FEATURES AND BENEFITS
Mathematics: Applications and Connections, Course 1

See page(s):

Integration	... of mathematical topics helps students to see mathematics as a whole.	
	Algebra lessons prepare students for first-year algebra.	22
	Other integrated topics: • geometry	145
	• measurement	164
	• statistics	163
	• probability	316
	• proportional reasoning	317
Applications	... show students how mathematics relates to the real world around them.	
	• Lessons open with an application or connection relevant to teenagers	232
	• *"When am I ever going to use this?"* answers the age-old question.	152
	• *School to Career* demonstrates careers in which mathematics is used.	185
	• *Math in the Media* helps students interpret mathematics in print.	279
Connections	... to other subject areas help students appreciate the role of mathematics in the other courses they are taking, such as science, social studies, and literature.	
	• *Chapter Projects*	177
	• Connection examples and exercises	168, 219
	• *Interdisciplinary Investigations*	392-393
Problem Solving	... activities and applications are integrated into every chapter.	
	• problem-solving strategies through *Thinking Labs*	150-151
	• 4-step problem-solving plan used throughout each chapter	4
	• Study Hints	207
Labs and Investigations	... provide students with an opportunity to explore, create mathematical models, and work cooperatively with a partner or group.	
	• Optional Hands-On Labs and Technology Labs provide a preview of the next lesson or can extend the concepts in the preceding lesson.	181, 197
	• Mini-labs introduce or reinforce concepts within a lesson.	202
	• Activities from *Interactive Mathematics: Activities and Investigations* provide additional options for extension activities in real-world settings.	2d
Ample Practice and Review	... reinforces new skills and concepts.	
	• Extra Practice for each lesson in the back of the text.	548-594
	• Mixed Review exercises in each exercise set	205
	• *Let the Games Begin* helps students maintain skills in previous lessons	121
Test Preparation and Assessment	... provides practice for local, state, and national tests.	
	• Test Practice questions in each exercise set	139
	• Standardized Test Practice at the end of each chapter includes multiple-choice and free-response questions.	174-175
	• Alternative Assessment options in the Study Guide and Assessment	173
	• A free-response test for each chapter in the back of the text.	595-607
Technology	... strand prepares students to function in a technological society through a variety of instruction and activities, including Technology Labs.	
	• scientific calculators	340
	• graphing calculators	26
	• spreadsheets	144
	• Internet Connections	135
Teacher Support	... in the *Teacher's Wraparound Edition* makes it easy for you to organize, present, and enhance the content. The extensive set of resource materials denoted in the Teacher's Edition helps you increase each student's chance for success.	

Glencoe
Mathematics
Applications and Connections

Course 1

 Glencoe McGraw-Hill

New York, New York Columbus, Ohio Woodland Hills, California Peoria, Illinois

Mathematics: Applications and Connections
Course 1

Student Edition
Teacher's Wraparound Edition
Spanish Student Edition

Applications

Classroom Games
Diversity Masters
Family Letters and Activities
Investigations and Projects Masters
School to Career Masters
Science and Mathematics Lab Manual

Meeting Individual Needs

Enrichment Masters
Investigations for the Special Education Student
Parent and Student Study Guide Workbook
Practice Masters
Spanish Parent and Student Study Guide Workbook
Spanish Study Guide and Assessment
Study Guide and Practice Workbook
Study Guide Masters
Transition Booklet

Technology/Multimedia

 CD-ROM Program

 Interactive Mathematics
Tools Software

Technology Masters

 MathPASS CD-ROM

Assessment/Evaluation

Assessment and Evaluation Masters

 MindJogger Videoquizzes

 Test and Review Software

Manipulatives/Modeling

Hands-On Lab Masters
Glencoe Mathematics Classroom Manipulative Kit
Overhead Manipulative Resources
Glencoe Mathematics Student Manipulative Kit

Teaching Aids

Answer Key Masters

 Answer Key Transparencies

Block Scheduling Booklet

 5-Minute Check Transparencies
Teaching Transparencies

Lesson Planning Guide
Solutions Manual

 Interactive Lesson Planner

Glencoe/McGraw-Hill

A Division of The **McGraw·Hill** *Companies*

Send all inquiries to:
Glencoe/McGraw-Hill
8787 Orion Place
Columbus, OH 43240-4027

ISBN: 0-07-822866-2 (Student Edition)
       0-07-822868-9 (Teacher's Wraparound Edition)

3 4 5 6 7 8 9 10 027/043 08 07 06 05 04 03 02 01

Dear Students, Teachers, and Parents,

Mathematics students are very special to us! That's why we wrote **Mathematics: Applications and Connections,** a math program designed specifically for you. The exciting, relevant content and up-to-date design will hold your interest and answer the question "When am I ever going to use this?"

As you page through your text, you'll notice the variety of ways math is presented for you. You'll see real-world applications as well as connections to other subjects like science, history, language arts, and music. You'll have opportunities to use technology tools such as the Internet, CD-ROM, graphing calculators, and computer applications like spreadsheets.

You'll appreciate the easy-to-follow lesson format. Each new concept is introduced with an interesting application or connection followed by clear explanations and examples. As you complete the exercises and solve interesting problems, you'll learn a great deal of useful math. You'll also have the opportunity to complete relevant Chapter Projects, Hands-On Labs, and Interdisciplinary Investigations. Test Practice, Test-Taking Tips, and Reading Math Study Hints will help you improve your test-taking skills.

Each day, as you use **Mathematics: Applications and Connections,** you'll see the practical value of math. You'll quickly grow to appreciate how often math is used in ways that relate directly to your life. If you don't already realize the importance of math in your life, you soon will!

Sincerely, The Authors

Kay McClain

Patricia S. Wilson

Patricia Frey

Linda Dritsas

Barbara Smith

Jack M. Ott

Ron Pelfrey

Beatrice Moore-Harris

David Molina

Meet Our Authors

William Collins
Director of The Sisyphus
* Mathematics Learning Center*
W.C. Overfelt High School
San Jose, CA

William Collins provides mathematics support services to the students of Overfelt and the East Side community. He also has many years of experience as a mathematics instructor and mathematics department chairperson. Mr. Collins received his B.A. in Mathematics and his B.A. in Philosophy from Herbert H. Lehman College, CUNY, and his M.S. in Mathematics Education from California State University, Hayward. He is active in several professional mathematics organizations.

Linda Dritsas
District Coordinator
Fresno Unified School District
Fresno, CA

Linda Dritsas is highly involved with the Fresno Urban Systemic Initiative. She received her B.A. and M.A. from California State University, Fresno, where she also taught. Ms. Dritsas has published numerous articles, workbooks, and other supplementary materials. She received the Edward Begle Award from the California Mathematics Council. Ms. Dritsas has is an active member of NCTM and the Association for Supervision and Curriculum Development.

Patricia Frey
Mathematics Department
* Chairperson*
Buffalo Academy for Visual and
* Performing Arts*
Buffalo, NY

Patricia Frey received her B.A. from D'Youville College in Buffalo, and her M.Ed. from the State University of New York at Buffalo. Her publications include articles in mathematics education journals as well as mathematics, computer, and calculator curriculum journals. Ms. Frey is a Woodrow Wilson fellow and a New York State Math Mentor. She is an active member of NCTM and other professional mathematics organizations.

Arthur C. Howard
Program Director for Secondary
* Mathematics*
Aldine Independent School District
Houston, TX

Arthur Howard is also an adjunct mathematics teacher at North Harris College and a member of the Executive Board of the Rice University School Mathematics Project. He received his B.S. in Mathematics and M.Ed. in Mathematics Education from the University of Houston. Mr. Howard is active in NCTM and has made presentations at local, state, regional, and national mathematics conferences.

Kay McClain
Lecturer
George Peabody College
Vanderbilt University
Nashville, TN

Kay McClain is currently working on a Ph.D. at Vanderbilt University. While a teacher at Mountain Brook Middle School in Birmingham, Alabama. she received the Presidential Award for Excellence in the Teaching of Mathematics and was a Woodrow Wilson Fellow. Ms. McClain received her B.A. for Auburn University and her Educational specialist degree from the University of Montevallo. She is an active member of NCTM.

David Molina
Adjunct Professor of Mathematics
* Education*
The University of Texas at Austin
Austin, TX

Dr. David Molina is the Associate Director of the Charles A. Dana Center. He earned his B.S. in Mathematics from the University of Notre Dame and his M.A. and Ph.D. in Mathematics Education from The University of Texas at Austin. Dr. Molina is active in every area of mathematics education. He has published numerous articles about professional development and educational technology.

Beatrice Moore-Harris
Staff Development Specialist
Bureau of Education and Research
Houston, TX

Beatrice Moore-Harris is a former middle school mathematics teacher and Mathematics Supervisor for the Houston and Fort Worth Independent School Districts. She received her B.A. from Prairie View A&M University. Ms. Moore-Harris is also a consultant and one of four official spokespersons for NCTM. She is also an active member of several professional mathematics organizations.

Jack M. Ott
Distinguished Professor of
Mathematics Education
University of South Carolina
Columbia, SC

Jack Ott has taught grades 5-12 and college. He recently received the South Carolina Council of Teachers of Mathematics Award for Outstanding Contributions in Mathematics Education. Dr. Ott received his A.B. from Indiana Wesleyan University, his M.A. from Ball State University, and Ph.D. from The Ohio State University. He has written articles for The Mathematics Teacher and The Arithmetic Teacher and has been a speaker at national and state mathematics conferences.

Ronald Pelfrey
Mathematics Consultant
Lexington, KY

Ronald S. Pelfry is a former middle school and high school mathematics teacher and district-level mathematics supervisor. He received his B.S., M.A., and Ed.D. from the University of Kentucky. Dr. Pelfrey has been active with NCTM and its local and state affiliates in Kentucky. He has been an author of several articles on curriculum and assessment, a speaker, and both a regional and state conference chair.

Jack Price
Professor, Mathematics
Education
California State Polytechnic
University
Pomona, CA

Past-president of the National Council of Teacher of Mathematics, Dr. Price teaches mathematics and mathematics methods classes to prospective teachers. He received his B.A. from Eastern Michigan University and his M.Ed. and Ed. D. from Wayne State University in Detroit. Dr. Price also serves on the Expert Panel on Mathematics and Science Education of the U.S. Department of Education and the standing mathematics committee for NAEP.

Barbara Smith
Mathematics Consultant
Unionville-Chadds Ford School
District
Kennett Square, PA

Barbara Smith is a former mathematics teacher with 13 years experience at the middle school level and 3 years at the high school level. She received her B.S. from Grove City College and her M.Ed. from the University of Pittsburgh. Ms. Smith is an active member of NCTM and has held offices in several state and local mathematics organizations.

Patricia S. Wilson
Associate Professor of Mathematics
Education
University of Georgia
Athens, GA

Patricia Wilson, a former middle school mathematics teacher, is currently working with preservice and inservice teachers. She received the Excellence in Teaching Award from the College of Education at the University of Georgia. Dr. Wilson received her B.S. from Ohio University and her M.A. and Ph.D. from The Ohio State University. She is an active member of NCTM and other professional mathematics organizations.

Academic Consultants and Teacher Reviewers

Each of the Academic Consultants read all 39 chapters in Courses 1, 2, and 3, while each Teacher Reviewer read two chapters. The Consultants and Reviewers gave suggestions for improving the Student Editions and the Teacher's Wraparound Editions.

ACADEMIC CONSULTANTS

Richie Berman, Ph.D.
Mathematics Lecturer and Supervisor
University of California, Santa Barbara
Santa Barbara, California

Robbie Bonneville
Mathematics Coordinator
La Joya Unified School District
Alamo, Texas

Cindy J. Boyd
Mathematics Teacher
Abilene High School
Abilene, Texas

Gail Burrill
Mathematics Teacher
Whitnall High School
Hales Corners, Wisconsin

Georgia Cobbs
Assistant Professor
The University of Montana
Missoula, Montana

Gilbert Cuevas
Professor of Mathematics Education
University of Miami
Coral Gables, Florida

David Foster
Mathematics Director
Robert Noyce Foundation
Palo Alto, California

Eva Gates
Independent Mathematics
Consultant
Pearland, Texas

Berchie Gordon-Holliday
Mathematics/Science Coordinator
Northwest Local School District
Cincinnati, Ohio

Deborah Grabosky
Mathematics Teacher
Hillview Middle School
Whittier, California

Deborah Ann Haver
Principal
Great Bridge Middle School
Virginia Beach, Virginia

Carol E. Malloy
Assistant Professor, Math Education
The University of North Carolina,
Chapel Hill
Chapel Hill, North Carolina

Daniel Marks, Ed.D.
Associate Professor of Mathematics
Auburn University at Montgomery
Montgomery, Alabama

Melissa McClure
Mathematics Consultant
Teaching for Tomorrow
Fort Worth, Texas

TEACHER REVIEWERS

Course 1

Carleen Alford
Math Department Head
Onslow W. Minnis, Sr. Middle School
Richmond, Virginia

Margaret L. Bangerter
Mathematics Coordinator K-6
St. Joseph School District
St. Joseph, Missouri

Diana F. Brock
Sixth and Seventh Grade Math Teacher
Memorial Parkway Junior High
Katy, Texas

Mary Burkholder
Mathematics Department Chair
Chambersburg Area Senior High
Chambersburg, Pennsylvania

Eileen M. Egan
Sixth Grade Teacher
Howard M. Phifer Middle School
Pennsauken, New Jersey

Melisa R. Grove
Sixth Grade Math Teacher
King Philip Middle School
West Hartford, Connecticut

David J. Hall
Teacher
Ben Franklin Middle School
Baltimore, Maryland

Ms. Karen T. Jamieson, B.A., M.Ed.
Teacher
Thurman White Middle School
Henderson, Nevada

David Lancaster
Teacher/Mathematics Coordinator
North Cumberland Middle School
Cumberland, Rhode Island

Jane A. Mahan
Sixth Grade Math Teacher
Helfrich Park Middle School
Evansville, Indiana

Margaret E. Martin
Mathematics Teacher
Powell Middle School
Powell, Tennessee

Diane Duggento Sawyer
Mathematics Department Chair
Exeter Area Junior High
Exeter, New Hampshire

Susan Uhrig
Teacher
Monroe Middle School
Columbus, Ohio

Cindy Webb
Title 1 Math Demonstration Teacher
Federal Programs LISD
Lubbock, Texas

Katherine A. Yule
Teacher
Los Alisos Intermediate School
Mission Viejo, California

Course 2

Sybil Y. Brown
Math Teacher Support Team-USI
Columbus Public Schools
Columbus, Ohio

Ruth Ann Bruny
Mathematics Teacher
Preston Junior High School
Fort Collins, Colorado

BonnieLee Gin
Junior High Teacher
St. Mary of the Woods
Chicago, Illinois

Larry J. Gonzales
Math Department Chair
Desert Ridge Middle School
Albuquerque, New Mexico

Susan Hertz
Mathematics Teacher
Revere Middle School
Houston, Texas

Rosalin McMullan
Mathematics Teacher
Honea Path Middle School
Honea Path, South Carolina

Mrs. Susan W. Palmer
Teacher
Fort Mill Middle School
Fort Mill, South Carolina

Donna J. Parish
Teacher
Zia Middle School
Las Cruces, New Mexico

Ronald J. Pischke
Mathematics Coordinator
St. Mary of the Woods
Chicago, Illinois

Sister Edward William Quinn I.H.M.
Chairperson Elementary Mathematics
  Curriculum
Archdiocese of Philadelphia
Philadelphia, Pennsylvania

Marlyn G. Slater
Title I Math Specialist
Paradise Valley USD
Paradise Valley, Arizona

Sister Margaret Smith O.S.F.
Seventh and Eighth Grade Math Teacher
St. Mary's Elementary School
Lancaster, New York

Pamela Ann Summers
Coordinator, Secondary Math/Science
Lubbock ISD
Lubbock, Texas

Dora Swart
Teacher/Math Department Chair
W. F. West High School
Chehalis, Washington

Rosemary O'Brien Wisniewski
Middle School Math Chairperson
Arthur Slade Regional School
Glen Burnie, Maryland

Laura J. Young, Ed. D
Eighth Grade Mathematics Teacher
Edwards Middle School
Conyers, Georgia

Susan Luckie Youngblood
Teacher/Math Department Chair
Weaver Middle School
Macon, Georgia

Course 3

Beth Murphy Anderson
Mathematics Department Chair
Brownell Talbot School
Omaha, Nebraska

David S. Bradley
Mathematics Teacher
Thomas Jefferson Junior High School
Salt Lake City, Utah

Sandy Brownell
Math Teacher/Team Leader
Los Alamos Middle School
Los Alamos, New Mexico

Eduardo Cancino
Mathematics Specialist
Education Service Center, Region One
Edinburg, Texas

Sharon Cichocki
Secondary Math Coordinator
Hamburg High School
Hamburg, New York

Nancy W. Crowther
Teacher, retired
Sandy Springs Middle School
Atlanta, Georgia

Charlene Mitchell DeRidder, Ph.D.
Mathematics Supervisor K-12
Knox County Schools
Knoxville, Tennessee

Ruth S. Garrard
Mathematics Teacher
Davidson Fine Arts School
Augusta, Georgia

Lolita Gerardo
Secondary Math Teacher
Pharr San Juan Alamo High School
San Juan, Texas

Donna Jorgensen
Teacher of Mathematics/Science
Toms River Intermediate East
Toms River, New Jersey

Statha Kline-Cherry, Ed.D.
Director of Elementary Education
University of Houston – Downtown
Houston, Texas

Charlotte Laverne Sykes Marvel
Mathematics Instructor
Bryant Junior High School
Bryant, Arkansas

Albert H. Mauthe, Ed.D.
Supervisor of Mathematics
Norristown Area School District
Norristown, Pennsylvania

Barbara Gluskin McCune
Teacher
East Middle School
Farmington, Michigan

Laurie D. Newton
Teacher
Crossler Middle School
Salem, Oregon

Indercio Abel Reyes
Mathematics Teacher
PSJA Memorial High School
Alamo, Texas

Fernando Rosa
Mathematics Department Chair
Edinburg High School
Edinburg, Texas

Mary Ambriz Soto
Mathematics Coordinator
PSJA I.S.D.
Pharr, Texas

Judy L. Thompson
Eighth Grade Mathematics Teacher
Adams Middle School
North Platte, Nebraska

Karen A. Universal
Eighth Grade Mathematics Teacher
Cassadaga Valley Central School
Sinclairville, New York

Tommie L. Walsh
Teacher
S. Wilson Junior High School
Lubbock, Texas

Marcia K. Ziegler
Mathematics Teacher
Pharr-San Juan-Alamo North High School
Pharr, Texas

Student Advisory Board

The Student Advisory Board gave the editorial staff and design team feedback on the design, content, and covers of the Student Editions. We thank these students from Crestview Middle School in Columbus, Ohio, and McCord Middle School in Worthington, Ohio, for their hard work and creative suggestions in making *Mathematics: Applications and Connections* more student friendly.

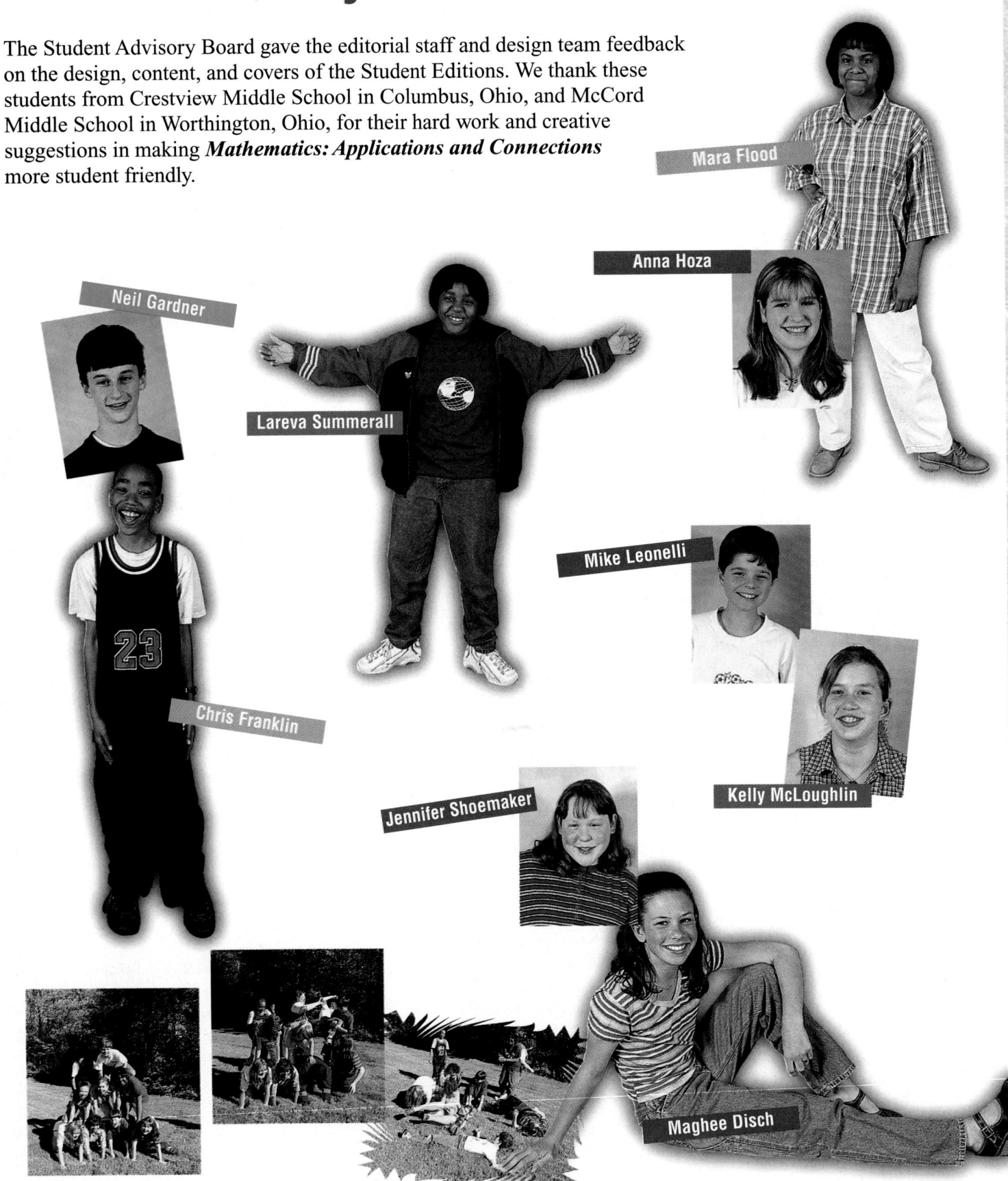

Mara Flood

Anna Hoza

Neil Gardner

Lareva Summerall

Mike Leonelli

Chris Franklin

Kelly McLoughlin

Jennifer Shoemaker

Maghee Disch

Table of Contents

CHAPTER 1

Problem Solving, Numbers, and Algebra

Let the **Games** Begin

- EXPO Bingo, **31**

SCHOOL to CAREER

- Business, **27**

interNET CONNECTION

Standardized Test Practice

Applications, Connections, and Integration Index, pages xxii–1.

Table of Contents

Statistics: Graphing Data

Table of Contents

Adding and Subtracting Decimals

Applications, Connections, and
Integration Index, pages xxii–1.

"O" is for Olympics, **128**

• The 1-Meter Dash, **121**

• Aviation, **99**

interNET CONNECTION

Standardized Test Practice

MATH IN THE MEDIA

• Tiger, **98**

CHAPTER 4 Multiplying and Dividing Decimals

Let the Games Begin

SCHOOL to CAREER

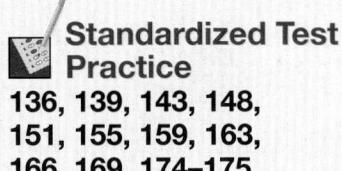

interNET CONNECTION

Standardized Test Practice

Using Number Patterns, Fractions, and Ratios

Applications, Connections, and
Integration Index, pages xxii–1.

- LCM Spin-Off, **209**

- Graphic Design, **185**

- Peanuts, **205**

interNET CONNECTION

Standardized Test Practice

Table of Contents

CHAPTER 6

Adding and Subtracting Fractions

Just "State" the Facts!, 264

• What Difference Does it Make?, **253**

• Cartography, **235**

Table of Contents

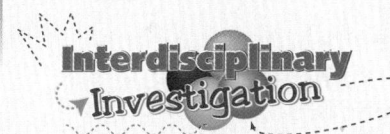

Just "State" the Facts!, **264**

• What Difference Does it Make?, **253**

• Cartography, **235**

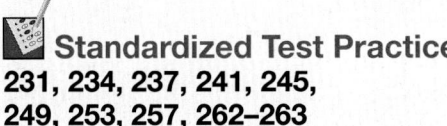

• Chapter Project, **227**
• Data Update, **234**
• School to Career, **235**
• Let the Games Begin, **253**
• Interdisciplinary Investigation, **265**
• Chapter Review, **258**
• Test Practice, **263**

Standardized Test Practice
231, 234, 237, 241, 245,
249, 253, 257, 262–263

CHAPTER 5

Using Number Patterns, Fractions, and Ratios

Applications, Connections, and
Integration Index, pages xxii–1.

CHAPTER 7
Multiplying and Dividing Fractions

Let the Games Begin

- Multiplication Mania, **276**

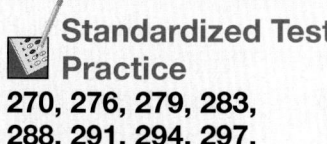
interNET CONNECTION

Standardized Test Practice

MATH IN THE MEDIA

- Peanuts, **279**

Applications, Connections, and
Integration Index, pages xxii–1.

Table of Contents

Let the Games Begin

• Fishin' for Matches, **343**

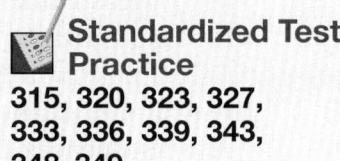

SCHOOL to CAREER

• Arts and Crafts, **328**

interNET CONNECTION

Standardized Test Practice

Geometry: Investigating Patterns

Applications, Connections, and
Integration Index, pages xxii–1.

That Is One Humongous Pie!, **392**

• Pento, **383**

• Architecture, **367**

MATH IN THE MEDIA

• Peanuts, **382**

• Chapter Project, **351**
• School to Career, **367**
• Let the Games Begin, **383**
• Interdisciplinary Investigation, **393**
• Chapter Review, **386**
• Test Practice, **391**

Standardized Test Practice
355, 357, 361, 366, 373,
378, 382, 390–391

Table of Contents

CHAPTER 10

Geometry: Understanding Area and Volume

Let the Games Begin

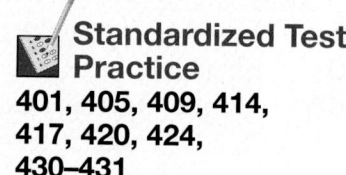
inter NET CONNECTION

Standardized Test Practice

CHAPTER 11 Algebra: Investigating Integers

Let the Games Begin

- Falling Off the Ends, **444**

SCHOOL to CAREER

- Statistics, **453**

 interNET CONNECTION

Standardized Test Practice

Table of Contents

Applications, Connections, and
Integration Index, pages xxii–1.

MATH IN THE MEDIA

Table of Contents

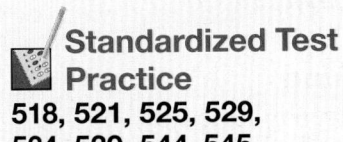

Applications, Connections, and
Integration Index, pages xxii–1.

Applications, Connections, and Integration Index

APPLICATIONS

Applications, Connections, and Integration Index

Applications, Connections, and Integration Index **XXV**

Applications, Connections, and Integration Index

Applications, Connections, and Integration Index

Algebra

Data Analysis, Statistics, and Probability

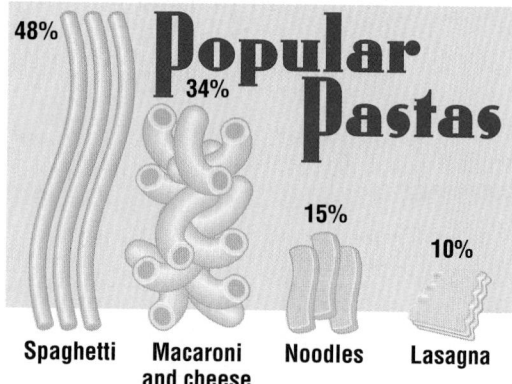

Source: National Pasta Association

Geometry and Spatial Sense, 366, 389, 452

Source: U.S. Census Bureau

Applications, Connections, and Integration Index

GLENCOE
Online

Mathematics

Visit the Glencoe Mathematics Internet Site for
Mathematics: Applications and Connections at

www.glencoe.com/sec/math/mac/mathnet

You'll find:

Chapter Review

Test Practice

Data Collection

Games

inter NET CONNECTION links to websites relevant to
Chapter Projects, Interdisciplinary Investigations, exercises

and much more!

About the Roller Coaster Hologram

The optimum viewing angle for the roller coaster hologram
on the cover of this textbook is a 45° angle. For best results,
view the hologram at this angle under a direct light source,
such as sunlight or incandescent lighting.

Table of Contents

Mathematics: Applications and Connections, Course 1

Pages T2-T31 provide a brief overview of the latest trends and research in mathematics education as well as to illustrate ways in which Glencoe has responded to these.

Chapter Overviews

Student Handbook

PATHWAYS TO SUCCESS

For the last several years, it's been difficult to find a newspaper or magazine that does not have an article about how poorly U.S. students score on international math exams compared to students from other countries such as Japan or Germany. For example, in the **Third International Mathematics and Science Study (TIMSS),** U.S. eighth grade students scored *below* the average for industrialized countries.

This result should not be surprising given the well-known study by James Flanders. He found that only 30-40% of the content in grades 6-8 of the most widely used K-8 mathematics series was new while algebra textbooks contained about 88% new content. (*Arithmetic Teacher*, "How Much of the Content in Mathematics Textbooks is New?", September 1987). This lack of new content in middle school combined with almost all new content in algebra 1 often leads to student frustration and failure in algebra 1. Flanders' research and the TIMSS data were both obtained before the first edition of *Mathematics: Applications and Connections* was published.

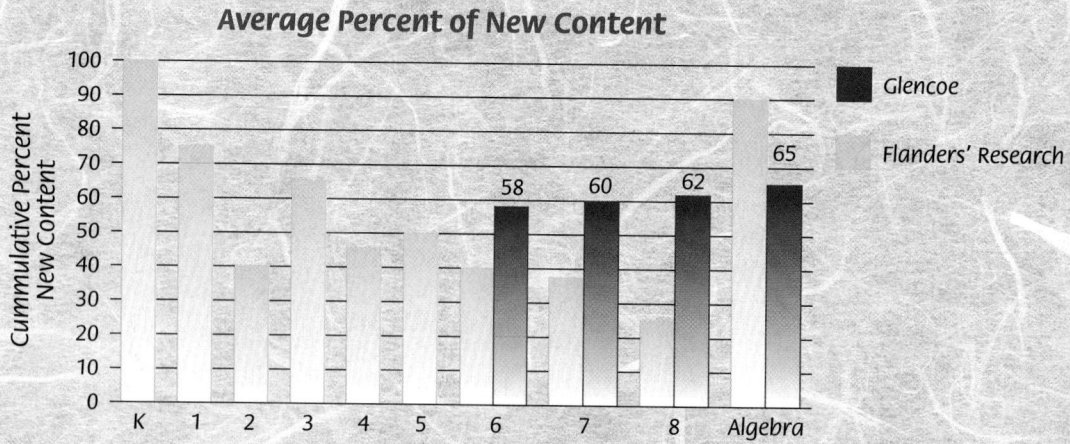

Average Percent of New Content

Note that the TIMSS data was collected when the programs described in the Flanders study were **very** widely used.

Glencoe changed this pattern with the publication of *Mathematics: Applications and Connections.*

Glencoe understands that the middle school experience is critical in preparing students for success in algebra 1 and geometry. **Mathematics: Applications and Connections** is designed to smooth the path to algebra and geometry by creating a program that has about the same amount of new material in Grade 6, Grade 7, and Grade 8 as well as in Glencoe's *Algebra 1*.

Here are some of the key findings from TIMSS and Glencoe's response.

TIMSS Finding

Achievement U.S. eighth-grade students test at about the international average in algebra, fractions, statistics, and probability. U.S. students do not do as well in geometry, measurement, and proportionality.

Curriculum The content taught in U.S. eighth-grade classrooms is at a seventh-grade level in comparison to other countries.

Curriculum Topic coverage in U.S. eighth-grade mathematics classes is not as focused as in Germany and Japan. (The U.S. curriculum is "a mile wide and an inch deep.)

Glencoe's Response

All mathematics topics are integrated throughout Course 1-3 of **Mathematics: Applications and Connections.**

Mathematics: Applications and Connections meets or exceeds international standards in grades 6-8. It emphasizes geometry, measurement, and proportionality, as well as algebra, fractions, and statistics.

Mathematics: Applications and Connections follows a structured scope and sequence that introduces, reinforces, and extends topics needed for success in algebra 1 and geometry.

In addition to Glencoe's progressive response to the Flanders' research and the TIMSS, here are some other key features and benefits that middle school mathematics educators asked us to include in **Mathematics: Applications and Connections.**

Feature

Integrated Content There is an emphasis on integrating algebra, geometry, measurement, proportional reasoning, statistics, probability, technology, and problem solving.

Applications and Connections Relevant, real-life applications and interdisciplinary connections are a part of every lesson. Every application and connection is written in an engaging style and often accompanied by colorful, high-interest photos, graphs, tables, and charts.

Test Preparation Every lesson has at least one multiple-choice *Test Practice* question. Every chapter has two pages of *Standardized Test Practice,* which includes multiple-choice test items, open-ended test items, and a *Test-Taking Tip.*

Benefit

Students will be prepared for success in algebra 1 and geometry, the gateway courses for success in college and careers.

Students are motivated to learn mathematics when it is interesting and related to their lives. Every page is designed to help you answer the question, "When am I ever going to use this?".

Test scores will increase because students will be prepared for success on state, national, and international standardized tests as well as classroom tests and end-of-course examinations.

As you examine **Mathematics: Applications and Connections,** you will see that this program will help you prepare your students for success in school and in their lives. As students use the program, they will repeatedly receive this message: "Math is for everyone...You can do it...You'll use it every day."

Mathematics: Applications and Connections— something good just got better!

BRIDGING THE GAP

From Elementary Mathematics to High School Mathematics

Students' experiences in middle school mathematics are crucial in preparing them for success in algebra and geometry.

Glencoe's **Mathematics: Applications and Connections** prepares all students for success in algebra and geometry. How? By introducing a variety of new concepts at the right time in the right way and by integrating them appropriately into all three courses. For example, integers are introduced in Chapter 11 of Course 1, in Chapter 5 of Course 2, and in Chapter 2 of Course 3. Because algebra and geometry are introduced in Chapter 1 in all three courses – and because both are reinforced throughout – students are much better prepared to take these courses in high school.

Manipulatives help students bridge the gap from the concrete to the abstract.

How does *Mathematics: Applications and Connections* help students bridge from the concrete, number-oriented mathematics in elementary school to abstract, symbol-centered algebra and geometry in high school? Many middle school students' learning styles lend themselves to concrete operations. They may not be able to grasp abstract concepts easily, but they can understand abstract concepts on a concrete level.

Shoe □ Jeff MacNelly

Hands-On Labs and Mini-Labs help students discover concepts on their own.

> "Hands-on experiential learning in which students take an active role and assume responsibility for their own learning is an integral part of the instructional practices of this program."
>
> Beatrice Moore-Harris, Author

Glencoe's *Mathematics: Applications and Connections* encourages students to **do** mathematics. **Hands-On Labs** give students hands-on experiences, with a partner or group, in discovering mathematical concepts for themselves. The **Hands-On Lab Masters** provide students with a way to record what they observe and discover in the Hands-On Labs. Students may also participate in shorter **Hands-On Mini-Labs** in which they investigate mathematical concepts within a lesson. **Hands-On Math** exercises provide even more opportunities for concrete learning.

The **Overhead Manipulative Resources** include a wealth of transparent manipulatives for use with overhead projectors such as a compass, spinner, counters, geoboard, and coordinate planes. A complete Teacher's Guide, correlated to the Hands-On Labs and Hands-On Mini-Labs, provides suggestions for demonstrations by the teacher or students.

The Glencoe **Mathematics Manipulative Kit** offers the tools students need to work through the Hands-On Labs and Hands-On Mini-Labs. A Teacher's Guide provides a correlation to all three courses.

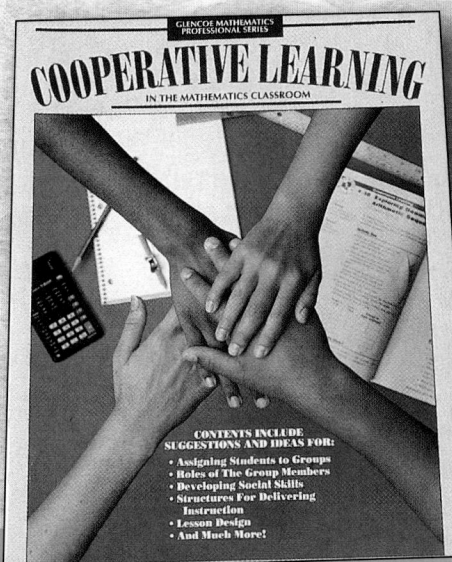

Cooperative Learning in the Mathematics Classroom, part of the Glencoe Mathematics Professional Series, provides suggestions for implementing cooperative learning techniques in your classroom.

Cooperative learning helps students with academic achievement and interpersonal skills.

In cooperative learning, small groups of students work as teams to share ideas, solve problems, and justify conclusions. At the same time, they develop vital skills in cooperating with others toward a common goal. The increased communication that takes place in cooperative learning experiences clarifies and strengthens individual students' understanding.

Glencoe's *Mathematics: Applications and Connections* offers an abundance of ways for students to learn cooperatively. **Chapter Projects** provide open-ended activities that often include collecting and organizing data. Students work together to explore, analyze, and report their results. **Interdisciplinary Investigations** relate mathematics to other content areas students are studying. These long-term projects are ideal for cooperative learning groups. The **Investigations and Projects Masters** provide students with ways to organize their explorations in the Chapter Projects and Interdisciplinary Investigations.

Hands-On Labs, Technology Labs, Thinking Labs, and **Mini-Labs** throughout all three courses of Mathematics: Applications and Connections also provide excellent opportunities for cooperative learning experiences. **Let the Games Begin** features interesting and fun games to help students reinforce and extend concepts.

Mathematics: Applications and Connections
Exemplifies NCTM Standards 2000

Mathematics: Applications and Connections thoroughly integrates all ten curriculum standards for grades 6-8 as outlined in the NCTM Standards 2000. For more information on the Standards, refer to pages 28–71 and 210–285 of *Principles and Standards for School Mathematics* ©2000 by the National Council of Teachers of Mathematics.

Glencoe has assigned numbers to the ten standards for ease of reference later in this text. The assigned reference numbers are listed in blue beside each standard.

Number and Operations Standard (1)

Course 1 (Chapters 1-13)
4-37, 46-85, 94-121, 132-148, 150-169, 178-180, 182-219, 228-241, 245-357, 268-301, 310-343, 352-366, 370-373, 375-383, 396-414, 416-425, 434-461, 464-467, 476-503, 514-534, 536-539

Course 2 (Chapters 1-13)
4-20, 28-35, 44-79, 88-121, 132-175, 184-217, 226-257, 268-307, 316-351, 362-373, 376-379, 382-385, 408-441, 450-481, 496-506, 510-517, 528-533, 538-553

Course 3 (Chapters 1-13)
4-47, 56-95, 104-129, 140-155, 158-177, 188-192, 194-199, 201-204, 206-212, 214-218, 232-267, 278-321, 330-373, 382-417, 428-444, 446-467, 476-481, 486-493, 495-507, 518-543, 546-548

Algebra Standard (2)

Course 1 (Chapters 1, 2, 4-13)
8-11, 16-31, 34-37, 46-57, 64-85, 133-139, 141-143, 149-155, 161-163, 167-169, 178-184, 197-201, 214-219, 243-245, 250-253, 273-283, 285-294, 296-301, 317-327, 330-343, 356-357, 370-373, 384-385, 398-409, 416-420, 425, 434-467, 476-503, 514-534, 536-539

Course 2 (Chapters 1-9, 11-13)
8-10, 12-33, 56-63, 66-69, 94-97, 133-136, 138-149, 197-200, 202-205, 207-217, 226-231, 234-245, 249-257, 284-288, 297-304, 317-320, 325-328, 332-335, 346-348, 360-365, 369-373, 376-379, 382-385, 388-397, 456-467, 469-481, 498-502, 510-513, 538-541

Course 3 (Chapters 1-13)
11-29, 32-47, 62-89, 92-95, 111-119, 140-147, 153-162, 167-177, 188-192, 194-212, 215-223, 232-234, 239-252, 257-260, 278-321, 330-373, 385-409, 414-417, 428-467, 476-479, 490-493, 528-533, 560-591

Geometry Standard (3)

Course 1 (Chapters 1, 3-13)
34-37, 102-111, 141-143, 149-155, 161-163, 178-181, 188-190, 198-201, 228-234, 238-241, 246-249, 268-272, 277-283, 296-301, 310-315, 317-327, 334-336, 340-353, 352-385, 396-425, 434-436, 445-448, 456-467, 484-487, 500-503, 522-534, 536-539

Course 2 (Chapters 1, 2, 4-10, 12)
17-20, 28-33, 56-59, 66-69, 146-147, 191-195, 215-217, 254-257, 292-300, 317-320, 362-365, 369-385, 388-397, 410-441, 490-517

Course 3 (Chapters 1-11, 13)
8-10, 17-25, 38-42, 81-83, 107-110, 118-123, 126-129, 148-151, 186-223, 239, 245-248, 253-256, 296-299, 301-314, 342-343, 357-373, 382-384, 386-389, 396-401, 404-417, 433-435, 442-444, 446-449, 452-467, 476-503, 560

Measurement Standard (4)

Course 1 (Chapters 1, 3-13)
4-7, 12-15, 28-31, 34-37, 95-104, 109-111, 118-121, 133-136, 145-155, 161-166, 188-190, 197-213, 228-234, 238-241, 246-249, 254-257, 268-283, 292-301, 312-315, 317-327, 334-336, 340-343, 352-355, 358-366, 370-373, 379-383, 396-414, 416-425, 434-436, 449-452, 459-461, 464-467, 484-487, 522-534, 536-539

Course 2 (Chapters 1-4, 7-9, 11, 12)
4-7, 54-55, 66-69, 74-76, 118, 148-149, 272-279, 284-287, 289-300, 305-307, 325-328, 360-385, 388-391, 469-472, 502-506

Course 3 (Chapters 1-9, 11)
38-47, 56-58, 62-72, 92-95, 118-119, 126-129, 148-151, 186-193, 196-199, 201-205, 213-214, 249-252, 265-267, 278-280, 301-311, 361-373, 396-401, 404-417, 482-485, 499-507

Data Analysis & Probability Standard (5)

Course 1 (Chapters 1-11, 13)
12-15, 34-37, 46-85, 105-108, 132-139, 141-143, 150-151, 157-159, 182-184, 206-209, 242, 250-253, 289-291, 316, 330-343, 358-361, 410-411, 434-439, 456-461, 514-539

Course 2 (Chapters 2-6, 8, 10, 11, 13)
44-63, 66-73, 88-121, 165-168, 172-175, 212-214, 253, 317-320, 342-345, 436-441, 459-467, 467-472, 528-553

Course 3 (Chapters 2-6, 10-12)
56-61, 73-76, 107-110, 120-123, 126-129, 140-177, 194-195, 200, 253-256, 260-264, 441, 450-451, 476-479, 516-531, 534-548

Problem Solving Standard (6)

Course 1 (Chapters 1-13)
4-37, 46-85, 94-121, 132-155, 157-169, 178-219, 229-257, 268-283, 285-301, 310-343, 352-385, 396-425, 434-467, 476-503, 514-539

Course 2 (Chapters 1-13)
4-35, 44-79, 88-121, 132-175, 184-217, 226-257, 268-287, 289-307, 316-351, 360-387, 408-441, 450-458, 460-481, 490-517, 528-553

Course 3 (Chapters 1-13)
4-47, 56-76, 78-95, 104-129, 140-177, 186-223, 232-267, 278-321, 330-373, 382-417, 428-431, 433-467, 476-507, 516-548, 560-591

Reasoning & Proof Standard (7)

Course 1 (Chapters 1-13)
4-37, 46-85, 94-121, 132-169, 178-219, 228-257, 268-283, 285-301, 310-343, 352-385, 396-425, 434-467, 476-503, 514-539

Course 2 (Chapters 1-13)
4-10, 12-23, 28-35, 44-79, 88-121, 132-175, 184-217, 226-257, 268-307, 316-351, 376-379, 382-387, 408-441, 450-458, 464-467, 490-517, 528-553

Course 3 (Chapters 1-13)
4-15, 17-47, 56-76, 78-95, 104-129, 140-177, 186-223, 232-267, 278-321, 330-373, 382-417, 428-431, 433-467, 476-507, 516-548, 560-591

Communication Standard (8)

Course 1 (Chapters 1-13)
4-37, 46-85, 94-121, 132-169, 178-219, 228-257, 268-301, 310-343, 352-385, 396-425, 434-467, 476-503, 514-539

Connections Standard (9)

Course 2 (Chapters 1-13)
4-10, 12-35, 44-79, 88-121, 132-175, 184-217, 226-257, 268-307, 316-351, 360-397, 408-441, 450-481, 490-517, 528-553

Course 3 (Chapters 1-13)
4-47, 56-76, 78-95, 104-129, 140-177, 186-223, 232-267, 278-321, 330-373, 382-417, 428-431, 433-467, 476-507, 516-548, 560-591

Connections Standard (9)

Course 1 (Chapters 1-13)
4-37, 46-85, 94-121, 133-139, 141-169, 178-180, 182-190, 193-219, 228-241, 243-257, 268-270, 273-283, 285-301, 312-343, 352-361, 364-366, 370-373, 375-383, 396-414, 416-425, 434-439, 441-461, 464-467, 476-487, 492-493, 496-503, 514-539

Course 2 (Chapters 1-13)
4-35, 44-79, 88-121, 132-136, 138-175, 184-194, 196-217, 226-257, 268-287, 289-307, 316-351, 360-361, 370-373, 382-385, 388-397, 408-441, 450-472, 478-481, 490-517, 528-553

Course 3 (Chapters 1-13)
4-15, 17-47, 56-76, 78-95, 104-129, 140-177, 186-192, 194-223, 232-267, 278-321, 330-373, 382-417, 428-431, 433-467, 476-507, 516-548, 560-591

Representation Standard (10)

Course 1 (Chapters 1-13)
4-25, 28-33, 46-85, 94-121, 132-136, 140-143, 145-148, 150-159, 167-169, 178-196, 198-205, 210-219, 228-231, 238-241, 243-257, 268-276, 280-288, 292-294, 296-300, 310-343, 352-385, 396-424, 434-452, 456-467, 476-491, 494-503, 514-521, 526-529, 531-534, 536-539

Course 2 (Chapters 1-13)
4-15, 17-20, 24-33, 44-59, 64-65, 70-76, 88-105, 108-117, 119-121, 138-145, 150-171, 184-191, 196-217, 226-231, 234-252, 254-257, 268-279, 282-307, 316-320, 325-328, 332-351, 360-385, 388-397, 410-437, 450-463, 468-472, 490-495, 498-517, 534-546, 551-553

Course 3 (Chapters 1-12)
17-29, 32-36, 38-47, 56-65, 69-76, 78-80, 84-85, 90-95, 104-123, 126-129, 140-146, 148-161, 167-170, 174-177, 186-199, 201-204, 210-213, 215-218, 235-239, 242-256, 261-264, 278-292, 300-304, 307-314, 335-341, 344-351, 357-373, 382-403, 408-417, 433-435, 442-444, 446-467, 476-502, 518-537

Motivating Middle School Students

Although these may be just complaints from our middle school students, they are legitimate questions that deserve answers. We at Glencoe realize that effective mathematics programs that really motivate middle school students must have more than strong content. They must demonstrate the usefulness of mathematics in a way that relates to student interests.

Mathematics: Applications and Connections makes math a part of students' daily school lives.

- **Applications** begin lessons with a real-life situation that points out how mathematics is used in students' everyday lives as well as in the world about them.
- **When am I ever going to use this?** gives an example of when the math concepts of the lesson will be useful in students' lives.
- **Connection** examples and exercises show how mathematics is used in other courses they may be taking such as Language Arts, Life Science, Geography, Music, Health, Physical Education, and Art.
- **Integration** examples and exercises illustrate how the math they are learning relates to mathematics courses they may take later such as Algebra, Geometry, and Probability and Statistics.

"The curriculum must go beyond the basics—to be relevant, it must be of interest to students and emphasize the usefulness of mathematics."

Ron Pelfrey, Author

Mathematics: Applications and Connections
invites students to look beyond their textbook to
see mathematics in the world.

Let the Games Begin gives students a fun
way to practice their math skills and learn to
interact positively with fellow students.

The **Family Activity** provides
an opportunity for students to
include their family members
in the math they are studying.

Cultural Kaleidoscope introduces students
to a variety of world cultures.

School to Career
features
demonstrate how
people use
mathematics in the
workplace and give
students
opportunities to
explore possible
avenues for future
careers.

Did You Know? features little
known facts to capture students'
interest.

Math in the Media includes cartoons,
graphs, advertisements, and other aspects
of the media that use mathematics to get a
point across.

Developing Problem Solving

According to the NCTM Standards, "Problem solving is the process by which students experience the power and usefulness of mathematics in the world around them. It is also a method of inquiry and application ... to provide a consistent context for learning and applying mathematics. Problem situations can establish a 'need to know' and foster the motivation for the development of concepts."

Problem solving is an integral part of every lesson in every course of Glencoe's *Mathematics: Applications and Connections.* How is this accomplished?

The **first chapter** of each course focuses on problem solving.
- Course 1:
  Problem Solving, Numbers, and Algebra
- Course 2:
  Problem Solving, Algebra, and Geometry
- Course 3: **Problem Solving and Algebra**

Thinking Labs in every chapter focus on problem-solving strategies, such as solving a simpler problem and working backward, and present opportunities to solve nonroutine problems.

Frequent **Problem-Solving Study Hints** suggest using various problem-solving strategies to investigate and understand mathematical content and apply strategies to new problem situations.

Reading Math Study Hints provide tips on how to read and interpret the language or symbolism of mathematics.

Study Hint
Reading Math The symbols < and > always point to the lesser of the two numbers.

Critical Thinking exercises in every lesson give students practice in developing and applying higher-order thinking skills.

Glencoe's *Mathematics: Applications and Connections* links practical problem solving to students' real-life interests. Mathematics becomes a vital force in the lives of middle school students as their eyes are opened to the relationship between mathematics and sports, shopping, and other teen interests. They "take ownership" of their skills by writing their own problems and presenting class projects connected to real life.

> "Problem solving is an integral component of this program. It requires students to think critically, examine new concepts, and then extend or generalize what they already know."
>
> **Linda Dritsas, Author**

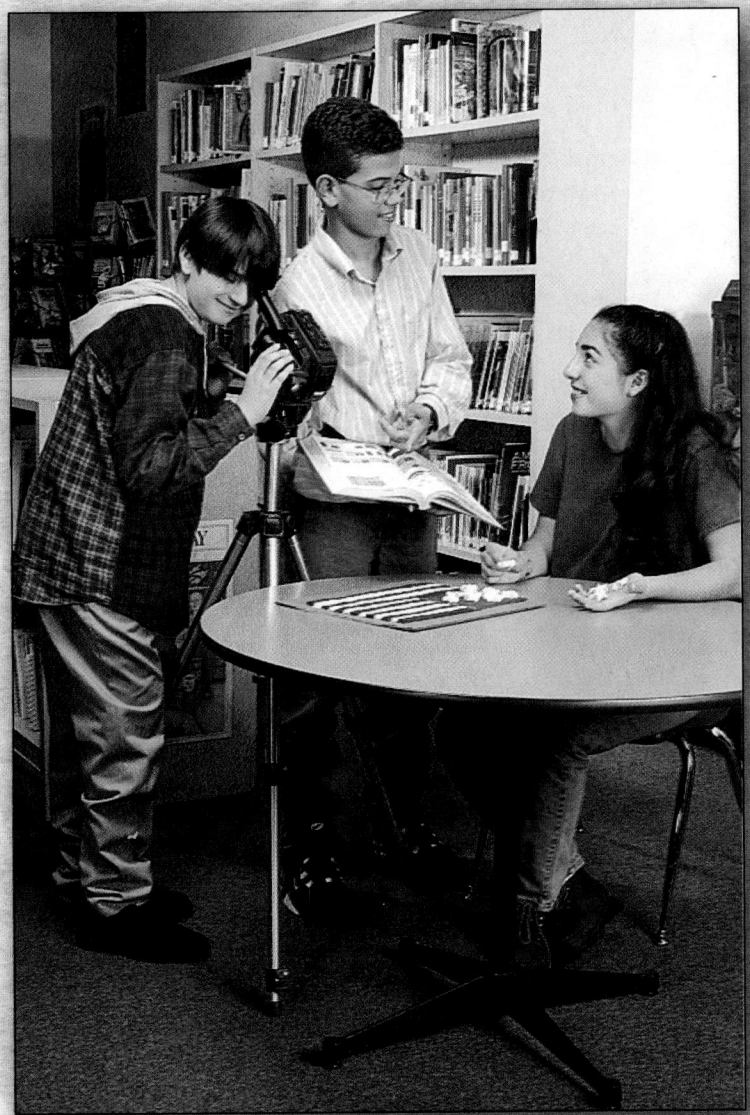

Most lessons begin with either a real-world **Application**, an interdisciplinary **Connection**, or content **Integration** that provides students with a reason to learn mathematics. Application, connection, and integration examples also occur throughout the texts to give students the opportunity to study completely worked-out problems.

Applications and Problem Solving exercises in every lesson directly link mathematics to real-world topics like entertainment, and to art, history, science, and other subjects.

CHAPTER Project

Interdisciplinary Investigation

The **Chapter Projects** and **Interdisciplinary Investigations** enable students to become more deeply engaged in a problem situation.

USING TECHNOLOGY

Is there a day that goes by when you don't encounter a computer-operated machine? The future world of our students will be even more involved in high technology. Clearly, technology is changing the workplace and the home at an increasingly rapid pace. Without technical mathematical skills, today's students will have little or no chance of finding good jobs.

Mathematics: Applications and Connections provides many opportunities for you to introduce your students to the world of technology as they learn mathematics.

Internet Connections throughout the Student Edition refer students to the Glencoe ***Mathematics: Applications and Connections*** site **www.glencoe.com/sec/math/mac/mathnet** that provides links to other websites on the Internet. These sites provide more information on the topics that students are studying.

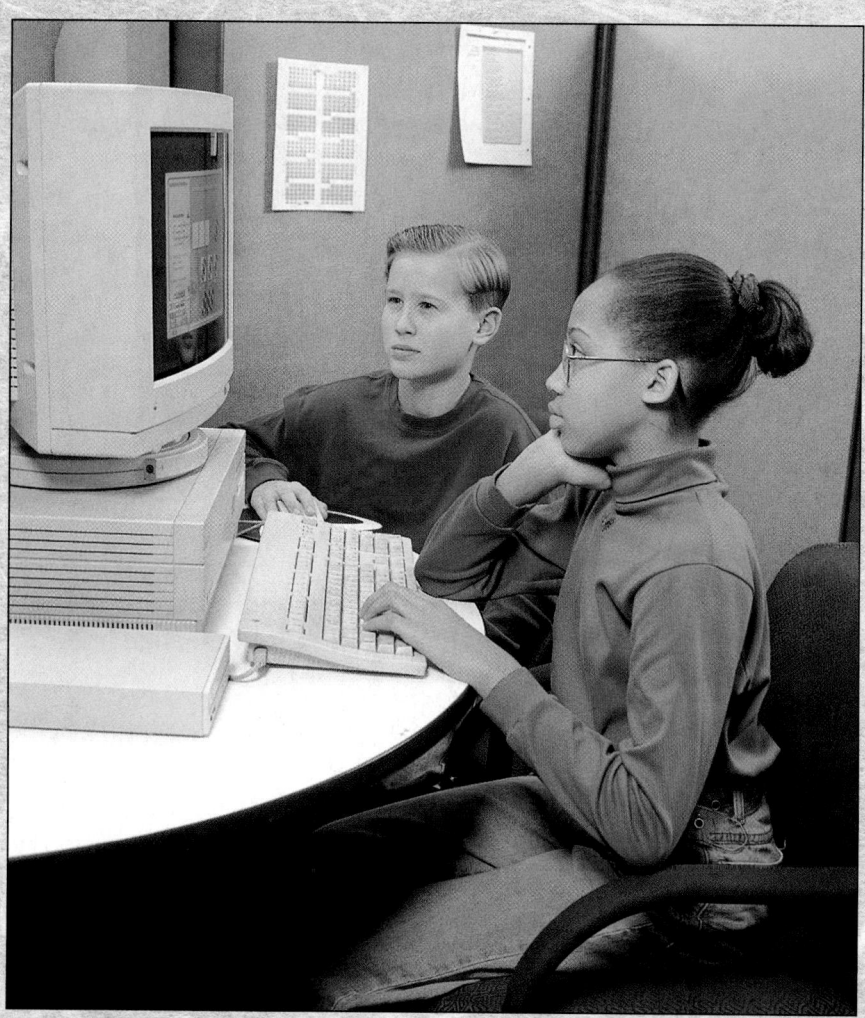

Technology Labs and **Mini-Labs** give students hands-on opportunities to use a computer or a graphing calculator to solve problems. Students learn how to use a spreadsheet to organize data and make predictions. Graphing calculator programs provide an introduction to logic and a way to perform calculations in a timely manner.

Technology Study Hints provide helpful suggestions on how students can use scientific calculators, graphing calculators, or software in studying the topics of the lesson.

In the **Chapter Projects** and **Interdisciplinary Investigations,** students are encouraged to use the Internet and application software like word processing, publishing software, and spreadsheets.

The **CD-ROM Program** for *Mathematics: Applications and Connections* contains a variety of activities correlated to each chapter. These include a Chapter Introduction and a Resource Lesson for each lesson in the Student Edition. The activities also include Interactive Lessons and Extended Activities for some of the lessons in the chapter. Every chapter includes an Assessment Game that is a cumulative review of skills they have learned.

MindJogger Videoquizzes feature a game show format that provides an alternative assessment and an entertaining way for your students to review chapter concepts and problem-solving skills.

CD-ROM Program, Course 2, Chapter 7

Interactive Mathematics Tools Software helps students gain mathematical power through interactive activities that combine video, sound, animation, graphics, and text.

All of the blackline masters for *Mathematics: Applications and Connections* are available on the **Electronic Teacher's Classroom Resources** CD-ROM. There's no need to carry a large array of booklets from room to room— just print out the masters you wish to use from a single CD-ROM that works on both Macintosh and Windows formats.

Using Projects

Doing mathematics is so much more effective than memorizing mathematics!

Mathematics: Applications and Connections gives you and your students several opportunities to engage in projects of varying lengths that put mathematics into motion.

The **Chapter Project** is introduced at the beginning of the chapter and sets in motion several activities that culminate with **Completing the Chapter Project** in the Chapter Study Guide and Assessment. Students apply the mathematics they learn in the chapter to various real-life situations. They are often asked to represent their results as a working model or in statistical graph form. Throughout the chapter, **Working on the Chapter Project** exercises remind students of the next steps in their project. These activities not only implement the mathematics student are learning, but give students the opportunity to work together as a team.

Interdisciplinary Investigation

The **Interdisciplinary Investigations** found at the ends of Chapters 3, 6, 9, and 12 show how the mathematics students have learned can be applied to other courses they may be taking. Each investigation uses the skills from the previous three chapters. In addition to the problem they are assigned to investigate, they are given writing assignments that explore other areas such as Language Arts, Foreign Language, Science, Health, Physical Education, and Social Studies.

Interactive Mathematics: Activities and Investigations

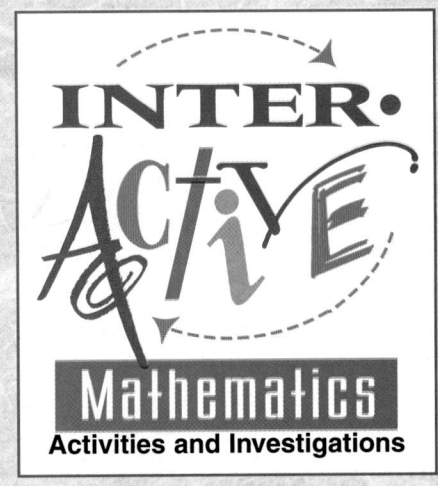

is based on a NSF-funded program that offers an innovative approach to teaching and learning middle school mathematics. Each of the 18 units that make up this comprehensive, activity-based program may be used to enhance chapters in *Mathematics: Applications and Connections.*

The interleaf pages of each chapter in the Teacher's Wraparound Edition highlight two activities from *Interactive Mathematics: Activities and Investigations* that are appropriate for that lesson. However, there are many other activities that may be useful.

The chart below summarizes the mathematical focus of each unit of *Interactive Mathematics: Activities and Investigations.*

Unit	Title	Mathematical Focus
Course 1		
1	From the Beginning	Building Math Power
2	A Million to One	Number Sense
3	Just the Right Size	Scale Drawings and Proportional Reasoning
4	Through the Looking Glass	Spatial Visualization
5	Get a Clue	Logical Reasoning
6	The Road Not Taken	Graph Theory and Networks
Course 2		
7	Take It From the Top	Building Math Power
8	Data Sense	Statistics and Data Analysis
9	Don't Fence Me In	Area and Perimeter
10	Against the Odds	Probability
11	Cycles	Algebra Patterns
12	Treasure Island	Geometry and Measurement
Course 3		
13	Start Your Engines	Building Math Power
14	Run for Cover	Surface Area and Volume
15	On the Move	Graphing and Functions
16	Growing Pains	Linear and Exponential Growth
17	Infinite Windows	Fractals and Chaos Theory
18	Quality Control	Applied Data Analysis

Glencoe has correlated *Mathematics: Applications and Connections (MAC)* with the *Interactive Mathematics: Activities and Investigations (IMAI)* units to provide a unique opportunity for you to tailor a program to your middle school students. Integrating the two programs allows you to emphasize areas and mathematical ideas that interest and fit the unique needs of the students in your class.

MAC Course 1 Chapter	IMAI Units 1-6	Other IMAI Units		MAC Course 2 Chapter	IMAI Units 7-12	Other IMAI Units		MAC Course 3 Chapter	IMAI Units 13-18	Other IMAI Units
1	1, 5			1	7			1	15	8
2	6	8		2	7	2		2	15	
3	2			3	8			3	16	3
4	2	7, 9		4	11	18		4	18	8
5	2, 3			5	11	16		5	14	4
6	3	11		6	11	15		6	16, 17	
7	3	10		7	9, 10			7	16, 17	
8	3	10		8	10	3		8	16, 17	3, 12
9	4	12		9	12			9	17, 18	10
10	4	14		10	9			10	15, 16	
11		11		11	10			11	14	
12		11		12	9	4, 14		12	17	6, 10
13	6	10		13	10	6		13	16	5

Interactive Mathematics: Activities and Investigations is available as individual units or as a three book series that groups Units 1-6, 7-12, and 13-18. Each unit also has a Classroom Instructional Resources binder that includes teaching instructions, blackline masters, transparencies, and guidance on using projects in the classroom.

For more information on *Interactive Mathematics: Activities and Investigations,* contact your nearest Glencoe Regional Office or call 1-800-334-7344.

Using Games in the Math Classroom

During the past few years, the use of games in the mathematics classroom has increased dramatically. These activities tend to be very motivational, and they often help improve students' attitudes toward mathematics in general. Because games are enjoyable, they allow students to learn and review mathematical skills and concepts while they unknowingly increase their problem-solving, logic, and computational skills.

Why Use Games? While mathematical games are not the only method you can use to provide individualized instruction or enrichment, they may be a very effective strategy. According to NCTM, most mathematical games serve one or more of the following functions.

- To develop concepts.
- To provide drill and reinforcement.
- To develop perceptual abilities.
- To provide opportunities for logical thinking and/or problem solving.

Therefore, mathematical games can be used in a number of different ways. You may want to use a game to introduce a new topic, thus encouraging students to employ discovery learning. You may want to use a game within the framework of your lesson instruction, for example, in the last few moments of a class period. Finally, you may want to use a game to review a concept previously taught.

The games presented in **Let the Games Begin** are designed to be useful and enjoyable to all students. Feel free to develop new and fun variations that will make each game your own.

More information on games is available from Glencoe on the Internet at **www.glencoe.com/sec/math/mac/mathnet.**

In addition to the games presented in the Student Edition, more games are available in the **Classrooms Games** booklet.

Multiple Learning Styles

People learn in many different ways. There are several different learning styles that help us approach and solve problems. Everyone possesses varying degrees of each of these learning styles, but the ways in which they combine and blend are as varied as the personalities of the individuals. Glencoe's *Mathematics: Applications and Connections* provides you with ways to accommodate students with these diverse learning styles.

Learning Style	Characteristics of Students	Activities in Student Edition
verbal/ linguistic	read regularly, write clearly, and easily understand the written word	**Communicating Mathematics** exercises ask students to tell, write, and explain mathematical concepts. Students also express what they have learned in their **Math Journals.**
logical	use numbers, logic, and critical thinking skills	Clearly-written **Examples** present important concepts, and **Critical Thinking** exercises extend those concepts. **Thinking Labs** encourage students to practice their logical thinking skills by using various strategies.
visual/ spatial	think in terms of pictures and images	**Integration** and **Hands-On Lab** exercises ask students to draw or show mathematical concepts through modeling, coordinate grids, charts, and graphs.
auditory/ musical	have "good ears" and can produce rhythms and melodies	Multimedia software, such as the **CD-ROM Program, MindJogger Videoquizzes,** and **Interactive Mathematics Tools Software,** can be easily incorporated into lessons.
kinesthetic	learn from touch, movement, and manipulating objects	**Hands-On Labs** and **Mini-Labs** provide for physical involvement in learning.
interpersonal	understand and work well with other people	**Chapter Projects, Interdisciplinary Investigations,** as well as **Hands-On Labs, Technology Labs,** and **Mini-Labs,** allow students to collaborate with others.
intrapersonal	have a realistic understanding of their strengths and weaknesses	**Math Journals, Portfolios,** and **Family Activities** help students personalize mathematics.
naturalist	can distinguish among, classify, and use features of the environment	**Application** and **Connection** examples and exercises show students how mathematics relates to the world around them.

As mathematics teacher, you may want to assign activities to students that accommodate their strongest learning styles, but frequently ask them to use their weakest learning styles. Additional activities are provided in the bottom margins of the lesson notes in the Teacher's Wraparound Edition.

The resources available in *Mathematics: Applications and Connections* guarantee that your classroom will be a multisensory environment, providing multiple paths for student learning.

Involving Parents and the Community

When children enter 6th grade, for a variety of reasons, it may become difficult for parents or guardians to remain on top of what's going on at school. The curricula grow more specialized, the typical middle school student becomes more independent of his or her parents, and multiple teachers replace the primary teacher of the elementary school years.

When parents do have the opportunity to meet with teachers, they often ask what they can do to motivate their children. Here are some ideas to share with parents. Developed by Reginald Clark of the Academy for Educational Development in Washington, D.C., they are designed to foster positive attitudes and boost learning.

- Share the fact that there is an inverse correlation between excessive TV viewing and high achievement in school.
- Stress the importance of seeing that their children complete homework assignments.
- Urge them to provide time, space, and materials needed for homework and reading.
- Remind them how important it is to listen to their children read and/or to read to their children.

Each chapter in Glencoe's **Mathematics: Applications and Connections** contains a suggested **Family Activity** for your students to complete with a family member. The **Family Letters and Activities** provide a letter and activity for each chapter to encourage students' families to become active participants in their students' learning.

Fostering Community Involvement

There are many ways to involve the community in your mathematics classroom and to share your learning with them.

- Send photos and press releases to your local newspaper to inform the community about the exciting things your students are learning.
- Have a "math career day" and invite local people to describe to students how they use math in their jobs.
- Set up a "shadow day" in which students spend a half-day "shadowing" people in the workplace who use math in their careers.
- Find out about – or implement your own – math fairs and competitions that give your students a chance to shine in the "outside world."

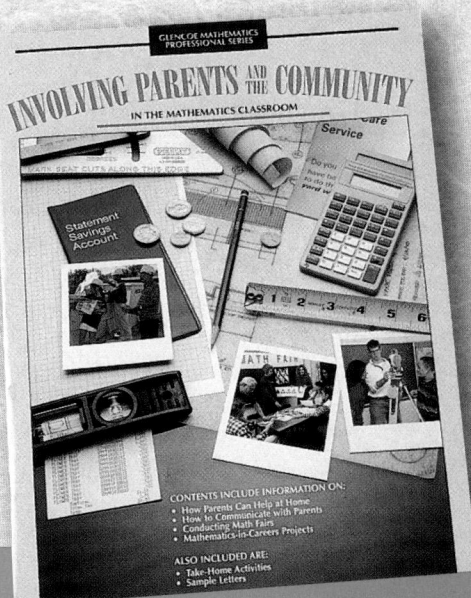

Involving Parents and the Community in the Mathematics Classroom, one of the booklets in Glencoe's Mathematics Professional Series, presents additional suggestions on how parents and the community can be active participants in supporting mathematics instruction.

Classroom Management

Meet Susan Uhrig. Mrs. Uhrig has taught in the Columbus Public Schools in Columbus, Ohio, for more than 25 years. She currently uses *Mathematics: Applications and Connections* in her classroom at Monroe Middle School.

Just one look at her classroom tells you that Mrs. Uhrig enjoys teaching middle school students. Their work is displayed throughout her bright classroom. Positive sayings on the bulletin boards encourage students to do their best. Manipulatives are kept out so they are easy to use—evidence that Mrs. Uhrig encourages her students to do mathematics.

Mrs. Uhrig says that she enjoys the diverse personalities of her students. You never know what challenges lie ahead each day! She organizes her classroom in ways that really get her students involved and keep their parents informed. Here are some of her ideas.

- Write the **assignment** and **objective** for the day on the chalkboard for students to copy when they come into class.
- Keep a **master notebook** where assignments are written so students can refer to the notebook if they miss a class.
- Have students keep assignment **logs** throughout the year. This helps students get and stay organized.

- Keep **manipulatives** on a table so they are easy to find and use. Mrs. Uhrig assigns several students to help distribute and collect manipulatives and calculators.
- Use "homework coupons" as a **reward** for special behavior.
- Have students write in their **journals** every day. Mrs. Uhrig has her students do the Check for Understanding exercises and 5-Minute Checks in their journals and allows them to refer to their journals during tests.
- Communicate with **parents and guardians** early and often. At the beginning of the year, Mrs. Uhrig sends each parent a letter that indicates her classroom policies. Throughout the year, she communicates with parents through student logs, interim reports, and grade cards.

There are many teachers like Mrs. Uhrig who, through years of experience, have acquired classroom management techniques that help their classrooms run smoothly. They also possess a wealth of knowledge about how to teach mathematics. Glencoe allows you to network with these teachers through the **Classroom Vignettes** in the Teacher's Wraparound Edition. Teachers from across the country share their ideas with you so that you may add to your own list of classroom management techniques.

Classroom Vignettes

Glencoe's unique **Classroom Vignettes** are classroom-tested teaching suggestions made by experienced mathematics educators. Each vignette was written by a teacher who uses Glencoe's *Mathematics: Applications and Connections* or by a Glencoe reviewer, consultant, or author. Glencoe thanks these outstanding mathematics educators for their unique contributions.

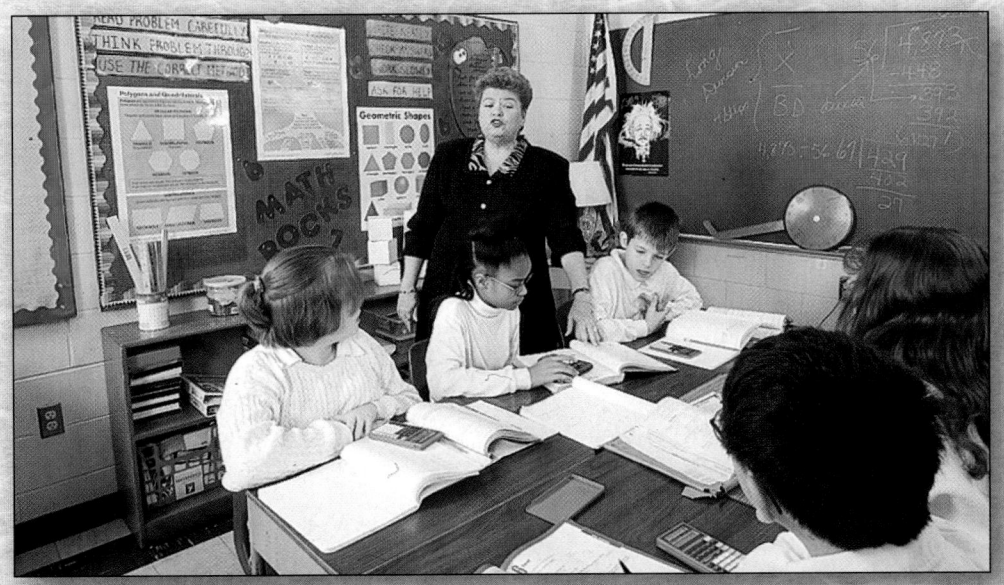

Research Activities

Glencoe's **Mathematics: Applications and Connections**, as well as the entire Glencoe Mathematics Series, is the product of ongoing, classroom-oriented research that involves students, teachers, curriculum supervisors, administrators, parents, and college-level mathematics educators.

The programs that make up the Glencoe Mathematics Series are currently being used by millions of students and tens of thousands of teachers. The key reason that Glencoe Mathematics programs are so successful in the classroom is the fact that each Glencoe author team is a mix of practicing classroom teachers, curriculum supervisors, and college-level mathematics educators. Glencoe's balanced author teams help ensure that Glencoe Mathematics programs are both practical and progressive.

Prior to publication of a Glencoe program, typical research activities include:
- a review of educational research and recommendations made by groups such as NCTM
- mail surveys of mathematics educators
- discussion groups involving mathematics teachers, department heads, and supervisors
- focus groups involving mathematics educators
- face-to-face interviews with mathematics educators
- telephone surveys of mathematics educators
- in-depth analyses of manuscript by a wide range of reviewers and consultants
- field tests in which students and teachers use pre-publication manuscript in the classroom

Feedback from teachers, curriculum supervisors, and even students who currently use Glencoe Mathematics programs is also incorporated as Glencoe plans and publishes new and revised programs. For example, Classroom Vignettes, which are printed in the *Teacher's Wraparound Editions*, are one result of this feedback.

All of this research and information is used by Glencoe's authors and editors to publish the best instructional resources possible.

Scope and Sequence

Mathematics: Applications and Connections is a comprehensive, well-balanced, three-course program that prepares middle school students for success in algebra and geometry. Through a carefully planned scope and sequence of mathematical topics, students encounter, practice, and extend their knowledge of mathematics to promote confidence and mastery.

The chart below shows the chapter titles for the three courses in *Mathematics: Applications and Connections.* The following pages present a detailed chart describing the depth to which each topic is covered.

Chapter	Course 1	Course 2	Course 3
1	Problem Solving, Numbers, and Algebra	Problem Solving, Algebra, and Geometry	Problem Solving and Algebra
2	**Statistics:** Graphing Data	Applying Decimals	**Algebra:** Using Integers
3	Adding and Subtracting Decimals	**Statistics:** Analyzing Data	Using Proportion and Percent
4	Multiplying and Dividing Decimals	Using Number Patterns, Fractions, and Percents	**Statistics:** Analyzing Data
5	Using Number Patterns, Fractions, and Ratios	**Algebra:** Using Integers	**Geometry:** Investigating Patterns
6	Adding and Subtracting Fractions	**Algebra:** Exploring Equations and Functions	Exploring Number Patterns
7	Multiplying and Dividing Fractions	Applying Fractions	**Algebra:** Using Rational Numbers
8	Exploring Ratio, Proportion, and Percent	Using Proportional Reasoning	Applying Proportional Reasoning
9	**Geometry:** Investigating Patterns	**Geometry:** Investigating Patterns	**Algebra:** Exploring Real Numbers
10	**Geometry:** Understanding Area and Volume	**Geometry:** Exploring Area	**Algebra:** Graphing Functions
11	**Algebra:** Investigating Integers	Applying Percents	**Geometry:** Using Area and Volume
12	**Algebra:** Exploring Equations	**Geometry:** Finding Volume and Surface Area	Investigating Discrete Math and Probability
13	Using Probability	Exploring Discrete Math and Probability	**Algebra:** Exploring Polynomials

Scope and Sequence

Legend
- ● Introduce
- ● Develop
- ● Reinforce

PROBLEM SOLVING

Course	1	2	3
Develop a plan	●	●	●
Strategies			
Look for a pattern	●	●	●
Solve a simpler problem	●	●	●
Act it out		●	●
Guess and check	●	●	●
Draw a diagram	●	●	●
Make a table	●	●	●
Work backward	●	●	●
Choose the method of computation	●	●	●
Make a list	●	●	●
Eliminate the possibilities	●	●	●
Determine reasonable answers	●	●	●
Make a model	●	●	●
Use a graph	●	●	●
Use an equation	●	●	●
Use logical reasoning	●	●	●
Use the Pythagorean Theorem	●	●	●
Use a Venn diagram	●	●	●
Use a frequency table	●	●	●
Use a spreadsheet	●	●	●
Use proportional reasoning			●

NUMBER AND OPERATIONS

Number Relationships

Decimals	1	2	3
Decimal concepts	●	●	●
Reading and writing	●	●	●
Decimal place value	●	●	●
Comparing and ordering	●	●	●
Rounding	●	●	●
Relating decimals and fractions	●	●	●
Relating decimals, ratios, and percents	●	●	●
Terminating and repeating decimals	●	●	●
Scientific notation		●	●
Powers of ten		●	●

Fractions	1	2	3
Fraction concepts	●	●	●
Writing mixed numbers as fractions	●	●	●
Mixed numbers and improper fractions	●	●	●

Course	1	2	3
Equivalent fractions	●	●	●
Comparing and ordering fractions	●	●	●
Simplifying fractions	●	●	●
Least common denominator (LCD)	●	●	●
Rounding and estimating fractions	●	●	●
Relating fractions and decimals	●	●	●
Relating fractions and percents		●	●

Proportional Reasoning

Ratio	1	2	3
Concept of ratio	●	●	●
Reading and writing ratios	●	●	●
Simplifying ratios	●	●	●
Relating ratios and fractions	●	●	●
Relating ratios and rates	●	●	●
Ratio and probability	●	●	●
The Golden Ratio			●

Proportion	1	2	3
Concept of proportion	●	●	●
Solving proportions	●	●	●
Property of proportion (cross product)	●	●	●
Scale drawings	●	●	●
Similar figures	●	●	●
Dilations		●	●
Indirect measurement		●	●

Percent	1	2	3
Concept of percent	●	●	●
Writing fractions and decimals as percent	●	●	●
Percents greater than 100% or less than 1%	●	●	●
Find percent of a number	●		●
Percent one number is of another		●	●
Finding number when percent is known		●	●
Percent proportion		●	●
Relating percent and ratio		●	●
Percent equation		●	●
Capture/recapture		●	●
Non-proportional relationships			●

Computations and Estimation

Order of operations	1	2	3
Order of operations	●	●	●

Decimals	1	2	3
Adding and subtracting	●	●	●
Multiplying by a whole number	●	●	●

Course	1	2	3
Multiplying two decimals	●	●	●
Dividing by a whole number	●	●	●
Dividing by decimals	●	●	●
Dividing with zeros in the quotient	●		
Fractions			
Adding and subtracting	●	●	●
Subtracting with renaming	●	●	●
Multiplying and dividing	●	●	●
Add and subtract mixed numbers	●	●	●
Multiply and divide mixed numbers	●	●	●
Percents			
Discount	●	●	●
Sales tax		●	
Simple interest		●	●
Percent of change		●	●
Integers			
Adding and subtracting		●	●
Multiplying and dividing		●	●
Estimation			
Whole numbers			
Rounding	●	●	●
Sums and differences	●	●	●
Products and quotients	●	●	●
Decimals			
Rounding	●	●	●
Sums and differences	●	●	●
Products and quotients	●	●	●
Fractions			
Sums and differences	●	●	●
Products and quotients	●	●	●
Percents	●	●	●
Use equivalent fractions, decimals, and percents			●
Strategies for estimating			
Rounding	●	●	●
Compatible numbers	●		
Capture-recapture		●	
Clustering	●	●	
Square roots		●	●
Area or volume	●	●	●
Mental math			
Divisibility patterns	●	●	●
Compatible numbers	●		
Solving equations mentally		●	
Finding percents			●
Powers of ten		●	
Using formulas	●	●	●

Number Systems and Number Theory

Course	1	2	3
Reading and writing whole numbers	●	●	●
Place value of whole numbers	●	●	●
Place value of decimals	●	●	●
Comparing and ordering			
Whole numbers	●	●	●
Decimals	●	●	●
Fractions	●	●	●
Integers	●	●	●
Rationals			●
Positive exponents	●	●	●
Negative exponents			●
Divisibility patterns	●	●	●
Prime and composite numbers	●	●	●
Relative primes			●
Prime factorization	●	●	●
Greatest common factor (GCF)	●	●	●
Least common multiple (LCM)	●	●	●
Scientific notation		●	●
Square roots		●	●
Factorials		●	●
Properties			
Properties of numbers		●	●
Distributive property	●	●	●
Property of proportions (cross products)	●	●	●
Properties of equality		●	●
Density property			●

PATTERNS AND FUNCTIONS

	1	2	3
Numeric patterns			
Sequences	●	●	●
Fibonacci sequence			●
Pascal's triangle		●	●
Divisibility patterns	●	●	●
Geometric patterns			
Recognizing geometry patterns	●	●	●
Tessellations	●	●	●
Fractals		●	
Represent relationships			
Tables	●	●	●
Graphs		●	●
Function rules		●	●
Analyze functional relationships			●
Use patterns and functions to solve problems	●	●	●

ALGEBRA

	1	2	3
Integers			
Reading and writing integers	●	●	●
Graphing integers on a number line	●	●	●
Comparing and ordering integers	●	●	●
Adding and subtracting integers	●	●	●

Course	1	2	3
Multiplying and dividing integers	●	●	●
Absolute value		●	●
Rational numbers			
Identify and simplify rational numbers			●
Properties of rational numbers			●
Density property			●
Rational numbers and decimals			●
Scientific notation			●
Comparing and ordering			●
Solving equations with rational number solutions			●
Real numbers			
Identify and classify real numbers			●
Square roots		●	●
Irrational numbers			●
Density property			●
Functions			
Function machine	●		●
Function tables	●	●	●
Linear functions			●
Analyze tables and graphs	●	●	●
Equations and expressions			
Concepts of variable, expression, equation	●	●	●
Order of operations		●	●
Evaluate algebraic expressions	●	●	●
Write algebraic expressions and equations		●	●
Solve addition and subtraction equations	●	●	●
Solve multiplication and division equations	●	●	●
Solve two-step equations	●	●	●
Solve equations with two variables		●	●
Solve inequalities		●	●
Solve equations with concrete methods	●	●	●
Solve equations with informal methods	●	●	●
Solve equations with formal methods		●	●
Graphing			
Integers on a number line	●	●	●
Irrational numbers on a number line			●
Inequalities on a number line		●	●
Points on a coordinate plane	●	●	●
Transformations on a coordinate plane	●	●	●
Functions	●	●	●
Linear functions			●
Quadratic functions			●
Equations		●	●
Systems of equations			●
Using graphing calculators		●	●
Polynomials			
Model with algebra tiles			●
Represent and simplify polynomials			●
Add, subtract, and multiply polynomials			●

Course	1	2	3
Factor polynomials			●
Multiply binomials			●
Apply algebra to real-world and math problems	●	●	●
Use spreadsheets and formulas	●	●	●

STATISTICS

Course	1	2	3
Taking a survey	●	●	●
Analyzing survey data	●	●	●
Organizing data			
Using a table to organize data	●	●	●
Frequency tables	●	●	●
Using tables to solve problems	●	●	●
Using matrices to organize data			●
Constructing and interpreting graphs			
Bar graphs	●	●	●
Circle graphs	●	●	●
Line graphs	●	●	
Stem-and-leaf plots	●	●	
Box-and-whisker plots	●	●	●
Line plots		●	●
Histograms			●
Scatter plots		●	●
Maps that show statistics			●
Choosing an appropriate display			●
Interpreting data			
Clusters		●	●
Mean, median, and mode	●	●	●
Range and quartiles	●	●	●
Misleading graphs and statistics	●	●	●
Making predictions from statistics	●	●	●
Making predictions from graphs	●	●	●
Making predictions from a sample	●	●	●

PROBABILITY

Course	1	2	3
Outcomes	●	●	●
Simple event	●	●	●
Independent events	●	●	●
Dependent events		●	●
Complementary events	●		
Experimental probability	●	●	●
Theoretical probability		●	●
Tree diagrams	●	●	●
Counting principle		●	●
Permutations and combinations	●	●	●
Probability and ratio	●	●	●
Fair and unfair games	●	●	●
Simulations or experiments	●	●	●
Area models	●	●	●
Capture-recapture		●	

Course	1	2	3
Punnett squares			●

GEOMETRY

Constructions
	1	2	3
Congruent segments	●		●
Perpendicular lines		●	●
Parallel lines		●	●
Segment bisectors	●		
Congruent angles	●		●
Angle bisectors	●		
Polygons, inscribed	●	●	●
Congruent triangles			●

Angles
	1	2	3
Classify and measure angles	●	●	●
Sum of angle measures		●	●
Parallel lines and transversal		●	●

Polygons
	1	2	3
Identify polygons	●	●	●
Classify triangles and quadrilaterals	●	●	●
Identify congruent figures	●	●	●
Using polygons as networks			●

Triangles
	1	2	3
Determine congruent triangles			●
Right triangle relationships (trigonometry)			●
Pythagorean Theorem		●	●
Special right triangles			●

Similarity
	1	2	3
Corresponding parts of similar figures	●	●	●
Identify similar figures	●	●	●
Scale drawings	●	●	●
Dilations	●	●	

Circles
	1	2	3
Circumference (radius, diameter)	●	●	●
Area	●	●	●
Perimeter	●	●	●

Area
	1	2	3
Rectangles	●	●	●
Parallelograms (base, height)	●	●	●
Trapezoids		●	●
Triangles	●	●	●
Circles	●	●	●
Square roots and area of squares		●	●
Pick's Theorem			●
Area and probability	●	●	

Transformations
	1	2	3
Translations, reflections, and rotations	●	●	●
Dilations		●	●
On the coordinate plane	●	●	●
Tessellations	●	●	●

Course	1	2	3
Symmetry	●	●	●

Solids
	1	2	3
Identify, draw three-dimensional figures	●	●	●
Nets	●	●	●
Surface area		●	●
Volume	●	●	●

Coordinate Geometry
	1	2	3
Graphing ordered pairs	●	●	●
Distance in the coordinate plane			●
Transformations on the coordinate plane	●	●	●

Patterns
	1	2	3
Recognizing geometric patterns	●	●	●
Symmetry	●	●	●
Tessellations	●	●	●
Fractals		●	

	1	2	3
Trigonometry			●
Inductive and deductive thinking			●

MEASUREMENT

Metric System
	1	2	3
Units of length, capacity, and mass	●	●	●
Changing units within the metric system	●	●	●

Customary system
	1	2	3
Units of length, capacity, and weight	●	●	●
Change units within the customary system	●	●	●

	1	2	3
Time	●		
Non-standard units	●		
Perimeter and circumference	●	●	●

Area
	1	2	3
Irregular figures	●	●	●
Rectangles	●	●	●
Parallelograms	●	●	●
Triangles	●	●	●
Circles	●	●	●
Trapezoids		●	●

Surface area
	1	2	3
Rectangular prisms		●	●
Triangular prisms			●
Cylinders		●	●

Volume
	1	2	3
Rectangular prisms	●	●	●
Cylinders		●	●
Pyramids and circular cones		●	●

	1	2	3
Relating area and perimeter	●		
Relating surface area and volume			●
Precision and significant digits			●
Indirect measurement		●	●

Legend ● Introduce   ● Develop   ● Reinforce

Planning Your

The charts on these two pages contain course planning guides for three types of classes. A Pacing Chart included in the interleaf of each chapter shows in greater detail the number of days suggested for all three types of pacing and which lessons are appropriate. This same pacing is repeated in the margin notes for each lesson for your convenience.

40- TO 50-MINUTE CLASS PERIODS

The chart below gives suggested pacing guides for two options, Standard and Honors, for four 9-week grading periods. The Standard option covers Chapters 1-12 while the Honors option covers Chapter 1-13.

The total number of days suggested for each option is 165 days. This allows for teacher flexibility in planning due to school cancellation or shortened class periods.

Grading Period	Standard		Honors	
	Chapter	**Days**	**Chapter**	**Days**
1	1	12	1	12
	2	14	2	14
	3	12	3	10
	4-1 to 4-2	4	4-1 to 4-4	7
2	4-3 to end	12	4-5A to end	8
	5	16	5	15
	6	13	6	12
			7-1 to 7-5	6
3	7	15	7-6 to end	8
	8	14	8	13
	9	14	9	12
			10-1 to 10-4B	8
4	10	13	10-5 to end	5
	11	15	11	13
	12	11	12	11
			13	11

Course of Study

The chart below gives a suggested pacing guide for teaching Course 1 using block scheduling in one semester (classes meet every day) or during the entire year (classes meet every other day). A total of 85 class periods is suggested to cover Chapters 1-12.

Chapter	Class Periods
1	6
2	7
3	6
4	8
5	8
6	7
7	8
8	7
9	7
10	7
11	8
12	6

For more detailed descriptions for lesson planning and pacing, please refer to the **Lesson Planning Guide** and the **Block Scheduling Booklet** for **Course 1** of *Mathematics: Applications and Connections.*

Problem Solving, Numbers, and Algebra

Previewing the Chapter

Overview

This chapter explores the problem-solving tools of a four-step plan, estimation, and algebraic equations. Students learn to estimate sums, differences, products, and quotients using rounding. They also evaluate numerical and algebraic expressions and investigate numerical patterns. Equations are solved using mental math and the guess-and-check strategy. The guess-and-check strategy is also applied to solving real-world problems.

Lesson (pages)	Lesson Objectives	NCTM Standards 2000	Standardized Tests	State/Local Objectives
1-1 (4–7)	Solve problems using the four-step plan.	1, 4, 6–10	MAT, SAT	
1-2 (8–11)	Solve problems using patterns.	1, 2, 6–10	MAT, SAT	
1-3 (12–15)	Estimate sums, differences, products, and quotients using rounding.	1, 4–10	CAT, CTBS, ITBS, SAT, TN	
1-4 (16–19)	Evaluate expressions using the order of operations.	1, 2, 6–10	CAT, CTBS, MAT, SAT, TN	
1-5A (20–21)	Model algebraic expressions.	1, 2, 6–10	CTBS, MAT, TN	
1-5 (22–25)	Evaluate numerical and simple algebraic expressions.	1, 2, 6–10	CAT, MAT, SAT	
1-5B (26)	Evaluate algebraic expressions by using a graphing calculator.	1, 2, 6–9	CAT, MAT, SAT	
1-6 (28–31)	Use powers and exponents in expressions.	1, 2, 4, 6–10		
1-7A (32–33)	Solve problems by using the guess-and-check strategy.	1, 6–10	MAT, SAT	
1-7 (34–37)	Solve equations by using mental math and guess and check.	1–9		

CAT = California Achievement Tests, CTBS = Comprehensive Tests of Basic Skills, ITBS = Iowa Tests of Basic Skills,
MAT = Metropolitan Achievement Tests, SAT = Stanford Achievement Tests, TN = Terra Nova
For the key to numbering of NCTM Standards 2000, see page T6.

Organizing the Chapter

 The **Interactive Lesson Planner** contains all of the blackline masters and transparencies. This CD-ROM also includes an easy-to-use lesson planning calendar.

LESSON PLANNING GUIDE

Lesson	Extra Practice (Student Edition)	Study Guide	Practice	Enrichment	Assessment & Evaluation	Classroom Games	Diversity	Hands-On Lab	School to Career	Science and Math Lab Manual	Technology	Transparencies A and B
1-1	p. 557	1	1	1								1-1
1-2	p. 557	2	2	2	15							1-2
1-3	p. 557	3	3	3								1-3
1-4	p. 558	4	4	4	14, 15						1	1-4
1-5A								39				
1-5	p. 558	5	5	5						1–4		1-5
1-5B												
1-6	p. 558	6	6	6	16	1–2					2	1-6
1-7A	p. 559											
1-7	p. 559	7	7	7	16		1	69	1			1-7
Study Guide/ Assessment					1–13, 17–19							

Columns under **BLACKLINE MASTERS (PAGE NUMBERS)**.

OTHER CHAPTER RESOURCES

Student Edition
Chapter Project, pp. 3, 15, 19, 41
School to Career, p. 27
Let the Games Begin, p. 31

Technology
MathPASS CD-ROM
Interactive Mathematics Tools Software

Teacher's Classroom Resources

Applications
Family Letters and Activities, pp. 1–2
Investigations and Projects Masters, pp. 17–20
Meeting Individual Needs
Transition Booklet, pp. 11–22, 25–26
Investigations for the Special Education Student, pp. 1–2

Teaching Aids
Answer Key Masters
Block Scheduling Booklet
Lesson Planning Guide
Solutions Manual

Professional Publications
Glencoe Mathematics Professional Series

Planning the Chapter

MindJogger Videoquizzes provide a unique format for reviewing concepts presented in the chapter.

ASSESSMENT RESOURCES

Student Edition

Mixed Review, pp. 11, 15, 19, 25, 30, 37

Mid-Chapter Self Test, p. 19

Math Journal, pp. 6, 14

Study Guide and Assessment, pp. 38–41

Performance Task, p. 41

Portfolio Suggestion, p. 41

Standardized Test Practice, pp. 42–43

Chapter Test, p. 595

Assessment and Evaluation Masters

Multiple-Choice Tests (Forms 1A, 1B, 1C), pp. 1–6

Free-Response Tests (Forms 2A, 2B, 2C), pp. 7–12

Performance Assessment, p. 13

Mid-Chapter Test, p. 14

Quizzes A–D, pp. 15–16

Standardized Test Practice, pp. 17–18

Cumulative Review, p. 19

Teacher's Wraparound Edition

5-Minute Check, pp. 4, 8, 12, 16, 22, 28, 34

Building Portfolios, p. 2

Math Journal, pp. 21, 26

Closing Activity, pp. 7, 11, 15, 19, 25, 31, 33, 37

Technology

Test and Review Software

MindJogger Videoquizzes

CD-ROM Program

MATERIALS AND MANIPULATIVES

Lesson 1-2
centimeter cubes*

Lesson 1-4
calculator

Lesson 1-5A
paper bags
popcorn

Lesson 1-5B
graphing calculator

Lesson 1-6
calculator

*Glencoe Manipulative Kit

PACING CHART

See pages T25–T27 for the Course Planning Calendar.

COURSE	DAY 1	DAY 2	DAY 3	DAY 4	DAY 5	DAY 6	DAY 7
Standard	Chapter Project	Lesson 1-1	Lesson 1-2	Lesson 1-3	Lesson 1-4	Lessons 1-5A & 1-5	
Honors	Chapter Project	Lesson 1-1	Lesson 1-2	Lesson 1-3	Lesson 1-4	Lessons 1-5 & 1-5B	
Block	Chapter Project & Lesson 1-1	Lessons 1-2 & 1-3	Lessons 1-4 & 1-5A	Lessons 1-5 & 1-6	Lessons 1-7A & 1-7	Study Guide and Assessment, Chapter Test	

The *Transition Booklet* (Skills 4–9, 11) can be used to practice rounding, adding, and subtracting whole numbers, and multiplying and dividing 1-digit numbers.

Interactive Mathematics:
Activities and Investigations

is an activity-based program that may be used as an enhancement for chapters in *Mathematics: Applications and Connections.*

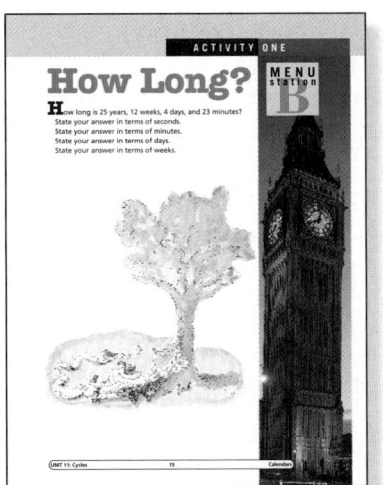

Unit 11, Activity One
Menu B
Use with Lesson 1-1.

Summary Students may work individually, in pairs, or in groups to convert a given amount of time into seconds, minutes, days, and weeks. After examination of the solutions by the class, students describe the methods they used to arrive at their solutions.

Math Connection Students examine time measurement units. After finding and interpreting information from the *Time Measurement Reference* in the Data Bank, they use logical reasoning and computation skills to solve conversion problems.

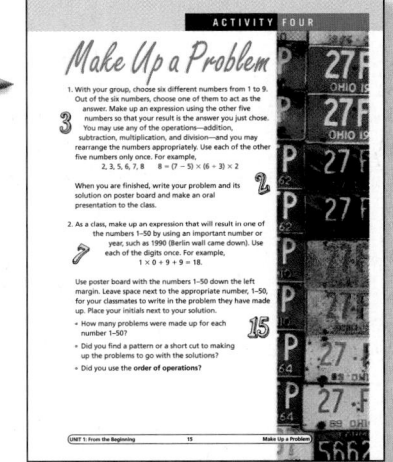

Unit 1, Activity Four
Make Up a Problem
Use with Lesson 1-4.

Summary Students choose six numbers from 1 to 9, use one of the six numbers as an answer, and make up an expression with the other five numbers equivalent to the answer. The class makes a poster displaying an expression equivalent to each number from 1 to 50.

Math Connection Students are asked to write an expression using addition, subtraction, multiplication, and division of whole numbers to represent a given solution. They use the order of operations during this activity.

DAY 8	DAY 9	DAY 10	DAY 11	DAY 12	DAY 13	DAY 14	DAY 15
Lesson 1-6	Lesson 1-7A	Lesson 1-7	Study Guide and Assessment	Chapter Test			
Lesson 1-6	Lesson 1-7A	Lesson 1-7	Study Guide and Assessment	Chapter Test			

Enhancing the Chapter

APPLICATIONS

Classroom Games, pp. 1–2

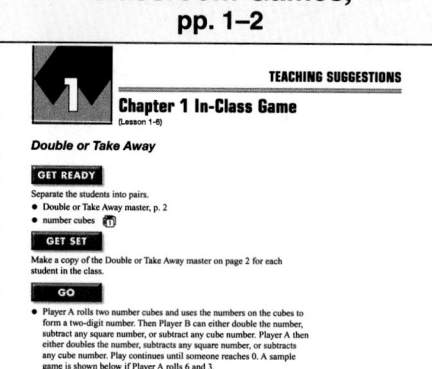

TEACHING SUGGESTIONS

Chapter 1 In-Class Game
(Lesson 1-6)

Double or Take Away

GET READY

Separate the students into pairs.
- Double or Take Away master, p. 2
- number cubes

GET SET

Make a copy of the Double or Take Away master on page 2 for each student in the class.

GO

- Player A rolls two number cubes and uses the numbers on the cubes to form a two-digit number. Then Player B can either double the number, subtract any square number, or subtract any cube number. Player A then either doubles the number, subtracts any square number, or subtracts any cube number. Play continues until someone reaches 0. A sample game is shown below if Player A rolls 6 and 3.

A	B
The number is 63.	Subtract 7² or 49. 63 − 49 = 14
Double 14. 28	Subtract 5² or 25. 28 − 25 = 3
Double 3. 6	Double 6. 12
Subtract 2³ or 8. 12 − 8 = 4	Subtract 2² or 4. 4 − 4 = 0

Player B is the winner of this round since he or she reached 0 first.
- Players alternate turns and receive 5 points when they win a round.

Variations:
- Have students find, for starting numbers 1 to 10, which player could win on the first move.
- Have students find, for starting numbers 1 to 100, which could give (a) a win on the first move, and (b) a win after two moves.

© Glencoe/McGraw-Hill   1   *Mathematics: Applications and Connections, Course 1*

Diversity Masters, p. 1

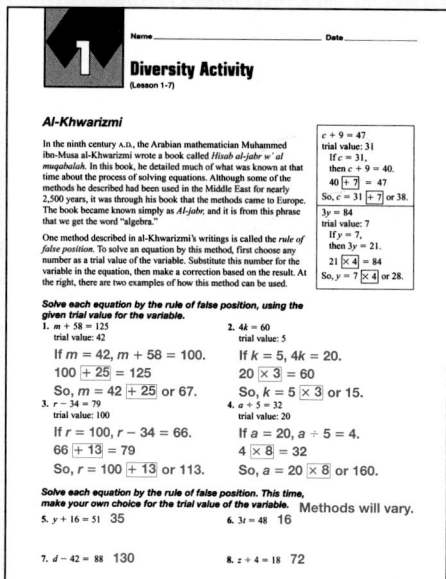

Name _____ Date _____

Diversity Activity
(Lesson 1-7)

Al-Khwarizmi

In the ninth century A.D., the Arabian mathematician Muhammed ibn-Musa al-Khwarizmi wrote a book called *Hisab al-jabr w' al muqabalah*. In this book, he detailed much of what was known at that time about the process of solving equations. Although some of the methods he described had been used in the Middle East for nearly 2,500 years, it was through his book that the methods came to Europe. The book became known simply as *Al-jabr*, and it is from this phrase that we get the word "algebra."

One method described in al-Khwarizmi's writings is called the *rule of false position*. To solve an equation by this method, first choose any number as a trial value of the variable. Substitute this number for the variable in the equation, then make a correction based on the result. At the right, there are two examples of how this method can be used.

$c + 9 = 47$
trial value: 31
If $c = 31$,
then $c + 9 = 40$.
$40 \boxed{+ 7} = 47$
So, $c = 31 \boxed{+ 7}$ or 38.

$3y = 84$
trial value: 7
If $y = 7$,
then $3y = 21$.
$21 \boxed{\times 4} = 84$
So, $y = 7 \boxed{\times 4}$ or 28.

Solve each equation by the rule of false position, using the given trial value for the variable.

1. $m + 58 = 125$
trial value: 42
If $m = 42$, $m + 58 = 100$.
$100 \boxed{+ 25} = 125$
So, $m = 42 \boxed{+ 25}$ or 67.

2. $4k = 60$
trial value: 5
If $k = 5$, $4k = 20$.
$20 \boxed{\times 3} = 60$
So, $k = 5 \boxed{\times 3}$ or 15.

3. $r − 34 = 79$
trial value: 100
If $r = 100$, $r − 34 = 66$.
$66 \boxed{+ 13} = 79$
So, $r = 100 \boxed{+ 13}$ or 113.

4. $a \div 5 = 32$
trial value: 20
If $a = 20$, $a \div 5 = 4$.
$4 \boxed{\times 8} = 32$
So, $a = 20 \boxed{\times 8}$ or 160.

Solve each equation by the rule of false position. This time, make your own choice for the trial value of the variable. Methods will vary.

5. $y + 16 = 51$ 35

6. $3r = 48$ 16

7. $d − 42 = 88$ 130

8. $z \div 4 = 18$ 72

© Glencoe/McGraw-Hill   T1   *Mathematics: Applications and Connections, Course 1*

School to Career Masters, p. 1

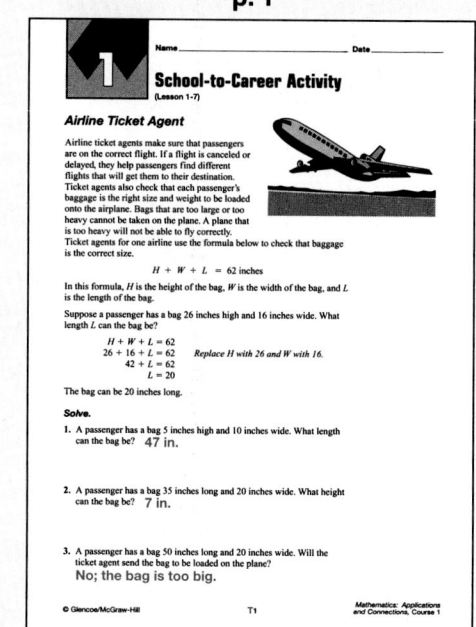

Name _____ Date _____

School-to-Career Activity
(Lesson 1-7)

Airline Ticket Agent

Airline ticket agents make sure that passengers are on the correct flight. If a flight is canceled or delayed, they help passengers find different flights that will get them to their destination. Ticket agents also check that each passenger's baggage is the right size and weight to be loaded onto the airplane. Bags that are too large or too heavy cannot be taken on the plane. A plane that is too heavy will not be able to fly correctly. Ticket agents for one airline use the formula below to check that baggage is the correct size.

$$H + W + L = 62 \text{ inches}$$

In this formula, H is the height of the bag, W is the width of the bag, and L is the length of the bag.

Suppose a passenger has a bag 26 inches high and 16 inches wide. What length L can the bag be?

$H + W + L = 62$
$26 + 16 + L = 62$ *Replace H with 26 and W with 16.*
$42 + L = 62$
$L = 20$

The bag can be 20 inches long.

Solve.

1. A passenger has a bag 5 inches high and 10 inches wide. What length can the bag be?   47 in.

2. A passenger has a bag 35 inches long and 20 inches wide. What height can the bag be?   7 in.

3. A passenger has a bag 50 inches long and 20 inches wide. Will the ticket agent send the bag to be loaded on the plane?
No; the bag is too big.

© Glencoe/McGraw-Hill   T1   *Mathematics: Applications and Connections, Course 1*

Family Letters and Activities, pp. 1–2

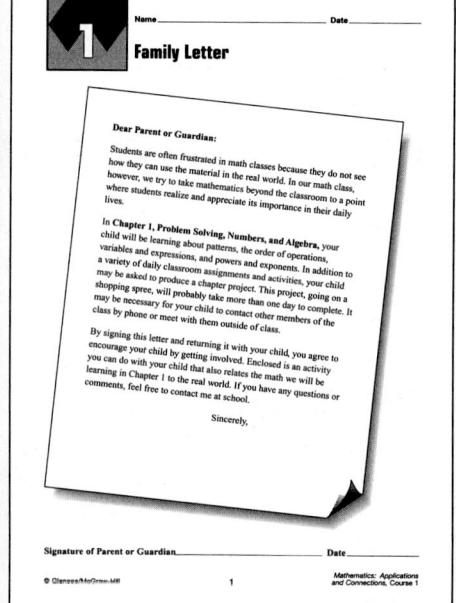

Name _____ Date _____

Family Letter

Dear Parent or Guardian:

Students are often frustrated in math classes because they do not see how they can use the material in the real world. In our math class, however, we try to take mathematics beyond the classroom to a point where students realize and appreciate its importance in their daily lives.

In **Chapter 1, Problem Solving, Numbers, and Algebra**, your child will be learning about patterns, the order of operations, variables and expressions, and powers and exponents. In addition to a variety of daily classroom assignments and activities, your child may be asked to produce a chapter project. This project, going on a shopping spree, will probably take more than one day to complete. It may be necessary for your child to contact other members of the class by phone or meet with them outside of class.

By signing this letter and returning it with your child, you agree to encourage your child by getting involved. Enclosed is an activity you can do with your child that also relates the math we will be learning in Chapter 1 to the real world. If you have any questions or comments, feel free to contact me at school.

Sincerely,

Signature of Parent or Guardian _____ Date _____

© Glencoe/McGraw-Hill   1   *Mathematics: Applications and Connections, Course 1*

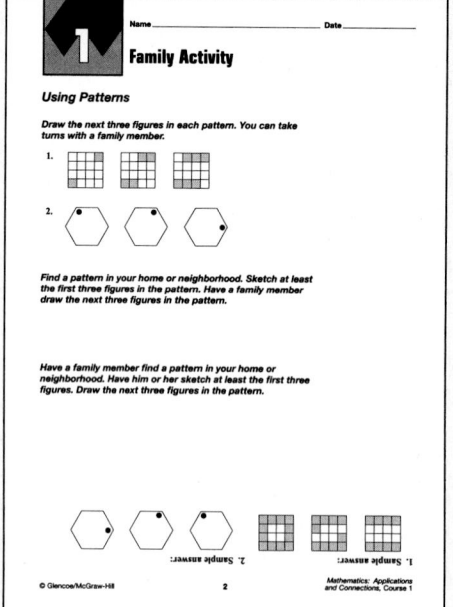

Name _____ Date _____

Family Activity

Using Patterns

Draw the next three figures in each pattern. You can take turns with a family member.

1.

2.

Find a pattern in your home or neighborhood. Sketch at least the first three figures in the pattern. Have a family member draw the next three figures in the pattern.

Have a family member find a pattern in your home or neighborhood. Have him or her sketch at least the first three figures. Draw the next three figures in the pattern.

1. Sample answer:

2. Sample answer:

© Glencoe/McGraw-Hill   2   *Mathematics: Applications and Connections, Course 1*

Science and Math Lab Manual, pp. 1–4

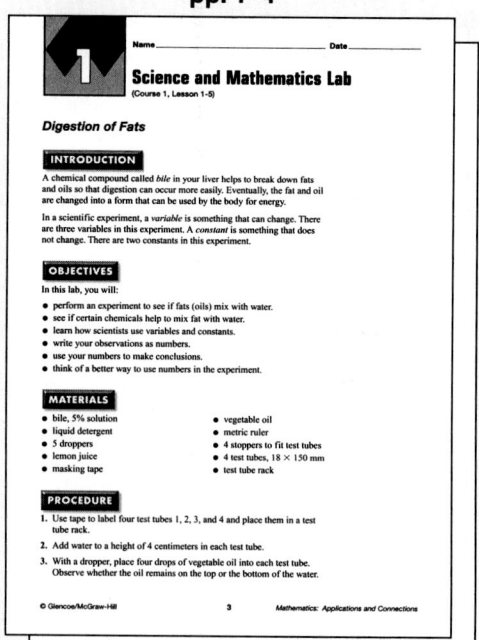

Name _____ Date _____

Science and Mathematics Lab
(Course 1, Lesson 1-5)

Digestion of Fats

INTRODUCTION

A chemical compound called *bile* in your liver helps to break down fats and oils so that digestion can occur more easily. Eventually, the fat and oil are changed into a form that can be used by the body for energy.

In a scientific experiment, a *variable* is something that can change. There are three variables in this experiment. A *constant* is something that does not change. There are two constants in this experiment.

OBJECTIVES

In this lab, you will:
- perform an experiment to see if fats (oils) mix with water.
- see if certain chemicals help to mix fat with water.
- learn how scientists use variables and constants.
- write your observations as numbers.
- use your numbers to make conclusions.
- think of a better way to use numbers in the experiment.

MATERIALS

- bile, 5% solution
- liquid detergent
- 5 droppers
- lemon juice
- masking tape
- vegetable oil
- metric ruler
- 4 stoppers to fit test tubes
- 4 test tubes, 18 × 150 mm
- test tube rack

PROCEDURE

1. Use tape to label four test tubes 1, 2, 3, and 4 and place them in a test tube rack.
2. Add water to a height of 4 centimeters in each test tube.
3. With a dropper, place four drops of vegetable oil into each test tube. Observe whether the oil remains on the top or the bottom of the water.

© Glencoe/McGraw-Hill   3   *Mathematics: Applications and Connections*

Hands-On Lab Masters, p. 69

1 Name_____ Date_____

Lab Activity
(Lesson 1-7)

Algebra: Solving Equations

Materials: cups, counters

Model each equation using cups and counters. Let a cup represent the variable and ○ represent the numbers. Use the guess-and-check strategy to solve each equation.

1. $c + 7 = 15$
2. $n - 5 = 9$
3. $6s = 18$
4. $d - 3 = 4$
5. $9 + e = 20$
6. $5y = 15$

© Glencoe/McGraw-Hill   69   *Mathematics: Applications and Connections, Course 1*

Assessment and Evaluation Masters, pp. 14–16

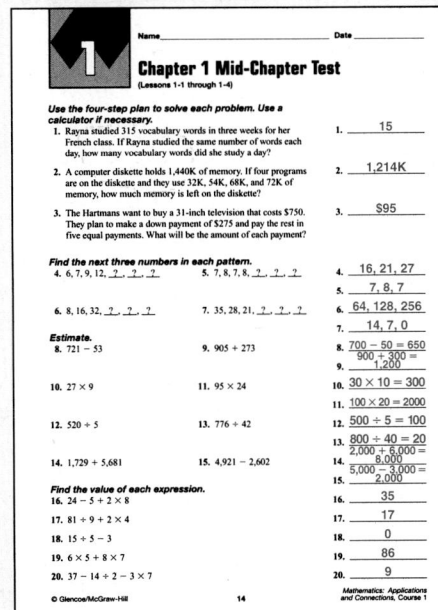

1 Name_____ Date_____

Chapter 1 Mid-Chapter Test
(Lessons 1-1 through 1-4)

Use the four-step plan to solve each problem. Use a calculator if necessary.

1. Rayna studied 315 vocabulary words in three weeks for her French class. If Rayna studied the same number of words each day, how many vocabulary words did she study a day?
1. 15

2. A computer diskette holds 1,440K of memory. If four programs are on the diskette and they use 32K, 54K, 68K, and 72K of memory, how much memory is left on the diskette?
2. 1,214K

3. The Hartmans want to buy a 31-inch television that costs $750. They plan to make a down payment of $275 and pay the rest in five equal payments. What will be the amount of each payment?
3. $95

Find the next three numbers in each pattern.

4. 6, 7, 9, 12, ?, ?, ?   5. 7, 8, 7, 8, ?, ?, ?
4. 16, 21, 27
5. 7, 8, 7

6. 8, 16, 32, ?, ?, ?   7. 35, 28, 21, ?, ?, ?
6. 64, 128, 256
7. 14, 7, 0

Estimate.

8. 721 − 53   9. 905 + 273
8. $700 − 50 = 650$
9. $900 + 300 = 1,200$

10. 27 × 9   11. 95 × 24
10. $30 × 10 = 300$
11. $100 × 20 = 2000$

12. 520 ÷ 5   13. 776 + 42
12. $500 ÷ 5 = 100$
13. $800 + 40 = 20$

14. 1,729 + 5,681   15. 4,921 − 2,602
14. $2,000 + 6,000 = 8,000$
15. $5,000 − 3,000 = 2,000$

Find the value of each expression.

16. 24 − 5 + 2 × 8
16. 35

17. 81 ÷ 9 + 2 × 4
17. 17

18. 15 + 5 − 3
18. 0

19. 6 × 5 + 8 × 7
19. 86

20. 37 − 14 ÷ 2 − 3 × 7
20. 9

© Glencoe/McGraw-Hill   14   *Mathematics: Applications and Connections, Course 1*

Name_____ Date_____

Chapter 1 Quiz A
(Lessons 1-1 and 1-2)

Use the four-step plan to solve each problem. Use a calculator if necessary.

1. On a trip to Florida, the Juarez family bought 4 adult plane tickets costing a total of $920. What was the cost of each ticket?
1. $230

2. Jill saved $12 per week for 50 weeks. How much did she save in all?
2. $600

Find the next three numbers in each pattern.

3. 222, 202, 182, ?, ?, ?   4. 3, 12, 48, ?, ?, ?
3. 162, 142, 122
4. 192, 768, 3,072

5. At the class play, 135 adult tickets were sold for $4 each, and 236 student tickets were sold for $2 each. How many more student tickets were sold than adult tickets?
5. 101

Name_____ Date_____

Chapter 1 Quiz B
(Lessons 1-3 and 1-4)

Round each number to the underlined place-value position.

1. 7,499   2. 495
1. 7,000
2. 500

Estimate using rounding.

3. 865 + 276   4. 78 − 56
3. $900 + 300 = 1,200$
4. $80 − 60 = 20$

5. 994 × 27   6. 4,106 ÷ 1,824
5. $1,000 × 30 = 30,000$
6. $4,000 ÷ 2,000 = 2$

Find the value of each expression.

7. 5 + 7 × 9   8. 36 − 27 + 3 + 1
7. 68
8. 28

9. 6 × 7 − 7 × 3   10. 10 + 2 + 15 + 3
9. 21
10. 10

© Glencoe/McGraw-Hill   15   *Mathematics: Applications and Connections, Course 1*

Technology Masters, pp. 1–2

1 Name_____ Date_____

Calculator Activity
(Lesson 1-4)

Order of Operations

Scientific calculators follow the correct order of operations.

Examples 1 Evaluate 18 + 3 × 2.

Enter: 18 [+] 3 [×] 2 [=]

If the display is 24, then the calculator follows the correct order of operations. If the display is 42, use parentheses to show the operation to be performed first as in the following example.

2 Evaluate 18 + (3 × 2).

Enter: 18 [+] [(] 3 [×] 2 [)] [=] 24

The correct answer is 24.

Use a calculator to find the value of each expression. Use parentheses if necessary.

1. 112 − 4 × 23   20   2. 15 + 12 + 2   21

3. 14 + 28 + 7   18   4. 25 + 10 − 5 + 5   34

5. 200 − 10 × 10 × 2   0   6. 12 + 4 × 2 + 8   14

7. 20 + 2 × 10   100   8. 114 + 10 − 9 × 9   43

9. 28 + 42 + 7 + 2   31   10. 125 − 100 − 25 + 5   20

CHALLENGE

11. 24 + 4 × 2 + 8 + 4 + 4   18   12. 75 + 5 × 5 + 10 × 10   100

© Glencoe/McGraw-Hill   T1   *Mathematics: Applications and Connections, Course 1*

1 Name_____ Date_____

Graphing Calculator Activity
(Lesson 1-6)

Exponents

You can use a graphing calculator to evaluate expressions involving exponents.

Example 1 Evaluate $5^4 + 6^3$.

Enter: 5 [^] 4 [+] 6 [^] 3 [ENTER] 661

So, $5^4 + 6^3 = 661$.

You can also use a graphing calculator to evaluate algebraic expressions that involve exponents. You store the variables' values in the memory before evaluating all of the expressions.

Example 2 Evaluate $x^3 + y^4$ if $x = 2$ and $y = 5$.

Enter: 2 [STO▶] [ALPHA] X [ENTER]
5 [STO▶] [ALPHA] Y [ENTER]
[ALPHA] X [^] 3 [+] [ALPHA] Y [^] 4 [ENTER] 633

So, $x^3 + y^4 = 633$ when $x = 2$ and $y = 5$.

Evaluate each expression.

1. $6 × 3^4 + 1$ 88   2. $4^3 + 10^7$ 10,001,024   3. $7^3 − 1^4 − 2^6$ 278

4. $4 + 3^5 − 2$ 240   5. $27 − 5^2 + 7^2$ 51   6. $6^6 − 5^5 + 4^4$ 43,787

7. $9^4 + 16 + 2^2 − 24 + 3$ 6,557   8. $10^3 − 9^3 + 8^3 − 7^4 + 6^5$ 5,816

Evaluate each expression if $x = 6$ and $y = 3$.

9. x^4 1,296   10. $y^3 + 2$ 245   11. $x^3 + 5^3$ 341

12. $x^3 + y^8$ 6,777   13. $3x^2 + y^4$ 189   14. $x^5 − 2y^4 − 126$ 1,259,586

15. xy^3 39,366   16. $5y^3 + 5x^3$ 40,095   17. $x^{10} − 10xy$ 60,465,996

18. $4xy + 2y^3 + xy − x^4 + y^{10}$ 57,897   19. $xy^3 + 5y + yx^2 + 5x$ 24,831

© Glencoe/McGraw-Hill   T2   *Mathematics: Applications and Connections, Course 1*

Investigations for the Special Education Student, pp. 1–2

Use with:
Course 1-Chapter 1
Course 2-Chapter 1
Course 3-Chapter 2

Investigation 1 Teacher's Guide

Vacation Getaways

Overview
This investigation shows how mathematics is connected to history and social studies. Not only will students improve their skills with decimal operations and map reading, but will they learn about a country of their choice—its history, geography, culture, and interesting facts. In order to accomplish this task, students will research and devise a detailed itinerary for a trip to their country, including a daily schedule and costs for each activity planned. Once completed, trip itineraries will be shared with or displayed for the class, and each student will be asked to locate his or her country on a world map.

Activity Goals
Students will:
• research a country of their choice.
• organize and plan a trip to that country, and
• make a budget for the trip.

Planning the Instruction
Prerequisite Skills
Students should have a significant amount of practice computing with whole numbers and decimals, figuring distances on a map, understanding time zone differences, and possibly converting from one currency to another.

Materials
• investigation worksheet
• calculators
• access to research materials

Time Needed
six 45-minute periods

Procedure
1. Explain that students' task is to plan a trip to a country of their choice. The trip should be for a minimum of 5 days, and the cost should not exceed $5,000. While on the trip, they should visit at least one historical, one scenic, and one entertaining point of interest.
2. Requirements for this task may include: contacting travel agents, auto clubs, airlines, or hotels to obtain current rates; consulting the library for information on the geography and history of the area to be visited; or gathering information about the area from relatives who have been there.
3. Have students complete the Preliminary Plan worksheet by estimating answers based on prior knowledge of the country.
4. Once the Preliminary Plan is done, students will begin the research necessary to find accurate, current responses to the preliminary plan questions.
5. To complete their final itinerary, students will use the information they have gathered to write a detailed schedule for each individual day of the trip, including the cost of each event.
6. If desired, have students type their final itineraries and share them with the class. Then, display each itinerary in the classroom and have students mark their country on a large world map.

Adaptations and Variations

The following are some ideas on how this investigation may be modified depending on student population.

LD
• Allow more time.
• If there seems to be a difficulty with students completing their research, allow students to have "research assistants" such as an older sibling or friend outside class to help with research.
• Allow students to type their responses and itinerary.

PH
• Help these students obtain research materials if access is difficult due to lack of mobility.
• If writing is a problem, allow students to type their work.

CD
• Arrange for someone to help students with the verbal portion of their research.
• If students are to share a summary of their trip orally, have them instead write a summary for the teacher or another student to read aloud.

BD
• Maintain close proximity during independent work time.

HI
• Have a student sign each oral summary.

VI
• Help students obtain enlarged print material. In addition, students may need an aide to help them with the visual portion of their research.

© Glencoe/McGraw-Hill   1   *Mathematics: Applications and Connections*

CHAPTER 1
Problem Solving, Numbers, and Algebra

Theme: Shopping

Many people enjoy the convenience of shopping by catalog from the comfort of their homes. Shopping by mail-order catalog generates almost $50 billion in sales annually.

The Internet is the newest rage in catalog shopping. From zero sales in 1994 to about $560 million in 1996, shopping on the Internet continues to grow.

Question of the Day A retailer decides to base shipping and handling charges on the volume of an item. The volume of an item is r^3. The charge is $3 times the volume. Find the cost if $r = 2$. **$24**

Assess Prerequisite Skills

Ask students to read through the list of objectives presented in "What you'll learn in Chapter 1." You may wish to ask them what each of the objectives means or if they have experienced or used any of these math concepts before.

Building Portfolios

A portfolio is each student's collection of work that expresses how the student has grown as a mathematics student. It does not necessarily include the best work done by the student, but rather should demonstrate improvement. You may want to have each student attach an explanation to each paper in the portfolio to state why it was chosen to be in the collection. Students should update their portfolios with the completion of each chapter.

Math and the Family

In the *Family Letters and Activities* booklet (pp. 1–2), you will find a letter to the parents explaining what students will study in Chapter 1. An activity appropriate for the whole family is also available.

What you'll learn in Chapter 1

- to solve real-world problems using the four-step plan,
- to estimate sums, differences, products, and quotients using rounding,
- to evaluate numerical and algebraic expressions, and
- to solve equations using mental math and the guess-and-check strategy.

OFFICIAL BASKETBALL FOR NCAA® CHAMPIONSHIPS

2 Chapter 1 Problem Solving, Numbers, and Algebra

CD-ROM Program

Activities for Chapter 1
- Chapter 1 Introduction
- Interactive Lessons 1-3, 1-5
- Assessment Game
- Resource Lessons 1-1 through 1-7

CHAPTER Project

CATALOG SHOPPING

In this project, you will use problem-solving strategies, estimation, and algebraic expressions to go on a shopping spree. You can use any catalog you wish for your shopping spree such as a sporting goods catalog or a novelty gift catalog.

Getting Started

- Look at the two shipping tables. Describe the method used by each catalog to determine the shipping charge.
- For each table, find the shipping charge for an item that costs $20 and weighs less than 5 pounds.

Table 1: Sporting Goods Catalog	
Shipping Charges	
For the first item	$5.99
Each additional item	$1.99
Rush Orders	
Next day air	$21.99*
Express delivery (2–3 days)	$9.99*
*Plus standard shipping charges	

Table 2: Novelty Gift Catalog	
Merchandise Total	**Shipping Charges**
up to $20.00	$4.95
$20.01 to $30.00	$5.95
$30.01 to $40.00	$6.95
$40.01 to $50.00	$7.95
$50.01 to $75.00	$8.95
$75.01 to $100.00	$9.95
$100.01 to $150.00	$12.95
$150.01 to $200.00	$15.95
1-Day Delivery	$9.99*
3-Day Delivery	$6.99*
*Plus standard shipping charges	

Technology Tips

- Use a **spreadsheet** to calculate the cost of the items and their shipping charges.
- Surf the **Internet** to see if any catalogs have websites.

inter NET CONNECTION   Data Update **For up-to-date** information on catalogs, visit:

www.glencoe.com/sec/math/mac/mathnet

Working on the Project

You can use what you'll learn in Chapter 1 to help you go on a shopping spree.

Page	Exercise
15	45
19	23
41	Alternative Assessment

inter NET CONNECTION

Glencoe has made every effort to ensure that the website links for *Mathematics: Applications and Connections* at **www. glencoe.com/sec/math/mac/mathnet** are current and contain appropriate content. However, these website links are not under Glencoe's control.

Instructional Resources ▶▶▶

A recording sheet to help students organize their data for the Chapter Project is shown at the right and is available in the *Investigations and Projects Masters*, p. 20.

CHAPTER Project NOTES

Objectives Students should
- learn to apply problem-solving strategies to real-life situations, such as catalog shopping.
- gain an understanding of estimation and algebraic expressions by applying them to catalog orders.

Project Pointer You may suggest that students begin a *Project Folder* to keep their work as they complete each stage of the Chapter Project. The completed project may also be added to their portfolios.

Using the Tables For Table 1, make sure students realize that the $1.99 is for *each* additional item. For example, if you buy six items, the shipping would be $5.99 + 5($1.99) = $15.94. For Table 2, emphasize that the shipping charges increase as the amount of money spent increases. It doesn't matter whether it's one item or twenty items.

Investigations and Projects Masters, p. 20

Name_____ Date_____

1 **Chapter 1 Project**

Shop 'Til You Drop!
Page 3, Getting Started

Page 15, Working on the Chapter Project, Exercise 45

Order Table	
Item Description	Price
Shipping Charges	
Total Charges	

Item Total	
Shipping Total	
Order Total	

Page 19, Working on the Chapter Project, Exercise 23

$(3 \times \$ \ Item \ 1) + (4 \times \$ \ Item \ 2) + \$ \ Shipping$
$(\ \times \$ \ \ ) + (\ \times \$ \ \ ) + \$ \ \ = \$ \ \_\_\_\_$

- *Study Guide Masters*, p. 1
- *Practice Masters*, p. 1
- *Enrichment Masters*, p. 1
- Transparencies 1-1, A and B

CD-ROM Program
- Resource Lesson 1-1

Recommended Pacing	
Standard	Day 2 of 12
Honors	Day 2 of 12
Block	Day 1 of 6

1 FOCUS

5-Minute Check

Find the value of each expression.
1. $17 + 5$ **22**
2. $65 + 12 + 37$ **114**
3. $86 - 49$ **37**
4. 6×52 **312**
5. $72 \div 4$ **18**

The 5-Minute Check is also available on **Transparency 1-1A** for this lesson.

Motivating the Lesson

Hands-On Activity Plan the solution to a story problem by writing each of the four steps on a separate sheet of paper. Mix up the sheets and ask students to put them in the correct order. Cover one of the sheets with a blank sheet and discuss how the exclusion of this step might affect other steps in the solution. Discuss each step in this way.

1-1 A Plan for Problem Solving

What you'll learn
You'll learn to solve problems using the four-step plan.

When am I ever going to use this?
The four-step plan gives you an organized method for solving problems.

The graph shows the number of years it took from the time a new technology was invented for it to be in one-half of U.S. homes. In what year was the telephone in one-half of U.S. homes? *This problem will be solved in Example 1.*

New Technology Catches On

Number of Years

Television (Introduced in 1946)	VCR (Introduced in 1975)	Personal Computer (Introduced in 1975)	Cable TV (Introduced in 1948)	Telephone (Introduced in 1876)
8	13	24	39	70

You can use a four-step plan to help solve this problem and other problems.

1. *Explore*
   - Read the problem carefully.
   - Ask yourself questions like, "What facts do I know?" and "What do I need to find out?"

2. *Plan*
   - See how the facts relate to each other.
   - Make a plan for solving the problem.
   - Estimate the answer.

3. *Solve*
   - Use your plan to solve the problem.
   - If your plan does not work, revise it or make a new plan.

4. *Examine*
   - Reread the problem.
   - Ask, "Is my answer close to my estimate?"
   - Ask, "Does my answer make sense for the problem?"
   - If not, solve the problem another way.

Cross-Curriculum Cue

Inform other teachers on your team that your students are studying problem-solving strategies. Suggestions for curriculum integration are:
Economics: consumer issues
Health: weekly caloric needs
Physical Science: formulas

Example 1

Real World APPLICATION

Inventions Refer to the beginning of the lesson. In what year was the telephone in one-half of U.S. homes?

Explore   The graph states that the telephone was invented in 1876 and that it took 70 years until one-half of U.S. homes had a telephone. You need to find the year when one-half of U.S. homes had a telephone.

Plan   To solve the problem, add the number of years it took until one-half of U.S. homes had a telephone to the year the telephone was invented.

Solve

year telephone was invented	plus	number of years until one-half of U.S. homes had a telephone
1876	+	70

$$1876 + 70 = 1946$$

By 1946, one-half of U.S. homes had a telephone.

Examine $1946 - 70 = 1876$. So the answer is correct.

Example 2

Real World APPLICATION

Work Tyler delivers newspapers each weekday. If Tyler works every weekday for one year, how many days does he work?

Explore   You know that Tyler delivers newspapers each weekday. You need to find out how many days Tyler works in one year.

Plan   Multiply the number of weekdays in each week, 5, by the number of weeks in one year, 52, to find the number of days Tyler works in one year.

Solve

number of weekdays in each week	times	number of weeks in one year
5	×	52

In one year, Tyler works 5×52 or 260 days.

(continued on the next page)

Lesson 1-1 A Plan for Problem Solving **5**

2 TEACH

Transparency 1-1B contains a teaching aid for this lesson.

Thinking Algebraically When students are solving the exercises in this lesson, have them write out the problems as equations to prepare them for algebraic expressions.

In-Class Examples

For Example 1
Refer to the graph at the beginning of the lesson. How many years are there between the time when one-half of all U.S. homes had cable TV and the time when one-half owned VCRs? **one year**

For Example 2
To help out an injured news carrier, Tyler delivered newspapers on weekends for one-half of a year. Including his weekday deliveries, how many days did he work that year? **312 days**

Teaching Tip In Examples 1 and 2, remind students to work carefully through the four-step process, even if the answer seems obvious.

Check for Understanding

If students need additional practice or instruction after completing Exercises 1–5, one of these options may be helpful.
- Extra Practice, see p. 557
- Reteaching Activity
- *Study Guide Masters*, p. 1
- *Practice Masters*, p. 1

Assignment Guide

Core: 7–13 odd, 15
Enriched: 6–14 even, 15

Additional Answers

1. Explore—Decide what facts you know and what you need to find out. Plan—Make a plan for solving the problem and estimate the answer. Solve—Solve the problem. Make a new plan if necessary. Examine—Check to see if your answer makes sense.

2. If your answer does not make sense, you will need to solve the problem another way.

Study Guide Masters, p. 1

Study Guide

A Plan for Problem Solving

A one-year subscription to a popular magazine costs $24. Ted is thinking of sharing the cost of the subscription equally with two friends. How much will each have to pay?

Explore	What do you know? A one-year subscription costs $24. Ted will share the cost equally with two friends. What are you trying to find? How much each friend will have to pay.
Plan	Since Ted will share with two friends, there are 1 + 2 or 3 people sharing the cost. Find the number of times 3 goes into $24.
Solve	$24 ÷ 3 = $8 Each friend will pay $8 toward the subscription.
Examine	The answer makes sense. 3 × $8 = $24

Use the four-step plan to solve each problem.

1. A record weight for a red snapper was 46 pounds. A record weight for a sturgeon was 468 pounds. About how many times heavier than the red snapper was the sturgeon?

   about 10 times

2. The distance from Chicago to Cleveland is 344 miles. Lisa plans to drive this distance in two days. If she drives 180 miles today, how many miles will she have to drive tomorrow?

   164 miles

3. On a certain day, 525 people signed up to play softball. If 15 players are assigned to each team, how many teams can be formed?

   35 teams

4. The Farrells want to buy a VCR that costs $460. They plan to make a down payment of $100 and pay the rest in eight equal payments. What is the amount of each payment?

   $45

5. Josita received $30 as a gift. She plans to buy two cassette tapes that cost $9 each and a deluxe headphone set that costs $25. How much money will she have left?

   $7

6. Tran wants to buy a bicycle that costs $192. He plans to save $6 each week. How many weeks will it take him to save enough money?

   32 weeks

© Glencoe/McGraw-Hill   T1   *Mathematics: Applications and Connections, Course 1*

Examine   There are 2 weekend days each week, Saturday and Sunday. So, in one year, there are 2 × 52 or 104 weekend days. Subtract 104 from 365 to find the number of weekdays. The result is 261. The answer is reasonable. *Why don't the number of weekend days and weekdays add up to 365?*

CHECK FOR UNDERSTANDING

Communicating Mathematics

Read and study the lesson to answer each question.

1. *Tell* how each step of the four-step plan for problem solving helps you solve a problem. **See margin.**

2. *Explain* why you should check to see whether your answer makes sense for the problem. **See margin.**

3. *Write a Problem* with an answer of $500 that uses addition. Ask a classmate to solve your problem using the four-step plan. **See students' work.**

Guided Practice

Use the four-step plan to solve each problem.

4. *School* Mika studied 224 vocabulary words in two weeks for his French class. If Mika studied the same number of words each day, how many vocabulary words did he study per day? **16 words**

5. *Computers* In 1993, about 5 million computers had CD-ROM drives. In 1997, there were three times as many computers with CD-ROM drives than in 1993. How many computers had CD-ROM drives in 1997? **about 15 million**

EXERCISES

Applications and Problem Solving

Use the four-step plan to solve each problem.

6. *Computers* A computer disk holds 720K of memory. If three programs are on the disk and they use 27K, 34K, and 52K of memory, how much memory is left on the disk? **607K**

7. *Geography* On a map of Tennessee, each inch represents approximately 18 miles. Travis is planning to travel from Nashville to Knoxville. If the distance on the map from Nashville to Knoxville is about 10 inches, approximately how far will he travel? **180 miles**

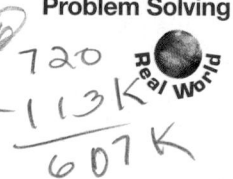

8. *Earth Science* On the first day of summer, Barrow, Alaska, has 24 hours of daylight, and Honolulu, Hawaii, has 13 hours and 26 minutes of daylight. How much more daylight does Barrow have than Honolulu? **10 h 34 min**

9. *Money Matters* The Anstines want to buy a 27-inch television that costs $390. They plan to make a down payment of $150 and pay the rest in six equal payments. What will be the amount of each payment? **$40**

■ Reteaching the Lesson ■

Activity Separate the class into groups. Provide each group with a store flyer that lists prices for items the store sells. Tell each group to choose any combination of 3 items from the list and to get as close to $25 as possible.

MathPASS CD-ROM

This CD-ROM offers a complete, self-paced mathematics curriculum. Each lesson includes a pretest, tutorial, guided practice, and posttest. MathPASS Lesson 1 is correlated to this Student Edition lesson.
For Windows & Macintosh

interNET
CONNECTION
For the latest postal statistics, visit www.glencoe.com/sec/mac/math/mathnet

13. 84,480 pennies
15. Yes; Sample answer: a team can score 7 field goals and 1 safety or 3 touchdowns, 2 two-point conversions, and 1 one-point conversion.

10. *Postal Service* Refer to the graph.
   a. How many more cards are sent for Valentine's Day than Father's Day? **824 million**
   b. How many more cards are sent for Valentine's Day than Mother's Day? **770 million**

11. *Life Science* To estimate the temperature in degrees Fahrenheit, you can count the number of times a cricket chirps in 15 seconds and then add that number to 40. What is the temperature if a cricket chirps 25 times in 15 seconds? **65°F**

ADD

12. *Money Matters* The student council at West Boulevard Middle School is planning their annual winter dance. Tickets to the dance cost $3 each. There are 345 students in the school. If each student buys one ticket, how much money would the student council collect? **$1,035**

MULT

13. *Measurement* Mrs. Hall challenged her class to determine the number of pennies it takes to reach one mile. If there are 16 pennies in one foot, how many pennies are in one mile? (*Hint*: 1 mile = 5,280 feet)

14. *Life Science* An adult male walrus weighs about 2,670 pounds. An adult female walrus weighs about 1,835 pounds. How many more pounds does an adult male walrus weigh than an adult female walrus? **835 pounds**

Holiday Mail
Average number of cards and letters mailed:

Valentine's Day 925 million
Mother's Day 155 million
Father's Day 101 million

Source: U.S Postal Service, Greeting Card Association

2. Sampl
The nu
cubes
build e
stairca
increa
4, 5, a

15. *Critical Thinking* Refer to the table. To score in either of the last two ways, a team must have scored a touchdown on the preceding play. Can a team score 23 points? Explain your answer.

For **Extra Practice**, see page 557.

Different Ways a Team Can Score in Football	
Touchdown	6 points
Field Goal	3 points
Safety	2 points
2-Point Conversion	2 points
1-Point Conversion	1 point

Lesson 1-1 A Plan for Problem Solving   **7**

═══ Extending the Lesson ═══

Enrichment Masters, p. 1

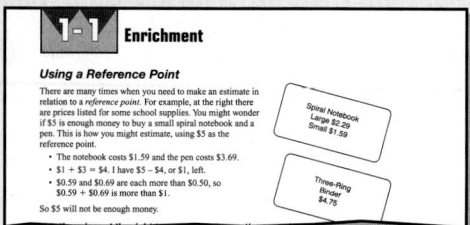
1-1 Enrichment

Using a Reference Point
There are many times when you need to make an estimate in relation to a *reference point*. For example, at the right there are prices listed for some school supplies. You might wonder if $5 is enough money to buy a small spiral notebook and a pen. This is how you might estimate, using $5 as the reference point.
• The notebook costs $1.59 and the pen costs $3.69.
• $1 + $3 = $4. I have $5 − $4, or $1, left.
• $0.59 and $0.69 are each more than $0.50, so $0.59 + $0.69 is more than $1.
So $5 will not be enough money.

Spiral Notebook Large $2.29 Small $1.59

Three-Ring Binder $4.79

Activity Have students ask their family members how they use mathematics in their jobs. As a class activity, use the responses to prepare a list of how mathematics is used on various jobs. Ask students to suggest other jobs they think require the use of mathematics.

Closing Activity
Speaking Separate students into groups of four. Within the groups, have each student explain one step of the problem-solving process.

$$
\begin{array}{r}
925 \\
-155 \\
\hline
770
\end{array}
$$

T

Practice Masters, p. 1

Name_____ Date_____

1-1 Practice

A Plan for Problem Solving

Use the four-step plan to solve each problem.

1. Kara is a member of the school swim team. She swims 35 laps at each practice. The swim team practices 4 days per week. How many laps does Kara swim in one month?
560 laps

2. The school band is having a car wash to raise money to purchase new uniforms. If they charge $4 per car, how many cars must band members wash to raise $208?
52 cars

3. When the Breen family left for their vacation, the car's odometer read 5,289 miles. Upon their return, the odometer read 6,035 miles. How many miles did the Breen family travel during their vacation?
746 miles

4. Kyle is renewing his subscription to his favorite computer magazine. The cost is $24 for 12 issues. What is the cost of each issue?
$2 per issue

5. The sixth-graders at Danville Middle School collected aluminum cans for a recycling project. Room 6A collected 137 cans; Room 6B collected 98 cans; Room 6C collected 164 cans. How many aluminum cans were collected in all?
399 cans

6. Carla enjoys collecting baseball cards. Her album contains 115 pages. Each page holds 9 baseball cards. How many baseball cards will there be in her in all? album when it is
1,035 cards

7. Chi-Sun went shopping for hiking supplies. He bought a knapsack for $22, a canteen for $5 and a compass for $12. How much money did he spend in all?
$39

8. Eva has saved $64 from her babysitting money. She needs 4 times this amount to buy a new bike. How much does the new bike cost?
$256

© Glencoe/McGraw-Hill   T1   Mathematics: Applications and Connections, Course 1

Instruct...
- *Study G...*
- *Practic...*
- *Enrichm...*
- Transpa...
- *Assess...*
  Master...
  CD-RO...
- *Res...*

Rec...	
Standar...	
Honors	
Block	

Use the...
solve e...

1. A wa...
   agre...
   widg...
   distr...
   widg...
   orde...
   yes

2. The...
   half-...
   sale...
   pack...
   for $...

Th...

ava...
for...

Motivat...

Commun...
such as f...
to give a...
pattern r...
example,...
football fi...
50, 40, 3...

In-Class Example

For Example 5
The band needs to make a triangular formation with 10 students at the base. How many students are needed? **55**

3 PRACTICE/APPLY

Check for Understanding
If students need additional practice or instruction after completing Exercises 1–6, one of these options may be helpful.
- Extra Practice, see p. 557
- Reteaching Activity
- *Study Guide Masters*, p. 2
- *Practice Masters*, p. 2

Additional Answer

3.
Number of Folds	1	2	3	4
Number of Thicknesses	2	4	8	16

Sample answer: The number of thicknesses doubles.

Study Guide Masters, p. 2

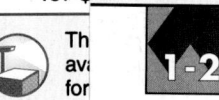

Example **5** INTEGRATION

Geometry The marching band wants to make a triangular formation on the football field. Triangular formations with 2, 3, 4, and 5 students at the base look as follows:

2   3   4   5

How many students are needed to make a triangular formation with 8 students at the base?

Explore You know the number of students needed to make a formation with 2, 3, 4, and 5 students at the base. You need to find the number of students needed to make a formation with 8 students at the base.

Plan Make a table to organize the information. Then, study the table to find a pattern.

Solve

Number of Students at Base	2	3	4	5	6	7	8
Total Number of Students Needed	3	6	10	15	?	?	?

21   28   36
+3 +4 +5 +6 +7 +8

The extra students needed increases by 1 each time. Use the pattern to complete the chart.

$15 + 6 = 21$ $21 + 7 = 28$ $28 + 8 = 36$

36 students will be needed to make a triangular formation with 8 students at the base.

Examine Draw a triangular formation with 8 dots at the base. Check to see if there are 36 dots in the formation.

CHECK FOR UNDERSTANDING

Communicating Mathematics

Read and study the lesson to answer each question.

1. *Draw* the first five phases of a geometric pattern. Then write a rule for finding the next shape in the pattern. **See students' work.**

2. *Write* a number pattern with six numbers. Then write a rule for finding the next number in the pattern. **See students' work.**

HANDS-ON MATH

3. Fold a piece of paper 1 time. Count the number of thicknesses. How many thicknesses are there when the paper is folded 2 times? 3 times? 4 times? Describe the pattern in the number of thicknesses. **See margin.**

10 Chapter 1 Problem Solving, Numbers, and Algebra

Reteaching the Lesson

Activity Give students a number and have them use the constant key (OP₁ or OP₂ on the calculator) to create a pattern of five numbers. Have them record the numbers. Then ask them to exchange papers with others to find the next two numbers in the pattern.

Error Analysis
Watch for students who think they find a pattern but who don't check that it works with all of the given numbers.
Prevent by encouraging students to write the operation for each succeeding number.

Guided Practice Find the next three numbers in each pattern. **5.** **8, 4, 2**

4. 0, 8, 16, 24, _?_, _?_, _?_ **32, 40, 48**   **5.** 128, 64, 32, 16, _?_, _?_, _?_

6. *Sports* Jamil and Mark are competing against each other in a tennis match. Their scores are shown below.

	Set 1	Set 2	Set 3	Set 4	Set 5
Jamil	6	2	6	4	6
Mark	3	6	3	6	?

If the pattern continues, what will Mark's score be in set 5? **3**

EXERCISES

Practice Find the next three numbers in each pattern.

8. 19, 22, 25
9. 512, 2,048, 8,192
10. 12, 6, 0
12. 243, 729, 2,187

7. 3, 4, 3, 4, _?_, _?_, _?_ **3, 4, 3**
9. 2, 8, 32, 128, _?_, _?_, _?_
11. 7, 8, 10, 13, _?_, _?_, _?_ **17, 22, 28**
13. Find the next three numbers in the pattern 1, 3, 7, 13, … . **21, 31, 43**

8. 7, 10, 13, 16, _?_, _?_, _?_
10. 36, 30, 24, 18, _?_, _?_, _?_
12. 3, 9, 27, 81, _?_, _?_, _?_

Applications and Problem Solving

14. *Fitness* Marcie is training for the swim team. On the first day, she swims 5 laps. The second day she swims 6 laps. The third day she swims 8 laps, and on the fourth day she swims 11 laps. **a. 15 laps**
  a. If this pattern continues, how many laps will she swim on the fifth day?
  b. On which day will she reach her goal of 33 laps? **day 8**

15. *Transportation* Isabel needs to take the bus home from the mall. She forgot her bus schedule but she remembers that the bus comes every 20 minutes. She also remembers that there is a bus at 12:30 P.M. What time does the first bus after 5:00 P.M. arrive? **5:10 P.M.**

16. *Geometry* Find the next two shapes in the pattern.

For **Extra Practice**, see page 557.

17. *Critical Thinking* What is the next number in the pattern 1, 2, 2, 4, 8, 32, … ? **256**

Mixed Review

18. *History* In July 1776, General George Washington had nearly 30,000 troops guarding New York City. After retreating through New Jersey to the Delaware River, only about 3,000 troops remained with him. How many troops did he lose? *(Lesson 1-1)* **27,000 troops**

19. *Standardized Test Practice* In its first year, Lucas Software had a profit of $2,763,000. The second year, their profit increased by $184,000. How much profit did Lucas Software have in the second year? *(Lesson 1-1)* **C**
  A $2,579,000   **B** $2,763,000   **C** $2,947,000   **D** $3,248,000

Lesson 1-2 Using Patterns **11**

Extending the Lesson

Enrichment Masters, p. 2

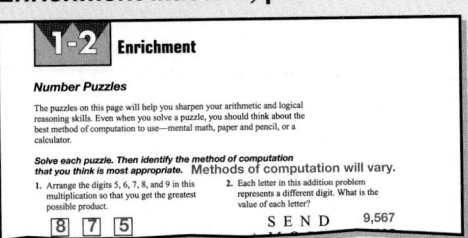

Activity The pattern 1, 1, 2, 3, 5, 8, … is called the *Fibonacci sequence*. Each number is the sum of the previous two numbers. Find the first 20 numbers in the sequence. Look for other patterns in the sequence. **1, 1, 2, 3, 5, 8, 13, 21, 34, 55, 89, 144, 233, 377, 610, 987, 1,597, 2,584, 4,181, 6,765. Sample answer: Every fifth number is divisible by 5.**

Lesson 1-2 **11**

- *Study Guide Masters*, p. 3
- *Practice Masters*, p. 3
- *Enrichment Masters*, p. 3
- Transparencies 1-3, A and B

 CD-ROM Program
- Resource Lesson 1-3
- Interactive Lesson 1-3

Recommended Pacing	
Standard	Day 4 of 12
Honors	Day 4 of 12
Block	Day 2 of 6

1 FOCUS

5-Minute Check
(Lesson 1-2)

Find the next three numbers for each pattern.

1. 2, 5, 8, 11, _?_ , _?_ , _?_
   14, 17, 20

2. 1, 3, 9, 27, _?_ , _?_ , _?_
   81, 243, 729

3. 25, 21, 17, 13, _?_ , _?_ , _?_
   9, 5, 1

4. 192, 96, 48, 24, _?_ , _?_ , _?_
   12, 6, 3

5. How many students in a marching band are needed to make a triangle formation with 6 students at the base?
   21

The 5-Minute Check is also available on **Transparency 1-3A** for this lesson.

Motivating the Lesson

Communication Have students read the opening paragraph of the lesson. Ask the following question. *Should you estimate or find an exact answer? Why?* Estimate; the question asks *about* how many wild horses are on public land in five states.

1-3 Estimation by Rounding

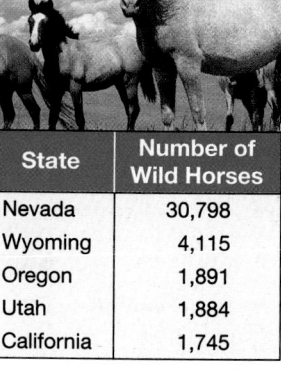

What you'll learn

You'll learn to estimate sums, differences, products, and quotients using rounding.

When am I ever going to use this?

Rounding can be used to estimate the total cost of items at a department store.

Wild horses can be found throughout the United States. The table shows the number of wild horses living on public lands in five western states. About how many wild horses are living on public lands in these five states?

To estimate the number of wild horses, you can use rounding. Round each number to the nearest thousand. Then add.

State	Number of Wild Horses
Nevada	30,798
Wyoming	4,115
Oregon	1,891
Utah	1,884
California	1,745

$$
\begin{array}{rcr}
30,798 & \rightarrow & 31,000 \\
4,115 & \rightarrow & 4,000 \\
1,891 & \rightarrow & 2,000 \\
1,884 & \rightarrow & 2,000 \\
+\ 1,745 & \rightarrow & +\ 2,000 \\
\hline
& & 41,000
\end{array}
$$

About 41,000 horses are living on public lands in the five states.

Let's review the rules for rounding.

Rounding Whole Numbers	Look at the digit to the right of the place being rounded. • The digit remains the same if the digit to the right is 0, 1, 2, 3, or 4. • Round up if the digit to the right is 5, 6, 7, 8, or 9.

 Example **1** Round 43 to the nearest ten.

On the number line, 43 is closer to 40 than it is to 50.

Look at the digit to the right of the tens place. Since 3 is less than 5, the digit in the tens place remains the same. 43 rounded to the nearest ten is 40.

Multiple Learning Styles

Interpersonal Have students work in groups to practice estimation problems. Ask each student to think up a problem about going to a grocery with money to buy several items. Have them try out their problems on the other students in the group.

② Round 252 to the nearest hundred.

252
200   250   300

On the number line, 252 is closer to 300 than it is to 200.

Look at the digit to the right of the hundreds place. Since the digit is 5, round up. That is, increase the digit in the hundreds place by one. The number 252 rounded to the nearest hundred is 300.

③ Round 9,973 to the nearest thousand.

9,973
9,000   9,500   10,000

On the number line, 9,973 is closer to 10,000 than it is to 9,000.

Look at the digit to the right of the thousands place. Round up since 9 is greater than 5. Thus, 9,973 rounded to the nearest thousand is 10,000.

Estimation is a useful skill that provides a quick answer when an exact answer is not needed.

Examples

④ Estimate the product of 7 and 64.

$$\begin{array}{ccc} 64 & \rightarrow & 60 \\ \times\,7 & \rightarrow & \times\,7 \\ \hline & & 420 \end{array}$$

⑤ Estimate the quotient of 112 and 23.

$$112 \div 23 \rightarrow 20\overline{)100}^{\,5}$$

Using estimation, you can also check to see whether an answer is reasonable.

Example

Real World APPLICATION

⑥ **Money Matters** Eduardo is shopping at Calyan's department store. He purchases a bag of candy, a mechanical pencil, and a package of baseball cards. The total bill is $9.12. He gives the cashier a $20 bill and receives $9.46 in change. Is this amount reasonable?

Round to the nearest dollar amount. Then subtract mentally.

$$\begin{array}{ccc} \$20.00 & \rightarrow & \$20 \\ -\,9.12 & \rightarrow & -\,9 \\ \hline & & \$11 \end{array}$$

Eduardo should have received about $11. So, the amount of $9.46 is *not* reasonable.

 Transparency 1-3B contains a teaching aid for this lesson.

Using Discussion Some students may be hesitant to make estimates using the methods presented, thinking that only exact answers are acceptable. Discuss situations in which estimates are more useful or descriptive than exact answers. **estimating the total cost of items to see if you have enough money**

In-Class Examples

For Example 1
a. Round 23 to the nearest ten. **20**

b. Round 86 to the nearest ten. **90**

For Example 2
a. Round 155 to the nearest hundred. **200**

b. Round 921 to the nearest hundred. **900**

For Example 3
a. Round 3,413 to the nearest thousand. **3,000**

b. Round 1,650 to the nearest thousand. **2,000**

For Example 4
a. Estimate the product of 3 and 18. **60**

b. Estimate the product of 13 and 92. **900**

For Example 5
a. Estimate the quotient of 157 and 42. **4**

b. Estimate the quotient of 96 and 12. **10**

For Example 6
Aaron went to a music store and bought 2 CDs at $11.59 each and a cassette for $8.39. He gave the cashier two $20 bills and got back $8.43 in change. Is this amount reasonable? **yes**

Teaching Tip Explain to students that estimates are useful when you don't need an exact answer and want to save time and work or when you don't have a pencil and paper handy.

Check for Understanding

If students need additional practice or instruction after completing Exercises 1–14, one of these options may be helpful.
- Extra Practice, see p. 557
- Reteaching Activity
- *Transition Booklet*, pp. 11–14, 17–18
- *Study Guide Masters*, p. 3
- *Practice Masters*, p. 3

Assignment Guide

Core: 15–43 odd, 46–52
Enriched: 16–42 even, 43, 44, 46–52

Additional Answers

1. On the number line, 957 is closer to 1,000 than to 900.

13. $500 \div 50 = 10$; not reasonable

36. $120 \div 2 = 60$; not reasonable

37. $5,000 + 5,000 = 10,000$; reasonable

38. $400 \times 4 = 1,600$; not reasonable

Study Guide Masters, p. 3

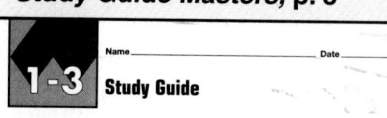

Communicating Mathematics

2. Sample answer: Round 517 to 500; round 192 to 200; 500 − 200 = 300 so 517 − 192 is about 300.

Read and study the lesson to answer each question.

1. *Tell* how you would round 957 to the nearest hundred by using the number line below. **See margin.**

$$\begin{array}{ccc} & 957 \\ 900 & 950 & 1,000 \end{array}$$

2. *Explain* how you would use rounding to estimate 517 − 192.

3. *Write* about a situation when you would use estimation. **See students' work.**

Guided Practice

10. $7.00 + $9.00 = $16.00; not reasonable

11. 900 − 400 = 500; reasonable

12. 200 × 6 = 1,200; reasonable

Round each number to the underlined place-value position.

4. 3̲5 40
5. 4̲24 400
6. 5̲42 540
7. 2̲96 300
8. 2,0̲88 2,000
9. 9̲,922 10,000

Estimate. State whether the answer shown is reasonable.

10. $6.67 + $8.99 = $12.66
11. 898 − 413 = 485
12. 215 × 6 = 1,290
13. 468 ÷ 52 = 14 **See margin.**

14. *Food* The average U.S. citizen eats about 47 pints of ice cream per year. The average Italian citizen eats about 22 pints per year. About how many more pints of ice cream does the average U.S. citizen eat than the average Italian citizen? **about 30 pints**

EXERCISES

Practice

Round each number to the underlined place-value position.

15. 9̲7 100
16. 5̲20 520
17. 5̲1 50
18. 1̲8 20
19. 4̲44 440
20. 8,1̲96 8,200
21. 5,5̲00 5,500
22. 9̲27 930
23. 3,7̲04 3,700
24. 3̲94 400
25. 5,6̲23 5,600
26. 3,6̲56 3,700
27. 9̲,716 10,000
28. 4̲,448 4,000
29. 1̲,888 2,000
30. 7̲,050 7,000

31. Round 9,438 to the nearest thousand. **9,000**

32. What is 6,612 rounded to the nearest hundred? **6,600**

33. 80 × 3 = 240; reasonable

34. $3.00 + $3.00 + $3.00 = $9.00; reasonable

35. 100 − 20 = 80; not reasonable

36–42. See margin.

Estimate. State whether the answer shown is reasonable.

33. 82 × 3 = 246
34. $3.32 + $3.34 + $3.21 = $9.87
35. 96 − 18 = 65
36. 121 ÷ 2 = 42
37. 4,901 + 5,002 = 9,903
38. 392 × 4 = 12,368
39. 765 − 234 = 531
40. 391 ÷ 23 = 17
41. $5.25 + $35.27 = $46.12
42. 2,914 × 3 = 8,742

Applications and Problem Solving

43. *Recycling* The average U.S. citizen uses about 190 pounds of plastic, 55 pounds of aluminum cans, 586 pounds of paper, and 325 pounds of glass per year. If these materials are recyclable, about how many pounds of these materials could be recycled by the average citizen in one year?
Sample answer: 200 + 60 + 600 + 300 = 1,160; about 1,160 lbs

■ Reteaching the Lesson ■

Activity Write a list of prices on the chalkboard for various items from a department store. Prepare several gift coupons for amounts ranging from $100 to $2,000. Hand out these coupons to students and ask them to shop from the list, getting as close to the amount on the coupon as possible.

Additional Answers

39. 800 − 200 = 600; reasonable
40. 400 ÷ 20 = 20; reasonable
41. $5.00 + $35.00 = $40.00; not reasonable
42. 3,000 × 3 = 9,000; reasonable

44. Travel The chart shows the approximate distance, in miles, between some U.S. cities. Suppose you travel from Raleigh, North Carolina, to Nashville, Tennessee. If you average 52 miles per hour, about how many hours will it take you to get there? **about 10 hours**

Mileage Chart

Approximate Mileages	Raleigh, NC	Albuquerque, NM	Nashville, TN	Minneapolis, MN	Portland, OR	Charleston, WV	Dallas, TX
Raleigh, NC		1,760	538	1,215	2,965	299	1,200
Albuquerque, NM	1,760		1,228	1,227	1,377	1,527	654
Nashville, TN	538	1,228		812	2,424	395	668
Minneapolis, MN	1,215	1,227	812		1,748	937	963
Portland, OR	2,965	1,377	2,424	1,748		2,572	2,041
Charleston, WV	299	1,527	395	937	2,572		1,141
Dallas, TX	1,200	654	668	963	2,041	1,141	

45. Working on the Refer to the tables on page 3.

45a. $75 + $36 + $21 + $6 + $2 + $2 + $10 = $152

  a. Suppose you place an order from the Sporting Goods Catalog. You order a pair of running shoes for $74.99, a hooded sweatshirt for $35.99, and a pair of shorts for $20.99. Estimate the total cost of the order including express delivery charges. **b. See students' work.**

  b. Choose a catalog from which you would like to order. Imagine you have $200 to spend. List the items you would like to order and their prices. Estimate the total cost of the order including shipping charges.

46. See margin.

46. Critical Thinking You want to purchase three items at a store for $4.43, $5.42, and $6.45. You have $15. To see if you have enough money, you estimate the total cost by rounding the cost of each item to the nearest dollar and adding. Will you have a problem making this purchase? Explain.

Mixed Review

47. Patterns Find the next three numbers in the pattern 1, 2, 4, 7, ... *(Lesson 1-2)* **11, 16, 22**

48. Geometry Find the next figure in the pattern. *(Lesson 1-2)*

49. School At Watson Middle School, the bells ring at 8:50 A.M., 8:54 A.M., 9:34 A.M., 9:38 A.M., and 10:18 A.M. each day. When do the next three bells ring? *(Lesson 1-2)* **10:22 A.M., 11:02 A.M., 11:06 A.M.**

50. Population In 1998, Denver had a population of 499,000 people, and Atlanta had a population of 404,000 people. How many more people were living in Denver than Atlanta? *(Lesson 1-1)* **95,000 people**

51. Standardized Test Practice The Changs' dot matrix printer prints four pages each minute. Hiro Chang has a history report that is 12 pages long. How long will it take the printer to print the report? *(Lesson 1-1)* **C**

  A 6 min   **B** 4 min   **C** 3 min   **D** 2 min

52. School Jill needs to hand out an equal number of counters to 23 students. If there are 522 counters, how many should she give each student? *(Lesson 1-1)* **22**

For **Extra Practice,** see page 557.

Lesson 1-3 Estimation by Rounding **15**

Exercise 45 asks students to advance to the next stage of work on the Chapter Project. You may ask students to consider how shipping charges in Exercise 45a will affect their estimates before they begin work.

4 ASSESS

Closing Activity

Modeling Give groups of students clothes catalogs. Have them pick out outfits, including shoes and socks. Ask them to estimate the cost of each outfit.

Additional Answer

46. $4 + $5 + $6 = $15. Since each cost is rounded down, the total cost will be greater than $15. You probably will not have enough money.

Practice Masters, p. 3

1-3 Practice

Estimation by Rounding

Round each number to the underlined place-value position.

1. <u>4</u>4 **40**	2. <u>6</u>5 **70**	3. <u>2</u>8 **30**
4. <u>6</u>17 **600**	5. <u>5</u>93 **600**	6. <u>4</u>52 **500**
7. <u>2</u>05 **700**	8. <u>6</u>99 **700**	9. <u>8</u>49 **800**
10. 1<u>0</u>9 **110**	11. 6<u>8</u>4 **680**	12. 2<u>7</u>1 **270**
13. <u>3</u>,150 **3,000**	14. <u>9</u>,738 **10,000**	15. <u>5</u>,426 **5,000**
16. <u>4</u>,549 **5,000**	17. 6,<u>6</u>55 **6,700**	18. 9,9<u>6</u>7 **9,970**
19. 1,3<u>6</u>9 **1,370**	20. <u>7</u>,510 **8,000**	21. 4,<u>0</u>87 **4,000**
22. <u>5</u>,435 **5,000**	23. 2,<u>9</u>03 **2,900**	24. 6,<u>2</u>58 **6,300**
25. 3,<u>0</u>09 **3,000**	26. 7,<u>4</u>99 **7,500**	27. <u>9</u>,501 **10,000**

Estimate. State whether the answer shown is reasonable.

28. 37 + 55 + 81 = 173   **40 + 60 + 80 = 180; yes**

29. 28 + 72 + 15 + 129 = 244   **30 + 70 + 20 + 130 = 250; yes**

30. 562 + 349 + 107 = 1,218   **600 + 300 + 100 = 1,000; no**

31. 418 + 689 + 104 = 1,411   **400 + 700 + 100 = 1,200; no**

32. $8.65 + $3.39 + $4.52 = $19.56   **$9 + $3 + $5 = $17; no**

33. 976 − 453 = 523   **1,000 − 500 = 500; yes**

34. 758 − 364 = 394   **800 − 400 = 400; yes**

35. $4.11 + $16.75 + $10.95 = $29.11   **$4 + $17 + $11 = $32; no**

© Glencoe/McGraw-Hill   T3   Mathematics: Applications and Connections, Course 1

Extending the Lesson

Enrichment Masters, p. 3

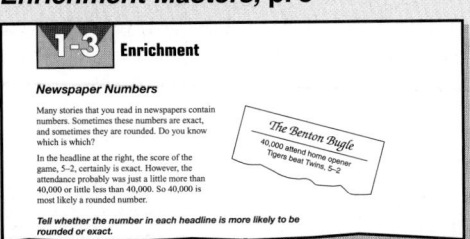

1-3 Enrichment

Newspaper Numbers

Many stories that you read in newspapers contain numbers. Sometimes these numbers are exact, and sometimes they are rounded. Do you know which is which?

The Benton Bugle
40,000 attend home opener
Tigers beat Twins, 5–2

In the headline at the right, the score of the game, 5–2, certainly is exact. However, the attendance probably was just a little more than 40,000 or little less than 40,000. So 40,000 is most likely a rounded number.

Tell whether the number in each headline is more likely to be rounded or exact.

Activity Interview the cafeteria staff to determine how they use estimation in their jobs. Focus questions on when and why exact numbers and estimates are useful. Write a report to be published in the class or school newspaper.

Instructional Resources

- *Study Guide Masters*, p. 4
- *Practice Masters*, p. 4
- *Enrichment Masters*, p. 4
- Transparencies 1-4, A and B
- *Assessment and Evaluation Masters*, pp. 14, 15
- *Technology Masters*, p. 1
- CD-ROM Program
  - Resource Lesson 1-4

Recommended Pacing	
Standard	Day 5 of 12
Honors	Day 5 of 12
Block	Day 3 of 6

1 FOCUS

5-Minute Check
(Lesson 1-3)

1. Round 535 to the nearest ten. **540**

Estimate. State whether the answer shown is reasonable.

2. 73 + 89 + 38 = 300
   70 + 90 + 40 = 200; **not reasonable**

3. 879 − 585 = 294
   900 − 600 = 300; **reasonable**

4. 1,679 × 31 = 52,049
   2,000 × 30 = 60,000; **reasonable**

5. 399 ÷ 19 = 20
   400 ÷ 20 = 20; **reasonable**

The 5-Minute Check is also available on Transparency **1-4A** for this lesson.

Motivating the Lesson

Hands-On Activity Have students use counters to represent 6 + 4 × 2. Discuss whether the correct answer is 20 or 14 and why. **14**

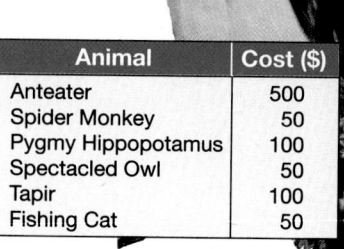

What you'll learn

You'll learn to evaluate expressions using the order of operations.

When am I ever going to use this?

Knowing how to follow the order of operations can help you find the total cost of zoo tickets for your class.

Word Wise

order of operations

The San Diego Zoo has more than 3,200 animals. Each year, the animal food bill is more than $685,000. Many people help reduce this cost by adopting an animal. The table shows the costs for adopting various zoo animals. How much would it cost to adopt 1 pygmy hippopotamus, 4 fishing cats, and 3 tapirs? *This problem will be solved in Example 4.*

Animal	Cost ($)
Anteater	500
Spider Monkey	50
Pygmy Hippopotamus	100
Spectacled Owl	50
Tapir	100
Fishing Cat	50

When more than one operation is used, we need to know which one to perform first so that everyone gets the same result. Mathematicians have come up with rules called the **order of operations**.

Order of Operations	1. Multiply and divide in order from left to right. 2. Add and subtract in order from left to right.

Examples

Find the value of each expression.

1 $15 + 7 - 3$

$$15 + 7 - 3 = 22 - 3 \quad \textit{Add 7 to 15.}$$
$$= 19 \quad \textit{Subtract 3 from 22.}$$

2 $3 + 6 \times 4 - 2$

$$3 + 6 \times 4 - 2 = 3 + 24 - 2 \quad \textit{Multiply 6 and 4.}$$
$$= 27 - 2 \quad \textit{Add 3 and 24.}$$
$$= 25 \quad \textit{Subtract 2 from 27.}$$

3 $14 \div 7 + 12 \times 3 - 9$

$$14 \div 7 + 12 \times 3 - 9 = 2 + 12 \times 3 - 9 \quad \textit{Divide 14 by 7.}$$
$$= 2 + 36 - 9 \quad \textit{Multiply 12 and 3.}$$
$$= 38 - 9 \quad \textit{Add 2 and 36.}$$
$$= 29 \quad \textit{Subtract 9 from 38.}$$

Multiple Learning Styles

Auditory/Musical Assign each of the four math operations a different sound—for example, a drum beat for division. Have one student find the value of an expression using the order of operations. Then have another student make the sounds in the same order that the first student evaluated the expression. Have students discuss whether the sounds came in the correct order.

Example 4

CONNECTION

Life Science Refer to the beginning of the lesson.

a. Write an expression for the cost of adopting 1 pygmy hippopotamus, 4 fishing cats, and 3 tapirs.

b. Find the cost of adopting the animals.

a.

cost for 1 hippo	plus	cost for 4 cats	plus	3 tapirs
$1 \times \$100$	$+$	$4 \times \$50$	$+$	$3 \times \$100$

b. Find the value of the expression.

$$1 \times \$100 + 4 \times \$50 + 3 \times \$100 = \$100 + 4 \times \$50 + 3 \times \$100$$
$$= \$100 + \$200 + 3 \times \$100$$
$$= \$100 + \$200 + \$300$$
$$= \$600$$

The cost of adopting the animals is $600.

Does your calculator follow the order of operations?

Using the Mini-Lab Scientific calculators follow the order of operations. Basic calculators may or may not. Find a calculator that does not follow the order of operations. Have students compare the answers found using this calculator with those found using a scientific calculator. Ask students what this shows about the importance of order of operations.

Teaching Tip To help students remember to multiply and divide before they add and subtract, suggest that they use the mnemonic **M**Y **D**EAR **A**UNT **S**ALLY. Remind students this does *not* necessarily mean to multiply before dividing or to add before subtracting.

TECHNOLOGY MINI-LAB

Work with a partner.

 calculator

Find the value of $5 + 8 \div 4 \times 3$.

Method 1
Use a calculator.

5 [+] 8 [÷] 4 [×] 3 [=] *11*

Method 2
Use paper and pencil.

Follow the order of operations.

$$5 + 8 \div 4 \times 3 = 5 + 2 \times 3$$
$$= 5 + 6$$
$$= 11$$

This calculator follows the order of operations.

Try This 1. See students' work.

1. Using your calculator, evaluate $3 + 2 \times 5 - 7$.

2. Evaluate this expression using paper and pencil and the order of operations. **6**

Talk About It

3. Compare your answers. Are they the same? If so, why are they the same? If not, why are they different? **See margin.**

Lesson 1-4 Order of Operations **17**

In-Class Examples

For Example 1
Find the value of each expression.
a. $28 - 4 + 9$ **33**
b. $103 + 15 - 8$ **110**

For Example 2
Find the value of each expression.
a. $24 + 3 \times 4 - 15$ **21**
b. $15 - 8 + 6 \times 3$ **25**

For Example 3
Find the value of each expression.
a. $16 \div 4 + 6 \times 2 - 5$ **11**
b. $13 + 56 \div 7 - 2 \times 4$ **13**

For Example 4
Refer to the beginning of the lesson. Find the cost of adopting 3 spectacled owls, 2 tapirs, 4 spider monkeys, and 1 anteater. **$1,050**

Additional Answer for the Mini-Lab

3. Whereas one calculator follows the order of operations, the other one performs the operations as they are entered into the calculator.

Check for Understanding

If students need additional practice or instruction after completing Exercises 1–7, one of these options may be helpful.
- Extra Practice, see p. 558
- Reteaching Activity
- *Study Guide Masters*, p. 4
- *Practice Masters*, p. 4
- Interactive Mathematics Tools Software

Assignment Guide

Core: 9–21 odd, 24–27
Enriched: 8–20 even, 21, 22, 24–27
All: Self Test, 1–10

Family Activity

Have students share with the class the projects they chose and the steps involved. Ask students to brainstorm activities in everday life that require a specific order of operations.

Additional Answer

1. **Multiply and divide from left to right. Then add and subtract from left to right.**

Study Guide Masters, p. 4

Name_____ Date_____

1-4 Study Guide

Order of Operations

To evaluate expressions, use the order of operations.

Order of Operations
1. Multiply and divide in order from left to right.
2. Add and subtract in order from left to right.

Example Find the value of $2 \times 8 - 42 \div 7 + 4$.

$2 \times 8 - 42 \div 7 + 4 = 16 - 42 \div 7 + 4$ *Multiply 2 and 8.*
$= 16 - 6 + 4$ *Divide 42 by 7.*
$= 10 + 4$ *Subtract 6 from 16.*
$= 14$ *Add 10 and 4.*

Find the value of each expression.

1. $15 + 4 \times 5 - 6$ **29**
2. $40 \div 8 - 3$ **2**
3. $9 \times 3 + 3$ **30**
4. $20 - 15 \div 3$ **15**
5. $2 \times 4 \times 5$ **40**
6. $18 \div 2 + 9 \times 2$ **27**
7. $3 + 7 - 5 + 2$ **7**
8. $4 \times 9 - 9 \times 4$ **0**
9. $15 \div 3 + 3 \times 5$ **20**
10. $45 \div 9 \div 5$ **1**
11. $18 \div 3 + 15 \div 3$ **26**
12. $50 - 5 \times 5 - 25$ **0**
13. $35 + 7 - 5$ **0**
14. $12 \times 2 - 5 \times 4$ **4**
15. $4 + 18 \div 3$ **10**
16. $150 \div 10 - 3 \times 5$ **0**
17. $7 + 2 \times 5$ **17**
18. $3 \times 8 - 16$ **8**
19. $80 \times 2 + 40 - 1$ **3**
20. $25 - 3 \times 4$ **13**
21. $2 + 4 \times 9 \div 12$ **5**
22. $45 - 40 + 1 \times 2$ **7**
23. $18 \div 2 \times 9$ **81**
24. $2 \times 5 \times 3$ **30**

© Glencoe/McGraw-Hill   T4   *Mathematics: Applications and Connections, Course 1*

Communicating Mathematics

Read and study the lesson to answer each question.

1. *List* each step of the order of operations. **See margin.**

2. *Identify* the first step when evaluating the expression $25 + 2 - 6 \div 3 \times 2$. **Divide 6 by 3.**

Guided Practice

Name the operation that should be done first. Then find the value of the expression.

3. $22 + 5 - 13$ **+; 14**
4. $13 - 4 + 7 \times 6$ **×; 51**
5. $9 \times 15 \div 5 + 6$ **×; 33**
6. $27 - 8 \div 4 \times 3$ **÷; 21**

7. *Money Matters* Mrs. Jamison's class is planning a trip to the zoo. Tickets cost $6 for children and $15 for adults.
   a. Write an expression for the total cost of 12 adult tickets and 28 children's tickets. **12 × $15 + 28 × $6**
   b. Find the total cost of the tickets. **$348**

Practice

Find the value of each expression.

8. $16 + 5 - 7$ **14**
9. $15 \times 8 - 3$ **117**
10. $85 \div 17 \times 14$ **70**
11. $29 + 56 \div 4$ **43**
12. $17 - 3 \times 4 + 6$ **11**
13. $21 + 18 \div 6 - 9$ **15**
14. $68 + 19 - 7 \times 5$ **52**
15. $19 + 45 \div 3 - 11$ **23**
16. $26 \div 13 + 9 \times 6 - 21$ **35**
17. $9 + 12 - 6 \times 4 \div 2$ **9**

18. Evaluate the expression $67 - 21 \div 7 \times 8 + 10$. **53**

19. Find the value of $21 \div 3 + 10 \times 9 - 42$. **55**

20. What is the value of 144 divided by 12 plus 3 times 7 minus 6? **27**

Family Activity

Ask a family member to help you make a list of the steps involved in a project around your home, such as painting a room. Discuss how the order of steps affects the result.

Applications and Problem Solving

 Real World

21. *Nutrition* The table shows the number of fat grams in one scoop of various ice cream flavors.

   a. Yoko ordered 2 scoops of chocolate chip ice cream and 1 scoop of pralines 'n cream. Robert ordered 3 scoops of chocolate almond. Write an expression for the total number of fat grams in the two orders. **2 × 15 + 1 × 14 + 3 × 18**

Flavor	Fat (g)
Chocolate Almond	18
Chocolate Chip	15
Pralines 'n Cream	14
Rainbow Sherbet	2

   b. Find the total number of fat grams in the two orders. **98 g**

Reteaching the Lesson

Activity Play "First Operation." Write expressions on index cards. Then write the order of operations on the chalkboard. Each player, in turn, chooses a card, performs the first operation, rewrites the expression, and then passes the card on to the next player who checks it for accuracy. Play continues until the last operation is performed.

Error Analysis

Watch for students who forget to always multiply and divide before they add and subtract.

Prevent by placing parentheses around the parts to be solved first.

22. **Entertainment** The Music Club is planning a production of a play. In order to determine the number of tickets they can sell, they need to know how many seats are in the auditorium. The auditorium has 3 sections, and each section has 24 rows. Sections A and C have 15 seats in each row and section B has 20 seats in each row.

    a. Write an expression for the total number of seats in the auditorium.

    b. How many seats are in the auditorium? **1,200 seats**

23. **Working on the CHAPTER Project** Refer to the tables on page 3.

    a. You decide to order 3 life-size cut-outs for $29.95 each from the Novelty Gift catalog. You also want 2 T-shirts that cost $16.95 each. Write an expression for the total cost of the order including shipping. Find the total cost of the order.

    b. Find a catalog from which you would like to order. Select 3 of one item and 4 of a different item. Write an expression for the total cost of your order including shipping. Find the total cost of the order.

22a. See Answer Appendix.

23a. See Answer Appendix.

23b. See students' work.

24. **Critical Thinking** Write an expression using four numbers and at least two of the operations $+$, $-$, $\times$, or $\div$ in which the value of the expression is 11. **Sample answer: $3 \times 2 + 6 - 1$**

Mixed Review

25. Round 9,046 to the nearest thousand. *(Lesson 1-3)* **9,000**

26. **Patterns** Find the next three numbers in the pattern 5, 10, 15, 20, … . *(Lesson 1-2)* **25, 30, 35**

27. **Standardized Test Practice** Brandi can run a mile in 7 minutes. At this rate, how long will it take her to run 8 miles? *(Lesson 1-1)* **B**

    A 58 min   **B** 56 min   **C** 54 min   **D** 15 min

For **Extra Practice**, see page 558.

Mid-Chapter Self Test

Use the four-step plan to solve each problem. *(Lesson 1-1)*

1. Thomas purchased a CD game. The total amount, including tax, was $43. How much change did he receive from $50? **$7**

2. On average, an elephant's heart beats 30 times per minute. At this rate, how many times would an elephant's heart beat in 1 hour? **1,800 times**

Find the next three numbers in each pattern. *(Lesson 1-2)*

3. 5, 13, 21, 29, _?_, _?_, _?_ **37, 45, 53**   4. 3, 12, 48, 192, _?_, _?_, _?_ **768, 3,072, 12,288**

Round each number to the underlined place-value position. *(Lesson 1-3)*

5. 1<u>5</u>4 **150**   6. <u>9</u>,511 **10,000**

7. Estimate 18,392 divided by 317. **$18,000 \div 300 = 60$**

Find the value of each expression. *(Lesson 1-4)*

8. $19 - 6 + 24$ **37**   9. $75 \div 3 - 8 \times 2$ **9**   10. $132 + 4 \times 9 \div 6 - 53$ **85**

Extending the Lesson

Enrichment Masters, p. 4

1-4 Enrichment

Operations Puzzles

Now that you have learned how to evaluate an expression using the order of operations, can you work backwards? In this activity, the value of the expression will be given to you. It is your job to decide what the operations or the numbers must be in order to arrive at that value.

Fill in each ☐ with $+$, $-$, $\times$, or $\div$ to make a true statement.

1. 48 ☐ 3 ☐ 12 = 12   2. 30 ☐ 15 ☐ 3 = 6

3. 24 ☐ 12 ☐ 6 ☐ 3 = 4   4. 24 ☐ 12 ☐ 6 ☐ 3 = 18

5. 4 ☐ 16 ☐ 2 ☐ 8 = 24   6. 45 ☐ 3 ☐ 3 ☐ 9 = 3

Activity Have students work in groups to determine how they would evaluate expressions such as $3 + 5 \times n = 24$.

Exercise 23 asks students to advance to the next stage of work on the Chapter Project. You may wish to have students check their calculations by adding the item costs individually.

4 ASSESS

Closing Activity

Writing Have students work in pairs to write, exchange, and evaluate expressions.

Chapter 1, Quiz B (Lessons 1-3 and 1-4) is available in the *Assessment and Evaluation Masters*, p. 15.

Mid-Chapter Test (Lessons 1-1 through 1-4) is available in the *Assessment and Evaluation Masters*, p. 14.

Mid-Chapter Self Test

The Mid-Chapter Self Test reviews concepts in Lessons 1-1 through 1-4. Lesson references are given so students can review concepts not yet mastered.

Practice Masters, p. 4

1-4 Practice

Order of Operations

Name the operation that should be done first. Then find the value of the expression.

1. $17 - 2 \cdot 4$ **$\times$; 9** 2. $24 \div 6 + 3$ **$\div$; 7** 3. $11 + 9 - 12$ **$+$; 8**

4. $30 + 6 \cdot 5$ **$\div$; 25** 5. $13 - 4 + 7$ **$-$; 16** 6. $8 \times 7 + 2$ **$\times$; 58**

7. $6 \cdot 7 - 2$ **$\times$; 40** 8. $36 \div 9 - 3$ **$\div$; 1** 9. $24 \times 2 + 6$ **$\times$; 8**

Find the value of each expression.

10. $2 + 4 \times 8$ **34** 11. $12 - 9 \div 3$ **9** 12. $8 \cdot 7 - 4$ **52**

13. $10 + 25 \div 5$ **15** 14. $6 + 24 \div 3 \times 2$ **22** 15. $15 - 9 \cdot 4 \div 12$ **12**

16. $8 \cdot 9 \div 6 - 4$ **8** 17. $54 \div 6 - 3 \times 2$ **3** 18. $2 \cdot 4 + 16 \div 8$ **10**

19. $6 + 21 \div 3 - 9$ **4** 20. $12 - 5 \times 6 \div 3$ **2** 21. $2 + 7 \cdot 8 \div 4$ **16**

22. $63 \div 9 + 12 - 2$ **17** 23. $3 \times 6 + 14 \div 2$ **25** 24. $7 \cdot 4 - 3 \cdot 8$ **4**

25. $9 + 18 \div 3 \times 5$ **39** 26. $7 + 8 - 3 + 5$ **17** 27. $7 \cdot 5 + 2 \cdot 3$ **41**

28. $20 - 5 \cdot 2$ **10** 29. $24 \div 8 + 2$ **5** 30. $18 + 24 + 12 \div 5$ **25**

31. $6 + 5 \cdot 2 + 4$ **20** 32. $75 \div 15 \cdot 4$ **20** 33. $45 + 22 + 11$ **47**

34. $32 \cdot 4 \div 2$ **64** 35. $9 + 4 - 2 \times 3$ **7** 36. $39 - 9 \cdot 3 + 6$ **18**

37. $15 \times 2 + 5 \times 6$ **60** 38. $10 + 53 - 60$ **3** 39. $32 - 4 \times 2 + 10$ **34**

© Glencoe/McGraw-Hill T4 *Mathematics: Applications and Connections, Course 1*

COOPERATIVE LEARNING

GET READY

Objective Students model algebraic expressions.

Optional Resources
Hands-On Lab Masters
• worksheet, p. 39

MANAGEMENT TIPS

Recommended Time
30 minutes

Getting Started Demonstrate how the paper bag represents some number. Place random numbers of popcorn in the bag and then count them.

Activities 1 and 2 on page 20 demonstrate the sum of some number and a known number. Emphasize that this sum changes according to the value of the "some number."

Activities 3 and 4 on page 21 increase the unknown quantity. Ask students how they would represent *three times some number*.
three bags

Teaching Tip Make sure students realize that the popcorn is defining the unknown quantity. For example, placing four pieces of popcorn in each of two bags changes the equation from $2x$ to $2(4)$.

1-5A Variables and Expressions

A Preview of Lesson 1-5

☐ paper bags

🍿 popcorn

In algebra, we often use unknown values. Consider the expression *the sum of three and some number*. The "some number" is an unknown value. When you assign a value to "some number," then you can find the value of the expression.

TRY THIS

Work with a partner.

1 To model the expression *the sum of three and some number*, place three pieces of popcorn next to an empty paper bag. The three pieces of popcorn represent the known value, 3. The bag represents the unknown value. It can contain any number of popcorn pieces.

the sum of three and some number

2 To evaluate the expression *the sum of three and some number*, follow these steps.

• Have one partner assign a value to "some number" by placing any number of the remaining pieces of popcorn in the bag.

• Empty the bag and count the pieces of popcorn that are in the bag. Add this to the other 3 pieces of popcorn. This total number is the value of the expression.

ON YOUR OWN

1. What is the "some number?" **the unknown value**

2. In the expression *the sum of three and some number*, replace "some number" with its known value. What is the value of the expression? **See students' work.**

3. Find the value of *some number plus eight* if "some number" is 5. **13**

4. *Look Ahead* Find the value of $m + 7$ if $m = 12$. **19**

20 Chapter 1 Problem Solving, Numbers, and Algebra

Have students complete Exercises 1–3 and 5–7. Encourage students to draw pictures to help them visualize the problems.

Use Exercises 4 and 8 to determine whether students understand the use of variables.

TRY THIS

Work with a partner.

3 To model the expression *two times some number,* place two bags in front of you. Each bag represents the same unknown value.

two times some number

4 To evaluate the expression *two times some number,* follow these steps.

- Have one partner assign a value to "some number" by placing the same number of pieces of popcorn in each bag.

- Empty the bags and count all of the pieces of popcorn. The number of pieces of popcorn is the value of the expression.

ON YOUR OWN

5. What is the "some number?"   **the unknown value**

6. In the expression *two times some number,* replace "some number" with its known value. What is the value of the expression?   **See students' work.**

7. How many bags would you need to model the expression *five times a number*?   **5 bags**

8. *Look Ahead* Find the value of $4 \times h$ if $h = 6$.   **24**

Lesson 1-5A HANDS-ON **LAB** **21**

Math Journal
Have students write a paragraph explaining how the models show variables. Have them include a description of how they could use the models if they forget the pattern they discovered in this lab.

Name_____ Date_____

Hands-On Lab
(Lesson 1-5A)

Variables and Expressions

On Your Own

1. What is the "some number?"   <u>the unknown value</u>

2. In the expression *the sum of 3 and some number,* replace "some number" with its known value. What is the value of the expression?   <u>See students' work.</u>

3. Find the value of *some number plus eight* if "some number" is 5.   <u>13</u>

4. **Look Ahead** Find the value of $m + 7$ if $m = 12$.   <u>19</u>

5. What is the "some number?"   <u>the unknown value</u>

6. In the expression *two times some number,* replace "some number" with its known value. What is the value of the expression?   <u>See students' work.</u>

7. How many bags would you need to model the expression *five times a number*?   <u>5 bags</u>

8. **Look Ahead** Find the value of $4 \times h$ if $h = 6$.   <u>24</u>

© Glencoe/McGraw-Hill   39   *Mathematics: Applications and Connections, Course 1*

Instructional Resources

- *Study Guide Masters*, p. 5
- *Practice Masters*, p. 5
- *Enrichment Masters*, p. 5
- Transparencies 1-5, A and B
- *Science and Math Lab Manual*, pp. 1–4

 CD-ROM Program
- Resource Lesson 1-5
- Interactive Lesson 1-5

Recommended Pacing	
Standard	Days 6 & 7 of 12
Honors	Days 6 & 7 of 12
Block	Day 4 of 6

1 FOCUS

 5-Minute Check
(Lesson 1-4)

Find the value of each expression.

1. $12 - 4 + 6 - 7$ **7**
2. $63 \div 7 + 16 \times 2$ **41**
3. $81 \div 9 + 6 - 5 \times 3$ **0**
4. $18 + 56 \div 8 - 3$ **22**
5. $5 \cdot 8 + 6 - 81 \div 9$ **37**

The 5-Minute Check is also available on **Transparency 1-5A** for this lesson.

Motivating the Lesson

Problem Solving Ask students what further information they would need to solve the following problems.

- If a pound of grapes costs $0.79, what is the total cost? **How many pounds of grapes were purchased?**
- How many buses are needed for 365 students? **How many students fit on a bus?**

Integration: Algebra
Variables and Expressions

What you'll learn

You'll learn to evaluate numerical and simple algebraic expressions.

When am I ever going to use this?

Knowing how to evaluate algebraic expressions can help you find the miles per gallon achieved by a car.

Word Wise

algebra
variable
algebraic expression
evaluate

Western Park Mall offers a gift wrapping service. The cost for gift wrapping is found by adding the length and the width of the box and multiplying by 5 cents. The table below shows how to find the cost of wrapping the most common size boxes. Study the pattern.

Length	Width	Length + Width	Cost (cents)
10	4	10 + 4	(10 + 4) × 5
12	6	12 + 6	(12 + 6) × 5
16	8	16 + 8	(16 + 8) × 5
20	10	20 + 10	(20 + 10) × 5

In mathematics, **algebra** is a language of symbols. By extending the table, using the letters L and W, the following table results.

Length	Width	Length + Width	Cost (cents)
L	W	$L + W$	$(L + W) \times 5$

The letters L and W are called **variables**. A variable is a symbol, usually a letter, used to represent a number. Any letter may be used as a variable. In this problem, the letter L represents length and W represents width.

The expression $(L + W) \times 5$ is called an **algebraic expression**. Algebraic expressions are combinations of variables, numbers, and at least one operation. $(L + W) \times 5$ is an algebraic expression for the cost of gift wrapping

The variables can be replaced with any number. Once the variables have been replaced, you can **evaluate**, or find the value of, the algebraic expression.

$$\left(L + W \right) \times 5$$

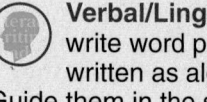 **Example** **1** Evaluate $14 + c$ if $c = 32$.

$$14 + c = 14 + 32 \quad \textit{Replace c with 32.}$$
$$= 46 \quad \textit{Add 14 and 32.}$$

Multiple Learning Styles

Verbal/Linguistic Ask students to write word problems that can be written as algebraic expressions. Guide them in the selection of topics, such as problems dealing with money, weight, or distance. Have them review their problems to make sure all necessary information is there. Then ask them to write the algebraic expressions for their problems.

Example **2** Evaluate $x - y$ if $x = 47$ and $y = 13$.

$x - y = 47 - 13$ *Replace x with 47 and y with 13.*

$\quad\ \ = 34$ *Subtract 13 from 47.*

In algebra, there are several ways to show multiplication.

$3 \cdot m$ $\boxed{\text{means}}$ $3 \times m$

$3m$ $\boxed{\text{means}}$ $3 \times m$

mn $\boxed{\text{means}}$ $m \times n$

Be sure to use the order of operations when you evaluate algebraic expressions.

Examples **3** Evaluate $3m + 2 \cdot 4$ if $m = 12$.

$3m + 2 \cdot 4 = 3 \times 12 + 2 \cdot 4$ *Replace m with 12.*

$\qquad\qquad = 36 + 2 \cdot 4$ *Multiply 3 and 12.*

$\qquad\qquad = 36 + 8$ *Multiply 2 and 4.*

$\qquad\qquad = 44$ *Add 36 and 8.*

Study Hint

Reading Math The expression $3m + 2 \cdot 4$ is read as three times m plus two times four.

4 Evaluate $4 + mn$ if $m = 6$ and $n = 2$.

$4 + mn = 4 + 6 \times 2$ *Replace m with 6 and n with 2.*

$\qquad\ \ = 4 + 12$ *Multiply 6 and 2.*

$\qquad\ \ = 16$ *Add 4 and 12.*

APPLICATION

Real World

5 **Hobbies** To find distance traveled, you can use the expression $r \times t$, where r represents rate and t represents time. Find the distance a hot air balloon traveled if its rate was 13 miles per hour and it traveled for 4 hours.

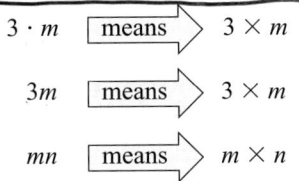

Evaluate $r \times t$ if $r = 13$ and $t = 4$.

$r \times t = 13 \times 4$ *Replace r with 13 and t with 4.*

$\qquad\ \ = 52$ *Multiply 13 and 4.*

The hot air balloon traveled 52 miles.

Lesson 1–5 Integration: Algebra   Variables and Expressions   **23**

  Transparency 1-5B contains a teaching aid for this lesson.

Reading Mathematics Algebra is used every day by scientists, engineers, and businesspeople. The variables and symbols used in algebra represent numbers and operations. Ask students what symbols they might find along a highway or at an airport and discuss what they mean.

In-Class Examples

For Example 1
Evaluate $c + 24$ if $c = 9$. **33**

For Example 2
Evaluate $x - y$ if $x = 18$ and $y = 6$. **12**

For Example 3
Evaluate $5m + 4 \cdot 5$ if $m = 8$. **60**

For Example 4
Evaluate $6 + mn$ if $m = 8$ and $n = 3$. **30**

For Example 5
How much would it cost to gift wrap a package that is 24 inches long and 18 inches wide if the algebraic expression for the cost of gift wrapping is $(L + W) \times \$0.06$? **$2.52**

Teaching Tip Note that for a product of a number and a variable, the number is usually written first, followed by the variable. For example, the product of m and 3 is expressed as $3m$, not $m3$.

Teaching Tip Point out to students that if x is the variable, they should refrain from using $\times$ for multiplication to avoid confusion.

Check for Understanding

If students need additional practice or instruction after completing Exercises 1–12, one of these options may be helpful.
- Extra Practice, see p. 558
- Reteaching Activity
- *Study Guide Masters,* p. 5
- *Practice Masters,* p. 5
- Interactive Mathematics Tools Software

Assignment Guide

Core: 13–39 odd, 41–46
Enriched: 14–38 even, 39–46

CHECK FOR UNDERSTANDING

Communicating Mathematics

Read and study the lesson to answer each question.

1. *Write* two algebraic expressions that mean the same as $5r$. $5 \times r$ or $5 \cdot r$

2. *Copy and complete* the chart.

Algebraic Expressions	Variables	Numbers	Operations
$4x - 2y$	x, y	4, 2	$-, \times$
$3r - 2s + 5t$	r, s, t	3, 2, 5	$-, +, \times$

3. *You Decide* Laura says that the value of $g + h \div 2$ when $g = 2$ and $h = 14$ is 8. Nicholas says the answer is 9. Who is correct? Explain your reasoning. Nicholas; $2 + 14 \div 2 = 9$

Guided Practice

Evaluate each expression if $a = 3$ and $b = 12$.

4. $a + 5$ 8
5. $48 \div b$ 4
6. $7ab$ 252
7. $2a + b$ 18

Evaluate each expression if $c = 5$, $d = 2$, and $f = 8$.

8. $f - d$ 6
9. $32 \div d$ 16
10. $6d + c$ 17
11. $c + d + f$ 15

12. *Geometry* The expression $\ell \times w$ gives the area of a rectangle. The letter ℓ represents the length of the rectangle, and w represents the width. Find the area of each rectangle.

a.
192 square meters

b.
630 square inches

EXERCISES

Practice

Evaluate each expression if $n = 5$ and $p = 7$.

13. $n + 5$ 10
14. $n \times 0$ 0
15. $4p - 6$ 22
16. $12 - n$ 7
17. $3np$ 105
18. $8 + p$ 15
19. $2n \times 6$ 60
20. $n \div 1$ 5
21. $p \times n$ 35
22. $2p - p$ 7
23. $3n + p$ 22
24. $21 \div 3 \times p$ 49

Evaluate each expression if $r = 6$, $s = 12$, and $t = 3$.

25. $s - t$ 9
26. $s \div 2$ 6
27. rt 18
28. $4 + 2r$ 16
29. $t \times 18$ 54
30. $48 \div s$ 4
31. $s - r + t$ 9
32. $rt - s$ 6
33. $3s - 4t$ 24
34. $4 + 2rt$ 40
35. $3rt - 2s$ 30
36. $s - 2r \div t$ 8

37. *Algebra* Find the value of $3z \div y$ if $y = 3$ and $z = 9$. 9

38. *Algebra* What is the value of $2xyz - 26$ if $x = 3$, $y = 6$, and $z = 10$? 334

24 Chapter 1 Problem Solving, Numbers, and Algebra

■ Reteaching the Lesson ■

Activity Ask students to write variables, numbers, and operation signs on individual paper squares. Have pairs of students take turns making up expressions by arranging the paper squares in different combinations, choosing numbers to replace the variables, and evaluating the expressions.

Applications and Problem Solving

Real World

39. Geometry To find the diameter of a circle, you can use the expression $2r$, where r is the length of the radius. Find the diameter of a circle whose radius is 6 inches. **12 inches**

6 in.

40. Travel To find the miles per gallon achieved by a car, you can use the expression $m = d \div g$ where m represents miles per gallon, d represents the distance traveled, and g represents the number of gallons of gasoline used.

a. Find the miles per gallon for a car that travels 180 miles on 5 gallons of gasoline. **36 mpg**

b. Find the miles per gallon for a car that travels 256 miles on 8 gallons of gasoline. **32 mpg**

41. Critical Thinking Christina and Shawon each have a calculator. Shawon starts at zero and adds three each time. Christina starts at 100 and subtracts seven each time. If they press their keys at the same time, will their displays ever show the same number at the same time? If so, what is the number? **yes; 30**

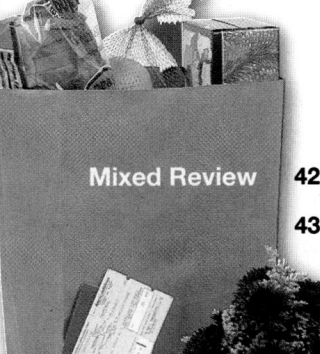

Mixed Review

42. Find the value of $36 \div 9 + 7 \times 2$. *(Lesson 1-4)* **18**

43. Evaluate $2 \times 18 \div 3 + 9$. *(Lesson 1-4)* **21**

 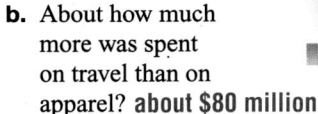

44. Shopping The graph shows how much consumers spent shopping on-line recently. *(Lesson 1-3)*

a. Estimate the total amount spent shopping on-line.

b. About how much more was spent on travel than on apparel? **about $80 million**

44a. Sample answer: $500 million

Shopping On-Line

$140	Computer products
$126	Travel
$85	Entertainment
$46	Apparel
$45	Gifts/flowers
$39	Food/drink

(millions)

45. Standardized Test Practice What number is missing from this pattern?
$\ldots, \square, 35, 41, 47, 53, \ldots$ *(Lesson 1-2)* **A**

A 29
B 31
C 26
D 24

For **Extra Practice**, see page 558.

46. Business In one month, Pam collected $51 from the customers on her paper route. If she owed the newspaper company $32, how much was her profit? *(Lesson 1-1)* **$19**

Lesson 1-5 Integration: Algebra   Variables and Expressions   **25**

Extending the Lesson

Enrichment Masters, p. 5

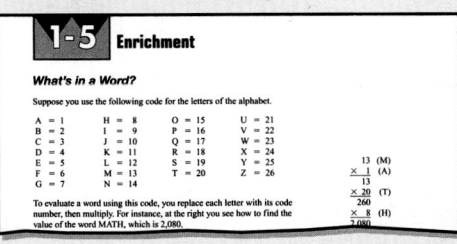

Activity Write an algebraic expression for each problem.
- Mei Ling counted 24 robins at her feeder. She saw other birds that were not robins. **24 + x**
- Suppose Mei Ling counted a total of 36 birds. How would you change the expression? **24 + x = 36**

TECHNOLOGY
LAB

GET READY

Objective Students evaluate algebraic expressions by using a graphing calculator.

Technology Resources
• TI-80, TI-81, TI-82, or TI-83 graphing calculator

MANAGEMENT TIPS

Recommended Time
40 minutes

Getting Started Allow students plenty of time to explore the various keys on their calculators. Have students practice using the alpha keys by entering their names. Also have them enter a few expressions to evaluate so they get used to how the different symbols look on the calculator screen.

Using a Graphing Calculator Discuss with students some of the advantages of using a graphing calculator for non-graphing calculations. Some advantages: larger screen, shows everything that is typed in and the answer, and the ability to store up to 26 numbers. Students can also re-evaluate the expression without re-keying every part of the expression by pressing 2nd ENTER and using the arrow keys to find the appropriate numbers to replace.

ASSESS

After students answer Exercises 1–8, ask them to develop a problem that would be difficult to do mentally. Then have them work the problem on the graphing calculator.

Use Exercise 9 to determine whether students understand evaluating expressions on a calculator.

GRAPHING CALCULATORS

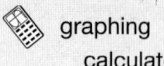

1-5B Evaluating Expressions

A Follow-Up of Lesson 1-5

graphing calculator

Graphing calculators observe the order of operations. So, you can enter an expression just as it is written to evaluate it. You can also use parentheses keys on a graphing calculator to indicate multiplication.

The expression appears on the screen as you enter it. On many calculators, the multiplication and division signs appear on the screen as * and /.

TRY THIS

Work with a partner.

Evaluate $3(x - 6) + 1$ if $x = 8$.

3 (8 − 6) + 1 ENTER   *You can use arrow keys to go back and correct any error you make by typing over it, or by using the [INS] (insert) key, or by using the* DEL *(delete) key.*

If $x = 8$, the value of $3(x - 6) + 1$ is 7.

If you discover that you entered the expression incorrectly, you can use the REPLAY feature to correct your error and reevaluate without reentering your expression. Press 2nd [ENTRY]. Then use the arrow keys to move to the location of the correction. After you make the correction, press ENTER to evaluate. You don't have to move the cursor to the end of the line.

ON YOUR OWN

Use a graphing calculator to evaluate each expression if $x = 4$, $y = 7$, and $z = 9$.

1. $12 - z$ **3**
2. $x + 9$ **13**
3. xy **28**
4. $2(18 - z)$ **18**
5. $x \div 2 + 12$ **14**
6. $\frac{2(z-x)}{(y-2)}$ **2**
7. $14 + \frac{3x}{2}$ **20**
8. $x(y + z) - x$ **60**

9. Evaluate the expression $5(3 + 8)$ with a scientific calculator and with a graphing calculator. Can you enter the expression the same way on both calculators? If not, explain the difference. **See Answer Appendix.**

26 Chapter 1 Problem Solving, Numbers, and Algebra

Math Journal

Have students write a paragraph that compares a graphing calculator, a scientific calculator, and a pencil and paper for evaluating expressions. Have students explain how to use the alpha key on a graphing calculator.

BUSINESS

Gary C. Comer
MAIL-ORDER BUSINESS OWNER

Gary C. Comer is the founder and Chairman of the Board of a major mail-order catalog. When he first founded the company in 1963, there was one catalog in which sailboat hardware and equipment was sold. Today, there are eight different catalogs. Consumers can purchase unique clothing and accessories, and products for the home.

If you are interested in owning your own mail-order business, you should consider taking courses in business management, accounting, and mathematics. A bachelor's degree in marketing and advertising, communications, business management, or accounting is also helpful.

For more information:
The Direct Marketing Association
1120 Avenue of the Americas
New York, NY 10036-6700

NET CONNECTION
www.glencoe.com/sec/
math/mac/mathnet

Someday, I'd like to start a mail-order business. I would travel around the world to find unusual products to sell in my catalog.

Your Turn
Design a catalog for a mail-order business you would like to start. Select a name for your company and describe and illustrate the products you want to sell.

More About Gary C. Comer
- Before he started his catalog company, Gary Comer was an advertising copywriter and an avid sailor. He won the North American Star Boat Championship, finished second in the World Star Boat Championship, and finished third in the Pan American Games. Then he decided to start a business that involved sailboat racing.
- The company originally sold sailboat equipment only. Now the company sells casual and tailored clothing, children's clothing, products for the home, and corporate gifts. On an average day, the catalog's phone lines handle between 40,000 and 50,000 calls. During the Christmas season, the company receives 100,000 calls daily.

Motivating Students
Mail-order catalogs are a popular way of selling retail merchandise. Many companies have catalogs in addition to retail outlets, or stores. Other companies sell their merchandise exclusively through catalogs. To begin a discussion of mail-order businesses, ask students these questions.
- Have you ever purchased anything from a catalog? If so, what? **Sample answer: sport cards, games, CDs, videotapes, clothing**
- Why might shopping by mail be preferable to shopping in a store? **Sample answer: convenience, many catalog companies take orders 24 hours a day, merchandise is delivered to your door, presents are delivered to the recipient**

Making the Math Connection
The owner of a mail-order business needs a thorough understanding of the mathematical aspects of retailing—keeping track of inventory, using sales figures to determine buying strategies, and computing profits and losses.

Working on *Your Turn*
Have students work in pairs. Make catalogs available to help students choose a design. Encourage them to use their creativity to illustrate and describe products so that customers would be eager to make purchases. Then have each pair give a brief oral presentation explaining their company and sharing their catalog with classmates.

*An additional School to Career activity is available on page 1 of the **School to Career Masters**.*

Instructional Resources

- *Study Guide Masters*, p. 6
- *Practice Masters*, p. 6
- *Enrichment Masters*, p. 6
- Transparencies 1-6, A and B
- *Assessment and Evaluation Masters*, p. 16
- *Classroom Games*, pp. 1–2
- *Technology Masters*, p. 2

 CD-ROM Program
- Resource Lesson 1-6

Recommended Pacing	
Standard	Day 8 of 12
Honors	Day 8 of 12
Block	Day 4 of 6

FOCUS

 5-Minute Check
(Lesson 1-5)

Evaluate each expression if r = 2 and s = 8.

1. $r \times 6$ 12
2. $s \div 4$ 2

Evaluate each expression if d = 3, f = 6, and g = 12.

3. $d + f + g$ 21
4. $g \div d + f$ 10
5. $6f - 4$ 32

The 5-Minute Check is also available on **Transparency 1-6A** for this lesson.

Motivating the Lesson

Hands-On Activity After reading the beginning of the lesson, have students use their calculators to find the product of $10 \cdot 10 \cdot 10 \cdot 10$. **10,000**
Then have them choose any number to multiply by itself several times.

1-6

Integration: Algebra
Powers and Exponents

What you'll learn
You'll learn to use powers and exponents in expressions.

When am I ever going to use this?
Knowing how to use powers and exponents can help you determine the amount of water needed to fill an aquarium.

Word Wise
factor
exponent
base
power
squared
cubed

The state of Hawaii has an area of more than 10,000 square miles. You can express 10,000 as the product $10 \cdot 10 \cdot 10 \cdot 10$.

When two or more numbers are multiplied, each number is called a **factor** of the product. For $3 \times 12 = 36$, 3 and 12 are factors of 36.

When the same factor is repeated, you can use an **exponent** to simplify the notation. An exponent tells how many times a number, called the **base**, is used as a factor.

$$10,000 = \underbrace{10 \cdot 10 \cdot 10 \cdot 10}_{four\ factors} = 10^{\underset{\uparrow}{4}} \leftarrow exponent$$
$$base \qquad 10^4\ is\ a\ power\ of\ 10.$$

A **power** is a number that is expressed using exponents. The powers 12^2, 5^3, and 7^4 are read as follows.

Symbols	Words
12^2	12 to the second power or 12 **squared**.
5^3	5 to the third power or 5 **cubed**.
7^4	7 to the fourth power.

Examples

1 Write $8 \cdot 8 \cdot 8 \cdot 8$ using exponents.

The base is 8.
Since 8 is a factor four times, the exponent is 4.
$8 \cdot 8 \cdot 8 \cdot 8 = 8^4$

2 Write 4^3 as a product. Then evaluate.

The base is 4.
The exponent 3 means that 4 is a factor three times.
$4^3 = 4 \cdot 4 \cdot 4$
$\quad = 64$

Since powers are a form of multiplication, the rules for the order of operations need to be expanded to include them.

Order of Operations	1. Do all powers before other operations.
	2. Multiply and divide in order from left to right.
	3. Add and subtract in order from left to right.

28   **Chapter 1** Problem Solving, Numbers, and Algebra

Multiple Learning Styles

 Kinesthetic Dried beans and two number cubes will be needed. Roll the number cubes. The greatest number will be the base. The other number will be the exponent. As you roll the cubes, have students write the expression and model it with beans. Then have them count the beans to evaluate the expression. For example, $4^3 - 4$ groups of 4 groups of 4 = 64 beans.

Example **3** Evaluate $5 \cdot 3^2 - 8$.

$5 \cdot 3^2 - 8 = 5 \cdot 9 - 8$ *Evaluate 3^2 first. $3^2 = 3 \cdot 3$ or 9.*

$ = 45 - 8$ *Multiply 5 and 9.*

$ = 37$ *Subtract 8 from 45.*

Powers and exponents are often used in algebra.

Examples

INTEGRATION

Algebra

4 Write $n \cdot n \cdot n \cdot n \cdot n$ using exponents.

The base is n.
Since n is a factor five times, the exponent is 5.
$n \cdot n \cdot n \cdot n \cdot n = n^5$

5 Write d^4 as a product.

The base is d.
The exponent 4 means that d is a factor four times.
$d^4 = d \cdot d \cdot d \cdot d$

6 Evaluate g^6 if $g = 3$.

$g^6 = 3^6$ *Replace g with 3.*

$ = 3 \cdot 3 \cdot 3 \cdot 3 \cdot 3 \cdot 3$

$ = 729$

You can also use a calculator to evaluate 3^6.

3 $\boxed{y^x}$ 6 $\boxed{=}$ *729*

> **Study Hint**
>
> Technology Many calculators have a $\boxed{y^x}$ key. You can use this key to evaluate powers. To find 12^4, enter 12 $\boxed{y^x}$ 4 $\boxed{=}$.

CHECK FOR UNDERSTANDING

Communicating Mathematics

Read and study the lesson to answer each question. **1. See margin.**

1. *Write* a paragraph explaining the terms *exponent, base,* and *power*.

2. *Demonstrate* how to evaluate 5^8 using a calculator. 5 $\boxed{y^x}$ 8 $\boxed{=}$ *390,625*

3. *You Decide* Esteban says that the value of $3^2 + 2^4 \cdot 6$ is 150. Tamika says the value is 105. Who is correct? Explain your reasoning.
Tamika; $3^2 + 2^4 \cdot 6 = 105$

Guided Practice **Write each product using exponents.**

4. $2 \cdot 2 \cdot 2 \cdot 2 \cdot 2 \cdot 2$ 2^6 5. $m \cdot m \cdot m \cdot m \cdot m$ m^5 6. $3 \cdot 3 \cdot 5 \cdot 5 \cdot 5$ $3^2 \cdot 5^3$

Write each power as a product.

7. c^3 $c \cdot c \cdot c$ 8. 4^7 $4 \cdot 4 \cdot 4 \cdot 4 \cdot 4 \cdot 4 \cdot 4$ 9. h^6 $h \cdot h \cdot h \cdot h \cdot h \cdot h$

Evaluate each expression.

10. 2^3 8   11. 10^5 100,000   12. $5^2 + 4 \cdot 2$ 33

13. *Foreign Languages* Mandarin Chinese is spoken by more people in the world than any other language. An estimated 10^9 people speak this language. About how many people in the world speak Mandarin Chinese?
about 1,000,000,000 people

Lesson 1–6 Integration: Algebra Powers and Exponents **29**

Additional Answer

1. **An exponent is a number that tells how many times a number, called the base, is used as a factor. A power is a number that is expressed using exponents.**

 Transparency 1-6B contains a teaching aid for this lesson.

Reading Mathematics Write the words *factor, exponent, base, power, squared,* and *cubed* on an overhead transparency. Say the words. Then write an example of each as you say it again. Label the examples. Then give students a word and have them identify the corresponding example. Conclude by pointing out that the term *power* is sometimes used to refer to the exponent itself.

> **In-Class Examples**
>
> **For Example 1**
> Write $5 \cdot 5 \cdot 5$ using exponents. 5^3
>
> **For Example 2**
> Write 6^5 as a product. Then evaluate. $6 \cdot 6 \cdot 6 \cdot 6 \cdot 6 = 7,776$
>
> **For Example 3**
> Evaluate $2 \cdot 6^3 + 7$. 439
>
> **For Example 4**
> Write $a \cdot a \cdot a \cdot a$ using exponents. a^4
>
> **For Example 5**
> Write k^6 as a product.
> $k \cdot k \cdot k \cdot k \cdot k \cdot k$
>
> **For Example 6**
> Evaluate r^3 if $r = 8$. 512

Teaching Tip Encourage students to expand their order of operations' mnemonic to include powers. For example, they could say **P**lease, **M**y **D**ear **A**unt **S**ally.

Check for Understanding
If students need additional practice or instruction after completing Exercises 1–13, one of these options may be helpful.
• Extra Practice, see p. 558
• Reteaching Activity
• *Study Guide Masters,* p. 6
• *Practice Masters,* p. 6

Additional Answers

27. $16 \cdot 16 \cdot 16 \cdot 16 \cdot 16 \cdot 16$

28. $a \cdot a \cdot a \cdot a \cdot a \cdot a \cdot a$

29. $x \cdot x \cdot x \cdot y \cdot y \cdot y \cdot y$

30. $b \cdot b \cdot c \cdot c \cdot c \cdot c \cdot d \cdot d \cdot d$

44. $10^3 = 1,000$

    $10^4 = 10,000$

    $10^5 = 100,000$

    $10^6 = 1,000,000$
To evaluate 10^{20}, attach 20 zeros to the number 1.

Study Guide Masters, p. 6

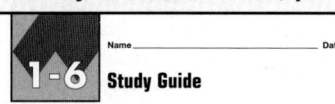

EXERCISES

Practice

Write each product using exponents.

14. $11 \cdot 11 \cdot 11$ **11^3**

15. $3 \cdot 3 \cdot 3 \cdot 3 \cdot 3 \cdot 3$ **3^6**

16. $w \cdot w \cdot w$ **w^3**

17. $3 \cdot 3 \cdot 4 \cdot 4 \cdot 4 \cdot 4$ **$3^2 \cdot 4^4$**

18. $15 \cdot 15 \cdot 8 \cdot 8$ **$15^2 \cdot 8^2$**

19. $r \cdot r \cdot r \cdot r$ **r^4**

20. $y \cdot y \cdot y \cdot z \cdot z$ **$y^3 \cdot z^2$**

21. $6 \cdot 6 \cdot 6 \cdot 1 \cdot 1 \cdot 1$ **$6^3 \cdot 1^3$**

22. $a \cdot a \cdot b \cdot b$ **$a^2 \cdot b^2$**

Write each power as a product. 27–30. See margin.

23. 14^2 **$14 \cdot 14$**

24. 21^4 **$21 \cdot 21 \cdot 21 \cdot 21$**

25. 7^5 **$7 \cdot 7 \cdot 7 \cdot 7 \cdot 7$**

26. $9^3 \cdot 2^4$ **$9 \cdot 9 \cdot 9 \cdot 2 \cdot 2 \cdot 2 \cdot 2$**

27. 16^6

28. a^7

29. $x^3 \cdot y^4$

30. $b^2 \cdot c^4 \cdot d^3$

Evaluate each expression.

31. 10^3 **1,000**

32. 6^3 **216**

33. 2^5 **32**

34. 16^2 **256**

35. 3 squared **9**

36. 4 cubed **64**

37. $4^5 + 3$ **1,027**

38. $4^2 \cdot 3^3 \cdot 6$ **2,592**

39. $4 \cdot 5^2 + 3$ **103**

40. *Algebra* What is the value of $x^3 + y^2$ if $x = 3$ and $y = 6$? **63**

41. Complete the table below.

$3^4 = 81$	$5^4 = 625$	$10^4 = 10,000$
$3^3 = 27$	$5^3 = 125$	$10^3 = 1,000$
$3^2 = 9$	$5^2 = 25$	$10^2 = 100$
$3^1 = 3$	$5^1 = 5$	$10^1 = \underline{?}$ **10**
$3^0 = \underline{?}$ **1**	$5^0 = \underline{?}$ **1**	$10^0 = \underline{?}$ **1**

Applications and Problem Solving

42. *Earth Science* A light year is the distance light travels in one year. The Milky Way galaxy is about 100,000 light years wide. Write 100,000 as a power with 10 as the base. **10^5**

43. *Geometry* The volume of a cube can be found by using the expression $V = s^3$, where s is the length of a side. The aquarium shown at the right is in the shape of a cube. What is its volume? *The volume will be expressed in cubic units.* **5,832 in^3**

18 in.

18 in.

18 in.

44. *Critical Thinking* Evaluate 10^3, 10^4, 10^5, and 10^6. Explain how you can evaluate 10^{20} without using a calculator. **See margin.**

Mixed Review

45. *Algebra* Evaluate the expression $ab - a$ if $a = 7$ and $b = 3$. *(Lesson 1-5)* **14**

46. **Standardized Test Practice** The Marcos family is going to a football game. Tickets cost \$5 for adults and \$2 for students. Mrs. Marcos will need 2 adult tickets and 4 student's tickets. Which expression could be used to find the cost in dollars of the tickets? *(Lesson 1-4)* **E**

  A $2 + \$5 \times 4 + \$2$

  B $\$5 + \$2 + 6$

  C $\$2 + 4 \times \$5 + 2$

  D $6 \times \$5 + \$2$

  E $2 \times \$5 + 4 \times \$2$

Investigations for the Special Education Student

This blackline master booklet helps you plan for the needs of your special education students by providing long-term projects along with teacher notes. Investigation 1, *Vacation Getaways,* may be used with this chapter.

MathPASS CD-ROM

This CD-ROM offers a complete, self-paced mathematics curriculum. Each lesson includes a pretest, tutorial, guided practice, and posttest. MathPASS Lesson 2 is correlated to this Student Edition lesson.
For Windows & Macintosh

47. Use rounding to estimate 398 + 688 + 241. Explain whether 1,337 is a reasonable answer. *(Lesson 1-3)* **400 + 700 + 200 = 1,300; reasonable**

48. *Patterns* Find the next three numbers in the pattern 7, 12, 17, 22, ... *(Lesson 1-2)* **27, 32, 37**

For **Extra Practice**, see page 558.

49. *School* The number of students at Aurora Junior High is half the number it was twenty years ago. If there were 758 students twenty years ago, how many students are there now? *(Lesson 1-1)* **379 students**

Let the Games Begin

EXPO Bingo

Math Skill
Powers and Exponents

Get Ready This game is for two to four players.

 calculator

Get Set Each player copies the EXPO bingo playing card onto a sheet of paper. Then each player selects 16 different powers and writes them in any of the upper right hand corner boxes. Choose a person to be the bingo caller.

EXPO BINGO CARD

				5^2	12^2	3^3	2^4
				7^2	2^3	8^2	3^2
				1^3	4^3	9^2	11^2
				6^2	14^2	5^3	15^2
				10^3	3^4	13^2	2^2

Go
- The caller reads one power at a time. Each player marks the space by writing the equivalent number in the larger box.
- The first player with four powers listed in any row, column, or diagonal wins.

interNET CONNECTION Visit www.glencoe.com/sec/math/mac/mathnet for more games.

■ Extending the Lesson ■

Enrichment Masters, p. 6

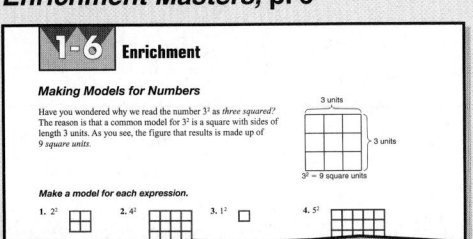

Let the Games Begin

Students can use the game to practice their knowledge of powers and exponents. Make sure students know how to enter expressions with exponents on their calculators so that the game proceeds smoothly and fairly. *Additional Resources for this game can be found on page 41 of the Classroom Games.*

---

4 ASSESS

Closing Activity
Speaking Write several expressions on the board that use the same factor multiple times. Ask student volunteers to describe how they would change these expressions to exponential expressions. Then have them evaluate the expressions using mental math or a calculator.

Chapter 1, Quiz C (Lessons 1-5 and 1-6) is available in the *Assessment and Evaluation Masters*, p. 16.

Practice Masters, p. 6

Objective Students solve problems by using the guess-and-check strategy.

Recommended Pacing	
Standard	Day 9 of 12
Honors	Day 9 of 12
Block	Day 5 of 6

1 FOCUS

Getting Started Have each student write *yes* or *no* on a scrap of paper. Ask them to guess how many students wrote *yes*. Then ask how they would check the total number of *yes* responses. **count the papers**

2 TEACH

Teaching Tip Encourage students to think of situations when they use guess-and-check. A common one is a multiple-choice math test. Instead of solving each problem and finding the answer among the choices, students often check each choice to see if it is an appropriate answer.

In-Class Example
Find a number such that the sum of that number and its double is 27. **9**

 PROBLEM SOLVING

1-7A Guess and Check

A Preview of Lesson 1-7

Yvonne and her friend Catalina are putting together a computer generated jigsaw puzzle. They are trying to decide the best way to start the puzzle. Let's listen in!

Yvonne

Do you know what the picture is supposed to look like?

I can't tell. Maybe we should start by finding the piece that will fit in the lower right-hand corner.

All right. Three of the four corner pieces are already in place. Let's look for the fourth corner piece.

It is the one that has a straight edge on the right side and on the bottom.

Yes! That piece looks like it will fit.

Catalina

THINK ABOUT IT

Work with a partner.

1. *Analyze* Catalina's and Yvonne's thinking. Do you agree with their thinking? Why or why not? **See students' work.**

2. *Think* of another way for Catalina and Yvonne to start the puzzle.

3. *Choose* the puzzle piece that will fit on the right side of the top left-hand puzzle piece. Explain your reasoning. **2–3. See margin.**

4. *Apply* what you have learned from Catalina's and Yvonne's situation to solve the following problem.

   Find an even number between 50 and 60 that is divisible by 2 and 3. **54**

32 Chapter 1 Problem Solving, Numbers, and Algebra

■ Reteaching the Lesson ■

Activity Have small groups of students use their calculators to create problems such as the following: *The product of a number and 14 is 210.* Have them exchange their problems with another group to solve using the guess-and-check strategy.

Additional Answers

2. Sample answer: Start by finding all the edge pieces.

3. The piece that is beside the top left-hand puzzle piece; it will connect to the corner piece.

For **Extra Practice**, see page 559.

ON YOUR OWN

5. The second step of the four-step plan for problem solving asks you to make a *plan* for solving the problem. *Tell* how you can use the **guess-and-check** strategy to help you make a plan for solving a problem. **See margin.**

6. *Write a Problem* that can be solved using the guess-and-check strategy. Then ask a classmate to solve the problem. **See students' work.**

7. *Explain* how you could use the guess-and-check strategy to answer Exercise 35 on page 36. **See margin.**

MIXED PROBLEM SOLVING

STRATEGIES
Look for a pattern.
Solve a simpler problem.
Act it out.
Guess and check.
Draw a diagram.
Make a chart.
Work backward.

Solve. Use any strategy.

8. *Money Matters* Kamaria earns $5 per hour baby-sitting. Last week, she worked 16 hours. How much money did Kamaria make? **$80**

9. *Life Science* Last week, the Mahoning Animal Shelter sent a total of 24 dogs and cats to new homes. There were 6 more dogs than cats. How many of each were adopted? **15 dogs, 9 cats**

10. *Entertainment* The chart below gives admission costs to Mount Carmel's health fair. Twelve people paid a total of $50 for admission. If 8 children attended the health fair, how many adults and senior citizens attended? **2 adults, 2 senior citizens**

11. There are 8 bones in the wrist, 14 in the fingers, and 5 in the palm.

Admission Costs	
Adults	$6
Children	$4
Senior Citizens	$3

11. *Life Science* Each hand in the human body has 27 bones. There are 6 more bones in your fingers than in your wrist. There are 3 fewer bones in your palm than in your wrist. How many bones are in each part of your hand?

12. *Money Matters* Refer to the chart below. Olivia and Imena each got a perm, a manicure, and a bottle of shampoo. About how much money did they spend? **about $180**

Alberto's Salon	
Cut/Style	$12
Perm	$56
Manicure	$17
Shampoo	$ 8

13. *Physical Science* Sound travels through air at a speed of 1,129 feet per second. At this rate, how far will sound travel in 1 minute? **67,740 feet per minute**

14. *Sports* Jamal's basketball team won twice as many games as they lost. They lost 8 games. How many games did they win? **16 games**

15. *Standardized Test Practice* Jorge purchased a new car. His loan, including interest, is $10,740. How much are his monthly payments if he has 60 payments to make? **B**
  A $195
  B $179
  C $135
  D $159
  E Not Here

Lesson 1-7A THINKING **LAB** 33

Check for Understanding
Use the results from Exercises 5–7 to determine if students comprehend the guess-and-check strategy.

Extra Practice If students need additional practice in problem solving, extra practice is available on the following pages.
- Guess and Check, see p. 559
- Mixed Problem Solving, see pp. 593–594

Assignment Guide
All: 5–15

4 ASSESS

Closing Activity
Writing Have students write word problems from everyday experiences that involve the guess-and-check strategy. Have them exchange problems and solve them.

Additional Answers
5. Sample answer: When making a plan to solve a problem, you can use the guess-and-check strategy to guess an answer and compare the answer to the problem. If your answer does not work, then you know to make another guess.

7. Sample answer: You could guess values for *p* to find what number divided by 5 is 45.

Extending the Lesson

Activity Give pairs of students play money and coins. Have them create a word problem about the money that can be solved using the guess-and-check strategy. Then have them exchange their problems with others for solving.

Sample problem: *Kevin has seven $1 bills, three quarters, six dimes, eight nickels, and four pennies. He wants to buy a book for $5.95. How much will he have left after the purchase? (Assume tax is included in the price.)* **$2.84**

- *Study Guide Masters,* p. 7
- *Practice Masters,* p. 7
- *Enrichment Masters,* p. 7
- Transparencies 1-7, A and B
- *Assessment and Evaluation Masters,* p. 16
- *Diversity Masters,* p. 1
- *Hands-On Lab Masters,* p. 69
- *School to Career Masters,* p. 1
- CD-ROM Program
  - Resource Lesson 1-7

Recommended Pacing	
Standard	Day 10 of 12
Honors	Day 10 of 12
Block	Day 5 of 6

1 FOCUS

5-Minute Check
(Lesson 1-6)

1. Write $6 \cdot 6 \cdot 6 \cdot 6$ using exponents. 6^4
2. Write 22^7 as a product. $22 \cdot 22 \cdot 22 \cdot 22 \cdot 22 \cdot 22 \cdot 22$
3. Evaluate $6^3 \cdot 8^2$. **13,824**
4. Evaluate r^3 if $r = 9$. **729**
5. In 1996, the population of Ecuador was estimated to be 117×10^5. About how many people lived there at that time? **about 11,700,000 people**

The 5-Minute Check is also available on **Transparency 1-7A** for this lesson.

Motivating the Lesson
Problem Solving Ask students what they need to know to determine whether the statement is true or false. *More red markers are sold each year than yellow markers.* **the number of red and yellow markers sold**

1-7
Integration: Algebra
Solving Equations

You'll learn to solve equations by using mental math and guess and check.

When am I ever going to use this?
Knowing how to solve equations can help you determine the number of new students in your school.

Word Wise
equation
solve
solution

> **Study Hint**
> Reading Math The equation $x - 4 = 5$ is read as *x minus four is equal to five.*

On March 23, 1775, ___?___ said, "*I know not what course others may take; but as for me, give me liberty, or give me death!*"

This sentence is neither true nor false until you fill in the blank. If you answer Patrick Henry, the sentence is true. If you answer George Washington, Harriet Tubman, or any other historical figure, the sentence is false.

In mathematics, an **equation** is a sentence that contains an equal sign, $=$. Equations can be either true or false.

$$34 - 12 = 22 \quad \textit{This equation is true.}$$
$$45 \times 2 = 100 \quad \textit{This equation is false.}$$

An equation like $x - 4 = 5$ is neither true nor false until x is replaced with a number.

Replace x with 10.

$$x - 4 = 5$$
$$10 - 4 \stackrel{?}{=} 5$$
$$6 = 5$$

This sentence is false.

Replace x with 9.

$$x - 4 = 5$$
$$9 - 4 \stackrel{?}{=} 5$$
$$5 = 5$$

This sentence is true.

When you replace a variable with a value that makes the equation true, you **solve** the equation. The replacement that makes the equation true is called a **solution** of the equation. The solution of $x - 4 = 5$ is 9.

> **Example**

1 Which of the numbers 3, 4, or 5 is the solution of $y + 8 = 12$?

Replace y with 3.	*Replace y with 4.*	*Replace y with 5.*
$y + 8 = 12$	$y + 8 = 12$	$y + 8 = 12$
$3 + 8 \stackrel{?}{=} 12$	$4 + 8 \stackrel{?}{=} 12$	$5 + 8 \stackrel{?}{=} 12$
$11 = 12$	$12 = 12 \checkmark$	$13 = 12$
This sentence is false.	This sentence is true.	This sentence is false.

The solution is 4 because replacing y with 4 results in a true sentence.

In Example 1, $y + 8 = 12$ was solved by replacing y with a number until a true sentence resulted.

Some equations can be solved mentally by using basic facts or arithmetic skills you already know well.

Solve each equation using mental math.

2 $2m = 10$

$2 \times 5 = 10$ *You know that $2 \times 5 = 10$.*

$10 = 10$

The solution is 5.

3 $7 = 5 + d$

$7 = 5 + 2$ *You know that $5 + 2 = 7$.*

$7 = 7$

The solution is 2.

You can also solve equations by using guess and check.

4 **School** Last year, the enrollment in Pointview Middle School was 695 students. This year there are 748 students. If n represents the number of new students, the equation $695 + n = 748$ results. Find the number of new students.

Use guess and check.

Try 50.	*Try 52.*	*Try 53.*
$695 + n = 748$	$695 + n = 748$	$695 + n = 748$
$695 + 50 \stackrel{?}{=} 748$	$695 + 52 \stackrel{?}{=} 748$	$695 + 53 \stackrel{?}{=} 748$
$745 = 748$	$747 = 748$	$748 = 748$ ✓
This sentence is false.	This sentence is false.	This sentence is true.

The solution is 53. So, there are 53 new students.

Study Hint

Estimation You know that 695 is about 700 and 748 is about 750. Think: $700 + 50 = 750$. So the answer should be close to 50.

CHECK FOR UNDERSTANDING

Communicating Mathematics

Read and study the lesson to answer each question.

1. *Write* an example of an algebraic expression. Write an example of an equation. How are they alike? How are they different? **See margin.**

2. *State* an equation with a solution of 7. **Sample answer: $x + 7 = 14$**

Lesson 1-7 Integration: Algebra   Solving Equations   **35**

■ Reteaching the Lesson ■

Activity Play "Equation Concentration." Use index cards in two different colors— one for equations, the other for solutions. Place all cards facedown. Each player, in turn, turns over two cards to try to make a match. The player with the most matches at the end of the game wins.

Additional Answer

1. Sample answer: Both algebraic expressions and equations can contain variables, operations, and numbers. Whereas an equation contains an equals sign, an algebraic expression does not contain an equals sign.

Assignment Guide

Core: 13–41 odd, 42–47
Enriched: 14–38 even, 40–47

Guided Practice

Tell whether the equation is *true* or *false* by replacing the variable with the given value.

3. $18 + j = 45; j = 29$ **false**

4. $y \div 7 = 35; y = 245$ **true**

Identify the solution to each equation from the list given.

5. $b + 5 = 12; 5, 6, 7$ **7**

6. $36 - h = 15; 21, 22, 23$ **21**

7. $72 \div d = 18; 3, 4, 5$ **4**

8. $16r = 96; 4, 5, 6$ **6**

Solve each equation mentally.

9. $4 + x = 13$ **9** **10.** $5w = 20$ **4** **11.** $z - 8 = 2$ **10**

12. *Shopping* Ana purchased a helmet and some reflectors for her bike. The cost of the helmet was $25. She spent a total of $32. **a. $25 + c = $32**

  a. Let c represent the cost of the reflectors. Write an equation that represents the total cost of the items.

  b. Solve your equation to find the cost of the reflectors. **$7**

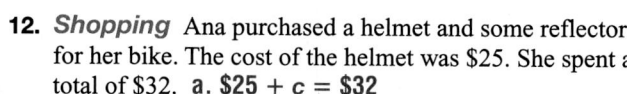

EXERCISES

Practice

Tell whether the equation is *true* or *false* by replacing the variable with the given value.

13. $p + 11 = 27; p = 16$ **true**

14. $4w = 24; w = 6$ **true**

15. $t - 15 = 32; t = 47$ **true**

16. $57 \div d = 21; d = 3$ **false**

17. $93 = 3v; v = 32$ **false**

18. $y \div 39 = 6; y = 234$ **true**

Identify the solution to each equation from the list given.

19. $8 + h = 23; 14, 15, 16$ **15**

20. $t - 6 = 3; 5, 7, 9$ **9**

21. $42 = 6a; 7, 8, 9$ **7**

22. $23 + n = 56; 31, 32, 33$ **33**

23. $b = 65 \div 5; 11, 13, 15$ **13**

24. $31 - m = 19; 10, 11, 12$ **12**

25. $k + 38 = 45; 7, 9, 11$ **7**

26. $76 \div q = 19; 3, 4, 5$ **4**

27. $11 = d \div 4; 41, 43, 44$ **44**

28. $7 \div g = 1; 6, 7, 8$ **7**

Solve each equation mentally.

29. $m - 9 = 17$ **26** **30.** $3 + j = 18$ **15** **31.** $12 = d + 5$ **7**

32. $22 = 2y$ **11** **33.** $24 \div w = 8$ **3** **34.** $4n = 32$ **8**

35. $p \div 5 = 45$ **225** **36.** $a = 4 + 13$ **17** **37.** $18 \div s = 9$ **2**

38. *Algebra* Which of the numbers 3, 6, or 9 is the solution of $7h = 63$? **9**

39. *Algebra* Find the solution of $176 = 11s$. **16**

Study Guide Masters, p. 7

Name_____ Date_____

1-7 Study Guide

Integration: Algebra
Solving Equations

An **equation** is a mathematical sentence that contains an equals sign. The **solution** is the number that makes the equation true.

Example

Warren spent $120 for theater tickets. If each ticket cost $20, how many tickets did Warren buy?

Let t equal the number of tickets.
The problem may be represented by this equation: $20 \times t = 120$.

Guess and check.

Replace t with 7.	Replace t with 6.
$20 \times t = 120$	$20 \times t = 120$
$20 \times 7 = 120$	$20 \times 6 = 120$
$140 = 120$	$120 = 120$ ✔
The sentence is false.	The sentence is true.

The solution is 6. Warren bought 6 tickets.

Identify the solution to each equation from the list given.

1. $15 + r = 21$ 5, 6, 7 **6**
2. $y \div 6 = 7$ 42, 48, 56 **42**
3. $5m = 40$ 6, 7, 8 **8**
4. $n = 7 + 21$ 3, 14, 28 **28**
5. $9 = 63 + b$ 7, 8, 9 **7**
6. $5w = 10$ 2, 25, 50 **2**

Solve each equation mentally.

7. $y = 10 + 6$ **16**
8. $p = 18 - 9$ **0**
9. $x + 6 = 4$ **24**
10. $h \div 5 = 25$ **125**
11. $3r = 15$ **5**
12. $a - 7 = 16$ **23**
13. $18 = 9 + v$ **9**
14. $28 = 4p$ **7**

© Glencoe/McGraw-Hill T7 Mathematics: Applications and Connections, Course 1

Classroom Vignette

"For practicing and reviewing for tests, I use small grease boards and markers. We review in a game format and students hold up their answers on the boards. They receive 1 point for each correct answer. Students bring in old tube socks to use as erasers."

Jan Wickboldt

Jan Wickboldt, Teacher
Clayton School
Clayton, WI

40. *Banking* Currency rates are calculated daily. If 140*d* represents the number of Spanish pesetas for each United States dollar, represented by *d*, how many pesetas will be received in exchange for $50? **7,000 pesetas**

41. *Food* Celina and Marcus went to a fast-food restaurant for lunch. Celina ordered a hamburger with cheese, one order of onion rings, and water. There are 19 grams of fat in one order of onion rings. There is a total of 65 grams of fat in the entire meal.

  a. Let *g* represent the number of grams of fat in a hamburger with cheese. Write an equation to find how many grams of fat are in a hamburger with cheese. **19 + *g* = 65**

  b. Solve your equation to find the number of grams of fat in a hamburger with cheese. **46 grams**

42. *Critical Thinking* Translate each sentence into an equation. Then solve.

  a. *Eight less than m is equal to 5.* **$m - 8 = 5$; 13**

  b. *The sum of h and 7 is equal to 18.* **$h + 7 = 18$; 11**

  c. *The product of 4 and 16 is equal to n.* **$4 \times 16 = n$; 64**

Mixed Review

43. *Standardized Test Practice* How is $2 \times 3 \times 3 \times 11$ expressed in exponential notation? *(Lesson 1-6)* **C**

  A $2 \times 2 \times 3 \times 11$

  B $2^3 \times 11$

  C $2 \times 3^2 \times 11$

  D $2 \times 2^3 \times 11$

44. *Algebra* Evaluate $3x - 2 \cdot 4 + y$ if $x = 7$ and $y = 1$. *(Lesson 1-5)* **14**

45. Find the value of $11 - 3 \div 3 + 2$. *(Lesson 1-4)* **12**

46. Sample answer: 40 miles per day

46. *Transportation* The steamer *Alaska* traveled 182 miles in 5 days. Use rounding to estimate how many miles it averaged each day. *(Lesson 1-3)*

47. *Sports* The graph shows the average cost of professional hockey, football, basketball, and baseball tickets. Camilia is planning to attend a hockey and a football game. About how much will she spend on the two tickets? *(Lesson 1-3)* **about $70**

Sports Ticket Costs

NFL	$35.74
NHL	$34.79
NBA	$31.80
MLB	$11.13

Source: Team Marketing Report

For **Extra Practice,**
see page 559.

Extending the Lesson

Enrichment Masters, p. 7

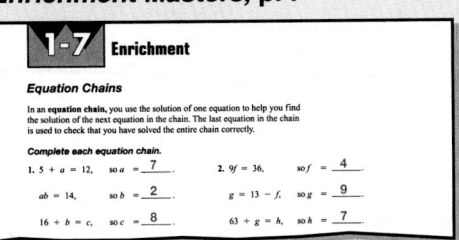

1-7 Enrichment

Equation Chains

In an **equation chain**, you use the solution of one equation to help you find the solution of the next equation in the chain. The last equation in the chain is used to check that you have solved the entire chain correctly.

Complete each equation chain.

1. $5 + a = 12$, so $a = $ __7__
   $ab = 14$, so $b = $ __2__
   $16 \div b = c$, so $c = $ __8__

2. $9f = 36$, so $f = $ __4__
   $g = 13 - f$, so $g = $ __9__
   $63 \div g = h$, so $h = $ __7__

Activity Ask students how they would solve this problem. Erik, Ana, and Gene collected 48 cans of food for the Hunger Drive. Ana brought in 23 cans. Erik collected 3 more cans than Gene. How many cans did they each collect?
48 = 23 + (3 + *g*) + *g*; Erik-14 cans; Gene-11 cans

Vocabulary

This section provides a listing of the new terms, properties, and phrases that were introduced in this chapter. Have students define each term and provide an example or two of it, if appropriate.

Understanding and Using the Vocabulary

These exercises check students' understanding of the terms by using a variety of verbal formats including matching, completion, and true/false.

A complete glossary of terms appears on pages 642–648. The glossary also appears in Spanish on pages 649–656.

interNET CONNECTION Chapter Review **For additional lesson-by-lesson review, visit:** www.glencoe.com/sec/math/mac/mathnet

Vocabulary

After completing this chapter, you should be able to define each term, concept, or phrase and give an example or two of each.

Algebra
algebra (p. 22)
algebraic expression (p. 22)
equation (p. 34)
evaluate (p. 22)
solution (p. 34)
solve (p. 34)
variable (p. 22)

Number and Operations
base (p. 28)
cubed (p. 28)
exponent (p. 28)
factor (p. 28)
order of operations (p. 16)
power (p. 28)
squared (p. 28)

Problem Solving
guess and check (p. 32)

Understanding and Using the Vocabulary

Choose the correct term or number to complete each sentence.

1. When finding the value of an expression, first (<u>multiply and divide</u>, add and subtract) in order from left to right.
2. $(7, \underline{h + 2})$ is an algebraic expression.
3. The base of 4^5 is ($\underline{4}$, 5).
4. When the same factor is repeated, a(n) (variable, <u>exponent</u>) can simplify the notation.
5. The factors of 12 are (<u>3 and 4</u>, 6 and 6).
6. Four cubed is written as (4^2, $\underline{4^3}$).
7. $2 \cdot 2 \cdot 2 \cdot 2 \cdot 2$ can be written as ($\underline{2^5}$, 5^2).
8. A symbol, usually a letter, used to represent a number is called a (<u>variable</u>, power).
9. If $d = 4$, then the value of the expression $14 - d$ is ($\underline{10}$, 18).
10. ($\underline{3x = 6}$, $2x + y$) is an equation.
11. The solution of $16 - g = 5$ is (21, $\underline{11}$).

In Your Own Words
12. *Summarize* the rules for the order of operations.

12. Sample answer: Do powers first. Next, do all multiplication and division in order from left to right. Then, do all addition and subtraction in order from left to right.

MindJogger Videoquizzes

MindJogger Videoquizzes provide an alternative review of concepts presented in this chapter. Students work in teams to answer questions, gaining points for correct answers. The questions are presented in three rounds.
Round 1 Concepts–5 questions
Round 2 Skills–4 questions
Round 3 Problem Solving–4 questions

Objectives & Examples

Upon completing the chapter, you should be able to:

● solve problems using the four-step plan *(Lesson 1-1)*

Use the four-step plan to solve.
Migina studied 2 hours each day for 10 days. How many hours has she studied?

Explore	Migina studied 2 hours each day for 10 days. Find the total number of hours studied.
Plan	Multiply 2 by 10.
Solve	$2 \times 10 = 20$ Migina studied 20 hours.
Examine	The answer makes sense and is reasonable.

● solve problems using patterns *(Lesson 1-2)*

Find the next three numbers for the pattern 1, 4, 7, 10, $\underline{?}$, $\underline{?}$, $\underline{?}$.

Each number is 3 more than the number before it.
$10 + 3 = 13 \quad 13 + 3 = 16 \quad 16 + 3 = 19$

The next three numbers are 13, 16, and 19.

● estimate sums, differences, products, and quotients using rounding *(Lesson 1-3)*

Estimate the product of 8 and 57.

$$\begin{array}{ccc} 57 & \to & 60 \\ \times\ 8 & \to & \times\ 8 \\ \hline & & 480 \end{array}$$

24. No; the total should be about $130.

Review Exercises

Use these exercises to review and prepare for the chapter test.

Use the four-step plan to solve each problem. 13. $39.92

13. *Money Matters* The Music Store sells compact discs for $9.98 each. If Lilla buys 4 CDs, how much will he spend?

14. *School* Tickets to the school dance cost $4 each. The dance committee collected a total of $352. How many students bought tickets? **88 students**

15. *History* In the 1932 presidential election, Franklin Roosevelt won with 472 electoral votes while Herbert Hoover had 59. How many electoral votes were cast? **531 votes**

Find the next three numbers or shapes in each pattern. 18. 225, 275, 325

16. 3, 6, 12, 24, $\underline{?}$, $\underline{?}$, $\underline{?}$ **48, 96, 192**

17. **See Answer Appendix.**

18. 25, 75, 125, 175, $\underline{?}$, $\underline{?}$, $\underline{?}$

19. 16, 24, 32, 40, $\underline{?}$, $\underline{?}$, $\underline{?}$ **48, 56, 64**

Round each number to the underlined place-value position.

20. $\underline{4}$,650 **5,000**   21. $\underline{2}$7 **30**

22. 5,3$\underline{2}$1 **5,320**   23. 6$\underline{5}$4 **650**

24. *Money Matters* Chapa purchases a coat for $91, a shirt for $17, and jeans for $24. The cashier asks for $163. Is this amount reasonable?

Objectives & Examples

This section reviews the skills and concepts of the chapter and shows completely worked examples.

Review Exercises

These exercises provide practice for the corresponding objectives.

Assessment and Evaluation Masters, pp. 3–4

Assessment and Evaluation

Six forms of Chapter 1 Test are available in the *Assessment and Evaluation Masters.*

Chapter 1 Test, Form 1B, is shown at the right. Chapter 1 Test, Form 2B, is shown on the next page.

1A	Multiple Choice	Honors
1B	Multiple Choice	Average
1C	Multiple Choice	Basic
2A	Free Response	Honors
2B	Free Response	Average
2C	Free Response	Basic

Objectives & Examples

evaluate expressions using the order of operations *(Lesson 1-4)*

Find the value of $6 + 12 \div 3$.

$$6 + 12 \div 3 = 6 + 4$$
$$= 10$$

evaluate numerical and simple algebraic expressions *(Lesson 1-5)*

Evaluate $2a + b$ if $a = 7$ and $b = 6$.

$$2a + b = 2 \times 7 + 6$$
$$= 14 + 6$$
$$= 20$$

use powers and exponents in expressions *(Lesson 1-6)*

Evaluate each expression.

$$4^3 = 4 \cdot 4 \cdot 4$$
$$= 64$$

$$6 \cdot 3^2 = 6 \cdot 3 \cdot 3$$
$$= 6 \cdot 9$$
$$= 54$$

solve equations by using mental math and guess and check *(Lesson 1-7)*

Solve $m - 2 = 7$ mentally.

$$9 - 2 = 7 \quad \textit{You know that}$$
$$7 = 7 \quad \textit{9 - 2 = 7.}$$

The solution is 9.

Review Exercises

Find the value of each expression.

25. $9 - 3 \times 2 - 1$ **2**

26. $3 \times 7 + 5 \times 9 \div 3$ **36**

27. $1 + 8 \div 4 - 1$ **2**

28. $4 + 8 - 6 + 10$ **16**

29. $2 \times 8 \div 4 + 3$ **7**

30. $30 \div 3 + 16 \div 4$ **14**

Evaluate each expression if $a = 4$, $b = 3$, and $c = 12$.

31. $c + a$ **16** **32.** $8 - b$ **5**

33. $2a - 1$ **7** **34.** $c - b - a$ **5**

35. $c + 3b$ **21** **36.** $3a - 4b$ **0**

37. $5a + 2c$ **44** **38.** $2ab - c$ **12**

Evaluate each expression.

39. 4^6 **4,096**

40. $5^2 \cdot 3^2 \cdot 4^2$ **3,600**

41. x^3 if $x = 5$ **125**

42. ten squared **100**

43. Write $t \cdot t \cdot t \cdot t \cdot t$ using exponents. t^5

44. Write 3^6 as a product. $3 \cdot 3 \cdot 3 \cdot 3 \cdot 3 \cdot 3$

Identify the solution to each equation from the list given.

45. $14a = 42$; 3, 4, 5 **3**

46. $b + 23 = 31$; 7, 8, 9 **8**

47. $9 = g \div 7$; 61, 62, 63 **63**

48. $y - 7 = 12$; 18, 19, 20 **19**

Solve each equation mentally.

49. $72 \div x = 8$ **9**

50. $m - 13 = 11$ **24**

51. $18 = 3w$ **6**

52. $12 + j = 21$ **9**

Assessment and Evaluation Masters, pp. 9–10

Name_____ Date_____

Chapter 1 Test, Form 2B

Find the next three numbers in each pattern.

1. 8, 14, 20, ?, ?, ? 1. _26, 32, 38_

2. 27, 23, 19, ?, ?, ? 2. _15, 11, 7_

3. 7, 14, 28, ?, ?, ? 3. _56, 112, 224_

4. 2, 6, 18, ?, ?, ? 4. _54, 162, 486_

Round each number to the underlined place-value position.

5. 6,244 5. _6,000_

6. 435 6. _400_

7. 1,324 7. _1,300_

8. 879 8. _900_

Estimate using rounding.

9. 743 + 578 9. _700 + 600 = 1,300_

10. 52 × 9 10. _50 × 10 = 500_

11. 267 − 113 11. _300 − 100 = 200_

12. 67 ÷ 8 12. _70 ÷ 10 = 7_

Find the value of each expression.

13. 24 − 8 × 2 13. _8_

14. 7 × 5 + 6 × 2 14. _47_

15. 3 + 4 × 5 − 1 15. _22_

16. 15 − 5 × 3 + 8 16. _8_

Evaluate each expression if $a = 7$, $b = 5$, and $c = 9$.

17. 8 + b + c 17. _22_

18. a + b × c 18. _52_

19. a − b + ab 19. _37_

20. ac − ab 20. _28_

© Glencoe/McGraw-Hill 9 *Mathematics: Applications and Connections, Course 1*

Chapter 1 Test, Form 2B (continued)

Evaluate.

21. 5^3 21. _125_

22. x^3 if $x = 12$ 22. _1,728_

23. eight squared 23. _64_

24. $2^4 + 3^2$ 24. _25_

Identify the solution to each equation from the list given.

25. x + 10 = 30; 20, 30, 40 25. _20_

26. 50 ÷ x = 25; 2, 75, 25 26. _2_

27. 3a = 21; 6, 7, 8 27. _7_

28. 85 − b = 70; 5, 15, 25 28. _15_

Solve each equation mentally.

29. 8m = 56 29. _7_

30. x − 12 = 4 30. _16_

31. p + 4 = 8 31. _32_

32. The sum of a number and its double is 24. Use the guess-and-check strategy to find the number. 32. _8_

33. At the library, 2,312 books were checked out on Friday, and 3,234 books were checked out on Saturday. Late charges of $74 and $87 were collected on Friday and Saturday, respectively. Find the total amount of late charges collected. 33. _$161_

© Glencoe/McGraw-Hill 10 *Mathematics: Applications and Connections, Course 1*

Test and Review Software

You may use this software, a combination of an item generator and item bank, to create your own tests or worksheets. Types of items include free response, multiple choice, short answer, and open ended.

CD-ROM Program

The CD-ROM Program contains an Assessment Game whose questions review the concepts in this chapter.

Applications & Problem Solving

53. *History* John F. Kennedy began his first term in the House of Representatives in January 1947. In November 1960, he was elected president of the United States. How long had he been in the legislature when he was elected president? *(Lesson 1-1)* **13 years 10 months**

54. *Fitness* Ricardo made a bar graph of the number of push-ups he did in 4 days. If the pattern continues, how many push-ups will he do on the seventh day? *(Lesson 1-2)* **32 push-ups**

Ricardo's Push-ups

55. *Travel* Kanya and her family are planning to go to Hawaii with a tour group. The cost of the trip is $964 per person. There are 63 people in the tour group. About how much money is needed for the tour group to go to Hawaii? *(Lesson 1-3)* **about $63,000**

56. *Guess and Check* The combined weight of two brothers is 300 pounds. One brother weighs 50 pounds more than the other. How much does each brother weigh? *(Lesson 1-7A)* **125 pounds, 175 pounds**

Alternative Assessment

● *Open Ended*

Suppose you are planning to buy a television that costs $410. The store has two payment plans. Plan 1 requires you to pay half of the purchase price up front and the remaining cost over 6 months, with a $5 fee added each month. Plan 2 requires you to make 12 equal payments of $50. Find the cost of each plan.

Plan 1: $440; Plan 2: $600
Suppose you have $250 in savings and you can afford a $50 monthly payment. Which payment plan should you choose? Explain your choice. **See margin.**

A practice test for Chapter 1 is provided on page 595.

● *Completing the* **CHAPTER Project**

Use the following checklist to complete your project

☑ The items and their costs are listed on the order form.

☑ The table of shipping charges is included.

☑ Pictures of the items are included.

☑ A list of advantages and disadvantages of mail-order shopping is included.

● Select one of the assignments from this chapter and place it in your portfolio. Attach a note to it explaining why you selected it.

Applications & Problem Solving

This section provides additional practice in solving real-world problems that involve the skills of this chapter.

Alternative Assessment

The *Open Ended* section provides students with a performance assessment opportunity to assess their work and understanding.

CHAPTER Project

Students should complete the final stages of their project and prepare a class demonstration of their results. A scoring guide for the project is available in the *Investigations and Projects Masters*, p. 19.

 Students should add to their portfolios at this time.

Assessment and Evaluation Masters, p. 13

Additional Answer for the Open Ended item
Plan 1 is the better choice. See students' explanations.

Performance Assessment

Additional performance assessment tasks for this chapter are included in the *Assessment and Evaluation Masters* on page 13. A scoring guide is also provided on page 25.

The Standardized Test Practice may be used to help students prepare for standardized tests. The test items are written in the same style as those in state proficiency tests and standardized tests like CAT, CTBS, ITBS, MAT, SAT, and Terra Nova. The test items cover skills and concepts covered up to this point in the text.

The pages can be used as an overnight assessment. After students have completed the pages, discuss how each problem can be solved, or provide copies of the solutions from the *Solutions Manual*.

Assessment and Evaluation Masters, p. 19

CHAPTER 1
Standardized Test Practice
Assessing Knowledge & Skills

Section One: Multiple Choice

There are twelve multiple-choice questions in this section. Choose the best answer. If a correct answer is *not here*, mark the letter for Not Here.

1. What is the value of 2^5? **B**
   A 10
   B 32
   C 25
   D 64

2. There will be 120 people at the annual orchestra awards banquet. Each table seats 8 people. Which procedure can be used to find the number of tables needed? **H**
   F Add 8 to 120.
   G Multiply 8 and 120.
   H Divide 120 by 8.
   J Subtract 8 from 120.

3. Find the value of the expression $121 \div 11 + 4 \cdot 8$. **B**
   A 120
   B 43
   C 12
   D 60

4. By scoring 2,491 points during the 1995-1996 regular season, Michael Jordan scored more points than any other NBA player. What is this number rounded to the nearest hundred? **J**
   F 2,490
   G 2,400
   H 2,590
   J 2,500

5. Evaluate mn if $m = 120$ and $n = 50$. **D**
   A 500
   B 600
   C 5,000
   D 6,000

Please note that Questions 6–12 have five answer choices.

6. Kenyatta is planning to buy a car that costs $9,786. To have a sunroof installed, the cost is $548 more. What is the price of the car with a sunroof? **G**
   F $9,334
   G $10,334
   H $10,024
   J $11,334
   K Not Here

7. A sign at the school bookstore read:

Item	Price
Calculator	$5
Notebook	$1
Combination Lock	$3
3-Ring Binder	$2

   Donavan purchased 3 notebooks, 2 binders, and a lock. Find the total cost of the items. **E**
   A $8
   B $7
   C $12
   D $9
   E $10

8. The students at Grant Middle School are selling candy bars as a fundraiser. Each class that sells 400 candy bars will earn a field trip to a water park. Lori's class has sold 207 candy bars. How many more candy bars must her class sell to earn a field trip? **F**
   F 193
   G 184
   H 173
   J 194
   K Not Here

◀◀◀ Instructional Resources

Another cumulative review is shown at the left and is available in the *Assessment and Evaluation Masters*, p. 19.

9. Cord Photography is having a sale on camera equipment.

Camera Package	
Camera	$178
Lens	$ 96
Camera Strap	$ 23

Which is the best estimate for the total amount of the camera package? **B**

A $100
B $300
C $400
D $200
E $600

10. The school cafeteria prepared 1,987 lunches last week. About how many lunches were prepared each day? **J**

F 600
G 700
H 500
J 400
K Not Here

11. Which is a reasonable estimate when 298 is subtracted from 702? **A**

A 400
B 500
C 900
D 1,000
E Not Here

12. Javiar drove his car for 4 hours at 45 miles per hour and for 3 hours at 50 miles per hour. Which expression could be used to find the total number of miles that Javier drove his car? **J**

F $45 \div 4 \times 50 \div 3$
G $45 + 50 \times 4$
H $45 + 4 \times 50 + 3$
J $45 \times 4 + 50 \times 3$
K Not Here

Test-Taking Tip

Many problems can be solved without much calculating if you understand the basic mathematical concepts. Always look carefully at what is asked, and think of possible shortcuts for solving the problem.

Section Two: Free Response

This section contains five questions for which you will provide short answers. Write your answers on your paper.

13. While installing gas pipes, Hector used pieces of pipe that measured 1 ft, 2 ft, 3 ft, and 4 ft. If he cut the pieces from a 20-ft pipe, how much pipe was left? **10 ft**

20 ft

14. Write $2 \times 3 \times 5 \times 5 \times 7$ in exponential notation. $2 \times 3 \times 5^2 \times 7$

15. Sue recycled 41 aluminum cans. Her friend Tammy gave her some more aluminum cans, and then she had recycled 62 cans. To find how many cans she was given, Sue wrote $c + 41 = 62$. What is the value of c? **21**

16. Find the value of $10 \times 10 + 10 \div 2$. **105**

17. Solve $t - 16 = 11$. **27**

inter NET CONNECTION Test Practice **For additional test practice questions, visit:**

www.glencoe.com/sec/math/mac/mathnet

Chapter 1 Standardized Test Practice **43**

Test-Taking Tip

Encourage students to underline key phrases in the question and cross out information that isn't needed.

Assessment and Evaluation Masters, pp. 17–18

Instructional Resources ▶▶▶

Additional standardized test practice is shown at the right and is available in the *Assessment and Evaluation Masters,* pp. 17–18.

Statistics: Graphing Data

Previewing the Chapter

Overview

This chapter explores graphing and statistics. Students learn to interpret and make frequency tables, bar graphs, line graphs, circle graphs, and stem-and-leaf plots. They use line graphs to make predictions. They find the mean, median, mode, and range of a set of data and learn to recognize when statistics and graphs are misleading. Students learn to solve problems by interpreting pictographs and bar graphs and by organizing data into a table and into a box-and-whisker plot. Students learn to graph ordered pairs in the first quadrant.

Lesson (pages)	Lesson Objectives	NCTM Standards 2000	Standardized Tests	State/Local Objectives
2-1 (46–49)	Make and interpret frequency tables.	1, 2, 5–10		
2-2 (50–53)	Choose appropriate scales and intervals for frequency tables.	1, 2, 5–10		
2-3 (54–57)	Construct bar graphs and line graphs.	1, 2, 5–10	MAT	
2-3B (58–59)	Solve problems by using a graph.	1, 5–10	CAT, MAT	
2-4 (60–63)	Interpret circle graphs.	1, 5–10	CAT, MAT, SAT	
2-5 (64–67)	Make predictions from line graphs.	1, 2, 5–10	MAT, SAT	
2-6 (68–70)	Construct stem-and-leaf plots.	1, 2, 5–10		
2-7 (71–75)	Find the mean, median, mode, and range to describe a set of data.	1, 2, 5–10	CTBS, ITBS, MAT, SAT, TN	
2-7B (76–77)	Display and summarize data in a box-and-whisker plot.	1, 2, 5–10		
2-8 (78–81)	Recognize when statistics and graphs are misleading.	1, 2, 5–10		
2-9 (82–85)	Use ordered pairs to locate points and organize data.	1, 2, 5–10	MAT	

CAT = California Achievement Tests, CTBS = Comprehensive Tests of Basic Skills, ITBS = Iowa Tests of Basic Skills, MAT = Metropolitan Achievement Tests, SAT = Stanford Achievement Tests, TN = Terra Nova
For the key to numbering of NCTM Standards 2000, see page T6.

Organizing the Chapter

 The **Interactive Lesson Planner** contains all of the blackline masters and transparencies. This CD-ROM also includes an easy-to-use lesson planning calendar.

LESSON PLANNING GUIDE

Lesson	Extra Practice (Student Edition)	BLACKLINE MASTERS (PAGE NUMBERS)										Transparencies A and B
		Study Guide	Practice	Enrichment	Assessment & Evaluation	Classroom Games	Diversity	Hands-On Lab	School to Career	Science and Math Lab Manual	Technology	
2-1	p. 559	8	8	8								2-1
2-2	p. 560	9	9	9								2-2
2-3	p. 560	10	10	10	43			70			4	2-3
2-3B	p. 560											
2-4	p. 561	11	11	11			2					2-4
2-5	p. 561	12	12	12	42, 43							2-5
2-6	p. 561	13	13	13								2-6
2-7	p. 562	14	14	14	44				2	5–8	3	2-7
2-7B								40				
2-8	p. 562	15	15	15		3–4						2-8
2-9	p. 562	16	16	16	44							2-9
Study Guide/ Assessment					29–41, 45–47							

OTHER CHAPTER RESOURCES

Student Edition
Chapter Project, pp. 45, 49, 57, 81, 89
Let the Games Begin, p. 75

Technology
 MathPASS CD-ROM

Interactive Mathematics Tools Software

Teacher's Classroom Resources

Applications
Family Letters and Activities, pp. 3–4
Investigations and Projects Masters, pp. 21–24
Meeting Individual Needs
Investigations for the Special Education Student, pp. 3–5

Teaching Aids
Answer Key Masters
Block Scheduling Booklet
Lesson Planning Guide
Solutions Manual

Professional Publications
Glencoe Mathematics Professional Series

Planning the Chapter

 MindJogger Videoquizzes provide a unique format for reviewing concepts presented in the chapter.

ASSESSMENT RESOURCES

Student Edition
Mixed Review, pp. 49, 53, 57, 63, 67, 70, 74, 81, 85
Mid-Chapter Self Test, p. 67
Math Journal, pp. 56, 69, 79
Study Guide and Assessment, pp. 86–89
Performance Task, p. 89
Portfolio Suggestion, p. 89
Standardized Test Practice, pp. 90–91
Chapter Test, p. 596

Assessment and Evaluation Masters
Multiple-Choice Tests (Forms 1A, 1B, 1C), pp. 29–34
Free-Response Tests (Forms 2A, 2B, 2C), pp. 35–40
Performance Assessment, p. 41
Mid-Chapter Test, p. 42
Quizzes A–D, pp. 43–44
Standardized Test Practice, pp. 45–46
Cumulative Review, p. 47

Teacher's Wraparound Edition
5-Minute Check, pp. 46, 50, 54, 60, 64, 68, 71, 78, 82
Building Portfolios, p. 44
Math Journal, p. 77
Closing Activity, pp. 49, 53, 57, 59, 63, 67, 70, 74, 81, 85

Technology
Test and Review Software
MindJogger Videoquizzes
CD-ROM Program

MATERIALS AND MANIPULATIVES

Lesson 2-1	Lesson 2-4	Lesson 2-7	Lesson 2-7B
newspaper	adding machine tape	bowls of beans	index cards
	cellophane tape	calculator	cardboard
	markers	index cards	markers
	tape measure*	spinners*†	push pins
	string		string

*Glencoe Manipulative Kit   †Glencoe Overhead Manipulative Resources

PACING CHART

See pages T25–T27 for the Course Planning Calendar.

COURSE	DAY 1	DAY 2	DAY 3	DAY 4	DAY 5	DAY 6	DAY 7
Standard	Chapter Project	Lesson 2-1	Lesson 2-2	Lesson 2-3	Lesson 2-3B	Lesson 2-4	Lesson 2-5
Honors	Chapter Project	Lesson 2-1	Lesson 2-2	Lesson 2-3	Lesson 2-3B	Lesson 2-4	Lesson 2-5
Block	Chapter Project & Lesson 2-1	Lessons 2-2 & 2-3	Lessons 2-3B & 2-4	Lessons 2-5 & 2-6	Lesson 2-7	Lessons 2-8 & 2-9	Study Guide and Assessment, Chapter Test

Interactive Mathematics:
Activities and Investigations

is an activity-based program that may be used as an enhancement for chapters in *Mathematics: Applications and Connections.*

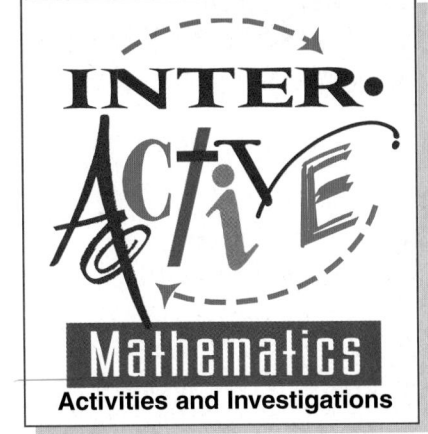

INTER•ACTIVE Mathematics
Activities and Investigations

Unit 8, Activity Three
Use with Lesson 2-3.

Summary Students work in groups to generate a list of statements about a double bar graph of the winner's and loser's Super Bowl scores. Then students write individual reports about any conclusions or trends they have interpreted from the graph and group discussion.

Math Connection Students analyze a set of data that is in the form of a double bar graph. They select a measure of central tendency to determine whether there are any trends in Super Bowl scores.

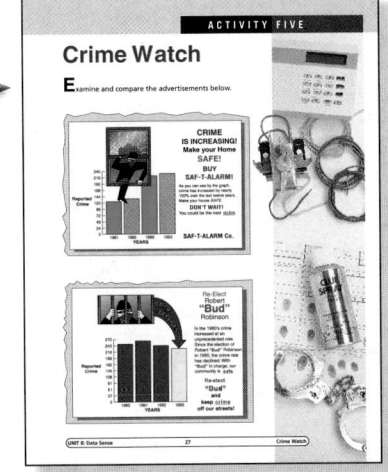

Unit 8, Activity Five

Use with Lesson 2-8.

Summary Students work in groups to discuss and analyze two advertisements showing different graphs in newspapers made using the same data. Each student then writes a letter to the editor of the newspaper describing the inconsistencies between the information presented in the two graphs.

Math Connection Students use two bar graphs that were constructed using the same data. A bar graph is used to compare quantities, with the length of each bar representing a number.

DAY 8	DAY 9	DAY 10	DAY 11	DAY 12	DAY 13	DAY 14	DAY 15
Lesson 2-6	Lesson 2-7		Lesson 2-8	Lesson 2-9	Study Guide and Assessment	Chapter Test	
Lesson 2-6	Lessons 2-7 & 2-7B		Lesson 2-8	Lesson 2-9	Study Guide and Assessment	Chapter Test	

Enhancing the Chapter

APPLICATIONS

Classroom Games, pp. 3–4

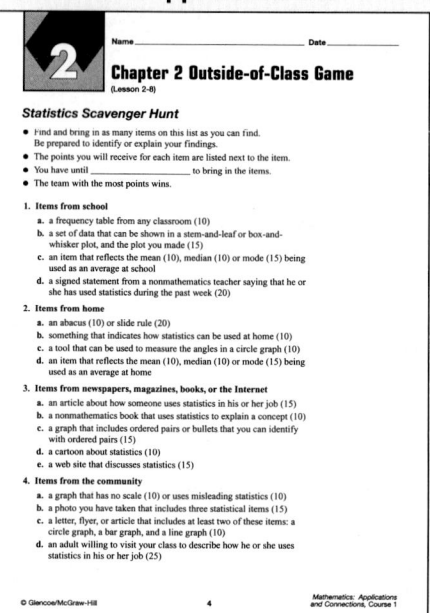

Diversity Masters, p. 2

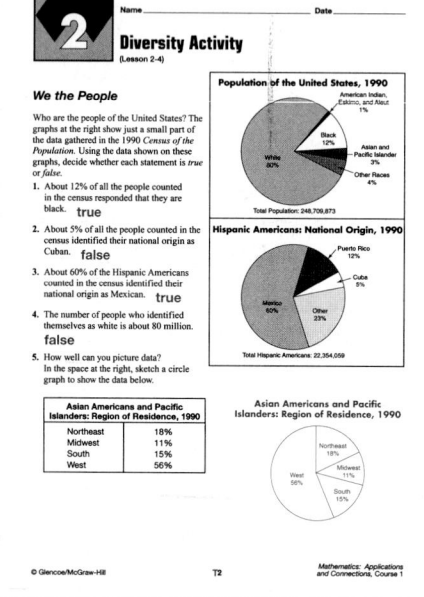

School to Career Masters, p. 2

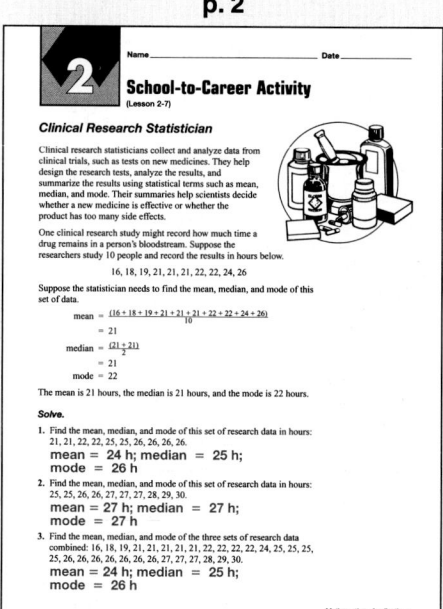

Family Letters and Activities, pp. 3–4

Science and Math Lab Manual, pp. 5–8

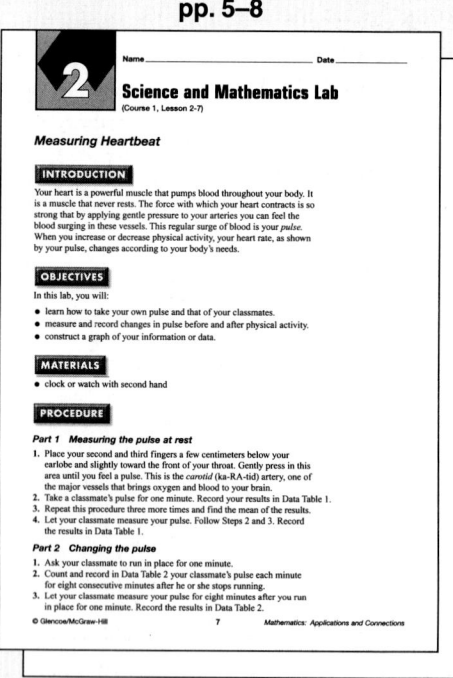

MANIPULATIVES/MODELING

Hands-On Lab Masters, p. 70

2 Name _____ Date _____

Lab Activity
(Lesson 2-3)

Bar Graphs and Line Graphs

Survey your classmates. Ask: "Including yourself, how many persons live in your household?" Answers will vary.

Number in Household	Tally	Frequency
2		
3		
4		
5		
6		
7		
8		
9		
10		

Make a bar graph of the frequency table on a separate sheet of paper.

Keep track of the number of minutes you spend doing some activity each day for one week. Then make a line graph of the data on a separate sheet of paper. See students' graphs.

Some examples that you may want to choose include the following: doing homework, reading for pleasure, watching TV, practicing music, exercising, talking on the phone, playing video games, working on a hobby.

Day of the Week	Time Spent (minutes)
Sun.	
Mon.	
Tues.	
Wed.	
Thurs.	
Fri.	
Sat.	

© Glencoe/McGraw-Hill   70   Mathematics: Applications and Connections, Course 1

ASSESSMENT/EVALUATION

Assessment and Evaluation Masters, pp. 42–44

2 Name _____ Date _____

Chapter 2 Mid-Chapter Test
(Lessons 2-1 through 2-5)

Refer to the table.

TV Times	
Interval	Frequency
7:00–8:00	4
8:00–9:00	6
9:00–10:00	15
10:00–11:00	13

1. How many people watched TV from 9:00 to 11:00?   1. **28**
2. Can you tell from the table if anyone watched only from 8:00 to 8:30?   2. **no**
3. What is the scale of the frequency data?   3. **7:00 to 11:00**   4. **31**

Five friends participated in a library reading program. The number of books each had read at its conclusion is as follows: Chris, 52; Amar, 33; Tenisha, 47; Wei, 21; Branwyn, 43.

4. What is the range of the data?   5. Books Read
5. Make a vertical bar graph showing these data.

Refer to the line graph.   **Sales for Third Quarter**
6. For what week were sales highest?   6. **week 12**
7. What four weeks had the same sales?   7. **weeks 5, 6, 9, and 11**
8. Predict the sales for week 14.   8. **about $9,000**

Refer to the circle graph.   **Favorite Food**
9. What type of food is most popular?   9. **pizza**
10. Which two types of food are equal in popularity?   10. **ice cream and hot dogs**

© Glencoe/McGraw-Hill   42   Mathematics: Applications and Connections, Course 1

Name _____ Date _____

Chapter 2 Quiz A
(Lessons 2-1 through 2-3)

At the annual flower show, people were asked to vote for their favorite flower. The results are as follows: Rose, 9; Tulip, 7; Lotus, 5; Iris, 6; Lily, 4.

Flower	Votes
Rose	9
Tulip	7
Lotus	5
Iris	6
Lily	4

1. Make a frequency table for the data.
2. What was the least popular flower?   2. **lily**
3. What scale would be used to make a vertical bar graph?   3. **0–10**
4. What interval would be used to make a vertical bar graph?   4. **2**
5. Make a vertical bar graph for the data.   5. Favorite Flowers

Name _____ Date _____

Chapter 2 Quiz B
(Lessons 2-4 and 2-5)

Refer to the circle graph.   **Favorite Vegetables**
1. Which vegetable is the least popular? the most popular?   1. **broccoli; corn**
2. Which two vegetables combined received more than half the votes?   2. **green beans and corn**

Refer to the line graph.   **Estimated Population for Sun City**
3. Predict the population of Sun City in 2004.   3. **about 5,000**
4. Predict the population of Sun City in 2008.   4. **about 7,000**
5. In what year will the population reach 8,000?   5. **2010**

© Glencoe/McGraw-Hill   43   Mathematics: Applications and Connections, Course 1

TECHNOLOGY/MULTIMEDIA

Technology Masters, pp. 3–4

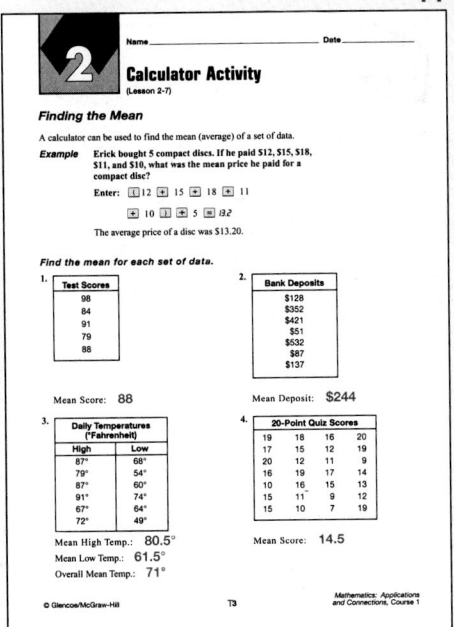

2 Name _____ Date _____

Calculator Activity
(Lesson 2-7)

Finding the Mean

A calculator can be used to find the mean (average) of a set of data.

Example   Erick bought 5 compact discs. If he paid $12, $15, $18, $11, and $10, what was the mean price he paid for a compact disc?

Enter: [ ] 12 [+] 15 [+] 18 [+] 11 [+] 10 [ ] [÷] 5 [=] *13.2*

The average price of a disc was $13.20.

Find the mean for each set of data.

1.
Test Scores
98
84
91
79
88

Mean Score: **88**

2.
Bank Deposits
$128
$352
$421
$51
$532
$87
$137

Mean Deposit: **$244**

3.
Daily Temperatures (°Fahrenheit)	
High	Low
87°	68°
79°	54°
87°	60°
91°	74°
67°	64°
72°	49°

Mean High Temp.: **80.5°**
Mean Low Temp.: **61.5°**
Overall Mean Temp.: **71°**

4.
20-Point Quiz Scores			
19	18	16	20
17	15	12	19
20	12	11	9
16	19	17	14
10	16	15	13
15	11	9	12
15	10	7	19

Mean Score: **14.5**

© Glencoe/McGraw-Hill   T3   Mathematics: Applications and Connections, Course 1

2 Name _____ Date _____

Graphing Calculator Activity
(Lesson 2-3)

Line Graphs

You can view a variety of graphs on a graphing calculator. Follow the steps shown to display a line graph of the data in the table.

Average Cost of New Major League Baseball Team	
Team	Cost (millions)
1969	$9
1977	$7
1993	$95
1998	$130

Step 1 First, clear all lists. Then, enter the data from the first column of the table under L1.

Enter: [2nd] [MEM] 4 [ENTER] [STAT] [ENTER] 1969 [ENTER] 1977 [ENTER] 1993 [ENTER] 1998 [ENTER]

Step 2 Enter the data from the second column of the table under L2.

Enter: [▶] 9 [ENTER] 7 [ENTER] 95 [ENTER] 130 [ENTER]

Step 3 Define the graph.

Enter: [2nd] [STAT PLOT] [ENTER] [ENTER] [▼] [▶] [ENTER] [▼] [2nd] [L1] [ENTER] [2nd] [L2] [ENTER] [ZOOM] 9

Display the data below in a line graph on a graphing calculator. (First, clear all lists.)

Number of Students Enrolled in 6th Grade	
Year	Students
1995	235
1996	219
1997	257
1998	289
1999	205

© Glencoe/McGraw-Hill   T4   Mathematics: Applications and Connections, Course 1

MEETING INDIVIDUAL NEEDS

Investigations for the Special Education Student, pp. 3–5

Use with:
| Course 1–Chapter 2 |
| Course 2–Chapter 3 |
| Course 3–Chapter 4 |

Investigation 2 Teacher's Guide

Commercial Success

Overview
This investigation gives students the opportunity to learn how important mathematics is in the business world. Students may work alone, with a partner, or in a small group to propose a brand-new product that is in demand. Then, students design, model, and test-market the product to determine its effectiveness. Success during the test-marketing process allows students to progress to the final stage—creating a business plan. This business plan, which is videotaped and presented to the class, includes a plan to market and sell the product.

Activity Goals
Students will:
• create a new product based on demand,
• graph data about the product, and
• develop a plan to market and sell the product.

Planning the Instruction
Prerequisite Skills
Students should have a significant amount of practice computing with whole numbers and collecting and graphing sets of data.

Materials
• investigation worksheets
• calculators
• graph paper
• supplies for making the product
• video camera or cassette recorder and tapes

Time Needed
• ten 45-minute periods

Procedure
1. Brainstorm product ideas with the class. Students should then agree on their own product idea.
2. Have students validate the demand for their product idea by surveying 20–50 people. If there is not sufficient demand, the students should rethink their product idea.
3. Using the Product Development worksheet, students will:
   a. design the product,
   b. list the steps needed to make the product,
   c. list the materials needed to make the product,
   d. estimate the cost to make the product.
4. Gather materials and have students create a model of the product.
5. Students should then test market their product by showing the model to the people surveyed originally, recording their opinions and comments, and summarizing the new data with a graph.
6. If test marketing was a success, have students devise a business plan using the Business Plan worksheet. Otherwise, revise the product according to the feedback from the survey.
7. Finally, have students write and videotape an advertisement for their product to present to the class.

Adaptations and Variations

The following are some ideas on how this investigation may be modified depending on student population.

LD • Allow more time.
• If graphing is difficult, use computer graphics.

PH • Decrease the number of people in the survey if access is a problem due to lack of mobility.
• If drawing is difficult, have students use computer graphics or provide a partner or aide to help them.

CD • Encourage students to work with a partner who is able to perform the verbal tasks in the investigation, such as asking survey questions or speaking on videotape.

BD • To prevent inappropriate behavior, monitor students closely and set aside a semiprivate place for them to work to avoid any distractions.
• Isolate from other students if a problem occurs.

HI • Have another student sign the advertisements.
• Allow students to sit close to the tape player.

VI • Decrease the number of people in the survey if mobility is an issue.
• Provide alternative ways for graphing data, such as using larger sheets of paper and thick markers, or use a computer with a large-screen monitor.

© Glencoe/McGraw-Hill   3   Mathematics: Applications and Connections

Statistics: Graphing Data

Theme: Pets

The Humane Society of the United States, founded in 1954, is an animal protection organization that also educates the public on the humane and proper care of pets.

In September 1997, the Society kicked off a new campaign called *First Strike* to educate the public on the connection between animal abuse and human violence.

Question of the Day In 1996, there were approximately 66 million cats and 55 million dogs in households. If 32 million households had cats and 36 million households had dogs, what is the mean number of cats and dogs per household? **cats, 2.1; dogs, 1.5**

Assess Prerequisite Skills

Ask students to read through the list of objectives presented in "What you'll learn in Chapter 2." You may wish to ask them what each of the objectives means or if they have experienced or used any of these math concepts before.

 Building Portfolios

Encourage students to revise their portfolios as they study this chapter. They may wish to include copies of the various surveys and graphs used in this chapter. These are good for future reference as well as reminders of what students have learned.

 Math and the Family

In the *Family Letters and Activities* booklet (pp. 3–4), you will find a letter to the parents explaining what students will study in Chapter 2. An activity appropriate for the whole family is also available.

What you'll learn in Chapter 2

- to interpret and make frequency tables, bar graphs, line graphs, circle graphs, and stem-and-leaf plots,
- to use graphs to solve problems and make predictions,
- to find the mean, median, mode, and range of a set of data,
- to recognize when statistics and graphs are misleading, and
- to graph points in a coordinate system.

44 Chapter 2 Statistics: Graphing Data

 CD-ROM Program

Activities for Chapter 2

- Interactive Lessons 2-1, 2-3
- Extended Activity 2-5
- Assessment Game
- Resource Lessons 2-1 through 2-9

CHAPTER Project

PETS ARE (HU)MANS' BEST FRIENDS

This project involves conducting a survey about pets. You will make tables and graphs from your survey and present them to the class. You should then compare the results of your survey to other students' surveys.

Getting Started

- Look at the class list below. How many students have no pets? How many pets are there altogether?
- Survey your classmates to determine the number and kind of pets they have.

Name	Number and Type of Pet	Total Pets
Kevin	2 dogs, 2 turtles	4
Carmen	2 dogs, 2 horses, 1 cat, 4 fish	9
Lawanda	1 dog, 3 cats	4
Heather	1 dog, 1 cat	2
Tiffany	2 dogs, 1 cat	3
Javier	1 cat, 1 hamster	2
Sonia	2 dogs, 2 cats, 20 fish	24
Matthew	1 dog	1
Denny	1 dog, 1 cat	2
Hisano	2 dogs, 1 turtle, 2 hamsters	5
Benito	1 dog, 1 cat, 6 fish, 1 hamster	9
Codi	4 cats, 3 dogs, 2 hamsters, 2 horses, 1 rabbit	12
Paquita	6 dogs, 3 cats, 3 birds, 2 snakes, 3 rats	17
Alvin	2 birds, 1 rabbit	3
Nikki	1 dog, 1 bird	2
Kyle	1 cat, 1 turtle	2
Malik	1 cat	1
Diego	1 dog, 1 snake, 1 fish	3
Cassi	5 rabbits, 2 dogs, 3 cats	10
Stephanie	1 dog, 2 cats, 1 horse	4
Lindsay	4 dogs, 5 horses, 5 cats	14
Tyrone	0	0
Michael	0	0
Judi	1 dog	1

Technology Tips

- Use **computer software** to make graphs of your data.
- Use an **electronic encyclopedia** to do your research.
- Use a **word processor.**

 interNET
CONNECTION   Research For up-to-date
information on pets, visit:

www.glencoe.com/sec/math/mac/mathnet

Working on the Project

You can use what you'll learn in Chapter 2 to help you make your presentation.

Page	Exercise
49	10
57	17
81	15
89	Alternative Assessment

---

 interNET
CONNECTION

Glencoe has made every effort to ensure that the website links for *Mathematics: Applications and Connections* at **www.glencoe.com/sec/math/mac/mathnet** are current and contain appropriate content. However, these website links are not under Glencoe's control.

Instructional Resources ▶▶▶

A recording sheet to help students organize their data for the Chapter Project is shown at the right and is available in the *Investigations and Projects Masters,* p. 24.

CHAPTER Project
NOTES

Objectives Students should
- make tables and graphs from a survey.
- compare different survey results.

Project Pointer You may suggest that students begin a *Project Folder* to keep their work as they complete each stage of the Chapter Project. The completed project may also be added to their portfolios.

Students may choose to survey number of pets *or* type of pet. This decision will help them determine the type of graph to use.

Using the Table After students take their surveys and complete tables similar to the one shown, have them make new tables that contain only the information they will use in their graphs.

Investigations and Projects Masters, **p. 24**

2	Chapter 2 Project

Name _____ Date _____

Pets Are (Hu)mans' Best Friends

Page 49, Working on the Chapter Project, Exercise 10

a.
Name	Tally	Frequency		Name	Tally	Frequency
Kevin				Paquita		
Carmen				Alvin		
Lawanda				Nikki		
Heather				Kyle		
Tiffany				Malik		
Javier				Diego		
Sonia				Cassi		
				Stephanie		
Matthew				Lindsay		
Denny				Tyrone		
Hisano				Michael		
Benito				Judi		
Codi						

b. Use a separate sheet of paper for your frequency table.

Page 57, Working on the Chapter Project, Exercise 17
a.   b.

Page 81, Working on the Chapter Project, Exercise 15
a. The set of data in order is:
    The mean number of pets per student is:
    The median number of pets is:
    The mode is:
b. The measure of central tendency that describes the data best is the:

© Glencoe/McGraw-Hill   24   *Mathematics: Applications and Connections, Course 1*

Instructional Resources

- *Study Guide Masters*, p. 8
- *Practice Masters*, p. 8
- *Enrichment Masters*, p. 8
- Transparencies 2-1, A and B
- CD-ROM Program
  - Resource Lesson 2-1
  - Interactive Lesson 2-1

Recommended Pacing	
Standard	Day 2 of 14
Honors	Day 2 of 14
Block	Day 1 of 7

1 FOCUS

5-Minute Check
(Chapter 1)

1. Estimate 378 + 245 using rounding. 400 + 200 = 600
2. Evaluate 12 ÷ 4 + 5 × 7. 38
3. Evaluate 9 + 6*a* if *a* = 4. 33
4. Write $6^2 \cdot 2^2$ as a product and evaluate.
   6 · 6 · 2 · 2 = 144
5. Solve *m* + 21 = 74 mentally. 53

The 5-Minute Check is also available on **Transparency 2-1A** for this lesson.

Motivating the Lesson

Problem Solving Ask students how they would organize a table of the ages of Olympic athletes.

2 TEACH

Transparency 2-1B contains a teaching aid for this lesson.

Teaching Tip In Example 1, emphasize to students the importance of checking the total number in the frequency column. Discuss what happens if the number is incorrect.

What **you'll learn**

You'll learn to make and interpret frequency tables.

When **am I ever going to use this?**

You can use frequency tables to keep track of votes in a class survey.

Word Wise
data
statistics
frequency table

Have you ever purchased something and the cashier asked you for your zip code? Zip codes are **data** that tell the store where its customers live. Data are pieces of information that are usually numerical. **Statistics** involves collecting, organizing, analyzing, and presenting data. In statistics, data are often organized in tables.

One type of table is a **frequency table**. A frequency table shows how many times each piece of data occurs. The frequency table below shows the results of a survey.

Favorite TV Show	Tally	Frequency
Show A	☰☰☰☰☰ III	28
Show B	☰☰☰☰☰ I	26
Show C	☰☰☰☰☰☰☰	35
Show D	☰☰☰☰☰☰	30
Show E	☰☰☰☰☰☰☰☰☰ IIII	44
Show F	☰☰☰	15

There is a tally mark for each response in the corresponding row. The total of each row of marks is given in the last column.

Example APPLICATION

Food Marian's Diner surveyed its customers to determine the favorite lunch item—hamburger (HB), hot-dog (HD), pizza (P), or sub (S). Make a frequency table of the responses shown at the right.

HD	HB	S	P
P	S	HB	HD
S	HB	HD	P
P	S	HB	P
P	S	HD	P
S	P	P	P

Explore   What do you know?

You know how each person responded.

You know how many people responded.

Plan   Draw a table with three columns and tally the responses.

Solve   In the first column, list each lunch item. In the second column, mark the tallies. In the third column, write the frequency or number of tallies.

Lunch Choice	Tally	Frequency
Hamburger	IIII	4
Hot Dog	IIII	4
Pizza	☰ ☰	10
Sub	☰ I	6

Multiple Learning Styles

 Auditory/Musical Provide students with copies of sheet music of children's songs and identify the notes in the treble clef. Have students make frequency tables of the notes by time value. Based on their results, have them make predictions of the most common notes. Test the predictions on several types of sheet music such as classical, modern, jazz, Top 40, and rock. Evaluate the success of their predictions.

> **Examine** Check to see if the total number of scores in the frequency column matches the number of responses in the original list. If it doesn't, you need to check your work.

You can use the information in a completed frequency table in many problem-solving situations.

Example 2

CONNECTION

Life Science Mr. Martinez' life science class is taking a field trip to the local zoo to do research for their class project. He decides to ask the students which behind-the-scenes tour they would like to take. They will take the tour receiving the most votes. Mr. Martinez made the frequency table below. Which tour should he schedule for the students?

Tour	Tally	Frequency
reptiles	⦀⦀ ⦀⦀ ⎸	11
large cats	⦀⦀ ⦀⦀⦀	8
pachyderms	⦀⦀⦀	3
birds	⦀⦀ ⎸	6

Look for the tour that has the most tally marks. Mr. Martinez should schedule a tour about reptiles.

HANDS-ON MINI-LAB

Work in groups of five.

 newspaper

Ten of the most commonly used words in written English are *the, and, of, to, in, is, you, that, it,* and *for.*

Try This

1. Select a portion of text from a newspaper article that is at least 4 inches long and 1 column wide.

2. Make a frequency table. Tally each time one of these ten words appears. **1–3. See students' work. Answers will vary.**

Talk About It

3. Which word appeared most often? Do you think it is the most commonly used word in written English?

4. Do you think the results would be the same if you selected a different section of the newspaper? Explain why or why not.

5. Do you think the results would be a lot different if you selected a portion of a novel instead of the newspaper? Explain why or why not. **4–5. Answers will vary.**

Check for Understanding

If students need additional practice or instruction after completing Exercises 1–5, one of the following options may be helpful.
- Extra Practice, see p. 559
- Reteaching Activity
- *Study Guide Masters*, p. 8
- *Practice Masters*, p. 8

Assignment Guide

Core: 6, 7, 9, 11–14
Enriched: 7–9, 11–14

Additional Answers

1. Sample answer: to make it easier to study the data.

2. Sample answer: *The Simpsons* was the favorite TV show.

5a.
Age	Tally	Frequency
10	I	1
11	I	1
12	ⅢⅠ	5
13	III	3
14	II	2

Study Guide Masters, p. 8

Name _____ Date _____

2-1 Study Guide

Frequency Tables

Members of a sixth-grade class were surveyed to determine when to hold the annual trip to the amusement park. The results are shown at the right. On what date should the trip be held?

Dates Reported			
June 9	June 2	June 9	June 8
June 2	June 9	June 8	June 9
June 9	June 2	June 9	June 1
June 2	June 9	June 9	June 9
June 8	June 2	June 9	June 1
June 2	June 9	June 2	June 2
June 8	June 9		

Explore What do you know?
You know how each person responded.
What do you need to know?
You are deciding on what date to take the trip.

Plan Make a frequency table.

Solve The frequency table shows that the greatest number of people want to take the trip on June 9.

Date	Tally	Frequency
June 1	II	2
June 2	ⅢⅢ III	8
June 8	IIII	4
June 9	ⅢⅢ ⅢⅢ II	12

Examine Since June 9 received the greatest number of votes, the annual trip should be held on June 9.

Solve.

1. The ages of students in the drama club at Grindstone Middle School are shown below.

11 12 11 13 14 13 13
12 12 12 12 11 10 13
13 14 12 11 12 13

Age	Tally	Frequency
10	I	1
11	IIII	4
12	ⅢⅢ II	7
13	ⅢⅢ I	6
14	II	2

a. Make a frequency table for the data.

b. What was the most common age of the drama club members? **12**

2. Twenty-one people were asked to name the state in which they were born. The data are shown below.

NY TX PA NY NY TX CA
NY CA CA CA NY PA PA
NY NY PA NY NY CA TX

State	Tally	Frequency
CA	ⅢⅢ	5
NY	ⅢⅢ IIII	9
PA	IIII	4
TX	III	3

a. Make a frequency table for the data.

b. In which state were the most people surveyed born? **NY**

c. How many of the people surveyed were born in New York State? **9**

© Glencoe/McGraw-Hill   T8   *Mathematics: Applications and Connections, Course 1*

Communicating Mathematics

Read and study the lesson to answer each question. 1–2. See margin.

1. *Tell* an advantage of organizing data into a frequency table.

2. *Write* a sentence to tell what you can conclude when you analyze the favorite TV show data in the frequency table on page 46.

HANDS-ON MATH

3. Use the newspaper article from the Mini-Lab on page 47 to make a frequency table of the letters used in the article. **a–d. See students' work.**

   a. Do you think the letter that appeared most often is used most often in the English language? Explain why or why not.

   b. Were any letters in the alphabet not in the article?

   c. What vowel appears most often?

   d. Compare your results with other classmates.

Guided Practice

4. *Physical Education* Coach Estes took a survey of the students in gym class to see which sport she should offer during the spring. She recorded the responses in the frequency table below.

Sport	Tally	Frequency
volleyball	ⅢⅢ ⅢⅢ	10
baseball	IIII	4
softball	ⅢⅢ III	8
basketball	ⅢⅢ II	7

   a. Copy the table and complete the frequency column.

   b. Which sport should Coach Estes offer? **volleyball**

5. The ages of the guests at Linn's birthday party are shown below.

14 12 13 12 12 14
13 10 11 12 13 12

   a. Make a frequency table of the data. **See margin.**

   b. What was the most common age of the guests? **12**

Applications and Problem Solving

Real World

Make a frequency table for each set of data. 6–8. See Answer Appendix.

6. To the nearest hour, how many hours of television did you watch last Saturday?

1 2 4 3 2 1 1 2 2 3

7. How many times were you absent in the last six weeks?

1 5 0 1 3 1 1 0 1
3 5 1 2 0 0 2 0 3

8. What were the daily high temperatures for September?

89 92 89 89 90 89 89 87 86 87
89 87 86 90 90 89 90 87 87 86
87 89 89 87 89 87 87 86 85 86

■ Reteaching the Lesson ■

Activity Have students think of a survey question with a *yes* or *no* answer, such as "Did you eat breakfast today?" Have them survey the class and make a frequency table of their results.

9a. Sample answer: All the shoes sold were between sizes 9 and 11.

9. *Business* The frequency table shows the sizes of shoes sold in August at the Athlete's Locker.

Size	Tally	Frequency
9	卌 卌 ‖	12
9½	卌 卌 卌 ‖	16
10	卌 卌 卌 卌 ‖‖	23
10½	卌 卌 ‖	11
11	卌 卌 卌	15

a. Describe the data shown in the table.

b. How many pairs of shoes were sold in August? **77 pairs of shoes**

c. Which size should the Athlete's Locker stock the most? **10**

10. *Working on the* **CHAPTER Project**

a. Make a frequency table that shows the number of pets owned by each student on the class list on page 45. **See students' work.**

b. Make a frequency table that shows the number of pets owned by each of your classmates. **See students' work.**

11. *Business* Refer to the frequency table below.

11a. Sample answer: Based on the data in the table, they should keep potato chips and corn chips well stocked.

11b. Answers will vary. Sample answer: There are too few to tell.

Favorite Snack Food of Food Mart Customers		
Snack Food	Tally	Frequency
potato chips	卌 ‖	6
tortilla chips	‖‖	3
corn chips	卌	5
pretzels	‖	2
popcorn	‖‖	3

a. Which snack(s) should Food Mart keep well stocked?

b. Are there any snacks that Food Mart should discontinue stocking? Explain.

12. *Critical Thinking* Refer to the beginning of the lesson. What are some reasons that a store would like to know the zip codes of its customers? **See margin.**

Mixed Review

13. **Standardized Test Practice** Name the number that is the solution of the equation $102 \div q = 17$. *(Lesson 1–7)* **A**

A 6   **B** 7

C 8   **D** 9

14. *Money Matters* Before buying a computer, Jocelyn called several computer stores to compare prices. The highest price was $2,349, and the lowest price was $1,788. Estimate the difference between the highest and lowest prices. *(Lesson 1–3)* **about $500**

For **Extra Practice,** see page 559.

Lesson 2-1 Frequency Tables **49**

Extending the Lesson

Enrichment Masters, p. 8

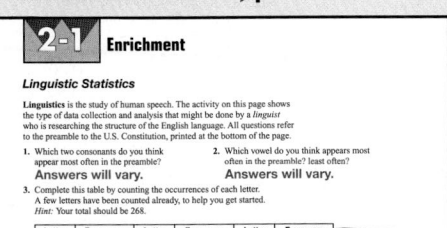

Activity Separate students into groups of three or four. Have them research how frequency tables are used in science, social studies, sports, conservation, or other areas. Have each group report to the class on its findings.

CHAPTER Project

Exercise 10 asks students to advance to the next stage of work on the Chapter Project. You may wish to have students work in groups to complete their frequency tables.

4 ASSESS

Closing Activity

Writing Have pairs of students write a description of a frequency table and how they might use it at school or at home. How might their teacher use one?

Additional Answer

12. Sample answer: The owner of the store could plan a special mailing to residents with the zip code that appears most.

Practice Masters, p. 8

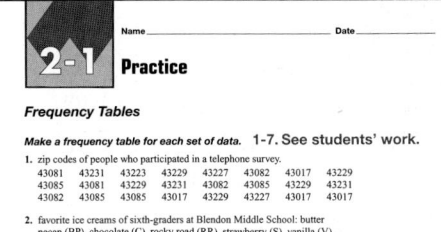

Instructional Resources

- *Study Guide Masters,* p. 9
- *Practice Masters,* p. 9
- *Enrichment Masters,* p. 9
- Transparencies 2-2, A and B

 CD-ROM Program
- Resource Lesson 2-2

Recommended Pacing	
Standard	Day 3 of 14
Honors	Day 3 of 14
Block	Day 2 of 7

1 FOCUS

 5-Minute Check
(Lesson 2-1)

Vivian kept track of the time she spent on the telephone for one week.

Telephone Calls		
Minutes	**Tally**	**Frequency**
1–14	IIII	4
15–29	HHT III	8
30–44	HHT HHT	10
45–59	HHT I	6

1. How many calls did Vivian make? **28**

2. How many calls were less than 30 minutes? **12**

3. How many calls were 30 minutes or longer? **16**

The 5-Minute Check is also available on **Transparency 2-2A** for this lesson.

Motivating the Lesson

Communication Discuss with students how or why the word *scale* may have evolved from the Latin word meaning ladder or staircase. Draw a picture of a ladder on the chalkboard and ask students to arrange a data set of temperatures or weights on the steps. Ask them what they think the word *interval* means.

2-2 Scales and Intervals

What you'll learn

You'll learn to choose appropriate scales and intervals for frequency tables.

When am I ever going to use this?

Knowing how to choose scales and intervals can help you make a bar graph or line graph.

Word Wise

interval
scale

For her history project, Margaret is investigating the early state legislature of Massachusetts. She uses an atlas to find how far each county seat is from the capital, Boston. The distances in miles are 65, 134, 37, 85, 22, 101, 90, 102, 7, 105, 2, 41, 28, and 42. How can Margaret organize this data so it is easier to study the distances? *This problem will be solved in Example 1.*

Margaret can group the data in **intervals**. To do this, she needs to determine the **scale** for her frequency table. The scale must include all of the data.

 Example 1
CONNECTION

History Refer to the beginning of the lesson. Organize Margaret's distance data into a frequency table.

Step 1 Determine the scale. Since the data includes distances from 2 to 134, begin the scale with 0 and end with 140.

Step 2 Determine the interval. To keep the number of intervals manageable, choose an interval of 20.

Step 3 Make the frequency table. Now Margaret can easily see the number of county seats in each interval.

All intervals need to be equal and not overlap.

Distances from County Seats to Boston		
Distance	**Tally**	**Frequency**
121–140	I	1
101–120	III	3
81–100	II	2
61–80	I	1
41–60	II	2
21–40	III	3
0–20	II	2

 Example 2
APPLICATION

Sports The scores of the Glencoe Scholarship Golf tournament are shown below.

74, 87, 88, 97, 75, 78, 76, 69, 84, 83, 86, 88, 92, 93, 72, 89, 85, 67, 77, 82, 84, 85, 99, 81

a. Determine an appropriate scale for the data.
b. Make a frequency table for the data.

50 Chapter 2 Statistics: Graphing Data

Investigations for the Special Education Student

This blackline master booklet helps you plan for the needs of your special education students by providing long-term projects along with teacher notes. Investigation 2, *Commercial Success,* may be used with this chapter.

a. A scale from 66 to 100 is appropriate because it includes all of the scores.

b. Since the scale is small, an interval of 5 is used in the table at the right.

Golf Scores		
Score	Tally	Frequency
96–100	II	2
91–95	II	2
86–90	IIIII	5
81–85	IIIIII	7
76–80	III	3
71–75	III	3
66–70	II	2

You can use a frequency table to organize data about a group of people, such as your classmates.

 MINI-LAB

Work with a partner.

 paper   pencil

Try This 1–3. Answers will vary.

1. Each person should ask ten classmates how many hours a week each of them spend on the telephone. Record each response. Combine your results with your partner.

2. Choose a scale and appropriate intervals for a frequency table.

3. Make a frequency table.

Talk About It 4. the most common responses

4. What does your frequency table tell you?

5. Compare your frequency table to a frequency table from another pair of classmates. Are the scale and intervals the same? Explain why or why not. **Answers will vary.**

CHECK FOR UNDERSTANDING

Communicating Mathematics

1–2. See margin.

Read and study the lesson to answer each question.

1. *Explain* how to find an appropriate scale for the data in the chart.

2. *Write* a sentence or two explaining how to determine an interval for the data in the chart.

Distances Traveled to School by Students in Mr. Alonzo's Class					
18	14	30	62	40	47
34	12	56	57	63	54
32	27	33	46	17	13

Additional Answers

1. Sample answer: The scale must include all of the data. Since the shortest distance is 12 and the longest distance is 63, a scale from 10 to 70 is appropriate.

2. Sample answer: Since the scale is 10 to 70, the best interval would be 10. This will provide a manageable number of intervals. Using 5 would have too many intervals and using 20 would have very few.

---

2 TEACH

 Transparency 2-2B contains a teaching aid for this lesson.

In-Class Examples

For Example 1

Organize this set of average temperatures (°F) in U.S. cities for the month of January into a frequency table.
21, 34, 13, 36, 41, 31, 49, 31, 49, 32, 50, 20, 42, 6, 29, 29, 29, 23, 16, 10, 22, 47, 32, 40, 26, 21, 25, 44, 27, 19, 44, 29

Average Temperatures		
°F	Tally	Frequency
46–50	IIII	4
41–45	IIII	4
36–40	II	2
31–35	IIIII	5
26–30	IIIIII	6
21–25	IIIII	5
16–20	III	3
11–15	I	1
6–10	II	2

For Example 2

The scores for a social studies test are shown below.
82, 41, 58, 99, 76, 84, 67, 97, 92, 85, 79, 83, 90, 84, 77, 63, 75, 91, 84, 88, 96, 73, 79, 80

a. Determine an appropriate scale for the data. **40 to 100**

b. Make a frequency table for the data.

Test Scores		
Score	Tally	Frequency
90–100	IIIIII	6
80–89	IIIIIIII	8
70–79	IIIIII	6
60–69	II	2
50–59	I	1
40–49	I	1

Using the Mini-Lab Encourage students to determine their own responses before beginning their surveys. As surveys are completed, circulate around the room to identify any difficulties in setting up frequency tables. Assign peer tutors as needed.

Check for Understanding

If students need additional practice or instruction after completing Exercises 1–7, one of these options may be helpful.
- Extra Practice, see p. 560
- Reteaching Activity
- *Study Guide Masters*, p. 9
- *Practice Masters*, p. 9
- Interactive Mathematics Tools Software

Assignment Guide

Core: 8, 10, 11, 13, 14, 16, 17, 19, 20–23
Enriched: 9, 10, 12, 13, 15, 16, 17–23

Additional Answer

6.

Amount	Tally	Frequency
20–24	I	1
15–19	II	2
10–14	⫫⫫	5
5–9	IIII	4
0–4		0

Study Guide Masters, p. 9

2-2 **Study Guide**

Name _____ Date _____

Scales and Intervals

The employees of Lake Products Corporation earn the following yearly salaries: $14,500; $26,000; $43,200; $23,700; $33,400; $15,500; $28,900; $31,100; $56,300; $41,000; $35,000; $24,700; $16,300; $20,000; $63,000; $8,100; $22,800; $9,700; $32,200; $19,300.

A scale from $0 to $69,999 may be used to make a frequency table that includes all of the salaries. The salaries may be divided into seven sections using an interval of $9,999.

The frequency table shows that most employees make between $10,000 and $39,999.

Employee Salaries		
Salary	Tally	Frequency
$60,000–$69,999	I	1
$50,000–$59,999	I	1
$40,000–$49,999	II	2
$30,000–$39,999	IIII	4
$20,000–$29,999	⫫⫫	5
$10,000–$19,999	⫫⫫	5
$0–$9,999	II	2

Determine the scale for a frequency table for each set of data.

1. 63, 89, 12, 45, 83, 62, 91, 44, 62, 42, 77, 9
0 to 100

2. 3,482; 1,955; 8,312; 6,605; 850; 7,831; 300; 5,067
0 to 10,000

3. 702, 593, 769, 104, 333, 210, 678, 996, 384, 339, 652, 151
0 to 1,000

Choose the best interval for a frequency table for each set of data.

4. the data in Exercise 1
a. 1 b. 10 c. 100

5. the data in Exercise 2
a. 10 b. 100 c. 1,000

6. the data in Exercise 3
a. 10 b. 100 c. 1,000

Choose the best number to end a scale for a frequency table for each set of data.

7. the data in Exercise 1
a. 0 b. 10 c. 100

8. the data in Exercise 2
a. 300 b. 1,000 c. 9,000

9. the data in Exercise 3
a. 100 b. 1,000 c. 9,000

© Glencoe/McGraw-Hill   T9   Mathematics: Applications and Connections, Course 1

HANDS-ON MATH

3. Using the data you collected for the Mini-Lab on page 51, make another frequency table to show how the scale and interval would change if you had asked your classmates how many *minutes* they spend on the phone. **See students' work.**

Guided Practice   Use the set of data below to answer Exercises 4–6.

$12, $8, $13, $6, $17, $7, $9, $13, $11, $10, $15, $20

4. What scale would you use in making a frequency table for this set of data? **Sample answer: 0 to 20**

5. Would an interval of 2 or 10 be better to use in making a frequency table for this set of data? Explain. **2; 10 is too large.**

6. Make a frequency table of the data. **See margin.**

7a. See Answer Appendix.

7. *Entertainment* Shelby's last eighteen video game scores were: 3,500; 10,200; 30,000; 65,300; 56,000; 28,200; 17,000; 43,200; 23,300; 41,900; 32,600; 29,100; 46,400; 39,500; 25,000; 37,800; 49,700; and 34,300.
   a. Make a frequency table for this set of data.
   b. In what interval are most of Shelby's scores? **Most of her scores were between 30,000 and 39,900.**

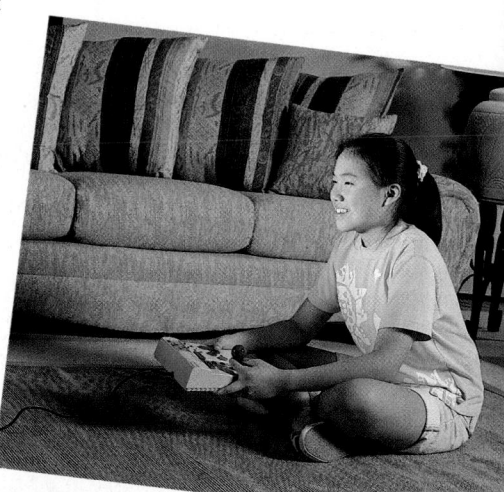

EXERCISES

Practice   Choose the better scale for a frequency table for each set of data.

8. 3, 17, 9, 6, 2, 5, 12 **b**   a. 0 to 10   b. 0 to 20
9. 53, 88, 25, 47, 50, 18, 15, 43 **a**   a. 0 to 99   b. 20 to 80
10. 245, 144, 489, 348, 36, 284, 150, 94, 220 **a**   a. 0 to 499   b. 0 to 999

Choose the best interval for a frequency table for each set of data.

11. the data in Exercise 8 **a**   a. 2   b. 10   c. 20
12. the data in Exercise 9 **c**   a. 4   b. 5   c. 10
13. the data in Exercise 10 **b**   a. 10   b. 100   c. 1,000

Make a frequency table for each set of data. **14–16. See Answer Appendix.**

14. the data in Exercise 8
15. the data in Exercise 9
16. the data in Exercise 10

Reteaching the Lesson

Activity Show the class several small containers containing varying numbers of dried beans. Ask students to count the beans in each container. Make a frequency table with the class. Have students determine the scale and intervals that organize the data.

Error Analysis

Watch for students who have difficulty choosing an appropriate scale.
Prevent by reminding them to use the highest and lowest numbers to determine the scale and to always include both numbers in the table.

Applications and Problem Solving

17a. No; since Texas is a much larger state, the distances will be larger. If she used the same scale the frequency table would not include all the distances.

17b. Sample answer: Yes; however, the table will have a large number of rows.

20. Sample answer: 21, 24, 34, 32, 31, 22, 23, 36, 35, 33, 32, 39, 34, 32, 23

Mixed Review

17. Geography Refer to the beginning of the lesson. Suppose Margaret decided to do her project on the state of Texas instead of Massachusetts.
a. Could she use the same scale she used for Massachusetts? Explain why or why not.
b. Could she use the same interval she used for Massachusetts? Explain why or why not.

18. Health Read the nutrition label on at least 15 different food items and record the number of milligrams (mg) of sodium per serving.
a. Make a frequency table of your data. **See students' work.**
b. What conclusions can you make from your table? **Answers will vary.**

19. Geography The highest elevation in states with mountains over 5,000 feet high are shown below.

State	Elevation (ft)	State	Elevation (ft)
Alaska	20,320	New Mexico	13,161
Arizona	12,633	New York	5,344
California	14,494	North Carolina	6,684
Colorado	14,433	Oregon	11,239
Hawaii	13,796	South Dakota	7,242
Idaho	12,662	Tennessee	6,643
Maine	5,268	Texas	8,749
Montana	12,799	Utah	13,528
Nebraska	5,424	Virginia	5,729
Nevada	13,140	Washington	14,410
New Hampshire	6,288	Wyoming	13,804

a. What scale would you use in making a frequency table for this set of data? **Sample answer: 5,000–20,999**
b. Make a frequency table of the data. **See margin.**

20. Critical Thinking Create a set of at least 15 pieces of data so that a frequency table of the data would need a scale from 20 to 40.

21. Sports The number of hits each player on the little league baseball team had in the last game of the season were 1, 3, 2, 4, 2, 3, 1, 0, and 2. Make a frequency table of the data. *(Lesson 2-1)* **See margin.**

22. Algebra Evaluate a^3 if $a = 2$. *(Lesson 1-6)* **8**

23. Standardized Test Practice A stereo receiver costs $659, speakers cost $472, and a compact disc player costs $326. Which is the best estimate for the total amount for this stereo system? *(Lesson 1-3)* **D**
A $900   B $1,100
C $1,200   D $1,500
E $1,900

For **Extra Practice**, see page 560.

Lesson 2-2 Scales and Intervals **53**

Extending the Lesson

Enrichment Masters, p. 9

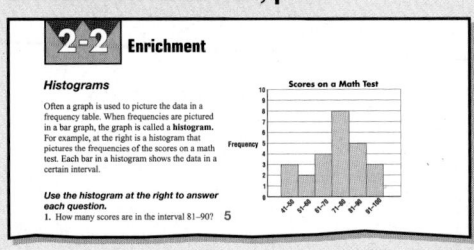

Activity Have students look through newspapers and almanacs for data that would probably not be organized in a frequency table. Ask students to describe the data and explain why a frequency table would not be appropriate.

---

4 ASSESS

Closing Activity
Modeling Ask students to measure the distance from their elbows to the tips of their little fingers. Have them gather this information and determine a scale for the data. Then have students separate into groups according to the interval they have selected.

Additional Answers
19b.

Elevation	Tally	Frequency
19,000–20,999	I	1
17,000–18,999		0
15,000–16,999		0
13,000–14,999	HHI III	8
11,000–12,999	IIII	4
9,000–10,999		0
7,000–8,999	II	2
5,000–6,999	HHI II	7

21.

Number of Hits	Tally	Frequency
0	I	1
1	II	2
2	III	3
3	II	2
4	I	1

Practice Masters, p. 9

2-2 Practice

Scales and Intervals

Choose the better scale for a frequency table for each set of data.
1. 27, 15, 39, 21, 58, 34, 46 **a**   a. 0 to 60   b. 10 to 50
2. 415, 258, 109, 374, 583, 116, 497, 601, 562 **b**   a. 0 to 600   b. 0 to 1,000
3. 18, 25, 40, 27, 11, 42, 13, 9, 36, 5 **a**   a. 0 to 50   b. 0 to 100
4. 5,096, 3,237, 8,924, 2,143, 9,451, 3,670, 7,182 **b**   a. 0 to 10,000   b. 2,000 to 10,000
5. 3, 4, 8, 6, 5, 3, 9, 7, 5, 6 **a**   a. 0 to 10   b. 1 to 5
6. 206, 247, 268, 219, 232, 193, 271, 254, 285 **b**   a. 0 to 300   b. 150 to 300
7. 13,500, 26,700, 39,200, 61,300, 42,800, 11,900, 25,600 **b** a. 0 to 70,000   b. 10,000 to 70,000
8. $96, $54, $78, $92, $63, $41, $59, $85, $97, $60 **b**   a. $50 to $90   b. $40 to $100

Choose the best interval for a frequency table for each set of data.
9. the data in Exercise 1   a. 1   **b.** 10   c. 100
10. the data in Exercise 2   a. 1   b. 10   **c.** 100
11. the data in Exercise 3   a. 1   **b.** 5   c. 100
12. the data in Exercise 4   **a.** 1,000   b. 5,000   c. 10,000
13. the data in Exercise 5   **a.** 1   b. 10   c. 100
14. the data in Exercise 6   a. 1   **b.** 15   c. 150
15. the data in Exercise 7   a. 100   b. 1,000   **c.** 10,000
16. the data in Exercise 8   a. 1   **b.** 10   c. 100

Make a frequency table for each set of data. 17-22. See students' work.
17. the data in Exercise 1   18. the data in Exercise 2
19. the data in Exercise 3   20. the data in Exercise 4
21. the data in Exercise 5   22. the data in Exercise 6

© Glencoe/McGraw-Hill   79   Mathematics: Applications and Connections, Course 1

Lesson 2-2   53

Instructional Resources

- *Study Guide Masters*, p. 10
- *Practice Masters*, p. 10
- *Enrichment Masters*, p. 10
- Transparencies 2-3, A and B
- *Assessment and Evaluation Masters*, p. 43
- *Hands-On Lab Masters*, p. 70
- *Technology Masters*, p. 4

 CD-ROM Program
  - Resource Lesson 2-3
  - Interactive Lesson 2-3

Recommended Pacing	
Standard	Day 4 of 14
Honors	Day 4 of 14
Block	Day 2 of 7

1 FOCUS

5-Minute Check
(Lesson 2-2)

1. Determine an appropriate scale for the following set of data. 24, 52, 44, 41, 87, 79, 43, 88, 63, 82, 20, 15, 50, 39, 69, 22 10–90

2. Make a frequency table for the data in Exercise 1.

Data	Tally	Frequency
10–30	IIII	4
31–50	IIII I	5
51–70	III	3
71–90	IIII	4

The 5-Minute Check is also available on **Transparency 2-3A** for this lesson.

Motivating the Lesson

Communication Ask students to read the opening paragraph of the lesson. Then ask these questions.
- Do you think that a graph is a better way to show this information? **yes**
- Why? **Sample answer: It is easier to see the difference in height of bars on a graph than to compare numbers in a table.**

2-3 Bar Graphs and Line Graphs

What you'll learn

You'll learn to construct bar graphs and line graphs.

When am I ever going to use this?

You can use a bar graph to compare the attendance at sporting events and a line graph to show population data.

Word Wise

bar graph
line graph

How do you wake up in the morning? Does someone wake you or do you use an alarm clock? The results of a survey of how 400 parents with children under 18 wake their children is shown in the frequency table.

Method	Frequency
Call Them	172
Alarm Clock	88
Wake On Their Own	64
Other	76

A graph is a more visual representation of data. A **bar graph** is used to compare the frequency of the amount in a category or class.

Example ① Use the data from the survey to draw a vertical bar graph.

Step 1 Draw and label both scales.

Step 2 Determine the scale for the vertical axis. Choose an interval that best represents the data and mark off equal spaces on the vertical scale.

> **Scale** The data includes numbers from 76 to 172, so begin the scale with 0 and end with 180.
>
> **Interval** Since the vertical scale needs to go from 0 to 180, use an interval of 20.

Step 3 Mark off equal spaces on the horizontal axis and label each with a method.

Step 4 Draw a bar for each method. The height of each bar represents the number of parents that use that method.

Step 5 Label the graph with a title.

How Parents Wake Up Their Children

Multiple Learning Styles

Visual/Spatial Have small groups use almanacs to find the temperatures over a 12-month period for a city of their choice. Ask groups to show the data in graphs on posterboards. Encourage a variety of cities among the groups, such as Minneapolis, Phoenix, and San Francisco so they can compare graphs.

To show how data changes over a period of time, you could use a **line graph**. A line graph is usually used to show the change and direction of change over time.

Example
APPLICATION

② Food Christopher takes a poll to find out how many soft drinks his classmates drink each day. The results are shown at the right. Draw a line graph using the data he collected.

Day	Frequency
Monday	27
Tuesday	22
Wednesday	18
Thursday	26
Friday	57
Saturday	61
Sunday	42

Step 1 Draw and label both scales.

Step 2 Determine the scale for the vertical axis. Choose an interval that best represents the data and mark off equal spaces on the vertical scale.

> **Scale** The data includes numbers from 18 to 61, so begin the scale with 0 and end with 70.

> **Interval** Since the vertical scale needs to go from 0 to 70, use an interval of 10.

Step 3 Mark off equal spaces on the horizontal scale and label them with the days of the week in order.

Step 4 Draw a dot to show the frequency for each day. Draw line segments to connect the dots.

Step 5 Label the graph with a title.

Study Hint

Technology You can use a graphing calculator to make a line graph without a title or labels. There are also many computer software programs available that will construct graphs as you enter the data.

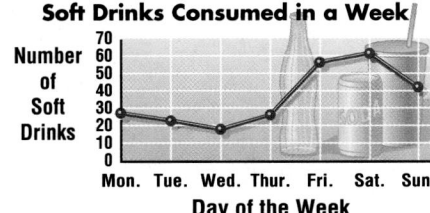

Soft Drinks Consumed in a Week

Number of Soft Drinks

Day of the Week

The graph shows that Christopher's classmates drink many more soft drinks on the weekend.

CHECK FOR UNDERSTANDING

Communicating Mathematics

Read and study the lesson to answer each question.

1. *Examine* the bar graph in Example 1. Tell which method for waking up children was used the most. **Call Them**

2. *Examine* the line graph in Example 2. Tell which day the students drank the least number of soft drinks. **Wednesday**

Lesson 2-3 Bar Graphs and Line Graphs   **55**

Classroom Vignette

"I fill a glass jar with color candies and have students estimate the total number of candies and how many are each color. We count the candy by placing them in cups of 10 for each color. We make a pictograph of the cups organized by color, labeling the axes and giving the graph a title."

Dora Brown, Teacher
Awtrey Middle School
Kennesaw, GA

Dora Brown

Transparency 2-3B contains a teaching aid for this lesson.

Reading Mathematics After reading the first paragraph on page 55 and discussing Example 2, ask students what changes and direction of change over time they observe.

In-Class Examples

For Example 1
A poll was taken to see how many minutes people read each day. The results showed women read 20 minutes; men, 15; teens, 25; and children, 10. Use the data to draw a vertical bar graph.

Daily Reading Time

Minutes

Population Surveyed

For Example 2
Draw a line graph to show the windchill factors at 35° F.

Thermometer Reading 35°F	
Wind Speed (mph)	**Windchill Factor (°F)**
5	33
10	22
15	16
20	12
25	8
30	6
35	4
40	3
45	2

Windchill Factors at 35°F

Windchill Factor (°F)

Wind Speed (mph)

Lesson 2-3   **55**

3 PRACTICE/APPLY

Check for Understanding

If students need additional practice or instruction after completing Exercises 1–6, you may find one of the following options helpful.
- Extra Practice, see p. 560
- Reteaching Activity
- *Study Guide Masters,* p. 10
- *Practice Masters,* p. 10
- Interactive Mathematics Tools Software

Assignment Guide

Core: 7–15 odd, 16, 18–21
Enriched: 8–14 even, 16, 18–21

Additional Answer

3. Sample answer: If the vertical scale is much higher than the highest value, it makes the graph flatter. Changing the interval does not affect either type of graph.

Study Guide Masters, p. 10

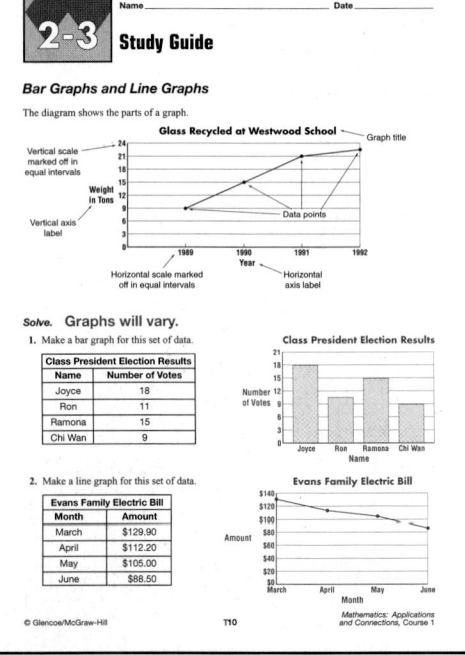

Math Journal

3. *Write* a sentence or two explaining how the vertical scale and the interval affect the look of a bar graph or line graph. **See margin.**

Guided Practice

Choose a scale and an interval for the vertical axis of a line graph for each set of data.

4. 28, 13, 9, 26, 19 **0–30; 5**

5. 18, 32, 52, 68, 56, 31 **0–70; 10**

6. *Transportation* The number of annual passengers arriving at and departing from airports are listed in the table.
   a. Choose an interval for a bar graph of the passenger data.
   b. Make a horizontal bar graph for the data. **See Answer Appendix.**
   a. 5,000 or 10,000

World's Busiest Airports	
Airport	Passengers (thousands)
Atlanta	73,500
Chicago-O'Hare	72,500
Los Angeles	61,200
London Heathrow	60,700
Dallas-Ft. Worth	60,500
Tokyo	51,200
Frankfurt	42,700
San Francisco	40,000
Paris	38,600

Source: Airports Council International

EXERCISES

Practice

Make a bar graph for each set of data. **7–10. See Answer Appendix.**

7. a vertical bar graph

Favorite Soft Drink	
Soft Drink	Frequency
Brand A	4
Brand B	15
Brand C	9
Brand D	19
Brand E	11
Brand F	8

8. a horizontal bar graph

Average Event Day Attendance (thousands)	
Sport	Attendance
NASCAR Races	83
NFL (football)	62
MLB (baseball)	31
NBA (basketball)	16
NHL (hockey)	14

Source: USA TODAY research

Make a line graph for each set of data.

9.

Average Snowfall for Brighton, Utah	
Month	Snow (in.)
Oct.	21
Nov.	50
Dec.	66
Jan.	69
Feb.	63
March	70
April	51
May	16

Source: *The USA TODAY Weather Almanac*

10.

Sales of Sing-Along Players in the U.S. (thousands)	
Year	Amount
1990	$77,900
1991	$94,800
1992	$119,000
1993	$116,000
1994	$86,900
1995	$94,300
1996	$82,100

Source: National Association of Music Merchants

Reteaching the Lesson

Activity Take a survey of the color of the shirts, blouses, or sweaters worn by students. Record the results in a frequency table. Have students determine the scale and interval. Draw a vertical bar graph and choose a title and labels for axes. Use masking tape to form the horizontal and vertical axes on the floor. Then have students model the bar graph by standing in the correct place based on the color of the top they are wearing.

Refer to the following tables for Exercises 11–15.

A.

Super Bowl Ticket Prices	
Year	Price
1967	$12
1972	15
1977	20
1982	40
1987	75
1992	150
1997	275

Source: The NFL

B.

Entertainment Expenses per Person	
Entertainment	Amount
Basic Cable	$110
Books	79
Home Video	73
Recorded Music	56
Daily Newspapers	49
Magazines	36
On-line/Internet	7

Source: Statistical Abstract of the United States

11. Determine a scale for the prices in Table A. **Sample answer: 0 to 300**

12. What would be the best interval for the amounts in Table B? Explain why you chose it. **12–13. See margin.**

13. Which table could be best represented with a line graph? Explain.

14. Make a bar graph for the data in Table B. **14–15. See Answer Appendix.**

15. Make a line graph for the data in Table A.

Applications and Problem Solving

16a. 18 million

16. *Geography* The line graph shows Australia's population growth.
   a. Estimate the population of Australia in 1991.
   b. Estimate the number of years it took for the population to double. **about 35 years**

Australia's Population

17. *Working on the* **CHAPTER Project** Refer to your frequency tables from Exercise 10 on page 49. **a–b. See students' work.**
   a. Make a bar graph using your frequency table from Exercise 10a.
   b. Make a bar graph using your frequency table from Exercise 10b.

18. Sample answer: Over half of my friends get a larger allowance.

18. *Critical Thinking* The bar graph shows the allowance of your five best friends. How might you use the information in this graph to argue for a raise in your allowance if you are currently getting $5 a week?

Weekly Allowances

Mixed Review

19. **Standardized Test Practice** Brianna's scores on her first six history quizzes were 76, 72, 83, 96, 81, and 85. Choose the best interval for a frequency table for this data. *(Lesson 2-2)* **B**

   A 10   **B** 5   **C** 2   **D** 1

For **Extra Practice**, see page 560.

20. *Algebra* Evaluate $ab - c$ if $a = 3$, $b = 16$ and $c = 5$. *(Lesson 1-5)* **43**

21. Evaluate $14 - 2 \times 5$. *(Lesson 1-4)* **4**

Lesson 2-3 Bar Graphs and Line Graphs   **57**

Extending the Lesson

Enrichment Masters, p. 10

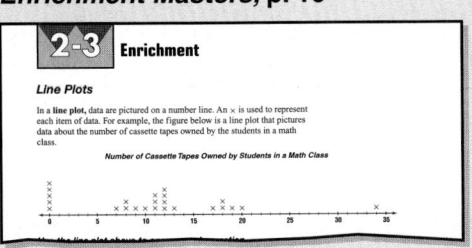

Activity Have students work in groups to look in news and financial magazines for bar and line graphs. Ask groups to compare information and determine whether the proper type of graph was used to display the data.

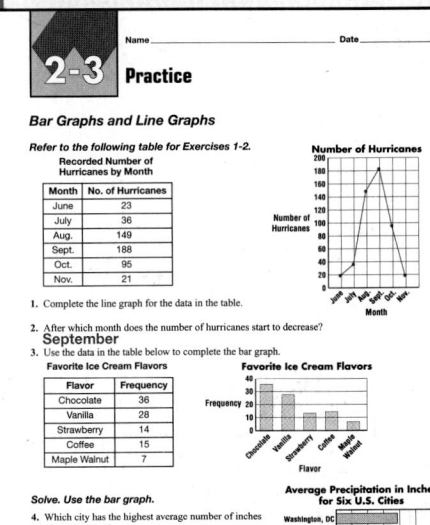

THINKING LAB

Objective Students solve problems by using a graph.

1 FOCUS

Getting Started Display a bar graph and a table on an overhead transparency. Using a timer, determine how long it takes students to find the greatest number represented by a bar on the graph and by a number in the table. Discuss how each is used.

2 TEACH

Teaching Tip Point out to students that a horizontal bar graph shows the same information as a vertical bar graph. Discuss reasons for making horizontal rather than vertical bar graphs.

In-Class Example

The pictograph shows circulation of four magazines. Refer to it for the following questions.

Magazine Circulation

Homes ▢▢▢▢▢▢
Scene ▢▢▮
Today ▢▢▢▢▢
Video ▢▢▢▢

▢ = 2 million copies

a. What was *Homes* circulation? **12 million**

b. What does the half-magazine for *Scene* mean? **1 million**

c. Which magazine had a circulation of 10 million copies? *Today*

THINKING LAB

2-3B Use a Graph

A Follow-Up of Lesson 2-3

The sixth grade class is planning a field trip to the science center. Their science teacher, Ms. Tai, has asked Steve and Maria to help her decide where they will stop for lunch. The choices are Burger Barn, Dairy Dine, Mardee's, Mickey's, and Sally's. Let's listen in!

Favorite Fast-Food Restaurant

I made a bar graph using our survey results. It looks like we should pick Burger Barn.

Steve

Yeah, but Ms. Tai told us it had to be healthy. I'm not sure Burger Barn is our best choice based on the pictograph I made.

What's a pictograph?

A pictograph is another type of graph used to compare numbers.

Well, Mardee's has the least amount of fat, but it's the least favorite.

How about Mickey's? It was the second most popular choice and the second lowest in fat!

Maria

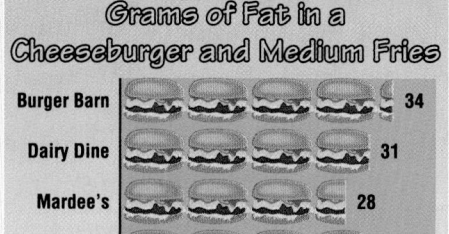

Grams of Fat in a Cheeseburger and Medium Fries

Burger Barn — 34
Dairy Dine — 31
Mardee's — 28
Mickey's — 30
Sally's — 32

🍔 = 8 grams fat

THINK ABOUT IT

1–2. See students' work.

1. *Compare* the two graphs to see if you agree with Maria's suggestion that they select Mickey's. Explain your answer.

2. *Analyze* the data in the two graphs to see what your second choice would be. Explain your answer.

58 Chapter 2 Statistics: Graphing Data

■ Reteaching the Lesson ■

Activity Use self-adhesive notes to conceal parts of a bar graph. Have students determine what information is missing and why it is needed. For example, without the vertical scale information on the fast-food graph, it is impossible to know the restaurant choices.

For **Extra Practice,** see page 560.

3. *Apply* what you have learned about the **use a graph** strategy to solve the following problem. **See margin.**

   Ms. Tai has suggested that students bring a sack lunch. Then they could stop to have dessert on the way home. The bar graph shows the fat grams in a chocolate shake at each of the restaurants. Which restaurant would you recommend and why?

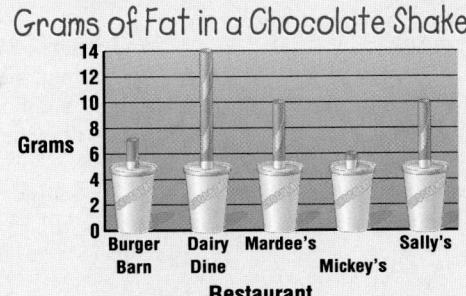

Grams of Fat in a Chocolate Shake

ON YOUR OWN

4–5. See students' work.

4. The second step of the 4-step plan for problem solving is *plan.* **Explain** how the type of graph helps you to make a plan for solving the problem.

5. *Write a Problem* that you could solve more easily if you could use a graph to examine the data in the problem.

6. *Examine* the line graph in Example 2 on page 55. Suppose Christopher's mother is going to buy 2-liter bottles of soft drinks. What day of the week would you recommend that she purchase based on the results shown in the graph? **See margin.**

MIXED PROBLEM SOLVING

STRATEGIES

Look for a pattern.
Solve a simpler problem.
Act it out.
Guess and check.
Draw a diagram.
Make a chart.
Work backward.

Solve. Use any strategy.

7. *Money Matters* Mr. Rivera bought 5 packages of batteries for $5.89 each. About how much did he spend? **$30**

8. *Algebra* Find x if the product of x and 28 is 252. **9**

9. *Travel* Ogima travels 345 miles per week. How far does he drive in four weeks? **1,380 miles**

10. *Money Matters* Laura collected $2.00 from each student to buy a gift for their teacher. If 27 people contributed, how much money was collected? **$54**

11. **Standardized Test Practice** The line graph shows the number of people in Lubbock and Garland from 1960 to 1990.

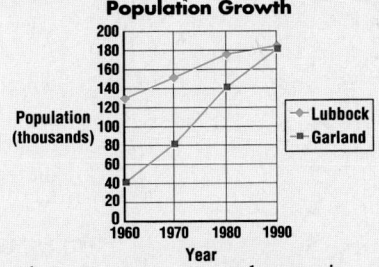

Population Growth

About how many more people were in Lubbock than in Garland in 1980? **C**

A 90,000 **B** 70,000
C 35,000 **D** 5,000

Check for Understanding
Use the results from Exercise 3 to determine whether students understand how to interpret bar graphs.

Extra Practice If students need additional practice in problem solving, extra practice is available on the following pages.
• Use a Graph, see p. 560
• Mixed Problem Solving, see pp. 593–594

Assignment Guide
All: 4–11

4 ASSESS

Closing Activity
Speaking Display a pictograph. Have small groups of students take turns posing questions about the graph for the rest of the class to answer. Ask why pictographs may be more difficult to interpret. **When there are partial pictures, it may be difficult to give an exact answer.**

Additional Answers
3. Sample answer: Mickey's; It is the second favorite and the healthiest.
6. Sample answer: Thursday, so she'd be prepared for the increased consumption on the weekend.

Extending the Lesson

Activity Have small groups of students determine how many minutes they each spend per day doing household chores. Have each group present its information in a bar graph or pictograph. Graphs can be based on minutes per day, per week, or per month. Then have groups predict how many minutes per year each student spends doing household chores.

Sample problem: *Michelle spends 45 minutes a day doing household chores. How many minutes does she spend per year on household chores?*
16,425 minutes

Instructional Resources

- *Study Guide Masters*, p. 11
- *Practice Masters*, p. 11
- *Enrichment Masters*, p. 11
- Transparencies 2-4, A and B
- *Diversity Masters*, p. 2
- CD-ROM Program
  - Resource Lesson 2-4

Recommended Pacing	
Standard	Day 6 of 14
Honors	Day 6 of 14
Block	Day 3 of 7

 5-Minute Check
(Lesson 2-3)

Refer to the graph for Exercises 1–3.

Average Temperatures Pittsburgh, PA

Source: *A Geography of Pennsylvania*

1. What is the temperature scale? **20°–80°**

2. What is the average temperature in July? **about 72°**

3. How much colder are days in November than in May? **about 20°**

 The 5-Minute Check is also available on **Transparency 2-4A** for this lesson.

Motivating the Lesson

Hands-On Activity Have students trace a circle. Ask them to think of it as a pizza. Have them name toppings. Tell them to divide their "pizza" into "slices" and choose a different topping for each slice. Discuss the results.

2-4 Reading Circle Graphs

What you'll learn
You'll learn to interpret circle graphs.

When am I ever going to use this?
Knowing how to interpret circle graphs can help you analyze a budget.

Word Wise
circle graph

In Lesson 2-3B, you learned how to interpret sets of data displayed in bar graphs and line graphs. In the Mini-Lab below, you will make a **circle graph**.

   MINI-LAB

Work with a partner. tape measure   markers

tape   adding machine tape   string

The table shows the age groups of all the people who listen to professional football radio broadcasts. You can use this data to make a circle graph.

Age Group	Percent
18–24	11%
25–34	27%
35–44	27%
45–54	17%
55–64	9%
65+	9%

Try This 1–4. See students' work.

1. Cut a piece of adding machine tape that is one meter long.

2. For each age group, mark the length in centimeters that corresponds to the percent. For example, the 18–24 age group is 11% so mark off 11 centimeters and label it accordingly.

3. Tape the ends of the adding machine tape together to form a circle. The labels should be facing the inside of the circle.

4. Stand your adding machine tape circle on a flat surface and locate its center. Tape one end of a piece of string to the center. Tape the other end to the point where the adding machine tape is joined together. Repeat with five more pieces of string joining the center to each mark on the tape.

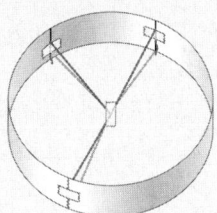

Talk About It 6–7. See margin.

5. What is the total of the percents? **100%**

6. Write a short paragraph describing the circle graph. Describe the sizes of the sections in relation to each other.

7. The circle graph you made represents the same information as the table. Discuss the advantages and disadvantages of each.

60 Chapter 2 Statistics: Graphing Data

Multiple Learning Styles

 Intrapersonal Find a circle graph that contains a topic of interest to students. Ask them which category they would have been in if surveyed. In what categories would their friends have been?

A circle graph is used to compare parts of a whole. The interior of the circle represents a set of data, and the pie-shaped sections are the parts. All the percents given in a circle graph must add up to 100%.

2 TEACH

 Transparency 2-4B contains a teaching aid for this lesson.

 Real World APPLICATION

Food The reasons why adults visit a fast food restaurant are shown in the circle graph.

a. What are the three most popular reasons for choosing a fast food restaurant?

b. How does fast service compare to location as a reason for choosing a fast food restaurant?

Choosing A Fast Food Restaurant

Convenient location 26%
Menu selection 16%
Fast service 12%
Reasonable prices 8%
Quality of food 25%
Various other 7%
Brand name 3%
Children's preference 2%
Cleanliness 1%

Source: *Maritz Marketing Ameripoll*

a. By looking at the sections of the circle graph, you can see that the three largest parts of the graph are location, food quality, and menu selection. So they are the three most popular reasons for choosing a fast food restaurant.

b. The section relating to location is about twice the size of the section relating to fast service. So, about twice as many people gave location as a reason as gave fast service.

CONNECTION ❷ Physical Science The circle graph shows what fuels are used to generate electric power in the U.S.

a. Which fuel is used to generate more electricity than the others combined?

b. Which two types of fuel together generate about the same amount of electricity as nuclear fuel?

Electric Power Sources

Coal 55%
Petroleum 2%
Hydroelectric 10%
Natural Gas 11%
Nuclear 22%

Source: Energy Information Administration

a. You can see that the section representing coal covers more than half of the circle. Therefore, it is used to generate more than the others combined.

b. If you combine the sections represented by natural gas and hydroelectric fuel, they are about the same size as nuclear fuel. So, they generate about the same amount of electricity as nuclear fuel.

Lesson 2-4 Reading Circle Graphs **61**

Using the Mini-Lab
Students may want to stand their tape on a piece of cardboard and use pins to stabilize it when adding the string.

In-Class Examples
For Example 1

Earth's Land Area

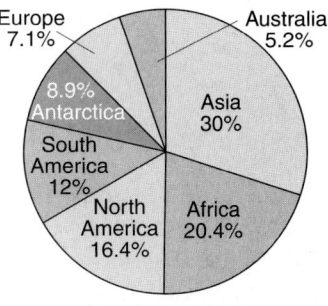

Europe 7.1%
Australia 5.2%
8.9% Antarctica
Asia 30%
South America 12%
North America 16.4%
Africa 20.4%

Source: National Geographic, Atlas of the World

a. What two continents make up more than half the continental land area? **Asia and Africa**

b. How many continents make up the other half? **5**

For Example 2

Major Sources of Marine Pollution

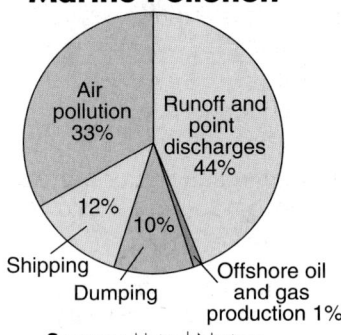

Air pollution 33%
Runoff and point discharges 44%
12%
10%
Shipping
Dumping
Offshore oil and gas production 1%

Source: United Nations Environment Program

a. What are the top two sources of marine pollution? **runoff and point discharges and air pollution**

b. Which two sources of pollution together have about the same result as runoff and point discharges? **air pollution and dumping or air pollution and shipping**

Additional Answers for the Mini-Lab

6. **Sample answer:** The larger the percent, the larger the part taken in the circle. The 25–34 and 35–44 age groups are each three times larger than each of the 55–64 and 65+ age groups. The 45–54 age group is almost twice as large as each of the 55–64 and 65+ age groups.

7. **Sample answer:** The circle graph allows you to see how all the parts are related.

3 PRACTICE/APPLY

Check for Understanding

If students need additional practice or instruction after completing Exercises 1–4, one of these options may be helpful.
- Extra Practice, see p. 561
- Reteaching Activity
- *Study Guide Masters,* p. 11
- *Practice Masters,* p. 11

Assignment Guide

Core: 5–10
Enriched: 5–10

Additional Answers

1. Sample answer: When you want to represent data that look at part to whole relationships.

2. The totals should be 100% because 100% represents the whole.

4a. 5%—Grilled Chicken, Turkey, and Tuna; 11%—Hamburgers, Ham & Cheese; 14%—Bologna; 21%—Other; 28%—Peanut Butter and Jelly

5a. 13%—Special; 15%—Egg Noodles; 31%—Short Pasta; 41%—Long Pasta

---

Study Guide Masters, p. 11

CHECK FOR UNDERSTANDING

Communicating Mathematics

Read and study the lesson to answer each question. 1–2. See margin.

1. *Explain* when it is best to use a circle graph.

2. *Write* what the total of the percents in a circle graph should be.

HANDS-ON MATH

3. The table shows the number of hours per week that students ages 12–18 use a computer at school. Use the same procedure you used in the Mini-Lab to make a circle graph of the data in the table. **See students' work.**

Time	Percent
Less than 1 hour	22%
1–2 hours	28%
2–4 hours	16%
4–6 hours	19%
More than 6 hours	11%
Don't know	4%

Source: *Consumer Electronics Manufacturers Association Survey*

Guided Practice

4. *Food* The circle graph shows the favorite sandwiches of children. a. See margin.

a. The percents are 5%, 11%, 14%, 21% and 28%. Match each percent with the appropriate section of the graph.

4b. **Sample answer: No; the combination of ham and cheese or hamburgers is not $\frac{1}{4}$ of the circle.**

b. Suppose hamburgers and ham and cheese were combined. Would the combination be preferred by $\frac{1}{4}$ of children? Explain.

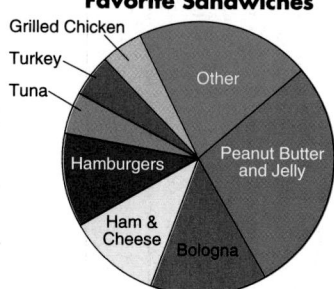

Favorite Sandwiches
Grilled Chicken
Turkey
Tuna
Other
Hamburgers
Peanut Butter and Jelly
Ham & Cheese
Bologna

Source: *Are You Normal?* by Bernice Kanner, St. Martin's, 1995

EXERCISES

Practice

5. *Food* The circle graph shows the retail sales by shape at the Pasta Factory Outlet.

5b. special and egg noodles
5d. special and egg noodles

a. The percents are 13%, 15%, 31% and 41%. Match each percent with the appropriate section of the graph. **See margin.**

b. Which two types of pasta have about the same amount of sales?

c. What percent of sales comes from short and long pasta? **72%**

d. Which two types together have about the same amount of sales as short pasta?

e. Which two types together account for about half of the sales? **either long pasta and special (54%) or short pasta and egg noodles (46%)**

Retail Sales by Pasta Shape
Special (lasagna, jumbo) 13%
Egg noodles 15%
Long pasta (spaghetti, linguini) 41%
Short pasta (elbow, twist, etc.) 31%

Reteaching the Lesson

Activity Have students randomly choose a colored paper scrap from a bag of 10 scraps. Record the results in a frequency table. Then construct a circle graph for the students to interpret. Ask questions such as: *Which color was chosen most often? How do you know?*

Error Analysis

Watch for students who have trouble interpreting a circle graph.

Prevent by reminding students that circle graphs show parts of a whole. If drawn correctly, the greatest numerical value should be the largest section.

6a. **14–17 and the under 14 age groups**

6c. **They are the same so the difference is 0.**

7a. **LP album, 7–12 in. singles and music videos**

6. *Money Matters* The circle graph shows the percent of people who purchase athletic shoes by age group.

a. What two age groups together make about half of all athletic shoe purchases?

b. What two age groups together make about one fourth of all athletic shoe purchases? **25–34 and 35–44**

c. What is the difference between the percent of people 65 and older and the 18–24 age group?

Who Buys Athletic Shoes?

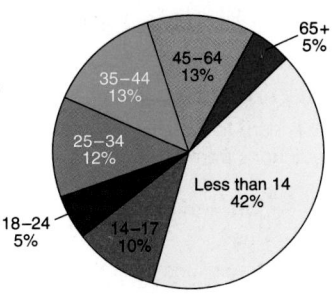

Source: *The Sporting Goods Market*

7. *Entertainment* The circle graph shows the format of recent pre-recorded music sales.

a. The two formats with the lowest percent of sales each had 1%. What are they?

b. Cassette album sales were five times cassette single sales and cassette single sales were five times as much as music video sales. The rest are CDs. What are the percents for each of these formats?
cassette single—5%; cassette album—25%; CDs—68%

Music Sales

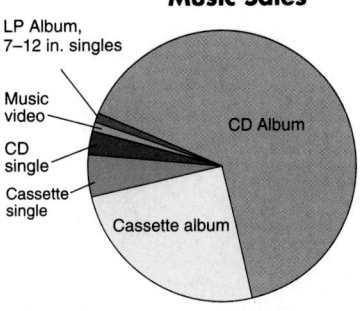

Source: RIAA

8. *Critical Thinking* Which would *not* be appropriate data to show in a circle graph? Explain your reasoning.

a. data showing what teens say would 'most' encourage them to volunteer

b. data showing how many hours parents help their children with homework each week

c. data showing the five most wasted foods in the United States

d. data showing why people dine out

b; It does not compare parts of a whole.

Mixed Review

9. *Life Science* Janet has a leaf collection that includes 15 birch, 8 willow, 5 oak, 10 maple, and 8 miscellaneous leaves. Make a bar graph for this data. *(Lesson 2-3)* **See Answer Appendix.**

10. **Standardized Test Practice** In March, an average of 280 videos were rented per day at Brian's Video Barn. Which is the best estimate for the number of videos rented for the whole month of March? *(Lesson 1-3)* **D**

A 3,000
B 6,000
C 8,000
D 9,000
E 10,000

For **Extra Practice,** see page 561.

Lesson 2-4 Reading Circle Graphs **63**

═══ **Extending the Lesson** ═══

Enrichment Masters, p. 11

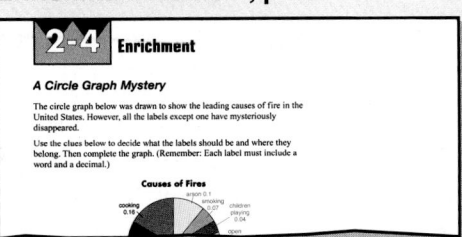

Activity Separate students into groups and have each group choose a feature of weather, such as temperature, wind speed, or humidity, to track and record for a week. Then have them organize the results into a color-coded circle graph. Encourage groups to display their graphs for the class to see.

4 ASSESS

Closing Activity

Speaking Have students compare circle graphs with bar and line graphs. Have them discuss how each graph is different from the others. Then display a circle graph from a newspaper or magazine. Have students ask each other questions about the information in the graph.

Practice Masters, p. 11

2-4 Practice

Reading Circle Graphs

Solve. Use the circle graph.

Customers' Favorite Pizza Toppings at Pizza Palace

1. Which pizza topping is the most popular? cheese
2. Which pizza topping is the least popular? onion
3. Which two toppings together are about as popular as cheese? mushroom and pepperoni
4. What percent of the toppings are meat? 36%

Solve. Use the circle graph.

Student Survey of Extra-Curricular Activities

5. Which extracurricular activity is the least popular? Chorus
6. Which extracurricular activity is about as popular as Band? Math Club
7. Which two activities together are about as popular as Drama Club? Band and Debating Team

© Glencoe/McGraw-Hill   T11   *Mathematics: Applications and Connections, Course 1*

Instructional Resources

- *Study Guide Masters*, p. 12
- *Practice Masters*, p. 12
- *Enrichment Masters*, p. 12
- Transparencies 2-5, A and B
- *Assessment and Evaluation Masters*, pp. 42, 43
- CD-ROM Program
  - Resource Lesson 2-5
  - Extended Activity 2-5

Recommended Pacing	
Standard	Day 7 of 14
Honors	Day 7 of 14
Block	Day 4 of 7

1 FOCUS

5-Minute Check
(Lesson 2-4)

Refer to the following graph for Exercises 1 and 2.

How Micah Spends His Allowance

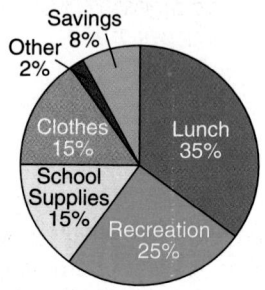

Savings 8%
Other 2%
Clothes 15%
School Supplies 15%
Lunch 35%
Recreation 25%

1. What percent of his allowance does Micah save? **8%**

2. For which two categories does he spend the same amount of money? **school supplies, clothes**

The 5-Minute Check is also available on **Transparency 2-5A** for this lesson.

Motivating the Lesson

Communication Refer to the beginning of the lesson and ask these questions.
- Does the graph show an increase or a decrease? **increase**
- What characteristic of this graph helps you make a prediction? **It shows a steady increase.**

What you'll learn

You'll learn to make predictions from line graphs.

When am I ever going to use this?

Making predictions can be used to plan housing and highway projects.

The line graph shows the population of the world since 1900. In 1992, the United Nations predicted that world population could increase to over 6 billion by the year 2000.

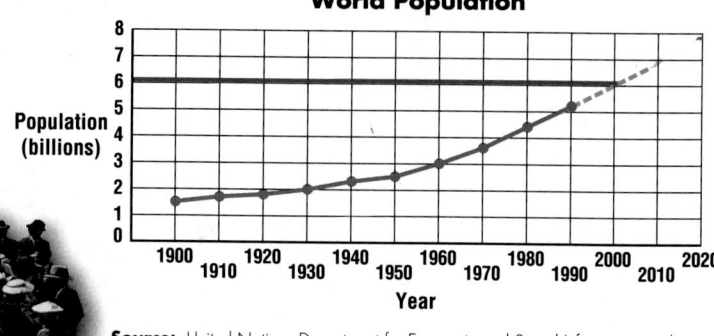

World Population

Source: United Nations Department for Economic and Social Information and Policy Analysis, Population Division.

Line graphs can be used to assist in making predictions as follows.

Step 1 Extend the graph as shown by the dashed line.

Step 2 Draw a horizontal line from the point where the extension intersects the 2000 gridline.

Step 3 You can see that the population of the world could be over 6 billion by the year 2000.

Example ① CONNECTION Geography Refer to the graph above.

a. **Predict the world population in the year 2020. Identify any assumptions you use to make your prediction.**

Extend the dashed line so it intersects the 2020 gridline. If the extension aligns with the segment between 1980 and 1990, world population could be about 8 billion by 2020.

b. **Suppose the population growth between 1990 and 2000 matches the rate of growth between 1940 and 1950 instead of between 1980 and 1990. What would the population be in the year 2000?**

The line segment between 1940 and 1950 is not as steep as the one between 1980 and 1990. The population would probably be less than 6 billion.

64 Chapter 2 Statistics: Graphing Data

Communicating Mathematics

Read and study the lesson to answer each question.

1. *Predict* the world population in 2010. Identify any assumptions you use to make your prediction. **See margin.**

2. *You Decide* Jamonte predicts that world population will be over 8 billion in 2010. Tashima predicts it will be less than 7 billion. Whose prediction do you agree with? Explain your reasoning. **See students' work.**

Guided Practice

3. *Sports* The line graph shows the winning times in the 3,000 meter steeplechase at the last thirteen Olympics.

Olympic 3,000-Meter Steeplechase, 1948–1996

Source: The Universal Almanac, 1997

   a. Would you have predicted the winning time in 1968? What might have happened? **Answers will vary.**

   b. Would you predict the winning time in 2004 to be under 8 minutes? Explain why or why not. **See students' work.**

EXERCISES

Practice

 inter·NET CONNECTION
For the latest weather statistics, visit: www.glencoe.com/sec/math/mac/mathnet

4a. 60°, 30°, 30°

4b. about 10–15° colder

4c. about 20° colder

4. *Earth Science* The line graph shows the average monthly temperature for three U.S cities. **4a–d. Sample answers given.**

   a. Predict the temperature for Galveston in December, Asheville in January, and Minneapolis in November.

Average Monthly Temperature

   b. How much colder would you expect it to be in Asheville than in Galveston in November?

   c. How much colder would you expect it to be in Minneapolis than in Asheville in December?

   d. How much colder would you expect it to be in Minneapolis than in Galveston in January? **about 45° colder**

Lesson 2-5 Making Predictions **65**

---

2 TEACH

 Transparency 2-5B contains a teaching aid for this lesson.

Thinking Algebraically Analyzing graphs and looking for patterns to predict an unknown value are the basics of the idea of *functions*. Ask students to describe the patterns for the graph on page 64.

In-Class Example

For the Example
Refer to the graph below.

Braking Distance for Cars on Dry Road

   a. Predict the braking distance of a car going 55 miles per hour. **140 feet**

   b. A car skidded 100 feet. How fast was it going? **about 46 miles per hour**

3 PRACTICE/APPLY

Check for Understanding
If students need additional practice or instruction after completing Exercises 1–3, one of these options may be helpful.
- Extra Practice, see p. 561
- Reteaching Activity
- *Study Guide Masters*, p. 12
- *Practice Masters*, p. 12

Additional Answer

1. Sample answer: If the extension aligns with the segment between 1980 and 1990, world population could be about 7 billion.

Reteaching the Lesson

Activity Have students use the following data to draw a line graph on the chalkboard and predict the average tuition and fees at state universities in the year 2000: 1989—$2,035; 1990—$2,159; 1991—$2,349; 1992—$2,410; 1993—$2,537; 1994—$2,689; 1995—$2,811.
Sample answer: $3,250

Average Annual Tuition at U.S. Colleges

Applications and Problem Solving

5. *Physical Science* Angelina and Bart each dropped a different ball from several distances and recorded the highest point of the first bounce. The graph shows their results. **5a–d. Sample answers given.**

Bounce Height

Height of Bounce (cm)

Distance Ball is Dropped (cm)

b. **It will bounce about as high as it did when dropped from 110 cm.**

a. What would you predict about Ball A if the distance it is dropped continues to increase? **It will continue to bounce higher.**

b. What would you predict about Ball B if the distance it is dropped continues to increase?

c. How might you explain these differences? **Ball A might be a Super Ball.**

d. Do you think that each ball will always give a higher bounce with a higher drop height? Explain. **No; at some point both balls will begin to level off. If you dropped Ball A from 100 feet it will not bounce 100 feet.**

6. *Sports* Tom and Jim have been running each afternoon preparing for the track team try-outs. They hope to qualify for the 1,600-meter run. The graph shows their best times over the last ten weeks.

Training Times

Time (min)

Weeks

7. The point where they cross indicates the times were the same.

a. Who has shown the most improvement? **Tom**

b. Who has the better times? **Jim**

c. Who do you predict will be the faster runner in 15 weeks? What will be his time? Explain. **Answers will vary.**

For **Extra Practice,** see page 561.

7. *Critical Thinking* Suppose the lines in Exercise 6 cross after week 12. What does the point where they cross represent?

Study Guide Masters, p. 12

2-5 **Study Guide**

Name_____ Date_____

Making Predictions

With this **line graph**, you can make predictions about the expected number of calories used while bicycling or playing tennis.

Calories Used in Ten Minutes

Calories

Weight in Pounds

── Playing Tennis ── Bicycling

Example About how many more calories can a 120-pound person expect to use bicycling for 10 minutes than playing tennis for 10 minutes?

From the graph, a 120-pound person will use about 60 calories playing tennis and about 82 calories bicycling for 10 minutes.

82 − 60 = 22

A 120-pound person can expect to use about 22 more calories in 10 minutes of bicycling.

Refer to the graph.

1. About how many calories can a 150-pound person expect to use bicycling for 10 minutes?
about 105 calories

2. About how many calories can a 110-pound person expect to use playing tennis for 10 minutes?
about 55 calories

3. About how many more calories can a 140-pound person expect to use bicycling for 10 minutes than playing tennis for 10 minutes?
about 30 more

4. About how many more calories will a 160-pound person use playing tennis for 10 minutes than a 100-pound person will use?
about 30

© Glencoe/McGraw-Hill   T12   Mathematics: Applications and Connections, Course 1

Mixed Review

8. *Food* Refer to the circle graph in Example 1 on page 61. Which two reasons together account for half of the responses? *(Lesson 2-4)*

8. See margin.

9. **Standardized Test Practice** If $m = 6$ and $n = 4$, find the value of the expression $2m - n$. *(Lesson 1-5)* **D**

    A 2   **B** 4   **C** 6   **D** 8

CHAPTER 2 — Mid-Chapter Self Test

Make a frequency table for the set of data. *(Lesson 2-1)*

1. To the nearest inch, how tall are you? **See Answer Appendix.**

    57   54   58   59   60   57   63   57   55   56   60   57

2. Use the set of data 58, 92, 23, 14, 62, 79, 43, 85, 91, 18, 50, 47, 25, 88. *(Lesson 2-2)*

   a. Choose the better scale for a frequency table for the data: 0 to 99 or 0 to 999. **0 to 99**

   b. Choose the best interval for a frequency table for the data: 1, 10, or 100 **10**

   c. Make a frequency table for this set of data. **See Answer Appendix.**

3. Make a bar graph for the data in the table at the right. *(Lesson 2-3)* **See Answer Appendix.**

Favorite Ice Cream Flavor	
Flavor	**Frequency**
Chocolate	7
Strawberry	9
Vanilla	5

4. The circle graph shows the average family size in the U.S. *(Lesson 2-4)* **a. four persons and three persons**

   a. Which two sizes of families together have about the same percent as the size with the greatest percent?

   b. What percent of all families have five or more members? **14%**

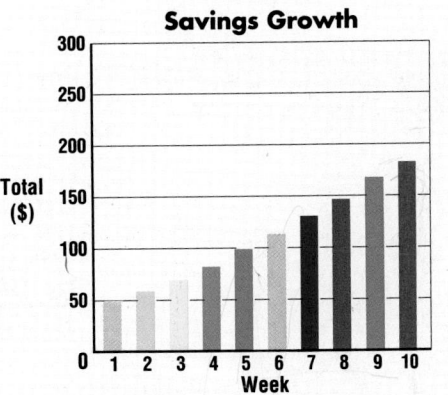

Family Size

Six persons 3%   Seven or more 2%
Five persons 9%
Four persons 21%
Two persons 42%
Three persons 23%

Source: U.S. Census Bureau

5c. Sample answer: No, the horizontal scale doesn't extend far enough.

5. *Economics* Keshia is saving her money to purchase a video game. She starts with $40 and adds $10 the first week, $11 the second week, $12 the third week, and so on. The graph at the right shows a record of her savings for the first 10 weeks. *(Lesson 2-5)*

   a. Estimate when Keshia will double her money (have at least $100). **the 5th week.**

   b. Estimate when she will double her money again (have at least $200). **the 11th week.**

   c. Can you predict when she might double her money again (have at least $400)? Explain your reasoning.

Savings Growth

Total ($) vs. Week (bar graph, values 0 to 300)

Extending the Lesson

Enrichment Masters, p. 12

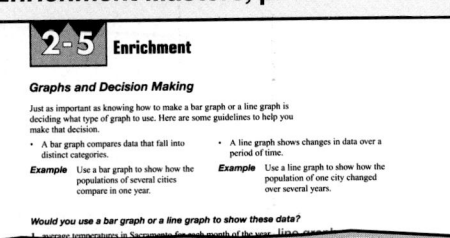

2-5 Enrichment

Graphs and Decision Making

Just as important as knowing how to make a bar graph or a line graph is deciding what type of graph to use. Here are some guidelines to help you make that decision.

- A bar graph compares data that fall into distinct categories.
- A line graph shows changes in data over a period of time.

Example Use a bar graph to show how the populations of several cities compare in one year.

Example Use a line graph to show how the population of one city changed over several years.

Would you use a bar graph or a line graph to show these data?

Activity Have pairs of students make up a graph of the expected weight gains of a science fiction creature. Suggest that they use a pencil or straw as the line of increase or decrease. Ask them to change the angle of the straightedge. Then have them determine how changing the angle affects the outcome.

Closing Activity

Writing Have students write a few sentences describing how graphs can be used to make predictions.

Chapter 2, Quiz B (Lessons 2-4 and 2-5) is available in the *Assessment and Evaluation Masters,* p. 43.

Mid-Chapter Test (Lessons 2-1 through 2-5) is available in the *Assessment and Evaluation Masters,* p. 42.

Mid-Chapter Self Test

The Mid-Chapter Self Test reviews concepts in Lessons 2-1 through 2-5. Lesson references are given so students can review concepts not yet mastered.

Additional Answer

8. convenient location and quality of food

Practice Masters, p. 12

2-5 Practice

Making Predictions
Refer to the graph for Exercises 1-6.

Ideal Weights for Adults
Weight (pounds) vs. Heights (line graph, Male and Female)

1. About how much should a woman weigh if she is 5'8"? **125 lb**
2. About how much should a man weigh if he is 5'11"? **180 lb**
3. About how tall should a man be if his ideal weight is 184 pounds? **6 feet**
4. About how tall should a woman be if her ideal weight is 121 pounds? **5'7"**
5. What would you expect the approximate ideal weight to be for a man 6'3" tall? **about 200 lb**
6. What would you expect the approximate ideal weight to be for a woman 6'1" tall? **about 148 lb**

Refer to the temperature graph for Exercises 7-9.

Average Daily High Temperature
Temperature (°F) vs. Month (line graph, Paris and Moscow)

7. Give the expected high temperature for Moscow in October. **46° F**
8. Give the expected high temperature for Paris in April. **60° F**
9. What month is the average daily high temperature the same for both Moscow and Paris? **July**

© Glencoe/McGraw-Hill   T 12   *Mathematics: Applications and Connections, Course 1*

- *Study Guide Masters*, p. 13
- *Practice Masters*, p. 13
- *Enrichment Masters*, p. 13
- Transparencies 2-6, A and B
- CD-ROM Program
  - Resource Lesson 2-6

Recommended Pacing	
Standard	Day 8 of 14
Honors	Day 8 of 14
Block	Day 4 of 7

1 FOCUS

5-Minute Check
(Lesson 2-5)

Refer to the graph for Exercises 1 and 2.

Rick's Test Results

1. Predict what Rick's score will be in week 6. **about 80**

2. At this rate, in what week will he earn a 100 on his test? **week 8**

 The 5-Minute Check is also available on **Transparency 2-6A** for this lesson.

Motivating the Lesson

Problem Solving Have students read the first paragraph of the lesson and decide whether most kids watch less than 10, 10 to 20, or more than 20 hours of television in a week. Record the responses.

2 TEACH

 Transparency 2-6B contains a teaching aid for this lesson.

Reading Mathematics Ask students to define *stem* and *leaf* in biological terms. Compare these characteristics with those of a stem-and-leaf plot.

What you'll learn

You'll learn to construct stem-and-leaf plots.

When am I ever going to use this?

You can use a stem-and-leaf plot to record a large set of data collected for a science project.

Word Wise

stem-and-leaf plot
stem
leaf

Did you know Although the length of the Iditarod race varies, the official distance is 1,049 miles—49 symbolizes the fact that Alaska was the 49th state.

 Example APPLICATION

2-6 Stem-and-Leaf Plots

D'Ante's brother told him that if he wants to improve his grades, he should watch less television and study more. D'Ante took a survey to find how many hours of television other kids in his grade watch in a week. The results are shown in the chart. What could D'Ante conclude from his data? *This problem will be solved in Example 2.*

2	18	23	14	13
4	5	9	11	13
21	3	19	8	16
9	10	3	3	10
12	15	4	16	19

One way to display a large data set to make it easy to read is to construct a **stem-and-leaf plot**. To display the data 25, 8, 14, 25, 12, and 21 in a stem-and-leaf plot, follow these steps.

Step 1 Find the least and the greatest number. Identify the tens digit in each. The least number, 8, has 0 in the tens place. The greatest number, 25, has 2 in the tens place.

Step 2 Draw a vertical line and write the tens digits from least to greatest to the left of the line. These digits form the **stems**.

$$
\begin{array}{c|c}
0 & \\
1 & \\
2 & \\
\end{array}
$$

Step 3 Write the units digits to the right of the line, with the corresponding stem. The units digits form the **leaves**.

$$
\begin{array}{c|c}
0 & 8 \\
1 & 4\ 2 \\
2 & 5\ 5\ 1 \\
\end{array}
$$

Step 4 Order the leaves in each row from least to greatest.

Stem	Leaf
0	8
1	2 4
2	1 5 5

Step 5 Include a key or an explanation.

$1|2 = 12$

Racing The Iditarod Dog Sled Race is more than 1,000 miles across Alaska. The distances between the checkpoints are shown in the chart.

a. Make a stem-and-leaf plot of the data.

b. In which interval do most of the distances fall? Why would this information be useful to competitors?

20	29	14	52	34
45	30	48	93	48
23	38	90	65	25
18	60	70	90	40
58	48	28	18	55
22				

Source: *USA TODAY* research

a. The least number is 14, and the greatest number is 93. So the stems start with 1 and end with 9.

Stem	Leaf
1	4 8 8
2	0 9 3 5 8 2
3	4 0 8
4	5 8 8 0 8
5	2 8 5
6	5 0
7	0
8	
9	3 0 0

Order the leaves from least to greatest.

➡

Stem	Leaf
1	4 8 8
2	0 2 3 5 8 9
3	0 4 8
4	0 5 8 8 8
5	2 5 8
6	0 5
7	0
8	
9	0 0 3

$1|4 = 14$ miles

Include 8 as a stem even though none of the numbers have an 8 in the tens place.

b. Most of the distances are between 20 and 48 miles. This information would be helpful in calculating the amount of supplies needed between checkpoints.

Example 2

APPLICATION

Surveys Refer to the beginning of the lesson. What could D'Ante conclude from his survey?

Make a stem-and-leaf plot of the survey data to make it easy to summarize. The stem 1 has the greatest number of leaves. D'Ante could conclude that most of the students watch 10-19 hours of television per week.

Stem	Leaf
0	2 3 3 3 4 4 5 8 9 9
1	0 0 1 2 3 3 4 5 6 6 8 9 9
2	1 3

$2|1 = 21$ hours

CHECK FOR UNDERSTANDING

Communicating Mathematics

Read and study the lesson to answer each question.

1. *Tell* when a stem-and-leaf plot would be the best way to represent a set of data. **when there are many numbers in a set of data**

Math Journal

2. *Explain* how a stem-and-leaf plot is like a bar graph. **See margin.**

3. *Find* a list of data in a magazine and make a stem-and-leaf plot. Describe how the plot summarizes the data. **See students' work.**

Guided Practice
4. 0, 1, 2, 3, 4

4. Determine the stems for the data set 9, 42, 33, 21, 11, 6, 40, 5, 5, 9.

5. Make a stem-and-leaf plot for the following set of data.

27, 53, 58, 34, 24, 36, 20, 38, 43, 45, 35, 54, 78, 47, 58, 36 **See Answer Appendix.**

6. *Traffic* Ms. Sangita recorded the number of cars that passed through the intersection in her neighborhood every morning for 3 weeks.

46	53	61	41	70	38	50
33	67	52	69	32	45	62
39	51	66	72	52	59	61

a. Make a stem-and-leaf plot of her data. **See Answer Appendix.**

b. In what intervals do most of the data fall? **between 50-59 and 60-69**

Lesson 2-6 Stem–and–Leaf Plots **69**

■ Reteaching the Lesson ■

Activity Have students use base-ten blocks to model the data that consist of two-digit numbers that you provide. Have students record the numbers of ten strips they use in the stems column of the stem-and-leaf plot, and the number of ones squares in the leaves column.

Additional Answer

2. The length of each row of numbers is like the length of bars on a graph.

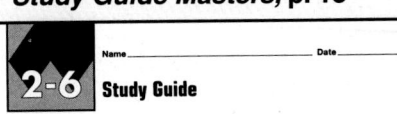

Lesson 2-6 **69**

Check for Understanding

If students need additional practice or instruction after completing Exercises 1–6, one of these options may be helpful.

- Extra Practice, see p. 561
- Reteaching Activity, see p. 69
- *Study Guide Masters,* p. 13
- *Practice Masters,* p. 13

Assignment Guide

Core: 7–15 odd, 16–18
Enriched: 8–12 even, 14–18

4 ASSESS

Closing Activity

Speaking Lead a class discussion on the advantages and disadvantages of a stem-and-leaf plot compared to a regular list of data. **Sample answers: Advantages: Stem-and-leaf plot is more concise, displays data in order, easy to interpret large sets of data; Disadvantage: original data must be reconstructed if being used another way.**

Practice Masters, p. 13

EXERCISES

Practice

Determine the stems for each set of data.

7. 41, 44, 28, 22, 39, 26, 33, 17, 14, 56, 22 **1, 2, 3, 4, 5**

8. 135, 106, 100, 132, 92, 136, 89, 128, 112 **8, 9, 10, 11, 12, 13**

9. 6, 15, 4, 3, 11, 22, 2, 9, 18, 20, 41, 45, 18 **0, 1, 2, 3, 4**

Make a stem-and-leaf plot for each set of data. **10–13. See Answer Appendix.**

10. 35, 29, 27, 28, 27, 30, 44, 33, 32, 45, 38, 28, 22, 21, 31, 31, 38, 24

11. 124, 99, 140, 133, 94, 130, 124, 167, 162, 92, 99, 132

14b. Sample answer: He probably will want the equipment around the 12th of October.

12. 92¢, 83¢, 94¢, 54¢, 85¢, 54¢, 96¢, 89¢, 75¢

13. Make a stem-and-leaf plot of the temperatures (°F) 57°, 34°, 57°, 56°, 27°, 58°, 46°, 53°, 28°, 34°, 9°, 56°, 57°, 45°, 34°, and 29°.

Applications and Problem Solving

14. *Agriculture* Cotton crops are typically harvested when all of the pods on the plants are open. Mr. Smotherman wants to rent harvesting equipment when all of the pods are open. The chart shows the dates in October during the past 19 years when the cotton pods were fully open.

10	19	12	21
18	7	11	16
12	18	20	14
15	16	8	22
9	12	13	

a. Make a stem-and-leaf plot of the data. **See Answer Appendix.**

b. Estimate what day Mr. Smotherman will need to rent the harvesting equipment.

15. *Life Science* As part of a science project, Lai'sung recorded the number of Monarch butterflies he saw every afternoon for one month during migrating season.

6	9	26	11	5
7	9	27	10	8
5	9	41	9	11
13	16	37	18	9
19	18	22	22	14
17	23	19	27	29

a. Make a stem-and-leaf plot of the data. **See Answer Appendix.**

b. On how many days did Lai'sung see more than 20 butterflies? **9 days**

16. *Critical Thinking* Refer to Exercise 6. The City Council told Ms. Sangita that they would place a traffic light at the intersection in her neighborhood if, on average, there were more than 50 cars that pass through the intersection each morning. Use the stem-and-leaf plot and one other type of graph of the same data to prepare an argument for the City Council meeting. **See students' work.**

Mixed Review
17. Sample answer: 400

17. *Business* Use the line graph to estimate sales in July at First Motors. *(Lesson 2-5)*

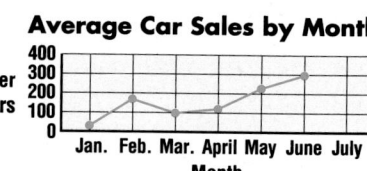

18. **Standardized Test Practice** If a passenger train travels at an average speed of 62 miles per hour, which is a good estimate for the number of hours it will take to travel 293 miles? *(Lesson 1-3)* **C**

  A 3 h   **B** 4 h   **C** 5 h   **D** 7 h   **E** 10 h

For **Extra Practice,** see page 561.

Extending the Lesson

Enrichment Masters, p. 13

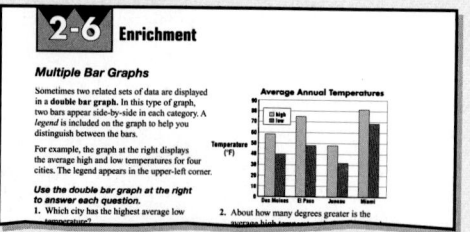

Activity Have students find the high and low temperatures for 15 cities in the U.S. Ask students to make a double stem-and-leaf plot for this data. Tell them that in a double stem-and-leaf plot, one column of stems has two columns of leaves—one on its left for one category and one on its right for the other.

Mean, Median, and Mode

What you'll learn

You'll learn to find the mean, median, mode, and range to describe a set of data.

When am I ever going to use this?

You can use mean, median, and mode to describe your classmates' allowances.

Word Wise

measures of central tendency
mean
median
mode
average
range

The table shows the prices of ten compact 35mm cameras.

It is often helpful to find one number to represent one aspect of a set of data. Some of these numbers are known as **measures of central tendency**. Three common measures of central tendency are **mean**, **median**, and **mode**.

Brand	Price
A	$160
B	$80
C	$230
D	$215
E	$180
F	$220
G	$170
H	$220
I	$300
J	$185

Each measure is a different type of **average**. When people use the word *average,* they are usually referring to the mean.

Mean	The mean of a set of data is the sum of the data divided by the number of pieces of data.

The mean of the camera prices is

$$\frac{160 + 80 + 230 + 215 + 180 + 220 + 170 + 220 + 300 + 185}{10} \text{ or } 196.$$

The median is another measure of central tendency.

Median	The median is the middle number when the data are arranged in numerical order.

Study Hint

Reading Math The median value means that there are just as many values above the median as below it.

To find the median camera price, first order the prices. Then find the middle number.

$$\underbrace{80 \quad 160 \quad 170 \quad 180 \quad 185}_{5 \ numbers} \quad \underbrace{215 \quad 220 \quad 220 \quad 230 \quad 300}_{5 \ numbers}$$

There are two middle numbers, 185 and 215. To find the median, you need to find the mean of these two numbers.

$$\frac{185 + 215}{2} \text{ or } 200$$

The median is 200, so the median price is $200.

Multiple Learning Styles

Interpersonal Give groups of students a price list from a consumer magazine for the top-rated brands of a particular product. Have each group study it and find the mean, median, and mode. Then have students discuss which measure best describes the "average" top-rated products.

Instructional Resources

- *Study Guide Masters,* p. 14
- *Practice Masters,* p. 14
- *Enrichment Masters,* p. 14
- Transparencies 2-7, A and B
- *Assessment and Evaluation Masters,* p. 44
- *School to Career Masters,* p. 2
- *Science and Math Lab Manual,* pp. 5–8
- *Technology Masters,* p. 3
- CD-ROM Program
  - Resource Lesson 2-7

Recommended Pacing	
Standard	Days 9 & 10 of 14
Honors	Days 9 & 10 of 14
Block	Day 5 of 7

1 FOCUS

5-Minute Check
(Lesson 2-6)

1. Make a stem-and-leaf plot for the following set of data.
46, 37, 32, 51, 48, 44, 33, 54, 39, 40, 56, 59

Stem	Leaf
3	2 3 7 9
4	0 4 6 8
5	1 4 6 9 5|1 = 51

2. The stem-and-leaf plot below shows scores on a test.

Stem	Leaf
9	0 3 7 9
8	1 1 2 7 8
7	3 4 5 5
6	2 5
5	
4	3 4|3 = 43

a. What was the highest score on the test? **99**

b. In which interval did most of the scores fall? **80–89**

The 5-Minute Check is also available on **Transparency 2-7A** for this lesson.

72 Chapter 2

Hands-On Activity Have students comparison shop in catalogs for one item such as a CD or video game. After they have four or five different prices, ask them how they would determine the average price for each item.

2 TEACH

Transparency 2-7B contains a teaching aid for this lesson.

In-Class Examples

For Example 1
Find the mean, median, and mode of the data in the following graph.

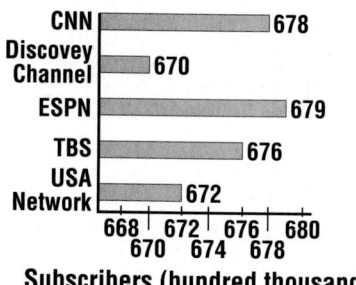

Top 5 Cable T.V. Networks, 1996

CNN 678
Discovey Channel 670
ESPN 679
TBS 676
USA Network 672

668 670 672 674 676 678 680

Subscribers (hundred thousands)

675,000; 676,000; no mode

For Example 2
What is the range of data for the graph in Example 1? **19,000**

A third measure of central tendency is the mode.

Mode	The mode of a set of data is the number(s) or item(s) that appear most often.

To find the mode of the camera price data, look for the dollar amount that appears most often. The amount $220 appears twice and is the mode. If Brand E would have cost $185, then $185 would have been listed twice also, and the data would have two modes. *A set of data may have no mode, one mode, or multiple modes.*

Example
Real World **APPLICATION**

① **Entertainment** The graph shows the number of channels available from different cable companies. Find the mean, median, and mode of the data.

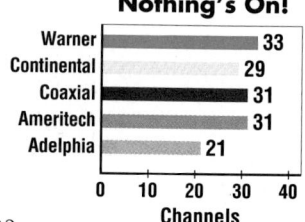

Nothing's On!

Warner 33
Continental 29
Coaxial 31
Ameritech 31
Adelphia 21

0 10 20 30 40
Channels

Did you know By the time American children reach age 18, they have, on average, watched 17,000 hours of television and seen 360,000 commercials.

Mean $\frac{21 + 31 + 31 + 29 + 33}{5}$ or 29

Mode The number 31 appears twice and is the mode.

Median The set of data in order is: 21   29   31   31   33.

The middle number is 31. The median is 31.

The stem-and-leaf plots show the test scores of two sixth grade science classes. Both classes have the same mean score, the same median score, and the same mode score. However, the individual scores are not all the same. How do the two sets of scores differ?

Third Period			**Fourth Period**	
2			2	0 8
3			3	5 8
4	3 5		4	5
5	2 4 5 6		5	0
6	0 0 0 8		6	0 0
7	2 5 8		7	2 5
8	1 5		8	8 9
9		$8|1 = 81$	9	1 6 8

Another aspect of data is how it is spread out. One way to describe the spread of a set of data is to use the **range**. The range is the difference between the greatest number and the least number in a set of data.

The range of the science test scores are as follows.

Third Period: 85 − 43 or 42   Fourth Period: 98 − 20 or 78

The scores of the fourth period class are more spread out, or dispersed, than those of the third period class.

Classroom Vignette

"We collect age information from the class by routing a chart in which students fill in their name, age in years and months, age in months, and birthday. Then students use the data in various ways determining the most appropriate statistical measures and methods for displaying the data."

Verlene B. DeWitt, Teacher
Lee Burneson Middle School
Westlake, OH

Verlene B. DeWitt

Example 2 Refer to the beginning of the lesson. What is the range of the camera prices?

First order the prices.

80 160 170 180 185 215 220 220 230 300

The range is 300 − 80 or 220.

The range of the camera prices is $220.

In this Mini-Lab, you'll use beans to learn more about measures of central tendency.

 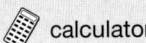

MINI-LAB

Work in groups of five.   bowl of beans   calculator

Try This

- Have one person in your group reach into the bowl and grab a handful of beans. Count and record the number of beans. Replace the beans in the bowl.
- Repeat the previous step for the other four members of your group.
- Find the mean, mode, and median of your group's results.

Talk About It 1–2. See students' work.

1. Suppose you add the number 4 to the set of data so that your group now has six pieces of data.
   a. Find the mean, mode, and median of the new set of data.
   b. Which measure of central tendency is affected the most?
   c. Which measure of central tendency is most representative of the data before adding the 4? after adding the 4?

2. Suppose you add the number 500 to your original set of data.
   a. Find the mean, mode, and median of the new set of data.
   b. Which measure of central tendency is affected the most?
   c. Which measure of central tendency is most representative of the data before adding the 500? after adding the 500?

3. the mean; Sample answer: Adding an extreme value can't affect the mode because it's a new value. It affects the median slightly because the middle value moves one position.

3. In general, which measure of central tendency is most affected by adding an extreme value? Explain.

CHECK FOR UNDERSTANDING

Communicating Mathematics

Read and study the lesson to answer each question. 1–2. See margin.

1. *State* which measure—mean, median, or mode—best represents the original set of data in the Mini-Lab. Explain your reasoning.

2. *Explain* how to find the median of a set of data that has an even number of data in the set.

Lesson 2-7 Mean, Median, and Mode **73**

Reteaching the Lesson

Activity Write a set of data on 3" × 5" cards with one number on each card. Have pairs of students arrange the cards in order from least to greatest. Have them find the mean on their calculators. Then have them find the mode and the median.

Error Analysis
Watch for students who have trouble differentiating mean, median, and mode. **Prevent by** association of common words: median of highway is in the middle; mode is one letter from *more*.

Using the Mini-Lab Ask students what was the most efficient way to count the beans. Ask students how they think their measures would change if they had 100 people in their group.

3 PRACTICE/APPLY

Check for Understanding
If students need additional practice or instruction after completing Exercises 1–6, you may find one of the following options helpful.
- Extra Practice, see p. 562
- Reteaching Activity
- *Study Guide Masters*, p. 14
- *Practice Masters*, p. 14
- Interactive Mathematics Tools Software

Additional Answers
1. The mean because the numbers do not differ greatly.
2. Find the mean of the two middle pieces of data.

Study Guide Masters, p. 14

Family Activity

Ask students to share with the class the graph they chose. Have them demonstrate how they found the mean, median, and mode and explain what each means.

4 ASSESS

Closing Activity
Writing Have pairs of students write a sentence to explain the method used to find each measure of central tendency.

Chapter 2, Quiz C (Lessons 2-6 and 2-7) is available in the *Assessment and Evaluation Masters*, p. 44.

Practice Masters, p. 14

2-7 Practice

Mean, Median, and Mode

Find the mean, median, mode, and range for each set of data.
1. 6, 9, 2, 4, 3, 6, 5 **5; 5; 6; 7**
2. 25, 18, 14, 27, 25, 14, 18, 25, 23 **21; 23; 25; 13**
3. 453, 345, 543, 345, 534 **444; 453; 345; 198**
4. 13, 6, 7, 13, 6 **9; 7; 6 and 13; 7**
5. 8, 2, 9, 4, 6, 8, 5 **6; 6; 8; 7**
6. 13, 7, 17, 19, 7, 15, 11, 7 **12; 12; 7; 12**
7. 1, 15, 9, 12, 18, 9, 5, 14, 7 **10; 9; 9; 17**
8. 28, 32, 23, 43, 32, 27, 21, 34 **30; 30; 32; 22**
9. 3, 9, 4, 3, 9, 4, 2, 3, 8 **5; 4; 3; 7**
10. 42, 35, 27, 42, 38, 35, 29, 24 **34; 35; 35 and 42; 18**
11. 157, 124, 157, 124, 157, 139 **143; 148; 157; 33**

Use the data below to answer Exercises 12–15.

After-School Activities	Cost per Hour
Piano	$14.00
Ballet	10.00
Swimming	5.00
Karate	15.00
Skating	12.00
Aerobics	5.00
Arts & Crafts	8.00
Drama	10.00
Scouts	2.00

12. What is the mode? **$5**
13. What is the median? **$10**
14. What is the mean? **$9.00**
15. If the price of swimming lessons went up to $6, would it change the
   a. mode? Why? **Yes; only one occurrence of 5.**
   b. median? Why? **No; still 4 numbers below 10.**
   c. mean? Why? **Yes; sum of data is different.**
   d. range? Why? **No; it's not the least or greatest amount.**

© Glencoe/McGraw-Hill   T 14   *Mathematics: Applications and Connections, Course 1*

HANDS-ON MATH

Guided Practice

3. Add a number to your original set of data in the Mini-Lab so that the mean and median stay the same. **See students' work.**

List the data in each set from least to greatest. Then find the median, mode, mean, and range. 5. **See Answer Appendix.**

4. 1, 2, 3, 5, 5, 7, 9; 5; 5; ≈ 4.6; 8

4. 3, 7, 1, 5, 5, 9, 2

5. 36, 26, 10, 57, 29, 83, 27, 88, 37

6. *Food* If 18 snacks in a vending machine cost 60¢ each, 9 snacks cost 50¢ each, and 8 snacks cost 80¢ each, what is the mean cost for all 35 snacks? **62¢**

EXERCISES

Find the mean, median, mode, and range for each set of data.

Practice

7. 44; 44; no mode; 22
8. 28; 27; 27; 10
9. 15; 15; 14 and 16; 4
10. 10; 9; 9; 11
12. 427.5; 430; 377 and 475; 300

7. 52, 48, 32, 40, 54, 38
8. 23, 27, 33, 31, 30, 27, 25
9. 13, 17, 16, 16, 14, 14, 16, 14
10. 9, 15, 9, 12, 7, 9, 15, 4
11. 31, 25, 18, 40, 31, 18, 26, 32, 39, 44, 37 **31; 31; 18 and 31; 26**
12. 475, 377, 273, 379, 477, 573, 475, 377, 385, 484

For **Extra Practice,** see page 562.

Refer to the beginning of the lesson for Exercises 13–15.

13. Suppose the Brand I camera was removed from the list. How would this affect the mean? **The mean would be lower.**

14. Suppose both the Brand I and the Brand B cameras were removed from the list. How would this affect the median? **It would not affect the median.**

15. If the Brand C camera cost as much as the Brand I camera, would this change the mean? Explain why or why not. **See Answer Appendix.**

Applications and Problem Solving

Family Activity

Find a bar graph in a newspaper or magazine in your home. Work with a family member to find the mean, median, and mode of the data in the graph.

16. *Earth Science* The Channel 6 meteorologist made the graph at the right.
   a. What was the mean high temperature for June? **88°**
   b. What was the range of the high temperatures? **7°**

Daily Highs for June

17. *Business Management* The manager of Dairy Land keeps a record of the sizes of the shakes sold. Would the mean, median, or mode be more useful to her? Explain. **See Answer Appendix.**

18. *Critical Thinking* List six numbers such that the mean is 14, the median is 14, the modes are 12 and 14, and the range is 5. **See Answer Appendix.**

Mixed Review

19. *Statistics* Construct a stem-and-leaf plot for 12, 7, 23, 9, 10, 20, 0, 4, 19, 13, 5, 7, 2, 13, 18, and 2. *(Lesson 2-6)* **See Answer Appendix.**

20. *Standardized Test Practice* Shamrock, Texas, had a population of 2,206 in 1996. What was the population rounded to the nearest thousand? *(Lesson 1-3)* **A**
   A 2,000   **B** 2,200   **C** 2,020   **D** 2,210

Extending the Lesson

Enrichment Masters, p. 14

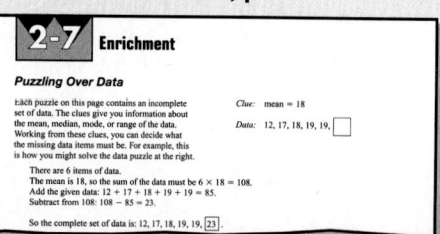

2-7 Enrichment

Puzzling Over Data

Each puzzle on this page contains an incomplete set of data. The clues give you information about the mean, median, mode, or range of the data. Working from these clues, you can decide what the missing data items must be. For example, this is how you might solve the data puzzle at the right.

Clue: mean = 18
Data: 12, 17, 18, 19, 19, ☐

There are 6 items of data.
The mean is 18, so the sum of the data must be 6 × 18 = 108.
Add the given data: 12 + 17 + 18 + 19 + 19 = 85.
Subtract from 108: 108 − 85 = 23.

So the complete set of data is: 12, 17, 18, 19, 19, 23.

Activity Check store catalogs for the range of prices of a favorite item. If you were the store's marketing manager, would you use the range, mean, mode, or median to advertise the items? Explain your reasons.

What's the Average?

Get Ready   This game is for four players.

 4 index cards   calculator   2 spinners

> **Math Skill**
> **Mean,**
> **Median,**
> **and Mode**

Get Set
- Each player should write five whole numbers on an index card. The numbers should be from 1 through 10.
- Label the spinner that has three equal regions with the words *mean, mode,* and *median.*

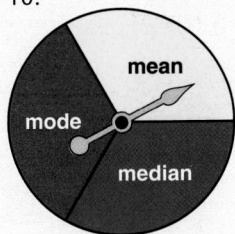

- Label the spinner that has four equal regions with the words *add/increase, add/decrease, remove/increase,* and *remove/decrease.*

Go
- Mix the index cards and turn them facedown.
- The first player randomly selects a card and spins each spinner once. Then the player adjusts the data set as instructed. For example, if the player gets *mode* and *add/decrease,* the player must add a piece of data to the data set so the mode decreases. If the player gets *median* and *remove/increase,* the player must remove a piece of data from the data set so the median of the set increases.
- The other members then check.
- A player scores two points for each correct solution and loses one point for each incorrect solution.
- The first player to get 10 points wins.

 Visit www.glencoe.com/sec/math/mac/mathnet for more games.

Lesson 2-7 Mean, Median, and Mode   **75**

Instructional Resources

Hands-On Lab Masters
- spinners, p. 20

Manipulative Kit
- spinners

Overhead Manipulative Resources
- spinners

You may wish to use an overhead transparency spinner to demonstrate the instructions. Encourage students to devise a pattern that will help them change the mean, median, and mode. For example, to add/increase the median, you would add a number that is larger than the median.
Additional resources for this game can be found on page 42 of the ***Classroom Games.***

MathPASS
CD-ROM

This CD-ROM offers a complete, self-paced mathematics curriculum. Each lesson includes a pretest, tutorial, guided practice, and posttest. MathPASS Lesson 3 is correlated to this Student Edition lesson.
For Windows & Macintosh

GET READY

Objective Students display and summarize data in a box-and-whisker plot.

Optional Resources
Hands-On Lab Masters
• number lines, p. 16
• worksheet, p. 40

MANAGEMENT TIPS

Recommended Time
45 minutes

Getting Started Have students find examples of line graphs and convert them to vertical bar graphs, using counters to represent the vertical numbers. Then they should practice finding the median of the horizontal axis.

The **Activity** deals with quartiles. Explain that quartiles are just fourths of the data. Compare *quartile* to *quarter*. The upper quartile is the upper fourth of the data. The lower quartile is the lowest fourth of the data.

HANDS-ON
LAB

 index cards

 cardboard

 markers

 push pins

 string

COOPERATIVE LEARNING

2-7B Box-and-Whisker Plots

A Follow-Up of Lesson 2-7

Did you know you can analyze a set of data by looking at its shape? In this lab, you will show the shape of a set of data by drawing a *box-and-whisker plot*. A box-and-whisker plot displays and summarizes a set of data.

TRY THIS

Work in groups of four.

Make a box-and-whisker plot for the data 20, 10, 22, 25, 18, 22, 16, 26, 23, 27, 14, and 19.

Step 1 Draw a number line on a piece of cardboard. Label it with an appropriate scale. Since the data goes from 10 to 27, begin the scale with 10 and end with 29.

10 11 12 13 14 15 16 17 18 19 20 21 22 23 24 25 26 27 28 29

Step 2 Copy each number from the data set on an index card. Place each number in its appropriate place above the number line.

22

10   14 16 18 19 20   22 23   25 26 27

10 11 12 13 14 15 16 17 18 19 20 21 22 23 24 25 26 27 28 29

Step 3 Mark the median and the *extreme* (least and greatest) *values* in the data by placing push pins on the number line. Label each number. The data is now separated into two halves.

22

10   14 16 18 19 20   22 23   25 26 27

10 11 12 13 14 15 16 17 18 19 20 21 22 23 24 25 26 27 28 29

lower   median   upper
extreme   extreme

76 Chapter 2 Statistics: Graphing Data

Step 4 Now find the median of each half of the data. Mark each by placing a push pin on the number line. The median of the lower half of the data is called the *lower quartile.* The median of the upper half of the data is called the *upper quartile.* Label these on the number line. The data is now separated into fourths or *quartiles,* each having the same number of data.

Step 5 Draw a box using the quartiles as the left and right edges. Then draw a line segment through the median.

Step 6 Construct the whiskers. Tie a piece of string between the lower quartile and the least number. Tie another piece of string between the upper quartile and the greatest number.

The box-and-whisker plot shows that the bottom fourth of the data is fairly spread out while the top fourth has a small range.

1,3. See Answer Appendix.

ON YOUR OWN

1. *Draw* a box-and-whisker plot for 37, 12, 25, 9, 33, 17, 51, 45, 35, and 39.
2. If the whiskers in a box-and-whisker plot are longer than the box, what does this tell you about the data? **See margin.**
3. *Reflect Back* Make a box-and-whisker plot for the data in the stem-and-leaf plot in Example 2 on page 69.

 Math Journal Have students summarize what they've learned about box-and-whisker plots and when they might be useful.

Have students complete Exercises 1 and 2. Watch for students who may have difficulty determining the upper and lower quartiles. Remind them to divide the data into fourths to find the quartiles.

Use Exercise 3 to determine whether students understand box-and-whisker plots.

Additional Answer

2. Sample answer: The middle half of the data is tightly clustered and the lower and upper fourths of the data are widely dispersed.

Hands-On Lab Masters, p. 40

- *Study Guide Masters*, p. 15
- *Practice Masters*, p. 15
- *Enrichment Masters*, p. 15
- Transparencies 2-8, A and B
- *Classroom Games*, pp. 3–4
- CD-ROM Program
  - Resource Lesson 2-8

Recommended Pacing	
Standard	Day 11 of 14
Honors	Day 11 of 14
Block	Day 6 of 7

1 FOCUS

5-Minute Check
(Lesson 2-7)

Find the mean, median, mode, and range for each set of data.

1. 2, 5, 6, 8, 4, 7, 8, 9, 5
   6, 6, 5 and 8, 7

2. 13, 80, 23, 45, 13, 81, 25
   40, 25, 13, 68

On a sale rack at a store, 20 CDs cost $5 each, 15 CDs cost $4 each, and 5 CDs cost $7 each. Use this data for Exercises 3–5.

3. What is the mean? $4.88
4. What is the mode? $5
5. What is the median? $5

The 5-Minute Check is also available on **Transparency 2-8A** for this lesson.

Motivating the Lesson

Problem Solving Ask students to read the opening paragraph of the lesson. Then have them look at the two graphs. Ask the following questions.
- How are the graphs the same?
  Sample answer: They show the same information.
- How are they different?
  Sample answer: There are more intervals in Graph 2; the intervals are larger in Graph 1.

What you'll learn
You'll learn to recognize when statistics and graphs are misleading.

When am I ever going to use this?
Knowing how to recognize misleading statistics will help you make informed decisions.

During political campaigns, politicians often use statistics to make a point. In a recent election, opposing candidates presented the two graphs shown below.

- Do both graphs show the same information?

- Which graph suggests a drastic cut in government spending? Which graph suggests fairly steady spending?

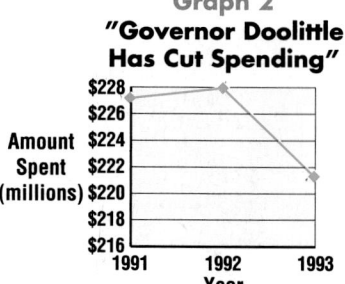

Graph 1
"Governor Doolittle Continues Spending"

Amount Spent (millions): $300, $250, $200, $150, $100, $50, $0
Year: 1991, 1992, 1993

Graph 2
"Governor Doolittle Has Cut Spending"

Amount Spent (millions): $228, $226, $224, $222, $220, $218, $216
Year: 1991, 1992, 1993

Both graphs represent the same data. By using a different scale, each candidate was able to take the same information and tell a very different story.

Graph 2 is a result of an expanded vertical scale. For this reason, Graph 2 is visually misleading when compared to the complete scale in Graph 1. This should be indicated using a small "break" in the vertical axis as shown at the right. This shows that the axis is not to scale between $0 and $220.

$228, $226, $224, $222, $220, $0

Example 1
CONNECTION

Geography The graphs display the same data.

a. **Is Graph A misleading? Explain.**

Graph A is misleading because there is no title and there are no labels on either scale. It should also include a break in the vertical axis between 0 and 30.

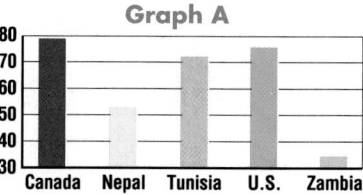

Graph A
80, 70, 60, 50, 40, 30
Canada, Nepal, Tunisia, U.S., Zambia

b. Is Graph B misleading? Explain.

Graph B is not misleading. The scales are labeled, and the graph includes a title.

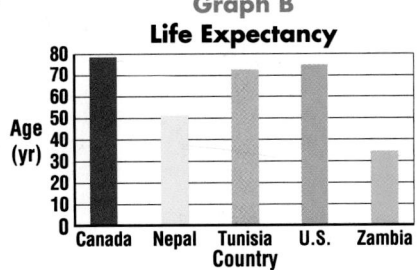

Graph B
Life Expectancy

Age (yr) — Country: Canada, Nepal, Tunisia, U.S., Zambia

Another way statistics can be misleading is by not using the best measure of central tendency.

Example 2 APPLICATION

Allowances The results of a class survey on weekly allowances are shown in the table. Felipe told his sister that the average allowance was $7, Megan told her parents the average was $5, and Alba told her brother the average was $4.45.

Allowance	Frequency
$7	6
$6	0
$5	5
$4	1
$3	4
$2	2
$1	2

a. How can all three people think they are correct?

b. Which do you think is the best measure and why?

a. Each person used a different measure of central tendency to describe the set of data. Felipe used the mode, Megan used the median, and Alba used the mean.

b. The mode is misleading because $7 is also the highest allowance. The median is misleading because $5 is the second highest allowance. In this case, the best measure is the mean.

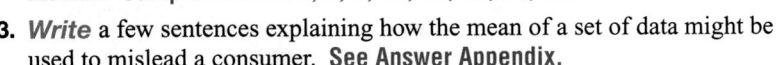

CHECK FOR UNDERSTANDING

Communicating Mathematics

Read and study the lesson to answer each question.

1. *Describe* at least two ways that a graph can be misleading. **See margin.**

2. *Write* a set of eight pieces of data that would best be represented by the median. **Sample answer: 2, 8, 9, 10, 12, 13, 14, 100**

3. *Write* a few sentences explaining how the mean of a set of data might be used to mislead a consumer. **See Answer Appendix.**

Guided Practice

Tell whether the *mean*, *median*, or *mode* would be best to describe each set of data. Explain each answer.

4. **mean — all numbers about the same**

4. 500, 400, 390, 405, 390

5. car buyer's favorite color **See margin.**

6. populations of California, Texas, New York, Florida, Pennsylvania, and Idaho **Median — Idaho is much less than the rest.**

Lesson 2-8 Misleading Statistics **79**

Additional Answers

1. Sample answer: using different scales and not having a title

5. mode—want to find the most frequent

Transparency 2-8B contains a teaching aid for this lesson.

Using Applications For the amounts below, have students determine which measure of central tendency they might choose as a basis for their weekly allowance. **mode** Ask them which measure they might use if they were parents. **mean**

$4 $6 $5 $7 $7

In-Class Examples

For Example 1
The graphs display the same information about life expectancy of women in various countries. Which graph is misleading? Explain. **Graph A; no labels and vertical axis skips from 0 to 50 and 50 to 70**

Graph A
Life Expectancy

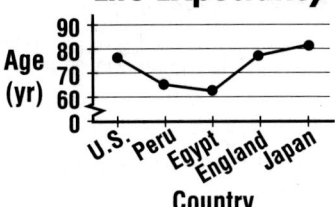

Graph B
Life Expectancy

Age (yr) — Country: U.S., Peru, Egypt, England, Japan

For Example 2
The speeds at which animals can travel in a quarter-mile distance are shown below. The mode is 30, the median is 40, and the mean is 38.5. Which average best represents the data? **median**

Speed (mph)	Frequency
61	1
50	3
45	2
40	3
35	3
30	4
9	1

Check for Understanding

If students need additional practice or instruction after completing Exercises 1–7, one of these options may be helpful.

- Extra Practice, see p. 562
- Reteaching Activity
- *Study Guide Masters*, p. 15
- *Practice Masters*, p. 15

Assignment Guide

Core: 8, 9–13 odd, 16–19
Enriched: 8–12 even, 13, 14, 16–19

7a. Graph B is misleading because the distance between 0 and 25 is the same as the distance between 25 and 30.

Study Guide Masters, p. 15

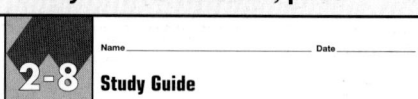

7. *Stock Market* The graphs below display the same information.

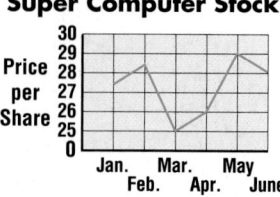

a. Explain why these graphs look different.

b. If a stockbroker wanted to convince a customer to invest in the stock market, which graph would she probably show the customer? Explain.
Graph A because it shows a general rise in price

EXERCISES

Practice

8a. Sample answer: Graph B; it does not go as high giving the impression that the rates are lower.

8b. Sample answer: Graph B; it looks like the calls are cheaper.

8. *Money Matters* A local telephone company employee made two graphs to show the cost of calling Port Arthur.

a. Which graph makes a call to Port Arthur look more economical? Why?

b. Which graph would you show to a telephone customer? Explain.

c. Which graph would you show to a company stockholder? Explain. **Sample answer: Graph A; it looks like the company is getting more**

Determine the measure of central tendency that you think is best for each category. Explain your choice.

Home	Condo	Cape Cod	Ranch	Split Level	2–Story
Bathrooms	1	1	$1\frac{1}{2}$	2	$2\frac{1}{2}$
Bedrooms	2	2	2	4	5
Taxes	$1,200	$2,080	$1,800	$1,740	$2,990
Price	$62,900	$99,450	$124,800	$114,900	$239,400

9. $1\frac{1}{2}$; median

9. number of bathrooms

10. number of bedrooms 2; mode

11. taxes $1962; mean

12. price $114,900; median

13. *Money Matters* An advertisement for *CD Spins* states that their average price for a CD is $11. How may the owner of *CD Spins* be using average to give the impression of lower prices? **There may be a few very low priced CDs, thus giving a lower average.**

14. *Language Arts* Dora is writing a book report on a book about Henry Aaron entitled *I Had A Hammer*. To show that Aaron is the lifetime home run leader, Dora draws the graphs below.

Graph A
Lifetime Home Run Leaders

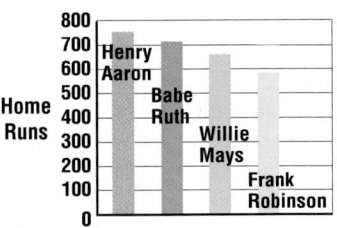

Graph B
Lifetime Home Run Leaders

b. Graph B; Sample answer: The scale is consistent.

a. Which graph makes it look like Willie Mays hit about twice as many home runs as Frank Robinson? **Graph A**

b. Which graph should Dora use for a presentation? Explain.

c. How could Graph A be changed to be less misleading? **Show a break in the vertical axis.**

Henry Aaron

15a. mean: 134 ÷ 24 ≈ 5.6 or 6 pets; median: 3 pets; mode: 2 pets

15. *Working on the* **CHAPTER Project** Refer to your frequency tables from Exercise 10 on page 49.

a. Find the mean, median, and mode for the data in your frequency table from Exercise 10a.

b. Tell which measure of central tendency you think would be best to describe this set of data. Explain your answer. **See margin.**

16. *Critical Thinking* Find a graph in a newspaper or magazine. Redraw the graph so that the data appear to show different results. Which graph describes the data better? Explain. **See students' work.**

Mixed Review

17. *Standardized Test Practice* The Chill hockey team played 32 games. They scored a total of 128 goals. What was the mean (average) number of goals scored per game? *(Lesson 2-7)* **A**

A 4
B 5
C 96
D 160

18. Sample answer: 100 to 150

18. *Sports* Erica's bowling scores last weekend were 119, 134, 135, 125, 143, and 130. What is an appropriate scale for her scores? *(Lesson 2-2)*

For **Extra Practice**, see page 562.

19. *Patterns* Find the next three numbers in the pattern 1, 4, 9, 16, ... *(Lesson 1-2)* **25, 36, 49**

Lesson 2-8 Misleading Statistics **81**

Extending the Lesson

Enrichment Masters, p. 15

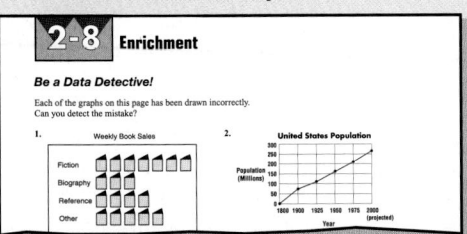

Activity Have small groups of students use the financial page of a daily newspaper to track the price of a stock over a period of one month. Have them determine whether a graph or a measure of central tendency best illustrates the performance of the stock.

Exercise 15 asks students to advance to the next stage of work on the Chapter Project. You may wish to have students work together to discuss the best measure of central tendency. If students can't reach a consensus, have them include all choices and reasons for each.

4 ASSESS

Closing Activity

Speaking Have students supply the words *mean*, *median*, and *mode* as you read the guidelines from the lesson for the best use of measures of central tendency. Then have them discuss examples of how information can be misleading in a graph.

Additional Answer

15b. Sample answer: The median best represents the data. The student with 24 pets has a big effect on the mean.

Practice Masters, p. 15

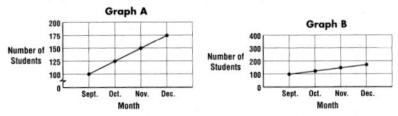

Lesson 2-8 **81**

Instructional Resources

- *Study Guide Masters*, p. 16
- *Practice Masters*, p. 16
- *Enrichment Masters*, p. 16
- Transparencies 2-9, A and B
- *Assessment and Evaluation Masters*, p. 44

 CD-ROM Program
- Resource Lesson 2-9

Recommended Pacing	
Standard	Day 12 of 14
Honors	Day 12 of 14
Block	Day 6 of 7

1 FOCUS

5-Minute Check
(Lesson 2-8)

Ruth's Cookie Sales

Ina's Cookie Sales

Ruth and Ina sold cookies for a week.

1. At first glance, which student appears to be the better salesperson? **Ruth**

2. Which student actually sold the most boxes? **Ina**

3. Which graph is misleading? **Ruth's**

 The 5-Minute Check is also available on **Transparency 2-9A** for this lesson.

2-9

Integration: Geometry
Graphing Ordered Pairs

What you'll learn

You'll learn to use ordered pairs to locate points and organize data.

When am I ever going to use this?

In geography, latitude and longitude are used to separate Earth into a coordinate grid.

Word Wise

coordinate system
origin
x-axis
y-axis
ordered pair
x-coordinate
y-coordinate

In the cartoon, how do the other students know who the machine has caught daydreaming?

Notice how the chart on the front of the machine forms a grid pattern. The grid is used to identify the daydreamer by using a code similar to what is used on road maps. Obviously, everyone knows how to locate the seat designated by 4-B.

CLOSE TO HOME JOHN McPHERSON

In mathematics, we can locate a point by using a **coordinate system**.

 The coordinate system is formed when two number lines intersect at their zero points. This point is called the **origin**. The horizontal number line is called the **x-axis**, and the vertical number line is called the **y-axis**.

You can name any point on a coordinate system by using an **ordered pair** of numbers. The first number in an ordered pair is called the **x-coordinate**, and the second number is called the **y-coordinate**. An ordered pair is written in this form:

$$(4, 2)$$

x-coordinate ↑ ↑ *y-coordinate*

The *x*-coordinate represents the number of horizontal units the point is from 0, and the *y*-coordinate represents the number of vertical units it is from 0.

82 Chapter 2 Statistics: Graphing Data

Motivating the Lesson

Hands-On Activity Have students determine the coordinates of their seat assignments in a manner similar to the one in the opening paragraph of the lesson.

Example ① Name the ordered pair for point K.

Start at the origin. Move right along the *x*-axis until you are under point *K*. Since you moved two units to the right, the *x*-coordinate of the ordered pair is 2.

Now move up until you reach point *K*. Since you moved up 4 units, the *y*-coordinate is 4.

The ordered pair for point *K* is (2, 4).

You can also graph a point on a coordinate system. To graph a point means to place a dot at the point named by an ordered pair.

Example ② Graph each point.

a. A(6, 4)
Start at the origin. Move 6 units to the right on the *x*-axis. Then move 4 units up to locate the point. Draw a dot and label the dot *A*.

b. B(7, 0)
Start at the origin. Move 7 units to the right on the *x*-axis. Since the *y*-coordinate is 0, stop here. Draw a dot and label the dot *B*.

Ordered pairs can also be used to show how data are related.

Example ③
INTEGRATION

Algebra Pazi went bowling at The Bowling Castle. Games were $2 each. If *x* represents the number of games she bowled, the expression 2*x* gives the total cost.

a. Make a list of ordered pairs in this form: (number of games bowled, cost of games).

b. Then graph the ordered pairs.

(continued on the next page)

Lesson 2-9 Integration: Geometry Graphing Ordered Pairs **83**

Transparency 2-9B contains a teaching aid for this lesson.

Reading Mathematics Much of mathematics involves symbolism with distinct meanings. Make sure students understand what the expression *B*(4, 2) means.

In-Class Examples

For Example 1
Name the ordered pair for point *M*. **(3, 2)**

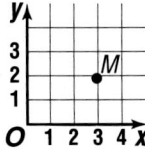

For Example 2
Graph each point.
a. *C* (5, 3)
b. *D* (0, 5)

For Example 3
Rhaghad went to play putt-putt. Games were $3 each. If *x* represents the number of games she played, the expression 3*x* gives the total cost.
a. Make a list of ordered pairs in this form: (number of games played, cost of games).

x (games)	3*x*	*y* (cost)	(*x*, *y*)
1	3(1)	3	(1, 3)
2	3(2)	6	(2, 6)
3	3(3)	9	(3, 9)

b. Graph the ordered pairs.

Check for Understanding

If students need additional practice or instruction after completing Exercises 1–10, one of these options may be helpful.
- Extra Practice, see p. 562
- Reteaching Activity
- *Study Guide Masters*, p. 16
- *Practice Masters*, p. 16

Assignment Guide
Core: 11–31 odd, 33–37
Enriched: 12–30 even, 31–37

Additional Answers

3. Sample answer: Raul; to graph (8, 3) you move 8 units right and 3 units up and to graph (3, 8) you move 3 units right and 8 units up.

10.

Study Guide Masters, p. 16

Did you know? On February 2, 1997, Jeremy Sonnenfeld, a college sophomore, became the first person to bowl a 900 series (3 perfect games in a row) in the 101-year history of the American Bowling Congress.

a. Evaluate the expression 2x for 1, 2, and 3 games. A table of ordered pairs that result is shown below.

b.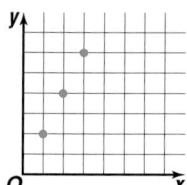

x (games)	2x	y (cost)	(x, y)
1	2 (1)	2	(1, 2)
2	2 (2)	4	(2, 4)
3	2 (3)	6	(3, 6)

(3, 6) means 3 games cost $6.

CHECK FOR UNDERSTANDING

Read and study the lesson to answer each question.

Communicating Mathematics
1. From the origin, go 7 units right, then up 9 units.
2. See students' work.

1. *Tell* how to graph the ordered pair (7, 9).
2. *Draw* a coordinate system and label the origin, x-axis, and y-axis.
3. *You Decide* Lina says that the ordered pairs (8, 3) and (3, 8) name the same point. Raul disagrees. Who is correct and why? **See margin.**

Guided Practice

Use the grid at the right to name the point for each ordered pair.

4. (3, 7) **B**   5. (9, 5) **F**   6. (0, 8) **A**

Use the grid at the right to name the ordered pair for each point.

7. E **(8, 0)**   8. D **(6, 3)**   9. C **(5, 6)**

10. See margin for graph. Sample answer: The points appear to be in a straight line.

10. *Physical Science* Odell and Elise conducted an experiment to see how the mass of an object affected the distance a spring stretched. On graph paper, draw a coordinate grid. Then graph the ordered pairs (mass, distance). Use the x-axis for mass and the y-axis for distance. What did they observe?

Stretching of a Spring	
Mass	Distance
100 g	3 cm
200 g	6 cm
300 g	9 cm
400 g	12 cm
500 g	15 cm

EXERCISES

Practice

Use the grid at the right to name the point for each ordered pair.

11. (9, 3) **C**   12. (5, 9) **Y**
13. (2, 0) **K**   14. (5, 1) **Z**
15. (1, 7) **Q**   16. (8, 2) **F**
17. (5, 6) **L**   18. (0, 2) **J**
19. (7, 5) **M**   20. (3, 4) **D**

2-9 Study Guide

Name _____ Date _____

Integration: Geometry
Graphing Ordered Pairs

In mathematics, we lokate points by using a **coordinate system**. This system is formed when two number lines intersect at their zero points. This point is called the **origin**, and is labeled with an O. The horizontal number line is called the **x-axis**, and the vertical number line is called the **y-axis**.

You can name any point on a coordinate system by using an **ordered pair** of numbers. The first number is called the **x-coordinate**, and the second number is called the **y-coordinate**.

Examples 1 **Name the ordered pair for point W.**

Start at the origin. Move right along the x-axis until you are under point W. Since you moved three units to the right, the x-coordinate of the ordered pair is 3.

Now move up until you reach point W. Since you moved up 1 unit, the y-coordinate of the ordered pair is 1. The ordered pair for point W is (3, 1).

2 **Graph P(0, 2).**

Start at the origin. Since the x-coordinate is 0, do not move any units to the right on the x-axis. Move 2 units up to locate the point. Draw a dot and label the point P.

Use the grid at the right to name the point for each ordered pair.

1. (0, 4) **L**   2. (3, 6) **N**
3. (2, 1) **J**   4. (1, 8) **K**
5. (7, 5) **M**   6. (5, 3) **H**

Graph each point.

7. A(1, 5)   9. X(6, 0)
8. F(9, 2)   10. D(4, 8)

© Glencoe/McGraw-Hill   T16   Mathematics: Applications and Connections, Course 1

Reteaching the Lesson

Activity Have students use a state map and locate different cities using the letter and number pairs. Discuss the importance of being able to locate places on a map. Have students construct a map of their neighborhood and draw a grid. Have them list ordered pairs that identify neighborhood landmarks.

Error Analysis

Watch for students who go up for the x value and across for the y value.
Prevent by reminding students to go alphabetically. The **x** value is **h**orizontal. The **y** value is **v**ertical.

Use the grid at the right to name the ordered pair for each point.

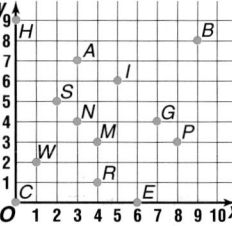

21. G **(7, 4)**   22. R **(4, 1)**

23. A **(3, 7)**   24. P **(8, 3)**

25. H **(0, 9)**   26. I **(5, 6)**

27. C **(0, 0)**   28. M **(4, 3)**

29. B **(9, 8)**   30. S **(2, 5)**

Applications and Problem Solving

31. *Art* Draw a coordinate grid. Number each axis from 0 to 20. Draw a picture on your grid. List the ordered pairs of points where sides of the drawing meet. Have a classmate draw your picture by graphing your ordered pairs and connecting the dots. **See students' work.**

32. *Cartography* The grid is a simplified version of the map of present-day Washington, D.C.

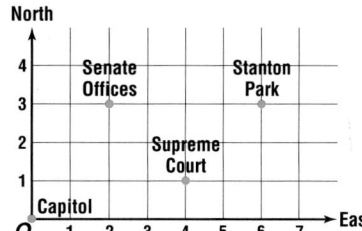

   a. Which ordered pair indicates the location of the Supreme Court? **(4, 1)**

   b. Which location does (6, 3) indicate? **Stanton Park**

34. Sample answer: 81; All the test scores except 49 are greater than the mean.

33. *Critical Thinking* Write a short paragraph that tells how graphing ordered pairs compares to graphing statistical data in bar graphs or line graphs. **See students' work.**

Mixed Review

34. *Statistics* Find the mean for the set of Tim's history test scores: 88, 90, 87, 91, 49. Why is this a misleading statistic? *(Lesson 2-8)*

35. **Standardized Test Practice** Four girls have heights of 152, 158, 164, and 168 centimeters. Which height is a reasonable average height of the girls? *(Lesson 2-7)* **C**

   A 120 cm   **B** 140 cm   **C** 160 cm

   D 180 cm   **E** 200 cm

36. *Life Science* Make a horizontal bar graph for the set of data in the chart. *(Lesson 2-3)* **See Answer Appendix.**

For **Extra Practice**, see page 562.

37. *Algebra* Solve the equation $56 \div n = 8$. *(Lesson 1-7)* **7**

Top Animal Speeds (mph)	
Antelope	61
Cheetah	70
Coyote	43
Elk	45
Gazelle	50
Gray Fox	42
Hyena	40
Lion	50
Quarterhorse	47.5
Wildebeest	50
Zebra	40

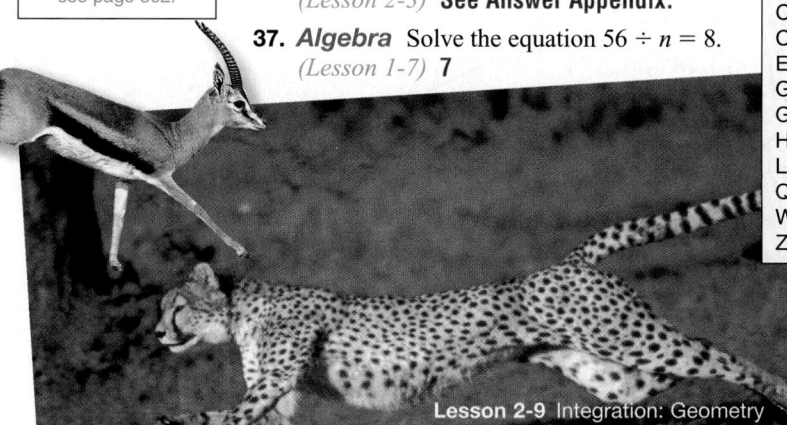

Extending the Lesson

Enrichment Masters, p. 16

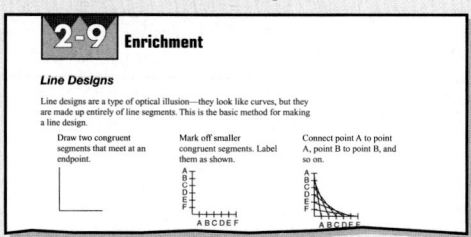

2-9 Enrichment

Line Designs

Line designs are a type of optical illusion—they look like curves, but they are made up entirely of line segments. This is the basic method for making a line design.

Activity Display these ordered pairs: (4, 1), (8, 3), (14, 6). Show students that these points lie on the same line. Then display: (6, 4), (10, 4), (20, 8), (11, 4), (2, 0), (26, 12). Have students identify which points also lie on the line. Ask students to identify a "rule" for how the x values are related to the y values.
Sample answer: $2 \cdot y - 2 = x$

Study Guide and Assessment

Vocabulary

This section provides a listing of the new terms, properties, and phrases that were introduced in this chapter. Have students define each term and provide an example or two of it, if appropriate.

Understanding and Using the Vocabulary

These exercises check students' understanding of the terms by using a variety of verbal formats including matching, completion, and true/false.

Glossaries A complete glossary of terms appears on pages 642–648. The glossary also appears in Spanish on pages 649–656.

Additional Answer

11. **Sample answer:** A bar graph represents data using rectangles to show the frequency of responses. A line graph uses dots at the frequency points connected by segments to show how data changes over time.

Vocabulary

After completing this chapter, you should be able to define each term, concept, or phrase and give an example or two of each.

Algebra
coordinate system (p. 82)
ordered pair (p. 82)
origin (p. 82)
x-axis (p. 82)
x-coordinate (p. 82)
y-axis (p. 82)
y-coordinate (p. 82)

Statistics and Probability
average (p. 71)
bar graph (p. 54)
box-and-whisker plot (p. 76)
circle graph (p. 60)
data (p. 46)
extreme value (p. 76)
frequency table (p. 46)

interval (p. 50)
leaf (p. 68)
line graph (p. 54)
lower quartile (p. 77)
mean (p. 71)
measures of central tendency (p. 71)
median (p. 71)
mode (p. 71)
range (p. 72)
scale (p. 50)
statistics (p. 46)
stem (p. 68)
stem-and-leaf plot (p. 68)
upper quartile (p. 77)

Problem Solving
use a graph (p. 58)

Understanding and Using the Vocabulary

Choose the letter of the term that best matches each phrase.

1. separates the scale into equal parts **f**
2. the sum of a set of data divided by the number of pieces of data **b**
3. a plot that uses place value to display a large data set **a**
4. the number that appears most often in a set of data **d**
5. the middle number when a set of data is arranged in numerical order **c**
6. the horizontal number line of a coordinate system **g**
7. the vertical number line of a coordinate system **i**
8. the first number in an ordered pair **h**
9. the second number in an ordered pair **j**
10. the name of a point on a coordinate system in the form (*x*-coordinate, *y*-coordinate) **e**

a. stem-and-leaf plot
b. mean
c. median
d. mode
e. ordered pair
f. interval
g. *x*-axis
h. *x*-coordinate
i. *y*-axis
j. *y*-coordinate
k. box-and-whisker plot

In Your Own Words

11. *Explain* the difference between a bar graph and a line graph. **See margin.**

86 Chapter 2 Statistics: Graphing Data

MindJogger Videoquizzes

MindJogger Videoquizzes provide an alternative review of concepts presented in this chapter. Students work in teams to answer questions, gaining points for correct answers. The questions are presented in three rounds.
Round 1 Concepts–5 questions
Round 2 Skills–4 questions
Round 3 Problem Solving–4 questions

Objectives & Examples

Upon completing this chapter, you should be able to:

● make and interpret frequency tables *(Lesson 2-1)*

Make a frequency table for this list of favorite fruits.

| banana | grapes | apple | banana |
| apple | apple | grapes | apple |

Fruit	Tally	Frequency
apples	IIII	4
bananas	II	2
grapes	II	2

● choose appropriate scales and intervals for frequency tables *(Lesson 2-2)*

Find an appropriate scale and an interval for 7, 11, 24, 9, 16, 19, and 18.

scale = 0 to 25, interval of 5

● construct bar graphs and line graphs *(Lesson 2-3)*

Number of Pets in Animal Shelter	
Season	Pets
Winter	65
Spring	75
Summer	85
Autumn	70

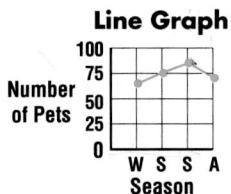

Line Graph

● interpret circle graphs *(Lesson 2-4)*

Magazine Sales by Grade

Sixth graders sold the most subscriptions, earning $906.80.

6th $906.80
7th $489.50
8th $616.75

Review Exercises

Use these exercises to review and prepare for the chapter test.

Make a frequency table for each set of data.

12. How many brothers and sisters do you have? **See Answer Appendix.**

3	1	2	0	4	1
2	1	0	1	3	1
0	2	1	3	1	0

13. What is your favorite color? **See Answer Appendix**

blue	red	pink	blue	orange
red	blue	red	red	yellow
green	blue	brown	pink	green

Choose an appropriate scale and an interval for each set of data. 15–17. See Answer Appendix.

14. 4, 7, 6, 9, 2, 3, 6 **scale = 0 to 10, interval 2**

15. 13, 38, 9, 23, 17, 43, 23

16. 16, 8, 9, 15, 10, 11, 17, 4, 7, 15

17. 138, 152, 112, 127, 173, 136, 98, 125, 145

18. Make a line graph from the data below.

Alma's Grades During Junior High	
Grade	Frequency
A	3
B	9
C	5
D	1
F	0

19. Make a vertical bar graph of the data in Exercise 18. **18–19. See Answer Appendix.**

Use the graph.

20. What is the most common race time? **42.8–54.9 minutes**

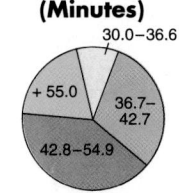

10K Race Times (Minutes)

30.0–36.6
+ 55.0
36.7–42.7
42.8–54.9

Objectives & Examples

This section reviews the skills and concepts of the chapter and shows completely worked examples.

Review Exercises

These exercises provide practice for the corresponding objectives.

Assessment and Evaluation Masters, **pp. 31–32**

Assessment and Evaluation

Six forms of Chapter 2 Test are available in the *Assessment and Evaluation Masters* as shown in the chart.

Chapter 2 Test, Form 1B, is shown at the right. Chapter 2 Test, Form 2B, is shown on the next page.

1A	Multiple Choice	Honors
1B	Multiple Choice	Average
1C	Multiple Choice	Basic
2A	Free Response	Honors
2B	Free Response	Average
2C	Free Response	Basic

Additional Answer

22.
Stem	Leaf
4	5 8
5	1 3 6
6	0 2 5 6 8
7	2 3 7 9
8	0 4

$4|5 = 45°$

Assessment and Evaluation Masters, pp. 37–38

Chapter 2 Test, Form 2B

Refer to the frequency table.

Passes Completed	
Interval	Frequency
0–4	3
5–8	6
9–12	9
13–16	8
17–20	5

1. How many players completed 9 or more passes? 1. __22__
2. Can you tell from the table if any player completed exactly 12 passes? 2. __no__
3. Can you tell from the table how many players completed 12 or fewer passes? If so, how many? 3. __yes, 18__

Points scored by five basketball players in a game: Majko, 26; Ertl, 32; Min, 11; Naylor, 8; Ben, 17
4. Make a stem-and-leaf plot for the data. 4.
Stem	Leaf
0	8
1	1 7
2	6
3	2
5. What is the range of the data? 5. __24__
6. Make a vertical bar graph showing these data. 6. Points scored

Refer to the bar graph.
7. In what month were sales the least? 7. __August__
8. How many cameras were sold in April? 8. __7__

Refer to the circle graph.
9. Which type of dessert is most popular? 9. __pie__
10. Which two types of desserts together are equal to about one half of the desserts? 10. __pie and pudding or ice cream and cake__

© Glencoe/McGraw-Hill 37 *Mathematics: Applications and Connections, Course 1*

Chapter 2 Test, Form 2B (continued)

When Tessa totaled the tips she had earned while working at Badlands Steak-a-Rama, she found she had earned $89 in July, $110 in Aug., $120 in Sept., $100 in Oct., $120 in Nov., and $97 in Dec. Use the data to find the following.
11. mean 11. __$106__
12. median 12. __$105__
13. mode 13. __$120__
14. Use the tip data above to make a line graph. 14. Tips Earned
15. Name two ways to make your graph misleading. 15. Sample answers: Make scale uneven, omit labels.
16. Does the mean, median, or mode best describe the data? 4, 20, 26, 29, 30? 16. __median__

Refer to the line graph.
17. Predict the average February temperature. 17. __15°__
18. Predict the average May temperature. 18. __45°__

Refer to the grid.

19. Name the point for the ordered pair (1, 2). 19. __F__
20. Name the ordered pair for point J. 20. __(4, 1)__

© Glencoe/McGraw-Hill 38 *Mathematics: Applications and Connections, Course 1*

Objectives & Examples

● make predictions from line graphs *(Lesson 2-5)*

Average Height for Adolescent Males

A male could be about 69 in. tall at age 17.

● construct stem-and-leaf plots *(Lesson 2-6)*

49, 58, 42, 63, 55, 42, 59, 44

Stem	Leaf
4	2 2 4 9
5	5 8 9
6	3

$4|2 = 42$

● find the mean, median, mode, and range of a set of data *(Lesson 2-7)*

117, 98, 104, 108, 104, 111

$$mean = \frac{117 + 98 + 104 + 108 + 104 + 111}{6} \text{ or } 107$$

$$median = \frac{104 + 108}{2} \text{ or } 106 \quad mode = 104$$

range = 117 − 98 or 19

● recognize when statistics and graphs are misleading *(Lesson 2-8)*

Choose the best measure of central tendency for the set $4, $4, $20, $23, $24, $27, and $30.

The median would be best. The mode is misleading because $4 is the lowest amount.

● use ordered pairs to locate points and organize data *(Lesson 2-9)*

Graph (6, 2).

Review Exercises

21. Would you expect the winning time in the year 2000 to be more or less than 2 minutes 15 seconds? **less**

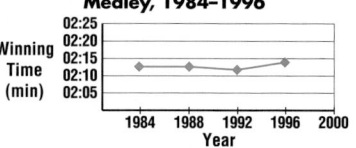

Women's 200-meter Individual Medley, 1984–1996

22. Make a stem-and-leaf plot for the following temperatures (°F). **See margin.**
60°, 53°, 68°, 72°, 66°, 80°, 73°, 51°, 62°, 48°, 56°, 84°, 77°, 45°, 79°, 65°

Use the following set of data for Exercises 23–26. 17, 31, 30, 34, 22, 26, 28, 22, 15

23. Find the mode. **22**
24. Find the median. **26**
25. Find the mean. **25**
26. Find the range. **19**

Tell whether the *mean*, *median*, or *mode* would be best to describe each set of data.

27. $10, $55, $60, $77, $79, $85, $85, $89
28. choices for Homecoming Queen **mode**
29. 81°, 84°, 85°, 87°, 88°, 90°, 91°, 98°

27. **median** 29. **mean**

Use the grid to name the point for each ordered pair.
30. (1, 4) **B** 31. (4, 1) **A**

Use the grid to name the ordered pair for each point.
32. E **(6, 0)** 33. C **(3, 6)**

Test and Review Software

You may use this software, a combination of an item generator and item bank, to create your own tests or worksheets. Types of items include free response, multiple choice, short answer, and open ended.

CD-ROM Program

The CD-ROM Program contains an Assessment Game whose questions review the concepts in this chapter.

Applications & Problem Solving

34. *Entertainment* The frequency table shows the number of hours per week sixth graders play video games. *(Lesson 2-1)*

a. In what interval did most of the responses fall? **3-4 h**

Hours Playing Video Games per Week	
0–2	10
3–4	11
5–6	5
7–8	3

b. How many people play video games less than 5 hours per week? **21 people**

35. *Television* A survey of the number of minutes a junior high student watches TV on a school day produced the following data.

95, 85, 69, 75, 90, 45,
92, 65, 50, 40, 75

Make a stem-and-leaf plot for the data. *(Lesson 2-6)* **See Answer Appendix.**

36. *Use a Graph* Was the marriage rate in 1980 higher or lower than in 1990? *(Lesson 2-3B)* **higher**

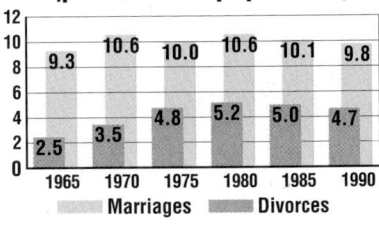

U.S. Marriage and Divorce Rates (per 1,000 of population)

Marriages: 1965: 9.3, 1970: 10.6, 1975: 10.0, 1980: 10.6, 1985: 10.1, 1990: 9.8
Divorces: 1965: 2.5, 1970: 3.5, 1975: 4.8, 1980: 5.2, 1985: 5.0, 1990: 4.7

Alternative Assessment

● Open Ended

Suppose you are the owner of a company. You want to convince a group of investors to contribute money so you can expand your business. Your monthly profits the past year are shown in the table.

January	$2,645	July	$3,200
February	$2,200	August	$2,900
March	$2,205	September	$2,050
April	$2,900	October	$1,950
May	$2,750	November	$2,400
June	$3,050	December	$3,250

Find the mean, median, and mode.

Explain how you would determine whether to present the mean, median, or mode as your "average" monthly profit. **See margin.**

A practice test for Chapter 2 is provided on page 596.

● Completing the CHAPTER Project

Use the following checklist to make sure your presentation is complete.

☑ You have included the frequency tables, bar graphs, and calculations of mean, median, and mode.

☑ The two new bar graphs show the types of pets in both classes.

☑ Your fact sheet about your favorite pet includes a picture or drawing of the pet, the cost of taking care of the pet for one year, and any other interesting facts about the pet.

PORTFOLIO Choose a topic of interest to you. Take a survey to collect data about it. Make a frequency table and a bar or line graph. Place all of these materials in your portfolio.

Applications & Problem Solving

This section provides additional practice in solving real-world problems that involve the skills of this chapter.

Alternative Assessment

The **Open Ended** section provides students with a performance assessment opportunity to evaluate their work and understanding.

CHAPTER Project

Students should complete the final stages of their project and prepare a class demonstration of their results. A scoring guide for the project is available in the *Investigations and Projects Masters*, p. 23.

PORTFOLIO Students should add to their portfolios at this time.

Assessment and Evaluation Masters, p. 41

Additional Answer for the Open Ended item

You would use the measure of tendency that shows the greatest profit. $2,625; $2,697.50; $2,900; The mode shows the greatest profit.

Performance Assessment

Additional performance assessment tasks for this chapter are included in the *Assessment and Evaluation Masters* on page 41. A scoring guide is also provided on page 53.

Chapter 2 Performance Assessment

Instructions: Demonstrate your knowledge by giving a clear, concise solution to each problem. Be sure to include all relevant drawings and to justify your answers. You may show your solutions in more than one way or investigate beyond the requirements of the problems.

1. Use the following table to answer each question.

Planet	Average Distance from Sun
Mercury	36,000,000 miles
Earth	93,003,000 miles
Jupiter	483,900,000 miles
Neptune	2,796,700,000 miles

a. Draw a misleading graph of the average distances from the Sun to the planets listed above.

b. Did you draw a pictograph, bar graph, or line graph? Why?

c. Why is the graph misleading?

d. Tell how to change the graph so that it is not misleading.

e. Tell why a circle graph would be inappropriate for this data.

f. Predict the average distance from the Sun to Venus. Venus is between Mercury and Earth. Check your prediction in an encyclopedia.

2. The scores in the Indianapolis Golf Tournament were 71, 73, 66, 75, 71, 82, 69, 72, 74, 64, 77, 71, 73, 70, 78, and 69.

a. Find the mean, median, and mode for the set of golf scores. Round to the nearest tenth.

b. These measures are said to be measures of central tendency. Explain in your own words what a measure of central tendency is.

c. Tell what a stem-and-leaf plot is. Make one for the golf data.

d. Choose a scale and interval and form a frequency table for the set of golf scores. Label your table.

e. List the ordered pairs you would use to graph the data.

f. Construct a line graph for the data in your table. Label your graph.

g. Tell what the line graph shows.

© Glencoe/McGraw-Hill   41   *Mathematics: Applications and Connections, Course 1*

The Standardized Test Practice may be used to help students prepare for standardized tests. The test items are written in the same style as those in state proficiency tests and standardized tests like CAT, CTBS, ITBS, MAT, SAT, and Terra Nova. The test items cover skills and concepts covered up to this point in the text.

The pages can be used as an overnight assessment. After students have completed the pages, discuss how each problem can be solved, or provide copies of the solutions from the *Solutions Manual*.

Assessment and Evaluation Masters, p. 47

Section One: Multiple Choice

There are twelve multiple-choice questions in this section. Choose the best answer. If a correct answer is *not here,* mark the letter for Not Here.

1. How is the product $3 \times 3 \times 5 \times 5 \times 7$ expressed in exponential notation? **D**
   - A $3 \times 3 \times 5 \times 5 \times 7$
   - B $3 \times 3 \times 5^2 \times 7$
   - C $3^2 \times 5 \times 5 \times 7$
   - D $3^2 \times 5^2 \times 7$

2. What is the value of $8 + 6 \times 10$? **F**
   - F 68
   - G 120
   - H 140
   - J 480

3. If $n = 4$, $m = 3$, and $x = 12$, what is the value of $x \cdot m + n$? **B**
   - A 19
   - B 40
   - C 24
   - D 84

4. Which average would be best to describe this data? **H**
   $$195, 188, 70, 185, 190$$
   - F range
   - G mean
   - H median
   - J mode

5. Evaluate the expression $c - b$ if $c = 9$ and $b = 3$. **B**
   - A 3
   - B 6
   - C 9
   - D 12

90 Chapters 1–2 Standardized Test Practice

6. Minato found 5 seashells. His friend Soto gave him some more, and then he had 10. To find out how many seashells he was given, Minato wrote $x + 5 = 10$. What is the value of x? **G**
   - F 2
   - G 5
   - H 15
   - J 35

Please note that Questions 7–12 have five answer choices.

7. Three chimpanzees weigh 62, 75, and 72 pounds. Which weight is a reasonable average weight of the chimpanzees? **C**
   - A 80 lb
   - B 75 lb
   - C 70 lb
   - D 65 lb
   - E 60 lb

8. The graph shows the number of visitors who toured Gund Arena on Saturday.

   How many people altogether toured the arena before 3:00 P.M.? **J**
   - F 275
   - G 350
   - H 400
   - J 500
   - K 550

◀◀◀ Instructional Resources

Another cumulative review is shown at the left and is available in the *Assessment and Evaluation Masters,* p. 47.

9. Jason bought 6 hockey tickets that ranged in price from $7 to $10. Which is a reasonable cost for all 6 tickets? **C**

  A $25

  B $40

  C $54

  D $70

  E $85

10. Serena's scout troop collected 4,230 aluminum cans for a service project. Scott's class collected 3,348 cans. How many more cans did Serena's scout troop collect than Scott's class? **H**

  F 756

  G 880

  H 882

  J 892

  K Not Here

11. The base price of a mini-van is $18,876. With an air conditioner, the mini-van costs $678 more. What is the price of the mini-van with an air conditioner? **E**

  A $19,454

  B $19,444

  C $18,954

  D $18,198

  E Not Here

12. Every class that sells 400 tickets to the school carnival earns a bowling party. Kylie's class sold 209 tickets. How many more tickets must her class sell to earn the bowling party? **H**

  F 101

  G 181

  H 191

  J 211

  K Not Here

Test-Taking Tip ◆ THE PRINCETON REVIEW

You may be able to eliminate all or most of the answer choices by estimating. Also, look to see which answer choices are not reasonable for the information given in the problem.

Section Two: Free Response

This section contains four questions for which you will provide short answers. Write your answers on your paper.

13. Translate the sentence into an equation and solve. $7 + r = 22$; **15**
  The sum of 7 and r is equal to 22.

14. Find the mode, median, and mean for the set of data. 72, 68, 59, 83, 74, 52
  no mode; 70,68

15. If $14 + p = 39$, what is the value of p? **25**

16. The line graph shows the number of houses sold in Mentor and Medina from 1960 to 1990.

House Sales

About how many more houses were sold in Mentor than in Medina in 1980? **75**

interNET CONNECTION Test Practice **For additional test practice questions, visit:** www.glencoe.com/sec/math/mac/mathnet

---

Assessment and Evaluation Masters, pp. 45–46

CHAPTER 3

Adding and Subtracting Decimals

Previewing the Chapter

Overview

This chapter explores comparing, ordering, adding, and subtracting decimals through ten-thousandths. Students learn to measure length in metric units and to estimate decimal sums and differences using rounding and clustering. Students also learn to determine whether answers to problems are reasonable.

Lesson (pages)	Lesson Objectives	NCTM Standards 2000	Standardized Tests	State/Local Objectives
3-1A (94)	Model decimals through hundredths.	1, 6–10	CTBS, TN	
3-1 (95–98)	Model, read, and write decimals.	1, 4, 6–10	CTBS, MAT, TN	
3-2A (100–101)	Measure length in metric units.	1, 4, 6–10	CAT	
3-2 (102–104)	Show relationships among metric units of length and measure line segments.	1, 3, 4, 6–10	CAT, MAT	
3-3 (105–108)	Compare decimals and order a set of decimals.	1, 3, 5–10	ITBS, MAT, SAT	
3-4 (109–111)	Round decimals.	1, 3, 4, 6–10	CTBS, ITBS, SAT, TN	
3-5 (112–115)	Estimate decimal sums and differences.	1, 6–10	CAT, CTBS, ITBS, SAT, TN	
3-6A (116–117)	Determine whether answers to problems are reasonable.	1, 6–10	CTBS, MAT, SAT, TN	
3-6 (118–121)	Add and subtract decimals.	1, 4, 6–10	CAT, CTBS, ITBS, MAT, SAT, TN	

CAT = California Achievement Tests, CTBS = Comprehensive Tests of Basic Skills, ITBS = Iowa Tests of Basic Skills, MAT = Metropolitan Achievement Tests, SAT = Stanford Achievement Tests, TN = Terra Nova
For the key to numbering of NCTM Standards 2000, see page T6.

The **Interactive Lesson Planner** contains all of the blackline masters and transparencies. This CD-ROM also includes an easy-to-use lesson planning calendar.

LESSON PLANNING GUIDE

Lesson	Extra Practice (Student Edition)	BLACKLINE MASTERS (PAGE NUMBERS)										Transparencies A and B
		Study Guide	Practice	Enrichment	Assessment & Evaluation	Classroom Games	Diversity	Hands-On Lab	School to Career	Science and Math Lab Manual	Technology	
3-1A								41				
3-1	p. 563	17	17	17								3-1
3-2A								42				
3-2	p. 563	18	18	18	71							3-2
3-3	p. 563	19	19	19	70, 71			71			6	3-3
3-4	p. 564	20	20	20			3					3-4
3-5	p. 564	21	21	21	72							3-5
3-6A	p. 564											
3-6	p. 565	22	22	22	72	5–6				3	5	3-6
Study Guide/ Assessment					57–69, 73–75							

OTHER CHAPTER RESOURCES

Student Edition

Chapter Project, pp. 93, 115, 120, 125
Math in the Media, p. 98
School to Career, p. 99
Let the Games Begin, p. 121

Technology

MathPASS CD-ROM
Interactive Mathematics Tools Software

Teacher's Classroom Resources

Applications
Family Letters and Activities, pp. 5–6
Investigations and Projects Masters, pp. 25–28
Meeting Individual Needs
Transition Booklet, pp. 5–8, 11–20, 29–30
Investigations for the Special Education Student, p. 7

Teaching Aids
Answer Key Masters
Block Scheduling Booklet
Lesson Planning Guide
Solutions Manual

Professional Publications
Glencoe Mathematics Professional Series

Planning the Chapter

 MindJogger Videoquizzes provide a unique format for reviewing concepts presented in the chapter.

ASSESSMENT RESOURCES

Student Edition
Mixed Review, pp. 98, 104, 108, 111, 115, 121
Mid-Chapter Self Test, p. 111
Math Journal, pp. 114, 119
Study Guide and Assessment, pp. 122–125
Performance Task, p. 125
Portfolio Suggestion, p.125
Standardized Test Practice, pp. 126–127
Chapter Test, p. 597

Assessment and Evaluation Masters
Multiple-Choice Tests (Forms 1A, 1B, 1C), pp. 57–62
Free-Response Tests (Forms 2A, 2B, 2C), pp. 63–68
Performance Assessment, p. 69
Mid-Chapter Test, p. 70
Quizzes A–D, pp. 71–72
Standardized Test Practice, pp. 73–74
Cumulative Review, p. 75

Teacher's Wraparound Edition
5-Minute Check, pp. 95, 102, 105, 109, 112, 118
Building Portfolios, p. 92
Math Journal, pp. 94, 101
Closing Activity, pp. 98, 104, 108, 111, 115, 117, 121

Technology
Test and Review Software
MindJogger Videoquizzes
CD-ROM Program

MATERIALS AND MANIPULATIVES

Lesson 3-1A
base-ten blocks*

Lesson 3-1
base-ten blocks*

Lesson 3-2A
tape measure*

Lesson 3-2
tape measure*

Lesson 3-3
grid paper†
marker

Lesson 3-6
meterstick
number cubes*
spinners*†
counters*†

*Glencoe Manipulative Kit

†Glencoe Overhead Manipulative Resources

PACING CHART

See pages T25–T27 for the Course Planning Calendar.

COURSE	DAY 1	DAY 2	DAY 3	DAY 4	DAY 5	DAY 6	DAY 7
Standard	Chapter Project	Lessons 3-1A & 3-1		Lessons 3-2A & 3-2		Lesson 3-3	Lesson 3-4
Honors	Chapter Project	Lesson 3-1	Lesson 3-2	Lesson 3-3	Lesson 3-4	Lesson 3-5	Lesson 3-6A
Block	Chapter Project & Lesson 3-1A	Lessons 3-1 & 3-2A	Lessons 3-2 & 3-3	Lessons 3-4 & 3-5	Lessons 3-6A & 3-6	Study Guide and Assessment, Chapter Test	

The *Transition Booklet* (Skills 1–2, 4–8, 13) can be used to practice basic operations with whole numbers and review measuring length.

Interactive Mathematics:
Activities and Investigations

is an activity-based program that may be used as an enhancement for chapters in **Mathematics: Applications and Connections.**

Unit 12, Activity One,
Mall Measures
Use with Lesson 3-2.

Summary Students work individually in groups to develop their own unit of linear measure and a system for using that unit to measure objects.

Math Connection Students use what they know about units of length and systems of measurement to create the "rules" for their new system of measure.

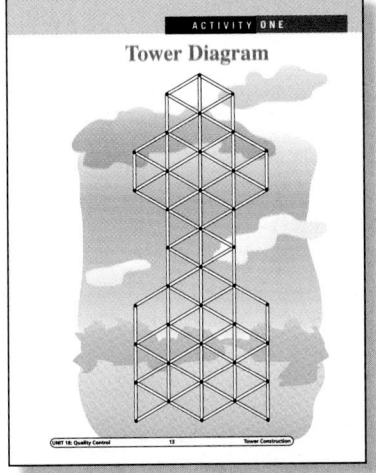

Unit 18, Activity One
Use with Lesson 3-6A.

Summary Students work in groups as construction contractors. Each group estimates the time and amount of raw materials needed to build a tower. Then they construct a tower, record the amount of time it took to build the tower, and write a report.

Math Connection Students use estimation, measurement, geometry, spatial visualization, and accuracy to estimate how many construction materials are needed to build a tower. At every stage they need to determine how reasonable their measurements are.

DAY 8	DAY 9	DAY 10	DAY 11	DAY 12	DAY 13	DAY 14	DAY 15
Lesson 3-5	Lesson 3-6A	Lesson 3-6	Study Guide and Assessment	Chapter Test			
Lesson 3-6	Study Guide and Assessment	Chapter Test					

Enhancing the Chapter

APPLICATIONS

Classroom Games, pp. 5–6

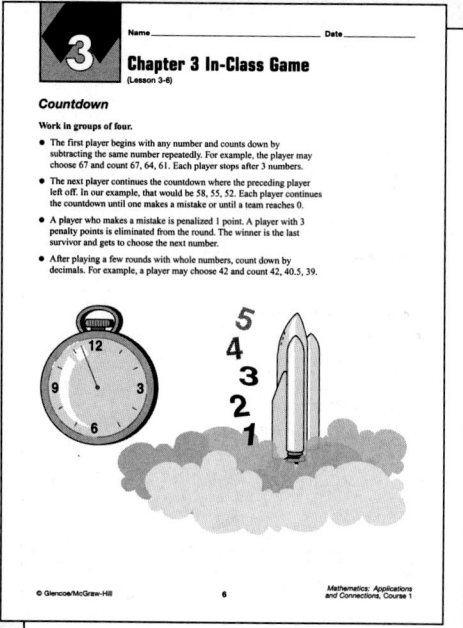

Chapter 3 In-Class Game
(Lesson 3-6)

Countdown

Work in groups of four.

- The first player begins with any number and counts down by subtracting the same number repeatedly. For example, the player may choose 67 and count 67, 64, 61. Each player stops after 3 numbers.
- The next player continues the countdown where the preceding player left off. In our example, that would be 58, 55, 52. Each player continues the countdown until one makes a mistake or until a team reaches 0.
- A player who makes a mistake is penalized 1 point. A player with 3 penalty points is eliminated from the round. The winner is the last survivor and gets to choose the next number.
- After playing a few rounds with whole numbers, count down by decimals. For example, a player may choose 42 and count 42, 40.5, 39.

Diversity Masters, p. 3

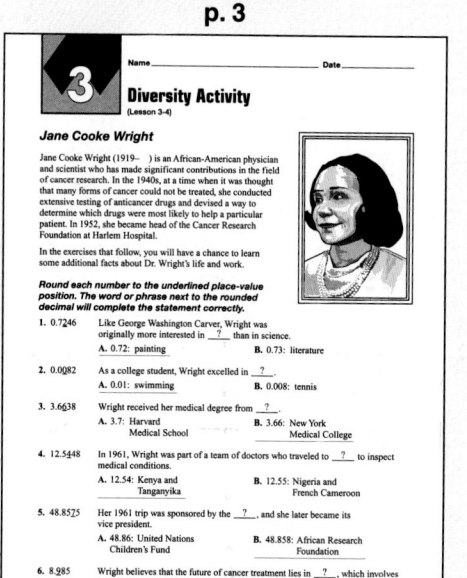

Diversity Activity
(Lesson 3-4)

Jane Cooke Wright

Jane Cooke Wright (1919–) is an African-American physician and scientist who has made significant contributions in the field of cancer research. In the 1940s, at a time when it was thought that many forms of cancer could not be treated, she conducted extensive testing of anticancer drugs and devised a way to determine which drugs were most likely to help a particular patient. In 1952, she became head of the Cancer Research Foundation at Harlem Hospital.

In the exercises that follow, you will have a chance to learn some additional facts about Dr. Wright's life and work.

Round each number to the underlined place-value position. The word or phrase next to the rounded decimal will complete the statement correctly.

1. 0.7246   Like George Washington Carver, Wright was originally more interested in __?__ than in science.
   A. 0.72: painting   B. 0.73: literature

2. 0.0082   As a college student, Wright excelled in __?__.
   A. 0.01: swimming   B. 0.008: tennis

3. 3.6638   Wright received her medical degree from __?__.
   A. 3.7: Harvard Medical School   B. 3.66: New York Medical College

4. 12.5448   In 1961, Wright was part of a team of doctors who traveled to __?__ to inspect medical conditions.
   A. 12.54: Kenya and Tanganyika   B. 12.55: Nigeria and French Cameroon

5. 48.8575   Her 1961 trip was sponsored by the __?__, and she later became its vice president.
   A. 48.86: United Nations Children's Fund   B. 48.858: African Research Foundation

6. 8.985   Wright believes that the future of cancer treatment lies in __?__, which involves treating patients with a combination of drugs rather than a single drug.
   A. 8.99: polychromy   B. 9.0: polychemotherapy

School to Career Masters, p. 3

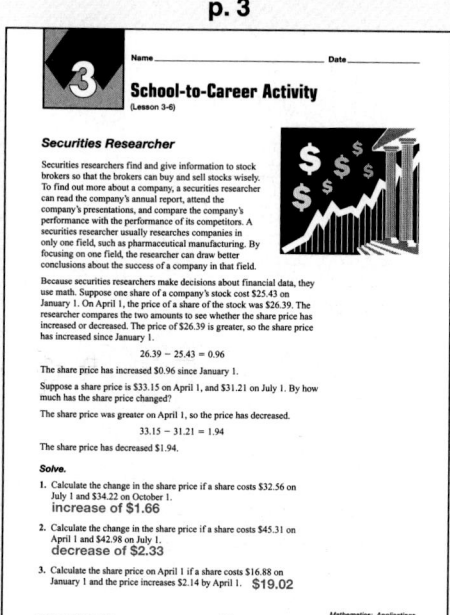

School-to-Career Activity
(Lesson 3-6)

Securities Researcher

Securities researchers find and give information to stock brokers so that the brokers can buy and sell stocks wisely. To find out more about a company, a securities researcher can read the company's annual report, attend the company's presentations, and compare the company's performance with the performance of its competitors. A securities researcher usually researches companies in only one field, such as pharmaceutical manufacturing. By focusing on one field, the researcher can draw better conclusions about the success of a company in that field.

Because securities researchers make decisions about financial data, they use math. Suppose one share of a company's stock cost $25.43 on January 1. On April 1, the price of a share of the stock was $26.39. The researcher compares the two amounts to see whether the share price has increased or decreased. The price of $26.39 is greater, so the share price has increased since January 1.

$$26.39 - 25.43 = 0.96$$

The share price has increased $0.96 since January 1.

Suppose a share price is $33.15 on April 1, and $31.21 on July 1. By how much has the share price changed?

The share price was greater on April 1, so the price has decreased.

$$33.15 - 31.21 = 1.94$$

The share price has decreased $1.94.

Solve.

1. Calculate the change in the share price if a share costs $32.56 on July 1 and $34.22 on October 1.
   increase of $1.66

2. Calculate the change in the share price if a share costs $45.31 on April 1 and $42.98 on July 1.
   decrease of $2.33

3. Calculate the share price on April 1 if a share costs $16.88 on January 1 and the price increases $2.14 by April 1. **$19.02**

Family Letters and Activities, pp. 5–6

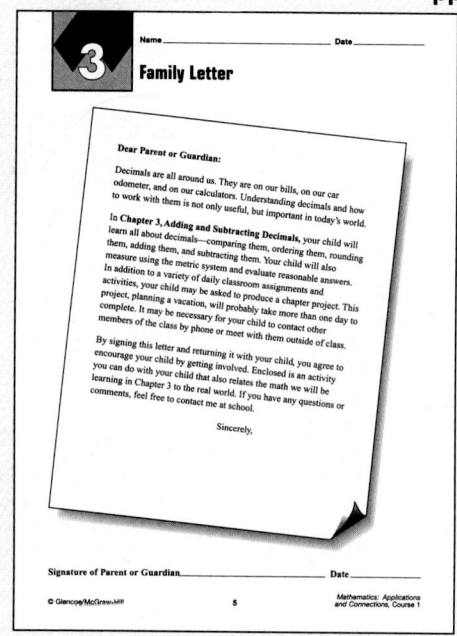

Family Letter

Dear Parent or Guardian:

Decimals are all around us. They are on our bills, on our car odometer, and on our calculators. Understanding decimals and how to work with them is not only useful, but important in today's world.

In **Chapter 3, Adding and Subtracting Decimals**, your child will learn all about decimals—comparing them, ordering them, rounding them, adding them, and subtracting them. Your child will also measure using the metric system and evaluate reasonable answers. In addition to a variety of daily classroom assignments and activities, your child may be asked to produce a chapter project. This project, planning a vacation, will probably take more than one day to complete. It may be necessary for your child to contact other members of the class by phone or meet with them outside of class.

By signing this letter and returning it with your child, you agree to encourage your child by getting involved. Enclosed is an activity you can do with your child that also relates the math we will be learning in Chapter 3 to the real world. If you have any questions or comments, feel free to contact me at school.

Sincerely,

Signature of Parent or Guardian _____ Date _____

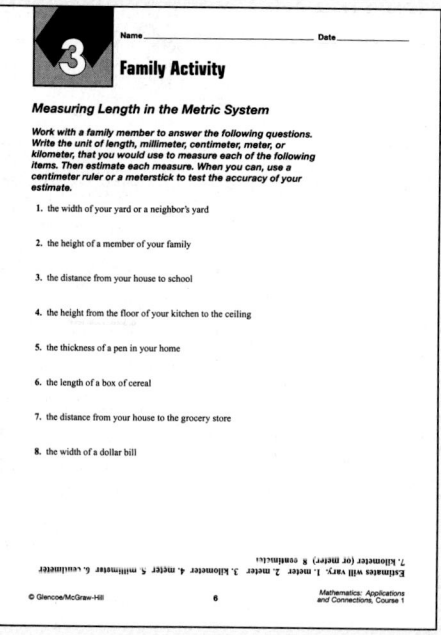

Family Activity

Measuring Length in the Metric System

Work with a family member to answer the following questions. Write the unit of length, millimeter, centimeter, meter, or kilometer, that you would use to measure each of the following items. Then estimate each measure. When you can, use a centimeter ruler or a meterstick to test the accuracy of your estimate.

1. the width of your yard or a neighbor's yard

2. the height of a member of your family

3. the distance from your house to school

4. the height from the floor of your kitchen to the ceiling

5. the thickness of a pen in your home

6. the length of a box of cereal

7. the distance from your house to the grocery store

8. the width of a dollar bill

Estimates will vary. 1. meter 2. meter 3. kilometer 4. meter 5. millimeter 6. centimeter 7. kilometer (or meter) 8. centimeter

92e   Chapter 3

MANIPULATIVES/MODELING

Hands-On Lab Masters, p. 71

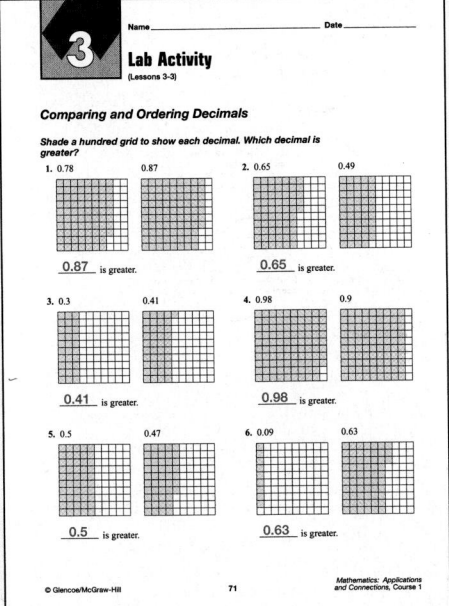

ASSESSMENT/EVALUATION

Assessment and Evaluation Masters, pp. 70–72

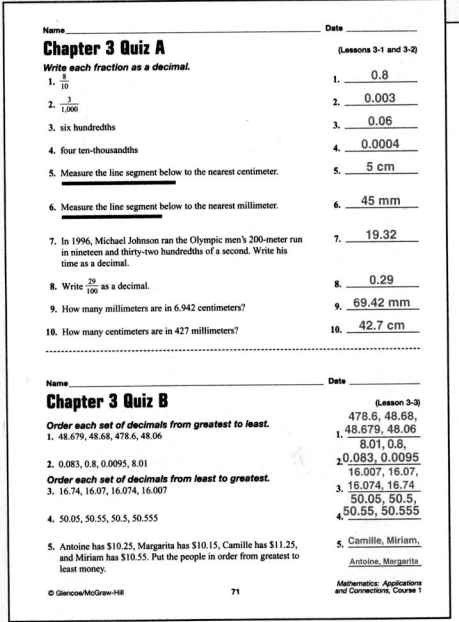

TECHNOLOGY/MULTIMEDIA

Technology Masters, pp. 5–6

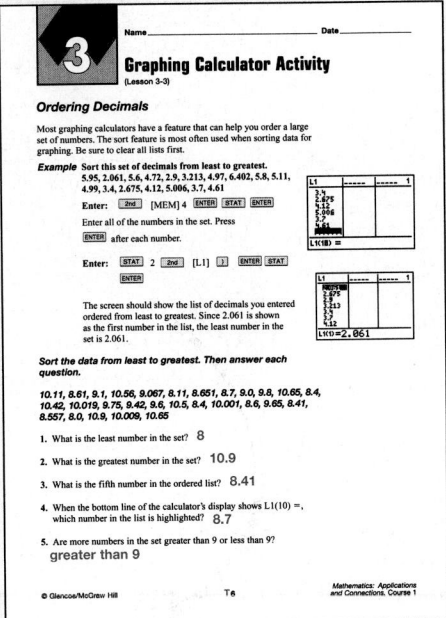

MEETING INDIVIDUAL NEEDS

Investigations for the Special Education Student, p. 7

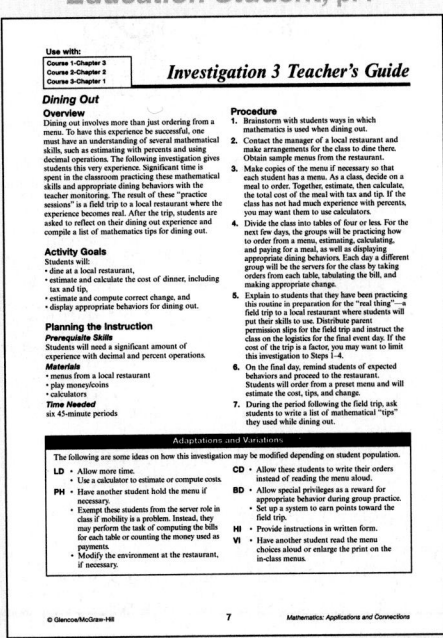

Theme: Travel

One of the most important parts of vacation planning is transportation.

It is a five- or six-hour flight from the West Coast to Honolulu International Airport. The flights may continue on to other islands, but just as often, students will need to arrange separate, inter-island flights. How much money each student spends on transportation depends on many factors, including how many people are in the party and how far in advance the ticket is purchased.

Question of the Day Caitlin, her brother, and her grandparents are flying to Hawaii from New York. Each ticket is $986.50, and additional tax is $47.81 per ticket. Estimate the cost for Caitlin's family to fly to Hawaii. **$4,200** Then use a calculator to find the exact cost. **$4,137.24**

Assess Prerequisite Skills

Ask students to read through the list of objectives presented in "What you'll learn in Chapter 3." You may wish to ask them what each of the objectives means or if they have experienced any of these types of problems before.

 Building Portfolios

Encourage students to revise their portfolios as they study this chapter. They may find some lessons more challenging than others and wish to include work that shows how they have improved their mathematical skills.

 Math and the Family

In the *Family Letters and Activities* booklet (pp. 5–6), you will find a letter to the parents explaining what students will study in Chapter 3. An activity appropriate for the whole family is also available.

CHAPTER 3 Adding and Subtracting Decimals

What you'll learn in Chapter 3

- to model, read, write, compare, order, and round decimals,
- to show relationships between metric units of length and estimate and measure line segments,
- to determine whether answers are reasonable, and
- to estimate and find sums and differences of decimals.

 CD-ROM Program

Activities for Chapter 3
- Chapter 3 Introduction
- Interactive Lessons 3-1A, 3-3
- Assessment Game
- Resource Lessons 3-1 through 3-6

CHAPTER Project

VACATION DESTINATION

In this project, you will add and subtract decimals to help you plan a one- or two-week vacation for your family. You will need to research the cost of transportation, lodging, food, and admission to any tourist attractions that you want to visit.

Getting Started

- Look at the table. Estimate the cost for two adults and two children to attend each of the three tours. Make a bar graph to compare your estimates.
- How could you estimate the cost for 4 people to attend the Hawaiian Luau?

Costs for Selected Activities on Maui, Hawaii

Activity	Costs	
Whale Watching Tour	$27.50 (adult, over 12)	$15.00 (children, 12 and under)
Tropical Plantation Tour	$8.50 (adult, over 12)	$3.50 (children, 12 and under)
Bike Tour from Haleakala Crater	$59.00 (basic, all ages)	$99.00 (deluxe, all ages)
Snorkeling Cruise to Molokini	$33.00 (afternoon, all ages)	$39.95 (morning, all ages)
Hawaiian Luau	$44.95 (all ages)	
Parasailing	$29.95 (morning, all ages)	$39.95 (anytime, all ages)

Technology Tips

- Use a **spreadsheet** to find the cost of your vacation.
- Use **computer software** to help you make graphs.
- Use a **word processor**.

 inter NET CONNECTION Research For up-to-date information on family vacations, visit:

www.glencoe.com/sec/math/mac/mathnet

Working on the Project

You can use what you'll learn in Chapter 3 to help you make your plans.

Page	Exercise
115	35
120	34
125	Alternative Assessment

Instructional Resources ▶▶▶
A recording sheet to help students organize their data for the Chapter Project is shown at the right and is available in the *Investigations and Projects Masters*, p. 28.

CHAPTER Project
N O T E S

Objectives Students should
- understand rounding, estimating, adding, and subtracting decimals.
- be able to solve problems using decimals.

Project Pointer You may suggest that students begin a *Project Folder* to keep their work as they complete each stage of the Chapter Project. The completed project may also be added to their portfolios.

Students who use computer software for their graphs should think carefully about their scale so that the graph is not misleading. You may want them to sketch a graph on paper first, so that they know what a reasonable graph will be for their data.

Using the Table Students need to be careful reading the table. Some of the costs are different by age and some are not. Students may want to explore why that difference exists. Also, they may want to investigate why some activities are less expensive during certain times of the day. Emphasize that all costs are per person.

***Investigations and Projects Masters*, p. 28**

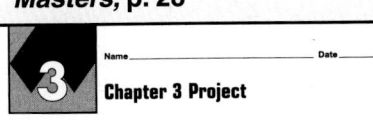

GET READY

Objective Students model decimals through hundredths.

Optional Resources
Hands-On Lab Masters
• base-ten models, p. 1
• worksheet, p. 41

Overhead Manipulative Resources
• decimal models

Manipulative Kit
• base-ten blocks
CD-ROM Program
• Interactive Lesson 3-1A

MANAGEMENT TIPS

Recommended Time
30 minutes

Getting Started Have students read the first paragraph and identify the base-ten models. Lead them to think of the ones block shown as a ones block that has been divided into 100 equal parts. Then ask the following questions.
• How would you describe the tenths and hundredths blocks?
• When would you use these numbers?

Activities 1 and 2 involve trading tenths blocks and hundredths blocks. When modeling the trade for students, have them describe your actions and justify the trade of tenths for hundredths. Have them determine the result before counting the hundredths.

ASSESS

Before modeling Exercises 1–3, encourage students to predict the answers. Have them describe their prediction methods. Discuss whether their predictions were right or wrong and why.

Use Exercise 4 to determine whether students understand modeling decimals with base-ten blocks.

COOPERATIVE LEARNING

, base-ten blocks

3-1A Decimals Through Hundredths

A Preview of Lesson 3-1

You know that base-ten blocks can be used to model whole numbers. Did you know that they can also be used to model decimals? For decimals, the blocks have the meanings shown at the right.

ones   tenths   hundredths

TRY THIS

Work in groups of four.

1 Model three tenths by using base-ten blocks.

• You can also model three tenths by trading the tenths for hundredths. How many hundredths are there?

2 Show four tenths and seven hundredths with base-ten blocks. What decimal have you modeled?

• Trade the tenths for hundredths and count the hundredths blocks.

• There are 47 blocks, so 47 hundredths is the decimal modeled.

ON YOUR OWN

1. Three tenths is the same as how many hundredths? **thirty hundredths**
2. Show six tenths and four hundredths with base-ten blocks. Trade the tenths for hundredths. How many hundredths do you have now? **See margin.**
3. How many tenths are the same as ninety hundredths? Model using base-ten blocks. **9 tenths; See Answer Appendix for model.**
4. *Look Ahead* If you separated a hundredth block into 100 equal parts, what decimal would be modeled by seventeen of the new parts? **17 ten-thousandths**

94 Chapter 3 Adding and Subtracting Decimals

Additional Answer
2. See students' work; 64 hundredths

 Math Journal Have students write a description of how base-ten blocks can be used to model decimals. Make sure the description is detailed enough so that they can use it as a reference later.

Decimals Through Ten-Thousandths

What you'll learn

You'll learn to model, read, and write decimals.

When am I ever going to use this?

You can use decimals to record winning times at a track meet.

Word Wise
place value

Did you know The duration of the average blink is about three tenths of a second.

Close your eyes and then open and close them as fast as you can. You have just modeled what happens when a camera takes a picture. The time a 35-millimeter camera's shutter stays open can range from a second to less than a millisecond.

A millisecond is $\frac{1}{1,000}$ of a second. What are some other ways to express $\frac{1}{1,000}$?

Decimals are another way to write fractions when the denominators are 10, 100, 1,000, and so on. We use **place-value** positions to name decimals.

In a decimal, the decimal point separates the ones place and the tenths place. The fraction $\frac{1}{1,000}$ can be written as the decimal 0.001 or in words as *one-thousandth*.

ones	tenths	hundredths	thousandths
0 •	0	0	1

Example

INTEGRATION ① **Statistics** Charmaine asked 100 students at Western Hills Middle School to identify their favorite animal. 42 out of 100 or $\frac{42}{100}$ said their favorite animal is a dog.

a. Model the decimal for $\frac{42}{100}$.

Display forty-two hundredths blocks. Trade forty blocks for four tenths blocks.

$\frac{42}{100}$

b. Write the decimal in a place-value chart.

There are four tenths and two hundredths in the model. Write 4 in the tenths place and 2 in the hundredths place.

ones	tenths	hundredths
0 •	4	2

c. Write the decimal in words.

Notice that the last digit, 2, is in the hundredths place. The decimal in words is *forty-two hundredths*.

Lesson 3-1 Decimals Through Ten-Thousandths **95**

Instructional Resources

- *Study Guide Masters,* p. 17
- *Practice Masters,* p. 17
- *Enrichment Masters,* p. 17
- Transparencies 3-1, A and B
- CD-ROM Program
  - Resource Lesson 3-1

Recommended Pacing	
Standard	Days 2 & 3 of 12
Honors	Day 2 of 10
Block	Day 2 of 6

1 FOCUS

5-Minute Check
(Chapter 2)

Refer to the table for Exercises 1–3.

Camcorder Prices	
1988	$1,025
1989	$750
1990	$880
1991	$1,060
1992	$1,150

1. What did the camcorder cost in 1992? **$1,150**

2. Find the mean, median, and mode of the prices. **$973; $1,025; no mode**

3. Make a line graph for the data in the table.

 The 5-Minute Check is also available on **Transparency 3-1A** for this lesson.

✳ Cross-Curriculum Cue

Inform the teachers on your team that your students are studying decimals. Suggestions for curriculum integration are:
Health: body temperature
Geography: distance
Earth Science: precipitation
Physical Education: speed

Multiple Learning Styles

Interpersonal Have small groups of students play "Decimal Match-Ups." Use two sets of matching cards (decimals and word names). Set a timer and challenge students to match as many cards as possible before time runs out.

Motivating the Lesson

Hands-On Activity Have students create designs using centimeter grid paper and colored markers or crayons. Give them directions for coloring such as, *Color six hundredths red.*

2 TEACH

 Transparency 3-1B contains a teaching aid for this lesson.

Reading Mathematics When looking at part c of Example 1, point out that when reading a decimal, the last digit gives the place-value name.

In-Class Examples

For Example 1
One hundred birds live in a bird sanctuary. Fifteen are parrots.
a. Write the decimal for the model. **0.15**

b. Write the decimal in a place-value chart.

c. Write the decimal in words. **fifteen hundredths**

For Example 2
a. Model the decimal for $1\frac{3}{10}$.

b. Write the decimal in a place-value chart.

c. Write the decimal in words. **one and three tenths**

You can also write mixed numbers, such as $3\frac{7}{10}$, as decimals.

Example 2

a. Model the decimal for $3\frac{7}{10}$.

b. Write the decimal in a place-value chart.

c. Write the decimal in words.

a. Display three ones and seven tenths blocks.

Study Hint

Reading Math The mixed number $3\frac{7}{10}$ is read as *three and seven tenths*. The number 3.7 is also read as *three and seven tenths*.

b. Write 3 in the ones place and 7 in the tenths place.

c. The decimal is *three and seven tenths*.

To write very small decimals, you can extend the place-value chart farther to the right.

Example 3

CONNECTION

Life Science The egg of the Vervain hummingbird weighs about $\frac{128}{10,000}$ ounce.

a. Write this fraction as a decimal in a place-value chart.

b. Write the decimal in words.

a.

b. The last digit, 8, is in the ten-thousandths place. So the decimal is *one hundred twenty-eight ten-thousandths*.

Classroom Vignette

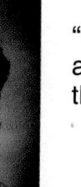

"We have fun using a Koosh ball to represent a decimal point and acting out decimal numbers as I or another student read them out."

Patricia A. Maestranzi, Teacher
Woodbury School
Salem, NH

Patricia A. Maestranzi

Communicating Mathematics

Read and study the lesson to answer each question.

1. *Write* the fraction, decimal, and word name for the decimal shown by the model. **0.05, $\frac{5}{100}$, five hundredths**

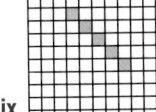

3. Mercedes is correct because the last digit, 8, is in the thousandths place.

2. *Draw* a model for 2.25. **See Answer Appendix.**

3. *You Decide* Elizabeth says that thirty-eight thousandths is written as 0.0038. Mercedes says that it is written as 0.038. Who is correct? Explain.

Guided Practice

Write each fraction or mixed number as a decimal.

4. $\frac{9}{10}$ **0.9**   5. $\frac{43}{100}$ **0.43**   6. $\frac{563}{1,000}$ **0.563**   7. $4\frac{29}{10,000}$ **4.0029**

8. Write four and three tenths as a decimal. **4.3**

9. Write seven hundred two ten-thousandths as a decimal. **0.0702**

10. *Auto Racing* In 1996, Buddy Lazier of Vail, Colorado, won the Indianapolis 500 with an average speed of one hundred forty-seven and nine hundred fifty-six thousandths miles per hour. Write the speed as a decimal. **147.956 mph**

Practice

Write each fraction or mixed number as a decimal.

19. 47.047
20. 3.0027
21. 172.0001

11. $\frac{3}{10}$ **0.3**   12. $\frac{99}{100}$ **0.99**   13. $\frac{7}{100}$ **0.07**   14. $10\frac{1}{10}$ **10.1**

15. $19\frac{53}{100}$ **19.53**   16. $\frac{375}{1,000}$ **0.375**   17. $\frac{9}{1,000}$ **0.009**   18. $\frac{5,561}{10,000}$ **0.5651**

19. $47\frac{47}{1,000}$ 20. $3\frac{27}{10,000}$ 21. $172\frac{1}{10,000}$ 22. $\frac{2,384}{1,000}$ **2.384**

Write each expression as a decimal.

23. twenty and nine tenths **20.9**

24. eleven hundredths **0.11**

25. three and three thousandths **3.003**

26. one hundred nine and fifteen thousandths **109.015**

27. eight hundred one ten-thousandths **0.0801**

28. 610.0306

28. six hundred ten and three hundred six ten-thousandths

Applications and Problem Solving

29. *Industrial Technology* A micrometer caliper is a device used to measure the thickness of an object. Many metric micrometer calipers can measure to one hundredth of a millimeter. Write one hundredth as a decimal. **0.01**

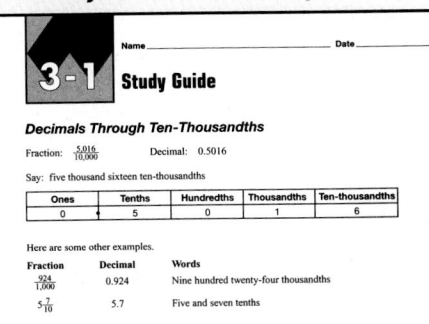

Lesson 3-1 Decimals Through Ten-Thousandths **97**

■ Reteaching the Lesson ■

Activity Display a place-value chart on an overhead transparency. Write a decimal in the place-value chart. Have students model the decimal using base-ten blocks. Students may also work in pairs to challenge each other with decimals to model.

In-Class Example

For Example 3

A hockey rink is about $\frac{379}{10,000}$ of a mile long.

a. Write the fraction as a decimal in a place-value chart.

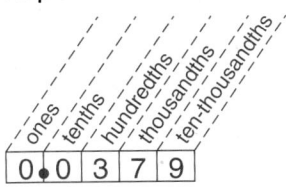

ones	tenths	hundredths	thousandths	ten-thousandths
0 • 0	3	7	9	

b. Write the decimal in words. **three hundred seventy-nine ten-thousandths**

3 PRACTICE/APPLY

Check for Understanding

If students need additional practice or instruction after completing Exercises 1–10, you may find one of the following options helpful.

• Extra Practice, see p. 563
• Reteaching Activity
• *Transition Booklet,* pp. 5–6
• *Study Guide Masters,* p. 17
• *Practice Masters,* p. 17
• 🖥 Interactive Mathematics Tools Software

Assignment Guide

Core: 11–29 odd, 31–35
Enriched: 12–28 even, 29–35

Study Guide Masters, p. 17

Name_____ Date_____

3-1 Study Guide

Decimals Through Ten-Thousandths

Fraction: $\frac{5,016}{10,000}$ Decimal: 0.5016

Say: five thousand sixteen ten-thousandths

Ones	Tenths	Hundredths	Thousandths	Ten-thousandths
0	5	0	1	6

Here are some examples.

Fraction	Decimal	Words
$\frac{924}{1,000}$	0.924	Nine hundred twenty-four thousandths
$5\frac{7}{10}$	5.7	Five and seven tenths

Write each fraction as a decimal.

1. $\frac{31}{100}$ 2. $\frac{9}{100}$ 3. $\frac{4}{10,000}$ 4. $\frac{35}{1,000}$
   0.31   0.09   0.0004   0.035

5. $\frac{1,654}{10,000}$ 6. $\frac{1}{10}$ 7. $\frac{6}{1,000}$ 8. $\frac{3}{10}$
   0.1654   0.1   0.006   0.3

Write each expression as a decimal.

9. two hundred fifty-one thousandths   10. one and eleven hundredths
   0.251   1.11

11. eight hundredths   12. seventy and fifty-six thousandths
    0.08   70.056

13. five hundred and two ten-thousandths   14. thirty-six ten-thousandths
    500.0002   0.0036

© Glencoe/McGraw-Hill   T17   Mathematics: Applications and Connections, Course 1

Closing Activity

Speaking Write several decimals on the chalkboard. Give a clue such as "Find the decimal that has a six in the thousandths place." The student who names the decimal gets to give a clue for another decimal, and so on.

---

30. four hundred fifty-five and ninety-eight hundredths dollars

Mixed Review

30. *Banking* As a safeguard against error, the dollar amount on a check is written in both standard form and in words. Write $455.98 in words.

31. *Critical Thinking* Use the digits 0, 0, 5, 7 to make the greatest possible decimal and the least possible decimal. **greatest: 0.750; least: 0.057**

32. *Geometry* *(Lesson 2-9)*

   a. Which of the points on the graph has the coordinates (0, 4)? *M*

   b. Write the coordinates of point *N*. **(4, 3)**

33. **Standardized Test Practice** Seven salespeople at Kip's Keyboards sold 13, 14, 10, 6, 3, 25, and 13 keyboards during the month of February. What is the mean for this set of data? *(Lesson 2-7)* **B**

   A 3   **B** 12   **C** 13   **D** 25

34. An interval of 5 would be best to form a scale because 1 is too small and 100 is too big.

34. *Statistics* Tammy took a survey of ten of her classmates to find the number of hours each person reads for pleasure each week. The results were 3, 0, 6, 10, 2, 20, 19, 8, 2, and 4. Would an interval of 1, 5, or 100 be best to form a frequency table of the data? Explain. *(Lesson 2-2)*

35. *Money* Martin collected $38 for the holiday children's fund. Phyllis collected half as much. Use the four-step plan to determine how much money Phyllis collected. *(Lesson 1-1)* **$19**

For **Extra Practice,** see page 563.

MATH IN THE MEDIA

Tiger *by Bud Blake*

2. No; Ten-thousandths as a decimal is 0.010. The 1 is not in the tenths place.

1. Write one tenth as a decimal. **0.1**

2. Suppose Hugo had said he learned ten thousandths of what he was supposed to. Would he be talking about the same amount? Explain.

Practice Masters, p. 17

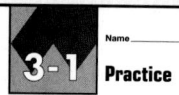

Name_____ Date_____

3-1 Practice

Decimals Through Ten-Thousandths

Write each fraction or mixed number as a decimal.

1. $\frac{8}{10}$ **0.8**   2. $\frac{19}{100}$ **0.19**   3. $\frac{7}{100}$ **0.07**   4. $\frac{26}{100}$ **0.26**

5. $\frac{32}{100}$ **0.32**   6. $\frac{5}{100}$ **0.05**   7. $\frac{4}{10}$ **0.4**   8. $\frac{11}{100}$ **0.11**

9. $\frac{6}{100}$ **0.06**   10. $\frac{48}{100}$ **0.48**   11. $\frac{93}{100}$ **0.93**   12. $\frac{2}{10}$ **0.2**

13. $\frac{407}{1,000}$ **0.407**   14. $\frac{9}{1,000}$ **0.009**   15. $\frac{2,351}{10,000}$ **0.2351**

16. $\frac{63}{10,000}$ **0.0063**   17. $\frac{742}{1,000}$ **0.742**   18. $\frac{8}{10,000}$ **0.0008**

19. $\frac{914}{10,000}$ **0.0914**   20. $\frac{3,806}{10,000}$ **0.3806**   21. $\frac{59}{1,000}$ **0.059**

Write each expression as a decimal.

22. thirteen hundredths **0.13**

23. two and forty-nine hundredths **2.49**

24. six and eight hundredths **6.08**

25. thirty-nine and two tenths **39.2**

26. eighty-three hundredths **0.83**

27. seven tenths **0.7**

28. forty-five and two ten-thousandths **45.0002**

29. thirty-one thousandths **0.031**

30. four thousandths **0.004**

31. twelve and nine hundred five ten-thousandths **12.0905**

© Glencoe/McGraw-Hill   T17   *Mathematics: Applications and Connections, Course 1*

■ Extending the Lesson ■

Enrichment Masters, p. 17

3-1 Enrichment

Decimal Letters

The letter A at the right was created by shading part of a hundreds square. There are 26 parts shaded, so the *value* of the letter A is 26 hundredths, or 0.26.

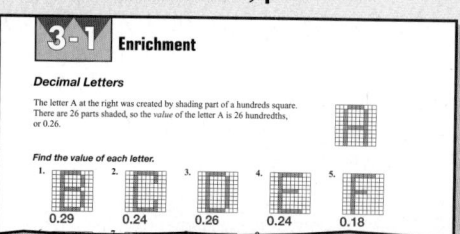

Find the value of each letter.

1. **B** 0.29   2. **C** 0.24   3. **D** 0.26   4. **E** 0.24   5. **F** 0.18

MATH IN THE MEDIA

Review with students different decimals that are equal to one tenth. For example, ten hundredths or one hundred thousandths.

Aviation

Mayte Greco
PILOT

Mayte Greco took flying lessons as a teenager. Now, the mother of five children, she is a pilot and owns her own air charter company in Florida. She also volunteers one day a week to search for Cuban refugees on rafts. She then radios the Coast Guard and waits until they come to the rescue.

Most companies that employ pilots require at least two years of college. To become a pilot for an airline company, you will need a college degree. Courses in engineering, meteorology, physics and mathematics are helpful in preparing for a pilot's career.

For more information:
Air Line Pilots Association
535 Herndon Parkway
P.O. Box 1169
Herndon, VA 22070

interNET CONNECTION
www.glencoe.com/sec/
math/mac/mathnet

I'd like to fly people to their favorite vacation spots. I could stop there for a day or two myself!

Your Turn
Research the future of careers in flying. Will more pilots be needed in the next 10 to 20 years? What are the salaries for pilots?

Motivating Students

As students learned in the chapter opener on pages 92–93, vacations often include a trip on an airplane. Aviation is an important part of recreation and entertainment, as well as business, trade, and government. There are many opportunities to explore in the aviation industry. Students may be interested in a career in that or a related field. To start the discussion, you may ask students questions about aviation history.

- When was the first airplane flight and who achieved it? **December 17, 1903, at Kitty Hawk, North Carolina; Wilbur and Orville Wright**
- When did the first jet airplane fly? **August 1939**
- How fast does the supersonic jet *Concorde* fly? **about 1,200 mph**

Making the Math Connection

When small planes ascend and descend, the barometric pressure changes by small amounts. These changes affect the altimeter, or altitude, setting. The pilot needs to make adjustments by adding and subtracting the pressures, which are measured in decimals, to and from the altimeter readings.

Working on *Your Turn*

Remind students that a career in aviation is not restricted to being a pilot. There are varied jobs associated with aviation that they can check out. These include working for commercial airlines, federal and state aviation boards, the U.S. Armed Forces, and NASA, or working in airport management or aerospace research, design, or manufacturing.

More About Mayte Greco

- Mayte Greco's parents left Cuba following the revolution led by Fidel Castro in 1958. Mayte was a baby when her parents settled in Miami, Florida. When she was growing up, her father would take her to the airport to watch airplanes coming and going.
- To become a pilot, Mayte Greco had to earn her "wings." A pilot's license requires hours of practice with a trained instructor, passing a written examination, and at least forty hours of flying time.

*An additional School to Career activity is available on page 3 of the **School to Career Masters**.*

HANDS-ON

GET READY

Objective Students measure length in metric units.

Optional Resources
Hands-On Lab Masters
• worksheet, p. 42
Manipulative Kit
• tape measure

MANAGEMENT TIPS

Recommended Time
45 minutes

Getting Started Guide the class in measuring the width of a chair seat. Help them find the answer in meters, centimeters, and millimeters.

HANDS-ON LAB

COOPERATIVE LEARNING

3-2A Measurement

 tape measure

A Preview of Lesson 3-2

The basic unit of length in the metric system is the *meter*. All other metric units of length are defined in terms of the meter.

The chart below summarizes the most commonly used metric units of length.

Unit	Symbol	Meaning
millimeter	mm	thousandth
centimeter	cm	hundredth
meter	m	one
kilometer	km	thousand

A metric ruler or tape measure is easy to read. The ruler below is labeled using *centimeters*.

The pencil below is about 12 centimeters long.

To read *millimeters*, you count each individual unit or mark on the metric ruler. There are ten millimeter marks for each centimeter mark. The pencil is about 124 millimeters long.

$$124 \text{ mm} = 12.4 \text{ cm}$$

There are 100 centimeters in a meter. Since there are 10 millimeters in one centimeter, there are 10×100 or 1,000 millimeters in a meter. The pencil is $\frac{124}{1,000}$ of a meter or 0.124 meters long.

$$124 \text{ mm} = 0.124 \text{ m}$$

Work in groups of four.

Copy the table. Using a tape measure, measure the objects and complete the table.

See students' work.

Object	Measure		
	m	cm	mm
height of door	X		
width of door		X	
length of classroom	X		
length of math book		X	
length of pencil		X	
length of table or desk		X	
width of hallway	X		
length of sheet of paper		X	
length of chalkboard eraser		X	
length of your hand		X	
width of your little finger			X

1. On your table, mark the unit of measure that is most appropriate for each item. **See table.**

2. What pattern do you notice in the relationship between the measure you marked and the size of the object?

3. What patterns do you notice in the relationship between the numbers in the columns? **See margin.**

4. Look around your classroom. Select three objects that you think would be best measured in meters, three objects you think would be best measured in millimeters, and three objects you think would be best measured in centimeters. Explain your choices. **See margin.**

5. *Look Ahead* Copy the table below. Write the name of a common object that you think has a length that corresponds to each length in the first column. **Answers will vary.**

Length	Object
5 centimeters	
15 centimeters	
3 meters	
1 meter	
75 centimeters	

2. Answers will vary. Sample answer: The larger the object, the larger the unit that should be used.

The **Activity** demonstrates that different objects have different appropriate units of measure. After students have measured a variety of the objects, discuss what is meant by *appropriate units of measure*.

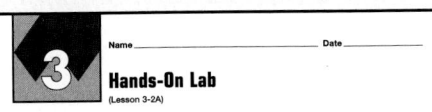

ASSESS

Have members of each group present some of their measurements to the class and what they chose as their appropriate unit of measure for that object. Discuss the appropriateness of the chosen unit.

Use Exercise 5 to determine whether students understand *appropriate units of measure*.

Additional Answers

3. Students should notice that the measures are related to powers of 10 and start to notice how decimals are used.

4. Answers will vary, but students should select larger objects for using meters and smaller objects when using centimeters and millimeters.

Hands-On Lab Masters, p. 42

Name _____ Date _____

3 Hands-On Lab
(Lesson 3-2A)

Measurement

Try This Answers will vary. Sample answers are given.

Object	Measure		
	m	cm	mm
height of door	x		
width of door		x	
length of classroom	x		
length of math book		x	
length of pencil		x	
length of table or desk		x	
width of hallway	x		
length of sheet of paper		x	
length of chalkboard eraser		x	
length of your hand		x	
width of your little finger			x

On Your Own
1. See students' work.
2. Sample answer: The larger the object, the larger the unit that should be used.
3. Students should notice that the measures are related to powers of 10 and start to notice how decimals are used.
4. Answers will vary, but students should select larger objects when using meters and smaller objects when using centimeters.

5. Look Ahead
Length	Object
5 centimeters	
15 centimeters	
3 meters	
1 meter	
75 centimeters	

Answers will vary.

© Glencoe/McGraw-Hill 42 *Mathematics: Applications and Connections, Course 1*

Math Journal
Have students write a paragraph about how to choose the most appropriate unit of measure and why this is important.

Instructional Resources
- *Study Guide Masters*, p. 18
- *Practice Masters*, p. 18
- *Enrichment Masters*, p. 18
- Transparencies 3-2, A and B
- *Assessment and Evaluation Masters*, p. 71

CD-ROM Program
- Resource Lesson 3-2

Recommended Pacing	
Standard	Days 4 & 5 of 12
Honors	Day 3 of 10
Block	Day 3 of 6

1 FOCUS

5-Minute Check
(Lesson 3-1)

Write each fraction or mixed number as a decimal.

1. $\frac{64}{1,000}$ **0.064**

2. $\frac{319}{10,000}$ **0.0319**

3. $5\frac{4}{10}$ **5.4**

Write each expression as a decimal.

4. thirty-eight thousandths **0.038**

5. twenty-nine and six ten-thousandths **29.0006**

The 5-Minute Check is also available on **Transparency 3-2A** for this lesson.

Motivating the Lesson

Communication Ask students how tall they are in centimeters and how they might find this out.

2 TEACH

Transparency 3-2B contains a teaching aid for this lesson.

Using the Mini-Lab Have students estimate heights of things in the classroom and compare these heights in meters and centimeters with their own heights.

3-2

Integration: Measurement

Length in the Metric System

What you'll learn

You'll learn to show relationships among metric units of lengths and to measure line segments.

When am I ever going to use this?

Metric units of length are used in cross country running, swimming, and track and field events.

Word Wise
metric system
meter

In the 1996 Summer Olympics, Michael Johnson became the first man to win both the 200-meter and 400-meter races.

Most Olympic events use the **metric system** to measure lengths. The basic unit of length in the metric system is the **meter**. All other metric units of length are defined in terms of the meter.

Decimals are used in the metric system. The chart summarizes the most commonly used metric units of length.

Unit	Symbol	Meaning	Size	Model
millimeter	mm	thousandth	0.001 m	thickness of a dime
centimeter	cm	hundredth	0.01 m	width of large paperclip
meter	m	one	1.0 m	width of doorway
kilometer	km	thousand	1,000 m	six city blocks

Examples

Write the unit of length: millimeter, centimeter, meter or kilometer, that you would use to measure each of the following. Then estimate each measure.

1 thickness of a nickel

Since a nickel is thin, the *millimeter* is the appropriate unit. The thickness of a nickel is a little more than the thickness of a dime, so the thickness of a nickel is about 2 millimeters.

2 length of a baseball bat

Since the length of a baseball bat is close to the width of a doorway, the *meter* is the appropriate unit. The length of a baseball bat is about 1 meter.

3 On the map, what is the distance between San Antonio and Houston in centimeters? in millimeters?

The distance is about 7.3 centimeters, or 73 millimeters.

102 **Chapter 3** Adding and Subtracting Decimals

Multiple Learning Styles

Kinesthetic Separate the class into groups, and have each group estimate the length of some part of the school. Each group member should measure and record that length using a different body part. Then have them measure that body part with an appropriate metric device. For example, one person might measure the hallway with his or her foot. Another might measure it with an arm. The foot and arm are then measured to the nearest centimeter. Find the length of the hallway using that data to create a chart presenting the various measurements.

Example 4
CONNECTION

Life Science Use a centimeter ruler to measure the length of the body of the chameleon as shown in the photo below.

In the photo, the length of the body of the chameleon is about 9 centimeters.

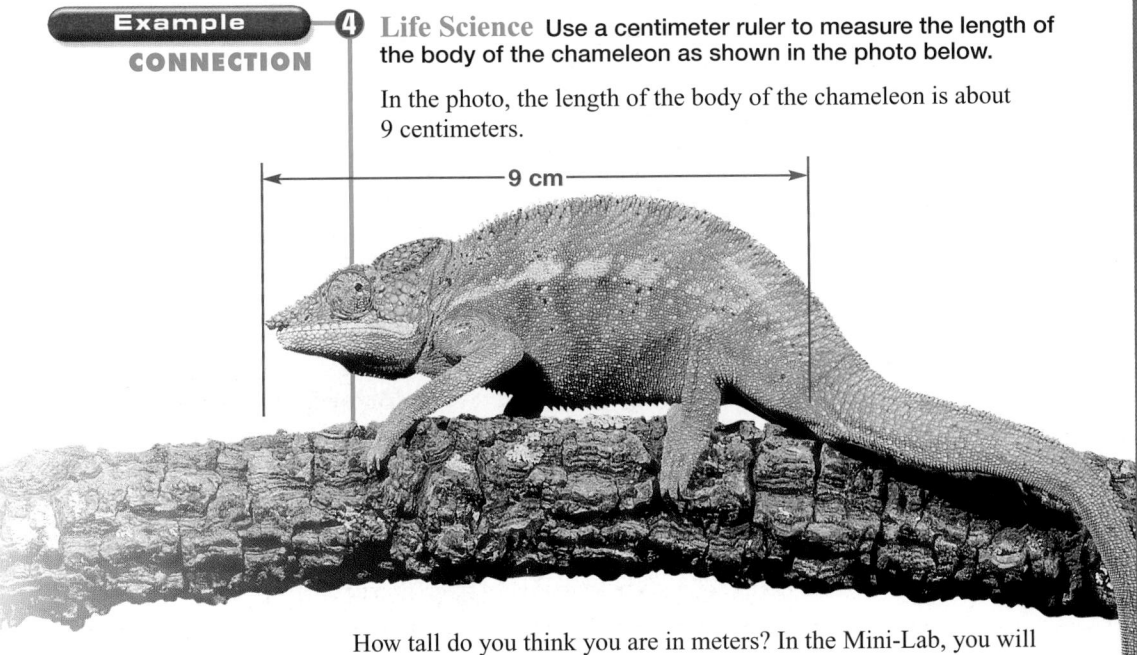

← 9 cm →

How tall do you think you are in meters? In the Mini-Lab, you will estimate and find heights in the metric system.

MINI-LAB

Work with a partner. ∿ string ⬚― tape measure

Try This
• Cut a length of string that is as long as your partner is tall.
• Estimate each other's height in centimeters and in meters. Then measure your string to find your height.

Talk About It
1. What is your height in centimeters? **Answers will vary.**
2. What is your height in meters? **Answers will vary.**
3. Write a paragraph explaining how you decide what metric unit to use to measure length. Use specific examples in your explanation.

3. Answers will vary. Students should conclude that the larger the object, the larger the unit that should be used.

Communicating Mathematics

CHECK FOR UNDERSTANDING

Read and study the lesson to answer each question.

1. *Draw* a line that is 10.5 centimeters long. **See students' work.**

2. *Tell* whether you would use centimeters or meters to measure the length of this book. Explain your answer. **See Answer Appendix.**

HANDS-ON MATH

3. Collect everyone's height data from the Mini-Lab. Organize the data and draw a bar graph to display the data. **See students' work.**

Lesson 3-2 Integration: Measurement Length in the Metric System **103**

Reteaching the Lesson

Activity Place a clear centimeter ruler on the overhead. Place a jumbo paper clip above the ruler. Have students model the activity and determine the lengths of their paper clips in millimeters and in thousandths of a meter. Continue with other items.

Error Analysis

Watch for students who are confused about the placement of the decimal point when converting a fraction to a decimal. **Prevent by** showing them a simple rule. For example, point out that 100 has *two* zeros, and the last digit in centimeters, or hundredths, is *two* places to the right of the decimal point.

In-Class Examples

Write the unit of length that you would use to measure each of the following. Then estimate each measure.

For Example 1
Width of a nickel
cm, about 2 cm

For Example 2
Width of an average window
m, about 1 m

For Example 3
On the map, what is the distance in centimeters between Austin and Houston along U.S. Route 290? in millimeters? **5.7 cm; 57 mm**

For Example 4
Measure the widest part of the chameleon's body, located just behind the foreleg. **about 3.5 cm**

3 PRACTICE/APPLY

Check for Understanding

If students need additional practice or instruction after completing Exercises 1–8, you may find one of the following options helpful.
• Extra Practice, see p. 563
• Reteaching Activity
• *Transition Booklet*, pp. 29–30
• *Study Guide Masters*, p. 18
• *Practice Masters*, p. 18

Study Guide Masters, p. 18

Name _____ Date _____

3-2 **Study Guide**

Integration: Measurement
Length in the Metric System

A dime is about one millimeter (1 mm) thick.
| 1 mm

A sugar cube is about one centimeter (1 cm) wide.
1 cm

A kitchen counter is about one meter (1 m) high.

Nine times the length of a football field, including end zones, is about 1 kilometer (1 km).

Use a centimeter ruler to measure each line segment.

1. —
   1.4 cm
2. ————
   8.9 cm
3. ——
   2.1 cm
4. ————
   10.5 cm
5. —
   0.7 cm
6. ———
   5.6 cm

Use a centimeter ruler to measure one side of each square.

7. ▢ 1.2 cm
8. ▢ 1.7 cm
9. ▢ 2.5 cm
10. ▢ 0.8 cm
11. ▢ 1.7 cm
12. ▢ 2.0 cm

© Glencoe/McGraw-Hill   T18   *Mathematics: Applications and Connections, Course 1*

4 ASSESS

Closing Activity

Modeling Have students demonstrate how the decimal point moves when expressing measurements in meters or in tenths, hundredths, or thousandths of a meter by measuring the same object all four ways.

Chapter 3, Quiz A (Lessons 3-1 and 3-2) is available in the *Assessment and Evaluation Masters,* p. 71.

Additional Answer

22. Sample answer: centigrade, centipede, century

Practice Masters, p. 18

Guided Practice

Write the unit of length: millimeter, centimeter, meter or kilometer, that you would use to measure each of the following. Then estimate each measure.

4. the length of a football field
   m; about 110 m
5. the width of a quarter
   cm; about 2.5 cm

Use a centimeter ruler to measure each line segment.

6. ————————
   4.4 cm or 44 mm
7. ——————
   3.2 cm or 32 mm

8. *Sports* Runners often participate in races that are 10 kilometers long. How many meters are in 10 kilometers? **10,000 meters**

EXERCISES

Practice

9. cm; about 90 cm
10. mm; 8 mm

Write the unit of length: millimeter, centimeter, meter or kilometer, that you would use to measure each of the following. Then estimate each measure.

9. the length of a skateboard
10. the thickness of a pencil
11. the height of a giraffe
    m; about 5 m
12. the length of a swimming pool
    m; about 50 meters

Use a centimeter ruler to measure each line segment.

13. ——— 1.3 cm or 13 mm
14. ——— 1.9 cm or 19 mm
15. ——— 3.8 cm or 38 mm
16. ——— 5.4 cm or 54 mm

Use a centimeter ruler to measure one side of each figure.

17.
    3 cm or 30 mm
18. 2.5 cm or 25 mm
19.
    2 cm or 20 mm

23. See students' work.
24. 0.49 m, 55 cm, 999 mm, 0.0037 km, 3.9 m

20. How many millimeters are in 6.8 centimeters? **68 mm**
21. How many centimeters are in 3 meters? **300 cm**

Applications and Problem Solving

22. *Language Arts* The metric prefix *cent* means *hundred*. Make a list of words that contain this prefix. **See margin.**
23. *Geometry* On a sheet of centimeter grid paper, draw a square such that the perimeter (distance around the square) is 20 centimeters.
24. *Critical Thinking* Order from least to greatest.
    0.0037 km   3.9 m   55 cm   0.49 m   999 mm

Mixed Review

25. **Standardized Test Practice** Choose the decimal that represents *twelve and sixty-three thousandths.* *(Lesson 3-1)* **C**
    A 1206.3   B 120.63   C 12.063   D 0.12063

For **Extra Practice,** see page 563.

26. *Statistics* Construct a horizontal bar graph using the guinea pig weights of 1.8, 1.754, 2.09, 1.91, and 2.1 pounds. *(Lesson 2-3)* **See Answer Appendix.**
27. *Algebra* Find the value of $3x - 2y$ if $x = 6$ and $y = 4$. *(Lesson 1-5)* **10**

Extending the Lesson

Enrichment Masters, p. 18

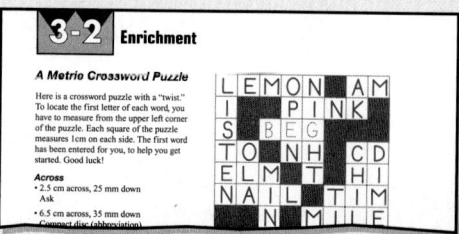

Activity Have students make a scale drawing of the classroom on centimeter grid paper. Then have them construct a cardboard model of the drawing. Display the drawings and models in the classroom.

Comparing and Ordering Decimals

What you'll learn

You'll learn to compare decimals and order a set of decimals.

When am I ever going to use this?

Knowing how to compare and order decimals can help you find library books.

Mrs. Lee's science class is studying acids and bases. Acidity is expressed using the pH scale, which ranges from 0 to 14.

Substance	pH
apple	2.9
baking soda	9.0
carrot	5.1
drinking water	7.0
household ammonia	13.0
lemon	2.1
lye	14.0
rainwater	5.8
tomato	4.2

The results of Carmen's group are shown in the table.

Carmen's group needs to compare the pH of the carrot and of rainwater, 5.1 and 5.8, respectively. There are two ways to compare decimals. You can compare the digits in each place-value position, or you can use a number line.

Method 1 Use place value.

Line up the decimal points of the two numbers. Then start at the left, comparing the digits in the same place-value position that are not equal. The decimal with the greater digit is the greater decimal.

> **Study Hint**
>
> Reading Math
> Remember that the symbol < is read as *is less than* and the symbol > is read as *is greater than*. The symbol always points toward the lesser number.

carrot: 5.**1**
rainwater: 5.**8**

1 and 8 are not equal. 1 tenth < 8 tenths, so 5.1 < 5.8.

Method 2 Use a number line.

On a number line, numbers to the right are greater than numbers to the left.

5.1 is left of 5.8, 5.1 < 5.8.

Since 5.1 < 5.8, the carrot is more acidic than the rainwater.

Example

1 Which is greater, 2.037 or 2.033?

Method 1 Use place value.

2.03**7**   *Line up decimal points.*
2.03**3**   *Starting at the left, compare each place-value.*

7 and 3 are not equal.

7 thousandths > 3 thousandths, so 2.037 > 2.033.

(continued on the next page)

Lesson 3-3 Comparing and Ordering Decimals   **105**

Investigations for the Special Education Student

This blackline master booklet helps you plan for the needs of your special education students by providing long-term projects along with teacher notes. Investigation 3, *Dining Out,* may be used with this chapter.

Instructional Resources
- *Study Guide Masters,* p. 19
- *Practice Masters,* p. 19
- *Enrichment Masters,* p. 19
- Transparencies 3-3, A and B
- *Assessment and Evaluation Masters,* pp. 70, 71
- *Hands-On Lab Masters,* p. 71
- *Technology Masters,* p. 6
- CD-ROM Program
  - Resource Lesson 3-3
  - Interactive Lesson 3-3

Recommended Pacing	
Standard	Day 6 of 12
Honors	Day 4 of 10
Block	Day 3 of 6

1 FOCUS

5-Minute Check
(Lesson 3-2)

Use a centimeter ruler to draw a line segment having the given length.

1. 2.8 centimeters
2. 4 centimeters
3. 3.6 centimeters
4. Draw a square with sides 1.5 centimeters long.
   1–4. See students' work.
5. How many millimeters are in 3.2 centimeters? **32**

The 5-Minute Check is also available on **Transparency 3-3A** for this lesson.

Motivating the Lesson
Problem Solving Ask students how they would determine which item weighs more:
- a turkey that weighs 19.68 pounds
- a turkey that weighs 19.75 pounds

Compare the decimal portion of each weight; 0.75 > 0.68 so 19.75 > 19.68.

Transparency 3-3B contains a teaching aid for this lesson.

Using the Mini-Lab A brief review with base-ten blocks may be needed by some students. When students are finished, lead them to make a generalization based on their findings.

In-Class Examples

For Example 1
Which is greater, 3.048 or 3.045? **3.048**

For Example 2
Which is the greatest number, 1.32, 1.305, or 1.3? **1.32**

For Example 3
Tanisha is doing research at the library. She has a stack of books to return to the shelves. Help her order the call numbers on the books from least to greatest: 389.426, 389.4, 389.42, 389.342. **389.342, 389.4, 389.42, 389.426**

Teaching Tip While discussing Example 2, stress the importance of lining up the decimal points before comparing.

1. The area of the shaded sections are equal.
2. The area of the shaded sections are equal.

Method 2 Use a number line.
Compare the decimals on a number line.

2.037 is to the right of 2.033. So 2.037 > 2.033.

You can also use grid paper to compare decimals.

Work with a partner. ▨ grid paper ✐ pencil or marker

Try This
- Each person should draw a 10-by-10 square on grid paper.
- One person should shade a grid to show 0.4 or four tenths.
- The other person should shade a grid to show 0.40 or forty hundredths.

Talk About It
1. How do the two grids compare?
2. Shade two more grids to show 0.6 and 0.60. Compare the two grids. What can you say about them?

You can annex, or place zeros to the right of a decimal so that each decimal has the same number of decimal places.

Example 2 Which is the greatest number, 19.48, 19.481, or 19.4?

Line up the decimal points.	*Annex a zero so that each has the same number of decimal places.*
19.48	19.480
19.481 ➡	19.481
19.4	19.400

Since 8 hundredths is greater than 0 hundredths, 19.480 > 19.400.
Since 1 thousandth is greater than 0 thousandths, 19.481 > 19.480.
The greatest number is 19.481.

MathPASS CD-ROM

This CD-ROM offers a complete, self-paced mathematics curriculum. Each lesson includes a pretest, tutorial, guided practice, and posttest. MathPASS Lesson 4 is correlated to this Student Edition Lesson.
For Windows & Macintosh

Example ③
Real World **APPLICATION**

Sports The table shows the top rebounder for each team in the Midwest Division of the NBA for the 1997 regular season. Order the rebounding averages from least to greatest.

For the latest sports statistics, visit:
www.glencoe.com/sec/math/mac/mathnet

Player	Team	Rebounds/Game
Barkley	Houston	13.5
Green	Dallas	7.9
Malone	Utah	9.9
Gugliotta	Minnesota	8.7
Er. Johnson	Denver	11.1
Perdue	San Antonio	9.8
Reeves	Vancouver	8.1

Use a number line to order the average number of rebounds.

```
      7.9 8.1  8.7      9.8 9.9      11.1                13.5
       ↓  ↓    ↓         ↓↓           ↓                   ↓
  ├──┼──●●┼──●──┼──┼──●●┼──┼──┼──●──┼──┼──┼──┼──●──┼──┤
  7  7.5  8  8.5  9  9.5 10 10.5 11 11.5 12 12.5 13 13.5 14
```

The rebounding averages in order from least to greatest are 7.9, 8.1, 8.7, 9.8, 9.9, 11.1, and 13.5.

CHECK FOR UNDERSTANDING

Communicating Mathematics

Read and study the lesson to answer each question.

1. *Draw* a number line that compares 3.89 and 3.91. **See Answer Appendix.**

2. **Sample answer: Since 1.018 is greater, it is to the right of 1.01.**

2. *Tell* how the decimals 1.018 and 1.01, graphed on the number line, compare.

```
   1.01                         1.018
    ↓                            ↓
  ──┼──────┼──────────┼──────────┼──────→
   1.01             1.015       1.02
```

HANDS-ON MATH

3. Use base-ten blocks to compare 1.63 and 1.54. **See students' work.**

Guided Practice

State the greatest number in each group.

4. 6.02 or 6.20 **6.20**

5. 0.042, 0.06 or 0.051 **0.06**

6. 198.6, 198.06, 189.5, or 198.067 **198.6**

Order each set of decimals from least to greatest.

7. 13.507; 13.05; 13.9; 13.84 **13.05, 13.507, 13.84, 13.9**

8. **0.002, 0.09, 0.19, 0.2, 0.21, 2.1, 21.9**
8. 0.2; 0.09; 0.19; 0.21; 2.1; 21.9; 0.002

9. **389.225, 388.404, 388.246, 385.867, 385.841**

9. *Sports* The table shows the scores for the top five teams in women's gymnastics at the 1996 Summer Olympics. Order the scores from greatest to least.

Team	Score
China	385.867
Romania	388.246
Russia	388.404
Ukraine	385.841
USA	389.225

Lesson 3-3 Comparing and Ordering Decimals   **107**

---

3 PRACTICE/APPLY

Check for Understanding
If students need additional practice or instruction after completing Exercises 1–9, you may find one of the following options helpful.
• Extra Practice, see p. 563
• Reteaching Activity
• *Transition Booklet*, pp. 7–8
• *Study Guide Masters*, p. 19
• *Practice Masters*, p. 19

Assignment Guide

Core: 11–27 odd, 28–32
Enriched: 10–24 even, 26–32

Study Guide Masters, p.19

3-3 **Study Guide**

Name _____ Date _____

Comparing and Ordering Decimals

Which is greater, 25.692 or 25.6902?
Line up the decimal points.
Start at the left. Find the first place in which the digits are different.

	Compare the digits.	The decimal with the greater digit is greater.
25.692 25.6902	2 is greater than 0. 2 > 0	25.692 > 25.6902

Order decimals by comparing them two at a time.

State the greater number in each group.

1. 0.042 or 0.422   **0.422**
2. 7.398 or 7.378   **7.398**
3. 76.1423 or 76.142   **76.1423**
4. 1.53 or 1.0053   **1.53**
5. 14.358 or 14.374   **14.374**
6. 0.092 or 0.192   **0.192**
7. 709.12 or 790.21   **790.21**
8. 5.0045 or 5.0405   **5.0405**
9. 12.2 or 2.222   **12.2**

Order each set of decimals from least to greatest.

10. 6.583   **6.065**
    6.843   **6.269**
    6.065   **6.583**
    6.269   **6.843**

11. 456.73   **456.23**
    465.32   **456.37**
    456.37   **456.73**
    456.23   **465.32**

12. 0.004   **0.004**
    0.04   **0.035**
    0.035   **0.04**
    0.305   **0.305**

Order each set of decimals from greatest to least.

13. 1.16   **1.16**
    0.616   **1.066**
    1.066   **0.616**
    0.06   **0.06**
    0.016   **0.016**

14. 91.5   **95.51**
    95.155   **95.155**
    9.05   **91.5**
    19.005   **19.005**
    95.51   **9.05**

15. 745.0003   **745.333**
    745.303   **745.303**
    745.03   **745.03**
    745.333   **745.003**
    745.003   **745.0003**

© Glencoe/McGraw-Hill   T19   Mathematics: Applications and Connections, Course 1

Reteaching the Lesson

Activity Have students use a newspaper to find sports statistics such as batting averages. Then ask them to order the averages from greatest to least. Point out that these are actually decimals, so 0.324 is greater than 0.299.

Error Analysis
Watch for students who consistently make errors in comparing decimals. **Prevent by** having these students use base-ten models to shade each decimal before comparing.

Lesson 3-3   **107**

Closing Activity

Modeling Play "So You Think You Have the Greatest Decimal?" Have students write decimals, 1 per card, on 3″ × 5″ index cards. Make 36 cards. Then divide the cards among the players. To play, each player reveals the top card. The player with the greatest decimal takes the cards. Play continues until all cards have been used.

Chapter 3, Quiz B (Lesson 3-3) is available in the *Assessment and Evaluation Masters*, p. 71.

Mid-Chapter Test (Lessons 3-1 through 3-3) is available in the *Assessment and Evaluation Masters*, p. 70.

Additional Answer

31. Sample Answer: 95, 91, 93, 89; no number occurs more often than the others

---

Practice Masters, p. 19

EXERCISES

Practice

State the greatest number in each group.

10. 16.099 or 160.98 **160.98**

11. 0.331 or 0.303 **0.331**

12. 18.607 or 18.06 **18.607**

13. 1.018 or 1.01 **1.018**

14. 0.03, 0.31, or 0.039 **0.31**

15. 47.553, 47.5, or 47.053 **47.553**

16. 547.484 or 547.4843 **547.4843**

17. 0.068, 0.07, or 0.7 **0.7**

Order each set of decimals from least to greatest.

18.	94.7	**94.7**	**19.**	15	**14.95**	**20.**	37.5	**35.7**
	101.1	**98.5**		15.8	**15**		35.7	**35.849**
	99.7	**99.7**		14.95	**15.01**		35.849	**36.06**
	98.5	**101.1**		15.01	**15.8**		36.06	**37.5**

Order each set of decimals from greatest to least.

21.	0.025	**0.0316**	**22.**	43.8	**43.8**	**23.**	379.8778	**397.877**
	0.0316	**0.0306**		42.998	**43.6789**		378.87	**379.9**
	0.0306	**0.025**		43.16	**43.16**		397.877	**379.88**
	0.0249	**0.0249**		42.022	**42.998**		379.9	**379.8778**
	0.0208	**0.0208**		43.6789	**42.022**		379.88	**378.87**

26. 745.2, 745.23, 745.231, 745.325, 745.412

24. Which is the least, 10.59 or 10.599? **10.59**

25. Which is the greatest, 0.0621, 0.603, or 0.06? **0.603**

Applications and Problem Solving

27a. 2.1, 2.9, 4.2, 5.1, 5.8, 7.0, 9.0, 13.0, 14.0

28. $1.70-César;
$0.79-Eric;
$1.07-Beatriz;
$1.18-Antonio;
$0.89-Dexter

26. *Library Science* Shannon has to return the stack of books shown at the right to the library shelves. Order the call numbers on the books from least to greatest.

27. *Statistics* Refer to the beginning of the lesson.
  a. Order the substances from the most acidic to the most basic.
  b. What is the median pH reading? **5.8**

28. *Critical Thinking* Antonio has more money than Beatriz. Antonio has less money than César. Dexter has $0.10 more than Eric. Use the decimals at the right to determine how much money each person has.

Mixed Review

For **Extra Practice**, see page 563.

29. *Measurement* Measure the line segment. *(Lesson 3-2)*
  5.7 cm or 57 mm

30. Write thirty-seven thousandths as a decimal. *(Lesson 3-1)* **0.037**

31. *Statistics* Make up a set of data that has no mode and state why it has no mode. *(Lesson 2-7)* **See margin.**

32. **Standardized Test Practice** Florida has 67 counties. What is this number rounded to the nearest ten? *(Lesson 1-3)* **C**
  A 60 **B** 65 **C** 70 **D** 75

Extending the Lesson

Enrichment Masters, p. 19

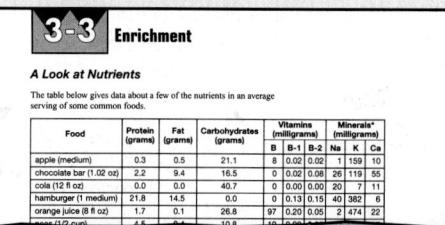

Activity Have students use the catalog system at the local or school library to find a book on any topic of interest. Have them look for the call number and then find the book in the stacks. You may suggest that students research how call numbers are assigned.

Rounding Decimals

What you'll learn

You'll learn to round decimals.

When am I ever going to use this?

Knowing how to round decimals is helpful in estimating with money.

A Mexican restaurant created the world's largest burrito in Anaheim, California, on July 31, 1995. It weighed 4,217 pounds and was 3,112.99 feet long. Do you think the weight and length were reported this way in the local papers?

Newspapers often round numbers so it is easier to read. The length of the burrito may have been reported as 3,113 feet.

Decimals may be rounded to any place-value position.

Instructional Resources

- *Study Guide Masters*, p. 20
- *Practice Masters*, p. 20
- *Enrichment Masters*, p. 20
- Transparencies 3-4, A and B
- *Diversity Masters*, p. 3
- CD-ROM Program
  - Resource Lesson 3-4

Recommended Pacing	
Standard	Day 7 of 12
Honors	Day 5 of 10
Block	Day 4 of 6

1 FOCUS

Example **1** **Round 1.63 to the nearest tenth.**

To round 1.63, look at the number line below.

1.63

On the number line, 1.63 is closer to 1.6 than it is to 1.7.

1.63 rounded to the nearest tenth is 1.6.

LOOK BACK

You can refer to Lesson 1-3 for information on rounding whole numbers.

You can also round decimals without using a number line.

Rounding Decimals	• Look at digit to the right of the place being rounded. • The digit remains the same if the digit to the right is 0, 1, 2, 3, or 4. • Round up if the digit to the right is 5, 6, 7, 8, or 9.

Example **2**

Money Matters Ayashe purchased a carbon monoxide detector for $27.44. To the nearest dollar, how much did she spend?

Look at the digit to the right of the ones place.

27.44   *Since 4 < 5, the digit in the*
↑   *ones place stays the same.*
ones place

To the nearest dollar, Ayashe spent $27.

Lesson 3-4 Rounding Decimals   **109**

5-Minute Check
(Lesson 3-3)

State the greatest number in each group.

1. 63.08 or 63.18 **63.18**
2. 0.5214, 0.521, or 0.52 **0.5214**
3. 75.481, 75.4182, or 75.4818 **75.4818**
4. Order the decimals from least to greatest: 97.490, 97.4, 97.482, 97.4826. **97.4, 97.482, 97.4826, 97.490**
5. Order the decimals from greatest to least: 55.711, 55.701, 55.7, 54.777, 55.071. **55.711, 55.701, 55.7, 55.071, 54.777**

The 5-Minute Check is also available on **Transparency 3-4A** for this lesson.

Motivating the Lesson

Communication Have small groups of students construct number lines with decimals in tenths from 74.0 to 76.0. Give each group a penny to slide along the number line. Have them record where the farthest point of the penny stops. Then have them discuss whether it is closer to 74.0, 75.0, or 76.0.

Classroom Vignette

"To practice rounding decimals, we create a human number line. Some students represent increments on the number line and others, numbers to be rounded. We discuss how each number is to be rounded and then the "rounded" student stands behind the appropriate person on the number line."

Joy Donlin, Teacher
Bates Middle School
Annapolis, MD

2 TEACH

Transparency 3-4B contains a teaching aid for this lesson.

Using Number Lines Have students use a number line to round a decimal to the tenth, hundredth, or whole number if they have difficulties.

In-Class Examples

For Example 1
Round 8.46 to the nearest tenth. **8.5**

For Example 2
A bakery manager says the cost per store-made roll is $0.169. To the nearest cent, how much is this? **$0.17**

For Example 3
Round 0.3928 to the nearest hundredth. **0.39**

3 PRACTICE/APPLY

Check for Understanding

If students need additional practice or instruction after completing Exercises 1–8, you may find one of the following options helpful.
- Extra Practice, see p. 564
- Reteaching Activity
- *Study Guide Masters*, p. 20
- *Practice Masters*, p. 20

***Study Guide Masters*, p. 20**

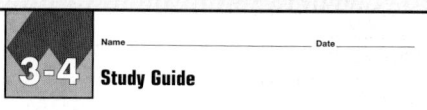

Example **3** Round 3.4672 to the nearest hundredth.

Look at the digit to the right of the hundredths place.

$$3.4672 \qquad \textit{Round up since } 7 > 5.$$
↑
hundredths place

3.4672 rounded to the nearest hundredth is 3.47.

CHECK FOR UNDERSTANDING

Communicating Mathematics

Read and study the lesson to answer each question.

1. *Explain* how to round $10.79 to the nearest dollar. **See Answer Appendix.**

2. *Draw* a number line to show why 2.983 rounded to the nearest tenth is 3.0. **See Answer Appendix.**

3. Sharon is correct. Carlos rounded to the nearest hundred.

3. *You Decide* Sharon says that 456.789 rounded to the nearest hundredth is 456.79. Carlos says it is 500. Who is correct? Explain.

Guided Practice

Round each number to the underlined place-value position.

4. 0.2<u>8</u> **0.3**   5. 8.2<u>0</u>2 **8.20**   6. 0.<u>1</u>487 **0.1**   7. 1<u>9</u>.59 **20**

8. *Money Matters* The unit price of a twenty-ounce bottle of a soft drink is $0.0445 per ounce. How much is this to the nearest cent? **$0.04**

EXERCISES

Practice

Round each number to the underlined place-value position.

9. 1<u>8</u>.44 **18**   10. 0.8<u>4</u>9 **0.85**   11. 20.<u>4</u>5 **20.5**   12. 2.4<u>8</u>5 **2.49**

13. 49.<u>7</u>75 **49.8**   14. 68.<u>8</u>8 **68.9**   15. 19.7<u>7</u>5   16. 48.<u>8</u>02 **48.8**

15. 19.78
18. 42.79
19. 7.000

17. 99.<u>9</u>8 **100.0**   18. 42.7<u>8</u>96   19. 6.99<u>9</u>8   20. 4.0<u>0</u>4 **4.00**

21. Round $1.69 to the nearest dollar. **$2.00**

22. Round 49,237.1589499 to the nearest ten-thousandth.
49,237.1589

Applications and Problem Solving

23. *Entertainment* KTXQ in Dallas, Texas, can be found by tuning to 102.1 on the radio. The DJs round the call number to the nearest whole number. What number do the DJs use to refer to KTXQ? **102**

24. *Money Matters* Gasoline prices are usually calculated to the thousandth place. If you purchased gas that cost $1.199 per gallon, what price would you say you paid? **$1.20**

■ Reteaching the Lesson ■

Activity Play "Rounds." Use two cubes, one with six different decimals in thousandths (for example, 8.754) and the other with the words "tenths," "hundredths," and "whole number" written twice on opposite faces. Have students take turns rolling the cubes and rounding the decimal to the place indicated.

MathPASS CD-ROM

This CD-ROM offers a complete, self-paced mathematics curriculum. Each lesson includes a pretest, tutorial, guided practice, and posttest. MathPASS Lesson 5 is correlated to this Student Edition Lesson.
For Windows & Macintosh

Family Activity

Interview family members about when they use rounding. Ask how they decide to what place value a number should be rounded.

Mixed Review

27. See Answer Appendix.

For **Extra Practice**, see page 564.

25. *Critical Thinking* The table shows the average density of the nine planets. If you had to determine the mean, median, and mode of this set of data, would you round to the nearest tenth, nearest whole number, or use the exact numbers? Explain. **See Answer Appendix.**

Planet	Grams per cubic cm
Mercury	5.42
Venus	5.25
Earth	5.52
Mars	3.94
Jupiter	1.33
Saturn	0.69
Uranus	1.27
Neptune	1.71
Pluto	2.03

26. Order the decimals 2.9, 2.38, 2.474, 2.91, and 2.88 from greatest to least. *(Lesson 3-3)* **2.91, 2.9, 2.88, 2.474, 2.38**

27. *Statistics* Is the mean a misleading measure of central tendency for this set of data: 17, 21, 20, 19, 17, 21, 18, 22, and 21? Explain. *(Lesson 2-8)*

28. *Standardized Test Practice* The graph shows the number of boys and girls who signed up to play in the Northtown Youth Soccer League. Which is a reasonable conclusion that can be drawn from the information in the graph? *(Lesson 2-3)* **B**

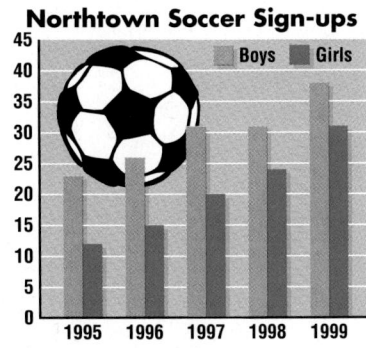

Northtown Soccer Sign-ups

A More girls than boys signed up for soccer in 1998.

B The number of girls playing soccer has been catching up with the number of boys since 1995.

C The number of boys who joined soccer decreased every year.

D Girls did not want to play soccer before 1995.

E There were more soccer sign-ups in 1997 than any other year.

CHAPTER 3

Mid-Chapter Self Test

Express each fraction as a decimal. *(Lesson 3-1)*

1. $\frac{7}{10}$ **0.7**   **2.** $\frac{43}{100}$ **0.43**   **3.** $\frac{681}{1,000}$ **0.681**   **4.** $\frac{409}{10,000}$ **0.0409**

Measure each line segment to the nearest centimeter. *(Lesson 3-2)*

5. ———————— **3 cm**   **6.** ———————————— **5 cm**

7. *Library* Miguel Aguilar went to the library to get some information about bees for a project. He is looking for books with the call numbers 638.178 and 638.186. Which number comes first? *(Lesson 3-3)* **638.178**

Round each number to the underlined place-value position. *(Lesson 3-4)*

8. 6.8 **7**   **9.** 3.401 **3.40**   **10.** 181.98 **182.0**

Lesson 3-4 Rounding Decimals **111**

Extending the Lesson

Enrichment Masters, p. 20

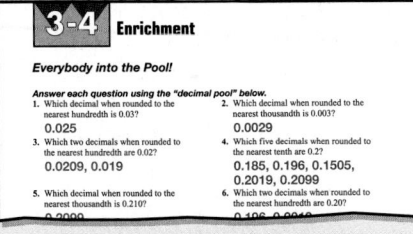

3-4 Enrichment

Everybody into the Pool!

Answer each question using the "decimal pool" below.
1. Which decimal when rounded to the nearest hundredth is 0.03? 0.025
2. Which decimal when rounded to the nearest thousandth is 0.003? 0.0029
3. Which two decimals when rounded to the nearest hundredth are 0.02? 0.0209, 0.019
4. Which five decimals when rounded to the nearest tenth are 0.2? 0.185, 0.196, 0.1505, 0.2019, 0.2099
5. Which decimal when rounded to the nearest thousandth is 0.210? 0.2099
6. Which two decimals when rounded to the nearest hundredth are 0.20?

Activity Have pairs of students divide whole numbers on their calculators and then round the quotients to the nearest whole number, tenth, or hundredth. Have them determine a method for rounding decimals with more than three digits to the right of the decimal point.

Assignment Guide

Core: 9–23 odd, 25–28
Enriched: 10–22 even, 23–28
All: Self Test, 1–10

Family Activity

Have students share what they found out about rounding from their family members. Discuss the different situations.

4 ASSESS

Closing Activity
Speaking Have groups of students discuss the steps they use to round a decimal to the nearest tenth, hundredth, or whole number. One representative from each group should present the steps to the class.

Mid-Chapter Self Test

The Mid-Chapter Self Test reviews the concepts in Lessons 3-1 through 3-4. Lesson references are given so students can review concepts not yet mastered.

Practice Masters, p. 20

3-4 Practice

Rounding Decimals

Round each number to the underlined place-value position.
1. 1.726 **1.73**
2. 54.38 **54**
3. 0.58 **0.6**
4. 0.9142 **0.91**
5. 80.659 **80.7**
6. 232.1 **232**
7. 1.063 **1.1**
8. 0.55 **0.6**
9. 0.8194 **0.8**
10. 0.496 **0.50**
11. 3.0182 **3.018**
12. 71.405 **71.4**
13. 9.63 **10**
14. 32.71 **32.7**
15. 2.671 **2.67**
16. 4.0507 **4.051**
17. 89.95 **90.0**
18. 0.134 **0.13**
19. 5.893 **5.9**
20. 520.6 **521**
21. 0.7098 **0.710**
22. 1.845 **1.85**
23. 34.55 **34.6**
24. 29.25 **29.3**
25. 56.0924 **56.092**
26. 1,199.7 **1,200**
27. 0.46 **0.5**
28. 0.3546 **0.4**

© Glencoe/McGraw-Hill   T20   *Mathematics: Applications and Connections, Course 1*

Lesson 3-4 **111**

- *Study Guide Masters*, p. 21
- *Practice Masters*, p. 21
- *Enrichment Masters*, p. 21
- Transparencies 3-5, A and B
- *Assessment and Evaluation Masters*, p. 72

 CD-ROM Program
- Resource Lesson 3-5

Recommended Pacing	
Standard	Day 8 of 12
Honors	Day 6 of 10
Block	Day 4 of 6

1 FOCUS

 5-Minute Check
(Lesson 3-4)

1. Draw a number line to show how to round 7.39 to the nearest tenth.

```
              7.39
               ↓
├───┼───┼───┤
7.3    7.35    7.4
```

Round each number to the underlined place-value position.

2. 32.1̲09   32.1

3. 7̲.65   8

4. 4.43̲8   4.44

5. 6.8̲611   6.9

The 5-Minute Check is also available on **Transparency 3-5A** for this lesson.

Motivating the Lesson

Problem Solving Ask students to read the opening paragraph of the lesson. Ask the following questions:
- Should you estimate or find the exact answer? Explain.
  Estimate; the question asks for an estimate by using the word *about*.
- Glancing quickly at the graph, would you guess the cost was about $10 billion? $15 billion?
  no; yes

3-5 Estimating Sums and Differences

***What* you'll learn**
You'll learn to estimate decimal sums and differences.

***When* am I ever going to use this?**
You'll estimate sums and differences when you need to determine if you have enough money to pay for the groceries in your cart.

Word Wise
clustering

Do you participate in a sport? The graph shows the cost of treating sports injuries in emergency rooms in a recent year. About how much did treating these injuries cost?

Since you only need to know about how much the cost was, you can estimate. One way to estimate is to round the amounts to the same place-value position and then add.

Where Does It Hurt?

Sport	Injuries	Cost (billions)
Cycling	599,874	$4.29
Basketball	693,933	$3.60
Snow skiing	330,289	$2.40
Football	390,180	$2.20
Skating, all types	322,311	$1.96

Source: *Consumer Product Safety Commission, American Academy of Orthopedic Surgeons*

Round each number to the nearest billion.

$$
\begin{aligned}
\$4.29 &\rightarrow \$4 \\
\$3.60 &\rightarrow \$4 \\
\$2.40 &\rightarrow \$2 \\
\$2.20 &\rightarrow \$2 \\
+\$1.96 &\rightarrow +\$2 \\
\hline
&\$14
\end{aligned}
$$

The cost of sports injuries was about $14 billion.

 Example **APPLICATION** **①**

Advertising The table shows the household exposure of the top ten advertisers on prime-time TV between August 26 and September 1. About how many households were exposed to Advertiser 1's and Advertiser 2's ads?

To estimate, round each number to the nearest hundred million.

Advertiser	Household Exposure (millions)
1	390.4
2	216.5
3	183.4
4	172.7
5	172.6
6	136.6
7	131.4
8	126.3
9	106.7
10	106.6

$$
\begin{aligned}
390.4 &\rightarrow 400 & \text{\textit{9 > 4, so round up.}} \\
+216.5 &\rightarrow +200 & \text{\textit{1 < 5, so the digit stays the same.}} \\
\hline
&600
\end{aligned}
$$

About 600 million households were exposed to Advertiser 1's and Advertiser 2's ads.

112 Chapter 3 Adding and Subtracting Decimals

Examples
CONNECTION

Earth Science The largest cut diamond is the 545.67-carat gem known as the Golden Jubilee. Before it was cut, it weighed 775.50 carats. About how many carats of the uncut diamond were not used?

$$
\begin{array}{rcl}
775.50 & \to & 776 \\
-545.67 & \to & -546 \\
\hline
& & 230
\end{array}
$$
Round to the nearest carat. Then subtract.

About 230 carats of the uncut diamond were not used.

APPLICATION

③ Money Matters Several video games are on sale. The sale price for Video game A is $42.99, and the sale price for Video game B is $55.88.

a. About how much less is Video game A than Video game B?

$$
\begin{array}{rcl}
\$55.88 & \to & \$56 \\
- 42.99 & \to & - 43 \\
\hline
& & 13
\end{array}
$$
Round to the nearest dollar. Then subtract.

Video game A is about $13 less than Video game B.

b. If you bought both games while they were on sale, about how much would they cost?

$$
\begin{array}{rcl}
\$55.88 & \to & \$56 \\
+42.99 & \to & +43 \\
\hline
& & 99
\end{array}
$$
Round to the nearest dollar. Then add.

The games would cost about $99.

Clustering is another way you can estimate sums and differences. Clustering is used when numbers are close to the same number.

Example
APPLICATION

④ Business The table shows the charges for business related calls and faxes made by Mrs. Moore last week. About how much were her business related phone charges last week?

Minutes	Amount ($)
1.0	0.31
1.0	0.28
1.0	0.28
1.0	0.26
1.0	0.30

Since each amount is about $0.30, add this amount 5 times.

$$0.30 + 0.30 + 0.30 + 0.30 + 0.30 = 1.50$$

Mrs. Moore spent about $1.50 last week.

Lesson 3-5 Estimating Sums and Differences **113**

Transparency **3-5B** contains a teaching aid for this lesson.

Reading Mathematics Ask students what they think *clustering* means and have them give specific examples. **gathering similar people or things together; stars, grapes, peanuts, buildings**

In-Class Examples

For Example 1
Refer to the table in Example 1. About how many households were exposed to Advertiser 5 and Advertiser 6 ads? **about 300 million**

For Example 2
Annual precipitation in Seattle, Washington, is about 37.19 inches. The city of Spokane receives only about 16.49 inches annually. About how much more precipitation does Seattle receive than Spokane? **about 21 inches**

For Example 3
A cassette that regularly sells at $9.98 is on sale for $6.29.
a. About how much less is the sale price? **about $4.00**
b. If you bought one on sale and one at regular price, about how much would they cost? **about $16.00**

For Example 4
The Adventure Club decided to hold monthly aluminum can recycling drives. The table shows the amount of money collected each month. About how much money did the club collect per month? altogether? **about $45; about $135**

Month	Money
March	$45.45
April	$45.19
May	$44.95

3-6A Reasonable Answers

A Preview of Lesson 3-6

Objective Students determine whether an answer is reasonable.

Recommended Pacing	
Standard	Day 9 of 12
Honors	Day 7 of 10
Block	Day 5 of 6

1 FOCUS

Getting Started Discuss the table with students. Round each year of CD shipments. Discuss the differences of rounding to the nearest ones, tens, or hundreds place.

2 TEACH

Teaching Tip Students may not understand what is *reasonable*. Using the CD table, discuss situations when you would round to the tens, hundreds, or thousands place. For example, a distributor would round 662.1 million up to 1 billion to impress buyers. However, an advertiser might round to 660 million to promote more advertising. Then have students work through Exercises 1–4.

In-Class Example

Roberta has $65 to spend on sports equipment. She decides to buy a bat for $29.95, 2 balls for $4.59 each, and a batting glove for $14.89. She thinks she will have enough left over to buy a cap for $15. Does this seem reasonable? **no**

Additional Answer

2. **Sample answer: Brian rounded to the nearest 1,000 and Akira rounded to the nearest 100.**

Akira and Brian were shopping for CDs and noticed there were hundreds of CDs. Let's listen in!

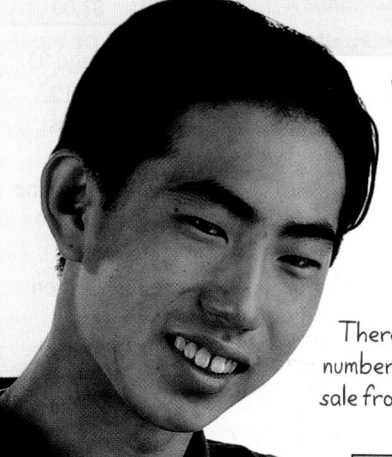

Wow! Look at the selection they have here. Do you think over a billion CDs have been sold yet?

I know where we can find the answer. I have an almanac in my backpack. We were using it today in social studies class. Let's look.

There it is. The table shows the number of CDs that were shipped for sale from 1984 to 1994.

Akira

How did you figure that? There were less than 700 million CDs shipped that year.

Year	CDs Shipped (millions)
1984	5.8
1985	22.6
1986	53.0
1987	102.1
1988	149.7
1989	207.2
1990	286.5
1991	333.3
1992	407.5
1993	495.4
1994	662.1

It looks like almost a billion CDs were shipped in 1994 alone!

Brian

THINK ABOUT IT

1. **Compare and contrast** Akira's and Brian's thinking. Whose estimate do you think is correct? Explain why. **Answers will vary.**

2. **Explain** why both boys might be considered correct. **2–4. See margin.**

3. **Choose** two years when a total of about 200 million CDs were shipped. Explain your reasoning.

4. **Apply** what you have learned from Akira and Brian's situation to solve the following problem.

   Kelsey buys a small beanbag animal for $5.54. She pays for the purchase with a $20 bill. Which is a more reasonable estimate for the amount of change she should receive: $12 or $15? Explain why.

■ Reteaching the Lesson ■

Activity Have students work in pairs to choose strategies for the exercises. Encourage students to try more than one strategy for each exercise. They should find that some strategies work better on some problems than on others.

Additional Answers

3. **Sample answer: If you round to the nearest hundred, the 1986 and 1987 amounts or the 1987 and 1988 amounts total 200 million. If you round to the nearest ten, the 1986 and 1988 amounts total 200 million.**

4. **$15 is more reasonable because $20 − $6 = $14 and $14 is closer to $15 than $12.**

For **Extra Practice**, see page 564.

ON YOUR OWN

5. The last step of the 4-step plan for problem solving asks you to *examine* your solution. *Explain* how the place value to which you round affects how you examine a solution.

6. *Write* a definition of a reasonable answer in your own words.

7. *Explain* how the strategies you used in estimating with large decimal numbers can be applied to estimating with small decimal numbers.

5–7. See students' work.

MIXED PROBLEM SOLVING

STRATEGIES
Look for a pattern.
Solve a simpler problem.
Act it out.
Guess and check.
Draw a diagram.
Make a chart.
Work backward.

Solve. Use any strategy.

8. *Write a Problem* using the following numbers and phrases: $4.59; 3 centimeters; 75° F; 9:00 A.M., and 6 hours. **See students' work.**

9. *Statistics* During the fall fund-raising project, Roberta's class sold magazine subscriptions. The pictograph shows how many magazines they sold during a 6-week period.

Subscriptions Sold Per Week

Week

4 subscriptions = ▪

a. How many subscriptions were sold during week 3? **See margin.**

b. What does the half-magazine shown during week 4 mean? **See margin.**

c. During what week did the class sell 16 subscriptions? **See margin.**

10. *Sports* Suppose 235,532 people attended a 4-game home stand to see the Texas Rangers during the 1997 season. Which is a more reasonable estimate for the number of people that attended each game: 50,000 or 60,000? Explain. **See margin.**

11. *Statistics* Based on the data in the table on page 116, what would you predict about the shipment of CDs from 1995 to 2000? Explain how you made your prediction. **See margin.**

12. *Education* Robert E. Lee High School will graduate 678 seniors on June 8. The ceremony will be held in the gymnasium. The gymnasium holds 2,100 people in addition to the graduates. Is it reasonable to offer each graduate three tickets for family and friends? Explain. **See margin.**

13. **Standardized Test Practice** Which diagram does *not* show 0.7? **B**

A

B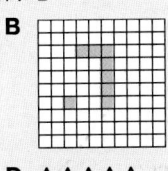

C
0.7
0.0   1.0

D △△△△△
△△△△△

Lesson 3-6A THINKING **LAB**   **117**

Extending the Lesson

Activity Have pairs of students interview the librarian or department heads to determine how they estimate budget figures each year. Have students ask questions such as: *What checking methods are used to determine the accuracy of the figures? What would happen if the figures were not accurate?*

Sample problem: *The art teacher needs to have at least half a ream of paper per student per year. A ream costs $8.95. The teacher has 180 students during the year. What would be a reasonable budget for paper?* **$900**

---

3 PRACTICE/APPLY

Check for Understanding
Use the results from Exercise 4 to determine whether students comprehend how to determine whether an answer is reasonable.

Extra Practice If students need additional practice in problem solving, extra practice is available on the following pages.
- Determine Reasonable Answers, see p. 564
- Mixed-Problem Solving, see pp. 593–594

Assignment Guide

All: 5–13

4 ASSESS

Closing Activity
Writing Have students imagine that during the course of the school year they are going to get 5 hours of math homework each night, for a total of 1,750 hours. Have them write a paragraph describing how they can determine whether that number of hours makes sense. **A more reasonable answer would be 900 hours.**

Additional Answers
9a. They sold 12 subscriptions during week three.

9b. Since each symbol means 4 subscriptions, a half-magazine means 2 subscriptions.

9c. They sold 16 subscriptions during week two.

10. 60,000 is more reasonable because 235,532 is closer to 240,000 than 200,000 and 240,000 ÷ 4 = 60,000.

11. Sample answer: By drawing a line graph and extending it to match the segment between 1993 and 1994, over 1.6 million CDs will be distributed in 2000.

12. Sample answer: yes; 2,100 ÷ 3 = 700. Since there are 678 seniors, this is a reasonable plan.

- *Study Guide Masters*, p. 22
- *Practice Masters*, p. 22
- *Enrichment Masters*, p. 22
- Transparencies 3-6, A and B
- *Assessment and Evaluation Masters*, p. 72
- *Classroom Games*, pp. 5–6
- *School to Career Masters*, p. 3
- *Technology Masters*, p. 5

 CD-ROM Program
- Resource Lesson 3-6

Recommended Pacing	
Standard	Day 10 of 12
Honors	Day 8 of 10
Block	Day 5 of 6

1 FOCUS

5-Minute Check
(Lesson 3-5)

Estimate using rounding.
1. 0.463 + 0.729
   0.5 + 0.7 = 1.2
2. 29.542 − 11.116
   30 − 11 = 19

Estimate using clustering.
3. 11.75 + 11.89 + 11.60 + 12
   48
4. 8.75 + 9.22 + 9.48 + 8.99
   36
5. Mona saw CDs on sale for $8.95 each. About how much money will she need to buy three CDs? **about $27**

 The 5-Minute Check is also available on **Transparency 3-6A** for this lesson.

Motivating the Lesson
Hands-On Activity Separate students into pairs and give each pair three number cubes. Have students take turns rolling the cubes, writing down the three numbers in any order to represent dollars and cents. Tell students this figure is the amount of money they can "deposit in their accounts." After three turns each, ask them to add up their own figures to see who has the greater sum. Point out that they are adding decimals.

3-6 Adding and Subtracting Decimals

What you'll learn
You'll learn to add and subtract decimals.

When am I ever going to use this?
You'll add and subtract decimals when you balance your checking account.

The table shows the top ten movies based on money earned on a recent weekend. What was the total earned by the top four movies?

In order to find the total, you need to add the four numbers.

Adding decimals is like adding whole numbers. Make sure that you line up the decimal points before you add or subtract.

Movie	Money Earned (millions)
A	$45.1
B	25.5
C	17.4
D	17.3
E	17.25
F	8.1
G	5.6
H	4.4
I	3.4
J	1.4

$$
\begin{array}{r}
\overset{2\ 1}{45.1} \\
25.5 \\
17.4 \\
+17.3 \\
\hline
105.3
\end{array}
$$

Estimate:
50 + 30 + 20 + 20 = 120

The top four movies earned a total of $105.3 million. The estimate shows that the answer is reasonable.

 Example 1
APPLICATION

Entertainment Refer to the table above. How much more money was earned by Movie A than by Movie J?

Explore What do you know?
You know how much money each movie earned.

What do you need to know?
You need to know how much more money Movie A earned than Movie J.

Plan You need to subtract the smaller amount earned from the larger amount earned.

Estimate first. 45 − 1 = 44

Solve
$$
\begin{array}{r}
\overset{4\ 11}{45.1} \\
-\ 1.4 \\
\hline
43.7
\end{array}
$$
Movie A earned $43.7 million more than Movie J.

Examine The estimate shows that the answer is reasonable.

Sometimes it is necessary to annex zeros in order to subtract decimals.

Examples

❷ Find the difference of 7 and 2.35.

Estimate: 7 − 2 = 5

7.00   *Annex two zeros.*
−2.35   *Rename and subtract.*

$$\begin{array}{r} \overset{6\ \ 910}{7.\cancel{0}\cancel{0}} \\ -2.35 \\ \hline 4.65 \end{array}$$

The estimate shows that the answer is reasonable.

Study Hint

Estimation When you use a calculator to add or subtract decimals, estimate to check that the result is reasonable. If it isn't, check to see if each decimal point was entered correctly.

---

❸ Find the sum of 47.68 and 7.8.

Estimate: 50 + 10 = 60

47.68 ⊞ 7.8 ⊜ 55.48

The estimate shows that the answer is reasonable.

INTEGRATION ❹ Algebra Evaluate $x + y$ if $x = 4.56$ and $y = 19.367$.

$x + y = 4.56 + 19.367$ *Replace x with 4.56 and y with 19.367.*

4.560   *Annex a zero and line up the decimal points.*
+19.367 *Add.*
23.927

The value is 23.927.

CHECK FOR UNDERSTANDING

Communicating Mathematics
2. Estimate: 4 + 0 + 2 = 6. Then line up the decimal points and add.

Guided Practice

Read and study the lesson to answer each question.

1. *Write* directions explaining how to subtract 2.67 from 3. **See margin.**
2. *Explain* how you would find the sum of 3.701, 0.49, and 2.4 using paper and pencil.
3. *Write* a paragraph explaining how adding and subtracting decimals compares to adding and subtracting whole numbers. **See students' work.**

Add or subtract.

4. 6.4 **9.7**   5. 1.34 **2.24**   6. 41.39 **18.22**   7. 3.7 **0.75**
   +3.3   +0.9   −23.17   −2.95

8. 67.38 − 37.46 **29.92**   9. 3.702 + 0.49 + 2.4 **6.592**

10. *Algebra* Solve the equation $c = 0.085 + 2.487$. **2.572**

Lesson 3-6 Adding and Subtracting Decimals **119**

Reteaching the Lesson

Activity Give groups of three students an addition or subtraction problem. Have one student line up the decimal points and another find the sum or difference. The third student checks the answer on a calculator. The group with the first correct answer makes up the next problem.

Error Analysis
Watch for students who forget to line up the decimal points before they add or subtract.
Prevent by having students turn their papers sideways and place the decimals vertically on the same ruled line.

---

2 TEACH

 Transparency 3-6B contains a teaching aid for this lesson.

Thinking Algebraically When estimating sums and differences of decimals, encourage students to write out their estimate with a variable. For example, in Example 2, they could write $7 − 2 = x$, and then find x.

In-Class Examples

For Example 1
Refer to the table on page 118 and find how much more money was earned by Movie C than by Movie E.
$0.15 million or $150,000

For Example 2
Find the difference of 90 and 9.85. **80.15**

For Example 3
Find the sum of 26.05 and 8.2. **34.25**

For Example 4
Evaluate $m + n$ if $m = 9.24$ and $n = 14.817$. **24.057**

Teaching Tip You may want to have students verify their computations by using a calculator.

3 PRACTICE/APPLY

Check for Understanding
If students need additional practice or instruction after completing Exercises 1–10, you may find one of the following options helpful.
- Extra Practice, see p. 565
- Reteaching Activity
- *Study Guide Masters*, p. 22
- *Practice Masters*, p. 22
- 🖥 Interactive Mathematics Tools Software

Additional Answer
1. Sample answer: Annex two zeros. Then line up the decimal points, rename, and subtract.

Lesson 3-6 **119**

CHAPTER Project

Exercise 34 asks students to advance to the next stage of work on the Chapter Project. Remind students to estimate an answer before working out the exact cost.

Practice   **Add or subtract.**

11. 2.3 **6.4**   **12.** 0.37 **0.92**   **13.** 0.67 **0.24**   **14.** 42.76 **11.17**
+4.1   +0.55   −0.43   −31.59

15. $6.78 **$11.77** **16.** 8 **14.76** **17.** 8.267 **1.747** **18.** 17.6 **12.87**
+ 4.99   +6.76   −6.52   −4.73

19. 6.6 − 4.58 **2.02**   **20.** 5.77 − 2.374 **3.396**

21. 0.563 + 5.8 + 6.89 **13.253**   **22.** 23.4 + 9.865 + 18.26 **51.525**

23. Find the sum of 84.34 and 67.235. **151.575**

24. How much is 46 minus 23.78? **22.22**

25. How much more than $102.90 is $115? **$12.10**

26. *Statistics* Find the average (mean) of 8.12, 7.6, and 8. Round to the nearest hundredth. **7.91**

Solve each equation.

27. $29.2 − 2.78 = b$ **26.42**   **28.** $e = 5.162 + 0.6099$ **5.7719**

29. $c = 4 − 1.9$ **2.1**   **30.** $478.98 − 46 = k$ **432.98**

31. *Algebra* What is the value of $a − b$ if $a = 34.6$ and $b = 23.88$? **10.72**

32. *Algebra* Evaluate $r + s + t$ if $r = 45.1$, $s = 16$, and $t = 8.091$. **69.191**

Applications and Problem Solving

Real World

33a. 2.6 pounds

33. *Food* The graph shows how many pounds of turkey the average person eats during the year.

  a. How many more pounds of turkey does the average person eat from October through December than from January through March?

  b. How many pounds of turkey does the average person eat in one year?
  18 pounds

GOBBLE, GOBBLE

Oct.-Dec. 6.3
July-Sept. 4.1
April-June 3.9
Jan.-March 3.7

Source: National Turkey Federation

34. *Working on the* CHAPTER Project Refer to the table on page 93. In Dawn's family, two people are over 12, and three are under 12. Find the exact cost for her family to take the Whale-Watching Tour and attend the Hawaiian Luau. **$324.75**

35. *Critical Thinking* Arrange the digits 1, 2, 3, 4, 5, 6, 7, and 8 into two decimals so that their difference is as close to 0 as possible. Use each digit only once. **0.2 − 0.1876543 = 0.0123457**

Study Guide Masters, p. 22

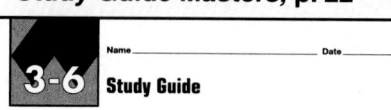

3-6 Name_____ Date_____
Study Guide

Adding and Subtracting Decimals

To add decimals, line up the decimal points.
Then add the same way you add whole numbers.

Examples **1** Find 0.465 + 0.292.   **2** Find 13.2 + 5.08 + 0.334.
        0.465   13.200
      + 0.292   5.080 ◄—*Annex zeros if necessary.*
        0.757   + 0.334
                                      18.614

To subtract decimals, line up the decimal points. Then subtract the same way you subtract whole numbers.

Examples **3** Find $155.36 − $24.17.   **4** Find 0.56 − 0.0277.
        $155.36   0.5600 ◄—*Annex zeros if necessary.*
       − 24.17   − 0.0277
        $131.19   0.5323

Add or subtract.

1. 0.352   **2.** 78.158   **3.** $9.63   **4.** 0.0123
     + 0.365   − 17.326   + 7.29   − 0.0028
     0.717   **60.832**   **$16.92**   **0.0095**

5. 2.011   **6.** $13.67   **7.** 0.0783   **8.** 9.054
     + 5.852   − 7.19   + 0.0238   − 4.038
     7.863   **$6.48**   **0.1021**   **5.016**

9. 5.014 + 12.3 + 0.4 **17.714**   **10.** 216.8 − 34.055 **182.745**

Solve each equation.

11. $m = 6.2 − 1.9$ **12.** $3.07 + 1.1 + 0.9 = k$ **13.** $44.15 − $1.99 = p$
     4.3   **5.07**   **$42.16**

14. $y = 0.075 + 1.2$ **15.** $v = 6.12 + 0.3 + 15.4$ **16.** $9 − 4.06 = c$
     1.275   **21.82**   **4.94**

© Glencoe/McGraw-Hill   T22   *Mathematics: Applications and Connections, Course 1*

120 **Chapter 3**

![MathPASS CD-ROM]

MathPASS CD-ROM

This CD-ROM offers a complete, self-paced mathematics curriculum. Each lesson includes a pretest, tutorial, guided practice, and posttest. MathPASS Lessons 6 and 7 are correlated to this Student Edition Lesson.
For Windows & Macintosh

Mixed Review

36. *Money Matters* Marta plans to buy a baseball for $6.50, a baseball glove for $37.99, and a baseball cap for $13.79. Estimate the cost of these items before tax is added. *(Lesson 3-5)* **$7 + $38 + $14 = $59**

37. **Standardized Test Practice** How long is the pencil in centimeters? *(Lesson 3-2)* **B**

    A 9 cm   **B** 8 cm

    C 7 cm   **D** 6 cm

38. *Statistics* Is the mode a misleading measure of central tendency for this set of data: 21, 20, 19, 13, 21, 18, 12, 21? Explain. *(Lesson 2-8)*

For **Extra Practice,** *see page 565.*

38. The mode is misleading because it is also the highest number in the set.

39. *Algebra* Identify the number that is the solution of the equation $42 \div h = 14$; 3, 4, or 5. *(Lesson 1-7)* **3**

The 1-Meter Dash

Get Ready This game is for two players.

    ⚃ 2 number cubes   ⊛ 2 spinners   ◑ 2 counters   📏 meterstick

Math Skill
Adding and Subtracting Decimals

Get Set
- Make a spinner that has two equal sections. Mark the sections with the words *add* and *subtract*.
- Each person starts with a counter at opposite ends of a meterstick.

Go
- The first player rolls the number cubes and spins the spinner.
- The player forms a decimal using the numbers on the number cube and then rolls the number cubes again.
- The player forms another decimal, performs the operation shown on the spinner, and then moves the counter that many centimeters along the meterstick. For example, suppose a player rolls a 2 and a 4, spins *subtract,* and then rolls a 5 and 6. That player could move $6.5 - 2.4$ or 4.1 centimeters.
- The winner is the first player to have their counter go beyond the other end of the meterstick.

 Visit www.glencoe.com/sec/math/mac/mathnet for more games.

Lesson 3-6 Adding and Subtracting Decimals **121**

CHAPTER 3 — Study Guide and Assessment

inter NET CONNECTION

Chapter Review **For additional lesson-by-lesson review, visit:** www.glencoe.com/sec/math/mac/mathnet

Vocabulary

After completing this chapter, you should be able to define each term, concept, or phrase and give an example or two of each.

Measurement
centimeter (p. 100)
meter (p. 102)
metric system (p. 102)
millimeter (p. 100)

Number and Operations
clustering (p. 113)
place value (p. 95)

Problem Solving
reasonable answers (pp. 116–117)

Understanding and Using the Vocabulary

Determine whether each statement is *true* or *false*. If the statement is false, replace the underlined word or number to make it true.

1. The number 0.07 is <u>greater</u> than 0.071. **false, less**

2. A millimeter equals <u>one thousandth</u> of a meter. **true**

3. A centimeter equals <u>one tenth</u> of a meter. **false, one hundredth**

4. When rounding decimals, the digit in the place being rounded should be rounded up if the digit to its right is <u>6</u>. **true**

5. The length of the cassette tape below is about 10 <u>millimeters</u>. **false, centimeters**

6. In 643.082 the digit 2 names the number two <u>hundredths</u>. **false, thousandths**

7. Six hundred and twelve thousandths written as a decimal is <u>0.612</u>. **false, 600.012**

8. Estimating 3.3 + 2.9 + 3.4 + 3.09 by computing 3 + 3 + 3 + 3 is an example of <u>clustering</u>. **true**

9. If the amount of your purchase is $6.74, then a reasonable amount of change from <u>$20</u> is $13.26. **true**

In Your Own Words

10. *Explain* when and why the clustering strategy is used to estimate sums. **See margin.**

MindJogger Videoquizzes

MindJogger Videoquizzes provide an alternative review of concepts presented in this chapter. Students work in teams to answer questions, gaining points for correct answers. The questions are presented in three rounds.
Round 1 Concepts–5 questions
Round 2 Skills–4 questions
Round 3 Problem Solving–4 questions

Objectives & Examples

Upon completing this chapter, you should be able to:

● model, read, and write decimals *(Lesson 3-1)*

Model $\frac{3}{100}$ using base-ten blocks.

Write $\frac{73}{100}$ as a decimal.

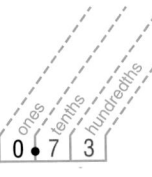

Write 7 in the tenths place and 3 in the hundredths place.

0 • 7 3

Write 0.024 in words.

The last digit, 4, is in the thousandths place. The decimal in words is *twenty-four thousandths*.

● show relationships among metric units of length and measure line segments *(Lesson 3-2)*

The line segment measures 4.1 centimeters or 41 millimeters.

Review Exercises

Use these exercises to review and prepare for the chapter test.

Write each fraction or mixed number as a decimal.

11. $\frac{8}{100}$ 0.08   12. $8\frac{9}{10}$ 8.9

13. $14\frac{17}{1,000}$ 14.017   14. $\frac{643}{10,000}$ 0.0643

Write each expression as a decimal.

15. two tenths 0.2

16. thirty-four hundredths 0.34

17. fifty-three thousandths 0.053

18. thirty and twelve ten-thousandths 30.0012

19. *Life Science* An amoeba is one of the larger creatures of the microscopic world. The length of a typical amoeba is 0.0008 meter. Write 0.0008 in words. **eight ten-thousandths**

Use a centimeter ruler to measure each line segment.

20. ———————— 4 cm

21. ———————————— 6 cm

22. ———— 2.5 cm

Use a centimeter ruler to measure one side of the figure.

23.   2 cm

Objectives & Examples

This section reviews the skills and concepts of the chapter and shows completely worked examples.

Review Exercises

These exercises provide practice for the corresponding objectives.

Assessment and Evaluation Masters, pp. 59–60

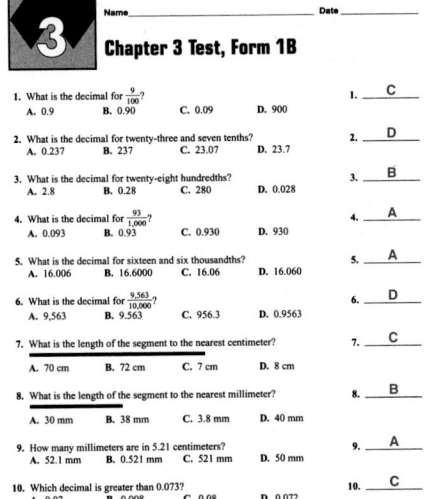

Assessment and Evaluation

Six forms of Chapter 3 Test are available in the *Assessment and Evaluation Masters* as shown in the chart.

Chapter 3 Test, Form 1B, is shown at the right. Chapter 3 Test, Form 2B, is shown on the next page.

1A	Multiple Choice	Honors
2A	Free Response	Honors
1B	Multiple Choice	Average
1C	Multiple Choice	Basic
2B	Free Response	Average
2C	Free Response	Basic

Assessment and Evaluation Masters, pp. 65–66

Name_____ Date_____

3 **Chapter 3 Test, Form 2B**

Write each fraction or mixed number as a decimal.
1. $2\frac{5}{10}$ 1. ____2.5____
2. $\frac{29}{1,000}$ 2. ___0.029___
3. $\frac{38}{100}$ 3. ___0.38____
4. $\frac{123}{10,000}$ 4. ___0.0123__
5. forty-four ten-thousandths   5. ___0.0044__
6. nineteen and three thousandths   6. ___19.003__

Measure each line segment to the nearest centimeter.
7. ▬▬▬▬▬   7. ___5 cm___
8. ▬▬▬▬   8. ___4 cm___

Measure each line segment to the nearest millimeter.
9. ▬▬▬▬   9. ___42 mm___
10. ▬▬▬▬   10. ___59 mm___
11. Estimate the height of a minivan using the metric system.   11. Sample answer: 2 m

State the greatest number in each group.
12. 0.315 or 0.0325   12. ___0.315___
13. 0.799, 0.08, or 0.8   13. ___0.8_____
14. 0.290, 0.30, 0.280   14. ___0.30____
15. Order the set of decimals from least to greatest: 0.038, 0.4, 0.35, 0.0005.   15. 0.0005, 0.038, 0.35, 0.4
16. Order the set of decimals from greatest to least: 0.089, 0.090, 0.009.   16. 0.090, 0.089, 0.009

© Glencoe/McGraw-Hill   65   Mathematics: Applications and Connections, Course 1

3 **Chapter 3 Test, Form 2B (continued)**

Round each number to the underlined place-value position.
17. 0.34<u>4</u>4   17. ___0.344___
18. 38.<u>9</u>49   18. ___38.9____
19. 4<u>3</u>.61   19. ___44_____
20. Round $1.32 to the nearest dollar.   20. ___$1_____

Estimate. Use any method.
21. $5.49 + $4.75 + $5.08   21. $5 + $5 + $5 = $15
22. 75.42 − 12.81   22. 75 − 13 = 62
23. 3.05 + 2.99 + 3.47 + 2.72   23. 3 + 3 +3 + 3 = 12
24. 70.4 − 35.1   24. 70 − 35 = 35
25. 98.2 + 25.46   25. 100 + 25 = 125

Add or subtract.
26. 89.4 + 78.56   26. ___167.96__
27. 98.1 − 17.89   27. ___80.21___
28. 50 − 9.3   28. ___40.7____
29. 4.9 + 3.876 + 13.029   29. ___21.805__
30. How much is 48 minus 35.47?   30. ___12.53___
31. Evaluate $r - s$ if $r = 6.792$ and $s = 3.9994$.   31. ___2.7926__

Solve.
32. Emily wants to buy notebooks at $2.95 each. She has $10 to spend. About how many notebooks can she buy?   32. ___3_____
33. Four same-priced items were purchased. Based on rounding, the estimate for the total was $20. What is the maximum price each item could have cost?   33. ___$5.49___

© Glencoe/McGraw-Hill   66   Mathematics: Applications and Connections, Course 1

Objectives & Examples

● **compare decimals and order a set of decimals** *(Lesson 3-3)*

Is 5.43 greater than 5.427?

Since 3 hundredths is greater than 2 hundredths, 5.43 is greater than 5.427.

Write 45.93, 46.4, 45.89, and 45.311 in order from least to greatest.

The decimals in order from least to greatest are 45.311, 45.89, 45.93, and 46.4.

● **round decimals** *(Lesson 3-4)*

Round 4.739 to the nearest tenth.

The digit to the right of the tenths place is 3. So, 7 remains the same.

4.739 rounded to the nearest tenth is 4.7.

● **estimate decimal sums and differences** *(Lesson 3-5)*

a. rounding

   7.79   →   7.8
   −2.32 → −2.3
                  5.5

b. clustering

   7.96 + 8.1 + 8.23 + 7.7 → 8 + 8 + 8 + 8
                           → 8 × 4 = 32

● **add and subtract decimals** *(Lesson 3-6)*

Find the difference of 7.3 and 2.89.

   6 1210
   7.3̶0̶   *Line up the decimal points.*
  −2.89   *Annex a zero.*
   4.41   *Rename and subtract.*

Review Exercises

State the greatest number in each group.

24. 5.218 or 5.207   **25.** 11.6 or 11.13

26. 13.02, 13.022, or 13.21 **13.21**
24. 5.218   25. 11.6

Order each set of decimals from least to greatest. **27. 0.0289, 0.0319, 0.032, 0.31**

27. 0.0319, 0.31, 0.032, 0.0289

28. 75.3, 7.598, 7.8, 75.6, 75.09
7.598, 7.8, 75.09, 75.3, 75.6

Order each set of decimals from greatest to least.

29. 6.32, 6.75, 6.39, 6.02 **6.75, 6.39, 6.32, 6.02**

30. 17.0463, 17.045, 17.023, 17.0201, 17.002
30. 17.023, 17.0201, 17.0463, 17.045, 17.002

Round each number to the underlined place-value position.

31. <u>7</u>.29 **7**   **32.** 76.8<u>0</u>2 **76.80**

33. 13.<u>5</u>81 **13.6**   **34.** 69.<u>9</u>99 **70.0**

Estimate. 35. $5 - 1 = 4$ 36. $30 + 20 = 50$

35. $4.86 - 1.131$ **36.** $34.29 + 17.58

37. $6.19 + 5.98 + 5.7 + 6 + 6.3$
$6 + 6 + 6 + 6 + 6 = 30$

38. *Money Matters* Inali worked three days last week. He earned $19.85 on Monday, $17.75 on Thursday, and $21.30 on Saturday. About how much did he earn in all? **about $60**

Add or subtract.

39.   15.63 **12.912** **40.**   4.63 **9.35**
         − 2.718   +4.72

41. $25.6 + 47.92 + 3.1 + 0.48$ **77.1**

42. Solve $x = 12 - 3.45$. **8.55**

Test and Review Software

You may use this software, a combination of an item generator and item bank, to create your own tests or worksheets. Types of items include free response, multiple choice, short answer, and open ended.

CD-ROM Program

The CD-ROM Program contains an Assessment Game whose questions review the concepts in this chapter.

Applications & Problem Solving

43. Inventory Control Cheryl works in a warehouse. She must place items on shelves according to their stock number. Arrange the set of stock numbers in order from least to greatest. *(Lesson 3-3)*

7,321.5   7,346.4   7,320.4
7,321.539   7,342.98   7,346.24

7320.4, 7321.5, 7321.539, 7342.98, 7346.24, 7346.4

44. Money Matters Lamont wrote a check for groceries. On the check, he wrote the amount of purchase as "Seventy-six and $\frac{32}{100}$ dollars." Write the amount as a decimal. *(Lesson 3-1)* **$76.32**

45. Money Matters Mr. Marlin bought three pairs of athletic shoes for his children. The shoes cost $39.99, $75.50, and $89.90. Estimate the amount of money Mr. Marlin spent on shoes. *(Lesson 3-5)* **about $210**

46. Reasonable Answers Jackson bought a pennant at a souvenir shop. He paid for the $7.59 pennant with a $10 bill. Should he expect about $4 or $2 in change? *(Lesson 3-6A)* **about $2**

Alternative Assessment

● **Open Ended**

Suppose you are planning a family picnic. The prices of the items you want are shown in the table.

Item	Cost
chips	2 bags for $4.48
bread	3 loaves for $3.29
cookies	12 for $3.50
apples	4 for $1.25

Estimate the cost to feed your family.
See students' work.

Suppose you bought the quantities listed in the cost column. Write the total dollar amount in words. If you have a $20 bill, would you expect about $10 or $8 in change?

twelve and $\frac{52}{100}$ dollars; about $8

A practice test for Chapter 3 is provided on page 597.

● Completing the **CHAPTER Project**

Use the following checklist to make sure your plan is complete.

☑ A schedule of travel times and activities.

☑ All travel costs including transportation, lodging, food, souvenirs, and entertainment. You may have to estimate the cost of some items.

☑ A paragraph describing why you chose your vacation spot.

● PORTFOLIO Write an example to illustrate using each type of estimation (rounding and clustering), and include them in your portfolio.

Applications & Problem Solving

This section provides additional practice in solving real-world problems that involve the skills of this chapter.

Alternative Assessment

The **Open Ended** section provides students with a performance assessment opportunity to evaluate their work and understanding.

CHAPTER Project

Students should complete the final stages of their project and prepare a class demonstration of their results. A scoring guide for the project is available in the *Investigations and Projects Masters*, p. 27.

PORTFOLIO Students should add to their portfolios at this time.

Assessment and Evaluation Masters, p. 69

Name_____ Date_____

3 **Chapter 3 Performance Assessment**

Instructions: Demonstrate your knowledge by giving a clear, concise solution to each problem. Be sure to include all relevant drawings and justify your answers. You may show your solutions in more than one way or investigate beyond the requirements of the problems.

1. Use the table to answer each question.

Amounts of Gases in Dry Air	
Gas	**Amount**
Nitrogen	$\frac{7,802}{10,000}$
Argon	ninety-four ten-thousandths
Oxygen	$\frac{201}{1,000}$
Other	$\frac{94}{10,000}$

  a. Write the amount of argon in dry air as a decimal.

  b. Write each fraction in the table as a decimal.

  c. Order the decimals from least to greatest.

  d. Find the total amount of oxygen and nitrogen in dry air.

  e. How much more oxygen than argon is there in dry air?

  f. Tell how to round a decimal without using a number line.

  g. Round each decimal in parts a and b to the nearest hundredth.

2. Refer to the rectangle. The perimeter of a rectangle is $l + l + w + w$.

  a. Use a centimeter ruler to measure the length and width of the rectangle.

  b. Estimate the perimeter of the rectangle. Explain why you would consider this a reasonable number for the perimeter of the rectangle.

© Glencoe/McGraw-Hill   69   *Mathematics: Applications and Connections, Course 1*

Performance Assessment

Additional performance assessment tasks for this chapter are included in the *Assessment and Evaluation Masters* on page 69. A scoring guide is also provided on page 81.

The Standardized Test Practice may be used to help students prepare for standardized tests. The test items are written in the same style as those in state proficiency tests and standardized tests like CAT, CTBS, ITBS, MAT, SAT, and Terra Nova. The test items cover skills and concepts covered up to this point in the text.

The pages can be used as an overnight assessment. After students have completed the pages, discuss how each problem can be solved, or provide copies of the solutions from the *Solutions Manual.*

Section One: Multiple Choice

There are twelve multiple-choice questions in this section. Choose the best answer. If a correct answer is *not here*, mark the letter for Not Here.

1. The class scores on a history quiz were: 8, 9, 8, 8, 7, 9, 10, 7, 10, 8, 8, 9, 9, 10, 9, and 8. What was the mode? **A**
   - A 8
   - B 8.5
   - C 8.56
   - D 8 and 9

2. Jodi keeps her fish in a tank that has a base 60 centimeters wide and 100 centimeters long. If she gets a tank that is 20 centimeters wider but with the same length as the older tank, what will be the dimensions of the new tank? **H**
   - F 40 cm by 100 cm
   - G 60 cm by 120 cm
   - H 80 cm by 100 cm
   - J 80 cm by 120 cm

3. Write $2 \times 3^3 \times 5 \times 7^2$ as the product of factors. **C**
   - A $2 \times 3 \times 5 \times 7$
   - B $2 \times 3 \times 3 \times 5 \times 7^2$
   - C $2 \times 3 \times 3 \times 3 \times 5 \times 7 \times 7$
   - D $3^3 \times 7^2$

4. What is the solution of $6a = 42$? **J**
   - F 4
   - G 5
   - H 6
   - J 7

5. Which shows the number *five and eighty-six thousandths?* **A**
   - A 5.086
   - B 5.0086
   - C 5.860
   - D 5.86

6. The graph shows the number of donuts sold at two stores.

DONUT SALES

About how many more donuts were sold at The Superstore than at Max's Market on Wednesday? **G**
   - F 0
   - G 20
   - H 40
   - J 60

Please note that Questions 7–12 have five answer choices.

7. A TV costs $975, a home theater system costs $395, and a VCR costs $169. Which is the best estimate for the total amount for this entertainment package? **D**
   - A $1,000
   - B $1,200
   - C $1,300
   - D $1,600
   - E $2,000

8. Four boxes of cereal have weights of 22, 11, 29, and 21 ounces. Which weight is a reasonable average weight of the 4 boxes of cereal? **J**
   - F 50 ounces
   - G 40 ounces
   - H 30 ounces
   - J 20 ounces
   - K 10 ounces

126 Chapters 1–3 Standardized Test Practice

Assessment and Evaluation Masters, p. 75

◀◀◀ **Instructional Resources**

Another cumulative review is shown at the left and is available in the *Assessment and Evaluation Masters,* p. 75.

9. A tree farm has 438 seedlings to be planted in 6 rows. How many seedlings need to be planted in each row? **B**
   - **A** 89
   - **B** 73
   - **C** 66
   - **D** 63
   - **E** Not Here

10. Lin paid $275.59 for a 25-inch color TV. The tax was $15.60. What was the price of the TV? **J**
    - **F** $291.19
    - **G** $269.99
    - **H** $260.99
    - **J** $259.99
    - **K** Not Here

11. If an airplane travels 435 miles per hour, how many miles will it travel in 5 hours? **D**
    - **A** 2,055 mi
    - **B** 2,075 mi
    - **C** 2,155 mi
    - **D** 2,175 mi
    - **E** Not Here

12. Each day Toru drives his delivery truck 2.75 kilometers to his first stop, 0.5 kilometer to his second stop, 7.8 kilometers to his third stop, and 5.42 kilometers back to the distribution center. How many kilometers does Toru drive his truck each day? **K**
    - **F** 15.47 km
    - **G** 13.47 km
    - **H** 13.22 km
    - **J** 4.4 km
    - **K** Not Here

 Test Practice For additional test practice questions, visit:

www.glencoe.com/sec/math/mac/mathnet

Test-Taking Tip THE PRINCETON REVIEW

You can prepare for taking standardized tests by working through practice tests like this one. The more you work with different styles of testing, the better you become at test taking.

Section Two: Free Response

This section contains eight questions for which you will provide short answers. Write your answers on your paper.

13. There will be 120 people at the music awards banquet. Each table seats 8 people. How can you find the number of tables needed? **divide 120 by 8**

14. Any number that makes an equation true is a(n) _____. **solution**

15. The lengths in miles of the Great Lakes are Lake Superior, 350; Lake Michigan, 307; Lake Huron, 206; Lake Erie, 241; and Lake Ontario, 193. What is the median of this data? **241 miles**

16. Round 5.99$\underline{9}$8 to the underlined place-value position. **6.000**

17. What is the value of $8 + 6 \times 10$? **68**

18. State the greater of the numbers, 1.089 or 1.09. **1.09**

19. Which measure of central tendency would be best to describe the colors of cars at a used car lot? **mode**

20. Evaluate the expression $a - b$ if $a = 42.2$ and $b = 35.9$. **6.3**

Assessment and Evaluation Masters, pp. 73-74

3 Chapter 3 Standardized Test Practice

Name_____ Date_____

1. Mrs. Moore's math class test scores are 74, 87, 92, 72, 89, 75, 67, 69, 84, 99, 86, and 75. Determine the range of the data.
   A. 75   B. 99   C. 32   D. 30   1. __C__

2. What would be an appropriate scale for the data in Question 1?
   A. 66 to 100   B. 68 to 99   C. 10   D. 70 to 100   2. __A__

3. How many millimeters are in 5.8 centimeters?
   A. 0.58 mm   B. 6 mm   C. 58 mm   D. 5 mm   3. __C__

4. Order the decimals from least to greatest. 9.99, 9.92, 10.25, 9.96
   A. 10.25, 9.99, 9.96, 9.92   B. 9.96, 9.92, 9.99, 10.25
   C. 9.92, 9.99, 9.96, 10.25   D. 9.92, 9.96, 9.99, 10.25   4. __D__

5. A fathom is equal to 1.8288 meters. For easier reference, this number is rounded to the nearest hundredth. What number is used?
   A. 1.8 m   B. 1.83 m   C. 1.829 m   D. 1.82 m   5. __B__

6. A dram is a British unit of weight equal to 3.88 grams. A standard aspirin tablet weighs eight hundred thirty six ten-thousandths drams. Write this weight as a decimal.
   A. 0.0836   B. 836.0010   C. 8.3006   D. 0.836   6. __A__

7. As a gift for her father, Yasuaki ordered books for $6.95, $9.95, $7.95, and $6.95. She had a coupon for $15 off her purchase. About what was the cost of her order after the coupon?
   A. $32   B. $16.50   C. $15   D. $17   7. __D__

8. The number of wins for the 1995-96 season for each team in the Central Division of the NBA were 41, 52, 25, 46, 72, 21, 46, 47. Determine the stems for this set of data.
   A. 2, 4, 5, 7   B. 1, 2, 5, 6, 7
   C. 2, 3, 4, 5, 6, 7   D. 1, 3, 5, 7   8. __C__

9. In science class, teams measured how far two frogs jumped in a certain amount of time. Stacey and Moira's frogs jumped 438.762 meters and 521.778 meters. What was the total distance for the two frogs?
   A. 960.540 m   B. 83.016 m
   C. 961 m   D. 959.540 m   9. __A__

10. To reach a friend's house, you have to walk 3 blocks east and 4 blocks north. If your house is at the origin, how could you represent your friend's house with an ordered pair?
    A. (4, 3)   B. (3, 4)   C. 7 blocks   D. You can't.   10. __B__

© Glencoe/McGraw-Hill   73   Mathematics: Applications and Connections, Course 1

3 Chapter 3 Standardized Test Practice (continued)

11. Evaluate $15 \div 3 + 27 \div 3$.
    A. 11   B. 4   C. 14   D. 16   11. __C__

12. A theater has 27 rows of main floor seats. Each row has 112 seats in it. All of the main floor seats are filled and 40 people are seated in the balcony. How many people are in the theater?
    A. 3,024   B. 3,064   C. 2,984   D. 1,192   12. __B__

13. What three types of graphs are commonly seen in newspapers?
    A. bar graphs, line graphs, circle graphs
    B. bar graphs, circle graphs, square graphs
    C. line graphs, calendar graphs, bar graphs
    D. circle graphs, triangle graphs, line graphs   13. __A__

14. Find the next three numbers in the pattern: 28, 32, 36, _?_, _?_, _?_.
    A. 38, 42, 46   B. 44, 48, 52
    C. 42, 44, 46   D. 40, 44, 48   14. __D__

15. Estimate $492 \div 5$.
    A. 98.4   B. 10   C. 100   D. 1,000   15. __C__

16. Solve $54 + a = 72$ using mental math.
    A. 126   B. 18   C. 13   D. 86   16. __B__

17. A movie theater owner calculates the income from a Saturday movie matinee by evaluating the expression $6.50A + 3.50C$, where A = adults and C = children. If $A = 25$ and $C = 105$, what is the income?
    A. $530   B. $770   C. $1300   D. $630   17. __A__

18. If you make a frequency chart for the letters in the title "Hail to the Chief," what letter is used most frequently?
    A. H   B. A   C. I   D. T   18. __A__

19. Evaluate $4 \cdot 6^2 + 3^3$.
    A. 181   B. 57   C. 67   D. 171   19. __D__

20. You are making a line graph for the average student ages in your school. The horizontal axis will be grade levels and the vertical axis will be average ages at each grade level. How do you expect the graph to appear?
    A. flat line   B. rising line
    C. falling line   D. cannot determine   20. __B__

© Glencoe/McGraw-Hill   74   Mathematics: Applications and Connections, Course 1

Instructional Resources ▶▶▶

Additional standardized test practice is shown at the right and is available in the *Assessment and Evaluation Masters*, pp. 73-74.

Interdisciplinary Investigation

Interdisciplinary Investigation

GET READY

This optional investigation is designed to be completed by a group of 4 or 5 students over several days or several weeks.

Mathematical Overview

This investigation utilizes the concepts from Chapters 1–3.
- converting time from minutes to seconds
- adding and subtracting decimals
- drawing statistical graphs

Time Management	
Gathering Data	30 minutes
Calculations	20 minutes
Creating Graphs	30 minutes
Summarizing Data	15 minutes
Presentation	10 minutes

Instructional Resources

- *Investigations and Projects Masters*, pp. 1–4
- *Hands-On Lab Masters*
  - grid paper, p. 11

Investigations and Projects Masters, p. 4

Name_____ Date_____

Interdisciplinary Investigation
(Student Edition, Pages 136–137)

What's for Dinner?

Use these tables to record your data.

Breakfast	Lunch	Dinner

Menu Item	Calories	Grams of Protein	Milligrams of Sodium	Grams of Fat
Total				

Menu Item	Calories	Grams of Protein	Milligrams of Sodium	Grams of Fat
Total				

© Glencoe/McGraw-Hill 4 *Mathematics: Applications and Connections, Course 3*

"O" IS FOR OLYMPICS

What do Atlanta, Georgia, and Athens, Greece, have in common? Both cities were sites for the modern Olympic Games. In 1896, Athens hosted the first modern Olympic Games with 13 nations participating. Now almost 200 nations compete every four years.

Are athletes today faster? How do the times of runners today compare to runners in 1896? Are swimmers getting faster every year? How do the times for men and women compare?

What You'll Do

In this investigation, you will collect data about an Olympic event. You will graph the data and predict future records in the event.

Materials calculator

 graph paper

Procedure

1. Work in groups of four. Find a source of winning Olympic times for each year that the games were held. Select one timed event in which both women and men participate. The event needs to have been held at least ten times. Two examples are the 100-meter dash and the 100-meter freestyle (swimming).

2. Separate your group into pairs. One pair will work with the men's times, and the other pair with the women's times for the event you selected. Make a table to display the times. Write all times in seconds. For example, 1 m 22.2 s is 60 s + 22.2 s or 82.2 s.

3. Graph your results.

4. Predict the winning times for men and women for the year 2012. Does your prediction seem reasonable?

Technology Tips

- Use a **calculator** to determine the mean and median.

- Use a **graphing calculator** or **graphing software** to display your graphs.

◄◄◄ Instructional Resources

A recording sheet to help students organize their data for this investigation is shown at the left and is available in the *Investigations and Projects Masters,* p. 4.

Cooperative Learning

This investigation offers an excellent opportunity for using cooperative learning groups. For more information on cooperative learning strategies and group management, see *Cooperative Learning in the Mathematics Classroom.*

Making the Connection

Use the Olympic data you collected as needed to help in these investigations.

Language Arts

Your friend says, "Men are better than women in sports and always will be." Write a letter to your friend stating whether you agree or disagree with this statement. Use the data from the investigation to support your opinion.

Foreign Language

Select a winner in an Olympic event from a country that speaks a foreign language that you know or are interested in. Write an article about the athlete's victory using that language.

Social Studies

Select a popular sport. Research the history of this sport and write a short report.

Go Further

- Predict when you think men and women will have the same time in the event you used in the investigation. What do you think the fastest time will ever be for that event?

- If possible, time everyone in your class in the 100-meter dash. How do the times compare to the Olympic times?

 Research For more information on the history of the Olympics, visit the website below.

Data Collection and Comparison To share and compare your data with other students in the U.S., visit:

www.glencoe.com/sec/math/mac/mathnet

 PORTFOLIO You may want to place your work on this investigation in your portfolio.

Working in Teams Each group of four should research various events that fit the criteria. They should then discuss and agree on what event to investigate. After they separate into pairs, each member of the pair should check the other's conversions, addition, and subtraction. They should work together to create an accurate and colorful graph.

Making the Connection

You may wish to alert other teachers on your team that your students may need their assistance in this investigation.
Language Arts Students need to edit and rewrite their letters until their wording is clear and effective. They need to support their statements with facts from their data.
Foreign Language Encourage students to use a foreign language dictionary and to ask a teacher of that language for help if necessary.
Social Studies Students should include the country of origin and the major countries where the sport is popular today.

***Investigations and Projects Masters*, p. 3**

SCORING GUIDE

Interdisciplinary Investigation
(Student Edition, Pages 136–137)

What's for Dinner?

Level	Specific Criteria
3 Superior	• Shows a thorough understanding of the concepts of expressing numbers as ratios and converting between fractions and percents. • Uses appropriate strategies to solve problems. • Computations are correct. • Written explanations are exemplary. • Charts, model, and any statements included are appropriate and sensible. • Goes beyond the requirements of some or all problems.
2 Satisfactory, with minor flaws	• Shows understanding of the concepts of expressing numbers as ratios and converting between fractions and percents. • Uses appropriate strategies to solve problems. • Computations are mostly correct. • Written explanations are effective. • Charts, model, and any statements included are appropriate and sensible. • Satisfies the requirements of problems.
1 Nearly Satisfactory, with obvious flaws	• Shows understanding of most of the concepts of expressing numbers as ratios and converting between fractions and percents. • May not use appropriate strategies to solve problems. • Computations are mostly correct. • Written explanations are satisfactory. • Charts, model, and any statements included are appropriate and sensible. • Satisfies the requirements of problems.
0 Unsatisfactory	• Shows little or no understanding of the concepts of expressing numbers as ratios and converting between fractions and percents. • Does not use appropriate strategies to solve problems. • Computations are incorrect. • Written explanations are not satisfactory. • Charts, model, and any statements included are not appropriate or sensible. • Does not satisfy the requirements of problems.

© Glencoe/McGraw-Hill 3 *Mathematics: Applications and Connections, Course 3*

ASSESS

You may wish to have students graph their results on posterboard for class presentation. During this presentation, ask students what they learned about time differences in men's and women's events and differences over the years covered.

Instructional Resources ▶▶▶
Sample solutions for this investigation are provided in the *Investigations and Projects Masters* on p. 2. The scoring guide for assessing student performance shown at the right is also available on p. 3.

Multiplying and Dividing Decimals

Previewing the Chapter

Overview

In this chapter, students learn to estimate decimal products, to multiply and divide decimals by whole numbers and decimals, and to round decimal quotients. The distributive property is used to compute products mentally. Finding the perimeter and area of figures and naming metric measurements is integrated into the chapter. Students learn to solve problems by first solving a simpler problem.

Lesson (pages)	Lesson Objectives	NCTM Standards 2000	Standardized Tests	State/Local Objectives
4-1A (132)	Use grid paper to multiply decimals by whole numbers.	1, 5–8, 10		
4-1 (133–136)	Estimate and find the products of decimals and whole numbers.	1, 2, 4–10	CAT, CTBS, ITBS, SAT, TN	
4-2 (137–139)	Compute products mentally using the distributive property.	1, 2, 5–9		
4-3A (140)	Use grid paper to multiply decimals.	1, 6–8, 10	CTBS, TN	
4-3 (141–143)	Multiply decimals.	1, 2, 3, 5–10	CAT, CTBS, ITBS, MAT, SAT, TN	
4-3B (144)	Explore how data and formulas are entered in a computer spreadsheet.	1, 6–9		
4-4 (145–148)	Find the perimeters and the areas of rectangles and squares.	1–4, 6–10	MAT, SAT	
4-4B (149)	Explore how perimeter and area are related.	2–4, 6–9		
4-5A (150–151)	Solve problems by first solving a simpler problem.	1–10	ITBS, MAT	
4-5 (152–155)	Divide decimals by whole numbers.	1–4, 6–10	CAT, CTBS, ITBS, SAT, TN	
4-6A (156)	Use base-ten blocks to divide decimals.	1, 7–10		
4-6 (157–159)	Divide decimals by decimals.	1, 5–10	CTBS, MAT, SAT, TN	
4-7 (161–163)	Divide decimals involving special cases of zero in the quotient.	1–4, 6–9	CTBS, MAT, TN	
4-8 (164–166)	Use metric units of mass and capacity.	1, 4, 6–9	ITBS, MAT, SAT	
4-9 (167–169)	Change units within the metric system.	1, 2, 6–10	CAT, CTBS, MAT, SAT, TN	

CAT = California Achievement Tests, CTBS = Comprehensive Tests of Basic Skills, ITBS = Iowa Tests of Basic Skills,
MAT = Metropolitan Achievement Tests, SAT = Stanford Achievement Tests, TN = Terra Nova
For the key to numbering of NCTM Standards 2000, see page T6.

Organizing the Chapter

 The **Interactive Lesson Planner** contains all of the blackline masters and transparencies. This CD-ROM also includes an easy-to-use lesson planning calendar.

LESSON PLANNING GUIDE

Lesson	Extra Practice (Student Edition)	BLACKLINE MASTERS (PAGE NUMBERS)										Transparencies A and B
		Study Guide	Practice	Enrichment	Assessment & Evaluation	Classroom Games	Diversity	Hands-On Lab	School to Career	Science and Math Lab Manual	Technology	
4-1A								43				
4-1	p. 565	23	23	23								4-1
4-2	p. 565	24	24	24							7	4-2
4-3A								44				
4-3	p. 566	25	25	25	99							4-3
4-3B												
4-4	p. 566	26	26	26							8	4-4
4-4B								45				
4-5A	p. 566											
4-5	p. 567	27	27	27	98, 99				4	73–76		4-5
4-6A								46				
4-6	p. 567	28	28	28		7–9						4-6
4-7	p. 567	29	29	29	100							4-7
4-8	p. 568	30	30	30								4-8
4-9	p. 568	31	31	31	100		4	72				4-9
Study Guide/ Assessment					85–97, 101–103							

OTHER CHAPTER RESOURCES

Student Edition
Chapter Project, pp. 131, 135, 143, 173
School to Career, p. 160
Let the Games Begin, p. 166

Technology
 MathPASS CD-ROM

 Interactive Mathematics Tools Software

Teacher's Classroom Resources

Applications
Family Letters and Activities, pp. 7–8
Investigations and Projects Masters, pp. 29–32

Meeting Individual Needs
Transition Booklet, pp. 21–28, 31–34
Investigations for the Special Education Student, pp. 9–12, 31–34

Teaching Aids
Answer Key Masters
Block Scheduling Booklet
Lesson Planning Guide
Solutions Manual

Professional Publications
Glencoe Mathematics Professional Series

Planning the Chapter

MindJogger Videoquizzes provide a unique format for reviewing concepts presented in the chapter.

ASSESSMENT RESOURCES

Student Edition

Mixed Review, pp. 136, 139, 143, 148, 155, 159, 163, 166, 169
Mid-Chapter Self Test, p. 155
Math Journal, pp. 138, 147, 162
Study Guide and Assessment, pp. 170–173
Performance Task, p. 173
Portfolio Suggestion, p. 173
Standardized Test Practice, pp. 174–175
Chapter Test, p. 598

Assessment and Evaluation Masters

Multiple-Choice Tests (Forms 1A, 1B, 1C), pp. 85–90
Free-Response Tests (Forms 2A, 2B, 2C), pp. 91–96
Performance Assessment, p. 97
Mid-Chapter Test, p. 98
Quizzes A–D, pp. 99–100
Standardized Test Practice, pp. 101–102
Cumulative Review, p. 103

Teacher's Wraparound Edition

5-Minute Check, pp. 133, 137, 141, 145, 152, 157, 161, 164, 167
Building Portfolios, p. 130
Math Journal, pp. 132, 140, 144, 149, 156
Closing Activity, pp. 136, 139, 143, 148, 151, 155, 159, 163, 166, 169

Technology

Test and Review Software
MindJogger Videoquizzes
CD-ROM Program

MATERIALS AND MANIPULATIVES

Lesson 4-1A
grid paper†
markers
scissors*

Lesson 4-3A
grid paper†
markers

Lesson 4-3B
computer
spreadsheet software

Lesson 4-4B
grid paper†
scissors*

Lesson 4-6A
base-ten blocks*

Lesson 4-8
index cards
tape

*Glencoe Manipulative Kit

†Glencoe Overhead Manipulative Resources

PACING CHART

See pages T25–T27 for the Course Planning Calendar.

COURSE	DAY 1	DAY 2	DAY 3	DAY 4	DAY 5	DAY 6	DAY 7
Standard	Chapter Project	Lessons 4-1A & 4-1		Lesson 4-2	Lessons 4-3A & 4-3		Lesson 4-4
Honors	Chapter Project	Lesson 4-1	Lesson 4-2	Lessons 4-3 & 4-3B		Lessons 4-4 & 4-4B	
Block	Chapter Project & Lesson 4-1A	Lessons 4-1 & 4-2	Lessons 4-3A & 4-3	Lessons 4-4 & 4-5A	Lessons 4-5 & 4-6A	Lessons 4-6 & 4-7	Lessons 4-8 & 4-9

The *Transition Booklet* (Skills 9–12, 14–15) can be used to practice multiplying and dividing by 1- and 2-digit numbers and measuring capacity and weight.

Interactive Mathematics:
Activities and Investigations

is an activity-based program that may be used as an enhancement for chapters in **Mathematics: Applications and Connections.**

Unit 2, Activity One, Menu B
Use with Lesson 4-5A.

Summary Students estimate how many beans, popcorn kernels, and rice are in three jars. They may want to solve a simpler problem by measuring out a small amount of the object being counted and use this information to make their estimation. Students write about their findings, post them around the room, and discuss the results.

Math Connection Students use proportional reasoning to solve the estimation problem. A proportion is an equation that shows that two ratios are equivalent. Students may solve a simpler problem as their problem-solving strategy.

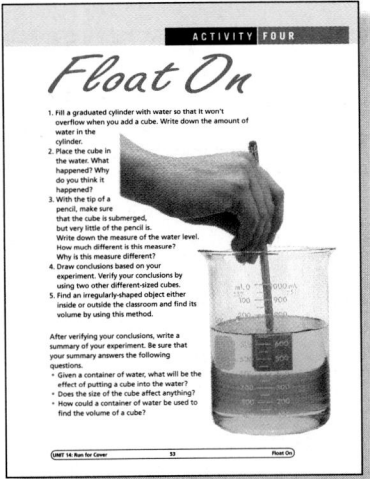

Unit 14, Activity Four
Use with Lesson 4-8.

Summary Students discover that by submerging a cube in water and noticing the difference in the water level, they can find the volume of solids. They then apply this method to find the volumes of irregularly shaped objects. Students also learn about Archimedes' principle and use it to predetermine whether objects will float or sink.

Math Connection Students use measurement and scientific experiments to determine the volume of solids and to determine whether objects will float or sink.

DAY 8	DAY 9	DAY 10	DAY 11	DAY 12	DAY 13	DAYS 14 & 15	DAY 16
Lesson 4-5A	Lesson 4-5	Lessons 4-6A & 4-6		Lesson 4-7	Lesson 4-8	Lesson 4-9, Study Guide & Assessment	Chapter Test
Lesson 4-5A	Lesson 4-5	Lesson 4-6	Lesson 4-7	Lesson 4-8	Lesson 4-9	Study Guide & Assessment, Chapter Test	
Study Guide and Assessment, Chapter Test							

APPLICATIONS

Classroom Games, pp. 7–9

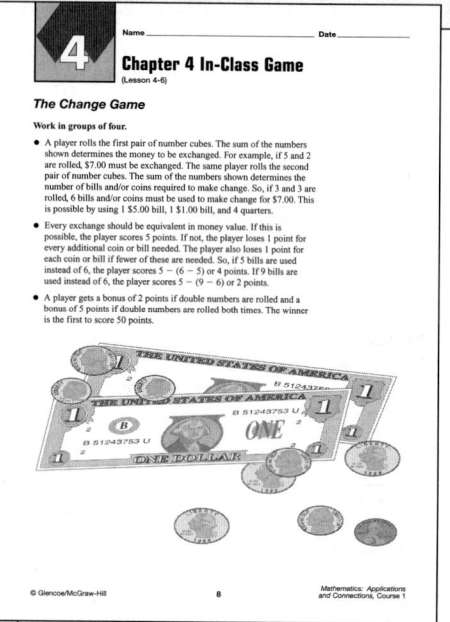

Diversity Masters, p. 4

School to Career Masters, p. 4

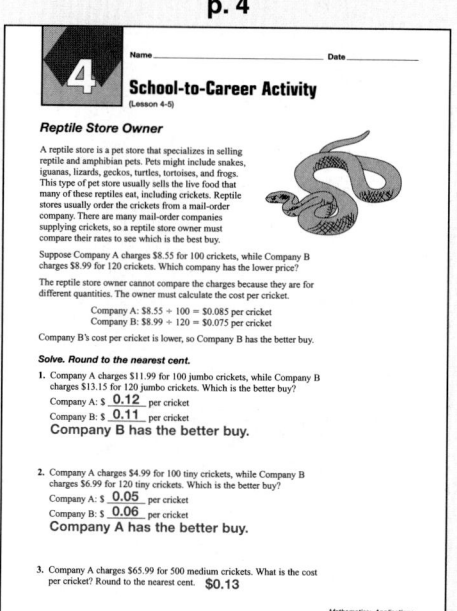

Family Letters and Activities, pp. 7–8

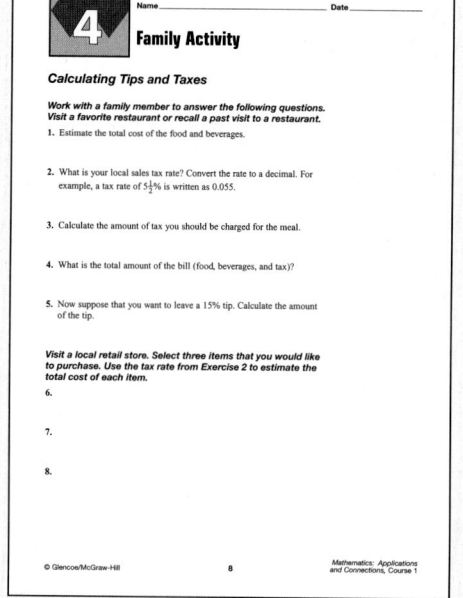

Science and Math Lab Manual, pp. 73–76

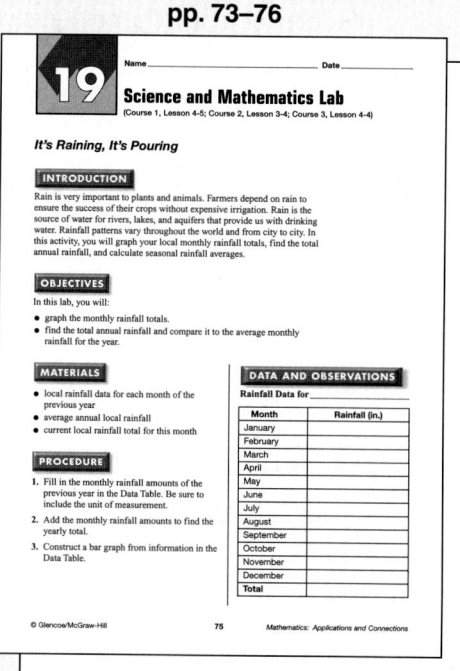

Hands-On Lab Masters, p. 72

Assessment and Evaluation Masters, pp. 98–100

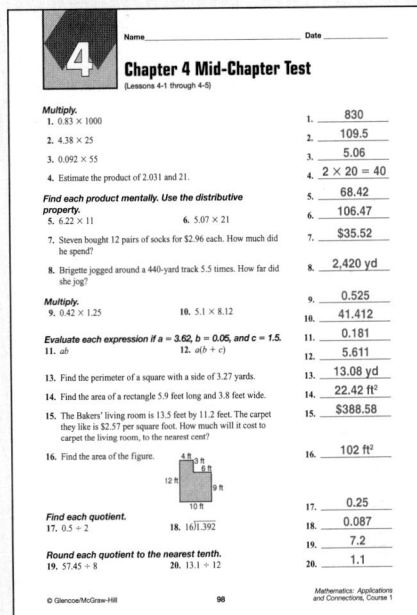

Technology Masters, pp. 7–8

Investigations for the Special Education Student, pp. 9–12, 31–34

Theme: Business

There are more than 22 million small businesses in the United States today. Not only do they employ more than half of the private workforce, they also account for more than 50 percent of the U.S. Gross Domestic Product. Many businesses begin with one person having an idea for a product or service. With the help of a staff and financial backing, one person's idea can become a thriving company.

Question of the Day Janelle and Lucy make necklaces and sell them for $3.75 each. A neighbor wants to order 125 as gifts for a family reunion. The girls will give him a discount of $0.25 per necklace on the first 100 necklaces and a discount of $0.50 per necklace for any additional. How much will his order cost? **$431.25**

Assess Prerequisite Skills

Ask students to read through the list of objectives presented in "What you'll learn in Chapter 4." You may wish to ask them what each of the objectives means or if they have experienced or used any of these math concepts before.

 Building Portfolios

Encourage students to revise their portfolios as they study this chapter. Have them include specific examples that illustrate their understanding of decimal multiplication and division.

 Math and the Family

In the *Family Letters and Activities* booklet (pp. 7–8), you will find a letter to the parents explaining what students will study in Chapter 4. An activity appropriate for the whole family is also available.

What you'll learn in Chapter 4

- to multiply and divide decimals by whole numbers and decimals,
- to use the distributive property to compute products mentally,
- to find the perimeters and areas of figures,
- to solve problems by first solving a simpler problem,
- to use metric units of mass and capacity, and
- to change units within the metric system

130 Chapter 4 Multiplying and Dividing Decimals

 CD-ROM Program

Activities for Chapter 4
- Chapter 4 Introduction
- Interactive Lessons 4-3, 4-4, 4-5, 4-6, 4-9
- Assessment Game
- Resource Lessons 4-1 through 4-9

CHAPTER Project

BE YOUR OWN BOSS!

Owning your own business can be a lot of work. But, it can be very rewarding. It also requires creativity. In this project, you will learn just a little of what goes into making a small business successful. After choosing a product you'd like to sell, you'll explain why you chose it and then determine its selling price. Then you should develop a pricing strategy for large orders. Finally, you need to design an advertisement for your product.

Getting Started

- Decide on a product to sell.
- Determine how much it will cost you to make this product.
- Decide on the price that you want to ask for your product.
- Decide whether you want to do any special promotions such as offering a discount on early orders.

Technology Tips

- Use a **spreadsheet** to organize your price chart and make calculations.
- Use **desktop publishing software** to design your advertisement.

 interNET CONNECTION   Research **For up-to-date information on starting a small business, visit:**

www.glencoe.com/sec/math/mac/mathnet

Working on the Project

You can use what you'll learn in Chapter 4 to help you sell your product.

Page	Exercise
135	32
143	30
173	Alternative Assessment

Chapter 4 **131**

 interNET CONNECTION

Glencoe has made every effort to ensure that the website links for *Mathematics: Applications and Connections* at **www. glencoe.com/sec/math/mac/mathnet** are current and contain appropriate content. However, these website links are not under Glencoe's control.

Instructional Resources ▶▶▶

A recording sheet to help students organize their data for the Chapter Project is shown at the right and is available in the *Investigations and Projects Masters*, p. 32.

GET READY

Objective Students use grid paper to multiply decimals by whole numbers.

Optional Resources
Hands-On Lab Masters
• grid paper, p. 11
• worksheet, p. 43

Overhead Manipulative Resources
• decimal models

MANAGEMENT TIPS

Recommended Time
30 minutes

Getting Started Have students read the first paragraph. Then ask questions such as the following.
• How would you represent the number 2? **2 10-by-10 squares**
• What decimal is represented by three columns? **0.3**

The **Activity** shows how to model decimal multiplication. As students are counting squares and finding products, ask what decimal each square represents. Ask how they would write 120 hundredths. Some students may find it helpful to use addition to find the product. For example, $0.60 + 0.60 = 1.20$.

ASSESS

Have students complete Exercises 1–4. Make sure students are shading the correct amount.

Use Exercise 5 to determine whether students understand the concept of multiplying decimals by whole numbers.

HANDS-ON LAB

COOPERATIVE LEARNING

4-1A Multiplying Decimals by Whole Numbers

A Preview of Lesson 4-1

 grid paper

 markers

 scissors

In this lab, you will use grid paper to draw decimal models. You can use decimal models to multiply a decimal by a whole number. Remember, □ represents one hundredth, ▯ represents one tenth, and ▢ represents one.

In the following activity, the number of rows will represent the first factor of the multiplication, and the number of columns will represent the second factor. The number of shaded rows or columns will represent the product.

TRY THIS

Work in groups of three.

To model 0.6×2, follow these steps.

Step 1 Draw two 10-by-10 squares on grid paper to represent the factor 2.

Step 2 Shade six rows to represent 0.6.

Step 3 Cut off the shaded rows and arrange them to form as many 10-by-10 squares as possible.

There is one 10-by-10 square, which is 1, and two rows, which is 0.2.

Therefore, $0.6 \times 2 = 1.2$.

ON YOUR OWN

Draw decimal models to show each product. 1–3. See Answer Appendix.

1. 4×0.6 **2.** 3×0.7 **3.** 0.5×5

4. Write a multiplication problem using decimals for the model shown. **0.7 × 4**

5. *Look Ahead* Find the product of 8 and 0.4 without using models. **3.2**

Math Journal

Have students write a paragraph explaining how models show the multiplication of decimals by whole numbers. Students should include an explanation of what one small square, one column, and one large square represent.

Multiplying Decimals by Whole Numbers

What you'll learn

You'll learn to estimate and find the products of decimals and whole numbers.

When am I ever going to use this?

Knowing how to multiply a decimal by a whole number can help you find the amount of money you earn.

Word Wise

compatible numbers

LOOK BACK
You can refer to Lesson 1-3 to review rounding.

Mrs. Sopher spends $2.25 for the Saturday and Sunday edition of her local newspaper. What does this cost per year? *This problem will be solved in Example 2.*

When multiplying a decimal by a whole number, multiply as with whole numbers. One way to determine where to place the decimal point in the product is to use estimation.

There are two methods to estimate products. You can use rounding or **compatible numbers**.

Method 1 Use rounding.

First, round each factor to its greatest place-value position. Then multiply. Do not round 1-digit factors.

Method 2 Use compatible numbers.

It is easy to find the product of compatible numbers mentally.

Examples

1 Find 9 × 78.42.

Estimate using rounding. Round 78.42 to 80. 9 × 80 = 720.

7 3 1
78.42   *Multiply as with whole numbers.*
×   9
‾‾‾‾‾‾
705.78 *Since the estimate is 720, place the decimal point after 5.*

Check with a calculator. 78.42 × 9 = 705.78 ✓

APPLICATION

2 **Money Matters** Refer to the beginning of the lesson. How much does Mrs. Sopher spend per year for newspapers?

Explore You know how much she spends each weekend. You want to know how much she spends in a year.

(continued on the next page)

Lesson 4-1 Multiplying Decimals by Whole Numbers **133**

4-1 Lesson Notes

Instructional Resources
- *Study Guide Masters*, p. 23
- *Practice Masters*, p. 23
- *Enrichment Masters*, p. 23
- Transparencies 4-1, A and B CD-ROM Program
- Resource Lesson 4-1

Recommended Pacing	
Standard	Days 2 & 3 of 16
Honors	Day 2 of 15
Block	Day 2 of 8

1 FOCUS

5-Minute Check
(Chapter 3)

1. Write three hundred ten-thousandths as a decimal. **0.0300**

2. Order 980.89, 980.08, 980.189, 890.86, 980.81, and 980.8 from greatest to least. **980.89, 980.81, 980.8, 980.189, 980.08, 890.86**

3. Estimate 18.05 + 39.95 using rounding. **20 + 40 = 60**

4. Subtract: 67.53 − 37.125. **30.405**

5. Add: 30.001 + 14.78. **44.781**

The 5-Minute Check is also available on **Transparency 4-1A** for this lesson.

Motivating the Lesson
Problem Solving Have students read the opening paragraph of the lesson. Ask the following question. *What estimation strategies could be used to find the cost per year for the newspaper?* **Sample answer: rounding**

 Cross-Curriculum Cue

Inform the teachers on your team that your students are studying decimal multiplication and division and metric measures. Suggestions for curriculum integration are:
Health: nutrition labels
Physical Science: formulas

Transparency 4-1B contains a teaching aid for this lesson.

Reading Mathematics Have groups of students find the dictionary definitions for *rounding* and *compatible*. Have them discuss how these definitions compare with how the words are used in this lesson.

In-Class Examples

For Example 1
a. Find 6.4 × 5. **32**
b. Find 3.08 × 7. **21.56**

For Example 2
During his professional basketball career, Wilt Chamberlain averaged 30.07 points per game for 1,045 games. How many points did he score in his career? **31,423 points**

For Example 3
a. Evaluate the expression 4*d* if *d* = 7.2. **28.8**
b. Evaluate the expression 5*s* if *s* = 0.014. **0.07**

Teaching Tip In Example 3, remind students that 3*a* is the same as 3 × *a*.

3 PRACTICE/APPLY

Check for Understanding
If students need additional practice or instruction after completing Exercises 1–11, one of these options may be helpful.
• Extra Practice, see p. 565
• Reteaching Activity
• *Transition Booklet,* pp. 21–22
• *Study Guide Masters,* p. 23
• *Practice Masters,* p. 23

Plan   There are 52 weeks in a year. Find $2.25 × 52.
Estimate using compatible numbers.

$2.25 → $2   *Round to the greatest place value.*
× 52   → ×50   *Round to 50 since it is easy to multiply 2 and 5 mentally.*

Since 2 × 5 = 10, then 2 × 50 = 100.

Solve

$$
\begin{array}{r}
\$2.25 \\
\times\ 52 \\
\hline
450 \\
1125 \\
\hline
117.00
\end{array}
$$
Since the estimate is 100, place the decimal point after 7.

Mrs. Sopher spends $117.00 a year for newspapers.

Examine   Compared to the estimate, the answer is reasonable.

You can also determine where to place the decimal point in the product by counting the number of decimal places in the decimal factor. The product must have the same number of decimal places. If more decimal places are needed, annex zeros.

Example
INTEGRATION

LOOK BACK
You can refer to Lesson 1-5 to review evaluating expressions.

3 Algebra Evaluate the expression 3*a* if *a* = 0.032.

3*a* = 3 × 0.032 *Replace a with 0.032.*

$$
\begin{array}{r}
0.032 \\
\times\ \ \ 3 \\
\hline
0.096
\end{array}
$$
← *three decimal places*
← *Annex a zero on the left to make three decimal places.*

Check your answer by adding.

$$
\begin{array}{r}
0.032 \\
0.032 \\
+\ 0.032 \\
\hline
0.096 \checkmark
\end{array}
$$

The product is 0.096.

CHECK FOR UNDERSTANDING

Communicating Mathematics

1. Sample answer: Round 40.32 to 40 and round 251 to 250. You can find 40 × 250 since 4 and 25 are compatible numbers.

Read and study the lesson to answer each question.

1. *Explain* how you could use compatible numbers to estimate the product of 40.23 and 251.

2. *Write* a multiplication problem for the model shown. **0.9 × 2**

■ Reteaching the Lesson ■

Activity Make multiplication cards that ask students to find the product of a decimal and a whole number. Then have groups of students play "Top of the Tower." Players choose a card, find the product, and add the product to a tower drawn on the chalkboard until they reach the sum of 1,000 (Top of the Tower).

3. You Decide Montega uses a calculator to find the product of 34.78 and 452. He gets 15,720.56 for an answer. Is the answer reasonable? Explain why or why not. **See margin.**

Guided Practice

Use estimation to place the decimal point in each product.

4. $0.88 \times 3 = 264$ **2.64**

5. $12.6 \times 19 = 2394$ **239.4**

6. $254 \times 3.82 = 97028$ **970.28**

Multiply.

7. 0.2
$\underline{\times 8}$ **1.6**

8. 5.02
$\underline{\times\ 3}$ **15.06**

9. 64×0.005 **0.32**

10. Algebra Evaluate the expression $12n$ if $n = 5.6$. **67.2**

11. Astronomy Pluto, normally the farthest planet from the Sun, is also the slowest. Its average speed around the Sun is 10,604 miles per hour. Earth, by contrast, travels 6.28 times faster. What is the average speed of Earth? **66,593.12 miles per hour**

EXERCISES

Practice

Multiply.

12. 0.6 **3.0**
$\underline{\times 5}$

13. 0.28 **1.12**
$\underline{\times\ 4}$

14. 2.03 **14.21**
$\underline{\times\ 7}$

15. 3.42 **30.78**
$\underline{\times\ 9}$

16. 0.007 **0.056**
$\underline{\times\ \ 8}$

17. 10.7 **64.2**
$\underline{\times\ 6}$

18. 0.67 **22.11**
$\underline{\times 33}$

19. 3.25 **2,606.5**
$\underline{\times 802}$

20. $1,250 \times 2.5$ **3,125**

21. 0.0125×754 **9.425**

22. $2,967 \times 0.071$ **210.657**

Solve each equation.

23. $x = 36 \times 0.007$

24. $4.8 \times 235 = y$

25. $p = 2,388 \times 1.65$

26. Algebra Evaluate $112d$ if $d = 0.98$. **109.76**

27. What is the solution of $n = 58.002 \cdot 367$? **21,286.734**

28. Will 11.7×5 be closer to 55 or 60? Explain. **See margin.**

29. How does knowing that $5^2 = 25$ help you find the answer to 5×0.5?

23. 0.252
24. 1128
25. 3,940.2
29. Sample answer: Since 0.5 is less than 5, 0.5×5 will be less than 25.

Applications and Problem Solving

30. Statistics The graph shows the broadcast television ratings for baseball. In which year were the ratings twice as high as the 1996 ratings? **1995**

FOUL BALL!

'93	Network A	3.8
'94	Network B	6.2
'95	Network B	5.8
'96	Network C	2.9

Sources: Major League Baseball and *USA TODAY* research

31. Money Exchange If the Japanese yen (¥) is worth $0.0078, what is the value of ¥ 3,750? **$29.25**

32. Working on the CHAPTER Project Determine how much it would cost someone to buy 1 item, 2 items, 3 items, . . . , through 10 items of your product. Organize this data in a table. **See students' work.**

Assignment Guide

Core: 13–31 odd, 33–37
Enriched: 12–28 even, 30, 31, 33–37

CHAPTER Project

Exercise 32 asks students to advance to the next stage of work on the Chapter Project. You may wish to have students consider offering quantity discounts. Have them show this discount in the table and determine how it would affect their profit.

Additional Answers

3. Sample answer: Yes; by rounding 34.78 to 30 and rounding 452 to 500, the product of 30 and 500 is 15,000.

28. Sample answer: It will be closer to 60 because 11.7 is closer to 12 and 5×12 is 60.

***Study Guide Masters*, p. 23**

Name_____ Date_____

4-1 Study Guide

Multiplying Decimals by Whole Numbers

When you multiply a decimal by a whole number, multiply as with whole numbers. The product must have the same number of decimal places as the decimal factor.

Examples **1** Find 6×5.43.

$\begin{array}{r} 5.43 \leftarrow \text{two decimal places} \\ \underline{\times\ 6} \\ 32.58 \leftarrow \text{two decimal places} \end{array}$

2 Find 120×0.056.

$\begin{array}{r} 0.056 \leftarrow \text{three decimal places} \\ \underline{\times\ 120} \\ 1\ 120 \\ \underline{5\ 6} \\ 6.720 \leftarrow \text{three decimal places} \end{array}$

Multiply.

1. 0.7
$\underline{\times\ 9}$
6.3

2. 0.78
$\underline{\times\ 17}$
13.26

3. 0.09
$\underline{\times\ 101}$
9.09

4. 6.2
$\underline{\times\ 12}$
74.4

5. 4.12
$\underline{\times\ 22}$
90.64

6. 10.4
$\underline{\times\ 221}$
2,298.4

7. 131.5
$\underline{\times\ 55}$
7,232.5

8. 0.3
$\underline{\times\ 494}$
148.2

9. $3,330 \times 0.05$
166.5

10. 75×0.003
0.225

11. 9×5.05
45.45

Solve each equation.

12. $f = 8 \times 0.006$
0.048

13. $a = 205 \times 0.22$
45.1

14. $t = 31 \times 1.12$
34.72

© Glencoe/McGraw-Hill

T23

Mathematics: Applications and Connections, Course 1

Closing Activity

Writing Have students use information in newspapers or magazines to write real-world problems that involve multiplying a decimal and a whole number.

---

33. Answers will vary.
Sample answer:
5 × 9.178

33. Critical Thinking Create a multiplication problem where the product is 45.89 and one of the factors is a whole number.

Mixed Review

34. Standardized Test Practice Jaden plans to buy a soccer ball for $21.99, soccer cleats for $45.50, and a soccer shirt for $14.79. What is the cost of these items before tax is added? *(Lesson 3-6)* **A**

A $82.28

B $81.18

C $80.28

D $80.18

E Not Here

Andy's Sit-Ups

35. Fitness The line graph shows Andy's progress doing sit-ups. How many sit-ups do you predict he will be doing in October? *(Lesson 2-5)* **Sample answer: 80**

37a. Sample answer: 800 points

37b. Sample answer: Use clustering to total the hundreds and use rounding to estimate to the nearest ten.

37c. Sample answer: You would round to the nearest ten because rounding to the nearest hundred they would all be the same.

36. School At Gillian School, there are 36 student council representatives as shown in the circle graph. Which grade (both boys and girls) has the most representatives? *(Lesson 2-4)* **7th grade**

Student Council Representatives

Girls 6th grade — 8
Boys 6th grade — 4
Girls 8th grade — 5
Boys 7th grade — 4
Boys 8th grade — 6
Girls 7th grade — 9

37. Sports The table shows the total points scored in the eight games in the second round of the midwest region during the 1997 NCAA Division I Women's Basketball Tournament. *(Lesson 1-3)*

a. Estimate the total points scored over the two days.

b. Explain how you could use a combination of methods to estimate the two-day total.

c. Suppose you wanted to make a bar graph comparing the total points scored in each game. Would you round to the nearest hundred or to the nearest ten? Explain.

For **Extra Practice**, see page 565.

Total Points Scored	
March 14	March 15
118	106
126	138
141	145
145	148

136 Chapter 4 Multiplying and Dividing Decimals

Practice Masters, p. 23

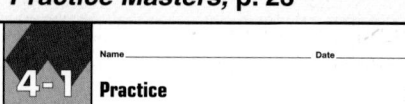

4-1 Practice

Multiplying Decimals by Whole Numbers

Use estimation to place the decimal point in each product.

1. 0.73 × 56 = 4088 **40.88**
2. 2.7 × 48 = 1296 **129.6**
3. 2.94 × 108 = 31752 **317.52**
4. 1.035 × 69 = 71415 **71.415**
5. 0.8 × 472 = 3776 **377.6**
6. 15.06 × 319 = 480414 **4,804.14**

Multiply.

7. 0.9 × 6 = **5.4**
8. 3.47 × 5 = **17.35**
9. 0.82 × 9 = **7.38**
10. 27.3 × 8 = **218.4**
11. 0.64 × 32 = **20.48**
12. 5.9 × 174 = **1,026.6**
13. 0.0358 × 216 = **7.7328**
14. 4.76 × 95 = **452.2**
15. 208.7 × 43 = **8,974.1**
16. 0.4 × 738 = **295.2**
17. 1.95 × 4,620 = **9,009**
18. 0.006 × 87 = **0.522**
19. 89.2 × 54 = **4,816.8**
20. 0.013 × 2,361 = **30.693**
21. 7.49 × 105 = **786.45**
22. 2.5 × 3,092 = **7,730**
23. 36 × 0.07 = **2.52**
24. 4.8 × 235 = **1,128**
25. 1.29 × 614 = **792.06**
26. 93 × 0.57 = **53.01**
27. 18 × 270.9 = **4,876.2**
28. 0.006 × 315 = **1.89**

29. Find the product of 58.2 and 67. **3,899.4**

30. What is 1,073 times 2.04? **2,188.92**

© Glencoe/McGraw-Hill   T23   Mathematics: Applications and Connections, Course 1

Extending the Lesson

Enrichment Masters, p. 23

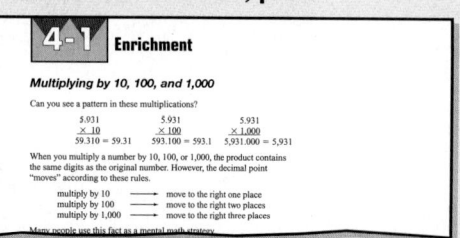

4-1 Enrichment

Multiplying by 10, 100, and 1,000

Can you see a pattern in these multiplications?

5.931 × 10 = 59.31
5.931 × 100 = 593.1
5.931 × 1,000 = 5,931

When you multiply a number by 10, 100, or 1,000, the product contains the same digits as the original number. However, the decimal point "moves" according to these rules.

multiply by 10 ⟶ move to the right one place
multiply by 100 ⟶ move to the right two places
multiply by 1,000 ⟶ move to the right three places

Many people use this fact as a mental math strategy.

Activity In the 1930s, a sixth grader could see a movie and buy a candy bar for $0.25. Have students determine the cost of a movie and a candy bar today. Then have them figure out the total cost for the whole class and compare that cost with what it would have been in the '30s.

Using the Distributive Property

What you'll learn

You'll learn to compute products mentally using the distributive property.

When am I ever going to use this?

Knowing how to use the distributive property can help you multiply mentally.

Word Wise

distributive property

Christine's drum teacher charges $15 for a lesson. If Christine had 4 lessons in November and 3 lessons in December, how much did she pay her drum teacher for those two months?

Before you solve this problem, let's look at another way to show multiplication, using grouping symbols such as parentheses. For example, you can write 3×5 as $3(5)$ or $(3)5$. Let's include parentheses with the rules for order of operations.

Order of Operations	1. Do all operations within grouping symbols first.
	2. Do all powers before other operations.
	3. Multiply and divide in order from left to right.
	4. Add and subtract in order from left to right.

Now go back to Christine's problem.

Method 1 To find the total cost of the lessons, you can multiply the charge per lesson by the total number of lessons.

$$\overset{\text{charge per lesson}}{\underset{\downarrow}{15}}(\overset{\text{number of lessons}}{\underset{\downarrow}{4 + 3}}) = 15(7) \quad \text{\textit{Use the order of operations. Add inside the parentheses first.}}$$

$$= 105$$

Method 2 You can find the cost for each month first, and then add to find the total cost of the lessons.

$$\overset{\text{money paid in November}}{\underset{\downarrow}{15 \times 4}} + \overset{\text{money paid in December}}{\underset{\downarrow}{15 \times 3}} = 60 + 45 \quad \text{\textit{Use the order of operations. Do the multiplication first.}}$$

$$= 105$$

The solution is the same using either method. Christine paid the drum teacher $105 for lessons in November and December. So, the following sentence is true.

$$15(4 + 3) = 15 \times 4 + 15 \times 3$$

This is an example of the **distributive property**.

Study Hint

Reading Math
Read the expression $15(4 + 3)$ as fifteen times the quantity four plus three.

Lesson 4-2 Using the Distributive Property **137**

Investigations for the Special Education Student

This blackline master booklet helps you plan for the needs of your special education students by providing long-term projects along with teacher notes. Investigation 4, *The Check's in the Mail,* and Investigation 11, *Super Star!,* may be used with this chapter.

Instructional Resources

- *Study Guide Masters,* p. 24
- *Practice Masters,* p. 24
- *Enrichment Masters,* p. 24
- Transparencies 4-2, A and B
- *Technology Masters,* p. 7
- CD-ROM Program
  - Resource Lesson 4-2

Recommended Pacing	
Standard	Day 4 of 16
Honors	Day 3 of 15
Block	Day 2 of 8

1 FOCUS

 5-Minute Check *(Lesson 4-1)*

Multiply.
1. 0.31
   $\times\ 4$
   1.24
2. 5.13
   $\times\ 2$
   10.26
3. 9.35×47 **439.45**
4. $5,285 \times 0.0261$ **137.9385**
5. A share of a certain stock sold for $22.1875. How much did 30 shares cost? **$665.63**

 The 5-Minute Check is also available on **Transparency 4-2A** for this lesson.

Motivating the Lesson

Communication After reading the opening paragraph of the lesson, ask students:
- How many steps would you use to solve the problem? **two or three steps**
- What operations would you use? **addition and multiplication**

2 TEACH

 Transparency 4-2B contains a teaching aid for this lesson.

Thinking Algebraically Compare the two definitions of the distributive property. Emphasize to students that the algebra definition is a general rule that works for any values of *a, b,* and *c.*

In-Class Examples

For Example 1
Find the products mentally using the distributive property.
a. 4 × 18 **72**
b. 7 × 13 **91**

For Example 2
Suppose you deliver weekly grocery flyers to earn extra money. You earn $0.42 per customer per week. You have 40 customers. How much will you make in a week? **$16.80**

3 PRACTICE/APPLY

Check for Understanding
If students need additional practice or instruction after completing Exercises 1–9, one of these options may be helpful.
• Extra Practice, see p. 565
• Reteaching Activity
• *Study Guide Masters,* p. 24
• *Practice Masters,* p. 24

Study Guide Masters, p. 24

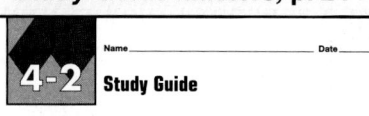

| | Distributive Property | Symbols: | Arithmetic | $5(3 + 6) = 5 \cdot 3 + 5 \cdot 6$ |
| | | | Algebra | For any numbers a, b, and c, $a(b + c) = ab + ac$. |

The distributive property allows us to solve problems in parts. This makes it easy to solve some multiplication problems mentally.

Examples

1 Find 6 × 45 mentally using the distributive property.

Estimate: 6 × 50 = 300

$$6 \times 45 = 6(40 + 5) \qquad \textit{Use 40 + 5 for 45.}$$
$$= 6 \times 40 + 6 \times 5$$
$$= 240 + 30$$
$$= 270 \qquad \textit{Compare to the estimate.}$$

APPLICATION
Real World

2 **Money Matters** Adria has a paper route to earn some extra money. She earns $0.18 per customer per week. If she has 80 customers, how much will she make weekly?

Estimate: 80 × $0.20 = $16

$$80 \times 0.18 = 80(0.1 + 0.08)$$
$$= 80 \times 0.1 + 80 \times 0.08$$
$$= 8 + 6.4$$
$$= 14.4$$

Adria will make $14.40. *Compare to the estimate.*

CHECK FOR UNDERSTANDING

Communicating Mathematics

Read and study the lesson to answer each question. 1–2. See margin.

1. *Tell* the order of operations you would use to find $9(8^2 + 6)$.

2. *Explain* how to use the distributive property to solve 5.5 × 8.

Math Journal

3. *Write* a paragraph explaining how the distributive property can help you solve a problem mentally. **See students' work.**

Guided Practice

4. Rewrite 12 × 5 + 12 × 8 using the distributive property.
12(5 + 8)

Find each product mentally. Use the distributive property.

7. 30 + 2 = 32

8. 7 × 30 + 7 × 0.9 = 210 + 6.3 = 216.3

5. 8 × 18 **80 + 64 = 144** 6. 52 × 3 **150 + 6 = 156** 7. 6.4 × 5

8. Find the product of 7 and 30.9 mentally.

9. *Money Matters* Emilio is taking Karate lessons. The instructor charges $25.00 for each lesson. If Emilio has 5 lessons in one month, how much does he owe the instructor? **100 + 25 = 125**

138 Chapter 4 Multiplying and Dividing Decimals

■ Reteaching the Lesson ■

Activity Make cards with multiplication problems such as 6 × 16 and 8.9 × 5. Highlight the number that can be rewritten using the distributive property (16 = 10 + 6; 8.9 = 8 + 0.9). Have students take turns choosing a card to find the product mentally.

Additional Answers

1. **First find 8^2. Then add 64 and 6. Finally, multiply 70(9).**

2. **Sample answer: Find the sum of 8 × 5 and 8 × 0.5.**

Practice

Rewrite each expression using the distributive property.

10. 4(30 + 6)
4 × 30 + 4 × 6

11. 3(20 + 7)
3 × 20 + 3 × 7

12. 15 × 20 + 15 × 0.4
15(20 + 0.4)

Find each product mentally. Use the distributive property.

13. 6 × 14 **84**

14. 103 × 7 **721**

15. 3 × 72 **216**

16. 2.4 × 11 **26.4**

17. 8.1 × 6 **48.6**

18. 20 × 4.3 **86**

19. 20.7 × 6 **124.2**

20. 14 × 110 **1,540**

21. 30 × 3.09 **92.7**

22. Find the product of 12 and 15 mentally. **180**

23. Mentally multiply 60 and 10.5. **630**

24. *Algebra* What is the value of 8(x + 0.7) if x is 30? **245.6**

Applications and Problem Solving

25. *Money Matters* The company that employs Mrs. Leshnock pays her 31.5¢ for each mile she drives her personal car for business purposes. How much money will she receive if she drives her car 50 miles on company business? **$15.75**

26. *Travel* The Garcia family drove from Houston to San Antonio. They filled their car's tank with 12.8 gallons of gas before they left Houston. They filled the tank with 10.2 gallons when they arrived in San Antonio. If gas cost $1.29 per gallon at both gas stations, how much did they spend on gas? **$29.67**

The Alamo in San Antonio, Texas

27. *Critical Thinking* Evaluate each expression.

a. 0.2(2 − 0.4) **0.32**

b. 0.1(1 − 0.5) **0.05**

c. 0.15(5 − 1.4) **0.54**

d. 0.75(10 − 0.25) **7.3125**

Mixed Review

28. **Standardized Test Practice** The sign below was on a sale rack. If Jhan bought 3 items from this sale rack, a reasonable total cost, without tax is — *(Lesson 4-1)* **C**

A $13.00.

B $26.00.

C $75.00.

D $100.00.

E $110.00.

SALE ITEMS!
$12.99
to
$29.99

29. *Weather* Washington, D.C., has an average annual precipitation of 35.86 inches. Round this amount to the nearest tenth. *(Lesson 3-4)* **35.9 in.**

30. *Statistics* The number of students in Mrs. Jing's history class during the first two weeks of the new semester were: 27, 31, 25, 19, 31, 32, 24, 26, 33, and 31. Construct a stem-and-leaf plot for the data. *(Lesson 2-6)* **See margin.**

For **Extra Practice**, see page 565.

Lesson 4-2 Using the Distributive Property **139**

Extending the Lesson

Enrichment Masters, p. 24

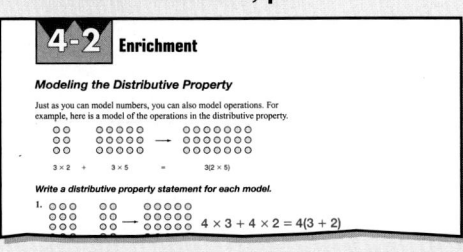

Activity Have pairs of students write problems involving multiplication of whole numbers and decimals. Have them determine whether they can solve the problems mentally using the distributive property. Then have them write generalizations about their strategies.

Assignment Guide

Core: 11–25 odd, 27–30
Enriched: 10–24 even, 25–30

4 ASSESS

Closing Activity

Speaking Give a multiplication example such as 8.7 × 30 and have students find the product mentally using the distributive property. Then ask a student to explain the process to the rest of the class and to give another example for the class to discuss and solve.

Additional Answer

30.

Stem	Leaf
1	9
2	4 5 6 7
3	1 1 1 2 3

3|1 = 31

Practice Masters, p. 24

Lesson 4-2 **139**

COOPERATIVE LEARNING

4-3A Multiplying Decimals

A Preview of Lesson 4-3

 grid paper

markers

In the Hands-On Lab on page 132, you used decimal models to multiply a whole number and a decimal. In this lab, you will use decimal models to multiply two decimals.

TRY THIS

Work with a partner.

1 To model 0.7×0.5, follow these steps.

• Draw a 10-by-10 square. Recall that each small square represents 0.01.

• Color seven rows of the model blue to represent 0.7.

• Color five columns of the model yellow to represent 0.5.

There are 35 small squares that are shaded green.

Therefore, $0.7 \times 0.5 = 0.35$.

2 To model 0.9×2.3, you need to draw three 10-by-10 squares.

• Line up the squares as shown.

• Color 9 rows blue to represent 0.9.

• Color 23 columns yellow to represent 2.3.

There are 207 small squares that are shaded green. This would cover two 10-by-10 squares, which is 2, and seven small squares, which is 0.07.

Therefore, $0.9 \times 2.3 = 2.07$.

ON YOUR OWN

Write a multiplication problem using decimals for each model. 2. 0.4 × 3.8

1. 0.6×1.9

2.

Use decimal models to show each product. 3–5. See Answer Appendix for models.

3. 0.4×0.6 **0.24**

4. 1.3×0.2 **0.26**

5. 2.5×1.1 **2.75**

6. *Look Ahead* Find the product of 1.7 and 2.2 without using models. **3.74**

140 Chapter 4 Multiplying and Dividing Decimals

 Math Journal Have students write an explanation of how models can be used to show the multiplication of decimals and how they might use models if they forget the pattern they learned in this lab.

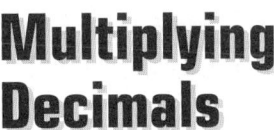

4-3 Multiplying Decimals

What you'll learn

You'll learn to multiply decimals.

When am I ever going to use this?

Knowing how to multiply decimals can help you find the amount of tip to leave at a restaurant.

On September 1, 1997, the minimum wage increased to $5.15 an hour. If Domingo works 17.5 hours a week and earns minimum wage, how much does he make each week before taxes?

To answer this question, you need to multiply 5.15 by 17.5. When you multiply decimals, multiply as with whole numbers. One way to place the decimal point is to use estimation.

Estimate: 5 · 20 = 100 Round 5.15 to 5 and 17.5 to 20.

$$
\begin{array}{r}
5.15 \\
\times 17.5 \\
\hline
2\,575 \\
36\,05 \\
51\,5 \\
\hline
90.125
\end{array}
$$
Multiply as with whole numbers.

Since the estimate is 100, place the decimal point after 0.

Rounded to the nearest penny, Domingo makes $90.13 before taxes.

Another way to place the decimal point in the product is by counting the decimal places in each factor. The product will have the same number of decimal places as the sum of the number of decimal places in the factors.

Examples

1 Find 2.4 · 5.9. *Estimate: 2 · 6 = 12*

$$
\begin{array}{r}
5.9 \\
\times 2.4 \\
\hline
23\,6 \\
118 \\
\hline
14.16
\end{array}
$$
← *one decimal place*
← *one decimal place*

← *two decimal places*

The product is 14.16. *Compared to the estimate, the answer is reasonable.*

2 Find 1.45 × 0.7. *Estimate: 1 × 1 = 1*

$$
\begin{array}{r}
1.45 \\
\times 0.7 \\
\hline
1.015
\end{array}
$$
← *two decimal places*
← *one decimal place*
← *three decimal places*

The product is 1.015.

Multiple Learning Styles

Logical Have students work in groups to plan a dinner for the class. They should collaborate on the menu and prepare a grocery list. Using recipes, grocery ads, and unit price comparisons, have them estimate the cost of the dinner. Encourage them to organize their data in tables.

 MathPASS CD-ROM

This CD-ROM offers a complete, self-paced mathematics curriculum. Each lesson includes a pretest, tutorial, guided practice, and posttest. MathPASS Lesson 8 is correlated to this Student Edition Lesson.

For Windows & Macintosh

4-3 Lesson Notes

Instructional Resources

- *Study Guide Masters*, p. 25
- *Practice Masters*, p. 25
- *Enrichment Masters*, p. 25
- Transparencies 4-3, A and B
- *Assessment and Evaluation Masters*, p. 99
- CD-ROM Program
  - Resource Lesson 4-3
  - Interactive Lesson 4-3

Recommended Pacing	
Standard	Days 5 & 6 of 16
Honors	Days 4 & 5 of 15
Block	Day 3 of 8

1 FOCUS

5-Minute Check
(Lesson 4-2)

1. Rewrite 5(20 + 6) using the distributive property.
   5 × 20 + 5 × 6

Find each product mentally. Use the distributive property.

2. 107 × 6 **642**
3. 5 × 6.3 **31.5**
4. 40 × 2.8 **112**
5. 0.6 × 15 **9**

 The 5-Minute Check is also available on **Transparency 4-3A** for this lesson.

Motivating the Lesson

Problem Solving Ask students how they would determine which craft material costs more.

- 8.5 yd of ribbon at $0.55 a yard
- 2.8 yd of lace at $1.82 a yard
  Sample answer: Estimate by multiplying; the lace costs more.

2 TEACH

 Transparency 4-3B contains a teaching aid for this lesson.

Using Logical Reasoning Have groups of students write riddles such as: *My product is 6.781. One of my factors is a decimal in tenths. How many decimal places does my other factor have?* **2**

3 PRACTICE/APPLY

Check for Understanding

If students need additional practice or instruction after completing Exercises 1–8, one of these options may be helpful.
- Extra Practice, see p. 566
- Reteaching Activity
- *Transition Booklet*, pp. 23–24
- *Study Guide Masters*, p. 25
- *Practice Masters*, p. 25
- Interactive Mathematics Tools Software

Assignment Guide

Core: 9–29 odd, 31–35
Enriched: 10–28 even, 29, 31–35

Study Guide Masters, p. 25

Name_____ Date_____

4-3 Study Guide

Multiplying Decimals

Multiply decimals just as you multiply whole numbers. The number of decimal places in the product is equal to the sum of the number of decimal places in the two factors.

Example   Multiply 0.16 and 1.025.

```
    1.025   ←—— three decimal places
  × 0.16    ←—— two decimal places
    6150
    1025
  0.16400   ←—— five decimal places
```

Multiply.

1. 0.5 × 20.2
   10.1
2. 1.2 × 2.3
   2.76
3. 0.055 × 3.2
   0.176

4. 0.014 × 0.4
   0.0056
5. 12.4 × 12.4
   153.76
6. 3.07 × 1.07
   3.2849

Solve each equation.

7. *c* = 15.5 × 3.3
   51.15
8. *x* = 202.1 × 1.14
   230.394
9. *a* = 0.008 × 65.3
   0.5224

Evaluate each expression if *m* = 0.09, *n* = 1.2, and *p* = 8.19.

10. *mn*
    0.108
11. *p*(*n* + *m*)
    10.5651
12. *pm*
    0.7371

© Glencoe/McGraw-Hill   T25   Mathematics: Applications and Connections, Course 1

Examples — ③ **Multiply 0.02 and 1.36.**   *Estimate: 0 · 1 = 0*

$$\begin{array}{r} 1.36 \\ \times 0.02 \\ \hline 0.0272 \end{array}$$ ← *two decimal places*
  ← *two decimal places*
  ← *To make four decimal places, annex a zero on the left.*

The product is 0.0272.

INTEGRATION ④ **Algebra** **Evaluate 4.3*n* if *n* = 10.89.**

4.3*n* = 4.3 · 10.89   *Replace n with 10.89.*

Estimate: 4 · 11 = 44

$$\begin{array}{r} 10.89 \\ \times\ 4.3 \\ \hline 3267 \\ 3356 \\ \hline 46.827 \end{array}$$ *Compare to the estimate.*

CHECK FOR UNDERSTANDING

Communicating Mathematics
1. Sample answer: The total decimal places of the factors are 5; **0.40563**

Guided Practice

Read and study the lesson to answer each question.

1. *Explain* how you know where the decimal point would go in the product 4.507 × 0.09 = 040563.

2. *Write* the multiplication sentence represented by the decimal model. **0.4 × 0.6**

3. Use estimation to place the decimal point in the product 3.4 · 1.2 = 408. **4.08**

Multiply.

4. 0.4 × 8.3 **3.32**
5. 8.54 · 3.27 **27.9258**
6. 39.6 × 2.417
   95.7132

7. Evaluate 0.002*y* if *y* = 3.9. **0.0078**

8. *Money Matters* Helaku wants to buy a new video game. The game he wants costs $41.99. The sales tax is calculated by multiplying the total of the merchandise by 0.0575. If the video game is the only thing Helaku purchases, how much sales tax will he pay? **$2.41**

EXERCISES

Practice   **Use estimation to place the decimal point in each product.**

9. 5.6 × 12.43 = 69608 **69.608**
10. 0.03 × 1.24 = 00372 **0.0372**

Multiply.

11. 0.35 · 1.4 **0.49**
12. 5.2 × 0.065 **0.338**
13. 3.06 · 4.28 **13.0968**
14. 0.9 × 0.15 **0.135**
15. 18.37 · 908.44
    16,688.0428
16. 0.003 × 0.012
    0.000036

Reteaching the Lesson

Activity Use transparency overlays and grid paper to illustrate multiplication. For example, illustrate 1.2 × 0.8 by covering one whole model and two rows of another model with a yellow overlay. Cover eight rows with a red overlay. Have students count the orange squares to find the product. **0.96**

Error Analysis

Watch for students who consistently place the decimal incorrectly in the product.

Prevent by asking students to explain the rules for multiplying decimals. Suggest that they estimate to check their answer.

Solve each equation.

17. $p = 1.3 \cdot 7.3$ **9.49**

18. $q = 0.3 \cdot 0.012$ **0.0036**

19. $0.6(0.031) = m$ **0.0186**

20. $28.2(4.4) = n$ **124.08**

Evaluate each expression if $a = 1.06$, $b = 0.002$, and $c = 5.5$.

22. 5.83212
23. 5.82788
24. 0.01166
27. 0.00696

21. ab **0.00212**   **22.** $a(b + c)$ **23.** $a(c - b)$ **24.** abc

25. Find the product of 24.8 and 4.389. **108.8472**

26. What is 2.15 multiplied by 3.84? **8.256**

27. *Algebra* What is the product of x and y if $x = 1.16$ and $y = 0.006$?

28. *Algebra* Find the value of prt if $p = \$250$, $r = 0.03$, and $t = 7.5$. **\$56.25**

Applications and Problem Solving

29. *Life Science* The graph shows a breakdown by age group of the 26.2 million Americans who were hearing impaired as of January, 1996. The number of people between the ages of 65 and 74 is 3.95 times the number of people in the 0-17 age group. Complete the graph by finding the number of people in the 65-74 age group. **5.41**

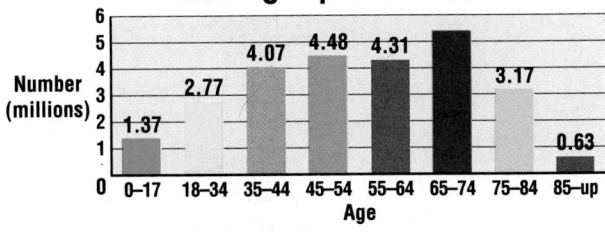

Hearing-Impaired Americans

Number (millions): 1.37, 2.77, 4.07, 4.48, 4.31, 3.17, 0.63

Age: 0–17, 18–34, 35–44, 45–54, 55–64, 65–74, 75–84, 85–up

Source: American Speech–Language–Hearing Association

30. *Working on the* **CHAPTER Project** Refer to the prices you determined in Exercise 32 on page 135. **a–b. See students' work.**

a. Suppose your after-tax prices are determined by multiplying the prices by 1.065. Find the after-tax price for your product.

b. Suppose your senior citizen discount is determined by multiplying the after-tax prices by 0.90. Find the discount prices.

31. *Critical Thinking* Write a multiplication problem where the product of two decimals is between 0.05 and 0.75. **Sample answer: 0.1×0.6**

32. $32 + 2 = 34$

Mixed Review

32. Find 8.5×4 mentally. Use the distributive property. *(Lesson 4-2)*

33. *Standardized Test Practice* Shanee recorded the number of miles she rode her bicycle each day for four days. Which list shows that data in correct order from least to greatest? *(Lesson 3-3)* **D**

A 7.6, 21.4, 13.7, 9.3

B 21.4, 13.7, 21.4

C 13.7, 7.6, 21.4, 9.3

D 7.6, 9.3, 13.7, 21.4

For **Extra Practice**, see page 566.

34. Express $\frac{8}{1,000}$ as a decimal. *(Lesson 3-1)* **0.008**

35. *Algebra* Evaluate y^3 if $y = 6$. *(Lesson 1-6)* **216**

Extending the Lesson

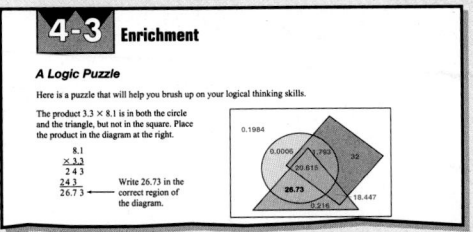
Activity Provide students with brochures for a local theme park, arcade, or game center. Have them use decimal multiplication to determine the cost of hosting a party for the entire class. Assume students will average 2.5 tokens or tickets for each game during the party.

---

4 ASSESS

Closing Activity

Speaking Have students summarize the rule for calculating the number of decimal places when multiplying decimals. Then have them explain how they can check their decimal point placement.

Chapter 4, Quiz A (Lessons 4-1 through 4-3) is available in the *Assessment and Evaluation Masters*, p. 99.

SPREADSHEETS

4-3B Reading Spreadsheets

A Follow-Up of Lesson 4-3

Objective Students explore how data and formulas are entered in a computer spreadsheet.

Technology Resources
Suggested spreadsheet software:
- *Lotus 1·2·3*
- *ClarisWorks*
- *Microsoft Excel*

MANAGEMENT TIPS

Recommended Time
45 minutes

Getting Started Make sure students understand the differences between data, labels, and formulas. Also make sure students understand a cell's address and how it is used in formulas.

Even though students have not studied percents yet, explain that the values they are entering in column C are the decimal form of the percent of discount. So $0.2 = 20\%$.

Teaching Tip Have students use a similar setup and enter prices and discounts from a local store's sale flyer. Suggest that they plan a shopping spree using the data.

ASSESS

After students answer Exercises 1–5, ask them how they could change the spreadsheet for different situations, such as inventories, employee discounts, and so on.

computer

 spreadsheet software

A computer *spreadsheet* arranges data and formulas in a column and row format. A spreadsheet is used for organizing and analyzing data.

A spreadsheet is made up of *cells*. A cell can contain data, labels, or formulas. Each cell has an address. A cell's address is a combination of the letter from the top of a particular column and the number from the left of a particular row. The cell B4 is the cell in column B and row 4. *Cell B4 in the spreadsheet below contains the amount $29.90.*

The spreadsheet below shows a price list for a retail store.

TRY THIS

Work with a partner.

The formulas in the cells in column D find the product of the numbers that are entered in columns B and C.

Use the spreadsheet to determine the discounts by making the following substitutions.

C2 = 0.2, C3 = 0.25, C4 = 0.15, C5 = 0.2, C6 = 0.35, C7 = 0.1

	A	B	C	D	E
1	Item	Regular Price	Rate of Discount	Discount	Sale Price
2	Blouse	$35.99		= B2*C2	= B2-D2
3	Skirt	$49.99		= B3*C3	= B3-D3
4	Jeans	$29.90		= B4*C4	= B4-D4
5	Shorts	$15.00		= B5*C5	= B5-D5
6	Sweatshirt	$18.99		= B6*C6	= B6-D6
7	T-Shirts	$19.95		= B7*C7	= B7-D7

ON YOUR OWN

1. Name the cell that holds the data $25.41. **E4**

2. What is stored in cell D5? **$3.00**

3. The formulas in the cells in column E find the difference of the numbers in column B and column D. Use the results from the activity above to determine each sale price. **$28.79, $37.49, $25.41, $12.00, $12.34, $17.95**

4. How could you use the spreadsheet to determine the amount of sales tax on each item? **See margin.**

5. Suppose column C was labeled *Quantity* and column D was labeled *Total*. Would the formulas in column D change? **No; you would still multiply.**

144 **Chapter 4** Multiplying and Dividing Decimals

Additional Answer
4. Sample answer: Add a column with the formula to find the amount of tax.

 Math Journal Have students write a paragraph explaining how the spreadsheet could be used to make a graph. Would they use a line graph or a bar graph for the given information?

4-4

Integration: Geometry
Perimeter and Area

What you'll learn

You'll learn to find the perimeters and the areas of rectangles and squares.

When am I ever going to use this?

Knowing how to find perimeter can help you buy the right amount of framing. Knowing how to find area can help you buy the right amount of paint or carpet.

Word Wise
perimeter
side
area

Alicia is redecorating her bedroom and wants to add a wallpaper border around the entire room. How much will she need?

Alicia needs to find the **perimeter** of the bedroom so she can know how much border to buy. The perimeter (*P*) of any closed figure is the distance around the figure. You can find the perimeter by adding the measures of the **sides** of the figure.

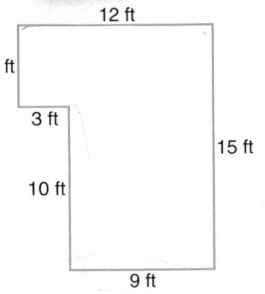

$$P = 15 + 9 + 10 + 3 + 5 + 12$$

$$P = 54$$

The perimeter of Alicia's room is 54 feet. So, Alicia needs 54 feet of wallpaper border.

To find the perimeter of a rectangle, add the measures of its four sides. Let *P* represent the measure of the perimeter, ℓ its length, and *w* its width.

$$P = \ell + w + \ell + w$$
$$P = \ell + \ell + w + w$$
$$P = 2\ell + 2w$$

Perimeter of a Rectangle	**Words:** The perimeter of a rectangle is two times the length (ℓ) plus two times the width (*w*).
	Symbols: $P = 2\ell + 2w$ **Model:**

Example ➊

Study Hint

Mental Math You can rewrite the formula for perimeter using the distributive property: $2\ell + 2w = 2(\ell + w)$.

Find the perimeter of a rectangle with a length of 18.3 meters and a width of 7.5 meters.

$$P = 2\ell + 2w$$
$$P = 2(18.3) + 2(7.5) \quad \textit{Replace } \ell \textit{ with 18.3 and w with 7.5.}$$
$$P = 36.6 + 15$$
$$P = 51.6$$

The perimeter is 51.6 meters.

Lesson 4-4 Integration: Geometry Perimeter and Area **145**

Instructional Resources
- *Study Guide Masters*, p. 26
- *Practice Masters*, p. 26
- *Enrichment Masters*, p. 26
- Transparencies 4-4, A and B
- *Technology Masters*, p. 8
- CD-ROM Program
  - Resource Lesson 4-4
  - Interactive Lesson 4-4

Recommended Pacing	
Standard	Day 7 of 16
Honors	Days 6 & 7 of 15
Block	Day 4 of 8

1 FOCUS

5-Minute Check
(Lesson 4-3)

Multiply.
1. $6.74 \cdot 3.28$ **22.1072**
2. $0.03 \cdot 0.002$ **0.00006**
3. Solve $x = 7.36 \cdot 20.544$. **151.20384**

Evaluate each expression if $a = 12.5$, $b = 3.08$, and $c = 0.009$.
4. $a(b + c)$ **38.6125**
5. abc **0.3465**

The 5-Minute Check is also available on **Transparency 4-4A** for this lesson.

Motivating the Lesson
Hands-On Activity Have small groups of students use toothpicks to make a closed figure. Let 1 toothpick = 10 feet. Have students determine methods for finding the distance around their figure and the amount of space covered by their figure.

Multiple Learning Styles

Visual/Spatial The region between Dallas, Texas, and Fort Worth, Texas, forms a rectangle made by Highway 20 on the south, Highway 408 and Loop 12 on the east, Highway 183 on the north, and Highway 183 and I-820 on the west. Have students use maps to determine other such regions that are either square or rectangular in shape. Then have them find the approximate perimeter and area of the region described.

Transparency 4-4B contains a teaching aid for this lesson.

Reading Mathematics Draw a rectangle on the chalkboard, including its dimensions. Also, write the words *perimeter, side, area, length,* and *width* on the board. Say each word. Have students use each word in a sentence about the figure. Discuss how the words *length* and *width* might be interpreted for different orientations of a rectangle.

In-Class Examples

For Example 1
Find the perimeter of a rectangle with a length of 22.86 meters and a width of 9.14 meters. **64 m**

For Example 2
Find the perimeter of a square poster whose sides each measure 91.44 centimeters. **365.76 cm**

For Example 3
Sandy is building a garden shed 11.2 feet long and 8.5 feet wide. How much floor material will she need? **95.2 ft²**

Teaching Tip Encourage students to always draw and label the figure (if an illustration is not included) and write the formula they will use before solving a problem.

Since each side of a square has the same length, you can multiply the measure of any of its sides (*s*) by 4 to find its perimeter. Thus, the formula for the perimeter of a square can be written as *P = 4s*.

Example 2 Find the perimeter of a square cement block whose sides each measure 17.875 inches.

17.875 in.

$P = 4s$
$P = 4 \times 17.875$ *Replace s with 17.875.*
$4 \boxed{\times} 17.875 \boxed{=} 71.5$

The perimeter of the cement block is 71.5 inches.

In addition to the perimeter, we often solve problems by using the **area** of a closed figure. Area is the number of square units needed to cover a surface.

By counting, you can see that the rectangle at the right has an area of 30 square units. You can also find its area by multiplying its length, 6 units, by its width, 5 units.

You can find the area of any rectangle by multiplying its length and its width.

| Area of a Rectangle | **Words:** The area of a rectangle is the product of its length (ℓ) and width (*w*). |
| | **Symbols:** $A = \ell \cdot w$ **Model:** |

Area is expressed in square units. For example, if the length and width are measured in feet, the area will be written in square feet, or ft².

Example 3 **Sports** International soccer fields are rectangular and measure 100 meters by 73 meters. A soccer field needs to be recovered with sod. How much sod do the groundskeepers need for the field?

$A = \ell \cdot w$
$A = 100 \cdot 73$ *Replace ℓ with 100 and w with 73.*
$A = 7,300$

The groundskeepers need 7,300 square meters of sod.

You can write the formula for the area of a square as $A = s^2$, because each side of a square has the same length.

Example ④ Find the area of a square whose sides measure 4.5 meters.

$A = s^2$

$A = 4.5^2$ *Replace s with 4.5.*

$A = 20.25$

4.5 m

The area of the square is 20.25 square meters.

CHECK FOR UNDERSTANDING

Communicating Mathematics

Read and study the lesson to answer each question. **1. See students' work.**

1. *Draw* and label a rectangle that has a perimeter of 36 units.

2. *Explain* how to find the area of a square.

> **2. Square the measure of one of its sides.**

Math Journal

3. Use grid paper to draw as many different rectangles as you can with a perimeter of 12 units. *Make a table* listing the length, width, perimeter, and area of each rectangle. Use the relationships between the lengths and widths to create formulas that could be used to find the perimeter and area of any rectangle. **See students' work.**

Guided Practice Find the perimeter of each figure.

4. **35 cm**
13 cm
9 cm
13 cm

5. 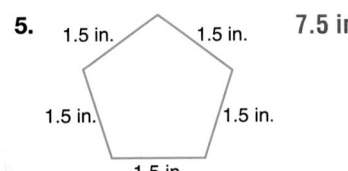 **7.5 in.**
1.5 in. 1.5 in.
1.5 in. 1.5 in.
1.5 in.

Find the perimeter and the area of each figure.

6.
rectangle | 2.6 m
8.8 m

$P = 22.8$ m; $A = 22.88$ m²

7.
square | 30.4 cm

$P = 121.6$ cm;
$A = 924.16$ cm²

8. What is the area of a rectangle with a length of 10.25 inches and a width of 8.5 inches? **87.125 in²**

EXERCISES

Practice Find the perimeter of each figure.

9.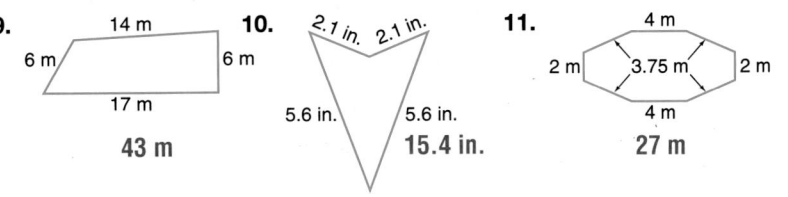
14 m
6 m
17 m
43 m

10. 2.1 in. 2.1 in.
5.6 in. 5.6 in.
15.4 in.

11.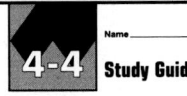
4 m
2 m 3.75 m 2 m
4 m
27 m

Lesson 4-4 Integration: Geometry Perimeter and Area **147**

In-Class Example
For Example 4
Find the area of a square whose sides measure 2.3 inches.
5.29 in²

3 PRACTICE/APPLY

Check for Understanding
If students need additional practice or instruction after completing Exercises 1–8, one of these options may be helpful.
- Extra Practice, see p. 566
- Reteaching Activity
- *Study Guide Masters*, p. 26
- *Practice Masters*, p. 26

Assignment Guide
Core: 9–21 odd, 23–26
Enriched: 10–18 even, 20–26

Study Guide Masters, p. 26

4 ASSESS

Closing Activity

Modeling Have students draw various rectangles and squares on grid paper and determine the length and width in grid units. Then have them find the perimeter and area of each figure.

Additional Answer
23.

Draw a diagram of one area in your home that is or could be carpeted. Find the dimensions of the area and record them on the diagram. How much carpet is needed to cover the area?

14. $P = 64$ ft;
   $A = 220$ ft²
15. $P = 12.8$ m;
   $A = 7.68$ m²

Applications and Problem Solving

16. $P = 49.2$ cm;
   $A = 151.29$ cm²
17. $P = 46.4$ in.;
   $A = 134.56$ in²

22. No; it will increase by two times the original length; see students' work.

Mixed Review

Find the perimeter and the area of each figure.

12.

rectangle — 7.25 ft — 12.5 ft
$P = 39.5$ ft;
$A = 90.625$ft²

13.
square — 1.5 in.
$P = 6$ in;
$A = 2.25$ in²

14. rectangle: ℓ, 22 ft; w, 10 ft
15. rectangle: ℓ, 4.8 m; w, 1.6 m
16. square: s, 12.3 cm
17. square: s, 11.6 in.

18. How many segments x units long will fit on the perimeter of each figure?

   a. x 4
   b. x 6

19. Find the area and perimeter of the figure made up of rectangles. **15 in²; 20 in.**

4 in. — 3 in. — 6 in. — 3 in. — 1 in.

20. *Gardening* Mrs. Collins has a rectangular strawberry garden that is 6.1 meters long and 2.5 meters wide.

   a. She wants to put a fence around her garden to keep the rabbits out. How much fencing does she need? **17.2 m**

   b. She needs to cover the garden with a net to keep birds from eating the strawberries. How much netting does she need? **15.25 m²**

21. *Sports* Badminton was added for the Summer Olympic games in Barcelona, Spain. A regulation badminton court has the measurements shown in the diagram.

   a. Tape is to be applied to the floor to form a badminton court's boundaries. Do you need to find the area or the perimeter to determine how much tape you need? **perimeter**

   20′ — 44′

   b. What is the area of the court? **880 ft²**

22. *Geometry* Suppose you increase a pair of opposite sides of a square by two units. Will the area of the rectangle be four more square units than the area of the square? Use a model in your explanation.

23. *Critical Thinking* Using the figure shown, draw another figure that has twice the area and still has the same perimeter. **See margin.**

24. *Algebra* Evaluate the expression zwx if $w = 0.2$, $x = 20.7$, and $z = 3.01$. *(Lesson 4-3)* **12.4614**

25. **Standardized Test Practice** Ernesto bought 7 spiral notebooks for his classes. Each notebook cost $2.29, including tax. What was the total cost of the notebooks? *(Lesson 4-1)* **C**

   A $8.93   **B** $16.93   **C** $16.03   **D** $17.03   **E** Not Here

For **Extra Practice**, see page 566.

148 Chapter 4 Multiplying and Dividing Decimals

Extending the Lesson

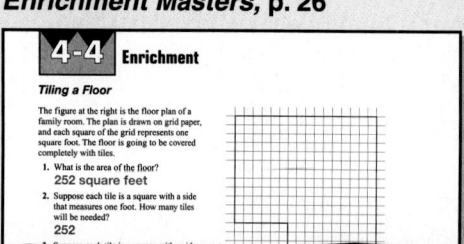
Activity Have students use a Computer Assisted Design (CAD) program to draw closed figures with designated perimeters. Have them determine, for example, how many different figures they can create that have a perimeter of 42 meters or an area of 110 square meters.

HANDS-ON LAB

COOPERATIVE LEARNING

4-4B Area and Perimeter

A Follow-up of Lesson 4-4

🔲 grid paper

In this lab, you will use grid paper to explore how perimeter and area are related.

TRY THIS

Work in groups of three.

Step 1 Copy the table at the right.

Step 2 On centimeter grid paper, draw a rectangle with a length of 6 and a width of 1.

Step 3 Find the perimeter and the area of the rectangle and record them in your table.

Step 4 Repeat Steps 2 and 3 for the remaining dimensions in your table.

Length	Width	Perimeter	Area
6	1		
5	2		
4	3		

ON YOUR OWN

1a–c. See Answer Appendix.

1. Each person in your group should copy the table at the right.

   a. One person should complete the table for all rectangles whose perimeter is 16 with whole number sides.

   b. Another person should complete the table for all rectangles whose perimeter is 18 with whole number sides.

   c. The third person should complete the table for all rectangles whose perimeter is 20 with whole number sides.

Length	Width	Area

2. Suppose you want to enclose a rectangular garden with the greatest area. **a. 13 feet long and 12 feet wide b. 12 feet by 12 feet**

   a. What would be the dimensions of the garden if you have 50 feet of fence?

   b. What would be the dimensions of the garden if you have 48 feet of fence?

3. What can you conclude about the relationship between area and perimeter?

4. *Reflect Back* Find the dimensions of a rectangle with the least perimeter possible if its area is 24 square units. **See margin.**

3. Sample answer: The longer the length and shorter the width, the lesser the area of the rectangular shape.

Lesson 4-4B HANDS-ON **LAB** **149**

Math Journal

Have students write a paragraph explaining how perimeter and area are related. Have them describe how they discovered the relationship between perimeter and area by making a table.

Additional Answer
4. 6 units long by 4 units wide

GET READY

Objective Students explore how perimeter and area are related.

MANAGEMENT TIPS

Optional Resources
Hands-On Lab Masters
• grid paper, p. 11
• worksheet, p. 45

Overhead Manipulative Resources
• centimeter grid

Recommended Time
45 minutes

Getting Started Ask students to find the dimensions of a rectangle drawn on centimeter grid paper. Then review the formulas for perimeter and area.

The **Activity** uses grid paper to explore perimeter and area relationships. Some students may wish to use a straightedge for accuracy in drawing lines. Have all students determine the lengths of the sides of their rectangles before they draw them.

ASSESS

Have students complete Exercises 1–3. Watch for students who confuse perimeter and area.

Use Exercise 4 to determine whether students understand the relationship between minimum perimeter and maximum area.

Objective Students solve problems by first solving a simpler problem.

Recommended Pacing	
Standard	Day 8 of 16
Honors	Day 8 of 15
Block	Day 4 of 8

1 FOCUS

Getting Started Have students act out the situation presented at the beginning of the lesson. Then have pairs of students work on Exercises 1–2. After discussing the results as a class, have the pairs solve Exercise 3.

2 TEACH

Teaching Tip Remind students to review what information they are given and what question is being asked before trying to solve the problems.

> **In-Class Example**
> A recipe that makes 6 servings of chili calls for 2 pounds of ground beef. How much ground beef is needed for 15 servings? **5 lb**

THINKING LAB PROBLEM SOLVING

4-5A Solve a Simpler Problem

A Preview of Lesson 4-5

Jemeka and Macy volunteered to plant some flowering bushes along the side of a neighborhood senior center. The wall of the building is 50 feet long. A gardener told them to plant the bushes 2 feet apart to give them room to grow. They are trying to determine how many plants to buy. Let's listen in!

50 divided by 2 is 25. I guess we need 25 plants.

I'm not sure that's right. Let's make it easier. Suppose the wall was 4 feet long. We'd need 3 bushes, not 2. Right?

Let's see. There would be one at the front corner, one in the middle 2 feet from the corner, and one at the back corner. When 3 bushes are planted 2 feet apart, the bushes on the end are 4 feet apart. You're right!

And if the wall was 6 feet long, we'd need one more bush for a total of 4 bushes. Is there a pattern here?

Macy

Yes! The number of plants needed is half the total distance plus one. So for this 50-foot wall, we'll need 26 plants, not 25. It was hard to see that until we worked with a shorter wall.

Jemeka

THINK ABOUT IT

Work with a partner.

1. *Explain* why Macy's first method of solving the problem seemed reasonable. **See margin.**

2. *Think* of another way the girls could have solved the problem. **Sample answer: Draw a diagram and count the plants.**

3. *Apply* what you have learned about the **solve a simpler problem** strategy to solve the following problem.

   Mike's Subs has made a submarine sandwich for eighteen people to share. How many cuts must be made to divide the sandwich equally among the eighteen people? **17 cuts**

150 Chapter 4 Multiplying and Dividing Decimals

■ Reteaching the Lesson ■

Activity Have students solve the problem below. Before they begin, ask how the problem can be simplified. *Find the number of 3-inch strips in 12 yards of string.* **144 strips**

Additional Answer

1. **Sample answer: She thought she was dividing the length into 2-foot sections.**

For **Extra Practice**, see page 566.

ON YOUR OWN

4. The last step of the 4-step plan for problem solving asks you to *examine* your solution. *Explain* how you can use estimation with decimals to help you examine a solution. **See margin.**

5. *Tell* why solving a simpler problem can sometimes help you solve a more difficult problem. **See margin.**

6. *Explain* how using the distributive property is similar to the solving a simpler problem strategy. **See margin.**

MIXED PROBLEM SOLVING

STRATEGIES

Look for a pattern.
Solve a simpler problem.
Act it out.
Guess and check.
Draw a diagram.
Make a chart.
Work backward.

Solve. Use any strategy.

7. *Gardening* Marco wants to fence in his tomato garden that is 8 feet by 6 feet. How much fencing does he need? **28 feet**

8. *Decorating* How many 1-foot square tiles are needed to cover a kitchen floor that is 14 feet by 10 feet? **140 tiles**

9. *Statistics* The bar graph shows revenues for several popular magazines.

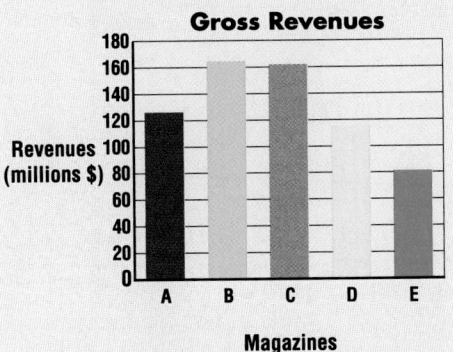

Gross Revenues

a. About how much higher were the revenues of magazine A than magazine E? **$40 million**

b. About how much higher were magazine B's revenues than magazine D's? **$50 million**

c. About how much more revenue did the magazine with the highest revenue have than magazine C? **$3 million**

10. *Decorating* The diagram shows Paula's dining room and living room area.

a. If she wants to carpet this area, how much carpet will she need? **528 ft²**

16 ft
12 ft
12 ft
24 ft
12 ft
28 ft

b. Draw another room that will use the same amount of carpet. **See students' work.**

11. *Sports* Luis bowled a 125, a 148, and a 162 during league competition. Before this competition, his average was 128 pins. Compare his previous average to his competition average. **See margin.**

12. *Entertainment* The Strand Theater seats 536 people. At last night's movie, there was one empty seat for every three people. How many people were in the movie theater? **402 people**

13. *Standardized Test Practice* Nick bought 5 packages of strawberries. Each package weighed 1.15 pounds. What was the weight of the 5 packages? **D**

A 4.85 lb
B 5.15 lb
C 5.45 lb
D 5.75 lb
E Not Here

■ Extending the Lesson ■

Activity Most building supply stores have brochures that give detailed descriptions for designing a kitchen. The brochures include cabinet and appliance dimensions, sample layouts, and suggested spacing. Have small groups of students use such a brochure to design a 16.5-foot by 12-foot kitchen. Then have them catalog shop to find the total cost of the items used.

Check for Understanding
Use the results from Exercise 4 to determine whether students understand how to solve a problem by breaking it down into simpler problems.

Extra Practice If students need additional practice in problem solving, extra practice is available on the following pages.
• Solve a Simpler Problem, see p. 566
• Mixed Problem Solving, see pp. 593–594

Assignment Guide
All: 4–13

4 ASSESS

Closing Activity
Writing Guide students to summarize the lesson by asking them to think of a simpler problem to solve the following. *Find the number of hours in 12 years.* **Sample answer: Multiply the number of hours in a day by 365. Then multiply that number by 12. Then have pairs of students create problems that can be solved using a simpler problem.**

Additional Answers
4. Sample answer: By estimating first, you can examine the solution to see if the decimal point is in the correct place.

5. Sample answer: This strategy allows you to break a difficult problem into manageable parts.

6. Sample answer: When you use the distributive property to solve a problem mentally, you solve two simpler problems and add.

11. His competition average was 17 pins higher than his previous average.

Instructional Resources

- *Study Guide Masters*, p. 27
- *Practice Masters*, p. 27
- *Enrichment Masters*, p. 27
- Transparencies 4-5, A and B
- *Assessment and Evaluation Masters*, pp. 98, 99
- *School to Career Masters*, p. 4
- *Science and Math Lab Manual*, pp. 73–76
- CD-ROM Program
  - Resource Lesson 4-5
  - Interactive Lesson 4-5

Recommended Pacing

Standard	Day 9 of 16
Honors	Day 9 of 15
Block	Day 5 of 8

1 FOCUS

5-Minute Check
(Lesson 4-4)
Find the perimeter and the area of each rectangle or square.

1.

2.7 ft
6.3 ft
18 ft, 17.01 ft²

2. rectangle: ℓ, 24 ft; w, 16 ft
80 ft, 384 ft²

3. square: s, 21 in. **84 in., 441 in²**

4. rectangle: ℓ, 8.22 m; w, 3.4 m
23.24 m, 27.948 m²

5. square: s, 8.4 mi **33.6 mi, 70.56 mi²**

The 5-Minute Check is also available on **Transparency 4-5A** for this lesson.

Motivating the Lesson
Hands-On Activity Give small groups of students play money (bills and coins). Have them divide different amounts of money equally among themselves.

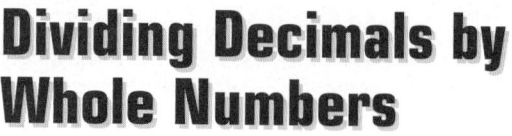

What you'll learn
You'll learn to divide decimals by whole numbers.

When am I ever going to use this?
Knowing how to divide a decimal by a whole number can help you find your share of a group purchase.

A package that included in-line skates, a helmet, and pads was on sale for $119.50. Josh didn't have enough money to pay for them so, in order to get the sale price, he put them on layaway. The store's layaway policy requires one payment now and a payment equal to that each week for 4 weeks. How much will he pay each time?

You need to divide $119.50 by 5.

First estimate. $100 \div 5 = 20$

When dividing a decimal by a whole number, place the decimal point in the quotient directly above the decimal point in the dividend. Then divide as you do with whole numbers.

$$
\begin{array}{r}
23.90 \\
5\overline{)119.50} \\
-10 \\
\hline
19 \\
-15 \\
\hline
4\,5 \\
-4\,5 \\
\hline
00
\end{array}
$$

Place the decimal point. Then divide as with whole numbers.

He needs to pay $23.90 each week. Checking this answer against the estimate, the answer is reasonable.

Examples

Find each quotient.

1 $29.8 \div 2$

Estimate: $30 \div 2 = 15$

$$
\begin{array}{r}
14.9 \\
2\overline{)29.8} \\
-2 \\
\hline
9 \\
-8 \\
\hline
1\,8 \\
-1\,8 \\
\hline
0
\end{array}
$$

Place the decimal point. Divide as with whole numbers.

$29.8 \div 2 = 14.9$

The estimate shows that the answer is reasonable.

2 $8.58 \div 12$

Estimate: $10 \div 10 = 1$

$$
\begin{array}{r}
0.715 \\
12\overline{)8.580} \\
-8\,4 \\
\hline
18 \\
-12 \\
\hline
60 \\
-60 \\
\hline
0
\end{array}
$$

Place the decimal point. Divide as with whole numbers. Annex a zero to continue dividing.

$8.58 \div 12 = 0.715$

The estimate shows that the answer is reasonable.

152 Chapter 4 Multiplying and Dividing Decimals

Usually when you divide with decimals, the answer does not come out even. You need to round the quotient to a specified place-value position. Always divide to one more place-value position than the place to which you are rounding.

Example 3
APPLICATION

Money Matters Katie and 5 of her friends bought a six-pack of fruit juice after their soccer game. Each friend wants to pay for her share. If the six-pack costs $3.29, how much does each friend owe to the nearest cent?

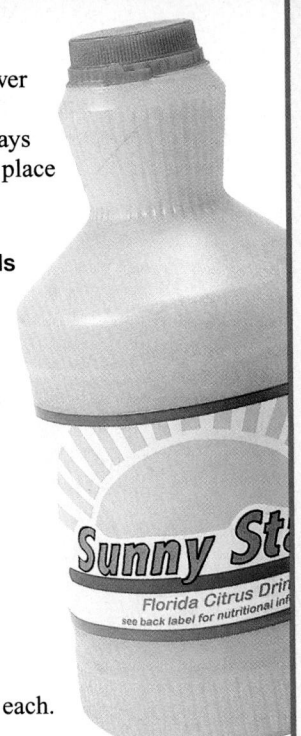

Sunny St
Florida Citrus Drir
see back label for nutritional inf

Study Hint

Estimation When dealing with money, always round the quotient up.

$$
\begin{array}{r}
0.548 \\
6\overline{)3.290} \\
-3\ 0 \\
\hline
29 \\
-24 \\
\hline
50 \\
-48 \\
\hline
2
\end{array}
$$

Estimate: 3.00 ÷ 6 = $0.50
Place the decimal point.
Annex a zero.
Divide to the thousandths place.

Katie and her five friends cannot pay $0.548 each. $0.548 rounded to the nearest cent is $0.55.

Each person owes $0.55. The estimate shows that the answer is reasonable.

CHECK FOR UNDERSTANDING

Communicating Mathematics

Read and study the lesson to answer each question. 2–3. See margin.

1. Sample answer: The estimate tells you the answer is close to 1.

1. *Explain* why you can use an estimate to place the decimal point in the quotient for 34.56 ÷ 25.

2. *Tell* how to round a quotient to a specific place-value position.

3. *You Decide* Payat uses a calculator to find 75.89 ÷ 38. He gets 1.997105263 for an answer. Is the answer reasonable? Explain.

Guided Practice

Find each quotient.

4. $13\overline{)15.6}$ **1.2**

5. $6\overline{)2.49}$ **0.415**

6. 55.6 ÷ 8 **6.95**

Round each quotient to the nearest tenth.

7. 55.39 ÷ 7 **7.9**

8. 78.75 ÷ 35 **2.3**

9. 111.37 ÷ 43 **2.6**

10. *Geometry* The perimeter of the square is 30.24 meters. What is the length of one side? **7.56 m**

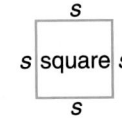

s square s

Lesson 4-5 Dividing Decimals by Whole Numbers **153**

2 TEACH

Transparency 4-5B contains a teaching aid for this lesson.

Using Connections Have pairs of students solve the following problem. *Howard has $57 to buy gifts for three people. If he spends an equal amount on each gift, how much can he spend on each person?* $19 Change $57 to $5.70 and have them solve the new problem. **$1.90**

Teaching Tip Before studying Example 1, review estimation using compatible numbers.

In-Class Examples

For Example 1
Find each quotient.
a. 82.8 ÷ 4 **20.7**
b. 36.4 ÷ 14 **2.6**

For Example 2
Find each quotient.
a. 7.56 ÷ 15 **0.504**
b. 2.18 ÷ 4 **0.545**

For Example 3
Mr. Schneider's class went to a movie theater. It cost $85.48 for 23 people. What was the cost per person rounded to the nearest cent? **$3.72**

3 PRACTICE/APPLY

Check for Understanding

If students need additional practice or instruction after completing Exercises 1–10, one of these options may be helpful.
• Extra Practice, see p. 567
• Reteaching Activity
• *Transition Booklet*, pp. 25–26
• *Study Guide Masters*, p. 27
• *Practice Masters*, p. 27

■ **Reteaching the Lesson** ■

Activity Play "I Can Estimate That," using division cards. Players reveal a card and challenge each other to get the closest estimate. Then they find the exact answer on a calculator. The player with the closest estimate gets the card. The player with the most cards wins.

Additional Answers

2. Always divide to one more place-value position than the place to which you are rounding.

3. Sample answer: Estimate 80 ÷ 40 = 2; The estimate shows that the answer is reasonable.

EXERCISES

Practice

Find each quotient.

11. $25\overline{)6.25}$ **0.25**
12. $16\overline{)117.44}$ **7.34**
13. $37\overline{)784.4}$ **21.2**
14. $475.2 \div 32$ **14.85**
15. $479.96 \div 52$ **9.23**
16. $256.36 \div 34$ **7.54**

Round each quotient to the nearest tenth.

17. $29.48 \div 11$ **2.7**
18. $28.56 \div 42$ **0.7**
19. $263.25 \div 81$ **3.3**

Round each quotient to the nearest hundredth.

20. $344.736 \div 76$ **4.54**
21. $650.23 \div 29$ **22.42**
22. $4.567 \div 21$ **0.22**

Solve each equation. **24. 0.8956**

23. $x = 29.37 \div 3$ **9.79**
24. $8.956 \div 10 = y$
25. $z = 302.5 \div 55$ **5.5**

26. Find 72.89 divided by 39 to the nearest thousandth. **1.869**
27. What is the solution of $m = 276.33 \div 61$? **4.53**
28. *Algebra* Evaluate $b \div c$ if $b = 34.56$ and $c = 32$. **1.08**

Applications and Problem Solving

29. *Money Matters* On Monday, Amber was paid $20 for watering her neighbor's plants the previous week. On Tuesday, her mother paid her $14 for raking 14 bags of leaves. She also made $10 baby-sitting on Friday. What was Amber's average pay for these three jobs? **$14.67**

30. *Sports* The Pickerington girls track team ran the 4-by-100 meter relay in 48.9 seconds. What was the average time of each runner? **12.225 seconds**

31. $0.19, $0.07, $0.06

31. *Spreadsheets* The spreadsheet shows the unit price for a jar of jelly. To find the unit price, divide the cost of the item by its size. Find the unit price for the next three items. Round to the nearest cent.

	A	B	C	D
1	Item	Cost	Size	Unit Price
2	Jelly	$1.59	12 oz	0.1325
3	Cereal	$3.35	18 oz	
4	Bread	$1.19	16 oz	
5	Ketchup	$0.89	14 oz	

32. *Money Matters* Suppose you wanted to fill a car's 12-gallon gas tank. If you can afford to spend $14.25 on gasoline, what price per gallon should you look for? Round to the nearest cent. **$1.19**

33. *Critical Thinking* Create a division problem that meets all of the following conditions. **Sample answer: 0.9984 ÷ 8**
   • the divisor is a whole number
   • the dividend is a decimal
   • the quotient is 0.125 when rounded to the nearest thousandth
   • the quotient is 0.12 when rounded to the nearest hundredth

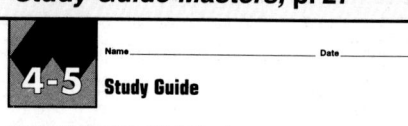

Mixed Review

34. *Geometry* Find the perimeter of the rectangle. (*Lesson 4-4*) **30.3 m**

11.75 m
3.4 m

35. *Weather* During two weeks of torrential rains, Antwon measured the rainfall. He recorded 11.33 centimeters in the first week and 15.75 centimeters in the second week. About how much rain fell in the two weeks? (*Lesson 3-5*) **about 27 cm**

36. *Careers* Prospective employees were told that the current employees' earnings averaged $475 a week. In the past, 6 people have earned weekly amounts of $200, $400, $410, $260, $320, and $1,260. Were the prospects being misled? Explain. (*Lesson 2-8*) **See margin.**

37. **Standardized Test Practice**
The line graph shows the number of people in Marysville and Plain City from 1960 to 1990. About how many more people were in Marysville than in Plain City in 1980? (*Lesson 2-3*) **B**

A 2,000 B 3,500
C 6,000 D 7,500

For **Extra Practice,** see page 567.

Population Growth

Population (1000's)

1960 1970 1980 1990

----- Marysville
.... Plain City

CHAPTER 4 — Mid-Chapter Self Test

1. *Money Matters* Mrs. Ortiz has bought a new car. Her payments will be $385.55 a month for 48 months. About how much will she pay in all? (*Lesson 4-1*) **$20,000**

Find each product mentally. Use the distributive property. (*Lesson 4-2*)

2. 6×17 **102**

3. 10.5×40 **420**

Solve each equation. (*Lesson 4-3*)

4. $a = 28.5 \cdot 0.61$ **17.385**

5. $b = 0.006(3.4)$ **0.0204**

6. *Geometry* Find the perimeter of a square if each side is 7.2 inches long. (*Lesson 4-4*) **28.8 in.**

Find the perimeter and the area of each figure. (*Lesson 4-4*)

7. rectangle 0.2 cm
4.7 cm
9.8 cm, 0.94 cm²

8. square
3.1 m
12.4 m, 9.61 m²

Round each quotient to the nearest hundredth. (*Lesson 4-5*)

9. $597.3 \div 62$ **9.63**

10. $69.597 \div 45$ **1.55**

Lesson 4-5 Dividing Decimals by Whole Numbers **155**

Extending the Lesson

Enrichment Masters, p. 27

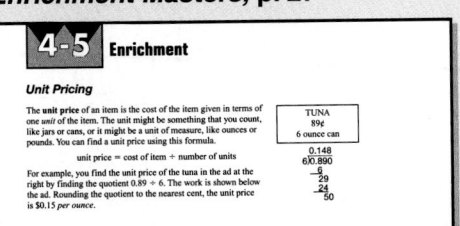

Activity Have pairs of students interview independent business owners. Have them ask how the skills taught in this lesson are used in business. Then have students use the information they have gathered to create word problems for classroom sharing.

GET READY

Objective Students use base-ten blocks to divide decimals.

Optional Resources
Hands-On Lab Masters
• base-ten models, p. 1
• worksheet, p. 46
Manipulative Kit
• base-ten blocks
Overhead Manipulative Resources
• decimal models

MANAGEMENT TIPS

Recommended Time
30 minutes

Getting Started Review modeling decimals. Read the first paragraph of the lesson aloud and display each model as you define it. Have students practice representing numbers such as 1.4, 2.3, 0.2, and 0.7.

Activities 1 and 2 involve modeling decimal division. Remind students to carefully count their models when they do the trading.

ASSESS

Have students complete Exercises 1–4. Watch for students who are not trading their blocks correctly or who are not grouping correctly at the end.

Use Exercise 5 to determine whether students understand how to divide decimals.

HANDS-ON
LAB

COOPERATIVE LEARNING

4-6A Dividing by Decimals

A Preview of Lesson 4-6

▦ base-ten blocks

In this lab, you will use base-ten blocks to model dividing a decimal by a decimal. Recall that each 10-by-10 block represents 1, each row or column represents 0.1, and each small square represents 0.01.

TRY THIS

Work with a partner.

❶ To model 1.2 ÷ 0.3, follow these steps.
• Place one and two tenths in front of you.

• Trade the ones block for tenths.

• Separate the tenths into groups of three tenths.

There are four groups of three tenths.
Therefore, 1.2 ÷ 0.3 = 4.

❷ To model 0.2 ÷ 0.04, follow these steps.
• Place two tenths in front of you.

• Trade the tenths blocks for hundredths.

• Separate the hundredths into groups of four hundredths.

There are five groups of four hundredths.
Therefore, 0.2 ÷ 0.04 = 5.

ON YOUR OWN

Use base-ten blocks to show each quotient. 1–4. See students' work for models.
1. 1.4 ÷ 0.7 **2**   **2.** 2.6 ÷ 0.2 **13**   **3.** 0.9 ÷ 0.03 **30**   **4.** 1.25 ÷ 0.25 **5**

5. *Look Ahead* Find the quotient for 2.4 ÷ 0.8 without using models. **3**

156 Chapter 4 Multiplying and Dividing Decimals

Have students write a paragraph explaining what expressions like 1.2 ÷ 0.3 mean when using models.

4-6

Dividing by Decimals

What you'll learn

You'll learn to divide decimals by decimals.

When am I ever going to use this?

Decimal division can be used to compare the rates of speed over different distances.

The circle graph shows where the United States exported $16.9 billion worth of cars in a recent year.

How many times greater was the value of the cars exported to Canada than to Japan?

You need to divide 7.8 by 2.4.

First, estimate the answer.

$$8 \div 2 = 4$$

The value of the cars exported to Canada was about 4 times greater than the value of the cars exported to Japan.

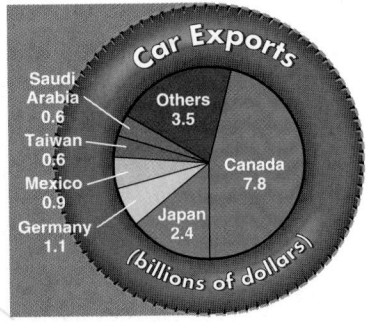

Source: U.S. Census Bureau

When dividing decimals by decimals, change the divisor to a whole number. To do this, multiply both the divisor and dividend by the same power of 10. Then divide as with whole numbers.

Multiply 7.8 and 2.4 by 10.

$$2.4\overline{)7.8} \rightarrow 2.4\overline{)7.8} \rightarrow 24\overline{)78.00}$$

$$\begin{array}{r} 3.25 \\ 24\overline{)78.00} \\ -72 \\ \hline 6\,0 \\ -4\,8 \\ \hline 1\,20 \\ -1\,20 \\ \hline 0 \end{array}$$

Multiply to check.

$$\begin{array}{r} 3.25 \\ \times 2.4 \\ \hline 1\,300 \\ 6\,50 \\ \hline 7.800 \quad \checkmark \end{array}$$

Study Hint

Mental Math When multiplying by powers of ten, move the decimal to the right as many places as the number of zeros in the power of ten.

The value of the cars exported to Canada was 3.25 times greater than the value of the cars exported to Japan. The estimate shows that the answer is reasonable.

Example 1 Find $8.84 \div 3.4$.

Estimate: $9 \div 3 = 3$

$$3.4\overline{)8.84} \rightarrow 34\overline{)88.4}$$

$$\begin{array}{r} 2.6 \\ 34\overline{)88.4} \\ -68 \\ \hline 20\,4 \\ -20\,4 \\ \hline 0 \end{array}$$

Multiply by 10.
Place the decimal point.
Divide as with whole numbers.

$8.84 \div 3.4 = 2.6$. The estimate shows that the answer is reasonable.

Check: $2.6 \times 3.4 = 8.84$ ✓

Lesson 4-6 Dividing by Decimals **157**

Multiple Learning Styles

Verbal/Linguistic Have students research decimal facts about animal sizes. For example, a 0.1-inch flea can jump 7.75 inches high. Have them use these facts to create word problems about living creatures. Separate students into groups to solve the problems.

MathPASS CD-ROM

This CD-ROM offers a complete, self-paced mathematics curriculum. Each lesson includes a pretest, tutorial, guided practice, and posttest. MathPASS Lesson 9 is correlated to this Student Edition lesson.
For Windows & Macintosh

Instructional Resources

- *Study Guide Masters*, p. 28
- *Practice Masters*, p. 28
- *Enrichment Masters*, p. 28
- Transparencies 4-6, A and B
- *Classroom Games*, pp. 7–9
- CD-ROM Program
  - Resource Lesson 4-6
  - Interactive Lesson 4-6

Recommended Pacing	
Standard	Days 10 & 11 of 16
Honors	Day 10 of 15
Block	Day 6 of 8

1 FOCUS

5-Minute Check
(Lesson 4-5)

Find each quotient.

1. $16\overline{)82.56}$ **5.16**
2. $56.7 \div 15$ **3.78**
3. Evaluate $(c - a) \div b$ if $a = 3.36$, $b = 21$, and $c = 63.84$. **2.88**
4. Round $85.3 \div 22$ to the nearest tenth. **3.9**
5. Round $5.068 \div 16$ to the nearest hundredth. **0.32**

The 5-Minute Check is also available on **Transparency 4-6A** for this lesson.

Motivating the Lesson

Communication Discuss with students how they would determine which macaroni has the lower price per kilogram.

- a 1.36-kilogram box at $2.49
- a 0.436-kilogram box at $0.57

2 TEACH

Transparency 4-6B contains a teaching aid for this lesson.

Using Critical Thinking Give students a division problem with the quotient's decimal point in the wrong place. Have them estimate the quotient and then use a calculator. Discuss how the error was made.

Lesson 4-6 **157**

In-Class Examples

For Example 1
Find each quotient.
a. 4.352 ÷ 3.2 **1.36**
b. 8.873 ÷ 1.9 **4.67**

For Example 2
Find each quotient.
a. 1.035 ÷ 0.023 **45**
b. 25.16 ÷ 0.068 **370**

For Example 3
Mrs. Sharvy's vegetable garden is 8.25 meters long. She wants to plant tomatoes 0.33 meter apart along the back border. How many plants does she need? **25**

3 PRACTICE/APPLY

Check for Understanding

If students need additional practice or instruction after completing Exercises 1–9, one of these options may be helpful.
- Extra Practice, see p. 567
- Reteaching Activity
- *Transition Booklet*, pp. 27–28
- *Study Guide Masters*, p. 28
- *Practice Masters*, p. 28

Study Guide Masters, p. 28

Examples ❷ Find 15.176 ÷ 0.028.

                     542.
0.028)15.176 → 28)15176.   *Multiply by 1,000.*
                 −140   *Place the decimal point.*
                  117   *Divide.*
                 −112
                   56
                  −56
                    0

15.176 ÷ 0.028 = 542 **Check:** 0.028 × 542 = 15.176 ✓

INTEGRATION ❸ **Measurement** Mr. Henderson's flower garden is 11.25 meters long. He wants to make a border along one side using bricks that are 0.25 meter long. How many bricks does he need?

                 45
0.25)11.25 → 25)1125   *Multiply by 100.*
               −100   *Place the decimal point.*
                125   *Divide.*
               −125
                  0

Mr. Henderson needs 45 bricks.

CHECK FOR UNDERSTANDING

Communicating Mathematics

Read and study the lesson to answer each question. **1–2. See margin.**

1. *Write* a decimal division problem that would require you to multiply the divisor and dividend by 10 before you divide.

2. *Explain* why the quotient for 2.35 ÷ 0.58 should be about 4.

Guided Practice

Find each quotient.

3. 2.7)51.3 **19**   4. 2.5)43.25 **17.3**   5. 0.18)124.92 **694**

6. 302.5 ÷ 5.5 **55**   7. 70.59 ÷ 1.3 **54.3**   8. 3.965 ÷ 0.065 **61**

9. *Algebra* Evaluate a ÷ b if a = 7.502 and b = 3.41. **2.2**

EXERCISES

Practice

Find each quotient.

10. 4.9)160.72 **32.8**   11. 0.98)109.76 **112**   12. 3.25)2,606.5 **802**

13. 3.6)1.44 **0.4**   14. 89.6)206.08 **2.3**   15. 0.008)0.0072 **0.9**

17. 2,967

16. 0.32 ÷ 0.005 **64**   17. 210.657 ÷ 0.071   18. 9.425 ÷ 0.0125 **754**

19. 0.0186 ÷ 0.031 **0.6** 20. 40.99524 ÷ 14.3   21. 5,885.9514 ÷ 703.22
                                        2.8668   **8.37**

158 Chapter 4 Multiplying and Dividing Decimals

■ Reteaching the Lesson ■

Activity Illustrate 2.5 ÷ 0.5 on the overhead projector using decimal models. Then multiply the divisor and the dividend by ten. Show 25 ÷ 5 with models. Guide students to conclude that multiplying the divisor and the dividend by a power of ten does not change the quotient.

Additional Answers

1. Sample answer: **1.84 ÷ 0.8**

2. Sample answer: When you multiply the divisor and dividend by 100, the problem becomes 235 ÷ 58. Estimate 240 ÷ 60 = 4.

Solve each equation.

22. $b = 17.01 \div 0.81$ **21**

23. $p = 94.16 \div 0.88$ **107**

24. $127.6625 \div 102.13 = x$ **1.25**

25. $0.0078 \div 0.002 = y$ **3.9**

26. What is 48.355 divided by 0.095? **509**

27. Find 7.502 divided by 2.2. **3.41**

28. *Algebra* Evaluate $s \div t$ if $s = 1.43$ and $t = 1.3$. **1.1**

29. *Algebra* Evaluate $(p + q) \div r$ if $p = 0.7$, $q = 1.4$, and $r = 2.5$. **0.84**

Applications and Problem Solving

30. *Sports* At the 1996 Olympics, American sprinter Michael Johnson set a world record of 19.32 seconds for the 200-meter dash. A honeybee can fly the same distance in 40.572 seconds. How many times faster than a honeybee is Michael Johnson? **2.1 times faster**

31. *Transportation* The Aero Spacelines Super Guppy, a converted Boeing C-97, can carry 87.5 tons. Tanks that weigh 4.5 tons each are to be loaded onto the Super Guppy. What is the maximum number of tanks it can transport? **19 tanks**

32. *Food* The table shows how many pounds of breakfast cereal are consumed each year by the average person in selected countries.

a. To the nearest tenth, how many times greater was the amount consumed in Great Britain than in France? **4.1**

b. To the nearest tenth, how many times greater was the amount consumed in the United States than in Canada? **2.0**

Country	Amount (lb)
Canada	6.02
France	1.78
Great Britain	7.34
South Korea	0.07
United States	11.9

33. *Critical Thinking* Replace each ■ to make a true sentence.

$$■.8 ■ 6 \div 0.35 = 2.5 ■$$
Sample answer: $0.896 \div 0.35 = 2.56$

Mixed Review

34. Find the quotient when 68.52 is divided by 12. *(Lesson 4-5)* **5.71**

35. Write the number 204.2398 in words. *(Lesson 3-1)* **See margin.**

36. **Standardized Test Practice**
The stem-and-leaf plot shows the high temperatures for 20 cities on February 23. Which interval had the fewest high temperatures? *(Lesson 2-6)* **C**

Stem	Leaf
2	5
3	0 2 4 5
4	1 2 6
5	
6	0
7	

$\quad ■ = 42$

A $20° - 29°$ **B** $30° - 39°$

C $50° - 59°$ **D** $70° - 79°$

For **Extra Practice,** see page 567.

37. *Algebra* Solve $b \times 6 = 42$ mentally. *(Lesson 1-7)* **7**

Extending the Lesson

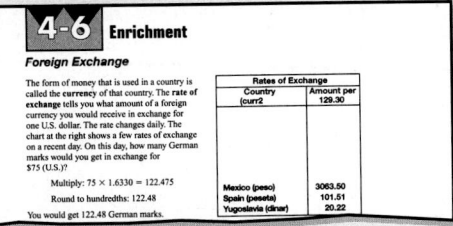
Activity Have groups of students write and solve word problems that involve dividing decimals. Have students use current newspapers, magazines, and catalogs to make the word problems relevant and realistic.

Assignment Guide

Core: 11–31 odd, 33–37
Enriched: 10–28 even, 30–37

4 ASSESS

Closing Activity

Speaking Write several problems on the chalkboard that involve dividing decimals by decimals. Give students clues to identify a problem such as, "To divide, the divisor and dividend would be multiplied by 100." Have the student who identifies the first problem provide the next clue. Continue for all problems.

Additional Answer

35. two hundred four and two thousand three hundred ninety-eight ten-thousandths

Motivating Students

Owning a small business is the dream of many people. Small business owners have the advantages of choosing the type of company they start, setting their own working hours and conditions, and earning profits from the company in addition to receiving a salary. To begin a discussion of small business ownership, ask students these questions.

- Are there any small businesses in your neighborhood? What are they? **Sample answer: video store, ice cream shop, service station, bakery**
- What would you need to start a small business? **Sample answer: money, a place to work , a product or service to sell, advertising**
- Why do you think some small businesses are more successful than others? **Sample answer: Some products and services are in higher demand than others.**

Making the Math Connection

Small business owners themselves often keep track of expenditures, sales, and inventory. They need to be able to add and subtract columns of numbers, calculate sales tax, and analyze financial data to determine profits and losses.

Working on *Your Turn*

Have students begin by forming groups and brainstorming ideas for small businesses. Have them choose five products or services to include in their survey. After conducting the survey, have groups discuss what their results would mean to someone attempting to start a small business.

*An additional School to Career activity is available on page 4 of the **School to Career Masters.***

SCHOOL to CAREER
BUSINESS

```
Cedric Walker
```
Small business owner

Cedric Walker is the co-owner, along with Cal Dupree, of the nation's only African-American-owned, operated, and performed circus. After spending three years doing research, Walker opened the circus in 1994.

A person who is interested in owning a small business should take classes in economics, mathematical analysis, business ethics, communications, mathematics of finance, and marketing. A college degree in communications, marketing, business law, business management, or accounting should be considered.

For more information:
The Young Entrepreneurs' Organization
10101 North Glebe Road
Arlington, VA 22207
(703) 519-6700

inter CONNECTION
www.glencoe.com/sec/math/mac/mathnet

> I can't wait to design my own product and start my own business!

Your Turn
Part of what makes a small business owner successful is offering a product or service that people need. Survey your class or your school and find out what people need that a small business could provide. Write a paragraph describing what you discovered and how you might be able to fill the need with your own small business.

160 Chapter 4 Multiplying and Dividing Decimals

More About Cedric Walker

- When Walker was 18, his father sent him to live with his uncle. He met the musical group the Commodores at his uncle's club and joined their road crew. He went on to a career in music promotion. He produced rap music shows such as the New York City Fresh Festival and gospel plays such as *A Good Man Is Hard to Find*.
- Walker set out to create an African-American variety show, then decided to make it a circus. He stresses that the circus is family entertainment. From a marketing standpoint, he believes the circus will be in business for many years to come.

4-7 Zeros in the Quotient

What you'll learn

You'll learn to divide decimals involving special cases of zero in the quotient.

When am I ever going to use this?

Knowing how to divide all kinds of decimals can help you find the unit cost of a jar of peanut butter.

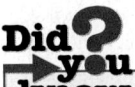

Did you know? The men's gymnastic team from Japan won the gold medal in the team combined exercises for five consecutive Olympics, from 1960 through 1976.

On March 30, 1980, Shigeru Iwasaki somersaulted backward 54.68 yards in 10.8 seconds. To the nearest hundredth, how many yards per second did he somersault?

First, estimate the answer.

$$50 \div 10 = 5$$

He went about 5 yards per second.

Method 1 Use a calculator.

54.68 ÷ 10.8 = *5.062962963*

To the nearest hundredth, he went 5.06 yards per second. Compared to the estimate, the answer is reasonable.

Method 2 Use paper and pencil.

You can see why a zero appears in this quotient.

$$
\begin{array}{r}
5.062 \\
10.8\overline{)54.68} \quad \rightarrow \quad 108\overline{)546.800} \\
-540 \\
\hline
6\,8 \\
-0 \\
\hline
6\,80 \\
-6\,48 \\
\hline
320 \\
-216 \\
\hline
104
\end{array}
$$

Divide to the thousandths place to round to the nearest hundredth. 68 < 108 so a zero is written in the quotient.

Example **1** Find $9.03 \div 0.301$.

$$
\begin{array}{r}
30.0 \\
0.301\overline{)9.030} \\
-9\,03 \\
\hline
00
\end{array}
$$

Write a zero in the ones place of the quotient.

$$9.03 \div 0.301 = 30.0$$

Check: $0.301 \times 30 = 9.03$ ✓

Lesson 4-7 Zeros in the Quotient **161**

MathPASS CD-ROM

This CD-ROM offers a complete, self-paced mathematics curriculum. Each lesson includes a pretest, tutorial, guided practice, and posttest. MathPASS Lesson 10 is correlated to this Student Edition lesson.
For Windows & Macintosh

4-7 Lesson Notes

Instructional Resources
- *Study Guide Masters*, p. 29
- *Practice Masters*, p. 29
- *Enrichment Masters*, p. 29
- Transparencies 4-7, A and B
- *Assessment and Evaluation Masters*, p. 100
- CD-ROM Program
  - Resource Lesson 4-7

Recommended Pacing	
Standard	Day 12 of 16
Honors	Day 11 of 15
Block	Day 6 of 8

1 FOCUS

5-Minute Check *(Lesson 4-6)*

Find each quotient.
1. $4.2\overline{)466.2}$ **111**
2. $5.8\overline{)21.46}$ **3.7**
3. $9.476 \div 1.03$ **9.2**
4. $173.28 \div 45.6$ **3.8**
5. Solve $a = 181.44 \div 15.12$. **12**

 The 5-Minute Check is also available on **Transparency 4-7A** for this lesson.

Motivating the Lesson

Communication Have students read the opening paragraphs of the lesson. Ask: *Why is there a zero in the tenths place of the quotient?* **There are no groups of 108 in a group of 68.**

2 TEACH

 Transparency 4-7B contains a teaching aid for this lesson.

Using Calculators Have students use a calculator to find quotients in decimal division problems they make up. Have them record any quotients with zeros in them. Then have them make a generalization based on their findings.

Example 2
Real World APPLICATION

Money Matters Mr. Alvarez put 11.5 gallons of gas in his van. If he paid $13.90, what was the price per gallon?

$$11.5\overline{)13.90} \rightarrow 115\overline{)139.000}$$ *Estimate: 10 ÷ 10 = 1*

```
        1.208
115)139.000
   −115
     24 0
    −23 0
      1 00
       −0
      1 000
      −920
        80
```

The price of the gasoline was about $1.21 per gallon.

CHECK FOR UNDERSTANDING

Communicating Mathematics

1. Sample answer: 4.53 ÷ 15

Math Journal

Read and study the lesson to answer each question. 2–3. See margin.

1. *Write* a decimal division problem that would require a zero in the quotient.
2. *Explain* how you could estimate the quotient for 17.5 ÷ 0.02.
3. *Write* a letter to a student explaining why 156.14 ÷ 14.8 is not 1.55.

Guided Practice

Find each quotient to the nearest hundredth.

4. 13)27 **2.08**
5. 36)145 **4.03**
6. 61)2,441 **40.02**
7. 75.3 ÷ 15 **5.02**
8. 0.68 ÷ 6 **0.11**
9. 3.41 ÷ 0.2 **17.05**

10. Solve $y = 15.25 ÷ 0.5$. **30.5**

11. *Algebra* Evaluate $d ÷ r$ if $d = 51.714$ and $r = 5.07$. **10.2**

EXERCISES

Practice

Find each quotient to the nearest hundredth.

12. 12)24.32 **2.03**
13. 0.25)75.25 **301**
14. 0.45)0.117 **0.26**
15. 24)125 **5.21**
16. 3.98)4.02 **1.01**
17. 7.89)86.3 **10.94**
18. 1.43 ÷ 13 **0.11**
19. 83.25 ÷ 4.11 **20.26**
20. 234.4 ÷ 11.2 **20.93**
21. 2.5 ÷ 0.24 **10.42**
22. 0.0125 ÷ 1.7 **0.01**
23. 95.23 ÷ 47.6 **2.00**

Solve each equation.

24. $g = 6.018 ÷ 5.9$ **1.02**
25. $d = 59.59 ÷ 0.59$ **101**
26. $7,576.4 ÷ 37.6 = f$ **201.5**
27. $3.3894 ÷ 4.2 = m$ **0.807**

28. What is 0.62524 divided by 30.8? **0.0203**

29. *Algebra* Evaluate $(a + b) ÷ c$ if $a = 0.016$, $b = 0.008$, and $c = 7.5$. **0.0032**

162   Chapter 4 Multiplying and Dividing Decimals

Reteaching the Lesson

Activity Have pairs of students model 0.53 ÷ 8 with base-ten blocks. Ask them how they would write the quotient. Then have them use their calculators to verify the answer. Continue with other examples that have zeros in the quotient.

Error Analysis
Watch for students who omit zeros before the decimal point.
Prevent by reminding students that without a preceding zero, a decimal point is easily overlooked—a $0.79 pen could become a $79 pen!

30. *Music* A compact disc has 11 tracks. If the entire CD takes 34.8 minutes to play, what is the average time for each track to the nearest hundredth of a minute? **about 3.16 minutes**

31. *Geometry* The area of the patio in the diagram is 27.36 square meters. The width of the patio is 4.5 meters. Find the length of the patio. **6.08 m**

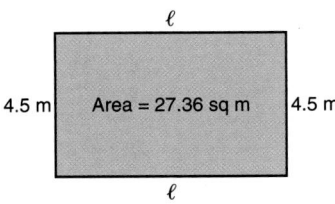

ℓ

4.5 m   Area = 27.36 sq m   4.5 m

ℓ

32. *Physical Science* Sound travels through air at 330 meters per second. How long will it take a bat's cry to reach its prey and echo back if the prey is 1 meter away? Round to the nearest thousandth of a second. **0.006 s**

33. *Critical Thinking* If a decimal greater than 0 and less than 1 is divided by a lesser decimal, would the quotient be always less, sometimes less, or never less than 1? **never**

Mixed Review

34. Find 5.06 divided by 2.3. *(Lesson 4-6)* **2.2**

35. *Standardized Test Practice* Mrs. Zacharias asked her mathematics students to decide whether 95 ceramic tiles, each measuring 1.5 feet-by-1.5 feet, would be enough to completely cover the floor of her classroom. What other piece of information would allow the students to answer the question? *(Lesson 4-4)* **D**
   A the weight of each tile
   B the number of classrooms in the school
   C the number of students in Mrs. Zacharias' classroom
   D the area of the classroom floor
   E the number of tiles in a package

36. See margin.

36. *Write a Problem* about a real-life situation involving the photo at the left that can be represented by a mean of 20° F. *(Lesson 2-7)*

37. *Statistics* Choose an appropriate scale for a frequency table for the following set of data: 24, 67, 11, 9, 52, 38, 114, and 98. *(Lesson 2-2)* **Sample answer: 0 to 120**

For **Extra Practice**, see page 567.

---

4 ASSESS

Closing Activity

Writing Have each student write a brief explanation of when zeros will appear in the quotient when dividing decimals.

Chapter 4, Quiz C (Lessons 4-6 and 4-7) is available in the *Assessment and Evaluation Masters,* p. 100.

Additional Answer

36. Sample answer: The low temperatures during the first week of February were 25°, 22°, 19°, 17°, 18°, 11°, and 28°.

Practice Masters, p. 29

4-7 Practice

Name _____ Date _____

Zeros in the Quotient

Find each quotient to the nearest hundredth.

1. 2.6)0.208 **0.08**   2. 1.2)0.0648 **0.05**   3. 15)4.53 **0.30**

4. 34)70.04 **2.06**   5. 4.2)42.294 **10.07**   6. 56.2)50.58 **0.9**

7. 18)729 **40.5**   8. 6.9)0.0207 **0.003**   9. 17.5)1.505 **0.09**

10. 7.2)4.68 **0.65**   11. 9.5)288.8 **30.4**   12. 3.8)34.39 **9.05**

13. 0.846 ÷ 1.2 **0.71**   14. 80.032 ÷ 1.6 **50.02**   15. 0.864 ÷ 24 **0.04**

16. 2.32 ÷ 58 **0.04**   17. 981.4 ÷ 14 **70.1**   18. 1.0034 ÷ 3.46 **0.29**

19. 0.0378 ÷ 6.3 **0.01**   20. 9.652 ÷ 1.9 **5.08**   21. 7.828 ÷ 76 **0.10**

22. 1,001 ÷ 25 **40.04**   23. 2.1843 ÷ 80.9 **0.03**   24. 9.66 ÷ 1.2 **8.05**

25. 75.84 ÷ 237 **0.32**   26. 0.3762 ÷ 41.8 **0.01**   27. 5.3 ÷ 106 **0.05**

© Glencoe/McGraw-Hill   T29   *Mathematics: Applications and Connections, Course 1*

Extending the Lesson

Enrichment Masters, p. 29

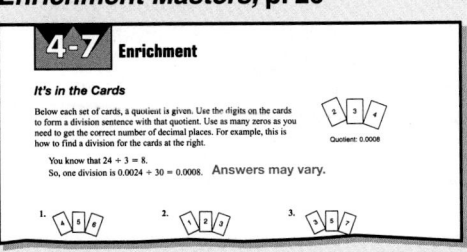

4-7 Enrichment

It's in the Cards

Below each set of cards, a quotient is given. Use the digits on the cards to form a division sentence with that quotient. Use as many zeros as you need to get the correct number of decimal places. For example, this is how to find a division for the cards at the right.

Quotient: 0.0008

You know that 24 ÷ 3 = 8.
So, one division is 0.0024 ÷ 30 = 0.0008. **Answers may vary.**

1. [4][8][3]   2. [7][5][0]   3. [3][8][5]

Activity Have students solve the following problem. *When 6.26 is divided by a number, the quotient is 2.08 and there is a remainder of 2. What is the number?* **3**

Instructional Resources

- *Study Guide Masters*, p. 30
- *Practice Masters*, p. 30
- *Enrichment Masters*, p. 30
- Transparencies 4-8, A and B
- CD-ROM Program
  - Resource Lesson 4-8

Recommended Pacing	
Standard	Day 13 of 16
Honors	Day 12 of 15
Block	Day 7 of 8

1 FOCUS

5-Minute Check
(Lesson 4-7)

Find each quotient to the nearest hundredth.

1. $55)\overline{115}$ **2.09**
2. $4.67 \div 38$ **0.12**
3. $83.7 \div 402.8$ **0.21**
4. Evaluate $r \div s$ if $r = 506.3$ and $s = 12.4$. Round to the nearest hundredth. **40.83**
5. Dinner for three costs $35.40. To the nearest cent, what is the cost for each person? **$11.80**

The 5-Minute Check is also available on **Transparency 4-8A** for this lesson.

Motivating the Lesson

Hands-On Activity Give small groups of students dried beans. Discuss the meanings of "mass." Without using a scale, have them describe how they would measure one kilogram of beans.

2 TEACH

Transparency 4-8B contains a teaching aid for this lesson.

Using a Balance Have students estimate the mass of various items in grams, milligrams, and kilograms. Have them use a pan balance and metric weights to check their work.

4-8

Integration: Measurement
Mass and Capacity in the Metric System

What you'll learn

You'll learn to use metric units of mass and capacity.

When am I ever going to use this?

Knowing how to use metric units of mass and capacity can help you solve problems in science class.

Word Wise

gram (g)
kilogram (kg)
milligram (mg)
liter (L)
milliliter (mL)

Pablo Lara is a weightlifter from Cuba who won the gold medal in the Olympics in Atlanta, Georgia. Pablo competed in the 76-kilogram division. This means his mass could be no more than 76 kilograms.

In the metric system, all units are defined in terms of a basic unit. The basic unit of mass in the metric system is the **gram (g)**. A **kilogram (kg)** is 1,000 grams, and a **milligram (mg)** is 0.001 gram.

Many items you use every day are measured in grams, kilograms, or milligrams.

- A small paper clip has a mass of about 1 gram.
- Your math textbook has a mass of about 1 kilogram.
- A grain of salt has a mass of about 1 milligram.

Examples

Did you know Pablo Lara lifted 451.75 pounds (204.9 kg) in the clean and jerk and 358 pounds (162.4 kg) in the snatch, yet he weighs only 167.5 pounds.

Write the unit of mass: milligram, gram, or kilogram, that you would use to measure each of the following. Then estimate the mass.

 a compact disc

Since a compact disc has a small mass, the *gram* is the appropriate unit.

The mass of a compact disc is about 50 grams.

 a laptop computer

Since a laptop computer has a mass close to several copies of your textbook, the *kilogram* is the appropriate unit.

The mass of a laptop computer is about 4 kilograms.

The basic unit of capacity in the metric system is the **liter (L)**. A liter is a little more than a quart. The **milliliter (mL)** is 0.001 liter. It takes 1,000 milliliters to make a liter.

- A small pitcher has a capacity of about 1 liter.
- An eyedropper has a capacity of about 1 milliliter.

Classroom Vignette

"To practice students' familiarity with the metric system, I have them work in groups and gather objects that they think will weigh a certain amount, such as 40 grams. You can do the same with length or units of capacity."

Judith J. Cardamone

Judith J. Cardamone, Teacher
East Middle School
Colorado Springs, CO

Write the unit of capacity: milliliter or liter, that you would use to measure each of the following. Then estimate the capacity.

3 a bathtub

Since a bathtub holds a large amount, the *liter* is the appropriate unit.

An average bathtub has a capacity of about 80 liters.

4 10 drops of food coloring

Since 10 drops of food coloring is a small amount, the *milliliter* is the appropriate unit.

The capacity is about 1 milliliter.

CHECK FOR UNDERSTANDING

Communicating Mathematics

Read and study the lesson to answer each question.

1. *Tell* which unit represents a greater mass, 1 gram or 1 kilogram. **kilogram**

2. *Explain* what a milliliter and a milligram have in common. **See margin.**

Guided Practice

Write the unit that you would use to measure each of the following. Then estimate the mass or capacity. **4. milligram; 500 mg**

3. the mass of a horse **kilogram; 500 kg**   4. an aspirin

5. a large bottle of soft drink **liter; 2 L**   6. a tennis ball **gram; 60 g**

7. *Food* A bread company makes loaves of bread that have a mass of 1 kilogram. A loaf of honey whole wheat is much larger than a loaf of blueberry apricot. Explain why this happens. **See margin.**

EXERCISES

Practice

Write the unit that you would use to measure each of the following. Then estimate the mass or capacity.

9. milliliter, 200 mL
10. milliliter, 1 mL
11. kilogram,100kg

8. gas in the tank of a car **liter, 50 L**   9. a bottle of cough syrup

10. vanilla used in a cookie recipe   11. the mass of an Olympic boxer

12. a can of soup **milliliter, 300 mL**   13. a bag of sugar **kilogram, 2 kg**

14. a glass of iced tea **milliliter, 350 mL**   15. a dollar bill **milligram, 1 mg**

16. a pitcher of water **liter, 2 L**   17. a canary **gram, 100 g**

18. the liquid in a thermometer **milliliter, 10 mL**   19. a table tennis ball **milligram, 500 mg**

20–22. See students' work.

Name an item that you think has the given measure.

20. about 250 mL   21. about 15 kg

Applications and Problem Solving

22. *Life Science* The human brain averages about 0.025 of a human's total body mass. Find your mass in kilograms and use a calculator to determine the approximate mass of your brain.

23. *Medicine* A pharmacist has 84.73 grams of a prescription medicine. She wants to separate it into 48 capsules. To the nearest thousandth, how many grams will go into each capsule? **1.765 g**

Lesson 4-8 Integration: Measurement Mass and Capacity in the Metric System   **165**

In-Class Examples

For Example 1
Write the unit of mass that you would use to measure a thumbtack. **gram**

For Example 2
Write the unit of mass that you would use to measure a cat. **kilogram**

For Example 3
Write the unit of capacity that you would use to measure the fruit juice in a punch recipe. **liter**

For Example 4
Write the unit of capacity that you would use to measure the amount of juice in one grape. **milliliter**

3 PRACTICE/APPLY

Check for Understanding
If students need additional practice or instruction after completing Exercises 1–7, one of these options may be helpful.
- Extra Practice, see p. 568
- Reteaching Activity
- *Transition Booklet*, pp. 31–34
- *Study Guide Masters*, p. 30
- *Practice Masters*, p. 30

Study Guide Masters, p. 30

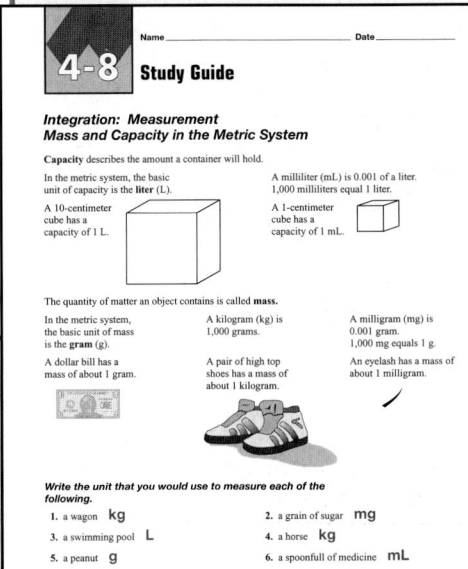

■ Reteaching the Lesson ■

Activity Have pairs of students use a scale to determine the mass of common materials such as pencils, books, and scissors. Have them record their findings and then arrange the items in order of increasing mass.

Additional Answers

2. Sample answer: They are both one-thousandth of the basic unit.

7. Sample answer: The fruit is heavier, so the loaf has to be smaller to have the same mass.

4 ASSESS

Closing Activity

Modeling Have students use clay to form different size balls that estimate various masses. To model capacity, tape pieces of paper together. Compare and discuss the different estimations.

Additional Answer

24b. Sample answer: The 6-pack is the better buy because you get more for the same amount of money.

---

24. *Money Matters* A can of soft drink contains 355 milliliters.
    a. How many milliliters are in a 6-pack of soft drink? **2,130 mL**
    b. Two liters of soft drink costs the same as a 6-pack of the same soft drink. Which is the better buy? Explain. **See margin.**

25. *Life Science* The table shows part of the recommended daily diet for a gibbon.
    a. Determine how many grams of carrots, bananas, and celery are needed in one week. **4,389 g**
    b. Is the amount of carrots, bananas, and celery in part a more or less than 4 kilograms?
    c. Visit a grocery store and select two or three of the items to weigh. About how many of these items would be needed for one week? **See students' work.**
    b. **more than 4 kg**

380 g lettuce
270 g orange
150 g spinach
143 g sweet potato
270 g banana
147 g carrot
210 g celery
210 g green beans

26. *Critical Thinking* Marva filled a 250-milliliter beaker with sand. She said its mass was 250 milligrams. Is she right? Explain.

Mixed Review

27. Divide 1,269.45 by 6.3. *(Lesson 4-7)* **201.5**

26. No, weight and capacity are not the same.

28. *Physical Science* One cubic meter of carbon dioxide has a mass of 1.977 kilograms. Round this number to the nearest tenth. *(Lesson 3-4)* **2.0**

29. *Standardized Test Practice* If a passenger train travels an average of 58 miles per hour, which is a good estimate for the number of hours it will take to travel 286 miles? *(Lesson 1-3)* **C**
    A 3 h   **B** 4 h   **C** 5 h   **D** 6 h   **E** 18 h

 For **Extra Practice,** see page 568.

Let the Games Begin

Scavenger Hunt

	Math Skill
	Metric Measurement

Get Ready This game is for three to four players.

 5 index cards per player   tape

Get Set Each player is assigned a unit of measure. For example, one player may have centimeters, another player may have liters, and the third player may have kilograms.

Go
• Each player will write their unit on each of the index cards and find items in the class that would best be measured using that unit.
• Players should pass their cards to the person on their left.
• The winner is the first player to tape the cards to the appropriate items.

interNET CONNECTION Visit www.glencoe.com/sec/math/mac/mathnet for more games.

Practice Masters, p. 30

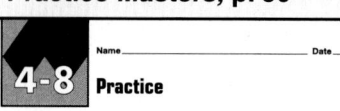

4-8 Practice

Name_____ Date_____

Integration: Measurement
Mass and Capacity in the Metric System

Write the unit that you would use to measure each of the following.

1. the mass of a bicycle **kg**
2. the mass of a pencil **g**
3. a glass of juice **mL**
4. a grain of sand **mg**
5. the mass of a penny **g**
6. the water in a swimming pool **L**
7. the mass of a feather **mg**
8. the mass of a bowling ball **kg**
9. hot chocolate in a large thermos **L**
10. a loaf of bread **g**
11. the mass of a whole watermelon **kg**
12. a cup of hot cider **mL**
13. the water in an aquarium **L**
14. the mass of a car key **g**
15. the mass of a vitamin pill **mg**
16. a can of soup **mL**
17. the mass of an egg **g**
18. the mass of a cat **kg**
19. the water in a team's cooler **L**
20. the mass of a sewing needle **mg**
21. the mass of mosquito **mg**
22. the liquid in a test tube **mL**
23. the mass of a student desk **kg**
24. the mass of a sandwich **g**
25. a bottle of expensive perfume **mL**
26. the mass of a sugar cube **mg**
27. the water in a washing machine **L**
28. the mass of a full bag of groceries **kg**
29. the mass of an apple **g**
30. the mass of a leaf **mg**

© Glencoe/McGraw-Hill   T30   Mathematics: Applications and Connections, Course 1

■ Extending the Lesson ■

Enrichment Masters, p. 30

4-8 Enrichment

Length, Mass, or Capacity?

When you encounter a problem about measurement, you won't necessarily see or hear one of the words *length, mass,* or *capacity.* Often you need to decide what type of measurement is involved, then choose the best unit of measure.

Tell whether each question most likely involves length, mass, or capacity.

1. Do I have enough milk to make this recipe? **capacity**
2. Do I have enough string to tie around this package? **length**
3. Will this punch bowl fit inside that box?
4. Will this amount of punch fit inside that bowl?

Let the Games Begin

You may want to have a fourth player on the team so that three players are matching the cards to the items and the fourth is judging correctness.

Integration: Measurement
Changing Metric Units

A chemistry experiment requires 3.05 grams of 3% hydrogen peroxide to produce one liter of oxygen. If a scientist wanted 24 liters of oxygen, how many kilograms of 3% hydrogen peroxide will she need? *This problem will be solved in Example 3.*

To change from one unit to another within the metric system, you either multiply or divide by powers of 10. The chart below shows the relationship between the units in the metric system and the powers of 10.

Study Hint

Mental Math Remember you can multiply or divide by a power of ten by moving the decimal point.

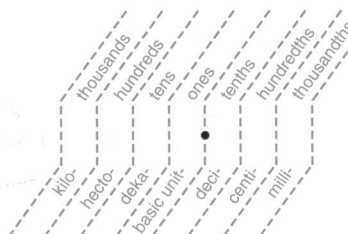

Each place value is ten times the place value to its right.

To change from a larger unit to a smaller unit, you need to multiply. To change from a smaller unit to a larger unit, you need to divide.

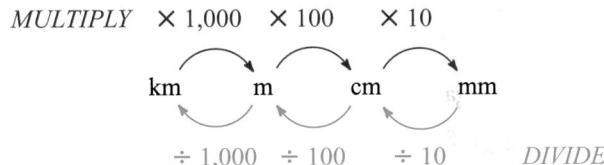

MULTIPLY $\times 1,000$ $\times 100$ $\times 10$

km   m   cm   mm

$\div 1,000$ $\div 100$ $\div 10$ *DIVIDE*

Examples

1 345 mL = _?_ L

To change from milliliters to liters, divide by 1,000 since 1 L = 1,000 mL.

$345 \div 1,000 = 0.345$
$345 \text{ mL} = 0.345 \text{ L}$

2 0.9 cm = _?_ mm

To change from centimeters to millimeters, multiply by 10 since 1 cm = 10 mm.

$0.9 \times 10 = 9$
$0.9 \text{ cm} = 9 \text{ mm}$

Lesson 4-9 Integration: Measurement Changing Metric Units   **167**

Classroom Vignette

"I have students copy the chart for converting within the metric system and show them how to move from what they know (are given) to what they need to know. The number of spaces moved left or right in the chart tells the students how many spaces to move the decimal point to the left or right."

Michelle Hutcheson

Michelle Hutcheson, Teacher
Evans Middle School
Newnan, GA

Transparency 4-9B contains a teaching aid for this lesson.

Mastering Basic Skills Have students practice multiplying and dividing by multiples of ten to prepare them for changing from one metric unit to another.

In-Class Examples

For Example 1
0.456 L = _?_ mL **456**

For Example 2
5 mm = _?_ cm **0.5**

For Example 3
A saltwater tank requires 11.26 grams of a certain salt and nutrient mixture for one liter of water. If Bob is filling a 45-liter tank, how many kilograms of the salt and nutrient mixture will he need? **0.5067 kg**

For Example 4
760 mg = _?_ g **0.76**

For Example 5
6.57 km = _?_ m **6,570**

Additional Answer

3. Sample answer: Parker and Dinh are both incorrect. Parker multiplied by 10 and Dinh divided by 10. They should have multiplied by 1,000.

Study Guide Masters, p. 31

4-9 Name _____ Date _____
Study Guide

Integration: Measurement
Changing Metric Units

The metric system is a base-10 system. The **meter** is the basic unit of length. The **liter** is the basic unit of capacity. The **gram** is the basic unit of mass.

Prefix	Meaning	Length	Capacity	Mass
kilo-	1,000	kilometer (km)	kiloliter (kL)	kilogram (kg)
hecto-	100	hectometer (hm)	hectoliter (hL)	hectogram (hg)
deka-	10	dekameter (dam)	dekaliter (daL)	dekagram (dag)
basic unit	1	meter (m)	liter (L)	gram (g)
deci-	0.1	decimeter (dm)	deciliter (dL)	decigram (dg)
centi-	0.01	centimeter (cm)	centiliter (cL)	centigram (cg)
milli-	0.001	millimeter (mm)	milliliter (mL)	milligram (mg)

Units may be changed by multiplying or dividing by multiples of 10.

Examples

1 3,500 mL = _____ L	2 7.6 km = _____ m	3 5,000 mg = _____ g
1,000 mL = 1 L	1km = 1,000 m	1,000 mg = 1 g
Divide 3,500 by 1,000.	Multiply 7.6 by 1,000.	Divide 5,000 by 1,000.
3,500 mL = 3.5 L	7.6 km = 7,600 m	5,000 mg = 5 g

Write whether you multiply or divide to change each measurement. Then complete.

1. 8.74 g = **8,740** mg multiply
2. 1,900 g = **1.9** kg divide
3. 6.21 L = **6,210** mL multiply
4. **5,600** g = 5.6 km multiply
5. 226 cm = **2.26**   divide
6. **5,114** g = 5.114 kg multiply
7. 890 mL = **0.89** L divide
8. **0.9** g = 900 mg divide
9. **610** cm = 6.1 m multiply
10. 0.6 kg = **600** g multiply
11. 0.5 km = **500** m multiply
12. **1,100** mm = 1.1 m multiply
13. **4** cm = 40 mm divide
14. 53.7 mL = **0.0537** L divide
15. 25 cm = **250** mm multiply

© Glencoe/McGraw-Hill   T31   *Mathematics: Applications and Connections, Course 1*

Physical Science Refer to the beginning of the lesson. How many kilograms of 3% hydrogen peroxide will the scientist need?

Explore You know it took 3.05 grams of 3% hydrogen peroxide to produce 1 liter of oxygen. You want to know how many kilograms are needed for 24 liters.

Plan Multiply 3.05 times 24 to find the number of grams needed. Then change this number from grams to kilograms.

Solve $3.05 \times 24 = 73.2$

Divide to change from smaller units to larger units.

$73.2 \div 1,000 = 0.0732$

She will need 0.0732 kilogram of 3% hydrogen peroxide.

Examine Since 1 g = 0.001 kg, the answer is reasonable.

> **Study Hint**
> Reading Math When a measurement is less than 1, the unit of measure stays singular. For example, 0.45 g is read as forty-five hundredths (of a) gram.

④ 0.45 g = _?_ mg

To change from grams to milligrams, multiply by 1,000 since 1 g = 1,000 mg.

$0.45 \times 1,000 = 450$

0.45 g = 450 mg

⑤ 8,960 m = _?_ km

To change from meters to kilometers, divide by 1,000 since 1 km = 1,000 m.

$8,960 \div 1,000 = 8.96$

8,960 m = 8.96 km

CHECK FOR UNDERSTANDING

Communicating Mathematics

Read and study the lesson to answer each question.

1. *Explain* how to change milliliters to liters. **divide by 1,000**

2. *Tell* whether you would use grams or kilograms to weigh a large screen television. **kilogram**

3. *You Decide* Parker and Dinh each changed 3.45 kilograms to grams. Parker's answer was 34.5 grams, and Dinh's answer was 0.345 grams. Who is correct? Explain your reasoning. **See margin.**

Guided Practice

Write whether you multiply or divide to change each measurement. Then complete.

4. 328 mL = _?_ L **divide; 0.328**
5. _?_ mm = 0.7 cm **multiply; 7**
6. _?_ g = 150 mg **divide; 0.15**
7. 5.02 kg = _?_ g **multiply; 5,020**
8. _?_ mL = 1.5 L **multiply; 1,500**
9. 150 m = _?_ km **divide; 0.15**

10. *Geography* The circumference of Earth is about 40,000 kilometers. How many meters is it around Earth? **40,000,000**

■**Reteaching the Lesson**■

Activity Have students make pairs of cards with equivalent metric measurement units on them. Play "Concentration" with students matching equivalent measures such as 500 mL and 0.5 L.

MathPASS CD-ROM

This CD-ROM offers a complete, self-paced mathematics curriculum. Each lesson includes a pretest, tutorial, guided practice, and posttest. MathPASS Lesson 11 is correlated to this Student Edition lesson.
For Windows & Macintosh

EXERCISES

Practice

Complete. 12. 0.253 14. 6.8 15. 5.24 17. 81.7 18. 0.149 19. 1.953

11. 210 mm = ? cm 2112. ? L = 253 mL   13. 2.5 L = ? mL **2,500**

14. 0.0068 kg = ? g   15. ? m = 524 cm   16. ? m = 2,400 mm **2.4**

17. ? mL = 0.0817 L   18. 149 mg = ? g   19. ? g = 1,953 mg

20. 0.593 km = ? m   21. 3.29 L = ? mL   22. 975 cm = ? mm

23. 5.25 kg = ? g   24. ? g = 427 mg   25. ? mL = 0.01 L **10**

26. ? cm = 6.908 km   27. 6,700 mg = ? kg   28. 1.2 km = ? mm

20. 593
21. 3,290
22. 9,750
23. 5,250
24. 0.427
26. 690,800
27. 0.0067

                                                   1,200,000

29. How many centimeters are in 0.58 meter? **58 cm**

30. Change 0.6 milligram to grams. **0.0006 g**

31. How many liters are in 213 milliliters? **0.213 L**

Applications and Problem Solving

32. *Earth Science* Seismic waves are waves generated by an earthquake. The focus of an earthquake is the point in Earth's interior where seismic waves originate. The focus can be between 5 and 700 kilometers below the surface of Earth. How many meters can the focus be below the surface? **between 5,000 and 700,000 meters**

33. *Food* A can holds 355 milliliters of soft drink. How many cans would equal 2 liters? **about 5.6 cans**

34. *Critical Thinking* A liter of water at 4°C has a mass of 1 kilogram. What is the mass of 1 milliliter of water at 4°C? **1 gram**

Mixed Review

35. *Measurement* To measure the water in a washing machine, would you use liters or milliliters as your units? *(Lesson 4-8)* **liters**

36. Find 4,507.72 divided by 8.5. *(Lesson 4-6)* **530.32**

37. *Algebra* Evaluate the expression $z + w$ if $z = 6.45$ and $w = 71.2$. *(Lesson 3-6)* **77.65**

38. **Standardized Test Practice** The graph shows the average number of greeting cards purchased by Americans recently. Which is a reasonable conclusion that can be drawn from the information in the graph? *(Lesson 2-3)* **D**

Greetings, America!

Number

| Age | |
Source: American Greetings Corporation

  A People over 65 buy the most greeting cards.

  B People 19 to 24 bought twenty times as many cards as people under 19.

  C The number of cards bought increases in every age group.

  D People 65 and older bought about five times as many cards as people 19 to 24.

  E People under 19 don't buy greeting cards.

For **Extra Practice**, see page 568.

Extending the Lesson

Enrichment Masters, p. 31

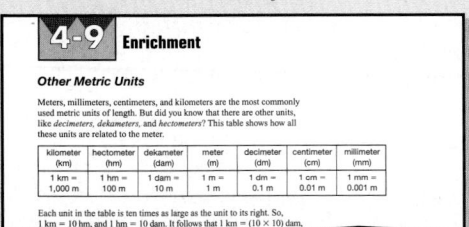

Activity Help students brainstorm things that may be measured in metric units, such as recorded snowfalls in one month. Ask them to draw a bar graph for their data, changing the metric unit of measure for the scale.

Vocabulary

This section provides a listing of the new terms, properties, and phrases that were introduced in this chapter. Have students define each term and provide an example or two of it, if appropriate.

Understanding and Using the Vocabulary

These exercises check students' understanding of the terms by using a variety of verbal formats including matching, completion, and true/false.

Glossaries A complete glossary of terms appears on pages 642–648. The glossary also appears in Spanish on pages 649–656.

Additional Answer

13. Sample answer: Round 6.9 to 7 and 88 to 90.
    $7 \times 90 = 630$

CHAPTER 4

Study Guide and Assessment

interNET CONNECTION Chapter Review **For additional lesson-by-lesson review, visit:** www.glencoe.com/sec/math/mac/mathnet

Vocabulary

After completing this chapter, you should be able to define each term, concept, or phrase and give an example or two of each.

Algebra
distributive property (p. 137)

Geometry
area (p. 146)
perimeter (p. 145)
sides (p. 145)

Number and Operations
compatible numbers (p. 133)

Measurement
gram (p. 164)
kilogram (p. 164)
liter (p. 164)
milligram (p. 164)
milliliter (p. 164)

Problem Solving
solve a simpler problem (pp. 150–151)

Understanding and Using the Vocabulary

State whether each sentence is *true* or *false*. If false, replace the underlined word or number to make a true sentence.

1. You can use compatible numbers to <u>estimate</u> products. **true**
2. Using the distributive property, $4(3 + 2) = 4 \cdot 3 + \underline{3} \cdot 2$. **false, 4**
3. The <u>area</u> of a rectangle is two times the length plus two times the width. **false, perimeter**
4. The perimeter of a rectangle with a length of 4 meters and a width of 1 meter is <u>5</u> meters. **false, 10**
5. The area of a rectangle is the <u>product</u> of its length and width. **true**
6. If each side of a square is 4.2 feet, then its <u>area</u> is 17.64 square feet. **true**
7. The basic unit of mass in the metric system is the <u>gram</u>. **true**
8. A <u>milligram</u> is 1,000 grams. **false, kilogram**
9. The basic unit of capacity in the metric system is the <u>liter</u>. **true**
10. It takes <u>0.001 milliliter</u> to make a liter. **false, 1,000 milliliters**
11. To change from a larger unit to a smaller unit, you need to <u>divide</u>. **false, multiply**
12. To change from a smaller unit to a larger unit, you need to <u>multiply</u>. **false, divide**

In Your Own Words

13. *Explain* how to estimate the product of 6.9 and 88. **See margin.**

170 Chapter 4 Multiplying and Dividing Decimals

MindJogger Videoquizzes

MindJogger Videoquizzes provide an alternative review of concepts presented in this chapter. Students work in teams to answer questions, gaining points for correct answers. The questions are presented in three rounds.

Round 1 Concepts–5 questions
Round 2 Skills–4 questions
Round 3 Problem Solving–4 questions

Objectives & Examples

Upon completing this chapter, you should be able to:

● estimate and find the products of decimals and whole numbers *(Lesson 4-1)*

Find 12.32 × 12.

12.32	*Estimate: 12 × 12 = 144*
× 12	*Multiply as with whole numbers.*
147.84	*Since the estimate is 144, place the decimal point after 7.*

● compute products mentally using the distributive property *(Lesson 4-2)*

Find 90 × 3.8:

Estimate: 90 × 4 = 360

$90 \times 3.8 = 90(3 + 0.8)$
$= 90 \times 3 + 90 \times 0.8$
$= 270 + 72$
$= 342$

● multiply decimals *(Lesson 4-3)*

Find 38.76 · 4.2.

38.76	← *two decimal places*
× 4.2	← *one decimal place*
7752	
15504	
162.792	← *three decimal places*

● find the perimeters and the areas of rectangles and squares *(Lesson 4-4)*

Find the perimeter and the area of the figure.

3.2 m

6.1 m

$P = 2\ell + 2w$	$A = \ell \cdot w$
$= 2(6.1) + 2(3.2)$	$= 6.1 \cdot 3.2$
$= 12.2 + 6.4$	$= 19.52 \text{ m}^2$
$= 18.6 \text{ m}$	

Review Exercises

Use these exercises to review and prepare for the chapter test.

Multiply.

14. 17.31 **692.40**
　　× 40

15. 2.15 **488.05**
　　×227

16. 38.5 × 791
30,453.5

17. 6 × 7.91 **47.46**

Solve each equation.

18. $m = 201 \times 3.94$ **791.94**

19. $51.2 \times 1,891 = r$ **96,819.2**

Find each product mentally. Use the distributive property.

20. 40 × 8.9 **356**

21. 30 × 10.76 **322.8**

22. 9 × 16 **144**

23. 5 × 6.8 **34**

Multiply. 24. 19.4902

24. 8.74 · 2.23

25. 0.04 × 5.1 **0.204**

26. 0.04 × 0.0063
0.000252

27. 11.089 · 5.6
62.0984

Solve each equation.

28. $d = 2.6 \cdot 3.9$
10.14

29. $112.45(4.8) = n$
539.76

Find the perimeter of each figure.

30.

4.3 km
2 km
4.9 km
11.2 km

31. **27.3 m**
8.3 m
4.2 m　4.7 m
10.1 m

33. 41 mi; 104.16 mi²

Find the perimeter and the area of each figure. 32. 66.2 in.; 202.5 in²

32. rectangle: $\ell = 25$ in.; $w = 8.1$ in.

33. rectangle: $\ell = 11.2$ mi; $w = 9.3$ mi

34. square: $s = 100$ m **400 m; 10,000 m²**

35. square: $s = 7.6$ ft **30.4 ft; 57.76 ft²**

Chapter 4 Study Guide and Assessment **171**

Objectives & Examples

This section reviews the skills and concepts of the chapter and shows completely worked examples.

Review Exercises

These exercises provide practice for the corresponding objectives.

***Assessment and Evaluation Masters*, pp. 87–88**

4

Chapter 4 Test, Form 1B

Name_____ Date_____

1. Multiply: 0.6 × 18.
   A. 18.6　B. 12.6　C. 10.8　D. 108　　　1. __C__

2. Multiply: $3.12 × 86.
   A. $24.35　B. $26.83　C. $243.51　D. $268.32　　2. __D__

3. Rewrite 8(10 + 7) using the distributive property.
   A. (8 × 10)(8 × 7)　B. (8 + 10)(8 + 7)
   C. 8 × 10 + 8 × 7　D. 8 × 10 + 7　　　3. __C__

4. To find 30 × 4.3 mentally using the distributive property, you would first think:
   A. 30 × 4.3 = 30(4 + 0.3).　B. 30 × 4.3 = 30 × 4 + 0.3.
   C. 30 × 4.3 = 30 + 4 + 0.3.　D. 30 × 4.3 = 30 × 4 × 0.3.　　4. __A__

5. Multiply: 0.42 × 1.8.
   A. 0.756　B. 7.56　C. 75.6　D. 756　　　5. __A__

6. Solve $a = 0.003 × 4.1$.
   A. 0.123　B. 0.0123　C. 12.3　D. 1.23　　6. __B__

7. Find the perimeter of the square.
   7.6 cm
   A. 15.2 cm　B. 57.76 cm　C. 5.776 cm　D. 30.4 cm　　7. __D__

8. Find the area of a rectangle with a length of 6.1 meters and a width of 4.3 meters.
   A. 10.4 m²　B. 26.23 m²　C. 2.623 m²　D. 20.8 m²　　8. __B__

9. Find the perimeter of the triangle.
   A. 18 ft　B. 27 ft　7.5 ft
   C. 13.5 ft　D. 36 ft　4.5 ft
   6 ft　　　9. __A__

10. Find the quotient: 47)110.92.
    A. 2.36　B. 23.6　C. 0.236　D. 236　　10. __A__

11. Evaluate $a ÷ b$ if $a = 104.5$ and $b = 38$.
    A. 0.275　B. 2.75　C. 27.5　D. 275　　11. __B__

12. Round the quotient to the nearest hundredth: 34)172.5.
    A. 50.73　B. 5.08　C. 5.07　D. 50.74　　12. __C__

© Glencoe/McGraw-Hill　　87　　*Mathematics: Applications and Connections, Course 1*

4

Chapter 4 Test, Form 1B (continued)

13. 78.35 must be multiplied by what power of ten to make a whole number?
    A. 10　B. 100　C. 1,000　D. 10,000　　13. __B__

14. 0.348 must be multiplied by what power of ten to make a whole number?
    A. 10　B. 100　C. 1,000　D. 10,000　　14. __C__

15. Evaluate $a ÷ b$ if $a = 27.9$ and $b = 0.9$.
    A. 31　B. 3.1　C. 0.31　D. 310　　15. __A__

16. Find the quotient: 0.72)11.52.
    A. 16　B. 1.6　C. 0.16　D. 0.016　　16. __A__

17. Find the quotient: 6.09 ÷ 0.3.
    A. 203　B. 0.203　C. 2.03　D. 20.3　　17. __D__

18. The area of a rectangle is 14.245 square meters. The length is 3.5 meters. What is the width?
    A. 4.7 m　B. 4.07 m　C. 47 m　D. 407 m　　18. __B__

19. What unit would you use to measure the mass of an apple?
    A. milligram　B. gram　C. kilogram　D. liter　　19. __B__

20. What unit would you use to measure the capacity of a hot tub?
    A. millimeter　B. gram　C. liter　D. kilogram　　20. __C__

21. What unit would you use to measure the mass of a pair of scissors?
    A. liter　B. milligram　C. kilogram　D. gram　　21. __D__

22. Change 9 grams to milligrams.
    A. 0.9 mg　B. 0.009 mg　C. 900 mg　D. 9,000 mg　　22. __D__

23. Change 186 millimeters to centimeters.
    A. 18.6 cm　B. 1.86 cm　C. 0.186 cm　D. 1,860 cm　　23. __A__

24. Oliver needs to mow the lawn shown below. What area will he mow?
    10 m
    4 m　4 m
    12 m　9 m
    4 m　4 m
    30 m
    A. 160 m²　B. 68 m²　C. 200 m²　D. 320 m²　　24. __A__

25. Mrs. Jankowski bought 6 videotapes that cost $28.95 each. About how much did the tapes cost in all?
    A. $120　B. $180　C. $150　D. $100　　25. __B__

© Glencoe/McGraw-Hill　　88　　*Mathematics: Applications and Connections, Course 1*

Assessment and Evaluation

Six forms of Chapter 4 Test are available in the *Assessment and Evaluation Masters* as shown in the chart.

Chapter 4 Test, Form 1B, is shown at the right. Chapter 4 Test, Form 2B, is shown on the next page.

1A	Multiple Choice	Honors
1B	Multiple Choice	Average
1C	Multiple Choice	Basic
2A	Free Response	Honors
2B	Free Response	Average
2C	Free Response	Basic

Assessment and Evaluation Masters, pp. 93–94

Objectives & Examples

● divide decimals by whole numbers *(Lesson 4-5)*

Find the quotient of 96.9 and 51.

$$
\begin{array}{r}
1.9 \\
51\overline{)96.9} \\
-51 \\
\hline
45\,9 \\
-45\,9 \\
\hline
0
\end{array}
$$

Estimate: 100 ÷ 50 = 2
Place the decimal point.
Divide as with whole numbers.

● divide decimals by decimals *(Lesson 4-6)*

Find the quotient of 166.14 and 21.3.

$$
21.3\overline{)166.14} \;\rightarrow\; 213\overline{)1661.4}^{\,7.8}
$$

Multiply the divisor and dividend by 10.

● divide decimals involving special cases of zero in the quotient *(Lesson 4-7)*

Find 571.2 ÷ 56.

$$
\begin{array}{r}
10.2 \\
56\overline{)571.2} \\
-56 \\
\hline
11 \\
-0 \\
\hline
11\,2 \\
-11\,2 \\
\hline
0
\end{array}
$$

● use metric units of mass and capacity *(Lesson 4-8)*

What unit of mass would you use to measure a chicken's egg?

Since a chicken's egg has a small mass, the *gram* is the appropriate unit.

● change units within the metric system *(Lesson 4-9)*

9.2 g = _?_ mg   *Multiply to change a larger*
9.2 g = 9,200 mg   *unit to a smaller unit.*

Review Exercises

Find each quotient.

36. 12.24 ÷ 36 **0.34**
37. 32)203.84 **6.37**
38. 1,000)17.97 **0.01797**
39. 5.2175 ÷ 10 **0.52175**
40. Round 38.86 ÷ 7 to the nearest tenth. **5.6**
41. Round 249.77 ÷ 13 to the nearest hundredth. **19.21**

Find each quotient.

42. 136.5 ÷ 35 **3.9**
43. 0.045)6.345 **141**
44. 0.081)43.254 **534**
45. 18.88 ÷ 3.2 **5.9**

Find each quotient to the nearest hundredth.

46. 7.38 ÷ 36 **0.21**
47. 24.3)0.243 **0.01**
48. 4.2)43.75 **10.42**
49. 8.134 ÷ 98 **0.08**

Solve each equation.

50. $h = 3{,}190.95 \div 4.5$ **709.1**
51. $77.1912 \div 14.2 = w$ **5.436**

Write the unit you would use to measure each of the following. Then estimate the mass or capacity. **55.** milliliter, 15 mL

52. a candy apple **gram, 200 g**
53. a stack of books **kilogram, 5 kg**
54. a pitcher of lemonade **liter, 3 L**
55. a dose of cough medicine

Complete.

56. 300 mL = _?_ L **0.3**
57. _?_ g = 1 mg **0.001**
58. _?_ m = 0.75 km **750**

Chapter 4 Test, Form 2B

Name_____ Date_____

1. Estimate: 4.8 × 69.   1. **5 × 70 = 350**

Multiply.
2. 0.72 × 26   2. **18.72**
3. 136 × 4.32   3. **587.52**
4. 8.97 × 6.8.   4. **60.996**
5. Solve m = 0.6 × 0.09.   5. **0.054**

Find each product mentally. Use the distributive property.
6. 102 × 8   6. **816**
7. 30.3 × 4   7. **121.2**

Find the perimeter of each figure.
8. 1.7 m, 0.8 m, 1.5 m   8. **4 m**

9. 5.6 cm, 2.9 cm   9. **17 cm**

10. Find the area of the square. 7.5 in.   10. **56.25 in²**

Find each quotient.
11. 8)28.96   11. **3.62**
12. 231.68 ÷ 32   12. **7.24**
13. 19.98 ÷ 0.74   13. **27**
14. 5.9)48.97   14. **8.3**

© Glencoe/McGraw-Hill   93   *Mathematics: Applications and Connections, Course 1*

Chapter 4 Test, Form 2B (continued)

Find each quotient.
15. 73.923 ÷ 12.3   15. **6.01**
16. 495.88 ÷ 98   16. **5.06**
17. Evaluate a ÷ b if a = 38.4 and b = 60.   17. **0.64**

Round each quotient to the nearest tenth.
18. 8.6 ÷ 7   18. **1.2**
19. 225.9 ÷ 42   19. **5.4**

Write the unit that you would use to measure each of the following. Then estimate the mass or capacity.
20. capacity of a soup bowl   20. **mL, 300 mL**
21. mass of a sofa   21. **kg, 40 kg**

Complete.
22. 897 mL = _?_ L   22. **0.897**
23. _?_ g = 4.6 kg   23. **4,600**
24. A room is 16.5 feet long by 13.7 feet wide. How many square feet of carpeting are needed to cover the room?   24. **226.05 ft²**
25. Isidro is fencing his yard. How much fencing does he need? 24 m, 8 m, 3 m, 10 m, 5 m, 14 m   25. **64 m**

© Glencoe/McGraw-Hill   94   *Mathematics: Applications and Connections, Course 1*

Test and Review Software

You may use this software, a combination of an item generator and item bank, to create your own tests or worksheets. Types of items include free response, multiple choice, short answer, and open ended.

CD-ROM Program

The CD-ROM Program contains an Assessment Game whose questions review the concepts in this chapter.

Applications & Problem Solving

59. Fitness Tyra exercises every morning by running once around a rectangular neighborhood. The length of the rectangle is 1.7 kilometers, and the width is 0.9 kilometer. How far does she run? *(Lesson 4-4)* **5.2 kilometers**

60. Solve a Simpler Problem The figure below is to be painted on a wall as part of a mural. Find the area of the figure. *(Lesson 4-5A)* **174 square feet**

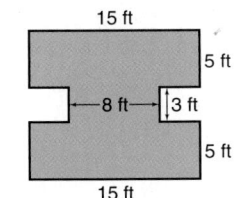

61. Money Matters Drew bought a new car and financed it over a 48-month period. The total of all the payments he will make is $15,336.96. How much is each car payment? *(Lesson 4-5)* **$319.52**

62. Money Matters Mariano wants to collect $131.25 to replace his friend's CD player that was lost in a fire. He is asking everyone to contribute $1.25. How many people will he need to collect from? *(Lesson 4-7)* **105 people**

Alternative Assessment

● **Open Ended**

Suppose you run a landscape company. The label on a bag of fertilizer states that it will cover 3 square meters. How can you determine how many bags to bring with you to fertilize your client's yard? **See margin.**

Suppose one client has a rectangular yard with dimensions of 7.3 meters by 5.2 meters. For how many bags of fertilizer will you charge the client?

It will take about 12.65 bags, so charge them for 13 bags.

● **Completing the CHAPTER Project**
Use the following checklist to make sure your project is complete.

☑ You have included your price chart for multiple items, your prices with tax included, and your senior citizen discount prices.

☑ Your paragraph describes why you chose the product that you did and how you determined its price.

☑ You have designed an advertisement for your product. Be sure to include your business name, a picture of the product, the price of the item, and anything else that you think would help sell the product.

 Select an item from this chapter that you feel shows your best work. Place it in your portfolio. Explain why you selected it.

A practice test for Chapter 4 is provided on page 598.

Chapter 4 Study Guide and Assessment **173**

Additional Answer for the Open Ended item
First, find the area of the yard in square meters. Then divide the area of the yard by 3 to find the number of bags.

 Performance Assessment

Additional performance assessment tasks for this chapter are included in the *Assessment and Evaluation Masters* on page 97. A scoring guide is also provided on page 109.

Applications & Problem Solving

This section provides additional practice in solving real-world problems that involve the skills of this chapter.

Alternative Assessment

The **Open Ended** section provides students with a performance assessment opportunity to evaluate their work and understanding.

 CHAPTER Project

Students should complete the final stages of their project and prepare a class demonstration of their results. A scoring guide for the project is available in the *Investigations and Projects Masters*, p. 31.

 Students should add to their portfolios at this time.

Assessment and Evaluation Masters, p. 97

Name_____ Date_____

4 | **Chapter 4 Performance Assessment**

Instructions: Demonstrate your knowledge by giving a clear, concise solution to each problem. Be sure to include all relevant drawings and justify your answers. You may show your solutions in more than one way or investigate beyond the requirements of the problems.

1. **a.** Use the 10-by-10 decimal models below to model 2 × 0.7. Find the product.

   b. Explain how to multiply 1.5 × 0.2 using the distributive property. Find the product.

   c. In your own words, tell how to multiply decimals.

2. **a.** Use models to find 2.4 ÷ 0.8. Show your work and explain each step.

   b. Estimate 0.15 ÷ 4. Then find the product. Show your work.

3. A chef wishes to serve strawberry shortcake for dinner.

   a. Tell how to change from larger units to smaller units of measure in the metric system. Tell how to change from smaller to larger units.

   b. A box of biscuit mix contains 2.26 kilograms. If 23 grams of biscuit mix are required for a shortcake, how many shortcakes can the chef make from each box? Round the quotient to the nearest tenth.

   c. The chef has 5.4 kilograms of strawberries. If he plans to serve 115 grams of strawberries with each shortcake, estimate the number of servings of strawberries he has. Explain each step.

   d. How many servings of strawberries does the chef have in part c?

   e. The front cover of the box of biscuit mix is 20 centimeters wide and 45 centimeters high. What are the perimeter and area of the cover of the box?

© Glencoe/McGraw-Hill   97   *Mathematics: Applications and Connections, Course 1*

Standardized Test Practice

The Standardized Test Practice may be used to help students prepare for standardized tests. The test items are written in the same style as those in state proficiency tests and standardized tests like CAT, CTBS, ITBS, MAT, SAT, and Terra Nova. The test items cover skills and concepts covered up to this point in the text.

The pages can be used as an overnight assessment. After students have completed the pages, discuss how each problem can be solved, or provide copies of the solutions from the *Solutions Manual*.

Assessment and Evaluation Masters, p. 103

4 Cumulative Review, Chapters 1-4

Name_____ Date_____

Perform the indicated operation. (Lessons 4-3, 3-6, 4-5, and 4-6)
1. 3.8×2.5 — 1. ___9.5___
2. $7.66 + 1.5$ — 2. ___9.16___
3. $38)\overline{53.2}$ — 3. ___1.4___
4. $0.27)\overline{0.999}$ — 4. ___37___

Evaluate. (Lessons 1-4, 1-6, and 1-5)
5. $7 + 6 \times 3 + 6$ — 5. ___31___
6. 7^4 — 6. ___2,401___
7. mn if $m = 8$ and $n = 25$ — 7. ___200___
8. x^6 if $x = 10$ — 8. ___1,000,000___
9. Order the following decimals from least to greatest: 0.003, 0.95, 0.2, 0.0056. (Lesson 3-3) — 9. ___0.003, 0.0056, 0.2, 0.95___

Golf Scores: 78, 136, 92, 100, 134, 92
10. What is the range of the golf scores? (Lesson 2-7) — 10. ___58___
11. What is the median of the golf scores? (Lesson 2-7) — 11. ___96___
12. Refer to the circle graph at the right. Which two flavors received about the same number of votes? (Lesson 2-4) — 12. ___chocolate and vanilla___

Favorite Flavors

13. The equation for finding the perimeter of a hexagon with six equal sides is $P = 6x$. If the length (s) of each side of a hexagon is 18 centimeters, find the perimeter. (Lesson 4-4) — 13. ___108 cm___

Estimate. (Lessons 3-5 and 1-3)
14. $0.716 + 0.855$ — 14. ___0.7 + 0.9 = 1.6___
15. 49×86 — 15. ___50 × 90 = 4,500___
16. $355 + 7$ — 16. ___350 ÷ 7 = 50___
17. $166 + 299$ — 17. ___170 + 300 = 470___
18. Change 1.9 kilograms to grams. (Lesson 4-9) — 18. ___1,900 g___
19. Find the area of the figure at the right. (Lesson 4-4) — 19. ___330 mm²___
20. Round $18.65 \div 3.8$ to the nearest hundredth. (Lesson 4-7) — 20. ___4.91___

© Glencoe/McGraw-Hill — 103 — Mathematics: Applications and Connections, Course 1

Section One: Multiple Choice

There are twelve multiple-choice questions in this section. Choose the best answer. If a correct answer is *not here*, mark the letter for Not Here.

1. Kenda found 18 crayons. Her classmate Marissa gave her some more, and then she had 42. To find out how many crayons she was given, Kenda wrote $18 + c = 42$. What is the value of c? **D**
   - **A** 60
   - **B** 52
   - **C** 34
   - **D** 24

2. The exponential form of $3 \times 3 \times 7 \times 7 \times 7 \times 11$ is $3^2 \times 7^? \times 11$. What should replace the question mark? **H**
   - **F** 1
   - **G** 2
   - **H** 3
   - **J** 7

3. Julian is 1.54 meters tall. How many centimeters tall is Julian? **C**
   - **A** 0.0154 cm
   - **B** 15.4 cm
   - **C** 154 cm
   - **D** 1,540 cm

4. Fairfield has an average precipitation of 35.22 inches in June and July. Round this amount to the nearest tenth. **G**
   - **F** 40
   - **G** 35.2
   - **H** 35.22
   - **J** 35.3

Please note that Questions 5–12 have five answer choices.

5. A sign in a store window reads as follows:

   ALL ITEMS
   $5.99
   to
   $13.99

   If Manny bought 3 items in the store, what would be a reasonable total cost? **C**
   - **A** $6.00
   - **B** $12.00
   - **C** $24.00
   - **D** $45.00
   - **E** $60.00

6. 8×3.21 is about— **F**
   - **F** 24.
   - **G** 32.
   - **H** 240.
   - **J** 320.
   - **K** 2,568.

7. Jesse wants to buy ice-cream cones for himself and 3 friends. Each cone costs $1.19. Which is the best estimate of the amount of money Jesse will need in order to buy the cones? **C**
   - **A** $1
   - **B** $3
   - **C** $5
   - **D** $7
   - **E** $9

◄◄◄ Instructional Resources

Another cumulative review is shown at the left and is available in the *Assessment and Evaluation Masters,* p. 103.

8. Aubrey charges $1.75 per hour for walking her neighbor's dogs. If she works for 8 hours, how much will she earn? **H**

   F $17.50

   G $16.00

   H $14.00

   J $7.50

   K Not Here

9. Three watermelons have weights of 18, 17, and 22 pounds. Which weight is a reasonable average weight of the three watermelons? **B**

   A 10 lb

   B 20 lb

   C 25 lb

   D 45 lb

   E 60 lb

10. Bill's Boy Scout troop collected $439 for the Muscular Dystrophy Association. Kelly's Girl Scout troop collected $672. How much more did Kelly's troop collect than Bill's? **G**

   F $133

   G $233

   H $243

   J $247

   K Not Here

11. Rashid cut a ribbon into 5 equal pieces. If each piece was 2.4 meters long, how long was the ribbon before he cut it? **C**

   A 0.48 m

   B 1.2 m

   C 12 m

   D 120 m

   E Not Here

12. Solve the equation $y = 43.1 + 7.256$. **G**

   F 51.456

   G 50.356

   H 11.566

   J 7.687

   K Not Here

Test-Taking Tip   THE PRINCETON REVIEW

Instead of waiting until the night before a test, allow yourself plenty of time to review the basic skills and formulas. If you prepare early, you will have time to find your weaknesses and ask for help.

Section Two: Free Response

This section contains seven questions for which you will provide short answers. Write your answers on your paper.

13. Five students took Mr. Castillo's history test. The scores were 93, 82, 95, 95, and 75. Find the mean, median and mode of the scores. **88, 93, 95**

14. Maria plans to buy dog food for $15.99, a bone for $5.79, and a dog toy for $2.99. What is the cost of these items before tax is added? **$24.77**

15. To measure the water in a swimming pool, would you use liters or milliliters? **liters**

16. Evaluate $(t + w) \div z$ if $t = 0.007$ $w = 0.014$, and $z = 2.5$. **0.0084**

17. 23.5 mL = _?_ L **0.0235**

18. Without computing, explain why 312.28 divided by 29.6 is not 105.5. **See margin.**

19. Which is a better buy, a 306-gram can of soup for $0.42 or a 539-gram can for $0.73? Explain. **See margin.**

 interNET CONNECTION   Test Practice **For additional test practice questions, visit:**

www.glencoe.com/sec/math/mac/mathnet

Chapters 1–4 Standardized Test Practice   **175**

Test-Taking Tip

Encourage students to set aside 15 to 30 minutes each night to review basic skills. Formulas can be written on flash cards to aid in self-testing.

Assessment and Evaluation Masters, pp. 101–102

4   Name_____ Date_____

Chapter 4 Standardized Test Practice

1. Keung rented a car for $19.99 a day plus $0.14 per mile. He kept the car one day and drove 391.8 miles. How much did he pay?   1. **B**
   A. $54.85   B. $74.84   C. $78.39   D. $411.93

2. Dalia is mowing yards to earn money. She decides to charge $0.01 per square foot. If she mows a yard that is 75 feet by 52 feet, how much should she charge?   2. **D**
   A. $390.00   B. $2.54   C. $25.40   D. $39

3. Centuries ago, for their inheritance, farmers would divide their land among their sons. If a farmer had 17.82 acres of land and divided it into 2.97-acre parcels, how many sons did he have?   3. **B**
   A. 5   B. 6   C. 7   D. 8

4. A bottle of window cleaner holds 973 milliliters of liquid. How many liters is that?   4. **D**
   A. 9.73 L   B. 0.0973 L   C. 97.3 L   D. 0.973 L

5. Write *twenty-seven and thirty-nine ten-thousandths* as a decimal.   5. **A**
   A. 27.0039   B. 27.39   C. 27.039   D. 27.3910

6. How many centimeters are in 3.5 kilometers?   6. **C**
   A. 3,500 cm   B. 0.0035 cm   C. 350,000 cm   D. 350 cm

7. Order the set of decimals from least to greatest. 23.2, 22.3, 23.08, 22.8, 22.08   7. **B**
   A. 22.08, 23.2, 23.08, 22.8, 22.3   B. 22.08, 22.3, 22.8, 23.08, 23.2
   C. 23.2, 23.3, 22.8, 22.08, 23.08   D. 22.3, 22.08, 22.8, 23.2, 23.08

8. Joshua and Sam are going to the movies. Joshua has $7.28 and Sam has $6.83. How much do they have together?   8. **A**
   A. $14.11   B. $13.01   C. $14.01   D. $13.11

9. Latoya is making a circle graph as part of a report. If the parts of the graph are in percents, what number should the parts add all of the parts?   9. **C**
   A. 50%   B. 1   C. 100%   D. can't tell

10. On the last math test, Jamil's class had the following scores: 98, 72, 65, 83, 91, 84, 90, 77, 96, 72, 91, 79, 85, 76, 97. When rounded to the nearest ones place, which two measures are equal?   10. **B**
    A. mean and mode   B. mean and median
    C. median and mode   D. none are equal

© Glencoe/McGraw-Hill   101   *Mathematics: Applications and Connections, Course 1*

4   **Chapter 4 Standardized Test Practice (continued)**

11. On a coordinate system, what three things must be labeled?   11. **D**
    A. origin, *x*-coordinate, *y*-coordinate
    B. data point, ordered pair, grid
    C. title, horizontal axis, vertical axis
    D. origin, *x*-axis, *y*-axis

12. Simplify: 28 ÷ 7 + 7 × 6 − 2.   12. **A**
    A. 44   B. 64   C. 8   D. 10

13. Simplify: 25 − 4 × 3 + 12 ÷ 6.   13. **B**
    A. 12   B. 15   C. 52.5   D. 12.5

14. Althea rented a car for $21 plus $0.12 per mile. If *m* represents the number of miles driven, then the algebraic expression $21 + $0.12*m* gives the cost for the car. Find the cost if Althea drove 342 miles.   14. **C**
    A. $7,223.04   B. $41.04   C. $62.04   D. $83.04

15. The volume of a cube can be found by using the expression $V = s^3$, where *s* is the length of a side. A shipping box is a cube with a side length of 2 feet. What is the volume of the box?   15. **B**
    A. 4 ft³   B. 8 ft³   C. 6 ft³   D. 10 ft³

16. The Hope diamond is a 45.52-carat blue diamond that is believed to have been cut from a 112-carat stone found in India in the 1600s. How many carats remained of the original stone after the Hope diamond was cut?   16. **A**
    A. 66.48   B. 157.52   C. 45.78   D. 44.40

17. Dominic purchased a shirt for $7.64. To the nearest dollar, how much is this?   17. **C**
    A. $7   B. $7.50   C. $8   D. $7.60

18. Estimate 43.768 − 37.419 using rounding.   18. **C**
    A. 6   B. 6.249   C. 7   D. 6.4

19. Rewrite 7(37) using the distributive property.   19. **B**
    A. 7(3) + 7(7)   B. 7(30) + 7(7)
    C. 7(3 + 7)   D. 7 + (3) + 7 + (7)

20. Christy and three friends went in together on a gift for their teacher. If the gift cost $23.49, how much does each friend owe to the nearest cent?   20. **D**
    A. $5.88   B. $7.83   C. $5.90   D. $5.87

© Glencoe/McGraw-Hill   102   *Mathematics: Applications and Connections, Course 1*

Additional Answers

18. Sample answer: If you round to compatible numbers, you can estimate that the quotient is 300 ÷ 30 = 10. This is not close to 105.5.

19. Sample answer: The 539-gram can of soup is a better buy. It costs 0.135¢ per gram while the 306-gram can costs 0.137¢ per gram.

Instructional Resources ▶▶▶

Additional standardized test practice is shown at the right and is available in the *Assessment and Evaluation Masters*, pp. 101–102.

Using Number Patterns, Fractions, and Ratios

Previewing the Chapter

Overview

This chapter helps students develop number sense and an understanding of fractions and ratios by investigating number patterns. Students learn to use the greatest common factor to simplify fractions and the least common multiple to order and compare them. They solve problems by making an organized list and use customary units of length. Students convert between decimals and fractions and explore terminating and repeating decimals.

Lesson (pages)	Lesson Objectives	NCTM Standards 2000	Standardized Tests	State/Local Objectives
5-1 (178–180)	Use divisibility rules for 2, 3, 5, 6, 9, and 10.	1, 2, 3, 6–10	CTBS, ITBS, MAT, SAT, TN	
5-2A (181)	Identify prime and composite numbers by using rectangular arrays.	2, 3, 6–8, 10		
5-2 (182–184)	Find the prime factorization of a composite number.	1, 2, 5–10	SAT	
5-3A (186–187)	Solve problems by making an organized list.	1, 6–10		
5-3 (188–190)	Find the greatest common factor of two or more numbers.	1, 3, 4, 6–10	CAT, CTBS, ITBS, MAT, SAT, TN	
5-4A (191–192)	Use models to represent fractions and equivalent fractions.	1, 6–8, 10	CAT, CTBS, TN	
5-4 (193–196)	Express fractions and ratios in simplest form.	1, 6–10	CTBS, ITBS, MAT, SAT, TN	
5-4B (197)	Determine the experimental probability for a given set of data.	1, 2, 4, 6–9	CTBS, SAT, TN	
5-5 (198–201)	Express mixed numbers as improper fractions and vice versa.	1–4, 6–10	CTBS, SAT, TN	
5-6 (202–205)	Measure line segments and objects with a ruler divided in halves, fourths, and eighths.	1, 4, 6–10		
5-7 (206–209)	Find the least common multiple of two or more numbers.	1, 4,–9	CAT, CTBS, ITBS, MAT, SAT, TN	
5-8 (210–213)	Compare and order fractions.	1, 4, 6–10	CAT, CTBS, ITBS, MAT, SAT, TN	
5-9 (214–216)	Express terminating decimals as fractions in simplest form.	1, 2, 6–10	CTBS, SAT, TN	
5-10 (217–219)	Express fractions as terminating and repeating decimals.	1, 2, 6–10		

CAT = California Achievement Tests, CTBS = Comprehensive Tests of Basic Skills, ITBS = Iowa Tests of Basic Skills, MAT = Metropolitan Achievement Tests, SAT = Stanford Achievement Tests, TN = Terra Nova
For the key to numbering of NCTM Standards 2000, see page T6.

Organizing the Chapter

 The **Interactive Lesson Planner** contains all of the blackline masters and transparencies. This CD-ROM also includes an easy-to-use lesson planning calendar.

LESSON PLANNING GUIDE

Lesson	Extra Practice (Student Edition)	BLACKLINE MASTERS (PAGE NUMBERS)										
		Study Guide	Practice	Enrichment	Assessment & Evaluation	Classroom Games	Diversity	Hands-On Lab	School to Career	Science and Math Lab Manual	Technology	Transparencies A and B
5-1	p. 568	32	32	32				73		77–80		5-1
5-2A								47				
5-2	p. 569	33	33	33			5					5-2
5-3A	p. 569											
5-3	p. 569	34	34	34	127							5-3
5-4A								48				
5-4	p. 570	35	35	35								5-4
5-4B								49				
5-5	p. 570	36	36	36	126, 127				5			5-5
5-6	p. 570	37	37	37								5-6
5-7	p. 571	38	38	38							10	5-7
5-8	p. 571	39	39	39	128	11–13						5-8
5-9	p. 571	40	40	40								5-9
5-10	p. 572	41	41	41	128					9–12	9	5-10
Study Guide/ Assessment					113–125, 129–131							

OTHER CHAPTER RESOURCES

Student Edition
Chapter Project, pp. 177, 196, 219, 223
Math in the Media, p. 205
School to Career, p. 185
Let the Games Begin, p. 209

Technology
 MathPASS CD-ROM

 Interactive Mathematics Tools Software

Teacher's Classroom Resources

Applications
Family Letters and Activities, pp. 9–10
Investigations and Projects Masters, pp. 33–36

Meeting Individual Needs
Transition Booklet, pp. 21–22, 25–26, 29–30
Investigations for the Special Education Student, pp. 13–14, 35–38

Teaching Aids
Answer Key Masters
Block Scheduling Booklet
Lesson Planning Guide
Solutions Manual

Professional Publications
Glencoe Mathematics Professional Series

Planning the Chapter

MindJogger Videoquizzes provide a unique format for reviewing concepts presented in the chapter.

ASSESSMENT RESOURCES

Student Edition
Mixed Review, pp. 180, 184, 190, 196, 201, 205, 209, 213, 216, 219
Mid-Chapter Self Test, p. 201
➡ Math Journal, pp. 179, 212
Study Guide and Assessment, pp. 220–223
Performance Task, p. 223
📋 Portfolio Suggestion, p. 223
Standardized Test Practice, pp. 224–225
Chapter Test, p. 599

Assessment and Evaluation Masters
Multiple-Choice Tests (Forms 1A, 1B, 1C), pp. 113–118
Free-Response Tests (Forms 2A, 2B, 2C), pp. 119–124
Performance Assessment, p. 125
Mid-Chapter Test, p. 126
Quizzes A–D, pp. 127–128
Standardized Test Practice, pp. 129–130
Cumulative Review, p. 131

Teacher's Wraparound Edition
5-Minute Check, pp. 178, 182, 188, 193, 198, 202, 206, 210, 214, 217
📋 Building Portfolios, p. 176
➡ Math Journal, pp. 181, 192, 197
Closing Activity, pp. 180, 184, 187, 190, 196, 201, 205, 209, 213, 216, 219

Technology
Test and Review Software
MindJogger Videoquizzes
CD-ROM Program

MATERIALS AND MANIPULATIVES

Lesson 5-2A
square tiles*

Lesson 5-4A
ruler*

Lesson 5-4B
number cube*

Lesson 5-5
ruler*

Lesson 5-6
tape measure*
string

Lesson 5-7
ruler*
scissors*
spinners†

Lesson 5-10
calculator

*Glencoe Manipulative Kit

†Glencoe Overhead Manipulative Resources

PACING CHART

See pages T25–T27 for the Course Planning Calendar.

COURSE	DAY 1	DAY 2	DAY 3	DAY 4	DAY 5	DAY 6	DAY 7
Standard	Chapter Project	Lesson 5-1	Lessons 5-2A & 5-2		Lesson 5-3A	Lesson 5-3	Lessons 5-4A & 5-4
Honors	Chapter Project	Lesson 5-1	Lesson 5-2	Lesson 5-3A	Lesson 5-3	Lessons 5-4 & 5-4B	
Block	Chapter Project & Lesson 5-1	Lessons 5-2A & 5-2	Lessons 5-3A & 5-3	Lessons 5-4A & 5-4	Lessons 5-5 & 5-6	Lessons 5-7 & 5-8	Lessons 5-9 & 5-10

The *Transition Booklet* (Skills 9, 11, 13) can be used to practice multiplying and dividing by 1-digit numbers and measuring length.

Interactive Mathematics:
Activities and Investigations

is an activity-based program that may be used as an enhancement for chapters in **Mathematics: Applications and Connections.**

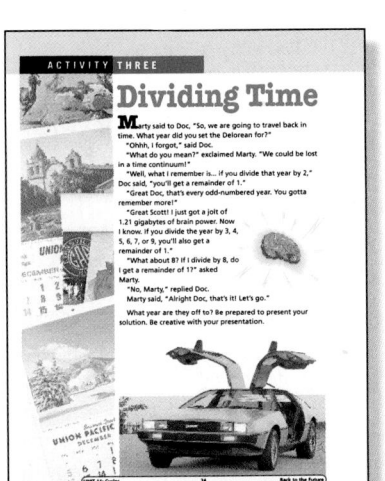

Unit 11, Activity Three
Dividing Time
Use with Lesson 5-1.

Summary Students work in groups to solve a problem involving different clock systems. They may solve the problem using various methods, including using common multiples, variables, and a guess-and-check process. Then the groups present their solutions to the class.

Math Connection Students solve a problem using multiple clock sizes. If students know their divisibility rules, they can use them to determine quickly for which year +1 is correct.

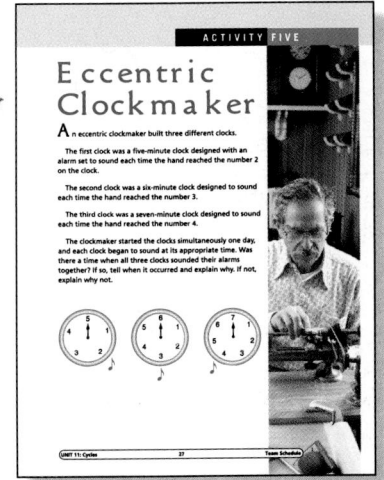

Unit 11, Activity Five
Eccentric Clockmaker

Use with Lesson 5-7.

Summary Students work in groups to determine when, if ever, all three clocks, each of different size and set to sound at different intervals, will sound simultaneously. The groups are then invited to share their solution and problem-solving methods with the class.

Math Connection Students explore cyclical patterns involving clocks of different sizes. They may use the least common multiple to solve the clock problem.

DAY 8	DAY 9	DAY 10	DAY 11	DAYS 12 & 13	DAY 14	DAY 15	DAY 16
(continue from Day 7)	Lesson 5-5	Lesson 5-6	Lesson 5-7	Lessons 5-8 & 5-9	Lesson 5-10	Study Guide and Assessment	Chapter Test
Lesson 5-5	Lesson 5-6	Lesson 5-7	Lesson 5-8	Lessons 5-9 & 5-10	Study Guide and Assessment	Chapter Test	
Study Guide and Assessment, Chapter Test							

Enhancing the Chapter

APPLICATIONS

Classroom Games, pp. 11–13

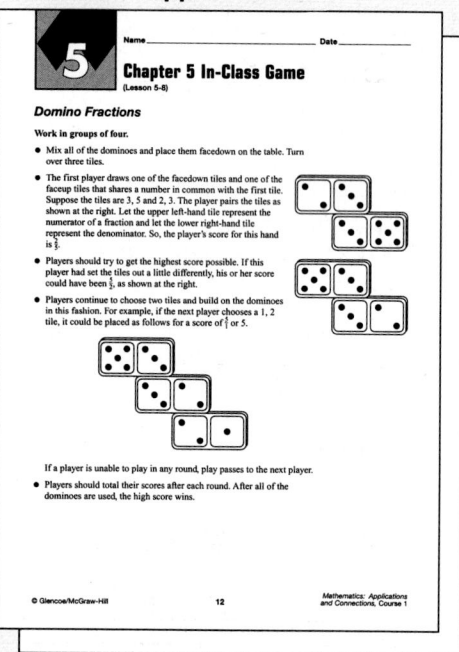

Diversity Masters, p. 5

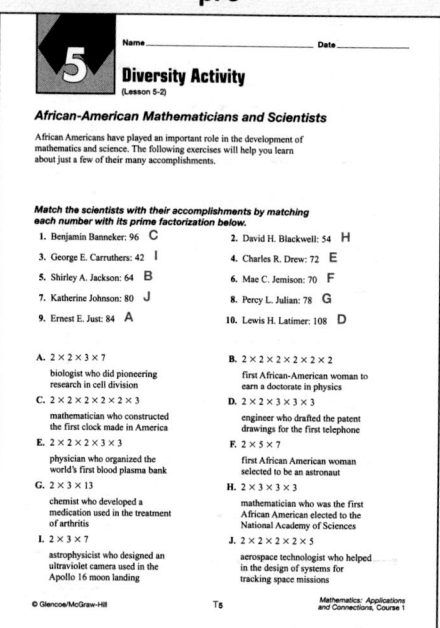

School to Career Masters, p. 5

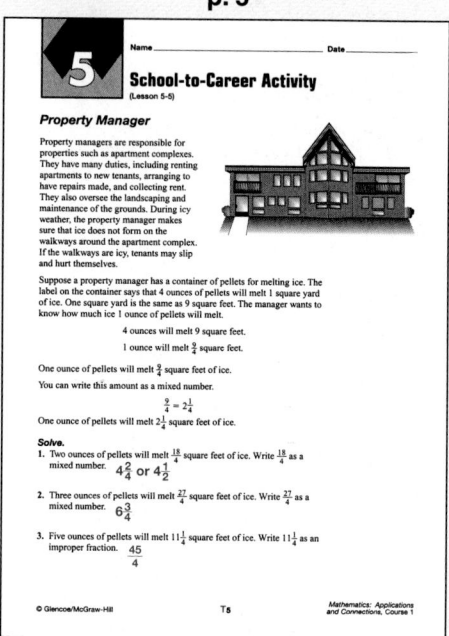

Family Letters and Activities, pp. 9–10

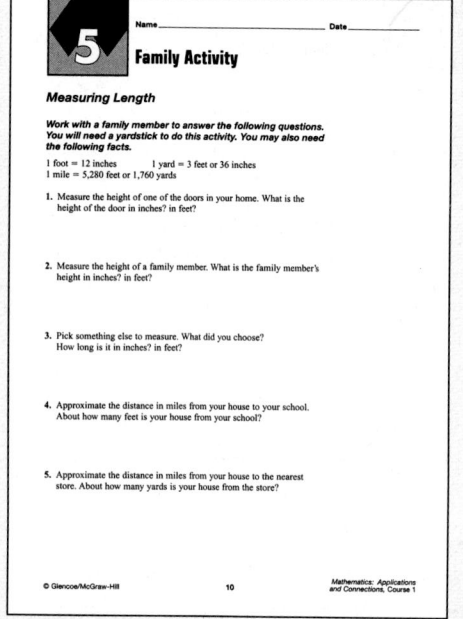

Science and Math Lab Manual, pp. 9–12

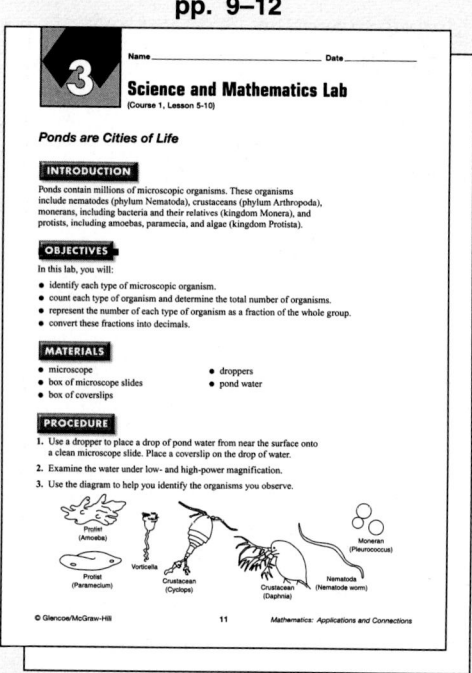

MANIPULATIVES/MODELING

Hands-On Lab Masters, p. 73

5 Lab Activity (Lesson 5-1)

Divisibility Patterns

1. List the numbers that divide 18 evenly. Use the rules for divisibility. **1, 2, 3, 6, 9, 18**

2. Take 18 beans. Separate them into groups evenly. The numbers you found in Exercise 1 will work as group numbers. Try to find all of the possible arrangements. Sketch each arrangement you find. **Sample answer:**

3. How many different numbers divide 18 evenly? **6** List each way.
   18 ÷ 1 = 18; 18 ÷ 2 = 9; 18 ÷ 3 = 6; 18 ÷ 6 = 3;
   18 ÷ 9 = 2; 18 ÷ 18 = 1

4. Put your 18 beans into a jar with everyone else's beans. Grab some more beans without counting. When you have the beans you want, count them. How many beans do you have? **Sample answer: 15**

5. What numbers will divide the number of beans you have evenly? Use your rules of divisibility. **Sample answer: 1, 3, 5, 15**

6. Separate your beans into groups evenly. Find all of the arrangements you can. Sketch each one. **Sample answer:**

7. How many different ways can you divide your beans? **Sample answer: 4**
   List the numbers represented by each grouping. **Sample answer:**
   15 ÷ 1 = 15; 15 ÷ 3 = 5; 15 ÷ 5 = 3; 15 ÷ 15 = 1

© Glencoe/McGraw-Hill   73   Mathematics: Applications and Connections, Course 1

ASSESSMENT/EVALUATION

Assessment and Evaluation Masters, pp. 126–128

5 Chapter 5 Mid-Chapter Test (Lessons 5-1 through 5-5)

Determine whether the first number is divisible by the second number.
1. 2,233; 9   2. 134; 2   **1. no   2. yes**

State whether each number is divisible by 2, 3, 5, 6, 9, or 10.
3. 945   4. 324   **3. 3, 5, 9   4. 2, 3, 6, 9**

Tell whether each number is prime, composite, or neither.
5. 221   6. 0   **5. composite   6. neither**

Find the prime factorization of each number for Questions 7–8.
7. 162   8. 140   **7. 2 × 3⁴   8. 2² × 5 × 7**

9. Fernando's grocery store has powdered, glazed, and iced donuts. These come in holes, mini, and regular sizes. How many different options are available to the customers? **9. 9**

Find the GCF of each set of numbers.
10. 77, 35   11. 88, 104, 136   **10. 7   11. 8**
12. 17, 153, 187   **12. 17**

Replace each ▥ with a number so that the fractions are equivalent.
13. 7/9 = ▥/45   14. 10/11 = ▥/66   **13. 54   14. 60**

State whether each fraction or ratio is in simplest form. If not, write each fraction or ratio in simplest form.
15. 39 to 270   16. 21/36   **15. no, 13 to 90   16. yes**

Express each mixed number as an improper fraction.
17. 15 2/7   18. 6 1/15   **17. 107/7   18. 91/15**

Express each improper fraction as a mixed number.
19. 155/20   20. 72/5   **19. 7 3/4   20. 14 2/5**

© Glencoe/McGraw-Hill   126   Mathematics: Applications and Connections, Course 1

Chapter 5 Quiz A (Lessons 5-1 through 5-3)

State whether each number is divisible by 2, 3, 5, 6, 9, or 10 for Questions 1–2.
1. 72   2. 315   **1. 2, 3, 6, 9   2. 3, 5, 9**

3. Find the prime factorization of 150. **3. 2 × 3 × 5 × 5**

4. Is 51 prime, composite, or neither? **4. composite**

5. Find the prime factorization of 40. **5. 2³ × 5**

6. A sweatshirt is available in white, black, or red and in three sizes: small, medium, and large. How many different types of sweatshirts are available? **6. 9**

Find the GCF of each set of numbers.
7. 35, 45   8. 52, 72   **7. 5   8. 4**
9. 15, 40   10. 27, 105, 126   **9. 5   10. 3**

Chapter 5 Quiz B (Lessons 5-4 and 5-5)

State whether each fraction or ratio is in simplest form. If not, write each fraction or ratio in simplest form.
1. 9/55   2. 54 to 60   **1. yes   2. no, 9 to 10**
3. 23:69   4. 8 out of 128   **3. no, 1:3   4. no, 1 out of 16**

Express each mixed number as an improper fraction.
5. 6 3/8   6. 22 1/4   **5. 51/8   6. 89/4**
7. 2 7/9   8. 40 3/5   **7. 25/9   8. 122/3**

Express each improper fraction as a mixed number.
9. 47/8   10. 165/40   **9. 5 5/8   10. 4 1/8**

© Glencoe/McGraw-Hill   127   Mathematics: Applications and Connections, Course 1

TECHNOLOGY/MULTIMEDIA

Technology Masters, pp. 9–10

5 Calculator Activity (Lesson 5-10)

Writing Fractions as Decimals

The U.S. Department of Health and Human Services recommends that no more than 3/10 of a total daily intake of 2,200 Calories should be from fat. How many Calories is that?

Express the fraction as a decimal and then multiply by 2,200.
Enter: 3 [÷] 10 [×] 2200 [=] **660**
The solution is 660 Calories.

Example Express 2 7/12 as a decimal.
Enter: 2 [+] 7 [÷] 12 [=] *2.5833333*
The solution is 2.583.

Express each fraction or mixed number as a decimal. Use bar notation to show a repeating decimal.
1. 3/8   **0.375**   2. 5/12   **0.416**   3. 2 3/4   **2.75**
4. 3/5   **0.6**   5. 1/9   **0.1**   6. 2 2/9   **2.2**
7. 7/10   **0.7**   8. 4/100   **0.04**   9. 2 3/11   **2.27**
10. 1 1/3   **1.3**   11. 21/35   **0.6**   12. 4 1/2   **7.5**
13. 3 5/8   **3.625**   14. 1 1/8   **1.125**   15. 21/1,000   **0.021**
16. 1 4/9   **1.4**   17. 3 3/4   **3.75**   18. 3 6/10   **3.6**
19. 84/16   **5.25**   20. 28/25   **3.92**   21. 1 1/3   **1.3**

© Glencoe/McGraw-Hill   T9   Mathematics: Applications and Connections, Course 1

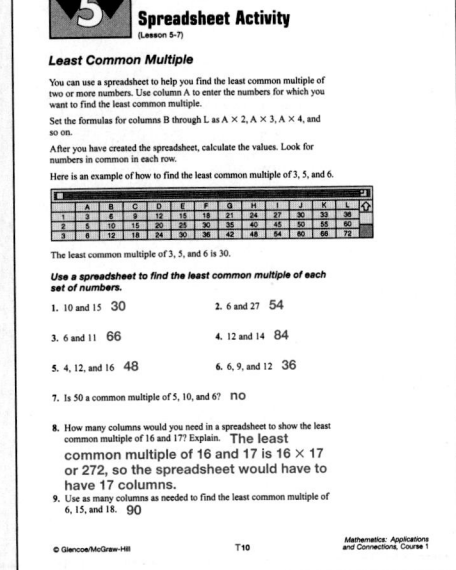

5 Spreadsheet Activity (Lesson 5-7)

Least Common Multiple

You can use a spreadsheet to help you find the least common multiple of two or more numbers. Use column A to enter the numbers for which you want to find the least common multiple.

Set the formulas for columns B through L as A × 2, A × 3, A × 4, and so on.

After you have created the spreadsheet, calculate the values. Look for numbers in common in each row.

Here is an example of how to find the least common multiple of 3, 5, and 6.

The least common multiple of 3, 5, and 6 is 30.

Use a spreadsheet to find the least common multiple of each set of numbers.
1. 10 and 15   **30**   2. 6 and 27   **54**
3. 6 and 11   **66**   4. 12 and 14   **84**
5. 4, 12, and 16   **48**   6. 6, 9, and 12   **36**

7. Is 50 a common multiple of 5, 10, and 6? **no**

8. How many columns would you need in a spreadsheet to show the least common multiple of 16 and 17? Explain. **The least common multiple of 16 and 17 is 16 × 17 or 272, so the spreadsheet would have to have 17 columns.**

9. Use as many columns as needed to find the least common multiple of 6, 15, and 18. **90**

© Glencoe/McGraw-Hill   T10   Mathematics: Applications and Connections, Course 1

MEETING INDIVIDUAL NEEDS

Investigations for the Special Education Student, pp. 13–14, 35–38

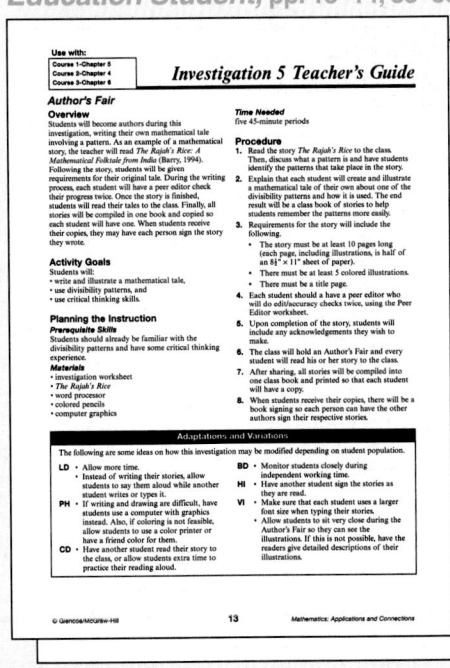

Use with:
Course 1–Chapter 5
Course 2–Chapter 4
Course 3–Chapter 4

Investigation 5 Teacher's Guide

Author's Fair

Overview
Students will become authors during this investigation, writing their own mathematical tale involving a pattern. As an example of a mathematical story, the teacher will read *The Rajah's Rice: A Mathematical Folktale from India* (Barry, 1994). Following the story, students will be given requirements for their original tale. During the writing process, each student will have a peer editor check their progress twice. Once the story is finished, students will read their tales to the class. Finally, all stories will be compiled in one book and copied so each student will have one. When students receive their copies, they may have each person sign the story they wrote.

Activity Goals
Students will:
• write and illustrate a mathematical tale,
• use divisibility patterns, and
• use critical thinking skills.

Planning the Instruction
Prerequisite Skills
Students should already be familiar with the divisibility patterns and have some critical thinking experience.
Materials
• investigation worksheet
• *The Rajah's Rice*
• word processor
• colored pencils
• computer graphics

Time Needed
five 45-minute periods

Procedure
1. Read the story *The Rajah's Rice* to the class. Then, discuss what a pattern is and have students identify the patterns that take place in the story.
2. Explain that each student will create and illustrate a mathematical tale of their own about one of the divisibility patterns and how it is used. The end result will be a class book of stories to help students remember the patterns more easily.
3. Requirements for the story will include the following.
   • The story must be at least 10 pages long (each page, including illustrations, is half of an 8½" × 11" sheet of paper).
   • There must be at least 5 colored illustrations.
   • There must be a title page.
4. Each student should have a peer editor who will do editing/accuracy checks twice, using the Peer Editor worksheet.
5. Upon completion of the story, students will include any acknowledgements they wish to make.
6. The class will hold an Author's Fair and every student will read his or her story to the class.
7. After sharing, all stories will be compiled into one class book and printed so that each student will have a copy.
8. When students receive their copies, there will be a book signing so each person can have the other authors sign their respective stories.

Adaptations and Variations

The following are some ideas on how this investigation may be modified depending on student population.

LD • Allow more time.
• Instead of writing their stories, allow students to say them aloud while another student writes or types it.

PH • If writing and drawing are difficult, allow students use a computer with graphics instead. Also, if coloring is not feasible, allow students to use a color printer or have a friend color for them.

CD • Have another student read their story to the class, or allow students extra time to practice their reading aloud.

BD • Monitor students closely during independent working time.

HI • Have another student sign the stories as they are read.

VI • Make sure that each student uses a larger font size when typing their stories.
• Allow students to sit very close during the Author's Fair so they can see the illustrations. If this is not possible, have the readers give detailed descriptions of their illustrations.

© Glencoe/McGraw-Hill   13   Mathematics: Applications and Connections

Theme: Publishing

Advertising did not become common in print until the 18th century although printing began in the 15th century. In the 19th century, advertising agencies were started as brokers for space in printed media. It was not until the 20th century that agencies actually produced the advertising messages.

Question of the Day Use the data in the table to write ratios of ads to articles for each magazine listed. Which has the highest ratio? **Magazine B** Which has the lowest ratio? **Magazine C** Discuss reasons for the numbers of ads in different magazines.

Assess Prerequisite Skills

Ask students to read through the list of objectives presented in "What you'll learn in Chapter 5." You may wish to ask them what each of the objectives means or if they have experienced or used any of these math concepts before.

 Building Portfolios

Encourage students to revise their portfolios as they study this chapter. Encourage them to write examples of real-life situations that require knowledge of each skill.

 Math and the Family

In the *Family Letters and Activities* booklet (pp. 9–10), you will find a letter to the parents explaining what students will study in Chapter 5. An activity appropriate for the whole family is also available.

Using Number Patterns, Fractions, and Ratios

What you'll learn in Chapter 5

- to use divisibility patterns to find the prime factorization and greatest common factor,
- to solve problems by making an organized list,
- to simplify fractions and to express mixed numbers as improper fractions and vice versa,
- to measure length in the customary system,
- to find the least common multiple of two or more numbers and compare and order fractions, and
- to write decimals as fractions and vice versa.

176 Chapter 5 Using Number Patterns, Fractions, and Ratios

 CD-ROM Program

Activities for Chapter 5
- Chapter 5 Introduction
- Interactive Lessons 5-3, 5-4, 5-7
- Extended Activity 5-2
- Assessment Game
- Resource Lessons 5-1 through 5-10

CHAPTER Project

HOT OFF THE PRESS

Imagine that you have been hired as a reviewer for a magazine publisher. Your job is to investigate competitors' magazines to determine what parts of the magazines have articles and what parts have advertisements. In this project, you will use fractions, ratios, and decimals to help you prepare a report that summarizes your findings. You can choose any four magazines for your project.

Getting Started

- Look at the table below. Find the total number of pages in each of the given magazines.
- Use the table to determine which magazine has the least number of pages of articles and advertisements. Which has the greatest number of pages of articles and advertisements?

| Magazine | Pages | | |
	Articles	Ads	Table of Contents
A	58	20	1
B	47	19	1
C	48	2	1
D	80	29	2

Technology Tips

- Use a **spreadsheet** to express fractions as decimals.
- Use computer **software** to make graphs.

 interNET CONNECTION For up-to-date information on magazines, visit:
www.glencoe.com/sec/math/mac/mathnet

Working on the Project

You can use what you'll learn in Chapter 5 to help you investigate magazines.

Page	Exercise
196	36
219	27
223	Alternative Assessment

interNET CONNECTION

Glencoe has made every effort to ensure that the website links for *Mathematics: Applications and Connections* at www.glencoe.com/sec/math/mac/mathnet are current and contain appropriate content. However, these website links are not under Glencoe's control.

Instructional Resources ▶▶▶

A recording sheet to help students organize their data for the Chapter Project is shown at the right and is available in the *Investigations and Projects Masters*, p. 36.

Instructional Resources

- *Study Guide Masters*, p. 32
- *Practice Masters*, p. 32
- *Enrichment Masters*, p. 32
- Transparencies 5-1, A and B
- *Science and Math Lab Masters*, pp. 77–80
- *Hands-On Lab Masters*, p. 73
   CD-ROM Program
  - Resource Lesson 5-1

Recommended Pacing	
Standard	Day 2 of 16
Honors	Day 2 of 15
Block	Day 1 of 8

1 FOCUS

 5-Minute Check
(Chapter 4)

Multiply.
1. 92.26×8 **738.08**
2. 12.35×0.76 **9.386**

Divide.
3. $712.5 \div 15$ **47.5**
4. $46.8 \div 2.5$ **18.72**
5. Complete: 41.6 kg = __?__ g.
   41,600

The 5-Minute Check is also available on **Transparency 5-1A** for this lesson.

Motivating the Lesson
Problem Solving Ask students how they would determine whether each statement is true or false without using division or estimation.
- There is no remainder in the quotient of $2,364 \div 2$. **true; ones digit is divisible by 2**
- The quotient of $98,633 \div 6$ is a whole number. **false; number is not divisible by 2 and 3**

Divisibility Patterns

You'll learn to use divisibility rules for 2, 3, 5, 6, 9, and 10.

When **am I ever going to use this?**
Knowing how to use divisibility rules can help you form groups when going on a field trip.

A popular brand of crayons were first introduced in 1903. Each box contained eight crayons. Today, crayons are sold in boxes of 8, 16, 24, 32, 48, 64, and 96 crayons. Suppose you have a box of 24 crayons. Can you divide the crayons evenly among three children?

To solve this problem, you can divide 24 by 3. $24 \div 3$ means to separate 24 into 3 equal groups.

```
8        +        8        +        8
        24
```

Since $8 + 8 + 8 = 24$, $24 \div 3 = 8$. The quotient, 8, is a whole number, so you can say that 24 is *divisible* by 3. The 24 crayons can be divided evenly among 3 children.

You can test for divisibility mentally by using divisibility rules. The divisibility rules for 2, 3, 5, 6, 9, and 10 are as follows.

A number is divisible by:

- 2 if the ones digit is divisible by 2.
- 3 if the sum of the digits is divisible by 3.
- 5 if the ones digit is 0 or 5.
- 6 if the number is divisible by both 2 and 3.
- 9 if the sum of the digits is divisible by 9.
- 10 if the ones digit is 0.

Examples

1 Is 46 divisible by 2?

The ones digit is 6. Since $6 \div 2 = 3$, 6 is divisible by 2. So, 46 is divisible by 2.

2 Is 428 divisible by 3?

The sum of the digits is $4 + 2 + 8$, or 14. Since 14 is not divisible by 3, 428 is not divisible by 3.

Check by using a calculator.

$428 \boxed{\div} 3 \boxed{=} \textit{142.66667}$ *Since the result is not a whole number, the remainder is not zero.*

428 is not divisible by 3.

178 Chapter 5 Using Number Patterns, Fractions, and Ratios

 Cross-Curriculum Cue

Inform the other teachers on your team that your students are studying number patterns, fractions, and ratios. Suggestions for curriculum integration are:

Economics: stock market
Statistics: ratio comparisons
Drafting: scale drawings

3 Is 2,736 divisible by 2, 3, 5, 6, 9, or 10?

2: Yes. The ones digit, 6, is divisible by 2.

3: Yes. The sum of the digits, 18, is divisible by 3.

5: No. The ones digit is not 0 or 5.

6: Yes. The number is divisible by both 2 and 3.

9: Yes. The sum of the digits, 18, is divisible by 9.

10: No. The ones digit, 6, is not 0.

So, of the given numbers, 2,736 is divisible by 2, 3, 6, and 9.

APPLICATION

Real World

4 **Gardening** Lyn has 4 dozen marigolds. She wants to plant the flowers in rows so that each row has the same number of flowers. Can she plant the flowers in 3 equal rows?

Explore You know that Lyn has 4 dozen marigolds. You need to find out whether she can plant the flowers in 3 equal rows.

Plan There are 12 in a dozen, so 4 dozen equals 48. Use divisibility rules to see whether 48 is divisible by 3.

Solve The sum of the digits, 12, is divisible by 3. Thus, she can plant the flowers in 3 equal rows.

Examine By using a model, you find that 48 flowers can be planted in 3 rows of 16.

CHECK FOR UNDERSTANDING

Communicating Mathematics

Read and study the lesson to answer each question. 2–3. See margin.

1. *Draw* a picture showing how a box of 24 crayons can be equally divided among 2, 6, or 12 children. **See Answer Appendix.**

2. *Explain* how to determine whether 129 is divisible by 3.

3. *Write* the divisibility rules for 2, 3, 5, 6, 9, and 10.

Guided Practice

Determine whether the first number is divisible by the second number.

4. 243; 3 **yes**   5. 2,081; 2 **no**   6. 963; 9 **yes**

State whether each number is divisible by 2, 3, 5, 6, 9, or 10.

7. 17 **none**   8. 104 **2**   9. 1,032 **2, 3, 6**

Lesson 5-1 Divisibility Patterns **179**

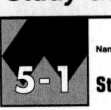

Check for Understanding

If students need additional practice or instruction after completing Exercises 1–10, one of these options may be helpful.
- Extra Practice, see p. 568
- Reteaching Activity, see p. 179
- *Transition Booklet*, pp. 25–26
- *Study Guide Masters*, p. 32
- *Practice Masters*, p. 32

Assignment Guide

Core: 11–35 odd, 36–40
Enriched: 12–32 even, 34–40

4 ASSESS

Closing Activity

Speaking Have students work in groups. Ask one member to call out a 3-digit number. Have them discuss whether the number is divisible by 2, 3, 5, 6, 9, or 10 and give reasons to support their answers. Continue until each group member has called out a number.

Additional Answer

35. Yes; each chaperone will have 15 students.

Practice Masters, p. 32

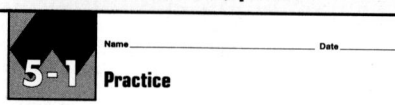

5-1 Practice

Divisibility Patterns

Determine whether the first number is divisible by the second number.

1. 527; 3 — no
2. 1,048; 6 — no
3. 693; 9 — yes
4. 1,974; 2 — yes
5. 305; 10 — no
6. 860; 5 — yes
7. 4,672; 9 — no
8. 2,310; 6 — yes
9. 816; 3 — yes
10. 13,509; 5 — no
11. 2,847; 2 — no
12. 192; 6 — yes

State whether each number is divisible by 2, 3, 5, 6, 9 or 10.

13. 36 — 2, 3, 6, 9
14. 450 — 2, 3, 5, 6, 9, 10
15. 192 — 2, 3, 6
16. 87 — 3
17. 264 — 2, 3, 6
18. 1,251 — 3, 9
19. 890 — 2, 5, 10
20. 738 — 2, 3, 6, 9
21. 2,601 — 3, 9
22. 675 — 3, 5, 9
23. 498 — 2, 3, 6
24. 2,019 — 3

Use mental math skills, paper and pencil, or a calculator to find a number that satisfies the given conditions. Sample answers are given.

25. a three-digit number divisible by both 2 and 9 — 198
26. a number divisible by both 5 and 6 — 60
27. a four-digit number divisible by 2, 3, and 9 — 3,096
28. a three-digit number divisible by 5, 6, and 9 — 630
29. a four-digit number divisible by 9 and 10 — 1,980
30. a five-digit number divisible by 5 and 9 — 14,625

© Glencoe/McGraw-Hill   T32   *Mathematics: Applications and Connections, Course 1*

---

10. *World Records* On February 28, 1898, in Milton, Massachusetts, Henry Helm Clayton and A.E. Sweetland set a record when their kite reached an altitude of 12,471 feet. Determine whether 12,471 is divisible by 2, 3, 5, 6, 9, or 10. **3**

EXERCISES

Practice

Determine whether the first number is divisible by the second number.

11. 435; 5 **yes**
12. 240; 10 **yes**
13. 624; 6 **yes**
14. 333; 9 **yes**
15. 1,330; 3 **no**
16. 1,752; 2 **yes**
17. 5,514; 3 **yes**
18. 507; 5 **no**
19. 11,112; 6 **yes**

State whether each number is divisible by 2, 3, 5, 6, 9, or 10.

20. 208 **2**
21. 576 **2, 3, 6, 9**
22. 175 **5**
23. 397 **none**
24. 403 **none**
25. 4,077 **3, 9**
26. 918 **2, 3, 6, 9**
27. 2,860 **2, 5, 10**
28. 9,910 **2, 5, 10**

32. Sample answer: 30

33. Sample answer: 90

29. Is 747 divisible by 9? **yes**
30. Is 8,760 divisible by 5? **yes**
31. Determine whether 3,517 is divisible by 6. **no**
32. Find a number that is divisible by both 3 and 5.
33. Find a number that is divisible by 2, 9, and 10.

Applications and Problem Solving

34. *Games* Reynaldo and two of his friends are going to play Old Maid. To play the card game, they need to deal out all of the cards. If there are 51 cards in the deck, will each player get the same number of cards? **Yes; each player will get 17 cards.**

35. *School* The sixth grade students at East Middle School are planning a trip to Grand Canyon National Park. There are 135 students and 9 chaperones. Will each chaperone have the same number of students in his or her group? **See margin.**

36. *Critical Thinking* How can you determine whether a number is divisible by 15? Explain. **Sample answer: if the number is divisible by 3 and 5.**

Mixed Review

37. *Measurement* How many grams are there in 0.05 kilogram? *(Lesson 4-9)* **50**

38. *Geometry* Find the perimeter of the figure. *(Lesson 4-4)* **43.0 ft**

39. Find the product of 17.241 and 16. *(Lesson 4-1)* **275.856**

14.5 ft
3.4 ft
6.1 ft
7.0 ft
3.6 ft
8.4 ft

40. **Standardized Test Practice** The Clothes Depot is having a sale on denim shirts. The prices of the shirts range from $19.99 to $35.99. If Zachary bought 4 denim shirts, what would be a reasonable total cost for the shirts? *(Lesson 3-5)* **C**

   A $60   B $70   C $120   D $160   E $180

For **Extra Practice,** see page 568.

Extending the Lesson

Enrichment Masters, p. 32

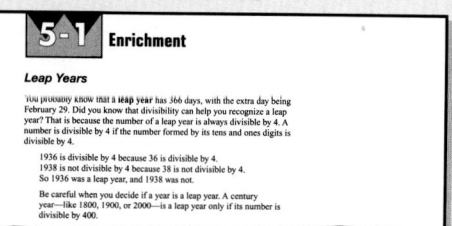

5-1 Enrichment

Leap Years

You probably know that a leap year has 366 days, with the extra day being February 29. Did you know that divisibility can help you recognize a leap year? That is because the number of a leap year is always divisible by 4. A number is divisible by 4 if the number formed by its tens and ones digits is divisible by 4.

1936 is divisible by 4 because 36 is divisible by 4.
1938 is not divisible by 4 because 38 is not divisible by 4.
So 1936 was a leap year, and 1938 was not.

Be careful when you decide if a year is a leap year. A century year—like 1800, 1900, or 2000—is a leap year only if its number is divisible by 400.

Activity Have small groups of students determine whether divisibility rules could be written for other numbers such as 4, 7, 8, and 11. Have them write out any rules that they find.

HANDS-ON LAB

COOPERATIVE LEARNING

5-2A Rectangular Arrays

A Preview of Lesson 5-2

square tiles

A *composite number* is a number that has more than two factors. A *prime number* is a number that has exactly two factors. You can use rectangular arrays to find out whether a number is composite or prime. *You can refer to Lesson 1-6 to review factors.*

TRY THIS

Work with a partner.

① Determine whether 6 is a prime number or a composite number.
  • Use 6 square tiles to build as many different-shaped rectangles as possible.

1 × 6   2 × 3

  • There is a rectangle that is 1 unit by 6 units and one that is 2 units by 3 units. So, the factors of 6 are 1, 2, 3, and 6.
Since 6 has four factors, it is a composite number.

② Determine whether 11 is a prime number or a composite number.
  • Use 11 square tiles to build as many different-shaped rectangles as possible.

1 × 11

  • There is one rectangle whose dimensions are 1 unit by 11 units. So, the factors of 11 are 1 and 11.
Since 11 has exactly two factors, it is a prime number.

ON YOUR OWN

1. Repeat the process with areas of 2 square units through 12 square units. **See Answer Appendix.**
2. Which numbers of square tiles had only one arrangement? **2, 3, 5, 7, 11**
3. Which numbers of square tiles had more than one arrangement? **4, 6, 8, 9, 10, 12**
4. Is there a relationship between a multiplication table and the number of arrangements you have? If so, describe it. **See margin.**
5. Make a guess about which numbers between 12 and 25 square units can have more than one rectangular shape. Explain why you selected those numbers. **See margin.**
6. *Look Ahead* Write a sentence describing the characteristics of prime and composite numbers. **See margin.**

Lesson 5-2A HANDS-ON LAB **181**

Additional Answers

4. The greater the number of arrangements, the more times the number appears on the multiplication table.

5. 12, 14, 15, 16, 18, 20, 21, 22, 24; these numbers have several factors.

6. Sample answer: A prime number has exactly 2 factors, 1 and the number itself. A composite number has more than 2 factors.

HANDS-ON 5-2A LAB Notes

GET READY

Objective Students identify prime and composite numbers by using rectangular arrays.

Optional Resources
Hands-On Lab Masters
• grid paper, pp. 11, 12
• worksheet, p. 47
Overhead Manipulative Resources
• algebra/area tiles
Manipulative Kit
• algebra/area tiles

MANAGEMENT TIPS

Recommended Time
30 minutes

Getting Started Have students practice making rectangles with the tiles or on grid paper. Make sure that students form complete rectangles. Show students how to model a rectangle with an area of 13 square units and one of 15 square units.

Activities 1 and 2 model prime and composite numbers. Explain that while rectangles can be positioned to look different, the shapes in this activity must have different widths and lengths. Tell students that a rectangle measuring 1 unit by 8 units is the same as a rectangle measuring 8 units by 1 unit.

ASSESS

Have students take turns modeling the rectangles and recording the findings. Also, to help students record all rectangles, have them start with a length of 1 unit. Then go to a length of 2 units, 3 units, and so on.

Have students write a paragraph that describes the patterns they discovered while modeling with the tiles.

- *Study Guide Masters*, p. 33
- *Practice Masters*, p. 33
- *Enrichment Masters*, p.33
- Transparencies 5-2, A and B
- *Diversity Masters*, p. 5

 CD-ROM Program
- Resource Lesson 5-2
- Extended Activity 5-2

Recommended Pacing	
Standard	Days 3 & 4 of 16
Honors	Day 3 of 15
Block	Day 2 of 8

1 FOCUS

 5-Minute Check
(Lesson 5-1)

Determine whether the first number is divisible by the second number.

1. 342; 6 **yes**
2. 795; 9 **no**

State whether each number is divisible by 2, 3, 5, 6, 9, or 10.

3. 113 **none**
4. 6,291 **3, 9**
5. Students at the Cassady School raised $98 for two homeless shelters in their town. Will they be able to give the same amount to each shelter? **yes**

The 5-Minute Check is also available on **Transparency 5-2A** for this lesson.

2 TEACH

Transparency 5-2B contains a teaching aid for this lesson.

Reading Mathematics Display the words *prime, composite, factor tree,* and *prime factorization.* Have students give an example of each. Write the examples below the words. Then have students use the words and the examples in a sentence.

5-2 Prime Factorization

What you'll learn

You'll learn to find the prime factorization of a composite number.

When am I ever going to use this?

Knowing how to find the prime factorization of a number can help you determine the possible dimensions of a box when given the box's volume.

Word Wise

composite number
prime number
prime factorization
factor tree

Each rectangle shown below has an area of 12 square units. The dimensions of the rectangles are 1 by 12, 2 by 6, and 3 by 4. So, the factors of 12 are 1, 2, 3, 4, 6, and 12.

1 × 12

2 × 6   3 × 4

Since 12 has six factors, it is a **composite number**. A composite number is any whole number greater than one with more than two factors.

In Lesson 5-2A, you found that there was only one rectangle you could make with 2, 3, 5, 7, and 11 square tiles. Numbers such as these are **prime numbers**. A prime number has exactly two factors, 1 and the number itself.

The numbers 0 and 1 are neither prime nor composite. Zero has an endless number of factors. The number 1 has only one factor, itself.

Example ① Determine whether 18 is a prime or composite number. Draw rectangles to explain your answer.

1 × 18

2 × 9   3 × 6

The factors of 18 are 1, 2, 3, 6, 9, and 18. Since 18 has more than two factors, it is a composite number.

Motivating the Lesson

Hands-On Activity Give pairs of students 40 small items, such as dried beans or paper clips. Have them separate the items into equal groups and record their findings. Challenge them to find as many equal groups as possible.

Multiple Learning Styles

 Visual/Spatial Have pairs of students use the geoboard's circular pattern. With colored rubber bands or string, students should hook the various intervals that represent different factors. Have students chart the information depicted on the geoboard and discuss. Repeat with a 24-peg board or a different composite number.

Every composite number can be expressed as a product of prime numbers. This is called the **prime factorization** of a number. To find the prime factorization of a number, you can use a **factor tree** or division.

Examples ② Find the prime factorization of 36.

Method 1 Use a factor tree.

Factor 36. 36 is divisible by 2.

Circle the prime number 2. How do you know 2 is prime?

Factor 18. Circle the prime number 2.

Factor 9. Circle the prime numbers 3.

LOOK BACK
You can refer to Lesson 1-6 to review exponents.

Method 2 Use division.

$$\begin{array}{r} 3 \\ 3\overline{)9} \\ 2\overline{)18} \\ 2\overline{)36} \end{array}$$

Begin with the least prime that is a factor. Then divide the quotient by the least possible prime factor. In this case, it is 2. Repeat until the quotient is prime.

The prime factorization of 36 is $2 \times 2 \times 3 \times 3$, or $2^2 \times 3^2$.

INTEGRATION ③ **Geometry** The volume of a box is found by multiplying its height, length, and width. If the measure of the volume of a box is 255, what could its dimensions be?

Find the prime factorization of 255.

255
3 × 85
5 × 17

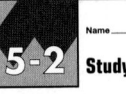

The prime factorization of 255 is $3 \times 5 \times 17$. So, 3, 5, and 17 are factors of 255. Thus, the dimensions of the box could be 3 by 5 by 17.

CHECK FOR UNDERSTANDING

Communicating Mathematics

Read and study the lesson to answer each question. 1–3. Answer Appendix.

1. *Draw* a picture to determine whether 10 is a prime or composite number.

2. *Explain* the difference between a prime number and a composite number.

3. *You Decide* Michelle says that the prime factorization of 120 is $2 \times 2 \times 2 \times 3 \times 5$. Lorenzo says that it is $2 \times 5 \times 3 \times 2 \times 2$. Who is correct? Explain your reasoning.

Lesson 5-2 Prime Factorization **183**

Reteaching the Lesson

Activity Have students use prime number cards to physically build a factor tree. Have them use self-adhesive notes to write composite numbers. As they factor each composite number, have them replace that note with a pair of factors (cards and/or other notes). Continue until the tree is composed totally of cards.

Error Analysis
Watch for students who rely on products in multiplication facts to determine whether a number is prime.
Prevent by reminding students that numbers such as 51 are not products in basic multiplication facts.

In-Class Examples

For Example 1
Determine whether 15 is a prime or composite number. Draw rectangles to explain your answer. **15 is a composite number.**

For Example 2
Find the prime factorization of 48. **$2 \times 2 \times 2 \times 2 \times 3$ or $2^4 \times 3$**

For Example 3
If the measure of the volume of a box is 609, what could its dimensions be? **3 by 7 by 29**

3 PRACTICE/APPLY

Check for Understanding
If students need additional practice or instruction after completing Exercises 1–12, one of these options may be helpful.
• Extra Practice, see p. 569
• Reteaching Activity
• *Transition Booklet*, pp. 21–22
• *Study Guide Masters*, p. 33
• *Practice Masters*, p. 33

***Study Guide Masters*, p. 33**

Name_____ Date_____

5-2 Study Guide

Prime Factorization

A **prime number** has exactly two factors, 1 and the number itself.

Example 1 13 is a prime number. It has only 1 and 13 as factors.

A **composite number** has more than two factors.
A composite number may be written as the product of prime numbers.

Example 2 Find the prime factorization of 48.

Factor 48.
Factor 6 and 8.
Factor 4.
Circle the prime numbers.

Write the prime numbers in order from least to greatest.
Check to see if the product is 48.
$2 \times 2 \times 2 \times 2 \times 3 = 48$

The numbers 0 and 1 are neither prime nor composite.
0 has an endless number of factors. 1 has only one factor, itself.

Find the prime factorization of each number.

1. 24
$2 \times 2 \times 2 \times 3$

2. 25
5×5

3. 70
$7 \times 5 \times 2$

4. 55
5×11

5. 44
$2 \times 2 \times 11$

6. 84
$2 \times 2 \times 3 \times 7$

7. 68
$2 \times 2 \times 17$

8. 121
11×11

9. 92
$2 \times 2 \times 23$

© Glencoe/McGraw-Hill   T33   *Mathematics: Applications and Connections, Course 1*

Lesson 5-2 **183**

Teaching Tip For Exercise 41, the Sieve of Eratosthenes works well for illustrating twin primes.

4 ASSESS

Closing Activity

Writing Ask students to write how they would find the prime factors of 35, 99, and 156. Then have them write the factors.

Additional Answer

41. 3 and 5, 5 and 7, 11 and 13, 17 and 19, 29 and 31, 41 and 43, 59 and 61, 71 and 73

Practice Masters, p. 33

Guided Practice

Tell whether each number is *prime*, *composite*, or *neither*.

4. 17 prime 5. 0 neither 6. 23 prime 7. 57 composite

Find the prime factorization of each number.

8. 49 7^2 9. 75 3×5^2 10. 32 2^5 11. 104 $2^3 \times 13$

12. *Geography* The state of North Carolina is made up of 100 counties. Express 100 as a product of primes. $2^2 \times 5^2$

EXERCISES

Practice

Tell whether each number is *prime*, *composite*, or *neither*.

13. 1 neither 14. 15 15. 29 prime 16. 44 composite
17. 45 18. 53 prime 19. 56 20. 31 prime
21. 87 composite 22. 110 composite 23. 93 composite 24. 114 composite

14. composite
17. composite
19. composite
25. $2 \times 3 \times 7$
33. $2 \times 3 \times 17$
35. $2^3 \times 3 \times 5$
38. $24 = 2^3 \cdot 3$;
$90 = 2 \cdot 3^2 \cdot 5$;
$98 = 2 \cdot 7^2$

Find the prime factorization of each number.

25. 42 26. 81 3^4 27. 65 5×13 28. 38 2×19
29. 17 prime 30. 24 $2^3 \times 3$ 31. 18 2×3^2 32. 40 $2^3 \times 5$
33. 102 34. 97 prime 35. 120 36. 48 $2^4 \times 3$

37. What is the least prime number that is greater than 80? **83**

38. Write 24, 90, and 98 as products of primes using exponents.

39. What is the greatest square of a whole number that divides 72 with a remainder of 0? What is the greatest cube of a whole number that divides 72 with a remainder of 0? **$36 = 6^2$; $8 = 2^3$**

Applications and Problem Solving

40. *Math History* In 1742, Christian Goldbach of Russia suggested that any even number greater than two could be expressed as the sum of two prime numbers. For example, $28 = 11 + 17$ and $30 = 13 + 17$. Find two prime numbers whose sum is the given number. **a–c. Sample answers given.**
a. 32 **13 + 19** b. 40 **17 + 23** c. 58 **41 + 17**

41. *Number Patterns* Twin primes are two prime numbers that are consecutive odd integers such as 3 and 5, 5 and 7, and 11 and 13. Find all of the twin primes that are less than 100. **See margin.**

42. *Critical Thinking* Every odd number greater than 7 can be expressed as the sum of three prime numbers. Which three prime numbers have a sum of 57? **Sample answer: 7 + 19 + 31**

Mixed Review

44. D

43. Determine whether or not 462 is divisible by 6. *(Lesson 5-1)* **yes**

44. **Standardized Test Practice** Seth purchased 3 CDs for $51.12. If each CD sold for the same amount, what was the price of each CD? *(Lesson 4-5)*
A $15.06 B $13.10 C $10.98 D $17.04 E Not Here

45. *Algebra* Evaluate $a - b$ if $a = 7.3$ and $b = 2.94$. *(Lesson 3-6)* **4.36**

46. *Statistics* Find the mean of the numbers 120, 112, 88, 100, 141, and 147. *(Lesson 2-7)* **118**

For **Extra Practice,** see page 569.

47. Write 17^7 as a product. *(Lesson 1-6)* $17 \times 17 \times 17 \times 17 \times 17 \times 17 \times 17$

Extending the Lesson

Enrichment Masters, p. 33

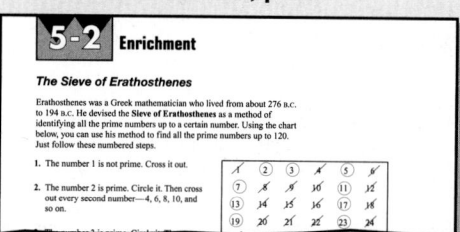

Activity Have students research *perfect, deficient,* and *abundant numbers.* Have them determine how they are related to factors of a number.

GRAPHIC DESIGN

CYBER GRAFIX

Kathryn Sharar Prusinski
GRAPHIC DESIGNER

I'd like to design graphics for a website.

Kathryn Sharar Prusinski is co-owner of CyberGraphix, a company that designs online magazines and other computer-related products. She holds a degree in advertising design and a certificate in advanced computer graphics. Ms. Prusinski designed several online materials for the Smithsonian and Sesame Street.

Most graphic designers have a bachelor's degree in graphic design, art, or art history. Graphic designers should have an understanding of computer technology, especially painting and graphic design tools. Computer and mathematics courses are an essential part of preparing for a career in graphics design.

For more information:
Graphic Arts Technical Foundation
200 Deer Run Road
Sewickley, PA 15143-2600

NET CONNECTION
www.glencoe.com/sec/math/mac/mathnet

Your Turn
Write and design a brochure that describes the advantages of a career in the graphic design industry.

School to Career: Graphic Design **185**

More About Kathryn Sharar Prusinski

- Kathryn Sharar Prusinski has a degree in Advertising Design from the Fashion Institute of Technology and a certificate in Advanced Computer Graphics from the Center for Media Arts. She also studied fine arts at Rutgers University and film animation at the School of Visual Arts in New York.

- Ms. Prusinski's on-line design credits include the following: the on-line magazine *National Geographic;* "NASA Space Challenge," a voyage with the astronauts on the space shuttle *Atlantis;* Disney's Gargoyles; and Saban's Mighty Morphin Power Rangers.

Motivating Students

Anyone who has created a poster or newsletter has tried graphic design. Graphic design can be employed for both commercial and artistic purposes. Its most popular use today is for the creation of websites on the Internet. To begin a discussion of graphic design, ask students these questions.

- What does the term *graphic design* mean? **a format that involves written words, drawings, engravings, photographs, or any combination of these items**
- What examples of graphic design are in the classroom? **Sample answer: bulletin board display, posters, textbooks**
- Why would someone creating a website need to understand graphic design? **to include text and illustrations in an interesting manner so that surfers will stop to read the site**

Making the Math Connection

Graphic designers need to understand angles, geometric shapes, area, and perimeter to lay out a design. Knowledge of scale and the ability to add, subtract, multiply, and divide using units of measure are also important.

Working on *Your Turn*

Have students separate into groups to brainstorm ideas for their brochures. Have them sketch their design ideas before creating the finished product. If possible, have students create their brochures on a computer.

*An additional School to Career activity is available on page 5 of the **School to Career Masters**.*

Objective Students solve problems by making an organized list.

Recommended Pacing	
Standard	Day 5 of 16
Honors	Day 4 of 15
Block	Day 3 of 8

1 FOCUS

Getting Started Ask students how they would determine which situation offers a greater variety of items.
- T-shirts available in 6 colors and 4 sizes
- 7 varieties of nuts, each in 3 package sizes

Suggest that students begin by listing the options.

2 TEACH

Teaching Tip An organized list will help students find a pattern and also determine whether all possibilities have been exhausted.

In-Class Example
How many 3-digit numbers can you make using the digits 4, 6, 8, and 9 if no repeated digits are allowed? **24 3-digit numbers**

THINKING LAB

PROBLEM SOLVING

5-3A Make a List

A Preview of Lesson 5-3

Harvi and Kendra are making a banner for spirit week using three sheets of paper. Harvi is trying to figure out how many different banners they can make using two colors of paper. Let's listen in!

Harvi

Our school colors are red and blue so we should use red and blue paper. How many different banners can we make using three sheets of paper?

Well, let's arrange the sheets of paper in different ways and see.

It's going to be hard to remember each arrangement. While you're arranging the paper, I'll list the possibilities.

Arrangements

That's a good idea.

Well, there are eight different possibilities.

RRR RRB RBR RBB
BRR BBR BRB BBB

Kendra

THINK ABOUT IT

Work with a partner.

1. **Analyze** the eight different possibilities. Do you agree or disagree with the possibilities? Explain your reasoning. **See students' work.**

2. **Think** of another way that Harvi and Kendra could have solved the problem.
   See students' work.

3. **Apply** the **make a list** strategy to solve the following problem.

   Molly's Muffin Shop sells apple, cranberry, blueberry, and strawberry muffins in three sizes: mini, regular, and jumbo. How many different options does a customer have to buy a muffin? **12 possible options**

186 Chapter 5 Using Number Patterns, Fractions, and Ratios

■ Reteaching the Lesson ■

Activity Give small groups of students a take-out pizza menu. Have them list all of the possible options available.

For **Extra Practice,** see page 569.

ON YOUR OWN

4. The third step of the 4-step plan for problem solving asks you to *solve* the problem. *Explain* the advantages of making an organized list over a random list when solving the problem. **See margin.**

5. *Write a Problem* that can be solved by making a list. Then ask a classmate to solve the problem. **See students' work.**

6. *Look Back* Explain how you can use the make a list strategy to answer Exercise 41 on page 184. **See margin.**

MIXED PROBLEM SOLVING

Solve. Use any strategy.

STRATEGIES
Look for a pattern.
Solve a simpler problem.
Act it out.
Guess and check.
Draw a diagram.
Make a chart.
Work backward.

7. *Manufacturing* A sweater company offers 6 different styles of sweaters in 5 different colors. How many combinations of style and color are possible? **30**

8. *Money Matters* Luisa saved $125 in May and $175 in June. How much does she need to save in July to average $150 per month in savings? **$150**

9. *Number Patterns* Colleen is planning to travel to Dallas, San Antonio, and Houston. She cannot decide in which order to schedule her visits. How many choices does she have? **6**

10. *Food* The graph shows that strawberry and grape jelly account for more than half of the yearly jelly sales in the United States. *About* how much more money is spent on strawberry and grape jelly than the other types of jelly? **Sample answer: $370 million–$300 million or $70 million.**

Yearly Jelly Sales

$366.2 million

$291.5 million

Strawberry and Grape

All others

Source: Nielsen Marketing Research

11. *Travel* The Guerrero's vacation lasted 12 days. They budgeted $75 per night for lodging and $65 per day for food. How much did they budget for these two items for the entire trip? **$1,680**

12. *Number Sense* How many different 2-digit numbers can you make using the digits 1, 3, 5, and 7 if no number is repeated? **12**

13. *Standardized Test Practice* Samantha is going on vacation. She has asked her neighbor to feed her 2 dogs while she is gone. Each dog eats 8.5 cans of dog food per week. What else do you need to know to find how many cans of food Samantha should buy before she goes on vacation? **C**
    A   the number of ounces in each can of dog food
    B   the price of one can of dog food
    C   the number of weeks Samantha will be on vacation
    D   the breed of each dog
    E   the weight of each dog

14. *Manufacturing* How many different license plates can you make with the letters M, N, and P and the numbers 1, 2, and 3 if each license plate starts with three letters and ends with three numbers? **36**

Lesson 5-3A **THINKING** **187**

Check for Understanding
Use the results from Exercise 3 to determine whether students understand how to make a list to solve a problem.

Extra Practice If students need additional practice in problem solving, extra practice is available on the following pages.
• Make a List, see p. 569
• Mixed Problem Solving, see pp. 593–594

Assignment Guide
All: 4–14

4 ASSESS

Closing Activity
Writing Have students list situations that are most easily answered by making a list. Suggest that they compare lists.

Additional Answers
4. **Sample answer: An organized list allows you to make sure you have all the possibilities.**

6. **Sample answer: Make a list of all consecutive integers. Then circle each pair of consecutive odd integers that are both prime.**

1   3   5   7

■ Extending the Lesson ■

Activity Have small groups of students contact local automobile dealers to obtain new-car brochures. Have them choose a model and list the types of options. Then have them determine how many cars the dealers would need to keep on the lot if they wanted to have all of the possible combinations available for their customers.

Instructional Resources

- *Study Guide Masters*, p. 34
- *Practice Masters*, p. 34
- *Enrichment Masters*, p. 34
- Transparencies 5-3, A and B
- *Assessment and Evaluation Masters*, p. 127

 CD-ROM Program
- Resource Lesson 5-3
- Interactive Lesson 5-3

Recommended Pacing	
Standard	Day 6 of 16
Honors	Day 5 of 15
Block	Day 3 of 8

1 FOCUS

 5-Minute Check
(Lesson 5-2)

Tell whether each number is *prime, composite,* or *neither*.

1. 49   composite
2. 67   prime

Find the prime factorization of each number.

3. 118 2×59
4. 90 $2 \times 3 \times 3 \times 5$ or $2 \times 3^2 \times 5$
5. The first prime number is 2. What is the fourteenth prime number?   43

The 5-Minute Check is also available on **Transparency 5-3A** for this lesson.

Motivating the Lesson

Communication Ask a student to read aloud the opening paragraph of the lesson. Discuss whether the greatest number of people is a product, a factor, or a sum, and why. **a factor because the larger groups are being separated into smaller groups**

2 TEACH

 Transparency 5-3B contains a teaching aid for this lesson.

5-3 Greatest Common Factor

What you'll learn

You'll learn to find the greatest common factor of two or more numbers.

When am I ever going to use this?

Knowing how to find the greatest common factor of two or more numbers can help you coordinate a parade.

Word Wise

greatest common factor (GCF)

Suppose that 27 flag line and 45 drill team members were selected to participate in the Flag Day parade. The parade director wants all members to line up in rows that have the same number of people. Flag line and drill team members will be in different rows. What is the greatest number of people that can be in each row?

To answer this question, you can use the factors of 27 and 45.

factors of 27: 1, 3, 9, 27
factors of 45: 1, 3, 5, 9, 15, 45

Notice that 1, 3, and 9 are common factors of both 27 and 45. The greatest of the common factors of two or more numbers is called the **greatest common factor (GCF)** of the numbers. So, the greatest common factor of 27 and 45 is 9.

The greatest number of people that can be in each row is 9.

To find the GCF of two or more numbers, you can make a list or use prime factorization.

Method 1 Make a list.
- List all of the factors of each number.
- Identify the common factors.
- The greatest of the common factors is the GCF.

Method 2 Use prime factorization.
- Write the prime factorization of each number.
- Identify all of the common prime factors.
- The product of the common prime factors is the GCF.

 Example 1 Find the GCF of 24 and 32 by making a list.

factors of 24: 1, 2, 3, 4, 6, 8, 12, 24   *List all of the factors*
factors of 32: 1, 2, 4, 8, 16, 32   *of each number.*

The common factors are 1, 2, 4, and 8.
The GCF of 24 and 32 is 8.

188   **Chapter 5** Using Number Patterns, Fractions, and Ratios

---

Classroom Vignette

"I assign a color to each of the first eight prime numbers. Students make up factor trees to find the prime factorization of a number. When they finish each tree, they circle each prime number with its appropriate color. They can then spot the factors that numbers have in common to find the GCF."

Frances S. Gattis, Teacher
Ware County Middle School
Waycross, GA

2 Find the GCF of 36 and 54 by using prime factorization.

```
      36              54
    ╱    ╲          ╱    ╲
   ②  ×  18        ②  ×  27        Write the prime
        ╱  ╲            ╱  ╲        factorization of
       ②ₓ  9          ③  ×  9       each number.
          ╱ ╲            ╱ ╲
         ③ × ③          ③ × ③
```

Did you know? The tree most commonly found in the United States is the Ponderosa pine.

The common prime factors are 2, 3, and 3.

The GCF of 36 and 54 is $2 \times 3 \times 3$, or 18.

CONNECTION

3 **Life Science** Kaja has 32 fir, 48 cedar, and 80 maple tree seedlings to sell at the annual Agriculture Fair. He wants to display them in rows with the same number of seedlings in each row with no mixing of rows.

   a. What is the greatest number of seedlings that he could put in each row?

   b. How many rows of each tree seedlings will there be?

   a. factors of 32: 1, 2, 4, 8, 16, 32   List all of the
      factors of 48: 1, 2, 3, 4, 6, 8, 12, 16, 24, 48   factors of
      factors of 80: 1, 2, 4, 5, 8, 10, 16, 20, 40, 80   each number.

      The common factors are 1, 2, 4, 8, and 16.
      The GCF of 32, 48, and 80 is 16.
      So, Kaja could put 16 tree seedlings in a row.

   b. Since $2 \times 16 = 32$, there would be 2 rows of fir seedlings.
      Since $3 \times 16 = 48$, there would be 3 rows of cedar seedlings.
      Since $5 \times 16 = 80$, there would be 5 rows of maple seedlings.

In-Class Examples

For Example 1
Find the GCF of 24 and 48 by making a list. **24**

For Example 2
Find the GCF of 32 and 48 by using prime factorization. **16**

For Example 3
There are 84 turkey sandwiches and 63 ham sandwiches to be placed on trays. Each tray should have only one kind of sandwich, and all trays should have the same number of sandwiches.
a. What is the greatest number of sandwiches that can be placed on one tray? **21**
b. How many trays of each type of sandwich will there be?
4 turkey trays, 3 ham trays

Teaching Tip As shown in Example 2, if a common factor occurs more than once, include it the number of times that it is common to the prime factorization of both numbers.

CHECK FOR UNDERSTANDING

Communicating Mathematics

Read and study the lesson to answer each question. 1–2. Answer Appendix.

1. *Explain* how to find the GCF of 12 and 18.

2. *Tell* how the GCF of two numbers could be one of the numbers. Give two examples.

Guided Practice

Find the GCF of each set of numbers by making a list.

3. 10, 15 **5**   4. 8, 30 **2**   5. 14, 35, 84 **7**

Find the GCF of each set of numbers by using prime factorization.

6. 15, 45 **15**   7. 8, 88 **8**   8. 16, 24, 72 **8**

9. *School* Carena has two rolls of streamers to use in decorating the school gym for a pep rally. One roll is 64 feet long, and the other roll is 72 feet long. If she wants to make all of the streamers the same length, what is the greatest length each streamer can be? **8 ft**

Lesson 5-3 Greatest Common Factor **189**

Study Guide Masters, p. 34

■ **Reteaching the Lesson** ■

Activity Display these numbers and their factors on an overhead transparency. Ask leading questions to help students find the GCF.
36: 1, 2, 3, 4, 6, 9, 12, 18, 36
90: 1, 2, 3, 5, 6, 9, 10, 15, 18, 30, 45, 90
GCF: 18

Using Technology The TI-83 calculator has a GCD function (greatest common divisor), which calculates the GCF for any pair of numbers. To use the function, press MATH , select NUM, and ENTER 9. Enter the first number, a comma, the second number, and the closing parenthesis. Press ENTER to obtain the GCF.

Check for Understanding

If students need additional practice or instruction after completing Exercises 1–9, one of these options may be helpful.
- Extra Practice, see p. 569
- Reteaching Activity
- *Study Guide Masters*, p. 34
- *Practice Masters*, p. 34
- Interactive Mathematics Tools Software

Assignment Guide

Core: 11–31 odd, 33–37
Enriched: 10–30 even, 31–37

---

4 ASSESS

Closing Activity

Speaking Ask students how knowing divisibility rules can help them when finding the GCF of two numbers.

Chapter 5, Quiz A (Lessons 5-1 through 5-3) is available in the *Assessment and Evaluation Masters*, p. 127.

Practice Masters, p. 34

Practice

Find the GCF of each set of numbers by making a list.

10. 8, 32 **8** **11.** 6, 44 **2** **12.** 42, 56 **14**

13. 75, 30 **15** **14.** 9, 18, 42 **3** **15.** 22, 55, 88 **11**

Find the GCF of each set of numbers by using prime factorization.

16. 16, 56 **8** **17.** 17, 34 **17** **18.** 35, 65 **5**

19. 96, 108 **12** **20.** 16, 52, 76 **4** **21.** 12, 18, 60 **6**

28. 54: 1, 2, 3, 6, 9, 18, 27, 54; 90: 1, 2, 3, 5, 6, 9, 10, 15, 18, 30, 45, 90; 1, 2, 3, 6, 9, 18.

Find the GCF of each set of numbers using either method.

22. 15, 36 **3** **23.** 21, 45 **3** **24.** 42, 90 **6**

25. 34, 85 **17** **26.** 6, 57, 99 **3** **27.** 19, 95, 152 **19**

28. List all of the factors of 54 and 90. Then list the common factors.

29. Find the GCF of 39, 48, and 51. **3**

30. Write two numbers whose GCF is 18. **Sample answer: 18 and 36**

Applications and Problem Solving

31. *Remodeling* Shawn is covering a portion of his bathroom wall with equal-sized ceramic square tiles. The portion of the wall to be tiled measures 16 inches wide and 72 inches long.
  a. What is the largest square tile that can be used so that no tiles will need to be cut? **8 in. by 8 in.**
  b. What is the total number of tiles Shawn will need? **18**

32. *Business* Marsha has 45 apples, 75 pears, and 105 oranges to sell at her family's farm market. She wants to put the fruit in bags so that there are the same number of pieces of each fruit in each bag without mixing the fruit.

32b. 3 bags of apples, 5 bags of pears, 7 bags of oranges

  a. What is the greatest number of pieces of fruit that can be put in each bag? **15**
  b. How many bags of each kind of fruit will there be?

33. *Critical Thinking* Two composite numbers that have 1 as their only common factor are said to be *relatively prime*. Find two composite numbers less than 25 that are relatively prime. **Sample answer: 8 and 9**

Mixed Review

36. Sample answer:
$4 + 4 + 4 + 4 + 4 = 20$

For **Extra Practice**, see page 569.

34. **Standardized Test Practice** Which expression represents the prime factorization of 378? *(Lesson 5-2)* **C**
  A $2 \times 3 \times 7^3$ **B** $2^3 \times 3 \times 7$ **C** $2 \times 3^3 \times 7$ **D** $2^3 \times 3^3 \times 7^3$

35. *Decorating* Antonieta is buying new carpet for her bedroom. If her bedroom measures 5.3 yards by 4.7 yards, how many square yards of carpeting will she need? *(Lesson 4-4)* **24.9 yd²**

36. Estimate $4.231 + 3.98 + 4 + 4.197 + 3.76$. *(Lesson 3-5)*

37. Write *nine and sixteen thousandths* as a decimal. *(Lesson 3-1)* **9.016**

Extending the Lesson

Enrichment Masters, p. 34

5-3 Enrichment

Getting From Here to There

At the right, you see a rectangle on a grid of squares. The rectangle is 4 units wide and 7 units long. The *diagonal path* of this rectangle crosses 10 squares of the grid.

For each rectangle, record the width, the length, and the diagonal path.

width 4
length 7
diagonal path 10

1. 2; 3; 4 2. 3; 4; 6 3.

Activity Have pairs of students make generalizations about the GCF of two prime numbers. Then have them compare these generalizations with generalizations about the GCF of two composite numbers.

COOPERATIVE LEARNING

5-4A Fractions and Ratios

A Preview of Lesson 5-4

ruler

You have used models to help you understand decimals. You can also use models to help you understand ratios and fractions. A *ratio* is a comparison of two numbers by division. The ratio comparing 3 to 4 can be stated as 3 out of 4, 3 to 4, 3:4, or $\frac{3}{4}$.

TRY THIS

Work with a partner.

1 Model the ratio 1 *out of* 4.
- Copy the rectangle shown.
- Separate the rectangle into four equal parts.
- Shade 1 part.

One out of four parts is shaded.

Therefore, the model represents the ratio *1 out of 4*. Note that the model also represents the fraction $\frac{1}{4}$.

2 Model the fraction $\frac{3}{5}$.
- Copy the rectangle shown.
- Separate the rectangle into five equal parts.
- Shade 3 parts.

Three out of five of the parts are shaded.

Therefore, the model represents the fraction $\frac{3}{5}$ as well as the ratio *3 out of 5*.

ON YOUR OWN

Write a ratio and a fraction for each model shown. 3. 5 out of 9, 5 to 9, or 5:9; $\frac{5}{9}$

1.

5 out of 6, 5 to 6, or 5:6; $\frac{5}{6}$

2.

3 out of 8,
3 to 8, or 3:8; $\frac{3}{8}$

3.

GET READY

Objective Students use models to represent fractions and equivalent fractions.

Optional Resources
Hands-On Lab Masters
- fraction models, pp. 3, 4
- worksheet, p. 48

Manipulative Kit
- ruler

MANAGEMENT TIPS

Recommended Time
45 minutes

Getting Started Have students read the opening paragraph of the lesson. Draw a variety of shapes and ask whether they can be divided into equal parts. Have students determine how they would divide a rectangle into equal parts.

Activities 1 and 2 model a single ratio or fraction. Emphasize to students that a fraction is just a way of writing a ratio.

Activity 3 models two fractions and compares them. Make sure that the two initial rectangles are identical. For students having difficulty drawing identical rectangles and dividing them into appropriate sections, you may opt to use the premade fraction models in the *Hands-On Lab Masters,* which are based on identical rectangles or circles.

ASSESS

Have students work in pairs. Ask them to represent a pair of equivalent fractions with a model. Then have them tell which fractions they have modeled.

Use Exercise 8 to determine whether students understand how to use models to represent and compare fractions and ratios.

Hands-On Lab Masters, p. 48

192   Chapter 5

TRY THIS

Work with a partner.

3 Compare $\frac{4}{6}$ and $\frac{2}{3}$.

• Draw two identical rectangles as shown.

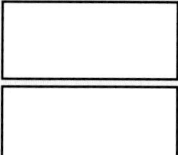

• Separate the upper rectangle into 6 equal parts. Separate the lower rectangle into 3 equal parts.

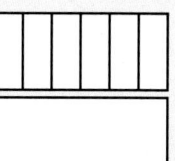

• Shade 4 parts of the upper rectangle and 2 parts of the lower rectangle.

$\frac{4}{6}$

$\frac{2}{3}$

Since the areas shaded are the same, the fractions are equivalent.

ON YOUR OWN

Write the pair of fractions represented by each model.

4. $\frac{1}{2}, \frac{4}{8}$

5. $\frac{3}{4}, \frac{6}{8}$

Draw models for each pair of fractions. Then tell whether the pair are equivalent.

6. $\frac{1}{3}, \frac{2}{6}$ **See Answer Appendix.**

7. $\frac{2}{8}, \frac{1}{4}$ **See Answer Appendix.**

8. *Look Ahead* What fraction is represented by the model shown? Name another fraction that is represented by the model. $\frac{2}{10}, \frac{1}{5}$

192   Chapter 5 Using Number Patterns, Fractions, and Ratios

| Math Journal | Have students write a description of how they used models to compare fractions and ratios and why models are helpful. Encourage them to include drawings. |

5-4 Simplifying Fractions and Ratios

What you'll learn

You'll learn to express fractions and ratios in simplest form.

When am I ever going to use this?

Knowing how to write fractions and ratios in simplest form can help you analyze baseball statistics.

Word Wise

ratio
equivalent fractions
simplest form

A roll of candy contains about 16 candies. Tyra has a roll in which 4 of the 16 candies are pink. You can compare the number of pink candies to the total number of candies using a **ratio**.

A ratio is a comparison of two numbers by division. The ratio that compares 4 to 16 can be written in several ways.

4 to 16	4 out of 16	4:16

Ratios can be expressed as fractions. In this case, the fraction is $\frac{4}{16}$.

You can write the fraction $\frac{4}{16}$ as $\frac{2}{8}$ and also as $\frac{1}{4}$. Fractions that name the same number are called **equivalent fractions**.

Method 1 Use a model.

 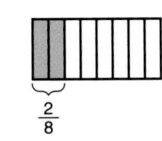

$\frac{1}{4}$ $\frac{2}{8}$

The rectangles are the same size and the same part or fraction of each rectangle is shaded. So, the fractions are equivalent. That is, $\frac{1}{4} = \frac{2}{8}$.

Method 2 Use paper and pencil.

$$\overset{\times 2}{\frac{1}{4} = \frac{2}{8}} \qquad \overset{\div 2}{\frac{2}{8} = \frac{1}{4}}$$

Multiply or divide the numerator and the denominator of a fraction by the same nonzero number.

Examples

Replace each ■ with a number so that the fractions are equivalent.

1 $\frac{3}{8} = \frac{■}{24}$

Since $8 \times 3 = 24$, multiply the numerator and denominator by 3.

$$\overset{\times 3}{\frac{3}{8} = \frac{■}{24}}, \text{ so } \frac{3}{8} = \frac{9}{24}.$$

2 $\frac{15}{25} = \frac{3}{■}$

Since $15 \div 3 = 5$, divide the numerator and denominator by 5.

$$\overset{\div 5}{\frac{15}{25} = \frac{3}{■}}, \text{ so } \frac{15}{25} = \frac{3}{5}.$$

Lesson 5-4 Simplifying Fractions and Ratios   **193**

5-4 Lesson Notes

Instructional Resources
- *Study Guide Masters*, p. 35
- *Practice Masters*, p. 35
- *Enrichment Masters*, p. 35
- Transparencies 5-4, A and B
- CD-ROM Program
  - Resource Lesson 5-4
  - Interactive Lesson 5-4

Recommended Pacing

Standard	Days 7 & 8 of 16
Honors	Days 6 & 7 of 15
Block	Day 4 of 8

1 FOCUS

5-Minute Check
(Lesson 5-3)

Find the GCF of each set of numbers.
1. 22, 46   **2**
2. 36, 54   **18**
3. 72, 39   **3**
4. 48, 56   **8**
5. 12, 45, 60   **3**

The 5-Minute Check is also available on **Transparency 5-4A** for this lesson.

Motivating the Lesson

Hands-On Activity Have pairs of students hold their hands behind their backs. On the count of three, have them put both hands out in front with any number of fingers outstretched. Have them express in simplest form the total number of fingers as a fraction of the total number possible (20). Have students do ten rounds and compare results.

Transparency 5-4B contains a teaching aid for this lesson.

Using Patterns As students examine Examples 1 and 2, have them identify whether they are seeking a number greater or less than the given numerator (or denominator). This determines whether they should divide or multiply. Expand this pattern to show that when simplifying, they always divide.

In-Class Examples

For Example 1
Replace ■ with a number so that $\frac{3}{8} = \frac{■}{24} \cdot \frac{9}{24}$

For Example 2
Replace ■ with a number so that $\frac{21}{28} = \frac{■}{4} \cdot \frac{3}{4}$

For Example 3
Write $\frac{3}{9}$ in simplest form. $\frac{1}{3}$

For Example 4
Write $\frac{35}{84}$ in simplest form. $\frac{5}{12}$

For Example 5
82 of the first 100 elements in the periodic table were discovered before 1900. Express the ratio 82:100 in simplest form. **41:50**

Teaching Tip After Example 4, stress that both the numerator and the denominator must be divided by the GCF when writing a fraction in simplest form. However, point out that a second division can be performed in case they did not use the GCF.

A fraction is in **simplest form** when the GCF of the numerator and denominator is 1. To write a fraction in simplest form, find the GCF of the numerator and the denominator. Then divide the numerator and denominator by the GCF.

3 Write $\frac{4}{10}$ in simplest form.

factors of 4: 1, 2, 4   *Find the GCF of the numerator*
factors of 10: 1, 2, 5, 10   *and the denominator.*

The GCF of 4 and 10 is 2.

$$\frac{4}{10} = \frac{2}{5} \qquad \text{\textit{Divide the numerator and}}$$
$$\text{\textit{denominator by the GCF, 2.}}$$

Since the GCF of 2 and 5 is 1, the fraction $\frac{2}{5}$ is in simplest form.

Study Hint

Technology You can use a fraction calculator to simplify fractions. For example, to simplify $\frac{4}{16}$, enter
4 [/] 16 [SIMP] [=] .
Repeat [SIMP] [=]
until the N/D → n/d does not appear on the screen.

4 Write $\frac{18}{21}$ in simplest form.

factors of 18: 1, 2, 3, 6, 9, 18   *Find the GCF of the numerator*
factors of 21: 1, 3, 7, 21   *and the denominator.*

The GCF of 18 and 21 is 3.

$$\frac{18}{21} = \frac{6}{7} \qquad \text{\textit{Divide the numerator and}}$$
$$\text{\textit{denominator by the GCF, 3.}}$$

Since the GCF of 6 and 7 is 1, the fraction $\frac{6}{7}$ is in simplest form.

INTEGRATION

5 **Statistics** Approximately 26 out of 100 American households have two or more VCR's. Express the ratio 26:100 in simplest form.

factors of 26: 1, 2, 13, 26   *Find the GCF.*
factors of 100: 1, 2, 4, 5, 10, 20, 25, 50, 100

The GCF of 26 and 100 is 2.

$$\frac{26}{100} = \frac{13}{50} \qquad \text{\textit{Simplify. Divide both the numerator}}$$
$$\text{\textit{and the denominator by the GCF, 2.}}$$

In simplest form, the ratio is 13:50.

Classroom Vignette

"I use colored candies to introduce fractions. Each group of students sorts and counts the pieces by color and finds the total number of pieces. Then they write the fraction representing each color's part of the whole bag. We post the results and students look for patterns in the product."

Sharon E. Eaton

Sharon E. Eaton, Teacher
Thunderbolt Middle School
Lake Havasu City, AZ

number cu...

Communicating Mathematics

Read and study the lesson to answer each question. **2. See margin.**

1. *Examine* the figure shown.
   a. Write the fraction that represents the shaded part of the figure. $\frac{8}{12}$
   b. Find the GCF of the numerator and denominator of the fraction. **4**
   c. Write the fraction in simplest form. $\frac{2}{3}$
   d. Draw a model that represents the fraction in simplest form. **See margin.**

2. *Explain* how you can tell whether a fraction is in simplest form.

Guided Practice

Replace each ■ with a number so that the fractions are equivalent.

3. $\frac{1}{3} = \frac{■}{27}$ **9**
4. $\frac{12}{16} = \frac{3}{■}$ **4**
5. $\frac{■}{5} = \frac{9}{15}$ **3**

State whether each fraction or ratio is in simplest form. If not, write each fraction or ratio in simplest form.

6. $\frac{5}{8}$ **yes**
7. 4 to 36 **no; 1 to 9**
8. $\frac{42}{49}$ **no;** $\frac{6}{7}$
9. 79:100 **yes**

10. *Statistics* Approximately 36 of every 100 people in the United States listen to compact discs on portable CD players. Express the ratio 36:100 as a fraction in simplest form. $\frac{9}{25}$

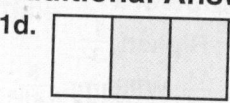

Practice

Replace each ■ with a number so that the fractions are equivalent.

11. $\frac{1}{2} = \frac{■}{8}$ **4**
12. $\frac{10}{15} = \frac{2}{■}$ **3**
13. $\frac{3}{4} = \frac{■}{12}$ **9**
14. $\frac{14}{18} = \frac{■}{9}$ **7**
15. $\frac{8}{9} = \frac{■}{27}$ **24**
16. $\frac{30}{35} = \frac{6}{■}$ **7**
17. $\frac{13}{78} = \frac{1}{■}$ **6**
18. $\frac{4}{5} = \frac{■}{40}$ **32**
19. $\frac{57}{60} = \frac{19}{■}$ **20**

State whether each fraction or ratio is in simplest form. If not, write each fraction or ratio in simplest form.

23. no; 3 out of 4
24. no; 4 to 11
27. no; 3:5
31. no; 1 out of 4

20. $\frac{4}{20}$ **no;** $\frac{1}{5}$
21. $\frac{10}{38}$ **no;** $\frac{5}{19}$
22. 8:25 **yes**
23. 18 out of 24
24. 28 to 77
25. $\frac{15}{100}$ **no;** $\frac{3}{20}$
26. $\frac{27}{54}$ **no;** $\frac{1}{2}$
27. 21:35
28. 41:85 **yes**
29. $\frac{42}{50}$ **no;** $\frac{21}{25}$
30. $\frac{11}{67}$ **yes**
31. 12 out of 48

32. Express the ratio 12 out of 144 in simplest form. **1 out of 12**

33. Write a fraction that can be expressed as $\frac{2}{3}$ in simplest form.
    Sample answer: $\frac{4}{6}$

Lesson 5-4 Simplifying Fractions and Ratios **195**

Work with a ...

To find the pro... these steps.
- Copy the cha...
- Estimate the ... it is rolled 6...
- Roll the num...
- Suppose the ... ratio, or exp... Based on y... 2? a 4? a 6?

1. $\frac{7}{48}$ 2. $\frac{5}{48}$

Six index ca...
chooses a c...
activity 48 ti...

1. What is th...
2. What is th...
3. What is t...
4. *Reflect* Write the...

Check for Understanding

If students need additional practice or instruction after completing Exercises 1–10, one of these options may be helpful.
- Extra Practice, see p. 570
- Reteaching Activity
- *Study Guide Masters*, p. 35
- *Practice Masters*, p. 35

Assignment Guide

Core: 11–35 odd, 37–42
Enriched: 12–32 even, 34, 35, 37–42

Additional Answers

1d.

2. Sample answer: The numerator and the denominator do not have any common factors other than 1.

Study Guide Masters, p. 35

Activity Have small groups of students play "Fraction Pairs." Make pairs of equivalent fraction cards. Place all cards facedown. Have players take turns picking two cards and determining whether they are matching pairs. One player may challenge another by drawing a model to prove that a match is incorrect.

Error Analysis

Watch for students who divide by a common factor that is not the greatest common factor and assume the fraction is simplified.

Prevent by asking students to examine the resulting fraction to see whether its numerator and denominator can be divided again.

Exercise 36
advance to ...
on the Chap...
should dete...
pages that i...
and ads.

Closing

Modeling

fractions su...
them mode...
equivalent....
models to ...

Addition

35a. Gwy...

Gon...

Bon...

35b. Ripk...

Practice

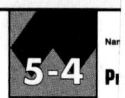

5-5 Lesson Notes

Instructional Resources
- *Study Guide Masters*, p. 36
- *Practice Masters*, p. 36
- *Enrichment Masters*, p. 36
- Transparencies 5-5, A and B
- *Assessment and Evaluation Masters*, pp. 126, 127
- *School to Career Masters*, p. 5
- CD-ROM Program
  - Resource Lesson 5-5

Recommended Pacing	
Standard	Day 9 of 16
Honors	Day 8 of 15
Block	Day 5 of 8

1 FOCUS

5-Minute Check
(Lesson 5-4)

State whether each fraction or ratio is in simplest form. If not, write it in simplest form.

1. $\frac{7}{32}$ simplest form

2. $\frac{6}{33}$ $\frac{2}{11}$

3. 35:40 7:8

4. $\frac{17}{85}$ $\frac{1}{5}$

5. Ten Americans in every 100 are hearing impaired. Write this as a fraction in simplest form. $\frac{1}{10}$

 The 5-Minute Check is also available on **Transparency 5-5A** for this lesson.

Motivating the Lesson

Problem Solving You would like to bring a fruit punch to class to celebrate your birthday. If you triple the recipe, $\frac{5}{8}$ cup grape juice will be $\frac{15}{8}$ cups, $\frac{3}{4}$ cup orange juice will be $\frac{9}{4}$ cups, and $\frac{2}{3}$ cup apple juice will be $\frac{6}{3}$ cups. How would you measure these amounts?

5-5 Mixed Numbers and Improper Fractions

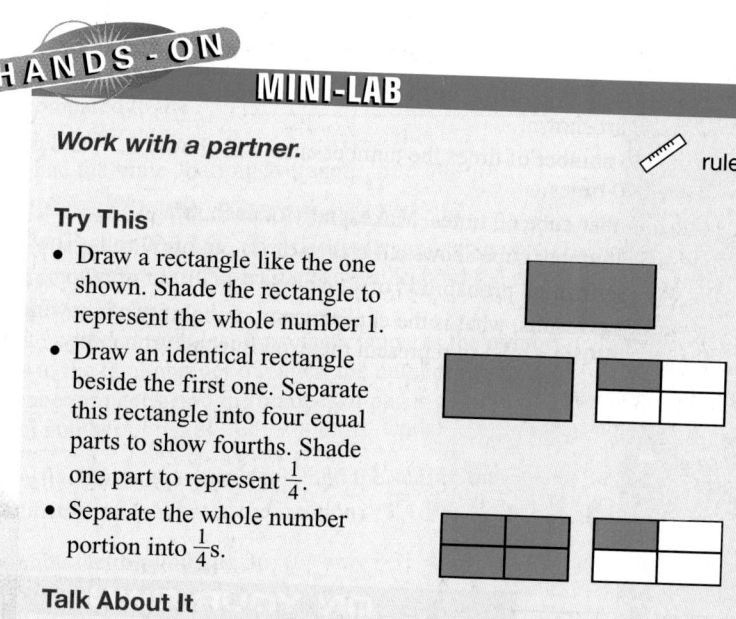

What you'll learn
You'll learn to express mixed numbers as improper fractions and vice versa.

When am I ever going to use this?
Knowing how to express numbers in different forms can help you determine the amounts of the ingredients when increasing a recipe.

Word Wise
mixed number
improper fraction

Tennis anyone? Tennis racquets come in a variety of grip sizes. Three of these are $4\frac{3}{8}$ inches, $4\frac{1}{4}$ inches, and $3\frac{7}{8}$ inches.

The numbers $4\frac{3}{8}$, $4\frac{1}{4}$, and $3\frac{7}{8}$ are examples of **mixed numbers**.

A mixed number shows the sum of a whole number and a fraction.

In the following Mini-Lab, you'll learn that mixed numbers can be written as fractions.

HANDS-ON MINI-LAB

Work with a partner. ruler

Try This
- Draw a rectangle like the one shown. Shade the rectangle to represent the whole number 1.
- Draw an identical rectangle beside the first one. Separate this rectangle into four equal parts to show fourths. Shade one part to represent $\frac{1}{4}$.
- Separate the whole number portion into $\frac{1}{4}$s.

Talk About It
1. How many shaded $\frac{1}{4}$s are there? 5
2. What fraction is equivalent to $1\frac{1}{4}$? $\frac{5}{4}$

A fraction, like $\frac{5}{4}$ or $\frac{6}{5}$, with a numerator that is greater than or equal to the denominator is called an **improper fraction**. To express a mixed number as an improper fraction, you can use a model.

198 Chapter 5 Using Number Patterns, Fractions, and Ratios

Investigations for the Special Education Student

This blackline master booklet helps you plan for the needs of your special education students by providing long-term projects along with teacher notes. Investigation 5, *Author's Fair*, and Investigation 12, *Yard Sale*, may be used with this chapter.

Example 1 Express $3\frac{1}{2}$ as an improper fraction.

Change the whole number into halves. Then count the total number of halves.

There are seven $\frac{1}{2}$s in $3\frac{1}{2}$. So, $3\frac{1}{2}$ can be expressed as $\frac{7}{2}$.

Study Hint

Reading Math
A mixed number like $3\frac{1}{2}$ is read as three and one half. $3\frac{1}{2}$ means $3 + \frac{1}{2}$.

A shortcut to writing a mixed number as an improper fraction is to first multiply the whole number by the denominator and add the numerator. Then write this sum over the denominator.

$$1\frac{1}{4} = \frac{(1 \times 4) + 1}{4} = \frac{5}{4}$$

Example 2 CONNECTION

Life Science The body of the vampire bat measures $2\frac{3}{4}$ inches. Express the body length of a vampire bat as an improper fraction.

$2\frac{3}{4} = \frac{(2 \times 4) + 3}{4}$ *Multiply 2 by 4 and add 3.*

$= \frac{11}{4}$ *Then write the result over 4.*

The body length of a vampire bat can be expressed as $\frac{11}{4}$ inches.

You can also express an improper fraction as a mixed number. To do this, divide the numerator by the denominator.

Example 3 Express $\frac{7}{3}$ as a mixed number.

Divide 7 by 3.

$\begin{array}{r} 2 \\ 3\overline{)7} \\ -6 \\ \hline 1 \end{array}$ *Write the remainder in the numerator of a fraction that has the divisor as the denominator.*

$\frac{7}{3} = 2\frac{1}{3}$

$\underbrace{}_{2}$ $\underbrace{}_{\frac{1}{3}}$

Lesson 5-5 Mixed Numbers and Improper Fractions **199**

Teaching Tip Before the Mini-Lab, show students that mixed numbers can be written as the sum of a whole number and a fraction by writing $1\frac{1}{4} = 1 + \frac{1}{4}$, $1\frac{3}{16} = 1 + \frac{3}{16}$, and $1\frac{1}{2} = 1 + \frac{1}{2}$.

Using the Mini-Lab Have students model other mixed numbers such as $\frac{9}{4}$, $\frac{6}{5}$, or $\frac{5}{3}$. Make sure students separate the whole number portion into the same number of parts as they separate the extra rectangle.

Transparency 5-5B contains a teaching aid for this lesson.

In-Class Examples

For Example 1
Express $3\frac{5}{8}$ as an improper fraction. $\frac{29}{8}$

For Example 2
The distance between the center of the pitcher's mound and home plate on a baseball diamond is $60\frac{1}{2}$ feet. Express this distance as an improper fraction. $\frac{121}{2}$ **feet**

For Example 3
a. Express $\frac{9}{8}$ as a mixed number. $1\frac{1}{8}$
b. Express $\frac{7}{2}$ as a mixed number. $3\frac{1}{2}$

MathPASS CD-ROM

This CD-ROM offers a complete, self-paced mathematics curriculum. Each lesson includes a pretest, tutorial, guided practice, and posttest. MathPASS Lessons 13 and 14 are correlated to this Student Edition lesson.
For Windows & Macintosh

CHECK FOR UNDERSTANDING

Communicating Mathematics

Read and study the lesson to answer each question. 1–3. See margin.

1. *Define* improper fraction.

2. *Write* a mixed number and an improper fraction for the model shown.

HANDS-ON MATH

3. *Fold* each of three paper plates into four equal parts to show fourths. Shade nine parts. What improper fraction do the shaded parts represent? What mixed number is equivalent to this improper fraction?

Guided Practice

Express each mixed number as an improper fraction.

4. $2\frac{1}{2}$ $\frac{5}{2}$ 5. $1\frac{2}{5}$ $\frac{7}{5}$ 6. $4\frac{3}{4}$ $\frac{19}{4}$

Express each improper fraction as a mixed number.

7. $\frac{11}{4}$ $2\frac{3}{4}$ 8. $\frac{13}{2}$ $6\frac{1}{2}$ 9. $\frac{24}{6}$ 4

10. Express *nine-fourths* as a mixed number. $2\frac{1}{4}$

EXERCISES

Practice

Express each mixed number as an improper fraction.

11. $3\frac{1}{5}$ $\frac{16}{5}$ 12. $2\frac{3}{8}$ $\frac{19}{8}$ 13. $1\frac{1}{8}$ $\frac{9}{8}$ 14. $4\frac{3}{4}$ $\frac{19}{4}$ 15. $1\frac{7}{9}$ $\frac{16}{9}$

16. $4\frac{5}{6}$ $\frac{29}{6}$ 17. $8\frac{2}{3}$ $\frac{26}{3}$ 18. $5\frac{8}{9}$ $\frac{53}{9}$ 19. $7\frac{3}{5}$ $\frac{38}{5}$ 20. $12\frac{4}{7}$ $\frac{88}{7}$

Express each improper fraction as a mixed number.

21. $\frac{19}{3}$ $6\frac{1}{3}$ 22. $\frac{13}{8}$ $1\frac{5}{8}$ 23. $\frac{15}{8}$ $1\frac{7}{8}$ 24. $\frac{17}{5}$ $3\frac{2}{5}$ 25. $\frac{29}{4}$ $7\frac{1}{4}$

26. $\frac{23}{6}$ $3\frac{5}{6}$ 27. $\frac{19}{9}$ $2\frac{1}{9}$ 28. $\frac{32}{8}$ 4   29. $\frac{25}{7}$ $3\frac{4}{7}$ 30. $\frac{48}{11}$ $4\frac{4}{11}$

31. Express *six and seven-eighths* as an improper fraction. $\frac{55}{8}$

32. Find the mixed number that is equivalent to *thirty-eight ninths.* $4\frac{2}{9}$

Applications and Problem Solving

Real World

33. See margin.

33. **Sports** To win the U.S. Triple Crown, a horse must win the Kentucky Derby, the Preakness Stakes, and the Belmont Stakes. The table shows the distance of each of these races. Express each distance as an improper fraction.

Race	Distance
Kentucky Derby	$1\frac{1}{4}$ mi
Preakness Stakes	$1\frac{3}{16}$ mi
Belmont Stakes	$1\frac{1}{2}$ mi

200   **Chapter 5** Using Number Patterns, Fractions, and Ratios

■ Reteaching the Lesson ■

Activity Have students take turns rolling two number cubes, once for the numerator and again for the denominator. Have them record the fraction. Then, if the fraction is improper, have them express it as a mixed number.

Additional Answer
33. Kentucky Derby—$\frac{5}{4}$; Preakness Stakes—$\frac{19}{16}$; Belmont Stakes—$\frac{3}{2}$

34. *Entertainment* The table shows the running time of some movies.

Movie	Running Time (min)
A	88
B	76
C	84
D	69

$\frac{88}{60}$

a. For each movie, write a fraction that compares the running time to the number of minutes in an hour.

b. Express each fraction as a mixed number in simplest form. **a–b. See Answer Appendix.**

35. *Critical Thinking* Explain, in your own words, how you can determine whether a fraction is less than, equal to, or greater than 1. **See Answer Appendix.**

Mixed Review **36.** Express $\frac{35}{42}$ in simplest form. *(Lesson 5-4)* $\frac{5}{6}$

$\begin{array}{r} 51 \\ \times 4 \\ \hline 204 \end{array}$

37. Find the prime factorization of 204. *(Lesson 5-2)* $2^2 \times 3 \times 17$

38. *Standardized Test Practice* Jalisa is planning to buy baseball cards that cost \$2.27 per pack including tax. How many packs of baseball cards can she buy with \$32? *(Lesson 4-6)* **C**

A 12 **B** 13 **C** 14 **D** 15 **E** Not Here

39. Write *thirteen hundredths* as a decimal. *(Lesson 3-1)* **0.13**

$2.27\sqrt{3200}$

$\begin{array}{r} 14 \\ 3200 \\ 227 \\ \hline 930 \\ -908 \\ \hline 220 \end{array}$

For **Extra Practice**, see page 570.

CHAPTER 5

Mid-Chapter Self Test

State whether each number is divisible by 2, 3, 5, 6, 9, or 10. *(Lesson 5-1)*

1. 435 **3, 5** 2. 827 **none** 3. 1,090 **2, 5, 10**

Find the prime factorization of each number. *(Lesson 5-2)*

4. 36 $2^2 \times 3^2$ 5. 88 $2^3 \times 11$ 6. 105 $3 \times 5 \times 7$

7. Find the GCF of 90 and 36. *(Lesson 5-3)* **18**

8. Express $\frac{12}{28}$ in simplest form. *(Lesson 5-4)* $\frac{3}{7}$

9. *Geography* Eight out of 50 states in the United States are located in the South Atlantic region. Express the ratio 8:50 in simplest form. *(Lesson 5-4)* **4:25**

10. Write a mixed number and an improper fraction for the model shown. *(Lesson 5-5)*

  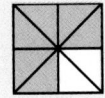

$2\frac{6}{8}$ or $2\frac{3}{4}$ and $\frac{22}{8}$ or $\frac{11}{4}$

Lesson 5-5 Mixed Numbers and Improper Fractions **201**

Extending the Lesson

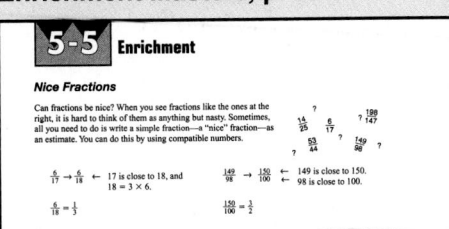
Activity Ask students to bring in recipes that include mixed numbers as measurements. Then have students practice writing the ingredients as improper fractions. Ask them why this skill might be necessary when making the recipe.

Instructional Resources

- *Study Guide Masters*, p. 37
- *Practice Masters*, p. 37
- *Enrichment Masters*, p. 37
- Transparencies 5-6, A and B
- CD-ROM Program

  - Resource Lesson 5-6

Recommended Pacing

Standard	Day 10 of 16
Honors	Day 9 of 15
Block	Day 5 of 8

1 FOCUS

5-Minute Check
(Lesson 5-5)

Express each mixed number as an improper fraction.

1. $3\frac{2}{7}$ $\frac{23}{7}$

2. $1\frac{5}{6}$ $\frac{11}{6}$

Express each improper fraction as a mixed number.

3. $\frac{14}{3}$ $4\frac{2}{3}$

4. $\frac{38}{12}$ $3\frac{1}{6}$

5. What improper fraction represents the mixed number six and five ninths?
$\frac{59}{9}$

The 5-Minute Check is also available on **Transparency 5-6A** for this lesson.

Motivating the Lesson

Hands-On Activity Have students use inch rulers to measure things in the classroom such as doors, desks, books, paper, chalk, and pencils. Have them determine whether it is best to express their measurements in inches, feet, or yards and then measure to the nearest whole unit.

5-6

What you'll learn

You'll learn to measure line segments and objects with a ruler divided in halves, fourths, and eighths.

When am I ever going to use this?

Knowing how to use the customary system can help you measure everyday objects.

Word Wise

inch
foot
yard
mile

Integration: Measurement
Length in the Customary System

Did you know that, for many people, the length of their arm is about 8 times the length of their index finger?

HANDS-ON MINI-LAB

Work with a partner.   📏 tape measure   ∿ string

Try This

- On a long piece of string, mark off eight segments using the length of your index finger. Measure this length to the nearest inch. Record.
- Measure the length of your arm from your shoulder to the end of your index finger to the nearest inch. Record.

Talk About It 1–2. See students' work.

1. How does the total length of the eight segments on the string compare to the actual length of your arm?
2. Divide the actual length of your arm by 8 to get an estimate of the length of your index finger. How does this estimate compare to the actual length of your index finger?

One of the most commonly used customary units of length is the **inch**. Some others are the **foot**, **yard**, and **mile**.

$$1 \text{ foot (ft)} = 12 \text{ inches (in.)}$$

$$1 \text{ yard (yd)} = 3 \text{ feet or } 36 \text{ inches}$$

$$1 \text{ mile (mi)} = 5{,}280 \text{ feet or } 1{,}760 \text{ yards}$$

To change from one unit to another unit in the customary system, you can use either multiplication or division.

Examples

1 4 ft = _?_ in.

Since 1 ft = 12 in., it follows that 4 feet equals 4 × 12, or 48 inches.

4 ft = 48 in.

2 15 ft = _?_ yd

Since 1 yd = 3 ft, it follows that 15 feet equals 15 ÷ 3, or 5 yards.

15 ft = 5 yd

Sometimes you need to measure objects using units less than an inch. Most rulers are separated into eighths.

Using the Mini-Lab You may suggest that once students have marked off one index length, they can fold the string to mark off the other seven lengths instead of laying their finger down each time.

Examples

3 Draw a line segment measuring $1\frac{3}{4}$ inches.

Find $1\frac{3}{4}$ on the ruler. Draw a line segment from 0 to $1\frac{3}{4}$.

INTEGRATION 4 Geometry

a. Find the length of $\overline{AD}$ to the nearest fourth inch.
b. Find the length of $\overline{AE}$ to the nearest eighth inch.
c. Find the length of $\overline{BC}$ to the nearest inch.

> **Study Hint**
> Reading Math The notation $\overline{AB}$ is read as line segment AB.

a. To the nearest fourth inch, the length of $\overline{AD}$ is $2\frac{1}{4}$ inches.

b. To the nearest eighth inch, the length of $\overline{AE}$ is $2\frac{5}{8}$ inches.

c. To the nearest inch, the length of $\overline{BC}$ is $2 - 1$, or 1 inch.

In-Class Examples

For Example 1
6 ft = _?_ in. **72**

For Example 2
36 ft = _?_ yd **12**

For Example 3
Draw a line segment measuring $2\frac{1}{4}$ inches. **Check students' drawings.**

For Example 4
Have students draw three line segments. Have them measure one to the nearest half inch, one to the nearest fourth inch, and the third to the nearest eighth inch. **Check students' drawings.**

Teaching Tip Before Example 3, if your students' rulers are divided into sixteenths, use an overhead transparency to show how to read it.

3 PRACTICE/APPLY

CHECK FOR UNDERSTANDING

Communicating Mathematics

Read and study the lesson to answer each question.

1. *Tell* how you would change 24 inches to feet. **Divide 24 by 12.**

2. *Explain* why $\frac{4}{16}$ inch is the same measure as $\frac{1}{4}$ inch. **See margin.**

HANDS-ON
MATH

3. A cubit is about 18 in. A span is about 8 to 9 in.

3. A *cubit* and a *span* are examples of *nonstandard units* of measurement. A cubit is the measure from a person's elbow to the end of the middle finger. A span is the measure from the end of the thumb to the end of the little finger as the hand is outstretched. *Use* a ruler or tape measure to find the approximate length of your cubit and your span in the customary system.

Lesson 5-6 Integration: Measurement Length in the Customary System **203**

Check for Understanding

If students need additional practice or instruction after completing Exercises 1–10, one of these options may be helpful.
- Extra Practice, see p. 570
- Reteaching Activity
- *Transition Booklet*, pp. 29–30
- *Study Guide Masters*, p. 37
- *Practice Masters*, p. 37

Additional Answer
2. In simplest form, $\frac{4}{16} = \frac{1}{4}$.

Reteaching the Lesson

Activity Write lengths, such as $1\frac{3}{8}$ inches, $2\frac{1}{4}$ inches, and so on, on the chalkboard. Have pairs of students create a design by taking turns drawing line segments of the given lengths. Have them use all of the segments at least once.

Error Analysis
Watch for students who read a ruler incorrectly.
Prevent by showing them how the lengths of the notches correspond to the fractional unit of measure.

Guided Practice

Complete.

4. 7 ft = $\underline{?}$ in. **84**

5. 36 in. = $\underline{?}$ ft **3**

Draw a line segment of each length.

6. $1\frac{1}{8}$ inches

7. $2\frac{1}{4}$ inches

Find the length of each line segment or object to the nearest half, fourth, or eighth inch.

8. ━━━━━━━━━━
$2\frac{1}{4}$ in.

9.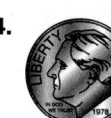
$\frac{7}{8}$ in.

10. *Auto Mechanics* Mrs. Huang uses wrenches of different sizes when working on cars. She needs to choose a wrench that will tighten the bolt shown. What size wrench will she need: $\frac{1}{2}$ inch, $\frac{5}{8}$ inch, or $\frac{3}{4}$ inch? $\frac{1}{2}$ in.

EXERCISES

Practice

Complete.

11. 60 in. = $\underline{?}$ ft **5**

12. 3 ft = $\underline{?}$ yd **1**

13. 3 yd = $\underline{?}$ in. **108**

14. 78 in. = $\underline{?}$ ft **6$\frac{1}{2}$**

15. 2 mi = $\underline{?}$ ft **10,560**

16. 225 ft = $\underline{?}$ yd **75**

Draw a line segment of each length. **17–22. See Answer Appendix.**

17. $1\frac{1}{4}$ inches

18. $1\frac{1}{2}$ inches

19. $\frac{3}{8}$ inch

20. 2 inches

21. $1\frac{5}{8}$ inches

22. $2\frac{1}{2}$ inches

Find the length of each line segment or object to the nearest half, fourth, or eighth inch.

23. ━━━━━
$\frac{1}{2}$ in.

24. (dime) $\frac{3}{4}$ in.

25. ⊓ $\frac{1}{2}$ in.

26. (paper clip) $1\frac{3}{8}$ in.

27. ━━━━━━ $1\frac{1}{4}$ in.

28. ━━━━━━━━━━ $2\frac{1}{2}$ in.

29. Which is greater: 16 inches or $1\frac{1}{2}$ feet? **$1\frac{1}{2}$ ft**

30. Order the measurements 1 yard, 24 inches, 4 feet, and 40 inches from least to greatest. **24 in., 1 yd, 40 in., 4 ft**

31. Order the measurements $\frac{1}{2}$ inch, $\frac{1}{8}$ inch, 1 inch, and $\frac{1}{4}$ inch from greatest to least. **See margin.**

32. Postal Service The first animated character to be featured on a 32-cent stamp was issued May 22, 1997, by the United States Postal Service. What is the measure of the width and height of the stamp to the nearest eighth inch? **width: 1 in., height: $1\frac{5}{8}$ in. or $1\frac{1}{2}$ in.**

33. Geometry Find the measure of each line segment.

a. $\overline{MN}$ **1 in.**   b. $\overline{MO}$ **$1\frac{3}{4}$ in.**   c. $\overline{MP}$ **$2\frac{1}{8}$ in.**

d. $\overline{MR}$ **$3\frac{7}{8}$ in.**   e. $\overline{NS}$ **3 in.**   f. $\overline{NO}$ **$\frac{3}{4}$ in.**

34. Critical Thinking How many eighth inches are in a foot? How many fourth inches are in a yard? **96 eighths; 144 fourths**

Mixed Review

35. Express $5\frac{3}{8}$ as an improper fraction. *(Lesson 5-5)* **$\frac{43}{8}$**

36. Find the greatest common factor of 45 and 75. *(Lesson 5-3)* **15**

37. Standardized Test Practice The sides of a regulation football field measure 120 yards and about 53.3 yards. About how far does a person have to walk to go all the way around a regulation football field? *(Lesson 4-4)* **C**

A 173.3 yd   **B** 246.6 yd   **C** 346.6 yd   **D** 6,396 yd

For **Extra Practice**, see page 570.

38. Solve the equation $n = 3.569 + 781.2$. *(Lesson 3-6)* **784.769**

MATH > IN THE MEDIA

Peanuts

1. Do you agree or disagree with the method Sally used to measure Snoopy's mouth? Explain. **See students' work.**

2. Tell how Sally got a measurement of 3 inches. **Subtract 6 in. from 9 in.**

■ Extending the Lesson ■

Enrichment Masters, p. 37

MATH > IN THE MEDIA

Tell students that measuring from one point to another on the ruler may be more accurate than measuring from the zero end. The end of a ruler can get broken or shortened, causing the first inch to be less than one inch.

Closing Activity

Modeling Have pairs of students find classroom items. Then have them measure the items to the nearest $\frac{1}{4}$ inch and $\frac{1}{8}$ inch and make a list of the items and their measurements. Encourage student pairs to compare lists.

Practice Masters, p. 37

5-6 Practice

Name_____ Date_____

Integration: Measurement
Length in the Customary System

Draw a line segment of each length.

1. $3\frac{1}{2}$ inches _____
2. $1\frac{5}{8}$ inches _____
3. $\frac{3}{4}$ inch _____
4. $4\frac{1}{4}$ inches _____
5. $2\frac{5}{8}$ inches _____
6. $3\frac{7}{8}$ inches _____

Find the length of each line segment to the nearest fourth inch.

7. _____ $2\frac{3}{4}$ inches
8. _____ $3\frac{1}{2}$ inches
9. _____ $4\frac{1}{4}$ inches
10. _____ $1\frac{3}{4}$ inches

Find the length of each object to the nearest eighth inch.

11. $1\frac{3}{8}$ in.   12. $2\frac{3}{4}$ in.

13. 3 in.   14. $1\frac{5}{8}$ in.

© Glencoe/McGraw-Hill   T 37   *Mathematics: Applications and Connections, Course 1*

Examine Each package of plates contains 10 plates. So, eight packages will contain 10×8, or 80 plates.

Each package of napkins contains 16 napkins. So, five packages will contain 16×5, or 80 napkins.

Each package of cups contains 8 cups. So, ten packages will contain 8×10, or 80 cups.

Since he will have exactly 80 of each item, the answer is correct.

CHECK FOR UNDERSTANDING

Communicating Mathematics

Read and study the lesson to answer each question.

1. *Define* least common multiple. **See margin.**

2. *Explain* to a classmate how to find the LCM of 8 and 12. **See margin.**

HANDS-ON MATH

3. Using paper strips, make a model to find the LCM of 5 and 6. What is the LCM of 5 and 6? **See student's work; 30**

Guided Practice

Determine whether the first number is a multiple of the second number.

4. 40; 5 **yes**   5. 32; 8 **yes**   6. 133; 3 **no**

Find the LCM for each set of numbers.

7. 3, 9 **9**   8. 5, 12 **60**   9. 2, 11 **22**   10. 9, 12, 15 **180**

11. 4 packages of hot dogs, 5 packages of hot dog buns, 2 packages of plates

11. *Party Planning* Refer to the chart shown. What is the least number of packages of each item that should be purchased so that there are the same number of hot dogs, hot dog buns, and plates?

The Food Shop	
Item	**Quantity**
Hot Dogs	10/pkg
Hot Dog Buns	8/pkg
Plates	20/pkg

EXERCISES

Practice

Determine whether the first number is a multiple of the second number.

12. 15; 9 **no**   13. 30; 6 **yes**   14. 14; 8 **no**

15. 32; 16 **yes**   16. 27; 4 **no**   17. 35; 3 **no**

18. 84; 7 **yes**   19. 115; 3 **no**   20. 142; 7 **no**

Find the LCM for each set of numbers. 31. 280   32. 224

21. 6, 12 **12**   22. 5, 8 **40**   23. 3, 7 **21**   24. 18, 24 **72**

25. 16, 20 **80**   26. 12, 21 **84**   27. 13, 16 **208**   28. 21, 28 **84**

29. 4, 6, 9 **36**   30. 15, 25, 75 **75**   31. 10, 35, 40   32. 14, 28, 32

33. What is the least common multiple of 3, 9, and 18? **18**

34. Find the LCM of 7, 8, and 28. **56**

Writing Fractions as Decimals

What you'll learn

You'll learn to express fractions as terminating and repeating decimals.

When am I ever going to use this?

Knowing how to express numbers in different forms can help you interpret weather statistics.

Word Wise

repeating decimal
bar notation

Home gardening has become a popular hobby. The top five vegetables grown in home gardens are tomatoes, peppers, onions, cucumbers, and beans. An estimated $\frac{2}{5}$ of home gardeners grow beans.

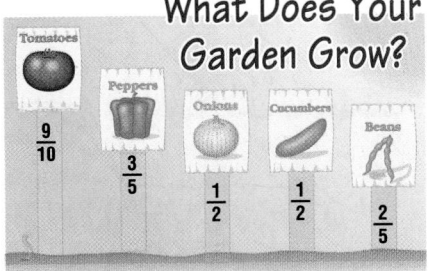

What Does Your Garden Grow?

Tomatoes $\frac{9}{10}$ Peppers $\frac{3}{5}$ Onions $\frac{1}{2}$ Cucumbers $\frac{1}{2}$ Beans $\frac{2}{5}$

Source: National Gardening Association, Gallup Organization

Any fraction can be written as a decimal using division.

$\frac{2}{5}$ means $2 \div 5$.

$$\begin{array}{r} 0.4 \\ 5\overline{)2.0} \\ -20 \\ \hline 0 \end{array}$$

Write 2 as 2.0.
Place the decimal point in the quotient. Divide as with whole numbers.

The fraction $\frac{2}{5}$ can be written as 0.4. A decimal like 0.4 is called a *terminating decimal* because the division ends, or terminates, when the remainder is zero.

Example ● **1** Express $\frac{1}{8}$ as a decimal.

$$\begin{array}{r} 0.125 \\ 8\overline{)1.000} \\ -8 \\ \hline 20 \\ -16 \\ \hline 40 \\ -40 \\ \hline 0 \end{array}$$ *Divide 1 by 8.*

Therefore, $\frac{1}{8} = 0.125$.

Lesson 5-10 Writing Fractions as Decimals **217**

Motivating the Lesson

Problem Solving Ask students how they would determine which basket of vegetables weighs more than $5\frac{1}{2}$ pounds.
- a 5.46-lb basket of tomatoes
- a 5.64-lb basket of peppers

5-10 Lesson Notes

Instructional Resources
- *Study Guide Masters,* p. 41
- *Practice Masters,* p. 41
- *Enrichment Masters,* p. 41
- Transparencies 5-10, A and B
- *Assessment and Evaluation Masters,* p. 128
- *Science and Math Lab Manual,* pp. 9–12
- *Technology Masters,* p. 9
- CD-ROM Program
  - Resource Lesson 5-10

Recommended Pacing	
Standard	Day 14 of 16
Honors	Day 13 of 15
Block	Day 7 of 8

1 FOCUS

5-Minute Check *(Lesson 5-9)*

Express each decimal as a fraction or mixed number in simplest form.

1. 0.4 $\frac{2}{5}$
2. 0.45 $\frac{9}{20}$
3. 3.675 $3\frac{27}{40}$
4. 22.52 $22\frac{13}{25}$
5. 17.8 $17\frac{4}{5}$

The 5-Minute Check is also available on **Transparency 5-10A** for this lesson.

2 TEACH

Transparency 5-10B contains a teaching aid for this lesson.

Reading Mathematics Have students look up the word "terminate" in the dictionary. Ask them to think of antonyms of the word. What other terms could be used for "repeating" decimal? Point out that a decimal equivalent of a fraction will always terminate or repeat. However, there are decimals such as π (3.14159265...) that do neither.

Teaching Tip When changing fractions to decimals, make sure students divide the numerator by the denominator rather than dividing the denominator by the numerator.

3 PRACTICE/APPLY

Check for Understanding

If students need additional practice or instruction after completing Exercises 1–8, one of these options may be helpful.
- Extra Practice, see p. 572
- Reteaching Activity
- *Study Guide Masters*, p. 41
- *Practice Masters*, p. 41

***Study Guide Masters*, p. 41**

Not all fractions are terminating decimals. Decimals like 0.5555555... are called **repeating decimals** because the digits repeat. The **bar notation** $0.\overline{5}$ can be used to indicate that the 5 digit repeats forever. Several repeating decimals are shown.

$0.433333333... = 0.4\overline{3}$ *The digit 3 repeats.*
$2.121212121... = 2.\overline{12}$ *The digits 12 repeat.*
$13.567567567... = 13.\overline{567}$ *The digits 567 repeat.*

Examples

2 Express $\frac{3}{11}$ as a decimal. Use bar notation to show a repeating decimal.

Method 1 Use paper and pencil.

```
   0.2727...
11)3.0000      Divide 3 by 11.
  −22
   80
  −77
   30
  −22
   80        The pattern will
  −77        continue.
    3
```

Method 2 Use a calculator.

3 ÷ 11 = 0.27272727

Therefore, $\frac{3}{11} = 0.2727...$ or $0.\overline{27}$.

3 **Earth Science** The average annual precipitation in Georgia is about $48\frac{3}{5}$ inches. How many inches of precipitation does Georgia average each month?

Divide $48\frac{3}{5}$ by 12. First, express $48\frac{3}{5}$ as a decimal.

48 + 3 ÷ 5 = 48.6 $48\frac{3}{5} = 48 + \frac{3}{5}$

Then divide by 12.

48.6 ÷ 12 = 4.05

Georgia averages about 4.05 inches of precipitation each month.

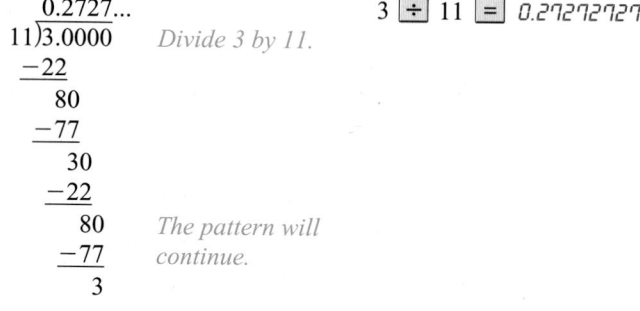

CHECK FOR UNDERSTANDING

Communicating Mathematics

1–2. See Answer Appendix.

Guided Practice

Read and study the lesson to answer each question.

1. *Explain* to a classmate how to express a fraction as a decimal.

2. *Give* an example of a terminating decimal and a repeating decimal.

Write each repeating decimal using bar notation.

3. 0.4444444... **0.$\overline{4}$**   4. 10.34343434... **10.$\overline{34}$**

218   Chapter 5 Using Number Patterns, Fractions, and Ratios

Reteaching the Lesson

Activity Have students work in pairs to write a fraction and its decimal equivalent. First, have them factor the denominator. If the denominator has factors other than 2 or 5, the decimal will not terminate. Then have them divide, knowing what type of decimal to expect.

Error Analysis

Watch for students who place the bar notation over more digits than actually repeat.

Prevent by reminding students to determine the pattern of repetition before placing the bar notation.

Express each fraction or mixed number as a decimal. Use bar notation to show a repeating decimal.

5. $\frac{3}{8}$ **0.375** 6. $2\frac{4}{11}$ **2.$\overline{36}$** 7. $\frac{7}{12}$ **0.58$\overline{3}$**

8. Express the fraction $\frac{7}{8}$ as a decimal. **0.875**

EXERCISES

Practice **Write each repeating decimal using bar notation.**

9. 0.77777777... **0.$\overline{7}$** 10. 1.33333333... **1.$\overline{3}$** 11. 2.45454545... **2.$\overline{45}$**

12. 17.0909090... **17.$\overline{09}$** 13. 0.83183183... **0.8$\overline{31}$** 14. 5.01289289... **5.01$\overline{289}$**

Express each fraction or mixed number as a decimal. Use bar notation to show a repeating decimal.

15. $\frac{3}{4}$ **0.75** 16. $4\frac{1}{5}$ **4.2** 17. $\frac{2}{9}$ **0.$\overline{2}$** 18. $2\frac{5}{8}$ **2.625**

19. $\frac{5}{11}$ **0.$\overline{45}$** 20. $7\frac{1}{3}$ **7.$\overline{3}$** 21. $\frac{11}{12}$ **0.91$\overline{6}$** 22. $\frac{7}{10}$ **0.7**

23. Express *four and one-eleventh* as a decimal. **4.$\overline{09}$**

24. Find the decimal equivalent of the fraction *four fifteenths*. **0.2$\overline{6}$**

Applications and Problem Solving

25. *Food* A chocolate drop weighs $\frac{1}{6}$ ounce. Find the decimal equivalent of $\frac{1}{6}$ ounce. **0.1$\overline{6}$ oz**

26. *Geography* Japan is a group of islands in the Pacific Ocean. Tokyo is Japan's largest city. The city receives about $5\frac{1}{8}$ inches of rain each month. How many inches of rain does Tokyo receive in a year? **61.5 in.**

27. *Working on the* CHAPTER Project Refer to the table you made on page 196 in Exercise 36.
   a. Express each of your fractions as a decimal. If necessary, round to the nearest hundredth. Which of your magazines has the highest decimal portion devoted to articles? to advertisements? Which has the lowest decimal portion devoted to articles? to advertisements?
   b. Make a bar graph for the set of data. **a–b. See students' work.**

28. *Critical Thinking* Tell how you can determine whether a fraction in simplest form will be expressed as a terminating or repeating decimal by looking at the denominator. **See margin.**

Mixed Review

29. 29$\frac{3}{4}$

29. *Earth Science* Mercury moves in its orbit at a speed of 29.75 miles per second. Write this speed as a mixed number in simplest form. *(Lesson 5-9)*

30. Find the LCM of 24 and 30. *(Lesson 5-7)* **120**

31. *Standardized Test Practice* Express 24 as a product of primes. *(Lesson 5-2)* **D**
   A $2 \times 4 \times 3$ **B** $2 \times 2 \times 2 \times 6$
   C $2 \times 2 \times 8$ **D** $2 \times 2 \times 2 \times 3$

For **Extra Practice**, see page 572.

32. Find $2 + 17 - 16 \div 4$. *(Lesson 1-4)* **15**

Extending the Lesson

Enrichment Masters, p. 41

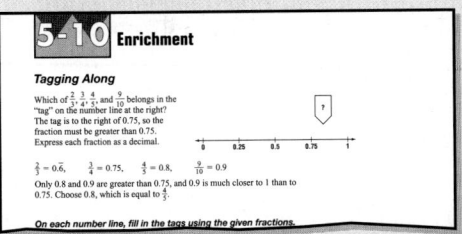

Activity Have small groups of students create a table of fractions and their decimal equivalents. Have students look for patterns in families of repeating decimals, such as $\frac{1}{9} = 0.1\overline{1}$, $\frac{2}{9} = 0.2\overline{2}$, $\frac{3}{9} = 0.3\overline{3}$.

Study Guide and Assessment

interNET CONNECTION Chapter Review For additional review, visit: www.glencoe.com/sec/math/mac/mathnet

Vocabulary

Vocabulary

This section provides a listing of the new terms, properties, and phrases that were introduced in this chapter. Have students define each term and provide an example or two of it, if appropriate.

Understanding and Using the Vocabulary

These exercises check students' understanding of the terms by using a variety of verbal formats including matching, completion, and true/false.

Glossaries A complete glossary of terms appears on pages 642–648. The glossary also appears in Spanish on pages 649–656.

Additional Answer

8. An inch is the most commonly used unit of length. 1 foot = 12 inches; 1 yard = 3 feet, or 36 inches; 1 mile = 5,280 feet, or 1,760 yards.

After completing this chapter, you should be able to define each term, concept, or phrase and give an example or two of each.

Number and Operations
bar notation (p. 218)
common multiples (p. 206)
composite number (pp. 181, 182)
equivalent fractions (p. 193)
factor tree (p. 183)
greatest common factor (GCF) (p. 188)
improper fraction (p. 198)

least common denominator (LCD) (p. 210)
least common multiple (LCM) (p. 206)
mixed number (p. 198)
multiple (p. 206)
prime factorization (p. 183)
prime number (pp. 181, 182)
ratio (pp. 191, 193)
repeating decimal (p. 218)
simplest form (p. 194)
terminating decimal (p. 214)

Measurement
foot (p. 202)
inch (p. 202)
mile (p. 202)
yard (p. 202)

Probability
experimental (p. 197)

Problem Solving
make a list (p. 186)

Understanding and Using the Vocabulary

Choose the letter of the term that best matches each phrase.

1. a comparison of two numbers by division **g**
2. the product of a number and any whole number **a**
3. a number having more than two factors **e**
4. numbers showing the sum of a whole number and a fraction **h**
5. a number having exactly two factors, 1 and itself **b**
6. the LCM of 15 and 9 **c**
7. the greatest common factor of 56 and 70 **f**

a. multiple
b. prime number
c. 45
d. improper fraction
e. composite number
f. 14
g. ratio
h. mixed number

In Your Own Words

8. *Explain* the relationship between inch, foot, yard, and mile. **See margin.**

Objectives & Examples

Upon completing this chapter, you should be able to:

● use divisibility rules for 2, 3, 5, 6, 9, and 10 *(Lesson 5-1)*

Is 630 divisible by 2, 3, 5, 6, 9, or 10?
It is divisible by 2, 3, 5, 6, 9, and 10.

Review Exercises

Use these exercises to review and prepare for the chapter test.

State whether each number is divisible by 2, 3, 5, 6, 9, or 10.

9. 51 **3**
10. 300 **2, 3, 5, 6, 10**
11. 423 **3, 9**
12. 1,250 **2, 5, 10**

MindJogger Videoquizzes

MindJogger Videoquizzes provide an alternative review of concepts presented in this chapter. Students work in teams to answer questions, gaining points for correct answers. The questions are presented in three rounds.
Round 1 Concepts–5 questions
Round 2 Skills–4 questions
Round 3 Problem Solving–4 questions

Objectives & Examples

● find the prime factorization of a composite number *(Lesson 5-2)*

The prime factorization of 16 is
$2 \times 2 \times 2 \times 2$ or 2^4.

● find the greatest common factor of two or more numbers *(Lesson 5-3)*

Find the GCF of 12 and 18.
factors of 12: 1, 2, 3, 4, 6, 12
factors of 18: 1, 2, 3, 6, 9, 18
The GCF of 12 and 18 is 6.

● express fractions and ratios in simplest form *(Lesson 5-4)*

Write $\frac{12}{36}$ in simplest form.
factors of 12: 1, 2, 3, 4, 6, 12
factors of 36: 1, 2, 3, 4, 6, 9, 12, 18, 36
The GCF of 12 and 36 is 12.

$$\frac{12}{36} = \frac{1}{3}$$
(÷12)

In simplest form, the fraction is $\frac{1}{3}$.

● express mixed numbers as improper fractions and vice versa *(Lesson 5-5)*

Express $1\frac{2}{3}$ as an improper fraction.
$$1\frac{2}{3} = \frac{(1 \times 3) + 2}{3}$$
$$= \frac{5}{3}$$

Review Exercises

Tell whether each number is *prime*, *composite*, or *neither*.

13. 37 prime
14. 78 composite
15. 1 neither
16. 47 prime

Find the prime factorization of each number.

17. 54 2×3^3
18. 75 3×5^2
19. 124 $2^2 \times 31$
20. 36 $2^2 \times 3^2$

Find the GCF of each set of numbers by making a list.

21. 30, 36 **6**
22. 39, 26 **13**

Find the GCF of each set of numbers by using prime factorization.

23. 18, 28 **2**
24. 12, 24, 30 **6**

Replace each ■ with a number so that the fractions are equivalent.

25. $\frac{5}{6} = \frac{\blacksquare}{24}$ **20**
26. $\frac{15}{35} = \frac{3}{\blacksquare}$ **7**

State whether each fraction or ratio is in simplest form. If not, write each fraction or ratio in simplest form.

27. $\frac{15}{18}$ no; $\frac{5}{6}$
28. 2 out of 9 **yes**
29. 14 to 16 no; 7 to 8
30. $\frac{24}{28}$ no; $\frac{6}{7}$

Express each mixed number as an improper fraction.

31. $3\frac{3}{5}$ $\frac{18}{5}$
32. $4\frac{2}{7}$ $\frac{30}{7}$

Express each improper fraction as a mixed number.

33. $\frac{19}{5}$ $3\frac{4}{5}$
34. $\frac{36}{7}$ $5\frac{1}{7}$

Chapter 5 Study Guide and Assessment **221**

Objectives & Examples

This section reviews the skills and concepts of the chapter and shows completely worked examples.

Review Exercises

These exercises provide practice for the corresponding objectives.

Assessment and Evaluation Masters, pp. 115–116

Name_____ Date_____

5

Chapter 5 Test, Form 1B

1. 216 is divisible by which of these numbers?
   A. 2, 3, 5, 6, and 9   B. 2, 3, 6, and 9
   C. 5, 6, and 10   D. 9 and 10   1. __B__

2. 144 is divisible by which of these numbers?
   A. 2, 3, 5, 6, and 9   B. 3, 6, and 10
   C. 9 and 10   D. 2, 3, 6, and 9   2. __D__

3. Which numbers are factors of 54?
   A. 2, 3, 6, and 12   B. 5, 6, and 9
   C. 10 and 27   D. 2, 3, 9, 18, and 27   3. __D__

4. Find the prime factorization of 84.
   A. 3 × 4 × 7   B. 2 × 2 × 3 × 7
   C. 2 × 42   D. 7 × 12   4. __B__

5. Which number is prime?
   A. 15   B. 28   C. 31   D. 33   5. __C__

6. What is the GCF of 28 and 36?
   A. 2   B. 4   C. 7   D. 9   6. __B__

7. What is the GCF of 8, 12, and 30?
   A. 2   B. 3   C. 4   D. 6   7. __A__

8. Which fraction is in simplest form?
   A. $\frac{18}{27}$ B. $\frac{50}{100}$ C. $\frac{32}{34}$ D. $\frac{9}{11}$ 8. __D__

9. Which ratio is in simplest form?
   A. 10 to 18   B. 27 to 36   C. 15 to 19   D. 18 to 20   9. __C__

10. Which fraction is *not* in simplest form?
    A. $\frac{7}{18}$ B. $\frac{9}{50}$ C. $\frac{7}{100}$ D. $\frac{11}{12}$ 10. __B__

11. Express $3\frac{2}{5}$ as an improper fraction.
    A. $\frac{17}{5}$ B. $\frac{5}{3}$ C. $\frac{10}{5}$ D. $\frac{30}{5}$ 11. __A__

12. Express $\frac{35}{4}$ as a mixed number.
    A. $8\frac{3}{4}$ B. $8\frac{4}{4}$ C. $\frac{3}{4}$ D. $8\frac{3}{35}$ 12. __A__

13. Find the length of the segment to the nearest fourth inch.   13. __D__

    A. 2 in.   B. $2\frac{3}{4}$ in.   C. $1\frac{3}{4}$ in.   D. $2\frac{1}{4}$ in.

© Glencoe/McGraw-Hill   115   *Mathematics: Applications and Connections, Course 1*

5

Chapter 5 Test, Form 1B (continued)

14. Complete: 18 in. = __?__ ft.
    A. $\frac{1}{2}$ B. 1   C. $1\frac{1}{2}$ D. 2   14. __C__

15. Find the LCM for 18 and 24.
    A. 36   B. 48   C. 54   D. 72   15. __D__

16. Which number is a multiple of 18?
    A. 9   B. 36   C. 52   D. 6   16. __B__

17. What is the LCD for $\frac{5}{6}$ and $\frac{4}{7}$?
    A. 2   B. 4   C. 12   D. 24   17. __C__

18. Which sentence is true?
    A. $\frac{2}{3} = \frac{4}{5}$ B. $\frac{2}{3}\frac{1}{3} < \frac{4}{3}$ C. $\frac{2}{3}\frac{1}{3} > \frac{4}{3}$ D. $\frac{4}{5} > \frac{2}{3}\frac{1}{3}$ 18. __C__

19. Which fraction is the greatest?
    A. $\frac{3}{4}$ B. $\frac{7}{8}$ C. $\frac{13}{16}$ D. $\frac{24}{32}$ 19. __B__

20. Express 0.48 as a fraction in simplest form.
    A. $\frac{48}{100}$ B. $\frac{24}{50}$ C. $\frac{12}{25}$ D. $\frac{12}{50}$ 20. __C__

21. Express 3.64 as a fraction in simplest form.
    A. $3\frac{16}{25}$ B. $3\frac{32}{50}$ C. $3\frac{64}{100}$ D. $\frac{16}{25}$ 21. __A__

22. Express $6\frac{11}{20}$ as a decimal.
    A. 6.5   B. 6.55   C. 0.55   D. 6.11   22. __B__

23. Express $\frac{5}{18}$ as a decimal. Use bar notation to show a repeating decimal.
    A. 0.27   B. 0.2̄7̄   C. 0.027   D. 27.7   23. __A__

24. At an ice cream store, three flavors of ice cream are available: chocolate, vanilla, and strawberry. Three types of toppings are available: marshmallow, pineapple, and hot fudge. If you choose one ice cream and one topping, how many combinations are possible?
    A. 3   B. 9   C. 6   D. 5   24. __B__

25. Raleigh has two lengths of cord for making bead bracelets. One is 18 inches long, and the other is 45 inches long. He wants to cut both cords into pieces, all having the same length. What is the longest length each cord can be?
    A. 3 in.   B. 6 in.   C. 5 in.   D. 9 in.   25. __D__

© Glencoe/McGraw-Hill   116   *Mathematics: Applications and Connections, Course 1*

Assessment and Evaluation

Six forms of Chapter 5 Test are available in the *Assessment and Evaluation Masters* as shown in the chart.

Chapter 5 Test, Form 1B, is shown at the right. Chapter 5 Test, Form 2B, is shown on the next page.

1A	Multiple Choice	Honors
1B	Multiple Choice	Average
1C	Multiple Choice	Basic
2A	Free Response	Honors
2B	Free Response	Average
2C	Free Response	Basic

Assessment and Evaluation Masters, pp. 121–122

Objectives & Examples

● measure line segments and objects with a ruler divided in halves, fourths, and eighths *(Lesson 5-6)*

Draw a line segment measuring $1\frac{3}{8}$ inches.

───────────

● find the least common multiple of two or more numbers *(Lesson 5-7)*

Find the LCM of 8 and 12.

multiples of 8: 0, 8, 16, 24, 32, …

multiples of 12: 0, 12, 24, 36, …

The LCM of 8 and 12 is 24.

● compare and order fractions *(Lesson 5-8)*

$\frac{3}{7}$ ● $\frac{4}{9}$ *The LCM of 7 and 9 is 63.*

$\frac{3}{7} = \frac{27}{63}$ (×9) $\frac{4}{9} = \frac{28}{63}$ (×7)

Since $\frac{27}{63} < \frac{28}{63}, \frac{3}{7} < \frac{4}{9}$.

● express terminating decimals as fractions in simplest form *(Lesson 5-9)*

Express 1.72 as a mixed number in simplest form.

$1.72 = 1\frac{72}{100}$ or $1\frac{18}{25}$

● express fractions as terminating and repeating decimals *(Lesson 5-10)*

Express $\frac{5}{6}$ as a decimal.

5 ÷ 6 = *0.833333…*

$\frac{5}{6} = 0.8\overline{3}$

Review Exercises

Draw a line segment of each length.

35. $1\frac{3}{4}$ inches   36. $2\frac{7}{8}$ inches

35–36. See Answer Appendix.

37. Find the length of the line segment to the nearest half, fourth, or eighth inch.

───── $1\frac{3}{4}$ in.

38. Determine whether 82 is a multiple of 12. **no**

Find the LCM for each set of numbers.

39. 15, 25 **75**   40. 28, 35 **140**

41. 7, 12 **84**   42. 12, 15, 20 **60**

Find the LCD for each pair of fractions.

43. $\frac{3}{5}, \frac{1}{4}$ **20**   44. $\frac{5}{6}, \frac{7}{8}$ **24**

Replace each ● with < , > , or = to make a true sentence.

45. $\frac{5}{9}$ ● $\frac{6}{11}$ **>**   46. $\frac{8}{12}$ ● $\frac{6}{9}$ **=**

Express each decimal as a fraction or mixed number in simplest form.

47. 0.8   48. 0.04

49. 3.65   50. 7.36

47. $\frac{4}{5}$ 48. $\frac{1}{25}$ 49. $3\frac{13}{20}$ 50. $7\frac{9}{25}$

Express each fraction or mixed number as a decimal. Use bar notation to show a repeating decimal.

51. $\frac{5}{8}$ **0.625**   52. $1\frac{5}{11}$ **1.45̄**

222   Chapter 5 Using Number Patterns, Fractions, and Ratios

Test and Review Software

You may use this software, a combination of an item generator and item bank, to create your own tests or worksheets. Types of items include free response, multiple choice, short answer, and open ended.

CD-ROM Program

The CD-ROM Program contains an Assessment Game whose questions review the concepts in this chapter.

Applications & Problem Solving

53. *Make a List* When school is cancelled because of snow, the superintendent has to call four radio stations to let them know. How many ways can the superintendent make the phone calls? *(Lesson 5-3A)*

54. *Landscaping* Brandon used $10\frac{1}{4}$ bags of mulch around the flower beds in his yard. Write $10\frac{1}{4}$ as an improper fraction. *(Lesson 5-5)* $\frac{41}{4}$

55. *Money Matters* Zu-Wang worked $6\frac{2}{5}$ hours last week. If he earns \$4.75 per hour, how much did he earn last week? *(Lesson 5-10)* **\$30.40**

53. 24 ways

56. *School* The graph shows the results of a survey on field trip preferences. Where do more students prefer to go on their field trip? *(Lesson 5-8)* **ZOO**

Zoo	$\frac{9}{20}$
Museum	$\frac{1}{4}$
State Capitol	$\frac{3}{10}$

Alternative Assessment

● *Open Ended*

Suppose you are buying party supplies for a younger sibling's birthday party. You find a package of 6 decks of cards, a package of 8 candy bars, and a package of 4 cans of modeling dough. How can you determine the least number of packages of cards, candy, and modeling dough to buy so that you have the same number of each? **Find the LCM of 4, 6, and 8.**

Find the least number of packages to buy so that you will have the same number of each item. If there will be 15 children at the party, what is the least number of packages of each item you would have to buy? **See margin.**

A practice test for Chapter 5 is provided on page 599.

● *Completing the* CHAPTER Project

Use the following checklist to make sure your report for your boss is complete.

- ☑ The table showing the number of pages of articles, ads, and table of contents in each issue of your magazines is included.

- ☑ The data comparing the number of pages of articles, ads, and table of contents to the total number of pages in each magazine is correct.

- ☑ The data showing what portion of each magazine is devoted to articles and ads is correct.

- ☑ The bar graphs of the data are included.

PORTFOLIO   Select one of the assignments from this chapter and place it in your portfolio. Attach a note to it explaining why you selected it.

Applications & Problem Solving

This section provides additional practice in solving real-world problems that involve the skills of this chapter.

Alternative Assessment

The *Open Ended* section provides students with a performance assessment opportunity to evaluate their work and understanding.

CHAPTER Project

Students should complete the final stages of their project and prepare a class demonstration of their results. A scoring guide for the project is available in the *Investigations and Projects Masters*, p. 35.

PORTFOLIO   Students should add to their portfolios at this time.

Assessment and Evaluation Masters, p. 125

Name_____ Date _____

Chapter 5 Performance Assessment

Instructions: Demonstrate your knowledge by giving a clear, concise solution to each problem. Be sure to include all relevant drawings and justify your answers. You may show your solutions in more than one way or investigate beyond the requirements of the problems.

1. Mr. Berkowitz is planning the half-time show for the first football game of the season. He expects 120 band members this year and needs to determine possible marching formations.

  a. Tell how to find the prime factorization of a number.

  b. Find the prime factorization of 120. Show your work.

  c. Give all possible rectangular formations the band can make.

  d. At one point in the show, the woodwind and brass sections of the band will march toward each other from the end zones in rows across the field of equal length. If there are 30 woodwinds and 50 in the brass section, what is the longest row possible? What is this number called?

  e. In the finale, band members in rows of 10 perform with members of the flag corp in rows of 6. What is the LCM of 6 and 10? If he wishes to use the same number of band members as flag corp members, what is the least number of rows of each that he can use?

2. A restaurant owner is planning a menu for the next day.

  a. She has $2\frac{5}{6}$ apple pies left. If each serving is one-sixth of a pie, how many servings does she have left? Write the answer as an improper fraction and as a decimal.

  b. She sells about 50 servings of pecan pie a day. How many pecan pies does she usually sell a day?

  c. If she is sold out of pecan pie, how many pies should she order for the next day?

  d. Write a word problem that uses mixed numbers. Solve and give the meaning of the answer.

3. Dominique is trimming a picture to fit in a frame. The frame measures 0.75 foot by 0.5 foot.

  a. Change the decimals to fractions.

  b. What are the measurements of the frame in inches? Show how you determine this.

Additional Answer for the Open Ended item

The LCM is 24. So, 4 packages of cards, 3 packages of candy, and 6 packages of modeling dough should be purchased. If 15 children attend the party, 3 packages of cards, 2 packages of candy, and 4 packages of modeling dough should be purchased.

◉ Performance Assessment

Additional performance assessment tasks for this chapter are included in the *Assessment and Evaluation Masters* on page 125. A scoring guide is also provided on page 137.

The Standardized Test Practice may be used to help students prepare for standardized tests. The test items are written in the same style as those in state proficiency tests and standardized tests like CAT, CTBS, ITBS, MAT, SAT, and Terra Nova. The test items cover skills and concepts covered up to this point in the text.

The pages can be used as an overnight assessment. After students have completed the pages, discuss how each problem can be solved, or provide copies of the solutions from the *Solutions Manual*.

Section One: Multiple Choice

There are thirteen multiple-choice questions in this section. Choose the best answer. If a correct answer is *not here*, choose the letter for Not Here.

1. Which is a true sentence? **A**

   A $0.5 > 0.48$

   B $0.48 > 0.5$

   C $1.4 > 2.5$

   D $5.01 < 4.08$

2. Find the area of the rectangle. **H**

   9.2 m

   2.4 m

   F 11.8 m^2 G 23.28 m^2

   H 22.08 m^2 J 90.4 m^2

3. Shalena's birthday is 7 weeks and 5 days away. How many days away is her birthday? **B**

   A 49 days

   B 54 days

   C 35 days

   D 12 days

4. Simplify the fraction $\frac{18}{144}$. **G**

   F $\frac{1}{6}$ G $\frac{1}{8}$

   H $\frac{1}{14}$ J $\frac{1}{12}$

5. Xavier High School has a student enrollment of 2,155 students. What is this number rounded to the nearest thousand? **A**

   A 2,000

   B 2,100

   C 2,150

   D 2,200

Please note that Questions 6–13 have five answer choices.

6. Greg purchased 4 paperback books. Each book costs between $4.99 and $8.99. What is a reasonable total cost for the books? **G**

   F $10   G $30

   H $15   J $45

   K $50

7. Mitena is buying 3 binders that cost $2.89 each and 4 pens that cost $0.49 each. Which expression can be used to find the total cost of the items? **B**

   A $3 \times 2.89 \times 4 \times 0.49$

   B $3 \times 2.89 + 4 \times 0.49$

   C $3 + 2.89 + 4 + 0.49$

   D $3 + 2.89 \times 4 + 0.49$

   E $3 \times 2.89 \div 4 \times 0.49$

8. The graph shows the number of teams who entered the annual 3-on-3-basketball tournament from 1994 to 1998.

Basketball Tournament

How many more teams entered the tournament in 1997 than in 1995? **F**

   F 60   G 30

   H 90   J 120

   K 150

Assessment and Evaluation Masters, p. 131

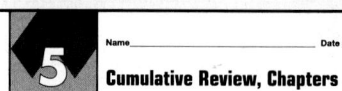

5   Name_____ Date_____

Cumulative Review, Chapters 1–5

Perform the indicated operation.

1. $56\overline{)190.4}$ 1. ___3.4___
2. 18×3.52 2. ___63.36___
3. $7.284 \div 1.2$ 3. ___6.07___

Evaluate.

4. $7 \times 12 + 6 \times 12$ 4. ___156___
5. n^3 if $n = 13$ 5. ___2,197___

Estimate.

6. $3.98 + 5.13 6. __$4 + $5 = $9__
7. 9.2×28.3 7. __$9 \times 30 = 270$__

8. Find the best interval for a frequency table for these scores: 91, 88, 83, 83, 90.   8. ___2___
9. Find the median of the following scores: 17, 13, 25, 22, 13.   9. ___17___
10. A United States one-dollar bill is 15.7 centimeters long and 6.6 centimeters wide. Find the perimeter.   10. ___44.6 cm___
11. Complete: 63 in. = _?_ ft.   11. ___$5\frac{1}{4}$ ft___
12. Change 3.8 kilograms to grams.   12. ___3,800 g___
13. Express $\frac{31}{5}$ as a mixed number.   13. ___$6\frac{1}{5}$___

Write as a decimal.

14. $\frac{81}{10,000}$ 14. ___0.0081___
15. $\frac{15}{16}$ 15. ___0.9375___

Order from least to greatest for Questions 16–17.

16. 0.006, 0.2, 0.03, 0.0008   16. __0.0008, 0.006, 0.03, 0.2__
17. $\frac{3}{4}, \frac{1}{8}, \frac{15}{16}, \frac{1}{2}$ 17. __$\frac{1}{8}, \frac{1}{2}, \frac{3}{4}, \frac{15}{16}$__
18. Find the GCF of 18 and 30.   18. ___6___
19. Express 0.06 as a fraction in simplest form.   19. ___$\frac{3}{50}$___
20. Find the LCM for 14, 15, and 21.   20. ___210___

© Glencoe/McGraw-Hill   131   *Mathematics: Applications and Connections, Course 1*

◀◀◀ Instructional Resources

Another cumulative review is shown at the left and is available in the *Assessment and Evaluation Masters*, p. 131.

9. If $n = 4.35 \div 1.5$, what is the value of n to the nearest tenth? **A**

- A 2.9
- B 0.09
- C 0.29
- D 1.2
- E Not Here

10. Nashala wants to buy movie tickets for herself and three friends. Each ticket costs $2.95. Which is the best estimate for the total cost of the tickets? **J**

- F $3
- G $6
- H $9
- J $12
- K Not Here

11. Find the value of $23 - 6 + 2 \times 5$. **C**

- A 195
- B 7
- C 27
- D 29
- E Not Here

12. The Framing Center charges $12.95 to frame one 3-inch by 5-inch picture. How much would it cost to frame three 3-inch by 5-inch pictures? **H**

- F $35.95
- G $42.99
- H $38.85
- J $45.79
- K Not Here

13. Solve $11.05 \div 0.65$. **D**

- A 9
- B 15
- C 14
- D 17
- E Not Here

Test Practice For additional test practice questions, visit:

www.glencoe.com/sec/math/mac/mathnet

Test-Taking Tip THE PRINCETON REVIEW

It is a good idea to review formulas before taking a standardized test. Usually the formulas are given in the test booklet, but reviewing the formulas before taking a test may give you an advantage.

Section Two: Free Response

This section contains six questions for which you will provide short answers. Write your answers on your paper. 16. $4\frac{57}{125}$

14. Erika's bowling scores were 119, 134, 135, 125, 143, and 135. What is the mode of her scores? **135**

15. What is the value of $y + 42$ if $y = 87$? **129**

16. Express the decimal 4.456 as a mixed number in simplest form.

17. Levon is shopping for groceries. He buys a 12-pack of cola for $3.98, a bottle of laundry detergent for $4.79, and 2 frozen pizzas for $5.86 each. What is the total cost of the items before tax is added? **$20.49**

18. What is the perimeter of a rectangular bulletin board that is 4 feet wide and 6 feet long? **20 ft**

19. Angel purchased a red, a black, and a blue T-shirt. The total cost for the shirts was $14.37. How much change should he receive from a $20 bill? **$5.63**

Chapters 1–5 Standardized Test Practice **225**

Assessment and Evaluation Masters, pp. 129–130

Instructional Resources ▶▶▶

Additional standardized test practice is shown at the right and is available in the *Assessment and Evaluation Masters,* pp. 129–130.

Adding and Subtracting Fractions

Overview

This chapter explores adding and subtracting fractions. Students round fractions and mixed numbers and estimate sums and differences. They learn to add and subtract fractions with like denominators, fractions with unlike denominators, and mixed numbers. Connections include problem solving by eliminating possibilities and adding and subtracting measures of time.

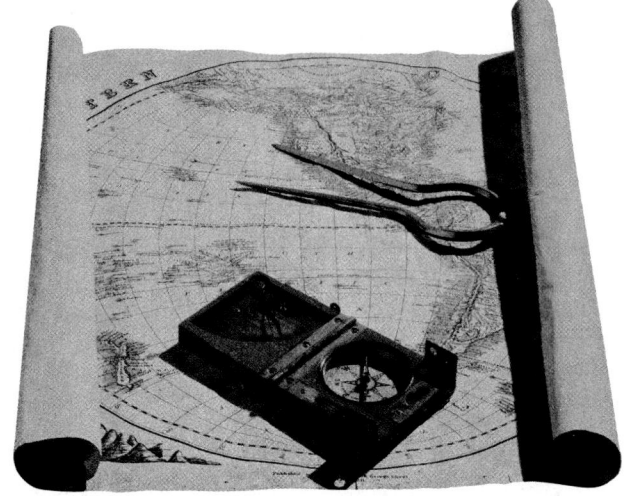

Lesson (pages)	Lesson Objectives	NCTM Standards 2000	Standardized Tests	State/Local Objectives
6-1 (228–231)	Round fractions and mixed numbers.	1, 3, 4, 6–10	SAT	
6-2 (232–234)	Estimate sums and differences of fractions and mixed numbers.	1, 3, 4, 6–9	CTBS, TN	
6-2B (236–237)	Solve problems by eliminating possibilities.	1, 6–9	MAT	
6-3 (238–241)	Add and subtract fractions with like denominators.	1, 3, 4, 6–10	CAT, CTBS, ITBS, MAT, SAT, TN	
6-4A (242)	Find common unit names for adding different objects.	5–8		
6-4 (243–245)	Add and subtract fractions with unlike denominators.	1, 2, 6–10	CAT, CTBS, ITBS, MAT, SAT, TN	
6-5 (246–249)	Add and subtract mixed numbers.	1, 3, 4, 6–10	CAT, CTBS, SAT, TN	
6-6 (250–253)	Subtract mixed numbers involving renaming.	1, 2, 5–10	CTBS, SAT, TN	
6-7 (254–257)	Add and subtract measures of time.	1, 4, 6–10		

CAT = California Achievement Tests, CTBS = Comprehensive Tests of Basic Skills, ITBS = Iowa Tests of Basic Skills, MAT = Metropolitan Achievement Tests, SAT = Stanford Achievement Tests, TN = Terra Nova
For the key to numbering of NCTM Standards 2000, see page T6.

Organizing the Chapter

 The **Interactive Lesson Planner** contains all of the blackline masters and transparencies. This CD-ROM also includes an easy-to-use lesson planning calendar.

LESSON PLANNING GUIDE

| Lesson | Extra Practice (Student Edition) | BLACKLINE MASTERS (PAGE NUMBERS) | | | | | | | | | | Transparencies A and B |
		Study Guide	Practice	Enrichment	Assessment & Evaluation	Classroom Games	Diversity	Hands-On Lab	School to Career	Science and Math Lab Manual	Technology	
6-1	p. 572	42	42	42					6			6-1
6-2	p. 572	43	43	43	155							6-2
6-2B	p. 573											
6-3	p. 573	44	44	44			6	74				6-3
6-4A								50				
6-4	p. 573	45	45	45	154, 155						12	6-4
6-5	p. 574	46	46	46		15–18						6-5
6-6	p. 574	47	47	47	156							6-6
6-7	p. 574	48	48	48	156						11	6-7
Study Guide/ Assessment					141–153, 157–159							

OTHER CHAPTER RESOURCES

Student Edition

Chapter Project, pp. 227, 231, 252, 261
School to Career, p. 235
Let the Games Begin, p. 253

Technology

 MathPASS CD-ROM

 Interactive Mathematics Tools Software

Teacher's Classroom Resources

Applications
Family Letters and Activities, pp. 11–12
Investigations and Projects Masters, pp. 37–40

Meeting Individual Needs
Investigations for the Special Education Student, pp. 15, 17–18

Teaching Aids
Answer Key Masters
Block Scheduling Booklet
Lesson Planning Guide
Solutions Manual

Professional Publications
Glencoe Mathematics Professional Series

Planning the Chapter

MindJogger Videoquizzes provide a unique format for reviewing concepts presented in the chapter.

ASSESSMENT RESOURCES

Student Edition

Mixed Review, pp. 231, 234, 241, 245, 249, 253, 257

Mid-Chapter Self Test, p. 249

Math Journal, pp. 230, 255

Study Guide and Assessment, pp. 258–261

Performance Task, p. 261

Portfolio Suggestion, p. 261

Standardized Test Practice, pp. 262–263

Chapter Test, p. 600

Assessment and Evaluation Masters

Multiple-Choice Tests (Forms 1A, 1B, 1C), pp. 141–146

Free-Response Tests (Forms 2A, 2B, 2C), pp. 147–152

Performance Assessment, p. 153

Mid-Chapter Test, p. 154

Quizzes A–D, pp. 155–156

Standardized Test Practice, pp. 157–158

Cumulative Review, p. 159

Teacher's Wraparound Edition

5-Minute Check, pp. 228, 232, 238, 243, 246, 250, 254

Building Portfolios, p. 226

Math Journal, p. 242

Closing Activity, pp. 231, 234, 237, 241, 245, 249, 253, 257

Technology

Test and Review Software

MindJogger Videoquizzes

CD-ROM Program

MATERIALS AND MANIPULATIVES

Lesson 6-3
grid paper†
colored pencils

Lesson 6-4A
pennies
nickels
pencils
pens

Lesson 6-5
paper plates
scissors*

Lesson 6-6
number cubes*
spinner*†

*Glencoe Manipulative Kit

†Glencoe Overhead Manipulative Resources

PACING CHART

See pages T25–T27 for the Course Planning Calendar.

COURSE	DAY 1	DAY 2	DAY 3	DAY 4	DAY 5	DAY 6	DAY 7
Standard	Chapter Project	Lesson 6-1	Lesson 6-2	Lesson 6-2B	Lesson 6-3	Lessons 6-4A & 6-4	
Honors	Chapter Project	Lesson 6-1	Lesson 6-2	Lesson 6-2B	Lesson 6-3	Lesson 6-4	Lesson 6-5
Block	Chapter Project & Lesson 6-1	Lessons 6-2 & 6-2B	Lessons 6-3 & 6-4A	Lesson 6-4 & 6-5	Lesson 6-6	Lesson 6-7	Study Guide and Assessment, Chapter Test

Interactive Mathematics:
Activities and Investigations

is an activity-based program that may be used as an enhancement for chapters in *Mathematics: Applications and Connections.*

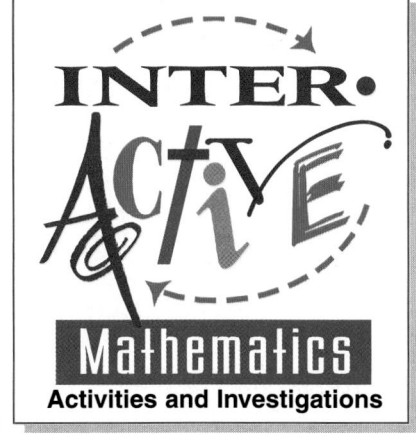

INTER·ACTIVE
Mathematics
Activities and Investigations

Unit 5, Activity One, Menu A
Use with Lesson 6-2B.

Summary Students work in groups to solve two cooperative logic puzzles. They then explain in writing the methods they used to arrive at their solutions.

Math Connection Students work cooperatively in groups to determine their own strategies in order to solve two logic puzzles. Each group is given two envelopes, one per puzzle, with the instructions for the puzzle on the outside and clue cards on the inside.

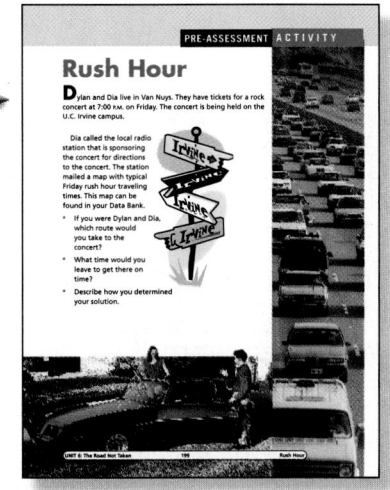

Unit 6, Pre-Assessment Activity
Use with Lesson 6-7.

Summary Students are given a map and a problem situation. They work in pairs or groups to determine the best route to travel and at which time they should begin their trip to ensure on-time arrival. Each group gives an oral presentation of their decisions.

Math Connection Students will be using their knowledge of discrete mathematics. Discrete mathematics is the study of objects and ideas that can be divided into distinct parts.

DAY 8	DAY 9	DAY 10	DAY 11	DAY 12	DAY 13	DAY 14	DAY 15
Lesson 6-5	Lesson 6-6		Lesson 6-7	Study Guide and Assessment	Chapter Test		
Lesson 6-6		Lesson 6-7	Study Guide and Assessment	Chapter Test			

APPLICATIONS

Classroom Games,
pp. 15–18

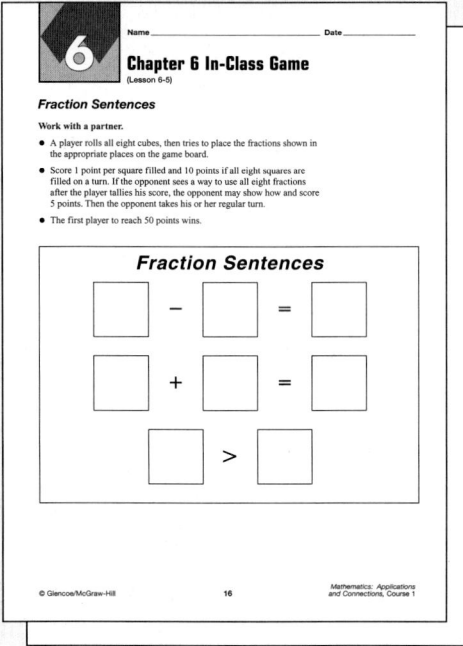

Diversity Masters,
p. 6

School to Career Masters,
p. 6

Family Letters and Activities,
pp. 11–12

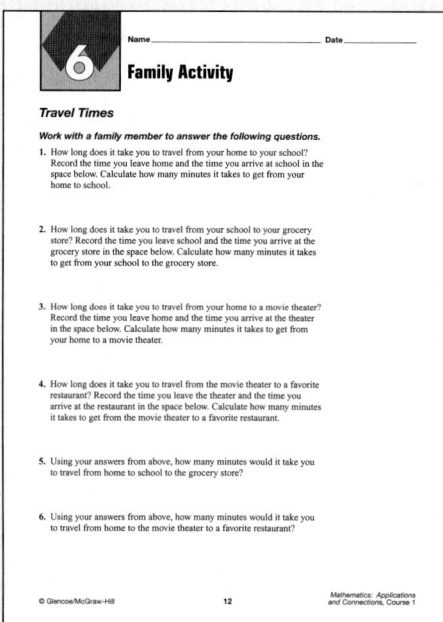

Hands-On Lab Masters, p. 74

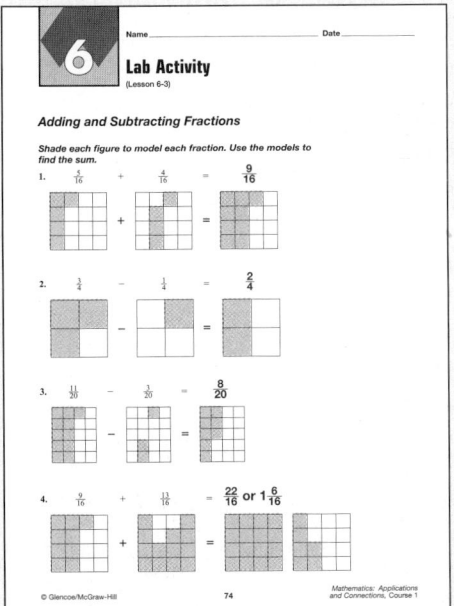

Assessment and Evaluation Masters, pp. 154–156

Technology Masters, pp. 11–12

Investigations for the Special Education Student, pp. 15, 17–18

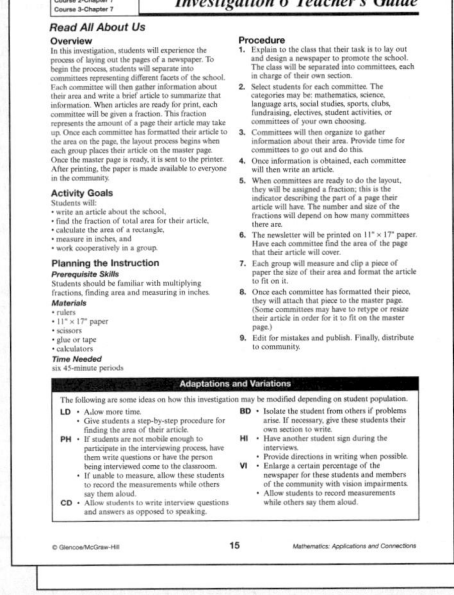

CHAPTER 6 — Adding and Subtracting Fractions

Theme: Maps

Buried treasures can be found with thorough research and modern technology. In 1988, Tommy Thompson and his crew found the remains of the *Central America* off the coast of South Carolina. Their researchers used first-hand narratives and newspaper accounts to map the location of the sunken ship. Today, remote-controlled vehicles and nuclear submarines are used to plumb the depths of the oceans looking for lost ships and their treasures.

Question of the Day Jeanne is following directions to Raphael's house. She travels $1\frac{1}{2}$ miles and turns left, $\frac{3}{4}$ mile and turns right, $\frac{1}{4}$ mile and turns left, and $2\frac{5}{8}$ miles and turns right. Then she continues $\frac{1}{3}$ mile to Raphael's house. How far has Jeanne traveled? $5\frac{11}{24}$ miles

Assess Prerequisite Skills

Ask students to read through the list of objectives presented in "What you'll learn in Chapter 6." You may wish to ask them what each of the objectives means or if they have experienced or used any of these math concepts before.

 Building Portfolios

Encourage students to revise their portfolios as they study this chapter. In addition to their maps, you may wish to have them include examples of the work they did to create the maps.

 Math and the Family

In the *Family Letters and Activities* booklet (pp. 11–12), you will find a letter to the parents explaining what students will study in Chapter 6. An activity appropriate for the whole family is also available.

 What you'll learn in Chapter 6

- to round fractions and mixed numbers,
- to estimate and find sums and differences of fractions and mixed numbers,
- to solve problems by eliminating possibilities, and
- to add and subtract measures of time.

 CD-ROM Program

Activities for Chapter 6
- Chapter 6 Introduction
- Interactive Lessons 6-3, 6-5, 6-6
- Assessment Game
- Resource Lessons 6-1 through 6-7

TRAIL TO THE
TREASURE TROVE

Countless stories and movies have been written about people in search of hidden or lost treasure. Often, these people found or bought maps describing the location of the treasure. In this project, you will create and draw your own map for locating a hidden treasure. You will then provide instructions so that someone can find your treasure by using your map.

Getting Started

- On your map, the distance between the starting point and the treasure, in a straight line, must be $5\frac{3}{4}$ inches.
- You will use the landmarks and distances shown in the table when you draw your map.

Landmarks	Distance
starting point to first landmark	$\frac{7}{8}$ in.
center of fountain to tallest oak tree	$1\frac{3}{8}$ in.
tallest oak tree to bench near pond	$2\frac{1}{2}$ in.
bench near pond to seal-shaped rock	$1\frac{5}{8}$ in.
last landmark to treasure	$1\frac{1}{8}$ in.

Technology Tips

- Use a **word processor** to list your instructions.
- Use **computer software** to draw your map.
- Use an **electronic encyclopedia** to learn more about maps and map making.

 interNET CONNECTION **Research** For up-to-date information on maps and map making, visit:

www.glencoe.com/sec/math/mac/mathnet

Working on the Project

You can use what you'll learn in Chapter 6 to help you make your treasure map.

Page	Exercise
231	34
252	37
261	Alternative Assessment

Instructional Resources ►►►

A recording sheet to help students organize their data for the Chapter Project is shown at the right and is available in the *Investigations and Projects Masters,* p. 40.

CHAPTER Project
N O T E S

Objectives Students should
- create and draw a map for locating hidden treasure.
- provide instructions to find the treasure using the map.

Project Pointer You may suggest that students begin a *Project Folder* to keep their work as they complete each stage of the Chapter Project. The completed project may also be added to their portfolios.

Have students develop a plan for creating a map that meets all of the distance requirements. Encourage them to see how many different ways they can place the landmarks and still have a total distance of $5\frac{3}{4}$ inches from the starting point to the treasure. Also point out that several requirements for the map will be given in the chapter.

Using the Table Make sure students understand that in addition to using the distances given for each landmark, they must also follow the guideline given for the total distance from the starting point to the treasure.

Investigations and Projects Masters, p. 40

6 Name_____ Date_____

Chapter 6 Project

Trail to the Treasure Trove

© Glencoe/McGraw-Hill   40   Mathematics: Applications and Connections, Course 1

Check for Understanding

If students need additional practice or instruction after completing Exercises 1–11, one of these options may be helpful.
- Extra Practice, see p. 572
- Reteaching Activity
- *Study Guide Masters,* p. 42
- *Practice Masters,* p. 42
- 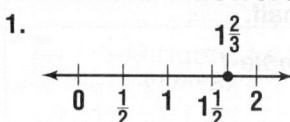 Interactive Mathematics Tools Software

Assignment Guide
Core: 13–33 odd, 35–39
Enriched: 12–32 even, 33, 35–39

Additional Answers

1.

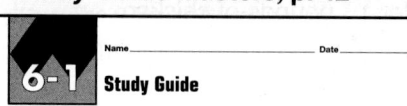

$$1\frac{2}{3}$$

0 $\frac{1}{2}$ 1 $1\frac{1}{2}$ 2

3. Sample answer: If the numerator is close in value to the denominator, round up. If the numerator is about half the denominator, round to $\frac{1}{2}$. If the numerator is much smaller than the denominator, round down.

Study Guide Masters, p. 42

CHECK FOR UNDERSTANDING

Communicating Mathematics

Read and study the lesson to answer each question. 1. See margin.

1. *Draw* a number line that shows how to round $1\frac{2}{3}$ to the nearest half.

2. *Describe* a situation where it would make sense to round a fraction up to the nearest unit.

3. *Write*, in your own words, how you know whether to round a fraction to 0, $\frac{1}{2}$, or 1 when rounding to the nearest half. **See margin.**

Guided Practice

2. Sample answer: When estimating the amount of wood needed to build a bookshelf.

Round each number to the nearest half.

4. $\frac{45}{8}$ $\frac{1}{2}$ 5. $3\frac{15}{16}$ 4   6. $\frac{4}{10}$ $\frac{1}{2}$ 7. $\frac{7}{10}$ $\frac{1}{2}$ 8. $5\frac{2}{5}$ $5\frac{1}{2}$

Tell whether each number should be rounded up or down.

9. the weight limit of a bridge **down**

10. the capacity of a container needed to hold $4\frac{3}{4}$ liters of gasoline **up**

11. *Measurement* Find the amount of water in the measuring cup to the nearest one-half cup.
$2\frac{1}{2}$ **cups**

EXERCISES

Practice

Round each number to the nearest half.

12. $1\frac{1}{10}$ 1   13. $\frac{5}{6}$ 1   14. $\frac{3}{8}$ $\frac{1}{2}$ 15. $6\frac{2}{3}$ $6\frac{1}{2}$ 16. $\frac{1}{5}$ 0

17. $\frac{9}{16}$ $\frac{1}{2}$ 18. $2\frac{4}{5}$ 3   19. $12\frac{1}{6}$ 12   20. $7\frac{3}{10}$ $7\frac{1}{2}$ 21. $4\frac{2}{9}$ 4

22. $\frac{1}{8}$ 0   23. $10\frac{7}{10}$ $10\frac{1}{2}$ 24. $\frac{1}{9}$ 0   25. $5\frac{3}{7}$ $5\frac{1}{2}$ 26. $\frac{27}{32}$ 1

Tell whether each number should be rounded up or down.

27. the amount of chili pepper needed for a pot of chili **down**

28. a patch for a $2\frac{1}{4}$-inch tear in a pair of jeans **up**

29. the depth of the stream where you are fishing while wearing hip boots **up**

30. the width of blinds to fit in a window $63\frac{3}{4}$ inches wide **down**

31. the weight of cargo on an airplane **up**

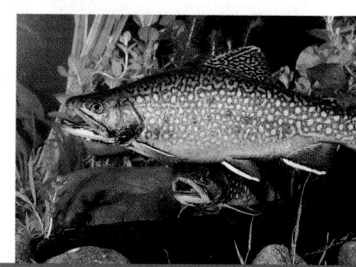

230   Chapter 6 Adding and Subtracting Fractions

■ Reteaching the Lesson ■

Activity You will need measuring cups, spoons, and a variety of containers. Have pairs of students fill the containers with water or a dry material such as uncooked oatmeal, beans, popcorn, or rice. Then have them measure the contents to the nearest half-unit.

32. $1\frac{1}{2}$ pounds,
1 pound isn't enough.

32. *Cooking* A recipe to make tacos calls for $1\frac{1}{4}$ pounds of ground beef. Should you buy a $1\frac{1}{2}$-pound package or a 1-pound package? Explain.

33. *Food* The graph shows the results of a survey of the food served at 28 major league baseball stadiums.

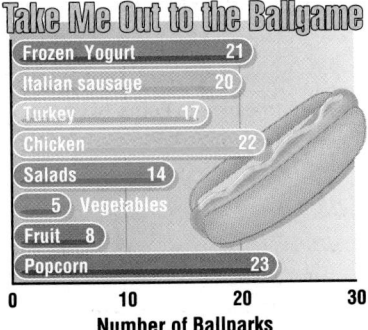

Take Me Out to the Ballgame

Frozen Yogurt	21
Italian sausage	20
Turkey	17
Chicken	22
Salads	14
Vegetables	5
Fruit	8
Popcorn	23

Number of Ballparks

a. Write a fraction to represent the number of stadiums that sell each type of food.

b. Which foods are sold in about half of the stadiums?

c. Which foods are sold in almost all of the stadiums? **popcorn, chicken, frozen yogurt**

33a. $\frac{23}{28}, \frac{2}{7}, \frac{5}{28}, \frac{1}{2},$
$\frac{11}{14}, \frac{17}{28}, \frac{5}{7}, \frac{3}{4}$
33b. salads, turkey

34. *Working on the* **CHAPTER Project** Refer to the table on page 227. Begin drawing your map. Choose the first two landmarks so that the distance between them is $1\frac{1}{2}$ inches when rounded to the nearest half inch. However, on your map, use the actual distance. **See margin.**

Mixed Review

35. *Critical Thinking* Name three mixed numbers that round to $5\frac{1}{2}$.
Sample answer: $5\frac{3}{8}, 5\frac{7}{16}, 5\frac{3}{5}$

36. Write $1\frac{5}{18}$ as a decimal using bar notation. *(Lesson 5-10)* **$1.2\overline{7}$**

37. *Measurement* One acre is about 0.0016 square mile. Write this decimal in words. *(Lesson 3-1)* **sixteen ten-thousandths**

38. *Statistics* Make a horizontal bar graph and one other type of graph for the set of data. *(Lesson 2-3)*

Raul's Earnings				
Monday	Tuesday	Wednesday	Thursday	Friday
$21.50	$13.75	$19.15	$20.00	$25.50

See Answer Appendix.

39. *Standardized Test Practice* A telephone operator answered 500 calls during the first three weeks of a month. She answered 137 calls the fourth week. A reasonable conclusion would be that the telephone operator answered — *(Lesson 1-3)* **D**

A less than 100 calls per week.

B between 100 and 125 calls per week.

C between 126 and 150 calls per week.

D between 151 and 175 calls per week.

E more than 175 calls per week.

For **Extra Practice**, see page 572.

Lesson 6-1 Rounding Fractions and Mixed Numbers **231**

Extending the Lesson

Enrichment Masters, p. 42

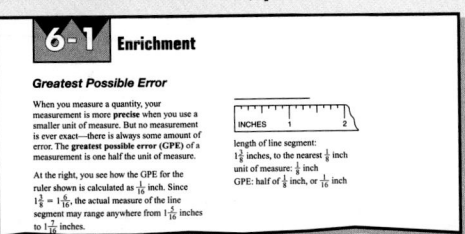

6-1 Enrichment

Greatest Possible Error

When you measure a quantity, your measurement is more **precise** when you use a smaller unit of measure. But no measurement is ever exact—there is always some amount of error. The **greatest possible error (GPE)** of a measurement is one half the unit of measure.

At the right, you see how the GPE for the ruler shown is calculated as $\frac{1}{16}$ inch. Since $1\frac{3}{8} = 1\frac{6}{16}$, the actual measure of the line segment may range anywhere from $1\frac{5}{16}$ inches to $1\frac{7}{16}$ inches.

length of line segment:
$1\frac{3}{8}$ inches, to the nearest $\frac{1}{8}$ inch
unit of measure: $\frac{1}{8}$ inch
GPE: half of $\frac{1}{8}$ inch, or $\frac{1}{16}$ inch

Activity Have pairs of students contrast examples of appropriate and inappropriate units of measurement for rounding. For example, the time spent mowing a lawn could be rounded to the nearest one-half hour, but even the nearest one-half minute would not be exact enough to record the finishing time in an Olympic race.

CHAPTER Project

Exercise 34 asks students to advance to the next stage of work on the Chapter Project. You may wish to provide students with blank tables to help them organize their information.

4 ASSESS

Closing Activity

Speaking Name a fraction and ask a student whether it should be rounded up, down, or to the nearest half unit. Then have that student name a fraction for someone else, and continue around the room until everyone has had a turn.

Additional Answer

34. Sample answer: The two landmarks can be either the center of the fountain and the tallest oak tree or the bench near the pond and the seal-shaped rock.

Practice Masters, p. 42

6-1 Practice

Name_____ Date_____

Rounding Fractions and Mixed Numbers

Round each number to the nearest half.

1. $\frac{4}{7}$ **$\frac{1}{2}$** 2. $1\frac{1}{9}$ **1** 3. $3\frac{11}{12}$ **4** 4. $\frac{2}{15}$ **0**

5. $6\frac{7}{13}$ **$6\frac{1}{2}$** 6. $2\frac{1}{3}$ **2** 7. $5\frac{6}{11}$ **$5\frac{1}{2}$** 8. $\frac{11}{14}$ **1**

9. $7\frac{3}{19}$ **7** 10. $\frac{1}{10}$ **0** 11. $9\frac{17}{20}$ **10** 12. $4\frac{8}{13}$ **$4\frac{1}{2}$**

13. $8\frac{4}{9}$ **9** 14. $1\frac{5}{12}$ **$1\frac{1}{2}$** 15. $\frac{3}{18}$ **0** 16. $3\frac{8}{9}$ **4**

17. $\frac{9}{16}$ **$\frac{1}{2}$** 18. $2\frac{11}{13}$ **3** 19. $5\frac{3}{20}$ **5** 20. $7\frac{9}{11}$ **8**

21. $10\frac{1}{4}$ **10** 22. $\frac{13}{15}$ **1** 23. $6\frac{4}{25}$ **6** 24. $8\frac{9}{19}$ **$8\frac{1}{2}$**

Tell whether each number should be rounded up, down, or to the nearest half unit.

25. the length of a strip of wallpaper to hang on a wall $7\frac{5}{8}$ feet high **round up**
26. the width of a turntable to fit into a stereo cabinet with a width of $18\frac{3}{8}$ inches **round down**
27. the length of a ribbon needed for a bow on a birthday present, accurate to $\frac{1}{2}$ inch **round to nearest $\frac{1}{2}$ inch**
28. the capacity of a punch bowl needed to hold $4\frac{5}{8}$ gallons of punch **round up**

Find the length of each line segment to the nearest one-half inch.

29. _____ **$\frac{1}{2}$ in.** 30. _____ **2 in.**

31. _____ **$2\frac{1}{2}$ in.** 32. _____ **1 in.**

© Glencoe/McGraw-Hill T42 *Mathematics: Applications and Connections, Course 1*

Instructional Resources
- *Study Guide Masters*, p. 43
- *Practice Masters*, p. 43
- *Enrichment Masters*, p. 43
- Transparencies 6-2, A and B
- *Assessment and Evaluation Masters*, p. 155

 CD-ROM Program
- Resource Lesson 6-2

Recommended Pacing	
Standard	Day 3 of 13
Honors	Day 3 of 12
Block	Day 2 of 7

1 FOCUS

5-Minute Check
(Lesson 6-1)

Round each number to the nearest half.

1. $\frac{1}{8}$ 0

2. $3\frac{9}{16}$ $3\frac{1}{2}$

3. $\frac{9}{11}$ 1

Tell whether each number should be rounded up or down.

4. the number of bricks to load in a $\frac{3}{4}$-ton pickup truck **down**

5. the length of paper needed to wrap several gifts **up**

 The 5-Minute Check is also available on **Transparency 6-2A** for this lesson.

2 TEACH

 Transparency 6-2B contains a teaching aid for this lesson.

Using Modeling Have students work in groups of three. Ask them to measure the lengths of their outstretched arms (fingertip to fingertip). Then have them hold hands with arms outstretched and estimate their combined length. Have them compare their estimates with others and with their actual combined length.

6-2 Estimating Sums and Differences

What you'll learn
You'll learn to estimate sums and differences of fractions and mixed numbers.

When am I ever going to use this?
You'll estimate sums and differences when planning what songs to record on a cassette tape.

Maxine is making a cassette tape of some of her favorite songs from her CD collection so that she can listen to them while she jogs. She has already recorded about $49\frac{3}{4}$ minutes of music on her 60-minute cassette tape. The songs she wants to record are about $3\frac{3}{4}$ minutes, $4\frac{1}{6}$ minutes, and $3\frac{1}{3}$ minutes long. Is there enough tape left to record all three songs? *This problem will be solved in Example 3.*

A good way to estimate the sum or difference of fractions is to round each fraction to the nearest half and then add or subtract.

Examples

Estimate. $\frac{1}{8} = 0$ $\frac{1}{2}$ 1

❶ $\frac{9}{16} - \frac{1}{8}$

$\frac{9}{16}$ rounds to $\frac{1}{2}$.

$\frac{1}{8}$ rounds to 0.

Subtract: $\frac{1}{2} - 0 = \frac{1}{2}$

$\frac{9}{16} - \frac{1}{8}$ is about $\frac{1}{2}$.

❷ $\frac{5}{6} + \frac{7}{12}$

$\frac{5}{6}$ rounds to 1.

$\frac{7}{12}$ rounds to $\frac{1}{2}$.

Add: $1 + \frac{1}{2} = 1\frac{1}{2}$

$\frac{5}{6} + \frac{7}{12}$ is about $1\frac{1}{2}$.

To estimate sums and differences of mixed numbers, round each number to the nearest whole number.

Example

Real World APPLICATION

❸ **Music** Refer to the beginning of the lesson. **Is there enough tape left to record all three songs?**

Explore You know how long the tape is, how much has been used, and the length of each of the three songs Maxine wants to record.

Plan Subtract to estimate the amount of time left on the tape. Then compare it to an estimate of the total length of the three songs.

Solve $49\frac{3}{4}$ rounds to 50.

Subtract: $60 - 50 = 10$

There are about 10 minutes left on the tape.

$3\frac{3}{4}$ rounds to 4.

$4\frac{1}{6}$ rounds to 4.

$3\frac{1}{3}$ rounds to 3.

Motivating the Lesson
Problem Solving Ask students how to estimate which pair of chores would take longer to finish.

- washing floors for $\frac{1}{2}$ hour and cleaning the garage for $2\frac{1}{4}$ hours

- washing the car for $1\frac{3}{4}$ hours and raking leaves for $\frac{1}{2}$ hour

Round each mixed number to the nearest whole number.

Add: $4 + 4 + 3 = 11$

The three songs need about 11 minutes of tape.

The time needed is greater than the time left on the tape. Maxine cannot record all three songs.

Examine Check by adding the total time for the three songs to the time already used.

Sometimes when estimating sums and differences of fractions and mixed numbers, you need to round all fractions up.

Example ④ **APPLICATION** Real World

Crafts Leon is making a wallet in a craft class. He plans to trim the wallet with a different color of leather. The wallet is $6\frac{3}{4}$ inches long and $3\frac{1}{2}$ inches wide. About how much leather trim does he need?

Leon wants to make sure he buys enough leather. He rounds up.

Since he wants to trim the entire wallet, he needs to estimate the perimeter of the wallet.

$6\frac{3}{4}$ rounds to 7, and $3\frac{1}{2}$ rounds to 4.

Estimate: $7 + 4 + 7 + 4 = 22$

Leon needs about 22 inches of leather trim.

$6\frac{3}{4}$ in.

$3\frac{1}{2}$ in.

CHECK FOR UNDERSTANDING

Communicating Mathematics

1. See Answer Appendix.

Read and study the lesson to answer each question.

1. *Draw* a number line that shows about where $2\frac{3}{4}$ is located.

2. *Explain* how you would estimate $3\frac{3}{4}$ minus $1\frac{1}{3}$. **Sample answer:** $4 - 1 = 3$

3. *You Decide* Nina wants to make a square picture frame that is $4\frac{3}{8}$ inches on each side. Should she buy 16 inches of framing material or 20 inches of framing material? Explain. **See Answer Appendix.**

Guided Practice

Estimate. **4–9. Sample answers are given.**

4. $\frac{7}{8} - \frac{5}{16}$ $1 - \frac{1}{2} = \frac{1}{2}$
5. $6\frac{7}{10} + 3\frac{5}{8}$ $7 + 4 = 11$
6. $\frac{1}{2} + \frac{4}{5}$ $\frac{1}{2} + 1 = 1\frac{1}{2}$

7. $2\frac{5}{12} - \frac{1}{3}$ $2\frac{1}{2} - \frac{1}{2} = 2$
8. $7\frac{1}{4} - 2\frac{3}{16}$ $7 - 2 = 5$
9. $5\frac{7}{12} + 9\frac{5}{6}$ $6 + 10 = 16$

10. *Write a Problem* in which you would need to estimate the difference between $5\frac{2}{3}$ and $1\frac{1}{4}$. **See Answer Appendix.**

Lesson 6-2 Estimating Sums and Differences **233**

■ **Reteaching the Lesson** ■

Activity Give pairs of students catalog pages that include measurements of curtains, furniture, or rugs. Have them use the information to create word problems involving estimating sums and differences of fractions and mixed numbers. Have them exchange their problems with others to solve.

Check for Understanding

If students need additional practice or instruction after completing Exercises 1–10, one of these options may be helpful.
- Extra Practice, see p. 572
- Reteaching Activity, see p. 233
- *Study Guide Masters*, p. 43
- *Practice Masters*, p. 43

Assignment Guide

Core: 11–29 odd, 31–36
Enriched: 12–26 even, 28–36

4 ASSESS

Closing Activity

Modeling Have pairs of students use fraction bars to estimate sums and differences. For example, have them use bars for $\frac{7}{12} + \frac{7}{8}$. To determine whether they need to round up, down, or to the nearest half, have them compare the $\frac{1}{2}$ model with $\frac{7}{12}$ and $\frac{7}{8}$. Then have them write $\frac{1}{2} + 1 = 1\frac{1}{2}$.

Chapter 6, Quiz A (Lessons 6-1 and 6-2) is available in the *Assessment and Evaluation Masters*, p. 155.

Practice Masters, p. 43

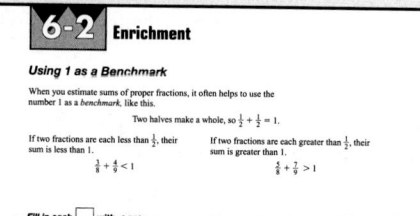

EXERCISES

Practice   **Estimate.** 11–27. Sample answers are given.

11. $\frac{7}{8} + \frac{5}{16}$ $1 + \frac{1}{2} = 1\frac{1}{2}$ **12.** $5\frac{1}{3} - 4\frac{3}{4}$ $5 - 5 = 0$ **13.** $8\frac{1}{4} - \frac{9}{16}$ $8 - 1 = 7$

14. $7\frac{4}{5} + 3\frac{1}{3}$ $8 + 3 = 11$ **15.** $\frac{9}{10} + \frac{1}{2}$ $1 + \frac{1}{2} = 1\frac{1}{2}$ **16.** $3\frac{3}{4} - 2\frac{7}{8}$ $4 - 3 = 1$

17. $\frac{2}{3} + 6\frac{3}{8}$ $1 + 6 = 7$ **18.** $2\frac{3}{10} - 1\frac{7}{8}$ $2 - 2 = 0$ **19.** $8\frac{5}{6} + \frac{1}{12}$ $9 + 0 = 9$

20. $11 - 1 = 10$
21. $22 + 5 = 27$
20. $11\frac{7}{16} - \frac{5}{9}$ **21.** $21\frac{5}{8} + 4\frac{3}{4}$ **22.** $12\frac{4}{5} + \frac{2}{3}$ $13 + 1 = 14$

23. $5 \text{ min} - 1 \text{ min} =$ **23.** About how much longer than $\frac{5}{6}$ minute is $4\frac{1}{2}$ minutes?
    4 min

24. Estimate the sum $3\frac{3}{10} + 2\frac{4}{5} + 3\frac{1}{3}$. $3 + 3 + 3 = 9$

25. $20 \text{ cups} - 11$ **25.** About how much more is $19\frac{3}{4}$ cups than $10\frac{7}{8}$ cups?
    $\text{cups} = 9 \text{ cups}$

26. Estimate the difference between $1\frac{3}{5}$ and $\frac{1}{6}$. $2 - 0 = 2$

27. Estimate the sum of $7\frac{1}{3}$, $6\frac{4}{5}$, $6\frac{3}{4}$, $7\frac{1}{10}$, and $6\frac{15}{16}$. $7 + 7 + 7 + 7 + 7 = 35$

Applications and Problem Solving

28. *Geometry* Estimate the perimeter of the rectangle.
$12 \text{ in.} + 3 \text{ in.} + 12 \text{ in.} + 3 \text{ in.} = 30 \text{ in.}$ $12\frac{1}{8}$ in. $2\frac{13}{16}$ in.

29. *Carpentry* A board that is $63\frac{5}{8}$ inches long is about how much longer than a board that is $62\frac{1}{4}$ inches long? $64 \text{ in.} - 62 \text{ in.} = 2 \text{ in.}$

inter NET CONNECTION
For the latest immigration statistics, visit:
www.glencoe.com/sec/math/mac/mathnet

30. *Geography* In 1994, about $\frac{3}{8}$ of the U.S. immigrants came from Latin America, about $\frac{1}{5}$ came from Canada and Europe, and about $\frac{1}{25}$ came from Africa and Australia. Asians made up the rest of the immigrant population.

  a. About what fraction of immigrants were from Latin America, Canada, and Europe? $\frac{1}{2} + 0 = \frac{1}{2}$

30b. $1 - \left(\frac{1}{2} + 0 + 0\right)$
     $= \frac{1}{2}$
  b. Estimate to find the fraction of immigrants from Asia.

31. *Critical Thinking* The estimate for the sum of two fractions is 1. If 2 is added to each fraction, the estimate for the sum of the two mixed numbers is 4. What are examples of the fractions? **Sample answer:** $\frac{5}{8}$ and $\frac{7}{16}$

Mixed Review **32.** **Standardized Test Practice** What is $6\frac{4}{7}$ rounded to the nearest half? *(Lesson 6-1)* **B**

  A 6   **B** $6\frac{1}{2}$ **C** 7   **D** $7\frac{1}{2}$

33. *Physical Science* Helium has a mass of 0.17 kilogram per cubic meter. Express this mass as a fraction in simplest form. *(Lesson 5-9)* $\frac{17}{100}$

34. Find the least common multiple of 7 and 21. *(Lesson 5-7)* **21**

For **Extra Practice,** see page 572.

35. *Measurement* Change 4 kilometers to centimeters. *(Lesson 4-9)* **400,000 cm**

36. Estimate $39.7 - 28.561$ using rounding. *(Lesson 3-4)* **10**

Extending the Lesson

Enrichment Masters, p. 43

Activity Choose a favorite recipe. Estimate the amount of ingredients needed to make enough for the whole class. Ask the cafeteria staff if there are any special requirements for adapting the recipe for a large group.

CARTOGRAPHY

Richard Jimenez
CARTOGRAPHER

Richard Jimenez is a cartographer for the U.S. Geological Survey. He creates maps of different areas of the United States. Mr. Jimenez is very skilled in accurately measuring distances and determining the location of any given place on a map by using coordinates.

A person who is interested in becoming a cartographer should take classes in geography, mathematics, mechanical drawing, and computer science. The mathematics courses should include algebra and trigonometry. A college degree in engineering or physical science is often required. College courses should include technical mathematics, drafting, and mapping.

For more information:
American Congress on Surveying and Mapping
5410 Grosvenor Lane, Suite 210
Bethesda, MD 20814

*inter*NET
CONNECTION
www.glencoe.com/sec/
math/mac/mathnet

> I use maps when I go hiking. Someday I'd like to create maps that people can use to travel around the world!

Your Turn

Plan a one-week vacation. Write a report about where you will travel, the sites you will visit along the way, and the distance and driving time for your trip. Include in your report a map to refer to while reporting your plan to the class.

School to Career: Cartography **235**

Motivating Students

People have been making maps for thousands of years. The oldest example that has been found is a clay tablet map created by a Babylonian in 2300 B.C. Maps grew more scientific beginning in the eighteenth century, when decorative illustrations were replaced by factual representations. To begin a discussion of cartography, ask students these questions.

- How were maps drawn before inventions were created to aid the process? **Cartographers used their own observations and explorers' accounts.**
- What do cartographers use today to help them draw maps? **aerial and satellite photographs, computer graphics**

Making the Math Connection

Measuring angles is extremely important in cartography. Also of importance are the abilities to add and subtract degrees of latitude and longitude, determine distances according to scale, plot points using coordinates, and depict a sphere on a plane.

Working on *Your Turn*

Encourage students to draw their maps based on written descriptions and photographs of the area, rather than relying on professionally created maps. Have them include the sites they are most interested in visiting. As they report their plan to the class, have them draw the route they plan to take on their map.

More About Richard Jimenez

- Richard Jimenez received a B.S. degree in Surveying and Mapping from Metropolitan State College in Denver, Colorado. As a cartographer, he has done analytical mapping, field work, digital mapping, and photogrammetry (making measurements using aerial photographs).

- Mr. Jimenez became a cartographer because he enjoyed relating mathematical measurements of land to nature. He believes it is important not to spend too much of one's time in front of a computer—after all, maps represent the real world.

*An additional School to Career activity is available on page 6 of the **School to Career Masters.***

THINKING LAB

6-2B Eliminate Possibilities

A Follow-Up of Lesson 6-2

Objective Students solve problems by eliminating possibilities.

Recommended Pacing	
Standard	Day 4 of 13
Honors	Day 4 of 12
Block	Day 2 of 7

1 FOCUS

Getting Started Ask students how they can determine which movie to see on a Saturday afternoon, considering they only have $2.00 each.
- a drama rated PG-13 at a second-run theater, which charges $2.00
- a spy thriller rated R at a first-run theater, which charges $3.50
- a comedy rated G at a second-run theater, which charges $1.50
- a rock music documentary rated PG at a first-run theater, which charges $6.00

eliminate the higher-priced movies and those with adult ratings

2 TEACH

Teaching Tip Suggest that students list the possible solutions to problems such as Exercise 12, crossing out the ones that are not reasonable.

In-Class Example

Carlito has $60 to buy clothes. Looking at the prices of the items below, what can he buy?
- shoes that cost $39.95
- a jacket that costs $69.95
- jeans that cost $29.95
- a shirt that costs $18.95
- a suit that costs $249.95

shoes, jeans, shirt, shirt and jeans, shirt and shoes, 2 jeans, 3 shirts

---

Cesar and Franco are planning to take the bus to the City Center Mall. They have a map and timetables for the bus routes through their neighborhood. Let's listen in.

There are seven different bus routes that leave the Northern Lights Park and Ride. Which one do we want?

And the number 1 and number 83 are east-west routes. We want to go south.

Cesar

Since it's Saturday, we can eliminate the three express routes. They only run on weekdays.

Number 87 doesn't go downtown, but we could pick up number 16 at Cassady Avenue.

But then we would have to pay twice. That leaves us with the number 9 bus. Let's check the timetables.

Franco

THINK ABOUT IT

Work with a partner.

1. **Tell** how Cesar and Franco eliminated possibilities to solve the problem.
2. **Explain** how estimating could help you to **eliminate possibilities.** See margin.
   1. **Sample answer: Franco and Cesar eliminated the routes that they could not take to see which route they could.**

3. **Apply** the eliminate possibilities strategy to solve the following problem.

   Mrs. Danko bought a ham that weighed $5\frac{1}{4}$ pounds and a turkey that weighed $13\frac{1}{2}$ pounds. About how many pounds of meat did she buy? **C**

   A 8 lb   B 10 lb   C 19 lb   D 20 lb

236   **Chapter 6** Adding and Subtracting Fractions

■ Reteaching the Lesson ■

Activity Have students work in small groups and brainstorm as many different sports as they can. Then have them refine their lists to only the sports which they can play on the school grounds on that day. Tell them to consider the weather, available equipment, and surroundings, and to give a reason for why they eliminated each sport from their lists.

Additional Answer

2. **Sample answer: Estimating gets you close to the actual answer. You could eliminate choices that aren't close to your estimate.**

For **Extra Practice**, see page 573.

ON YOUR OWN

4. The fourth step of the 4-step plan for problem solving asks you to *examine*. **Explain** how you can use the strategy of eliminating possibilities to examine a solution.
4–6. See margin.

5. *Write a Problem* that could be solved by eliminating possibilities.

6. *Reflect Back* Tell how the eliminating possibilities strategy would help you on a multiple-choice test.

MIXED PROBLEM SOLVING

10. about 44 feet

> **STRATEGIES**
> Look for a pattern.
> Solve a simpler problem.
> Act it out.
> Guess and check.
> Draw a diagram.
> Make a chart.
> Work backward.

Solve. Use any strategy.

7. Viho's father is 4 times as old as Viho. His grandfather is twice as old as Viho's father. The sum of their three ages is 104. How old is Viho, his father, and his grandfather? **See margin.**

8. **Standardized Test Practice** Last year, Fred's car odometer read 45,500.4. A year later the odometer reads 57,200.9. About how many miles did Fred drive over the past year? **C**

  A 1,000,000   **B** 200,000
  C 10,000   **D** 1,000
  E 100

9. *Money Matters* Candy bars are priced at 2 for 99¢. What will one candy bar cost? **50¢**

10. *Geometry* Mrs. Coe wants to buy fence to put around her rectangular flower bed. About how much fence will she need?

$13\frac{1}{4}$ ft $8\frac{1}{2}$ ft

11. *Food* Ani is preparing a meal for her friends. She wants to make three desserts — a cake, some cookies, and an apple pie. To make the cake, she needs $1\frac{1}{2}$ cups of flour. She needs $1\frac{1}{4}$ cups for the cookies, and $2\frac{3}{4}$ cups for the pie. About how much flour does she need to make the three desserts? **about 7 cups**

12. *Sports* Jill, Kai, Lyndsi, and Mykia are friends. Each of them is on one of the following school teams: basketball, golf, soccer, or tennis. Use the following information to determine who plays on each team. **See margin.**

> Jill is shorter than the girl who plays basketball. Kai only likes to play games played on a court. Lyndsi has a problem with her knee and cannot run. Mykia practices kicking a ball as part of her training.

13. *Fashion* A manufacturer offers four different styles of tennis shoes in white, black, and blue. How many combinations of style and color are possible? **12**

14. *Statistics* Is the mean of 123.9, 43.6, 120.89, 502.9, 12.7, and 72.34 about 150 or 15? Explain. **See margin.**

15. **Standardized Test Practice** Anita is making curtains for her room. She needs $12\frac{3}{4}$ yards of material for a larger window and $7\frac{1}{2}$ yards for a smaller window. She bought 30 yards of material. About how much will she have left after making the curtains? **D**

  A 21 yd
  B 20 yd
  C 19 yd
  D 10 yd
  E 5 yd

Lesson 6-2B THINKING **LAB** **237**

■ Extending the Lesson ■

Activity Have small groups of students write a multiple-choice quiz on estimating sums and differences of fractions and mixed numbers. Ask them to prepare an answer key. Then have the groups exchange their work with other groups to critique the answer key in terms of being able to use the eliminating possibilities strategy.

Check for Understanding
Use the discussion from Exercise 3 to determine whether students understand the eliminate possibilities strategy.

Extra Practice If students need additional practice in problem solving, extra practice is available on the following pages.
- Eliminate Possibilities, see p. 573
- Mixed Problem Solving, see pp. 593–594

Assignment Guide
All: 4–15

4 ASSESS

Closing Activity
Writing Have students write a paragraph explaining how eliminating possibilities can be used to solve a problem. Have them include a situation where they could apply this strategy.

Additional Answers
4. Estimate before getting the exact answer and then compare the exact answer to the estimate.

5. Sample answer: Is 15,840 ÷ 18 equal to 80, 88, 880, or 8,800?

6. Sample answer: By eliminating possibilities, especially obviously wrong choices, you can narrow down the choices until you arrive at the correct answer.

7. Viho is 8 years old, his father is 32, and his grandfather is 64.

12. Jill—tennis; Kai—basketball; Lyndsi—golf; Mykia—soccer

14. about 150; Sample answer: An estimate of the total is 800, and 800 ÷ 5 is greater than 100.

- *Study Guide Masters*, p. 44
- *Practice Masters*, p. 44
- *Enrichment Masters*, p. 44
- Transparencies 6-3, A and B
- *Diversity Masters*, p. 6
- *Hands-On Lab Masters*, p. 74

 CD-ROM Program
- Resource Lesson 6-3
- Interactive Lesson 6-3

Recommended Pacing	
Standard	Day 5 of 13
Honors	Day 5 of 12
Block	Day 3 of 7

1 FOCUS

5-Minute Check
(Lesson 6-2)

Estimate.

1. $\frac{5}{6} + \frac{1}{5}$ $1 + 0 = 1$
2. $7\frac{1}{8} - 4\frac{3}{5}$ $7 - 5 = 2$
3. $3\frac{6}{7} + 8\frac{3}{4}$ $4 + 9 = 13$
4. $5\frac{2}{3} - \frac{7}{13}$ $6 - \frac{1}{2} = 5\frac{1}{2}$
5. Estimate the amount of framing material needed for a picture that is $18\frac{3}{8}$ inches long and $10\frac{1}{2}$ inches wide.
   $19 + 11 + 19 + 11 = 60$ in.

 The 5-Minute Check is also available on **Transparency 6-3A** for this lesson.

Motivating the Lesson

Communication Ask students to read the opening paragraph of the lesson. Ask the following questions.

- If everyone in this class wanted to plant one square of a garden, how many squares would we need?
- What fraction of the garden would be planted if we put in four squares of tomatoes and five squares of peppers?

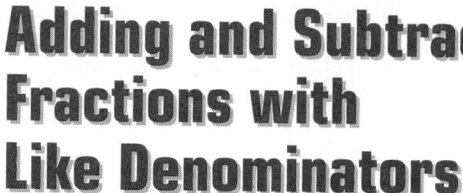

6-3 Adding and Subtracting Fractions with Like Denominators

You'll learn to add and subtract fractions with like denominators.

When am I ever going to use this?

You'll add and subtract fractions with like denominators when you work with equal parts of a whole, such as sections of a garden.

Word Wise
like fractions

John prepared an area for a vegetable garden. He used rope to make a 3-by-5 grid of squares. He planted green beans in the back three squares and corn in two squares. How much of the garden has he planted so far?

You can use grid paper to model this problem.

  MINI-LAB

Work with a partner. grid paper colored pencils

Try This

- On your grid paper, draw a rectangle like the one shown. Since a 3-by-5 grid has 15 squares, each one represents $\frac{1}{15}$.
- With a colored pencil, color three squares to represent the green beans.
- With a different colored pencil, color two more squares to represent the corn.

Talk About It

1. How many squares are colored? **5 squares**
2. What fraction represents the number of colored squares inside the rectangle? $\frac{5}{15}$ or $\frac{1}{3}$
3. If you color four more squares, what fraction would that represent? $\frac{9}{15}$ or $\frac{3}{5}$

Fractions with the same denominator are called **like fractions**. You add and subtract the numerators of like fractions the same way you add and subtract whole numbers. The denominator of the fraction names the units being added or subtracted.

From the Mini-Lab, we know that

3 fifteenths	*plus*	*2 fifteenths*	*equals*	*5 fifteenths.*
$\frac{3}{15}$	$+$	$\frac{2}{15}$	$=$	$\frac{5}{15}$ or $\frac{1}{3}$

John has planted $\frac{1}{3}$ of the garden so far.

Classroom Vignette

"I have students begin writing their addition and subtraction problems vertically in Lesson 6-3. This makes finding common denominators easier."

Doris Jones, Teacher
Creekland Middle School
Lawrenceville, GA

Adding Like Fractions	To add fractions with like denominators, add the numerators. Use the same denominator in the sum.

Example ❶ Find the sum of $\frac{3}{5}$ and $\frac{4}{5}$.

Estimate: $\frac{1}{2} + 1 = 1\frac{1}{2}$

$$\frac{3}{5} + \frac{4}{5} = \frac{3+4}{5}$$
$$= \frac{7}{5}$$
$$= 1\frac{2}{5}$$ *Compared to the estimate, the answer is reasonable.*

$$\frac{3}{5} \quad + \quad \frac{4}{5}$$

$1\frac{2}{5}$

Study Hint

Estimation Use rounding to estimate your answer before adding or subtracting. Then compare your answer to your estimate to see if it is reasonable.

Subtracting Like Fractions	To subtract fractions with like denominators, subtract the numerators. Use the same denominator in the difference.

Subtraction has three meanings. Each of these is shown in one of the following examples.

- to take away part of a set
- to find a missing addend
- to compare the size of two sets

Examples ❷ Reiko opened a carton of milk and drank $\frac{1}{4}$ of it. How much of the carton of milk is left?

Since 1 is equal to $\frac{4}{4}$, you need to find $\frac{4}{4} - \frac{1}{4}$.

$$\frac{4}{4} - \frac{1}{4} = \frac{4-1}{4}$$
$$= \frac{3}{4}$$

$\frac{3}{4}$ of the carton is left.

❸ Patrice was refilling her watering can. The can holds $\frac{7}{8}$ gallon of water. If it took $\frac{5}{8}$ gallon to fill it, how much water was already in the can?

LOOK BACK
Refer to Lesson 1-7 to review solving equations using mental math.

You can use mental math to solve this problem.

$x + \frac{5}{8} = \frac{7}{8}$ *Think: What plus $\frac{5}{8} = \frac{7}{8}$?*

$\frac{2}{8} + \frac{5}{8} = \frac{7}{8}$, so the watering can already contained $\frac{2}{8}$ or $\frac{1}{4}$ gallon.

Lesson 6-3 Adding and Subtracting Fractions with Like Denominators **239**

2 TEACH

Transparency 6-3B contains a teaching aid for this lesson.

Using the Mini-Lab You may wish to model the activity on an overhead transparency. Remind students that all fractions representing a portion of the garden will have a denominator of 15 unless simplified. Continue with other examples as needed.

In-Class Examples

For Example 1
Find the sum of $\frac{8}{9}$ and $\frac{5}{9}$. $1\frac{4}{9}$

For Example 2
Mario and his friends ate $\frac{4}{7}$ of a giant submarine sandwich. How much of the sub is left? $\frac{3}{7}$

For Example 3
The route from Ramon's house to the public library and then to school is $\frac{9}{10}$ mile. It is $\frac{3}{10}$ mile from the library to the school. What is the distance from Ramon's house to the library? $\frac{3}{5}$ mile

Teaching Tip Before Example 3, remind students to write fractions in their simplest form when answering a problem.

In-Class Example

For Example 4

A large orange weighs $\frac{11}{16}$ pound. A small orange weighs $\frac{5}{16}$ pound. How much more does the large orange weigh?

$\frac{3}{8}$ **pound**

3 PRACTICE/APPLY

Check for Understanding

If students need additional practice or instruction after completing Exercises 1–10, one of these options may be helpful.

- Extra Practice, see p. 573
- Reteaching Activity
- *Study Guide Masters,* p. 44
- *Practice Masters,* p. 44
- Interactive Mathematics Tools Software

Assignment Guide
Core: 11–31 odd, 32–36
Enriched: 12-28 even, 29–36

Study Guide Masters, p. 44

6-3 Study Guide

Name _____ Date _____

Adding and Subtracting Fractions with Like Denominators

To add fractions with like denominators, add the numerators.

Example 1 Find the sum of $\frac{7}{8} + \frac{5}{8}$.

$\frac{7}{8} + \frac{5}{8} = \frac{7+5}{8}$
$= \frac{12}{8}$
$= 1\frac{4}{8}$ or $1\frac{1}{2}$

To subtract fractions with like denominators, subtract the numerators.

Example 2 Find the difference between $\frac{9}{10}$ and $\frac{7}{10}$.

$\frac{9}{10} - \frac{7}{10} = \frac{9-7}{10}$
$= \frac{2}{10}$ or $\frac{1}{5}$

Add or subtract. Write each answer in simplest form.

1. $\frac{7}{12} + \frac{2}{12}$ $\frac{3}{4}$
2. $\frac{9}{10} - \frac{3}{10}$ $\frac{3}{5}$
3. $\frac{7}{9} + \frac{5}{9}$ $1\frac{1}{3}$
4. $\frac{7}{16} - \frac{3}{16}$ $\frac{1}{4}$
5. $\frac{5}{11} + \frac{6}{11}$ 1
6. $\frac{7}{8} - \frac{5}{8}$ $\frac{1}{4}$
7. $\frac{2}{3} + \frac{2}{3}$ $1\frac{1}{3}$
8. $\frac{11}{12} - \frac{5}{12}$ $\frac{1}{2}$
9. $\frac{3}{4} + \frac{3}{4}$ $1\frac{1}{2}$
10. $\frac{4}{5} - \frac{1}{5}$ $\frac{3}{5}$
11. $\frac{5}{6} + \frac{1}{6}$ 1
12. $\frac{7}{10} - \frac{1}{10}$ $\frac{3}{5}$
13. $\frac{2}{7} + \frac{4}{7}$ 1
14. $\frac{13}{16} - \frac{2}{16}$ $\frac{3}{4}$
15. $\frac{5}{8} + \frac{3}{8}$ 1

© Glencoe/McGraw-Hill   744   *Mathematics: Applications and Connections, Course 1*

Example **4** **CONNECTION**

Geography According to the 1990 census, about $\frac{12}{100}$ of the population of the United States lives in California. Another $\frac{7}{100}$ of the population lives in Texas. How much more of the population lives in California than in Texas?

$\frac{12}{100} - \frac{7}{100} = \frac{12 - 7}{100}$ *Subtract the numerators.*

$= \frac{5}{100}$ or $\frac{1}{20}$ *Simplify.*

About $\frac{1}{20}$ more of the population of the United States lives in California than in Texas.

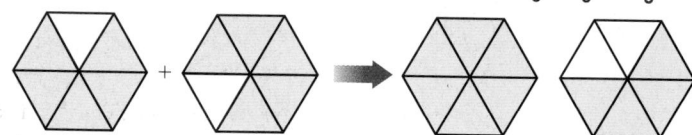

CHECK FOR UNDERSTANDING

Communicating Mathematics

1. **Sample answer:** Add numerators and keep the denominators the same.

Read and study the lesson to answer each question.

1. *Tell* a simple rule for adding and subtracting like fractions.

2. *Write* the addition sentence shown by the model. $\frac{5}{6} + \frac{5}{6} = 1\frac{2}{3}$

HANDS-ON MATH

3. *Make a model* to show the sum of $\frac{5}{8}$ and $\frac{5}{8}$. Write the sum as a mixed number. **See Answer Appendix.**

Guided Practice

Add or subtract. Write the answer in simplest form.

4. $\frac{3}{8} + \frac{1}{8}$ $\frac{1}{2}$

5. $\frac{3}{5} - \frac{2}{5}$ $\frac{1}{5}$

6. $\frac{7}{10} - \frac{3}{10}$ $\frac{2}{5}$

7. $\frac{5}{6} + \frac{5}{6}$ $1\frac{2}{3}$

8. Find the sum of $\frac{2}{3}$ and $\frac{2}{3}$. $1\frac{1}{3}$

9. What is $\frac{11}{12}$ minus $\frac{5}{12}$? $\frac{1}{2}$

10. *Food* Angie is making a punch mixture that calls for $\frac{3}{4}$ quart of grapefruit juice, $\frac{3}{4}$ quart of orange juice, and $\frac{3}{4}$ quart of pineapple juice. How much punch does the recipe make? $2\frac{1}{4}$ **quarts**

EXERCISES

Practice

Add or subtract. Write the answer in simplest form.

11. $\frac{7}{8} + \frac{5}{8}$ $1\frac{1}{2}$

12. $\frac{9}{16} - \frac{5}{16}$ $\frac{1}{4}$

13. $\frac{3}{4} - \frac{3}{4}$ 0

14. $\frac{3}{5} + \frac{4}{5}$ $1\frac{2}{5}$

15. $\frac{1}{3} + \frac{2}{3}$ 1

16. $\frac{3}{10} + \frac{5}{10}$ $\frac{4}{5}$

17. $\frac{5}{6} - \frac{1}{6}$ $\frac{2}{3}$

18. $\frac{11}{12} - \frac{7}{12}$ $\frac{1}{3}$

19. $\frac{5}{9} - \frac{2}{9}$ $\frac{1}{3}$

20. $\frac{5}{8} - \frac{1}{8}$ $\frac{1}{2}$

21. $\frac{11}{16} + \frac{13}{16}$ $1\frac{1}{2}$

22. $\frac{7}{15} + \frac{8}{15}$ 1

Reteaching the Lesson

Activity Have pairs of students roll two number cubes. The greater number is the denominator, and the other number is the numerator. Ask students to think of the greatest fraction that could be added to it so the sum is less than 1 and the difference is greater than 0. For example, if the fraction is $\frac{4}{6}$, $\frac{1}{6}$ could be added or subtracted.

Error Analysis

Watch for students who add both the numerator and the denominator.

Prevent by reminding students that denominators are never added or subtracted.

Solve each equation mentally. Write the solution in simplest form.

23. $a + \frac{2}{5} = \frac{4}{5}$ $\frac{2}{5}$ 24. $b = \frac{7}{8} + \frac{3}{8}$ $1\frac{1}{4}$ 25. $\frac{8}{9} - c = \frac{4}{9}$ $\frac{4}{9}$

26. How much longer than $\frac{7}{16}$ inch is $\frac{15}{16}$ inch? $\frac{1}{2}$ **inch**

27. Find the sum of $\frac{3}{10}$, $\frac{9}{10}$, and $\frac{7}{10}$. $1\frac{9}{10}$

28. How much more is $\frac{3}{4}$ cup than $\frac{1}{4}$ cup? $\frac{1}{2}$ **cup**

Applications and Problem Solving

29. **Carpentry** In industrial technology class, Namid made a plaque by gluing a piece of $\frac{3}{8}$-inch oak to a piece of $\frac{5}{8}$-inch poplar. What was the total thickness of the plaque? **1 inch**

30. **Food** Chad found $\frac{5}{8}$ of a pizza in the refrigerator. He ate $\frac{3}{8}$ of the original pizza. How much of the original pizza is left? $\frac{1}{4}$

31. **Life Science** The inner organs of an electric eel are located in the first $\frac{1}{5}$ of its body. The rest of the eel contains the organs that produce an electric current. How much of an eel produces an electric current? $\frac{4}{5}$

32. **Critical Thinking** Find the sum $\frac{1}{20} + \frac{19}{20} + \frac{2}{20} + \frac{18}{20} + \frac{3}{20} + \frac{17}{20} + \ldots + \frac{10}{20} + \frac{10}{20}$. Look for a pattern to help you. **10**

Mixed Review

33. Estimate $4\frac{1}{5} + 1\frac{7}{8}$. *(Lesson 6-2)*   **4 + 2 = 6**

34. **Test Practice** Order the fractions $\frac{7}{9}, \frac{2}{3}, \frac{2}{6}, \frac{5}{2}$, and $\frac{4}{9}$ from greatest to least. *(Lesson 5-8)*   **C**

A $\frac{7}{9}, \frac{5}{2}, \frac{4}{9}, \frac{2}{6}, \frac{2}{3}$

B $\frac{7}{9}, \frac{4}{9}, \frac{2}{6}, \frac{2}{3}, \frac{4}{9}$

C $\frac{5}{2}, \frac{7}{9}, \frac{2}{3}, \frac{4}{9}, \frac{2}{6}$

D $\frac{2}{6}, \frac{4}{9}, \frac{2}{3}, \frac{7}{9}, \frac{5}{2}$

35. Name a fraction to describe what part of the figure is shaded. *(Lesson 5-4)* $\frac{6}{8}$ **or** $\frac{3}{4}$

36. **Statistics** The number of days that it rained each month in Cincinnati, Ohio, was recorded for a complete year with the following results: 12, 17, 9, 21, 15, 7, 14, 7, 15, 22, 14, 19. Construct a stem-and-leaf plot for this data. *(Lesson 2-6)* **See margin.**

Extending the Lesson

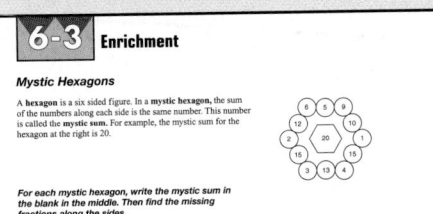

6-3 Enrichment

Mystic Hexagons

A **hexagon** is a six sided figure. In a **mystic hexagon**, the sum of the numbers along each side is the same number. This number is called the **mystic sum**. For example, the mystic sum for the hexagon at the right is 20.

For each mystic hexagon, write the mystic sum in the blank in the middle. Then find the missing fractions along the sides.

Activity Have students measure the tops of their desks or tables to the nearest $\frac{1}{2}$ inch and find the perimeter. Have students also measure the portion they actually use when their books and notebooks are out. Then have them subtract the perimeter of their work space from the perimeter of the entire surface.

Closing Activity

Modeling Have students use egg cartons and counters to model $\frac{3}{5} + \frac{1}{5} = \frac{4}{5}$ and $\frac{6}{7} - \frac{3}{7} = \frac{3}{7}$. Cut the cartons so there are 5 cups and 7 cups and have students place the counters in the cups.

Additional Answer

36.

Stem	Leaf
0	7 7 9
1	2 4 4 5 5 7 9
2	1 2 2|1 = 21

Practice Masters, p. 44

6-3 Practice

Adding and Subtracting Fractions with Like Denominators

Add or subtract. Write the answer in simplest form.

1. $\frac{2}{9} + \frac{4}{9}$ $\frac{2}{3}$ 2. $\frac{13}{16} - \frac{7}{16}$ $\frac{3}{8}$ 3. $\frac{5}{8} + \frac{7}{8}$ $1\frac{1}{2}$

4. $\frac{17}{18} - \frac{9}{18}$ $\frac{4}{9}$ 5. $\frac{13}{15} - \frac{4}{15}$ $\frac{3}{5}$ 6. $\frac{3}{4} + \frac{2}{4}$ $1\frac{1}{4}$

7. $\frac{11}{12} - \frac{7}{12}$ $\frac{1}{3}$ 8. $\frac{19}{20} - \frac{11}{20}$ $\frac{2}{5}$ 9. $\frac{8}{14} + \frac{8}{14}$ $1\frac{1}{7}$

10. $\frac{9}{10} - \frac{4}{10}$ $\frac{1}{2}$ 11. $\frac{4}{5} + \frac{1}{5}$ 1   12. $\frac{6}{7} + \frac{5}{7}$ $1\frac{4}{7}$

13. $\frac{10}{11} - \frac{2}{11}$ $\frac{8}{11}$ 14. $\frac{17}{18} + \frac{4}{18}$ $1\frac{1}{6}$ 15. $\frac{5}{6} + \frac{4}{6}$ $1\frac{1}{2}$

16. $\frac{13}{15} - \frac{13}{15}$ 0   17. $\frac{9}{16} + \frac{11}{16}$ $1\frac{1}{4}$ 18. $\frac{14}{15} - \frac{9}{15}$ $\frac{1}{3}$

19. $\frac{13}{20} - \frac{7}{20}$ $\frac{3}{10}$ 20. $\frac{11}{14} - \frac{5}{14}$ $\frac{3}{7}$ 21. $\frac{11}{18} + \frac{3}{18}$ $\frac{7}{9}$

22. $\frac{9}{11} + \frac{7}{11}$ $1\frac{5}{11}$ 23. $\frac{10}{13} - \frac{4}{13}$ $\frac{6}{13}$ 24. $\frac{9}{10} + \frac{7}{10}$ $1\frac{1}{5}$

Tell whether you would add or subtract to solve. Then solve.

25. Amber spent $\frac{2}{5}$ of an hour on her math assignment and $\frac{4}{5}$ of an hour studying for her science test. How much time did she spend doing her homework?
add; $\frac{2}{5} + \frac{4}{5} = 1\frac{1}{5}$ hours

26. Mr. Garcia planted $\frac{11}{16}$ of his fields with corn and $\frac{5}{16}$ of his fields with wheat. How much more of his fields were planted with corn than with wheat?
**subtract; $\frac{11}{16} - \frac{5}{16} = \frac{3}{8}$
More of his fields were planted with corn.**

© Glencoe/McGraw-Hill   T44   *Mathematics: Applications and Connections, Course 1*

HANDS-ON LAB

GET READY

Objective Students find common unit names for adding different objects.

Optional Resources
Hands-On Lab Masters
• worksheet, p. 50

MANAGEMENT TIPS

Recommended Time
15 minutes

Getting Started Have students read the opening paragraph of the lesson. Ask them to think of items in a department store that could have a common unit name. Ask students to think of reasons for a store to group objects into common units.

Some students may need encouragement when thinking of names for the sum of pennies and nickels. Guide them with questions such as the following. *What are they made of? What shape are they? What do we use them for? What is their value?*

The **Activity** has students make a list of common unit names for pennies and nickels and then for pencils and pens. Encourage the class to agree on the best unit names and to discuss why the names they chose are appropriate.

ASSESS

Have students complete Exercises 1–5. Make sure they see the connection between the idea of common unit names and common denominators. Students need to understand that $\frac{5}{10}, \frac{3}{6}, \frac{2}{4}$, and $\frac{4}{8}$ are equivalent fractions.

COOPERATIVE LEARNING

HANDS-ON LAB

 pennies and nickels

 pencils

 pens

6-4A Renaming Sums

A Preview of Lesson 6-4

If you had 7 cassette tapes and 5 CDs, how would you tell someone how many you have all together? Since you can't add tapes and CDs, you need to find a common unit name for them. You could name them 12 things, 12 objects, 12 recordings, or 12 albums. Probably the best unit name would be albums.

In this lab, you will find a common unit name for other common objects.

TRY THIS

Work with a partner.

• Choose one person to be the recorder.
• Put 4 pennies and 3 nickels together. Write as many unit names as you can think of to describe the sum of the pennies and nickels.
• Look at your list. Choose the best unit name for the pennies and nickels.
• Repeat the steps using pencils and pens.

1. **Sample answer: you rename the units so that the answer makes sense.**
4. **Sample answer: paper clips, staples, and rubber bands – paper holders**

ON YOUR OWN

1. Explain why you need a common unit name to find the sum.
2. Did you find that some unit names fit better than others? Explain why or why not. **See students' work.**
3. Make a graph showing the different units' names used by your class for the pennies and nickels. **See students' work.**
4. Make a list of different objects that could have a common unit name.
5. *Look Ahead* What do you think you need to do to find the sum of $\frac{1}{2}$ and $\frac{3}{4}$? **See margin.**

242 Chapter 6 Adding and Subtracting Fractions

Additional Answer
5. **Sample answer: Find a common denominator.**

 Math Journal

Have students write a paragraph explaining how a common unit name solves the problem of adding different objects. Include one or two examples of common unit names and what they describe.

Adding and Subtracting Fractions with Unlike Denominators

What you'll learn

You'll learn to add and subtract fractions with unlike denominators.

When am I ever going to use this?

You'll add and subtract fractions with unlike denominators when you analyze graphs.

LOOK BACK

You can refer to Lesson 5-8 to review LCD.

What would you do if you won $100,000? The graph shows how adults ages 35–50 said they would spend a $100,000 prize. What fraction of the money did the people surveyed say they would spend on a new car and a new home? *This problem will be solved in Example 1.*

To find the sum, you need a common unit name. In Lesson 6-4A, you came up with common unit names for a group of different objects. When you work with fractions with different, or unlike, denominators, you do the same thing.

To find the sum or difference of two fractions with unlike denominators, rename the fractions using the least common denominator (LCD). Then add or subtract and simplify.

I WON!!

Retirement $\frac{13}{50}$

College for children $\frac{9}{25}$

Take care of parents $\frac{1}{4}$

Take a dream vacation $\frac{1}{25}$

Toward a new car $\frac{1}{25}$

Toward a new home $\frac{3}{50}$

Source: Market Research Institute Survey

Examples

Real World APPLICATION

1 **Money Matters** Refer to the beginning of the lesson. What part of the $100,000 prize did people say they would spend on a new home and a new car?

Add $\frac{3}{50}$ and $\frac{1}{25}$.   *The LCD of $\frac{3}{50}$ and $\frac{1}{25}$ is 50.*

$\frac{3}{50} + \frac{1}{25} = \frac{3}{50} + \frac{2}{50}$ *Rename $\frac{1}{25}$ as $\frac{2}{50}$.*

$= \frac{3+2}{50}$

$= \frac{5}{50}$ or $\frac{1}{10}$

The people surveyed said they would spend $\frac{1}{10}$ of the prize on a new home and a new car.

2 Find $\frac{2}{3} - \frac{1}{2}$.

$\frac{2}{3} - \frac{1}{2} = \frac{4}{6} - \frac{3}{6}$ *The LCD of $\frac{2}{3}$ and $\frac{1}{2}$ is 6. Rename $\frac{2}{3}$ as $\frac{4}{6}$ and $\frac{1}{2}$ as $\frac{3}{6}$.*

$= \frac{4-3}{6}$ *Subtract the numerators.*

$= \frac{1}{6}$

Lesson 6-4 Adding and Subtracting Fractions with Unlike Denominators   **243**

Instructional Resources

- *Study Guide Masters*, p. 45
- *Practice Masters*, p. 45
- *Enrichment Masters*, p. 45
- *Transparencies 6-4, A and B*
- *Assessment and Evaluation Masters*, pp. 154, 155
- *Technology Masters*, p. 12
- CD-ROM Program
  - Resource Lesson 6-4

Recommended Pacing	
Standard	Days 6 & 7 of 13
Honors	Day 6 of 12
Block	Day 4 of 7

1 FOCUS

5-Minute Check
(Lesson 6-3)

Add or subtract. Write the answer in simplest form.

1. $\frac{3}{8} + \frac{1}{8}$ $\frac{1}{2}$
2. $\frac{7}{12} - \frac{4}{12}$ $\frac{1}{4}$
3. $\frac{9}{14} - \frac{6}{14}$ $\frac{3}{14}$
4. $\frac{4}{7} + \frac{6}{7}$ $1\frac{3}{7}$
5. How much more is $\frac{5}{9}$ gallon than $\frac{2}{9}$ gallon? $\frac{1}{3}$ **gallon**

The 5-Minute Check is also available on **Transparency 6-4A** for this lesson.

2 TEACH

Transparency 6-4B contains a teaching aid for this lesson.

Using Graphs Work with students to find the LCD for the circle graph at the beginning of the lesson. Add the fractions and remind students that circle graphs compare parts of a whole.

MathPASS CD-ROM

This CD-ROM offers a complete, self-paced mathematics curriculum. Each lesson includes a pretest, tutorial, guided practice, and posttest. MathPASS Lessons 17 and 18 are correlated to this Student Edition lesson.
For Windows & Macintosh

Motivating the Lesson

Communication Have students discuss how they would determine which cake has more sweetener.
- a chocolate chip cake that has $\frac{3}{4}$ cup of sugar and $\frac{1}{3}$ cup of brown sugar
- a black walnut cake that has $\frac{1}{2}$ cup of brown sugar and $\frac{2}{3}$ cup of corn syrup

In Chapter 1, you evaluated expressions when the variables were whole numbers. Now you can also evaluate expressions when the variables are fractions.

Example **INTEGRATION**

3 **Algebra** Evaluate $p - q$ if $p = \frac{5}{6}$ and $q = \frac{3}{4}$.

$p - q = \frac{5}{6} - \frac{3}{4}$ *Replace p with $\frac{5}{6}$ and q with $\frac{3}{4}$.*

$= \frac{10}{12} - \frac{9}{12}$ *Rename $\frac{5}{6}$ as $\frac{10}{12}$ and $\frac{3}{4}$ as $\frac{9}{12}$.*

$= \frac{10 - 9}{12}$ *Subtract the numerators.*

$= \frac{1}{12}$

CHECK FOR UNDERSTANDING

Communicating Mathematics

Read and study the lesson to answer each question.

1. *Explain* why you must rename fractions with unlike denominators when you add or subtract them. **See margin.**

2. *Tell* how to find the LCD for $\frac{2}{3}$ and $\frac{5}{8}$. **See margin.**

Guided Practice

Add or subtract. Write the answer in simplest form.

3. $\frac{3}{8} + \frac{1}{16}$ $\frac{7}{16}$ 4. $\frac{3}{5} - \frac{1}{10}$ $\frac{1}{2}$ 5. $\frac{1}{3} - \frac{1}{4}$ $\frac{1}{12}$ 6. $\frac{5}{6} + \frac{3}{4}$ $1\frac{7}{12}$

7. What is $\frac{2}{3}$ minus $\frac{5}{12}$? $\frac{1}{4}$ 8. Find the sum of $\frac{1}{2}$ and $\frac{4}{5}$. $1\frac{3}{10}$

9. *Algebra* Evaluate $c + d$ if $c = \frac{1}{4}$ and $d = \frac{5}{8}$. $\frac{7}{8}$

EXERCISES

Practice

Add or subtract. Write the answer in simplest form.

10. $\frac{5}{8} + \frac{1}{4}$ $\frac{7}{8}$ 11. $\frac{9}{16} - \frac{1}{2}$ $\frac{1}{16}$ 12. $\frac{7}{8} - \frac{3}{4}$ $\frac{1}{8}$ 13. $\frac{3}{5} + \frac{1}{2}$ $1\frac{1}{10}$

14. $\frac{2}{3} - \frac{1}{5}$ $\frac{7}{15}$ 15. $\frac{7}{10} - \frac{1}{6}$ $\frac{8}{15}$ 16. $\frac{1}{6} + \frac{3}{4}$ $\frac{11}{12}$ 17. $\frac{11}{12} - \frac{5}{8}$ $\frac{7}{24}$

18. $\frac{1}{4} + \frac{2}{3}$ $\frac{11}{12}$ 19. $\frac{3}{4} - \frac{2}{5}$ $\frac{7}{20}$ 20. $\frac{5}{8} + \frac{5}{6}$ $1\frac{11}{24}$ 21. $\frac{5}{9} - \frac{1}{12}$ $\frac{17}{36}$

22. Find the sum of $\frac{3}{8}$ and $\frac{5}{6}$. $1\frac{5}{24}$

23. How much is $\frac{7}{8}$ minus $\frac{1}{2}$? $\frac{3}{8}$

24. How much more is $\frac{3}{4}$ cup than $\frac{2}{3}$ cup? $\frac{1}{12}$ **cup**

25. How much longer than $\frac{9}{16}$ inch is $\frac{7}{8}$ inch? $\frac{5}{16}$ **inch**

26. What is the sum of $\frac{2}{3}, \frac{5}{8},$ and $\frac{7}{12}$? $1\frac{7}{8}$

Solve each equation. Write the solution in simplest form.

27. $x = \frac{3}{10} + \frac{9}{20}$ $\frac{3}{4}$ 28. $\frac{4}{5} + \frac{1}{2} = y$ $1\frac{3}{10}$ 29. $\frac{5}{6} - \frac{3}{4} = d$ $\frac{1}{12}$

30. *Algebra* Evaluate $j - k$ if $j = \frac{3}{4}$ and $k = \frac{1}{3}$. $\frac{5}{12}$

31. *Algebra* Evaluate $r + s$ if $r = \frac{3}{5}$ and $s = \frac{7}{10}$. $1\frac{3}{10}$

Applications and Problem Solving

32. *Money Matters* Refer to the graph at the beginning of the lesson. How much bigger is the part that would be spent on taking care of parents than on a dream vacation? $\frac{21}{100}$

33. *Life Science* Proper diet is essential to raising champion horses. Their diet usually consists of grain and hay. The table shows the prescribed amounts that three horses are fed each time, two times a day. How many cans of grain are needed to feed all three horses per feeding? $1\frac{1}{2}$

Horse's Name	Amount of Grain	Amount of Hay
Penny	$\frac{3}{4}$ can	2 slices
Fancy Free	$\frac{1}{4}$ can	3 slices
Max	$\frac{1}{2}$ can	2 slices

Family Activity

Find the recipes for two of your family's favorite desserts. Make a list of the total amount of each ingredient you would need to make both recipes.

34. *Carpentry* The Cabinet Shop made a desktop by gluing a sheet of oak veneer to a sheet of $\frac{3}{4}$-inch plywood. The total thickness of the desktop is $\frac{13}{16}$ inch. What was the thickness of the oak veneer? $\frac{1}{16}$

35. *Critical Thinking* A piece of wire was cut into thirds. One-third was used. One-fifth of the remaining wire was used. The piece that remains is 16 feet long. What was the original length of the wire? **30 feet**

Mixed Review

36. Find $\frac{3}{5} - \frac{1}{5}$. *(Lesson 6-3)* $\frac{2}{5}$

37. *Measurement* Find the width of your pencil to the nearest eighth inch. *(Lesson 5-6)* **Sample answer:** $\frac{2}{8}$ or $\frac{1}{4}$ in.

38. *Geometry* Find the perimeter of the figure. *(Lesson 4-4)* **44 m**

39. *Standardized Test Practice* Alphonse Bielevich caught an Atlantic codfish in New Hampshire that weighed 98.75 pounds. Donald Vaughn caught a Pacific codfish in Alaska that weighed 30 pounds. What is the difference in the weights of the two fish? *(Lesson 3-6)* **D**

    A 98.45 lb

    B 95.75 lb

    C 70 lb

    D 68.75 lb

    E Not Here

For **Extra Practice,** see page 573.

40. *Algebra* Solve the equation $17 - m = 4$. *(Lesson 1-7)* **13**

Lesson 6-4 Adding and Subtracting Fractions with Unlike Denominators   **245**

Extending the Lesson

Enrichment Masters, p. 45

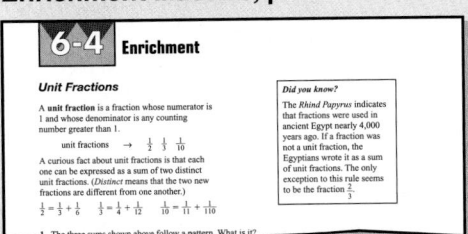

Activity Have students survey parents or other adults about the use of fractions and measurements in their work. Invite a parent or other adult to speak to the class about the use of fractions and the importance of accurate measurements in his or her career.

Family Activity

Have students bring recipes to class and explain how they determined the total amount of each ingredient needed. Suggest that students make one of the desserts with their family. Ask them how their knowledge of fractions helped them make the dessert.

4 ASSESS

Closing Activity

Writing Have students work in small groups to create word problems that can be solved by using equations that involve addition or subtraction of fractions. Ask them to use fractions that relate to the group; for example, the fraction of the group that has curly hair or blue eyes.

Chapter 6, Quiz B (Lessons 6-3 and 6-4) is available in the *Assessment and Evaluation Masters,* p. 155.

Mid-Chapter Test (Lessons 6-1 through 6-4) is available in the *Assessment and Evaluation Masters,* p. 154.

Practice Masters, p. 45

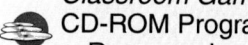

Instructional Resources
- *Study Guide Masters*, p. 46
- *Practice Masters*, p. 46
- *Enrichment Masters*, p. 46
- Transparencies 6-5, A and B
- *Classroom Games*, pp. 15–18

 CD-ROM Program
- Resource Lesson 6-5
- Interactive Lesson 6-5

Recommended Pacing	
Standard	Day 8 of 13
Honors	Day 7 of 12
Block	Day 4 of 7

1 FOCUS

 5-Minute Check
(Lesson 6-4)

Add or subtract. Write the answer in simplest form.

1. $\frac{2}{5} - \frac{1}{3}$ $\frac{1}{15}$

2. $\frac{3}{8} + \frac{2}{5}$ $\frac{31}{40}$

3. $\frac{9}{10} - \frac{1}{4}$ $\frac{13}{20}$

4. $\frac{1}{8} + \frac{1}{6}$ $\frac{7}{24}$

5. Evaluate $p - q$ if $p = \frac{2}{3}$ and $q = \frac{2}{5}$. $\frac{4}{15}$

The 5-Minute Check is also available on **Transparency 6-5A** for this lesson.

Motivating the Lesson

Problem Solving Ask students how they would solve the following problem. *Part of the daily diet of polar bears at the Bronx Zoo is $1\frac{1}{4}$ pounds of apples and a $1\frac{1}{2}$-pound mixture of oats and barley. What is the combined weight of these items?* $2\frac{3}{4}$ pounds

---

6-5 Adding and Subtracting Mixed Numbers

What you'll learn
You'll learn to add and subtract mixed numbers.

When am I ever going to use this?
You'll add and subtract mixed numbers when you work with lumber dimensions.

Sandy is taking a flight from Atlanta to San Antonio. Travel time is about $2\frac{3}{4}$ hours. When she reports to the gate, they tell her the flight has a $1\frac{1}{2}$-hour delay. In how many hours will she arrive in San Antonio?

You need to find $2\frac{3}{4} + 1\frac{1}{2}$. You can use models to solve the problem.

HANDS-ON MINI-LAB

Work with a partner. paper plates   scissors

Try This
- Place two paper plates in front of you to show the whole number 2 in the mixed number $2\frac{3}{4}$. Cut another paper plate into fourths. Place three fourths of the plate in front of you to show the fraction $\frac{3}{4}$ in the mixed number $2\frac{3}{4}$.

- Use more paper plates to show $1\frac{1}{2}$.

- Combine the pieces to make as many whole paper plates as you can.

Talk About It
1. How many whole paper plates do you have? **4**
2. What fraction is represented by the pieces of paper plate that you have left over? $\frac{1}{4}$
3. How long will it be before Sandy arrives in San Antonio?
4. Use paper plates to find $2\frac{3}{4} - 1\frac{1}{2}$.

3. $4\frac{1}{4}$ hours

4. $1\frac{1}{4}$; See students' work.

Multiple Learning Styles

 Naturalist Have students bring in samples from nature such as sticks, leaves, feathers, nuts, or pinecones. Have them measure the lengths of the items using fractional parts of customary measures. Then have students write problems that require adding or subtracting the lengths of the sticks, leaves, and so on.

The Mini-Lab suggests the following rule.

Adding and Subtracting Mixed Numbers	1. Add or subtract the fractions. 2. Then add or subtract the whole numbers. 3. Rename and simplify if necessary.

Examples

1 Find $4\frac{2}{3} - 2\frac{1}{3}$. *Estimate: 5 − 2 = 3*

Subtract the fractions.

$$\begin{array}{r} 4\frac{2}{3} \\ -2\frac{1}{3} \\ \hline \frac{1}{3} \end{array}$$

→

Subtract the whole numbers.

$$\begin{array}{r} 4\frac{2}{3} \\ -2\frac{1}{3} \\ \hline 2\frac{1}{3} \end{array}$$

2 Find $12\frac{1}{4} + 3\frac{5}{6}$. *Estimate: 12 + 4 = 16*

Add the fractions.

$$\begin{array}{r} 12\frac{1}{4} \\ +3\frac{5}{6} \\ \hline \end{array}$$

→

$$\begin{array}{r} 12\frac{3}{12} \\ +3\frac{10}{12} \\ \hline \frac{13}{12} \end{array}$$

→

Add the whole numbers.

$$\begin{array}{r} 12\frac{3}{12} \\ +3\frac{10}{12} \\ \hline 15\frac{13}{12} \end{array}$$ *Rename $\frac{13}{12}$ as $1\frac{1}{12}$.*

$15 + 1\frac{1}{12} = 16\frac{1}{12}$

INTEGRATION **3** **Algebra** Evaluate $x - y$ if $x = 5\frac{9}{10}$ and $y = 2\frac{1}{2}$.

$\begin{aligned} x - y &= 5\frac{9}{10} - 2\frac{1}{2} \quad \text{\textit{The LCM of 2 and 10 is 10.}} \\ &= 5\frac{9}{10} - 2\frac{5}{10} \quad \text{\textit{Rename $2\frac{1}{2}$ as $2\frac{5}{10}$.}} \\ &= 3\frac{4}{10} \text{ or } 3\frac{2}{5} \end{aligned}$

INTEGRATION **4** **Geometry** Find the perimeter of the triangle.

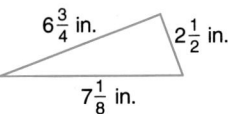
$6\frac{3}{4}$ in. $2\frac{1}{2}$ in. $7\frac{1}{8}$ in.

$P = 2\frac{1}{2} + 6\frac{3}{4} + 7\frac{1}{8}$ *The LCM of 2, 4, and 8 is 8.*

$P = 2\frac{4}{8} + 6\frac{6}{8} + 7\frac{1}{8}$ *Rename $\frac{1}{2}$ as $\frac{4}{8}$ and $\frac{3}{4}$ as $\frac{6}{8}$.*

$P = \frac{4 + 6 + 1}{8} + 2 + 6 + 7$ *Add the fractions. Then add the whole numbers.*

$P = \frac{11}{8} + 15$

$P = 15\frac{11}{8}$ or $16\frac{3}{8}$ *Rename $\frac{11}{8}$ as $1\frac{3}{8}$. $15 + 1\frac{3}{8} = 16\frac{3}{8}$.*

The perimeter of the triangle is $16\frac{3}{8}$ inches.

LOOK BACK
You can refer to Lesson 4-4 to review perimeter.

Lesson 6-5 Adding and Subtracting Mixed Numbers **247**

2 TEACH

 Transparency 6-5B contains a teaching aid for this lesson.

Using the Mini-Lab Each group will need at least four paper plates. If paper plates are not available, students can trace circles on sheets of paper and then cut them out.

Teaching Tip Before Example 1, stress the importance of adding and subtracting the fractions before adding and subtracting the whole numbers. This will encourage good habits for later work with renaming mixed numbers.

In-Class Examples
For Example 1
Find $12\frac{3}{8} - 5\frac{1}{8}$. $7\frac{1}{4}$

For Example 2
Find $3\frac{7}{9} + 15\frac{1}{6}$. $18\frac{17}{18}$

For Example 3
Evaluate $f + g$ if $f = 21\frac{4}{5}$ and $g = 6\frac{1}{10}$. $27\frac{9}{10}$

For Example 4
Find the perimeter of the trapezoid. $25\frac{7}{12}$ ft

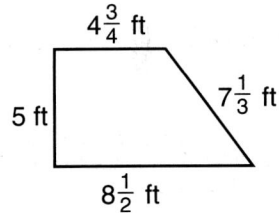
$4\frac{3}{4}$ ft $7\frac{1}{3}$ ft 5 ft $8\frac{1}{2}$ ft

Lesson 6-5 **247**

Check for Understanding

If students need additional practice or instruction after completing Exercises 1–11, one of these options may be helpful.
- Extra Practice, see p. 574
- Reteaching Activity
- *Study Guide Masters*, p. 46
- *Practice Masters*, p. 46

Assignment Guide

Core: 13–31 odd, 32–36
Enriched: 12–28 even, 29–36
All: Self Test, 1–10

Additional Answer

2. **Sample answer:** The length of a rectangle is $3\frac{5}{8}$ inches, and the width is $1\frac{1}{2}$ inches. How much longer is the length than the width?

CHECK FOR UNDERSTANDING

Communicating Mathematics

Read and study the lesson to answer each question.

1. *Tell* the first step you should take when adding or subtracting mixed numbers. **Sample answer: Find the LCM of the denominators.**

2. *Write a Problem* where you need to subtract $1\frac{1}{2}$ from $3\frac{5}{8}$. **See margin.**

HANDS-ON MATH

3. *Make a model* to show $2\frac{1}{4} + 2\frac{3}{4}$. **See Answer Appendix.**

Guided Practice

Add or subtract. Write the answer in simplest form.

4. $6\frac{3}{4} - 2\frac{1}{4}$ $4\frac{1}{2}$ 5. $7\frac{5}{8} + 3\frac{1}{8}$ $10\frac{3}{4}$ 6. $8\frac{9}{10} + 6\frac{1}{4}$ $15\frac{3}{20}$

7. $21\frac{4}{5} + 6\frac{3}{10}$ $28\frac{1}{10}$ 8. $11\frac{1}{3} - 8\frac{1}{6}$ $3\frac{1}{6}$ 9. $7\frac{2}{3} - \frac{3}{5}$ $7\frac{1}{15}$

10. *Algebra* Evaluate $j + k$ if $j = 9\frac{3}{5}$ and $k = 11\frac{3}{4}$. **$21\frac{7}{20}$**

11. *Life Science* A rare African giant frog was captured in 1989 on the Sanaga River, in Cameroon. The body of the frog measured $14\frac{1}{2}$ inches. With its legs fully extended, the frog was $34\frac{1}{2}$ inches long. How much longer was the frog when its legs were extended? **20 inches**

EXERCISES

Practice

Add or subtract. Write the answer in simplest form.

12. $4\frac{3}{5} + 2\frac{2}{5}$ 7 13. $3\frac{5}{6} - 1\frac{1}{6}$ $2\frac{2}{3}$ 14. $2\frac{1}{2} + 3\frac{2}{3}$ $6\frac{1}{6}$

15. $13\frac{1}{3} + 5\frac{3}{4}$ $19\frac{1}{12}$ 16. $8\frac{9}{10} - 6\frac{1}{4}$ $2\frac{13}{20}$ 17. $5\frac{3}{4} - 3\frac{1}{2}$ $2\frac{1}{4}$

18. $17\frac{3}{10} + 9\frac{1}{4}$ $26\frac{11}{20}$ 19. $7\frac{4}{5} + \frac{3}{5}$ $8\frac{2}{5}$ 20. $8\frac{1}{3} - 2\frac{1}{6}$ $6\frac{1}{6}$

21. $18\frac{5}{6} - 18\frac{5}{8}$ $\frac{5}{24}$ 22. $11\frac{3}{4} + 9\frac{3}{5}$ $21\frac{7}{20}$ 23. $14\frac{3}{5} - 5\frac{7}{16}$ $9\frac{13}{80}$

24. How much longer is $28\frac{1}{2}$ seconds than $23\frac{3}{10}$ seconds? **$5\frac{1}{5}$ seconds**

25. Find the sum of $4\frac{1}{5}$, $8\frac{7}{8}$, and $1\frac{7}{10}$. **$14\frac{31}{40}$**

Evaluate each expression if $a = 2\frac{3}{4}$, $b = 5\frac{1}{6}$, and $c = 7\frac{2}{3}$.

26. $a + b$ $7\frac{11}{12}$ 27. $c - b$ $2\frac{1}{2}$ 28. $a + c$ $10\frac{5}{12}$

Applications and Problem Solving

29. *Health* Dakota's baby sister weighed $7\frac{1}{2}$ pounds at birth. She weighed $8\frac{3}{4}$ pounds at her one-month checkup. How much weight did the baby gain? **$1\frac{1}{4}$ pounds**

Study Guide Masters, p. 46

Name_____ Date_____

6-5 **Study Guide**

Adding and Subtracting Mixed Numbers

Follow these steps to add and subtract mixed numbers.

Examples	Write equivalent fractions with a common denominator. Add or subtract the fractions.	Add or subtract the whole numbers. Rename and simplify. If necessary.

1 $4\frac{7}{8}$
$+ 3\frac{1}{2}$

2 $5\frac{4}{6}$
$- 3\frac{1}{2}$

Add or subtract. Write each answer in simplest form.

1. $6\frac{1}{4} + 2\frac{1}{4}$ $8\frac{1}{2}$ 2. $7\frac{7}{8} - 4\frac{2}{9}$ $3\frac{5}{9}$ 3. $8\frac{2}{3} + 2\frac{1}{3}$ 11

4. $6\frac{5}{7} - 5\frac{2}{7}$ $1\frac{3}{7}$ 5. $10\frac{1}{2} + 4\frac{1}{8}$ $14\frac{5}{8}$ 6. $12\frac{5}{6} - 3\frac{1}{3}$ $9\frac{1}{2}$

7. $7\frac{1}{10} + 2\frac{1}{5}$ $9\frac{3}{10}$ 8. $9\frac{1}{2} - 5\frac{1}{6}$ $4\frac{1}{3}$ 9. $5\frac{1}{4} + 2\frac{5}{8}$ $8\frac{3}{8}$

10. $18\frac{1}{4} - 6\frac{1}{4}$ 12 11. $5\frac{6}{7} + 4\frac{2}{3}$ $10\frac{11}{21}$ 12. $9\frac{3}{4} - 2\frac{1}{6}$ $7\frac{7}{12}$

© Glencoe/McGraw-Hill T46 Mathematics: Applications and Connections, Course 1

■ Reteaching the Lesson ■

Activity Write examples such as $2\frac{3}{4} + 5\frac{1}{8}$ on index cards. (Include subtraction examples also.) Have groups of three students add the fractions first, then the whole numbers, and simplify the answer. Have students take turns completing each part.

MathPASS CD-ROM

This CD-ROM offers a complete, self-paced mathematics curriculum. Each lesson includes a pretest, tutorial, guided practice, and posttest. MathPASS Lessons 19 and 20 are correlated to this Student Edition lesson.
For Windows & Macintosh

30a. $68\frac{2}{5}$ million acres

30d. more; Sample answer: $2\frac{9}{10}$ is $\frac{1}{10}$ more than $2\frac{4}{5}$

32. Sample answer: $1\frac{3}{4} + 2\frac{1}{2} = 4\frac{1}{4}$

30. *Agriculture* The table shows the acreage of crops planted in the United States in two different years.

   a. In year 1, how many more acres of wheat were planted than barley?

   b. Find the total acreage used to raise corn, wheat, cotton, and rice in year 1. **$172\frac{3}{5}$ million acres**

   c. How many more acres of soybeans were projected to be planted in year 2? **$4\frac{3}{5}$ million acres**

   d. Were more or fewer acres of rice projected to be planted in year 2? Explain.

Acreage (millions)		
Crop	Year 1	Year 2 (est.)
corn	$79\frac{1}{2}$	$81\frac{1}{2}$
wheat	$75\frac{3}{5}$	$69\frac{1}{5}$
soybeans	$64\frac{1}{5}$	$68\frac{4}{5}$
cotton	$14\frac{7}{10}$	$14\frac{1}{2}$
sorghum	$13\frac{1}{5}$	$10\frac{9}{10}$
barley	$7\frac{1}{5}$	7
oats	$4\frac{7}{10}$	$5\frac{3}{10}$
rice	$2\frac{4}{5}$	$2\frac{9}{10}$

Source: Agriculture Department Economic Research Service

31. *Write a Problem* that involves the two amounts of acreage of cotton given in the table in Exercise 30. **See margin.**

32. *Critical Thinking* Use the numbers 1, 2, 3, 4, 1, and 2 to create an addition of mixed numbers problem so that the sum is $4\frac{1}{4}$.

Mixed Review

33. **Standardized Test Practice** What is the perimeter of the figure? *(Lesson 6-4)* **D**

   A $\frac{16}{24}$ in.   **B** $\frac{16}{8}$ in.

   C 2 in.   **D** $2\frac{1}{2}$ in.

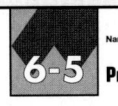
$\frac{1}{4}$ in. $\frac{3}{4}$ in. $\frac{7}{8}$ in. $\frac{5}{8}$ in.

34. Express $\frac{100}{6}$ as a mixed number. *(Lesson 5-5)* **$16\frac{2}{3}$**

35. *Measurement* If a rabbit has a mass of 800 grams, what is its mass in kilograms? *(Lesson 4-9)* **0.8 kg**

36. Estimate $21.1 + 19 + 20 + 20.3 + 20.1 + 18.8$. *(Lesson 3-5)*
   Sample answer: $20 + 20 + 20 + 20 + 20 + 20 = 120$

For **Extra Practice**, see page 574.

For **Extra Practice**, see page 574.

CHAPTER 6 — Mid-Chapter Self Test

1. *Food* You are not sure how much salt to put in a pot of chili. Should you put one-half teaspoon or one teaspoon of salt in the pot? Explain. *(Lesson 6-1)* **See margin.**

Estimate. *(Lesson 6-2)*

2. $4\frac{3}{4} - 2\frac{2}{5}$ $5 - 2 = 3$

3. $22\frac{3}{8} - 14\frac{9}{10}$ $22 - 15 = 7$

4. $9\frac{1}{3} + 5\frac{5}{6}$ $9 + 6 = 15$

Add or subtract. Write the answer in simplest form. *(Lessons 6-3, 6-4, and 6-5)*

5. $\frac{13}{20} - \frac{7}{20}$ $\frac{3}{10}$

6. $\frac{4}{5} + \frac{3}{5}$ $1\frac{2}{5}$

7. $\frac{2}{5} - \frac{1}{6}$ $\frac{7}{30}$

8. $\frac{3}{4} + \frac{7}{10}$ $1\frac{9}{20}$

9. $13\frac{2}{3} + 6\frac{1}{2}$ $20\frac{1}{6}$

10. $11\frac{5}{8} - 9\frac{2}{5}$ $2\frac{9}{40}$

Lesson 6-5 Adding and Subtracting Mixed Numbers   **249**

Extending the Lesson

Enrichment Masters, p. 46

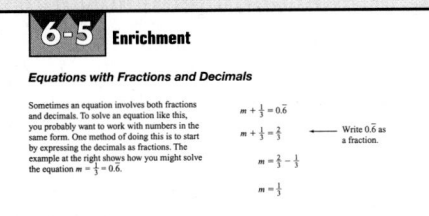

6-5 Enrichment

Equations with Fractions and Decimals

Sometimes an equation involves both fractions and decimals. To solve an equation like this, you probably want to work with numbers in the same form. One method of doing this is to start by expressing the decimals as fractions. The example at the right shows how you might solve the equation $m = \frac{1}{3} = 0.6$.

$m + \frac{1}{3} = 0.6$

$m + \frac{1}{3} = \frac{2}{3}$ Write 0.6 as a fraction.

$m = \frac{2}{3} - \frac{1}{3}$

$m = \frac{1}{3}$

Activity Challenge students to use what they know about decimals and fractions to solve the following problem. *Winona buys stationery for $0.99 a pound. She bought $3\frac{2}{5}$ pounds of pink paper and $1\frac{1}{2}$ pounds of purple paper. Not including tax, how much did Winona spend?* **$4.85**

---

4 ASSESS

Closing Activity

Speaking Name a sum or difference such as $2\frac{4}{7}$. Have students think of addition or subtraction problems that have this mixed number as the result. Then have students take turns giving each other sums or differences and finding corresponding problems.

Mid-Chapter Self Test

The Mid-Chapter Self Test reviews concepts in Lessons 6-1 through 6-5. Lesson references are given so students can review concepts not yet mastered.

Additional Answer

31. Sample answer: How much more cotton was planted in 1996 than was estimated to be planted in 1997?

Additional Answer for the Self Test

1. Sample answer: To avoid ruining the chili, you should round down to one-half teaspoon of salt. You can always add more.

Practice Masters, p. 46

6-5 Practice

Name _____ Date _____

Adding and Subtracting Mixed Numbers

Add or subtract. Write the answer in simplest form.

1. $2\frac{2}{3} + 4\frac{1}{9}$ $6\frac{5}{7}$ 2. $6\frac{3}{8} + 3\frac{3}{4}$ $10\frac{5}{9}$ 3. $8\frac{7}{12} - 5\frac{5}{12}$ $3\frac{1}{6}$

4. $10\frac{1}{2} - 2\frac{1}{5}$ $8\frac{1}{10}$ 5. $6\frac{5}{6} + \frac{3}{8}$ $7\frac{5}{24}$ 6. $9\frac{4}{5} + 2\frac{2}{3}$ $12\frac{7}{15}$

7. $7\frac{11}{16} - 3\frac{7}{16}$ $4\frac{1}{2}$ 8. $5\frac{8}{9} - 3\frac{1}{2}$ $2\frac{13}{18}$ 9. $8\frac{3}{4} + 6\frac{4}{5}$ $15\frac{3}{20}$

10. $13\frac{7}{10} - 8\frac{7}{15}$ $5\frac{1}{6}$ 11. $11\frac{1}{3} - 3\frac{4}{7}$ $8\frac{2}{21}$ 12. $3\frac{5}{9} + 7\frac{4}{9}$ 11

13. $9\frac{1}{2} + 3\frac{5}{9}$ $13\frac{7}{18}$ 14. $14\frac{7}{8} - 8\frac{1}{4}$ $6\frac{1}{8}$ 15. $12\frac{5}{12} - 5\frac{7}{18}$ $7\frac{1}{36}$

16. $8\frac{7}{10} + 7\frac{9}{10}$ $16\frac{3}{5}$ 17. $13\frac{7}{12} - 9\frac{1}{4}$ $4\frac{1}{3}$ 18. $2\frac{4}{7} + 7\frac{1}{2}$ $10\frac{3}{14}$

19. $14\frac{2}{3} + \frac{5}{6}$ $15\frac{1}{2}$ 20. $7\frac{1}{4} - 6\frac{1}{8}$ $1\frac{7}{24}$ 21. $10\frac{5}{6} - 3\frac{5}{6}$ 7

22. $8\frac{2}{7} + 3\frac{4}{5}$ $12\frac{3}{35}$ 23. $5\frac{6}{11} + 5\frac{1}{3}$ $11\frac{2}{33}$ 24. $9\frac{11}{12} - 7\frac{3}{4}$ $2\frac{9}{16}$

25. $4\frac{9}{10} - 3\frac{2}{5}$ $1\frac{1}{2}$ 26. $8\frac{2}{3} + 9\frac{5}{8}$ $18\frac{7}{24}$ 27. $7\frac{19}{20} - 4\frac{7}{10}$ $3\frac{1}{4}$

Solve each equation. Write the solution in simplest form.

28. $x = 2\frac{5}{6} + 3\frac{5}{7}$ $6\frac{5}{42}$ 29. $16\frac{5}{12} - 7\frac{5}{9} = n$ $9\frac{7}{36}$

30. $a = 18\frac{3}{20} - 5\frac{1}{15}$ $13\frac{1}{12}$ 31. $12\frac{7}{15} - 5\frac{1}{3} = c$ $7\frac{2}{15}$

© Glencoe/McGraw-Hill   T46   Mathematics: Applications and Connections, Course 1

Lesson 6-5   **249**

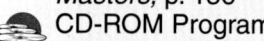
Recommended Pacing	
Standard	Days 9 & 10 of 13
Honors	Days 8 & 9 of 12
Block	Day 5 of 7

1 FOCUS

 5-Minute Check
(Lesson 6-5)

Add or subtract. Write the answer in simplest form.

1. $7\frac{5}{6} - 3\frac{3}{4}$ $4\frac{1}{12}$

2. $5\frac{2}{5} + 1\frac{3}{10}$ $6\frac{7}{10}$

3. $15\frac{5}{7} - 7\frac{1}{2}$ $8\frac{3}{14}$

4. Aaron bought $3\frac{5}{6}$ pounds of bananas and $4\frac{1}{2}$ pounds of oranges. How many pounds of fruit did he buy? $8\frac{1}{3}$ lb

5. Evaluate $a - b$ if $a = 3\frac{5}{12}$ and $b = 1\frac{3}{4}$. $1\frac{2}{3}$

 The 5-Minute Check is also available on **Transparency 6-6A** for this lesson.

Motivating the Lesson

Hands-On Activity Have students cut models from centimeter grid paper to illustrate renaming mixed numbers. The models below illustrate renaming $2\frac{1}{4}$ as $1\frac{5}{4}$.

What you'll learn
You'll learn to subtract mixed numbers involving renaming.

When am I ever going to use this?
You'll subtract mixed numbers involving renaming when you work with stock market prices.

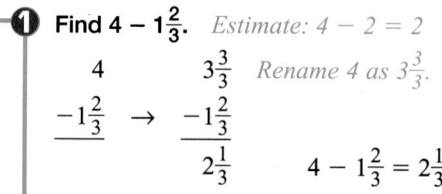 **LOOK BACK**
You can refer to Lesson 5-5 to review renaming mixed numbers.

Brenda belongs to a cycling club. The club meets and rides every weekend. Brenda rides during the week to stay in shape. On Tuesday she rode her bike $4\frac{1}{2}$ miles, and on Thursday she rode $6\frac{1}{4}$ miles. How much farther did she ride on Thursday? You need to subtract to compare the mileage.

$$6\frac{1}{4} \qquad 6\frac{1}{4}$$
$$-4\frac{1}{2} \rightarrow -4\frac{2}{4}$$

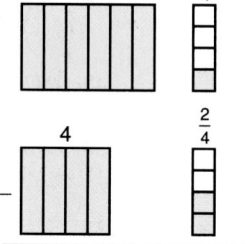

Notice that you cannot subtract $\frac{2}{4}$ from $\frac{1}{4}$. Rename $6\frac{1}{4}$ as $5\frac{5}{4}$.

$$6\frac{1}{4} \qquad 6\frac{1}{4} \qquad 5\frac{5}{4}$$
$$-4\frac{1}{2} \rightarrow -4\frac{2}{4} \rightarrow -4\frac{2}{4}$$
$$\overline{\qquad 1\frac{3}{4}}$$

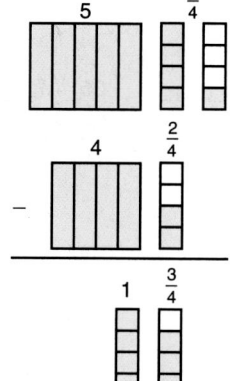

Brenda rode $1\frac{3}{4}$ miles farther on Thursday.

As shown above, sometimes it is necessary to rename the fraction of a mixed number as an improper fraction in order to subtract.

Example **1** Find $4 - 1\frac{2}{3}$. *Estimate: $4 - 2 = 2$*

$$4 \qquad\qquad 3\frac{3}{3} \quad \textit{Rename 4 as } 3\frac{3}{3}.$$
$$-1\frac{2}{3} \rightarrow -1\frac{2}{3}$$
$$\overline{\qquad 2\frac{1}{3}} \qquad 4 - 1\frac{2}{3} = 2\frac{1}{3}$$

Multiple Learning Styles

Verbal/Linguistic Have each pair of students create a large map on a piece of paper, labeling fractional lengths on it. Have them write a series of directions to travel a path on their map that would be achieved by adding or subtracting fractional lengths. Have groups exchange maps and directions and complete.

Examples ❷ Find $17\frac{1}{4} - 3\frac{5}{8}$.   *Estimate: 17 − 4 = 13*

Step 1 $17\frac{1}{4}$ → $17\frac{2}{8}$ *The LCM of 4 and 8 is 8.*
$-3\frac{5}{8}$ → $-3\frac{5}{8}$

Step 2 $17\frac{2}{8}$ → $16\frac{10}{8}$ *Since $\frac{5}{8}$ is greater than $\frac{2}{8}$, you must*
$-3\frac{5}{8}$ → $-3\frac{5}{8}$ *rename $17\frac{2}{8}$ as $16\frac{10}{8}$.*
$\overline{\phantom{-3\frac{5}{8}}13\frac{5}{8}}$

$17\frac{1}{4} - 3\frac{5}{8} = 13\frac{5}{8}$

CONNECTION ❸ **Life Science** A male California sea lion grows to be between $6\frac{1}{2}$ and 8 feet long. Find the difference between the greatest and least lengths.

Subtract $8 - 6\frac{1}{2}$.   *Estimate: 8 − 7 = 1*

8 → $7\frac{2}{2}$ *Rename 8 as $7\frac{2}{2}$.*
$-6\frac{1}{2}$ → $-6\frac{1}{2}$
$\overline{\phantom{-6\frac{1}{2}}1\frac{1}{2}}$

The difference between the greatest and least lengths is $1\frac{1}{2}$ feet.

CHECK FOR UNDERSTANDING

Communicating Mathematics

Read and study the lesson to answer each question.

1. *Draw* a model or use paper plates to show how to subtract $4\frac{1}{2} - 2\frac{3}{8}$. **See Answer Appendix.**

2. **Sample answer: The number being subtracted is $\frac{6}{8}$ or $\frac{7}{8}$.**

2. *Tell* why you might rename $3\frac{5}{8}$ as $2\frac{13}{8}$ in a subtraction problem.

3. *You Decide* Gail subtracted $10\frac{1}{5} - 3\frac{4}{5}$. Her answer was $6\frac{7}{5}$. Does Gail's answer make sense? How do you think Gail got her answer? **See Answer Appendix.**

Guided Practice

Complete.

4. $4\frac{1}{8} = 3\frac{\blacksquare}{8}$ **9**

5. $\blacksquare = 29\frac{4}{4}$ **30**

Subtract. Write the answer in simplest form.

6. $6\frac{3}{10}$ **$4\frac{1}{2}$**
   $-1\frac{4}{5}$

7. $11\frac{1}{6} - 8\frac{1}{3}$ **$2\frac{5}{6}$**

8. $7\frac{1}{4} - \frac{3}{5}$ **$6\frac{13}{20}$**

9. $3\frac{5}{8} - 2\frac{3}{4}$ **$\frac{7}{8}$**

10. *Transportation* The U.S. Department of Transportation regulations prohibit a truck driver from driving more than 70 hours in any 8-day period. Mr. Galvez has driven $53\frac{3}{4}$ hours in the last 6 days. How many more hours is he allowed to drive during the next 2 days? **$16\frac{1}{4}$ hours**

Lesson 6-6 Subtracting Mixed Numbers with Renaming **251**

Reteaching the Lesson

Activity Have pairs of students make and use drawings to model examples such as $12 - 3\frac{1}{4}$. Ask them to make enough shapes to show 12. Have them illustrate renaming by cutting one of the shapes. Then have them remove $3\frac{1}{4}$ to find the difference.

Error Analysis
Watch for students who forget to subtract the whole numbers.
Prevent by encouraging students to develop a habit of estimating and checking each answer.

---

2 TEACH

 Transparency 6-6B contains a teaching aid for this lesson.

Thinking Algebraically Tell students they can solve mixed number problems by renaming fractions as variables. After finding the LCM in Example 2, have students write an equation where x represents the numerator of the renamed mixed number $17\frac{1}{4}$.

Teaching Tip Before Example 1, as a review, write corresponding pairs of mixed numbers and improper fractions in random order on the chalkboard and have students match them.

In-Class Examples
Subtract. Write the answer in simplest form.

For Example 1
a. $15 - 4\frac{1}{5}$ $10\frac{4}{5}$

b. $21 - 8\frac{3}{7}$ $12\frac{4}{7}$

For Example 2
a. $4\frac{2}{5} - 2\frac{3}{4}$ $1\frac{13}{20}$

b. $7\frac{1}{9} - 3\frac{2}{3}$ $3\frac{4}{9}$

For Example 3
Mr. Jones is putting molding around two doors. He needs $17\frac{1}{6}$ feet of molding for a closet door and $16\frac{2}{3}$ feet of molding for the entry door. If he buys 35 feet of molding, how much molding will he have left after he finishes the doors? $1\frac{1}{6}$ ft

---

3 PRACTICE/APPLY

Check for Understanding
If students need additional practice or instruction after completing Exercises 1–10, one of these options may be helpful.
• Extra Practice, see p. 574
• Reteaching Activity
• *Study Guide Masters*, p. 47
• *Practice Masters*, p. 47

Lesson 6-6 **251**

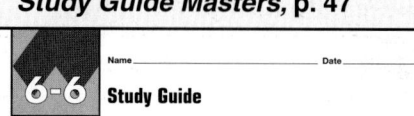

Exercise 37 asks students to advance to the next stage of work on the Chapter Project. You may wish to suggest to the students that they follow their instructions on their maps. This will ensure that their maps will make sense to others.

Study Guide Masters, p. 47

EXERCISES

Practice

Complete.

11. $3\frac{5}{8} = \blacksquare\frac{13}{8}$ **2**

12. $\blacksquare\frac{3}{10} = 5\frac{13}{10}$ **6**

13. $9\frac{2}{5} = 8\frac{\blacksquare}{5}$ **7**

14. $7\frac{\blacksquare}{3} = 6\frac{4}{3}$ **1**

15. $7\frac{13}{16} = 6\frac{\blacksquare}{16}$ **29**

16. $\blacksquare\frac{11}{12} = 7\frac{23}{12}$ **8**

Subtract. Write the answer in simplest form.

17. $\begin{array}{r} 30\frac{1}{4} \\ -24\frac{3}{4} \end{array}$ $5\frac{1}{2}$

18. $\begin{array}{r} 20\frac{1}{5} \\ -4\frac{3}{5} \end{array}$ $15\frac{3}{5}$

19. $\begin{array}{r} 5\frac{2}{5} \\ -1\frac{7}{10} \end{array}$ $3\frac{7}{10}$

20. $\begin{array}{r} 18\frac{3}{8} \\ -5\frac{3}{4} \end{array}$ $12\frac{5}{8}$

21. $7\frac{1}{3} - 2\frac{3}{4}$ $4\frac{7}{12}$

22. $15\frac{3}{8} - 9\frac{5}{6}$ $5\frac{13}{24}$

23. $16\frac{1}{6} - 8\frac{3}{4}$ $7\frac{5}{12}$

24. $13 - 8\frac{7}{8}$ $4\frac{1}{8}$

25. $30 - 20\frac{1}{4}$ $9\frac{3}{4}$

26. $6\frac{4}{5} - 1\frac{5}{6}$ $4\frac{29}{30}$

27. Find the difference between $11\frac{4}{7}$ and $3\frac{3}{5}$. $7\frac{34}{35}$

28. What is $2\frac{1}{2}$ less than $8\frac{1}{5}$? $5\frac{7}{10}$

Solve each equation. Write the solution in simplest form.

29. $f = 9\frac{1}{3} - 8\frac{2}{3}$ $\frac{2}{3}$

30. $p = 18\frac{5}{8} - 8\frac{3}{4}$ $9\frac{7}{8}$

31. $12\frac{3}{5} - 10\frac{5}{6} = t$ $1\frac{23}{30}$

Evaluate each expression if $a = 4\frac{1}{2}$, $b = 3\frac{2}{3}$, and $c = 2\frac{5}{6}$.

32. $a - b$ $\frac{5}{6}$

33. $a - c$ $1\frac{2}{3}$

34. $b - c$ $\frac{5}{6}$

Applications and Problem Solving

35a. softball; $2\frac{5}{8}$ to $3\frac{1}{8}$ in. larger

35b. softball; 1 to 2 ounces heavier

36. $8\frac{1}{2}$ in. by $2\frac{1}{2}$ in.

35. *Sports* Some of the differences between Olympic softball and Olympic baseball are listed in the table.

   a. Which sport's ball has the larger circumference? How much larger is it compared to the other sport's ball?

	Olympic Softball	Olympic Baseball
Size	$11\frac{7}{8}$ to $12\frac{1}{8}$ inches in circumference	9 to $9\frac{1}{4}$ inches in circumference
Weight	$6\frac{1}{4}$ to 7 ounces	5 to $5\frac{1}{4}$ ounces

   b. Which ball is heavier? How much heavier is it?

36. *Geometry* Suppose you fold the short side of an $8\frac{1}{2}$ inch-by-11 inch piece of paper to align with the long side. What are the dimensions of the rectangle at the side of the paper?

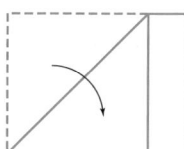

37. *Working on the* **CHAPTER Project** Refer to the table on page 227.

   a. Complete your map using the remaining landmarks. **See students' work.**

   b. How much longer is the path from the start, through the landmarks, to the treasure than the shortest distance between the start and the treasure? $1\frac{3}{4}$ in.

Study Guide

6-6 **Study Guide**

Name _____ Date _____

Subtracting Mixed Numbers with Renaming

Sometimes it is necessary to rename a mixed number as an improper fraction before you can subtract.

Examples

1 $6\frac{1}{4}$ → $6\frac{1}{4}$ You cannot subtract $\frac{3}{4}$ from $\frac{1}{4}$. → $5\frac{5}{4}$ Rename $6\frac{1}{4}$
$-2\frac{3}{4}$ → $-2\frac{3}{4}$ $-2\frac{3}{4}$ as $5\frac{5}{4}$.
                           $3\frac{3}{4}$ Then subtract.

2 8 → $7\frac{8}{8}$ Rename 8 as $7\frac{8}{8}$.
$-4\frac{5}{8}$ → $-4\frac{5}{8}$ Then subtract.
          $3\frac{3}{8}$

Complete.

1. $7\frac{1}{6} = \square\frac{11}{6}$ **6**

2. $4\frac{3}{4} = 3\frac{\square}{4}$ **7**

3. $2\frac{3}{8} = 1\frac{\square}{8}$ **11**

4. $9\frac{3}{8} = \square\frac{\square}{8}$ **8**

5. $10\frac{1}{3} = 9\frac{\square}{3}$ **4**

6. $15 = 14\frac{\square}{2}$ **2**

7. $20\frac{5}{12} = 19\frac{\square}{12}$ **17**

8. $13 = 12\frac{\square}{7}$ **7**

9. $6\frac{2}{5} = \square\frac{7}{5}$ **5**

Subtract. Write each answer in simplest form.

10. $5\frac{1}{3} - 3\frac{2}{3}$ $1\frac{2}{3}$

11. $12\frac{1}{6} - 7\frac{5}{6}$ $4\frac{1}{3}$

12. $8\frac{1}{8} - 3\frac{3}{8}$ $4\frac{3}{4}$

13. $9\frac{1}{4} - 4\frac{1}{2}$ $4\frac{3}{4}$

14. $12 - 1\frac{2}{5}$ $10\frac{3}{5}$

15. $8\frac{1}{2} - \frac{7}{8}$ $7\frac{5}{8}$

16. $15\frac{1}{4} - 9\frac{3}{4}$ $5\frac{1}{2}$

17. $7\frac{1}{3} - 3\frac{1}{12}$ $3\frac{7}{12}$

18. $22 - 10\frac{8}{9}$ $11\frac{1}{9}$

© Glencoe/McGraw-Hill   T47   *Mathematics: Applications and Connections, Course 1*

Classroom Vignette

"You may want to allow students to use the paper plate models they made in the Mini-Lab on page 246 to illustrate the renaming process used in subtracting mixed numbers."

Billie Pikur, Teacher
West Middle School
Rochester Hills, MI

Billie E. Pikur

38. *Critical Thinking* Write a problem where you must subtract with renaming and the difference is between $\frac{1}{3}$ and $\frac{1}{2}$.
Sample answer: What is $5\frac{1}{4} - 4\frac{7}{8}$?

Mixed Review **39.** Find the sum of $\frac{7}{8}$ and $1\frac{5}{6}$. Write the answer in simplest form. *(Lesson 6-5)* $2\frac{17}{24}$

40. Standardized Test Practice
Train A runs every 8 minutes and Train B runs every 6 minutes. If they both leave the station at 9:00 A.M., at what time will they next leave the station together? *(Lesson 5-7)* **A**

A 9:24 A.M.   **B** 9:48 A.M.
C 10:48 A.M.   **D** 12:00 P.M.

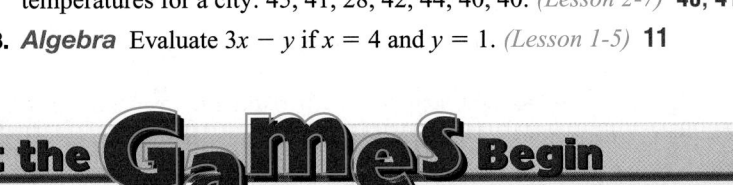

41. Find $586.1 \div 0.58$ to the nearest tenth. *(Lesson 4-7)* **1,010.5**

42. *Statistics* Find the mean and the median for the following set of low temperatures for a city: 45, 41, 28, 42, 44, 40, 40. *(Lesson 2-7)* **40; 41**

For **Extra Practice**, see page 574.

43. *Algebra* Evaluate $3x - y$ if $x = 4$ and $y = 1$. *(Lesson 1-5)* **11**

Let the Games Begin

What Difference Does It Make?

Get Ready   This game is for two players.

 2 number cubes   spinner

Get Set   Make the spinner shown.

Go
- Each player creates a mixed number by rolling the number cubes and spinning the spinner. For example, suppose a player rolls a 1 and a 6 and spins $\frac{2}{3}$. The player would record the mixed number $7\frac{2}{3}$.

- Each player creates a second mixed number using the same method.

- If the second mixed number is less than the first, the player should subtract it from the first.

- If the second mixed number is greater than the first, the player should add it to the first.

- Players continue to create mixed numbers and either add to or subtract from the previous result.

- The winner is the player with the smallest number after six rounds.

 Visit www.glencoe.com/sec/math/mac/mathnet for more games.

Lesson 6-6 Subtracting Mixed Numbers with Renaming **253**

Extending the Lesson

Enrichment Masters, p. 47

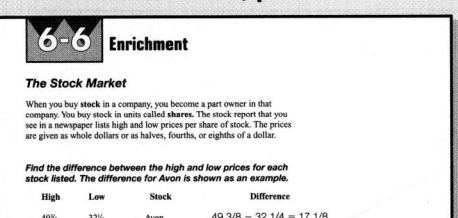

Let the Games Begin

Suggest to students before they start that finding the LCD of the fractions on the spinner may help them add or subtract more quickly during play. You may also choose to have students play in teams instead of in pairs.

Lesson 6-6   **253**

- *Study Guide Masters*, p. 48
- *Practice Masters*, p. 48
- *Enrichment Masters*, p. 48
- Transparencies 6-7, A and B
- *Assessment and Evaluation Masters*, p. 156
- *Technology Masters*, p. 11

 CD-ROM Program
- Resource Lesson 6-7

Recommended Pacing	
Standard	Day 11 of 13
Honors	Day 10 of 12
Block	Day 6 of 7

1 FOCUS

 5-Minute Check
(Lesson 6-6)

Complete.

1. $8\frac{2}{6} = 7\frac{\blacksquare}{6}$ 8

2. $10\frac{\blacksquare}{7} = 9\frac{12}{7}$ 5

Subtract. Write the answer in simplest form.

3. $20\frac{1}{4} - 15\frac{3}{4}$ $4\frac{1}{2}$

4. $11\frac{2}{5} - 8\frac{3}{10}$ $3\frac{1}{10}$

5. $22 - 13\frac{2}{7}$ $8\frac{5}{7}$

 The 5-Minute Check is also available on **Transparency 6-7A** for this lesson.

Motivating the Lesson

Problem Solving Have students read the introduction to the lesson and calculate how long they spend in math class each week.

What you'll learn

You'll learn to add and subtract measures of time.

When am I ever going to use this?

You'll add and subtract measures of time when you're trying to determine how long a flight will last.

Integration: Measurement
Adding and Subtracting Measures of Time

Demetria's school uses block scheduling. She has an A schedule and a B schedule. For example, she goes to math class this week on Monday, Wednesday, and Friday (A Schedule). Next week she will go to math class on Tuesday and Thursday (B Schedule). How much time will she spend in math class during the week when she only goes two days if each class is 1 hour and 30 minutes?

To add or subtract measures of time:
1. Add or subtract the seconds.
2. Add or subtract the minutes.
3. Add or subtract the hours.
Rename if necessary in each step.

1 hour (h) = 60 minutes (min)
1 minute = 60 seconds (s)

Tuesday: 1 h 30 min
Thursday: + 1 h 30 min
            2 h 60 min

Since 2 hours 60 minutes equals 3 hours, Demetria spends 3 hours in math class during weeks when she only goes two days.

 **Example** **APPLICATION** ❶ **Aerospace** The countdown for the launching of a spacecraft was stopped at 12 hours, 7 minutes, 36 seconds before launch. Another stop occurred 1 hour, 28 minutes, 10 seconds before launch. How far did the countdown progress between stops?

Estimate: 12 hours − 1 hour = 11 hours

   12 h   7 min 36 s   *Since you cannot subtract 28 min from 7 min,*
− 1 h 28 min 10 s   *you must rename 12 h 7 min as 11 h 67 min.*
           26 s

   12 h   7 min 36 s   →   11 h 67 min 36 s
− 1 h 28 min 10 s   − 1 h 28 min 10 s
           26 s   10 h 39 min 26 s

The countdown progressed 10 hours, 39 minutes, 26 seconds between the two stops.

Examples

APPLICATION ❷ **Travel** Josefina's flight is scheduled to leave Chicago at 11:14 A.M. and arrive in Houston at 1:36 P.M. How long will the flight last?

To answer this question, you need to find how much time has elapsed. Think of a clock.

11:14 A.M. to 12:00 noon   12:00 noon to 1:36 P.M.
   is 46 minutes.   is 1 hour 36 minutes.

The elapsed time is 46 min + 1 h 36 min or 1 h 82 min. Now rename 82 min as 1 h and 22 min.

1 h + 1 h 22 min = 2 h 22 min

Josefina's flight will last 2 hours and 22 minutes.

APPLICATION ❸ **Sports** Joan Benoit of the United States won the first women's Summer Olympic Games marathon in 1984. Her time was 2 hours, 24 minutes, 52 seconds. In the 1996 Summer Olympic Games, Fatuma Roba of Ethiopia won the marathon with a time of 2 hours, 26 minutes, 5 seconds. How much faster was Benoit's time?

Roba's time: 2 h 26 min 5 s   *Since you cannot subtract 52 s*
Benoit's time: − 2 h 24 min 52 s   *from 5 s, you must rename*
                                     26 min 5 s as 25 min 65 s.

   2 h 26 min 5 s →   2 h 25 min 65 s
− 2 h 24 min 52 s   − 2 h 24 min 52 s
                                  1 min 13 s

Benoit ran the marathon 1 minute, 13 seconds faster than Roba.

CHECK FOR UNDERSTANDING

Communicating Mathematics

Read and study the lesson to answer each question.

1. *Write* the number of minutes in 660 seconds. **11 minutes**

2. *Draw* clocks to show how much time elapses between when you leave home to go to school and when you return home from school. Then determine how much time has elapsed. **See Answer Appendix.**

3. *Write*, in your own words, how adding and subtracting measures of time is similar to adding and subtracting mixed numbers. **See margin.**

Lesson 6-7 Integration: Measurement   Adding and Subtracting Measures of Time   **255**

Additional Answer
3. Sample answer: Adding and subtracting measures of time is similar to adding and subtracting mixed numbers because you have to rename.

---

2 TEACH

Transparency 6-7B contains a teaching aid for this lesson.

Reading Mathematics Be sure students can read time numbers and labels from left to right correctly. Careful alignment of labels is necessary before adding or subtracting time.

In-Class Examples

For Example 1
In 1973, Secretariat won the Kentucky Derby in 1 minute, 59 seconds, and also won the Belmont Stakes in 2 minutes, 24 seconds. How much slower was Secretariat's time in the Belmont? **25 seconds**

For Example 2
If a 13-pound turkey is put in the oven at 11:20 A.M. and taken out at 4:30 P.M., how long did the turkey cook? **5 h 10 min**

For Example 3
Wesley Paul set an age group world record in the 1977 New York City Marathon. He ran the race in 3 hours 31 seconds. He was 8 years old at the time. Suppose he ran 2 hours 58 minutes 48 seconds in the practice before the race. How much faster was Wesley's practice time? **1 min 43 s**

Teaching Tip Compare adding or subtracting measures of time to adding and subtracting three-digit numbers. Remind students that renaming is not a new idea.

Check for Understanding

If students need additional practice or instruction after completing Exercises 1–13, one of these options may be helpful.

- Extra Practice, see p. 574
- Reteaching Activity
- *Study Guide Masters,* p. 48
- *Practice Masters,* p. 48

Assignment Guide

Core: 15–43 odd, 44–49
Enriched: 14–40 even, 41–49

Guided Practice **Complete.**

4. 8 h 18 min = 7 h $\underline{?}$ min **78**   **5.** 9 h 93 min 8 s = $\underline{?}$ h 33 min 8 s **10**

Add or subtract. Rename if necessary.

6.   5 h 34 min
    − 4 h 9 min
    1 h 25 min

7.   2 min 35 s
    + 8 min 10 s
    10 min 45 s

8.   9 h 20 min
    − 3 h 45 min
    5 h 35 min

9.   6 h   20 s
    − 2 h 9 min 40 s
    3 h 50 min 40 s

10.   12 h 40 min 30 s
    + 4 h 30 min 50 s
    17 h 11 min 20 s

Find the elapsed time.

11. 7:50 A.M. to 2:35 P.M.
    6 h 45 min

12. 10:30 P.M. to 6:15 A.M.
    7 h 45 min

13. *Money Matters* Kenny worked for the Moore family by baby-sitting this weekend. On Friday, he worked 3 hours and 15 minutes. On Saturday, he worked 4 hours and 45 minutes. If he gets paid $3.50 an hour, how much money did he make this weekend? **$28**

EXERCISES

Practice **Complete.**

14. 17 min 15 s = 16 min $\underline{?}$ s **75**

15. 4 h 8 min = 3 h $\underline{?}$ min **68**

16. 2 min 85 s = $\underline{?}$ min 25 s **3**

17. 42 h 5 min 87 s = 42 h $\underline{?}$ min $\underline{?}$ s **6; 27**

18. 2 h 23 min 28 s = 2 h 22 min $\underline{?}$ s **88**

19. 26 h 83 min 8 s = $\underline{?}$ h $\underline{?}$ min 8 s **27; 23**

Add or subtract. Rename if necessary.

20.   15 min 54 s
    − 9 min 50 s
    6 min 4 s

21.   7 h 20 min
    + 3 h 18 min
    10 h 38 min

22.   19 h 30 min
    − 12 h 40 min
    6 h 50 min

23.   5 h 25 min
    + 10 h 36 min
    16 h 1 min

24.   12 h 38 min
    − 3 h 46 min
    8 h 52 min

25.   15 h 8 min
    − 14 h 48 min
    20 min

26.   4 h 54 min
    + 12 h 6 min
    17 h

27.   4 min
    + 12 min 55 s
    16 min 55 s

28.   4 h 20 s
    − 3 h 45 s
    59 min 35 s

29.   18 h 25 min
    − 2 h 9 min 40 s
    16 h 15 min 20 s

30.   7 h 20 min
    + 2 h 48 min 10 s
    10 h 8 min 10 s

31.   3 h 35 min 40 s
    + 6 h 50 min 40 s
    10 h 26 min 20 s

32.   8 h
    − 3 h 20 min 15 s
    4 h 39 min 45 s

33.   6 h   20 s
    − 2 h 9 min 40 s
    3 h 50 min 40 s

34.   2 h 9 min 23 s
    − 1 h 10 min 32 s
    58 min 51 s

Study Guide Masters, p. 48

6-7 **Study Guide**

Name_____ Date_____

Integration: Measurement
Adding and Subtracting Measures of Time

To add measures of time, add the seconds, add the minutes, and add the hours. Rename if necessary.

Remember: 1 hour (h) = 60 minutes (min)
     1 minute (min) = 60 seconds (s)

Example 1   4 h 25 min 40 s
     + 5 h 30 min 25 s
     9 h 55 min 65 s   *Rename 65 s as 1 min 5 s.*
     9 h 55 min + 1 min 5 s = 9 h 56 min 5 s

To subtract measures of time, rename if necessary.
Then subtract seconds, subtract minutes, and subtract hours.

Example 2   7 h 15 min 40 s   *You cannot subtract 20 min from 15 min.*
     − 3 h 20 min 10 s
     6 h 75 min 40 s   *Rename 7 h 15 min as 6 h 75 min.*
     − 3 h 20 min 10 s   *Then subtract.*
     3h 55 min 30 s

Complete.

1. 14 min 85 s = ___15___ min 25 s

2. 9 h 5 min = 8 h ___65___ min

3. 3 h 20 min 7 s = 3 h ___19___ min ___67___ s

4. 7 h 9 min 25 s = ___6___ h ___69___ min 25 s

Add or subtract. Rename if necessary.

5. 6 h 20 min
   − 3 h 17 min
   3 h 3 min

6. 35 min 45 s
   + 12 min 12 s
   47 min 57 s

7. 12 h 15 min
   + 10 h 55 s
   22 h 1 min 10 s

8. 9 h 45 min 10 s
   − 3 h 30 min 50 s
   6 h 14 min 20 s

9. 1 h 55 min 12 s
   + 3 h 25 min 34 s
   5 h 20 min 46 s

10. 7 h 20 min
   − 2 h 9 min 10 s
   5 h 10 min 50 s

© Glencoe/McGraw-Hill   T48   Mathematics: Applications
and Connections, Course 1

Reteaching the Lesson

Activity Have students work in small groups to develop a chart of "A Day in the Life of a Sixth Grader." Have them record beginning and ending times for daily activities. Then have them determine how long each activity takes. Have them use their calculators to check their answers by determining if the total time is 24 hours.

Error Analysis

Watch for students who have difficulty renaming units of time.

Prevent by providing examples such as 85 seconds renamed as 1 minute 25 seconds.

Find the elapsed time.

35. 10:20 A.M. to 11:19 A.M. **59 min**   **36.** 6:30 A.M. to 12:35 P.M. **6 h 5 min**

37. 8:15 P.M. to 6:45 A.M. **10 h 30 min**   **38.** 8:05 A.M. to 4:15 P.M. **8 h 10 min**

39. 21 h 20 min 10 s 39. Find the sum of 7 hours, 25 minutes, 10 seconds and 13 hours 55 minutes.

40. How much time is there between 6:15 A.M. and 7:15 P.M.? **13 h**

Applications and Problem Solving

41. *Music* Orlando's piano lesson started at 4:45 P.M. and ended at 5:30 P.M. How long was his lesson? **45 min**

42. *Cooking* Rosalinda is making biscuits. She put the biscuits in the oven at 8:45 A.M. They need to bake for about 20 minutes. When should she check them? **9:05 A.M.**

43. *Travel* Peter flew from Tampa, Florida, to New York City. His plane left Tampa at 6:34 A.M., and the flight took 3 hours 55 minutes. What time did he arrive in New York City? **10:29 A.M.**

4^. *Critical Thinking* Bridgette is flying from Philadelphia to San Francisco visit her grandmother. Her flight leaves at 8:15 A.M. The non-stop flight akes about 6 hours. About what time will it be in San Francisco when Bridgette arrives? (*Hint:* Remember that there is a time difference between Philadelphia and San Francisco.) **11:15 A.M.**

Mixed Review

45. *Health* Joaquin is $65\frac{1}{2}$ inches tall. Jesús is $61\frac{3}{4}$ inches tall. How much taller is Joaquin than Jesús? *(Lesson 6-6)* $3\frac{3}{4}$ **in.**

46. *Cooking* Paul needs $2\frac{1}{4}$ cups of flour for making cookies, $1\frac{2}{3}$ cups for almond bars, and $3\frac{1}{2}$ cups for cinnamon rolls. How much flour does he need in all? *(Lesson 6-5)* $7\frac{5}{12}$ **cups**

47. **Standardized Test Practice** What is the greatest 3-digit number that is not divisible by 3 or 7? *(Lesson 5-1)* **B**

A 999

B 998

C 997

D 996

48. *Measurement* Which is the better estimate for the capacity of a glass of milk: 360 liters or 360 milliliters? *(Lesson 4-8)* **360 milliliters**

For **Extra Practice,** see page 574.

49. *Astronomy* The distance from Earth to the Sun is close to 10^8 miles. How many miles is this? *(Lesson 1-6)* **100,000,000 miles**

Lesson 6-7 Integration: Measurement   Adding and Subtracting Measures of Time   **257**

Extending the Lesson

Enrichment Masters, p. 48

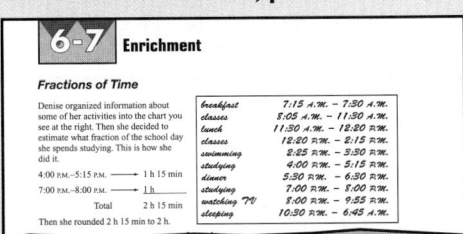

Activity Provide students with copies of pages from a bus or airline schedule. Ask them to plan a trip and use the schedules to calculate the amount of travel time.

Lesson 6-7   **257**

CHAPTER 6

Study Guide and Assessment

Chapter Review For additional lesson-by-lesson review, visit:
www.glencoe.com/sec/math/mac/mathnet

Vocabulary

This section provides a listing of the new terms, properties, and phrases that were introduced in this chapter. Have students define each term and provide an example or two of it, if appropriate.

Understanding and Using the Vocabulary

These exercises check students' understanding of the terms by using a variety of verbal formats including matching, completion, and true/false.

Glossaries A complete glossary of terms appears on pages 642–648. The glossary also appears in Spanish on pages 649–656.

Additional Answer

10. Sample answer: 8 hours 15 minutes should be renamed as 7 hours 75 minutes. Subtract 50 minutes from 75 minutes to get 25 minutes, and subtract 5 hours from 7 hours to get 2 hours.

Vocabulary

After completing this chapter, you should be able to define each term, concept, or phrase and give an example or two of each.

Number and Operations
like fractions (p. 238)

Problem Solving
eliminate possibilities (pp. 236–237)

Understanding and Using the Vocabulary

Choose the correct term or number to complete each sentence.

1. Rounded to the nearest half, $5\frac{1}{5}$ rounds to $\left(\underline{5}, 5\frac{1}{2}\right)$.

2. An estimate for $\frac{9}{20} + \frac{8}{9}$ is $\left(\frac{1}{2}, 1\frac{1}{2}\right)$.

3. The sum of $\frac{2}{5}$ and $\left(\frac{3}{5}, \frac{4}{5}\right)$ is $1\frac{1}{5}$.

4. (Denominators, <u>Numerators</u>) are subtracted when you subtract fractions with like denominators.

5. The (<u>LCD</u>, GCF) is the least common multiple of the denominators of unlike fractions.

6. The LCD of $\frac{1}{8}$ and $\frac{3}{10}$ is $\left(80, \underline{40}\right)$.

7. The solution of $x = 6\frac{7}{10} - 1\frac{1}{5}$ is $\left(5\frac{1}{2}, 5\frac{3}{5}\right)$.

8. The mixed number $9\frac{1}{4}$ can be renamed as $\left(8\frac{3}{4}, 8\frac{5}{4}\right)$.

9. The number of minutes in one hour and twenty minutes is $\left(120, \underline{80}\right)$.

In Your Own Words

10. *Explain* how to subtract 5 hours 50 minutes from 8 hours 15 minutes. **See margin.**

MindJogger Videoquizzes

MindJogger Videoquizzes provide an alternative review of concepts presented in this chapter. Students work in teams to answer questions, gaining points for correct answers. The questions are presented in three rounds.
Round 1 Concepts–5 questions
Round 2 Skills–4 questions
Round 3 Problem Solving–4 questions

Objectives & Examples

Upon completing this chapter, you should be able to:

● round fractions and mixed numbers
(Lesson 6-1)

Round to the nearest half.

$\frac{13}{16} \rightarrow 1$ *13 is close to 16.*

$\frac{5}{9} \rightarrow \frac{1}{2}$ *5 is about half of 9.*

$\frac{2}{11} \rightarrow 0$ *2 is much smaller than 11.*

● estimate sums and differences of fractions and mixed numbers *(Lesson 6-2)*

$\frac{13}{16} - \frac{5}{12} \rightarrow 1 - \frac{1}{2} = \frac{1}{2}$

$\frac{7}{8} + 8\frac{1}{5} \rightarrow 1 + 8 = 9$

● add and subtract fractions with like denominators *(Lesson 6-3)*

$\frac{7}{8} + \frac{5}{8} = \frac{7+5}{8}$

$= \frac{12}{8}$

$= 1\frac{4}{8} \text{ or } 1\frac{1}{2}$

Review Exercises

Use these exercises to review and prepare for the chapter test.

Round each number to the nearest half.

11. $\frac{9}{16}$ $\frac{1}{2}$ 12. $9\frac{2}{9}$ 9

13. $11\frac{4}{7}$ $11\frac{1}{2}$ 14. $\frac{9}{11}$ 1

Tell whether each number should be rounded up or down.

15. the diameter of a plant to put in an $11\frac{7}{8}$-inch pot   **down**

16. the weight limit of an elevator   **down**

17. the capacity of a pitcher needed to hold $\frac{7}{8}$ gallon of lemonade   **up**

18. the height of a truck that can go under a bridge   **up**

Estimate.

19. $8\frac{3}{16} - 4\frac{1}{4}$ $8 - 4 = 4$

20. $\frac{5}{8} + \frac{15}{16}$ $\frac{1}{2} + 1 = 1\frac{1}{2}$

21. $\frac{1}{8} + 4\frac{2}{3}$ $0 + 5 = 5$

22. $\frac{7}{8} - \frac{5}{12}$ $1 - \frac{1}{2} = \frac{1}{2}$

Add or subtract. Write the answer in simplest form.

23. $\frac{8}{15} + \frac{11}{15}$ $1\frac{4}{15}$

24. $\frac{4}{7} - \frac{1}{7}$ $\frac{3}{7}$

25. $\frac{7}{8} - \frac{1}{8}$ $\frac{3}{4}$

26. $\frac{5}{6} + \frac{5}{6}$ $1\frac{2}{3}$

Objectives & Examples

This section reviews the skills and concepts of the chapter and shows completely worked examples.

Review Exercises

These exercises provide practice for the corresponding objectives.

Assessment and Evaluation Masters, pp. 143–144

Chapter 6 Test, Form 1B

Name_____ Date_____

1. Round $\frac{15}{18}$ to the nearest half.
   A. 0   B. $\frac{1}{2}$ C. 1   D. none of these   1. __C__

2. Round $2\frac{1}{8}$ to the nearest half.
   A. 2   B. $2\frac{1}{2}$ C. 3   D. none of these   2. __A__

3. Estimate $4\frac{7}{8} + 6\frac{1}{4}$.
   A. 10   B. 11   C. 12   D. 13   3. __C__

4. Estimate $\frac{3}{32} - \frac{1}{16}$.
   A. 0   B. $\frac{1}{2}$ C. 1   D. $\frac{1}{4}$ 4. __A__

5. Roberto is buying blinds for a window that is $28\frac{3}{4}$ inches wide. Which is the best choice if the blinds come in these widths?
   A. 28 in.   B. $28\frac{1}{2}$ in.   C. 29 in.   D. 30 in.   5. __C__

6. Add: $\frac{13}{20} + \frac{3}{20}$.
   A. $\frac{4}{5}$ B. $\frac{2}{5}$ C. $\frac{16}{40}$ D. $\frac{8}{20}$ 6. __A__

7. Subtract: $\frac{14}{15} - \frac{7}{15}$.
   A. $\frac{12}{30}$ B. $\frac{4}{5}$ C. $\frac{6}{15}$ D. $\frac{7}{15}$ 7. __B__

8. A sheet of wood is $\frac{5}{8}$ inch thick. A planing machine will remove a $\frac{3}{32}$-inch layer of wood. How thick will the sheet be after the planing?
   A. $\frac{6}{32}$ inch   B. $\frac{1}{8}$ inch   C. $\frac{7}{16}$ inch   D. $\frac{1}{4}$ inch   8. __B__

9. Solve $m = \frac{9}{25} - \frac{3}{25}$.
   A. $\frac{6}{25}$ B. $\frac{12}{25}$ C. $\frac{12}{50}$ D. $\frac{6}{50}$ 9. __A__

10. Add: $\frac{7}{20} + \frac{3}{10}$.
    A. $\frac{10}{20}$ B. $\frac{10}{15}$ C. $\frac{1}{3}$ D. none of these   10. __D__

11. Subtract: $\frac{7}{15} - \frac{3}{10}$.
    A. $\frac{1}{30}$ B. $\frac{4}{25}$ C. $\frac{7}{60}$ D. $\frac{3}{30}$ 11. __A__

12. Add: $\frac{7}{15} + \frac{1}{3} + \frac{1}{5}$.
    A. $\frac{9}{23}$ B. $\frac{2}{5}$ C. $\frac{4}{225}$ D. $\frac{4}{5}$ 12. __D__

13. Solve $c = \frac{1}{2} - \frac{1}{4}$.
    A. $\frac{1}{4}$ B. $\frac{1}{2}$ C. $\frac{1}{3}$ D. none of these   13. __D__

© Glencoe/McGraw-Hill   143   *Mathematics: Applications and Connections, Course 1*

Chapter 6 Test, Form 1B (continued)

14. Subtract: $5\frac{11}{12} - 2\frac{5}{12}$.
    A. $3\frac{1}{2}$ B. $2\frac{2}{3}$ C. $3\frac{10}{30}$ D. $3\frac{1}{3}$ 14. __A__

15. Add: $9\frac{5}{8} + 2\frac{5}{6}$.
    A. $11\frac{5}{24}$ B. $12\frac{5}{24}$ C. $11\frac{29}{48}$ D. $11\frac{4}{7}$ 15. __B__

16. Evaluate $x - y$ if $x = 9\frac{5}{8}$ and $y = 4\frac{7}{16}$.
    A. $5\frac{7}{16}$ B. $4\frac{7}{16}$ C. $13\frac{13}{16}$ D. $13\frac{1}{4}$ 16. __A__

17. Evaluate $a + b$ if $a = 7\frac{1}{4}$ and $b = 8\frac{1}{2}$.
    A. $15\frac{1}{4}$ B. $15\frac{5}{6}$ C. $1\frac{1}{6}$ D. none of these   17. __B__

18. Subtract: $9\frac{1}{12} - 2\frac{1}{4}$.
    A. $7\frac{2}{3}$ B. $6\frac{1}{3}$ C. $7\frac{1}{48}$ D. $7\frac{1}{4}$ 18. __B__

19. Subtract: $20 - 6\frac{9}{10}$.
    A. $13\frac{7}{10}$ B. $14\frac{9}{10}$ C. $14\frac{1}{10}$ D. $13\frac{1}{10}$ 19. __D__

20. A metal pipe is $26\frac{7}{16}$ inches long. A plumber needs a $25\frac{1}{4}$-inch-long pipe. How much of the pipe does the plumber need to cut off?
    A. $\frac{11}{16}$ in.   B. $1\frac{11}{16}$ in.   C. $51\frac{11}{16}$ in.   D. $1\frac{1}{4}$ in.   20. __A__

21. Subtract: $5 - 1\frac{1}{3}$.
    A. $4\frac{2}{3}$ B. $4\frac{1}{3}$ C. $3\frac{2}{3}$ D. none of these   21. __C__

22. Add: 16 min 43 s
       $\underline{+ \ 9 \ min \ 17 \ s}$
    A. 25 min   B. 26 min
    C. 26 min 10 s   D. 25 min 50 sec   22. __B__

23. Subtract: 6 h
       $\underline{- \ 2 \ h \ 28 \ min \ 41 \ s}$
    A. 4 h 28 min 41 s   B. 3 h 28 min 41 s
    C. 3 h 31 min 19 s   D. 3 h 32 min 19 s   23. __C__

24. Jack baby-sat for his sister from 6:45 P.M. to 11:30 P.M. How long did he baby-sit?
    A. 5 h 15 min   B. 4 h 15 min   C. 4 h 45 min   D. 5 h 45 min   24. __C__

25. The science class set off two rockets. Rocket A was in the air 2 minutes 56 seconds. Rocket B was in the air 3 minutes 4 seconds. What was the difference in the air times of the rockets?
    A. 1 min 52 s   B. 52 s   C. 8 s   D. 1 min 8 s   25. __C__

© Glencoe/McGraw-Hill   144   *Mathematics: Applications and Connections, Course 1*

Assessment and Evaluation

Six forms of Chapter 6 Test are available in the *Assessment and Evaluation Masters* as shown in the chart.

Chapter 6 Test, Form 1B, is shown at the right. Chapter 6 Test, Form 2B, is shown on the next page.

1A	Multiple Choice	Honors
1B	Multiple Choice	Average
1C	Multiple Choice	Basic
2A	Free Response	Honors
2B	Free Response	Average
2C	Free Response	Basic

Objectives & Examples

Review Exercises

● add and subtract fractions with unlike denominators *(Lesson 6-4)*

$$\frac{7}{12} - \frac{11}{24} = \frac{14}{24} - \frac{11}{24}$$
$$= \frac{14 - 11}{24}$$
$$= \frac{3}{24} \text{ or } \frac{1}{8}$$

Add or subtract. Write the answer in simplest form.

27. $\frac{7}{10} - \frac{1}{5}$ $\frac{1}{2}$ **28.** $\frac{2}{3} + \frac{1}{4}$ $\frac{11}{12}$

29. $\frac{4}{9} + \frac{5}{6}$ $1\frac{5}{18}$ **30.** $\frac{2}{3} - \frac{1}{5}$ $\frac{7}{15}$

● add and subtract mixed numbers *(Lesson 6-5)*

$$11\frac{2}{3} \rightarrow 11\frac{16}{24}$$
$$+ 2\frac{3}{8} \rightarrow + 2\frac{9}{24}$$
$$13\frac{25}{24} = 13 + 1\frac{1}{24} \text{ or } 14\frac{1}{24}$$

Add or subtract. Write the answer in simplest form.

31. $7\frac{3}{7} - 2\frac{1}{7}$ $5\frac{2}{7}$ **32.** $8\frac{2}{3} + 1\frac{2}{3}$ $10\frac{1}{3}$

33. $9\frac{4}{5} - 8\frac{1}{2}$ $1\frac{3}{10}$ **34.** $11\frac{5}{8} - 3\frac{1}{6}$ $8\frac{11}{24}$

● subtract mixed numbers involving renaming *(Lesson 6-6)*

Find $4\frac{1}{4} - \frac{2}{3}$.

$$4\frac{1}{4} \rightarrow 4\frac{3}{12} \rightarrow 3\frac{15}{12}$$
$$- \frac{2}{3} \rightarrow - \frac{8}{12} \rightarrow - \frac{8}{12}$$
$$3\frac{7}{12}$$

$$4\frac{1}{4} - \frac{2}{3} = 3\frac{7}{12}$$

Subtract. Write the answer in simplest form.

35. $8\frac{1}{8}$ **36.** $7\frac{1}{6}$
$-3\frac{1}{4}$ $4\frac{7}{8}$ $-4\frac{1}{3}$ $2\frac{5}{6}$

37. $8 - 2\frac{2}{3}$ $5\frac{1}{3}$ **38.** $18\frac{7}{16} - 8\frac{3}{4}$ $9\frac{11}{16}$

Solve each equation. Write the solution in simplest form.

39. $f = 6\frac{1}{8} - \frac{1}{4}$ $5\frac{7}{8}$ **40.** $5\frac{2}{5} - 1\frac{7}{10} = h$ $3\frac{7}{10}$

● add and subtract measures of time *(Lesson 6-7)*

    3 h 50 min
  + 2 h 15 min
    5 h 65 min

Rename 65 min as 1 h and 5 min.

5 h + 1 h 5 min = 6 h 5 min

Complete.

41. 6 h 8 min = 5 h _?_ min **68**

42. 27 min 75 s = _?_ min _?_ s **28, 15**

Add or subtract. Rename if necessary.

43.   5 h 20 min   **44.**   7 h 45 min
      + 2 h 16 min   − 4 h 32 min
        7 h 36 min   3 h 13 min

45.   9 h 7 min   **46.**   2 h 35 min
      − 8 h 7 min 8 s   + 6 h 41 min
        59 min 52 s   9 h 16 min

Study Guide and Assessment

Assessment and Evaluation Masters, pp. 149–150

Name_____   Date_____

Chapter 6 Test, Form 2B

Round each number to the nearest half.
1. $\frac{5}{11}$ 1. ___$\frac{1}{2}$___
2. $\frac{19}{20}$ 2. ___1___
3. $3\frac{1}{16}$ 3. ___3___
4. $12\frac{1}{6}$ 4. ___12___

5. Jermaine is buying a lava lamp that he will store in a bookcase with shelves that are $11\frac{1}{4}$ inches apart. When looking for the lamp, should he round up or round down to determine its proper height?   5. ___down___

Estimate.
6. $7\frac{1}{10} - 4\frac{19}{20}$ 6. ___7 − 5 = 2___
7. $\frac{2\frac{1}{4}}{23} - \frac{1}{9}$ 7. ___1 − 0 = 1___
8. $\frac{17}{18} + \frac{9}{10}$ 8. ___1 + 1 = 2___
9. $3\frac{3}{4} + 2\frac{1}{3}$ 9. ___4 + 2 = 6___

Add or subtract. Write the answer in simplest form.
10. $\frac{7}{14} + \frac{4}{14}$ 10. ___$\frac{4}{7}$___
11. $\frac{7}{10} - \frac{2}{10}$ 11. ___$\frac{1}{2}$___
12. $\frac{1}{10} + \frac{2}{3}$ 12. ___$\frac{23}{30}$___
13. $\frac{4}{5} - \frac{1}{15}$ 13. ___$\frac{7}{10}$___
14. $7\frac{9}{16} - 3\frac{5}{16}$ 14. ___$4\frac{1}{4}$___
15. $5\frac{3}{4} + \frac{7}{8}$ 15. ___$6\frac{27}{40}$___
16. $6\frac{1}{16} + 6\frac{7}{16}$ 16. ___$12\frac{3}{8}$___
17. $12 - 3\frac{1}{15}$ 17. ___$8\frac{14}{15}$___
18. $18\frac{2}{3} - 14\frac{11}{20}$ 18. ___$3\frac{17}{20}$___

© Glencoe/McGraw-Hill   149   *Mathematics: Applications and Connections, Course 1*

Chapter 6 Test, Form 2B (continued)

Add or subtract. Write the answer in simplest form.
19. $5\frac{2}{3} - 2\frac{5}{6}$ 19. ___$2\frac{23}{30}$___
20. $10\frac{15}{16} - 3\frac{1}{4}$ 20. ___$7\frac{7}{32}$___
21. $3\frac{1}{2} + 2\frac{7}{10} + 1\frac{4}{5}$ 21. ___7___
22. $5\frac{1}{4} + 2\frac{5}{6}$ 22. ___$8\frac{7}{12}$___

23. Monica is going to buy a shirt for $15.99. Should she take $15 or $20 with her?   23. ___$20___

Solve each equation. Write the solution in simplest form.
24. $x = \frac{11}{24} + \frac{3}{24}$ 24. ___$\frac{2}{3}$___
25. $a = \frac{9}{14} - \frac{5}{14}$ 25. ___$\frac{2}{7}$___
26. $m = 9\frac{1}{2} + 6\frac{1}{10}$ 26. ___$15\frac{7}{10}$___
27. $y = 9\frac{2}{3} - 3\frac{3}{4}$ 27. ___$5\frac{11}{12}$___

28. A recipe calls for $\frac{1}{2}$ cup of pecans, $\frac{3}{8}$ cup of almonds, and $\frac{1}{4}$ cup of raisins. How many total cups of pecans, almonds, and raisins are in the recipe?   28. ___$1\frac{1}{8}$ cups___

29. A train is scheduled to leave at 6:40 A.M. and arrive at 9:10 A.M. that same day. How long is the scheduled trip?   29. ___2 h 30 min___

Add or subtract.
30.   4 h 39 min 22 s
    + 2 h 50 min 19 s   30. ___7 h 29 min 41 s___
31.   13 h 25 min
    − 11 h 50 min   31. ___1 h 35 min___
32.   3 h 18 min
    − 1 h 50 min   32. ___1 h 28 min___

33. Nicholas and Sarah watched two movies. One lasted 2 hours and 17 minutes, and the other lasted 3 hours and 21 minutes. How long were they watching the movies?   33. ___5 h 38 min___

© Glencoe/McGraw-Hill   150   *Mathematics: Applications and Connections, Course 1*

Test and Review Software

You may use this software, a combination of an item generator and item bank, to create your own tests or worksheets. Types of items include free response, multiple choice, short answer, and open ended.

CD-ROM Program

The CD-ROM Program contains an Assessment Game whose questions review the concepts in this chapter.

Applications & Problem Solving

47. Money Matters How much money should Danielle get from her purse to pay for a tape that costs $8.10: $8 or $8.50? *(Lesson 6-1)* **$8.50**

48. Food Lana wants to buy her lunch at school. She may choose one entree, one side dish, and one drink. How many lunch combinations are possible from today's menu? *(Lesson 6-2B)* **18**

Entree	Side Dish	Drink
cheeseburger	chips	milk
pizza	salad	juice
taco		water

49. Measurement Melinda walks $\frac{1}{2}$ mile to school in the morning and then $\frac{2}{3}$ mile to work after school. She gets a ride home after work from her dad. How many miles does she walk each day? *(Lesson 6-4)*

50. Jobs Gina began working at 9:15 A.M. and worked until 3:30 P.M. How long did she work? *(Lesson 6-7)* **6 h 15 min**

49. $1\frac{1}{6}$ **miles**

Alternative Assessment

● **Open Ended**

Suppose you are in charge of making costumes for a class play. You have determined you need $12\frac{2}{3}$ yards of blue fabric, $10\frac{5}{6}$ yards of pinstripe fabric, and $18\frac{1}{2}$ yards of white fabric. Tell how to estimate the sum or difference of mixed numbers. Estimate the total amount of fabric you need. **See Answer Appendix.**

Suppose you have 6 yards of floral fabric and you know you will use $4\frac{1}{8}$ yards. How much fabric will you have left? $1\frac{7}{8}$ **yards**

The play starts at 7:30 P.M. and ends at 9:18 P.M. How can you find the elapsed time without drawing clocks? How is finding elapsed time similar to subtracting mixed numbers involving renaming? **See Answer Appendix.**

A practice test for Chapter 6 is provided on page 600.

● **Completing the** **Project**

Use the following checklist to make sure your project is complete.

☑ You have included a list of instructions on how to use your map.

☑ You have included your map showing the location of the starting point, the four landmarks, and the treasure.

Add any finishing touches that you would like to make your project attractive.

 Select one of the assignments from this chapter that you found particularly challenging. Place it in your portfolio.

 Performance Assessment

Additional performance assessment tasks for this chapter are included in the *Assessment and Evaluation Masters* on page 153. A scoring guide is also provided on page 165.

Applications & Problem Solving

This section provides additional practice in solving real-world problems that involve the skills of this chapter.

Alternative Assessment

The **Open Ended** section provides students with a performance assessment opportunity to evaluate their work and understanding.

 Project

Students should complete the final stages of their project and prepare a class demonstration of their results. A scoring guide for the project is available in the *Investigations and Projects Masters*, p. 39.

PORTFOLIO Students should add to their portfolios at this time.

***Assessment and Evaluation Masters*, p. 153**

---

6   Name_____ Date_____

Chapter 6 Performance Assessment

Instructions: Demonstrate your knowledge by giving a clear, concise solution to each problem. Be sure to include all relevant drawings and justify your answers. You may show your solutions in more than one way or investigate beyond the requirements of the problems.

1. Jennifer is making grape jelly. She adds $\frac{1}{2}$ cup of water and $3\frac{1}{4}$ cups of sugar to 4 cups of crushed grapes.

  a. Tell how to estimate the sum or difference of mixed numbers.

  b. Estimate the total amount of ingredients in the jelly.

  c. Tell why you must find a common denominator before adding fractions.

  d. Find the total ingredients of Jennifer's jelly. Show the steps.

  e. Give three meanings of subtraction and an example of each.

  f. If Jennifer plans to make a total of 12 cups of ingredients, how many more cups of ingredients will she need? Show your work.

2. The Indianapolis 500 auto race is called the greatest spectacle in racing. The slowest winning time for the race was 6 hours 42 minutes 8 seconds in the first race in 1911. The fastest winning time was 1 hour 42 minutes 53 seconds in 1976.

  a. What is the difference between the winning times in 1911 and 1976? Explain each step.

  b. Suppose the fastest winning time for the race were 2 hours 41 minutes 18 seconds. What would be the difference between the fastest and slowest times for the race?

  c. Give several reasons such a race may be stopped early.

  d. If the race starts at 11:00 A.M. and the winner crosses the finish line at 2:38 P.M., what is the winning time for the race? Explain your reasoning.

Standardized Test Practice

The Standardized Test Practice may be used to help students prepare for standardized tests. The test items are written in the same style as those in state proficiency tests and standardized tests like CAT, CTBS, ITBS, MAT, SAT, and Terra Nova. The test items cover skills and concepts covered up to this point in the text.

The pages can be used as an overnight assessment. After students have completed the pages, discuss how each problem can be solved, or provide copies of the solutions from the *Solutions Manual*.

Assessment and Evaluation Masters, p. 159

Standardized Test Practice
Assessing Knowledge & Skills

Section One: Multiple Choice

There are twelve multiple-choice questions in this section. Choose the best answer. If a correct answer is *not here*, mark the letter for Not Here.

1. Which number sentence belongs to the same family of facts as $5 + 9 = 14$? **B**
   A $19 - 5 = 14$
   B $14 - 9 = 5$
   C $19 - 14 = 5$
   D $9 - 5 = 4$

2. Julio measures 250 grams of salt for a science experiment. What is the mass in kilograms? **G**
   F 0.0025 kg
   G 0.25 kg
   H 25 kg
   J 2,500 kg

3. What is the median of the following test scores? **D**

80	100	90	60	80	90	100
90	90	60	70	90	100	80

   A 75
   B 80
   C 85
   D 90

4. Which ordered pair is represented by point *M*? **J**
   F (3, 4)
   G (4, 2)
   H (1, 4)
   J (2, 4)

5. What is the LCD of $\frac{3}{8}$ and $\frac{5}{6}$? **C**
   A 14
   B 15
   C 24
   D 48

6. Which is the list of prime factors of 32? **F**
   F 2
   G 2, 16
   H 1, 32
   J 1, 2, 4, 8, 16, 32

Please note that Questions 7–12 have five answer choices.

7. Andy has asked one of his friends to feed his three dogs while he is away on vacation. Each dog eats $1\frac{1}{2}$ bags of dog food per week. What else do you need to know to find how many bags of food Andy should leave for his dogs to eat while he is away on vacation? **C**
   A the size of each of Andy's dogs
   B the price of each bag of dog food
   C the number of weeks Andy will be away on vacation
   D the amount of exercise the dogs need each day
   E the amount of dog food in 1 bag

8. A football game started at 2:40 P.M. and ended at 5:15 P.M. How long was the game? **G**
   F 2 h 15 min
   G 2 h 35 min
   H 3 h 15 min
   J 3 h 25 min
   K Not Here

◀◀◀ **Instructional Resources**
Another cumulative review is shown at the left and is available in the *Assessment and Evaluation Masters*, p. 159.

9. Which is a reasonable remainder when a number is divided by 5? **E**

A 8

B 7

C 6

D 5

E 4

10. Pedro bought 6 batteries for his radio. Each battery cost $1.79, including tax. What was the total cost of the batteries? **H**

F $6.24

G $10.24

H $10.74

J $11.74

K Not Here

11. Each day Matias drives his delivery truck 3.25 miles to his first stop, 4.23 miles to his second stop, 8.8 miles to his third stop, and 6 miles back to headquarters. How many miles does Matias drive the truck each day? **A**

A 22.28 miles

B 16.28 miles

C 8.42 miles

D 7.48 miles

E Not Here

12. Ron was making curtains for his room. He had 7 yards of material. It took $5\frac{1}{2}$ yards to make the curtains. How much material was not used for the curtains? **J**

F $12\frac{1}{2}$ yd

G $2\frac{1}{2}$ yd

H 2 yd

J $1\frac{1}{2}$ yd

K Not Here

Test-Taking Tip THE PRINCETON REVIEW

Most standardized tests have a time limit, so you must use your time wisely. Some questions will be easier than others. If you cannot answer a question quickly, go on to another. If there is time remaining when you are finished, go back to the questions that you skipped.

Section Two: Free Response

This section contains seven questions for which you will provide short answers. Write your answers on your paper.

13. When is the product of two decimals less than both factors? **when both factors are less than one**

14. *Geometry* Find the perimeter of the rectangle. **38 in.**

$6\frac{1}{2}$ in.

$12\frac{1}{2}$ in.

15. Write $\frac{35}{63}$ in simplest form. **$\frac{5}{9}$**

16. Express $\frac{18}{11}$ as a mixed number. **$1\frac{7}{11}$**

17. *Algebra* Evaluate $a + b$ if $a = \frac{7}{8}$ and $b = \frac{3}{16}$. **$1\frac{1}{16}$**

18. What is $12\frac{3}{15}$ minus $\frac{2}{5}$? **$11\frac{4}{5}$**

19. Find the elapsed time from 8:30 P.M. to 10:40 A.M. **14 h 10 min**

inter NET CONNECTION **Test Practice** For additional test practice questions, visit:

www.glencoe.com/sec/math/mac/mathnet

Test-Taking Tip

One of the important skills in test taking is time management. Remind students that they can answer several easier questions in the time they might otherwise spend trying to answer one question they find difficult.

Assessment and Evaluation Masters, pp. 157–158

Instructional Resources ▶▶▶

Additional standardized test practice is shown at the right and is available in the *Assessment and Evaluation Masters,* pp. 157–158.

Interdisciplinary
▼Investigation

This optional investigation is designed to be completed by a group of 4 or 5 students over several days or several weeks.

Mathematical Overview

This investigation utilizes the concepts from Chapters 1–6.
- rounding whole numbers
- writing fractions
- ordering whole numbers
- writing comparison ratios
- calculating perimeter

Time Management	
Gathering Data	30 minutes
Calculations	30 minutes
Summarizing Data	20 minutes
Presentation	15 minutes

Instructional Resources

- *Investigations and Projects Masters,* pp. 5–8

Investigations and Projects Masters, p. 8

Name_____ Date_____

Interdisciplinary Investigation
(Student Edition, Pages 264–265)

Just "State" The Facts!

Use this table to record your data.

2.

Cities (Metropolitan Areas) – 1990 Population ____			
City (Metropolitan Area)	Population	Population (Rounded)	Fraction
Other			
State Total			

3. Perimeter:

© Glencoe/McGraw-Hill   8   *Mathematics: Applications and Connections, Course 1*

JUST "STATE" THE FACTS!

Do you know the population of the largest city in the United States? According to the 1990 census, New York City had a population of 7,322,564. That is more than twice as many people as Los Angeles, the second largest city. In 1990, eight U. S. cities had populations over 1,000,000.

What You'll Do

In this investigation, you will choose a state and investigate what part of that state's population live in its largest cities.

Materials almanac calculator

Procedure

1. Work in groups of four. Each member of your group should choose a different state. Find a resource book, map, or website that lists the populations of the largest cities.

2. Make a table, similar to the one below, for your chosen state. List the ten largest cities in order from greatest to least population. Determine how many people live in the rest of the state and call that category "other."

Montana Cities – 1990 Population			
City	Population	Population (rounded)	Fraction
Billings	81,125	81,000	$\frac{81}{799}$
Great Falls	55,125	55,000	$\frac{55}{799}$
⋮	⋮	⋮	⋮
Other	498,357	498,000	$\frac{498}{799}$
State Total	799,065	799,000	

In column 2, write the population of each city. In column 3, round the population to the nearest thousand. In column 4, write a fraction to show the population of each city compared to the total population of the state. (Round the total population to the nearest thousand.)

Technology Tips

- Use a **spreadsheet** to record populations.

- Use a **graphing calculator** or **graphing software** to make graphs.

- Use a **word processor** to prepare your display.

- Surf the **Internet** for more information.

◄◄◄Instructional Resources

A recording sheet to help students organize their data for this investigation is shown at the left and is available in the *Investigations and Projects Masters,* p. 8.

Cooperative Learning

This investigation offers an excellent opportunity for using cooperative learning groups. For more information on cooperative learning strategies and group management, see *Cooperative Learning in the Mathematics Classroom.*

3. For your chosen state, use a map and the scale for the map to find the perimeter in miles. Place a string along each side and then add the lengths of string.

4. Prepare a display of the facts about your group's four states. Include some similarities and differences between the states.

Making the Connection

Use the data you collected about state population as needed to help in these investigations.

Language Arts

Imagine that the people of your chosen state stand on the perimeter and hold hands. Write directions for finding out whether there are enough people in the state to form a human border.

Science

Research the climate of your chosen state. Make a poster describing the climate. Include the high and low temperatures and draw a graph showing the amount of precipitation for each month.

Social Studies

Research the geography of your chosen state. Write a short report about the major geographic features of the state.

Go Further

- Make two or more different types of graphs comparing the populations of the cities in your chosen state and another student's state.

- Suppose that the state you chose has a random drawing for a prize. The names of all people in the state are included. What is the probability that the winner lives in the largest city?

 interNET CONNECTION Research For current information from the U.S. Bureau of the Census, visit:

www.glencoe.com/sec/math/mac/mathnet

 You may want to place your work on this investigation in your portfolio.

Working in Teams Be sure students use the most current information available. Each student should prepare his or her own table. Encourage students to choose states with fairly regular shapes to simplify finding the perimeter. Suggest that students check each other's perimeter measurements.

Making the Connection

You may wish to alert other teachers on your team that your students may need their assistance in this investigation. *Language Arts* Students should begin by figuring out how many people can span one mile. Tell them that the average arm span is $4\frac{1}{2}$ feet.

Science Students may wish to investigate how the climate affects population movement in their state. *Social Studies* Students may wish to include a discussion of how the geographic features affect the population distribution in their state. Have them make maps of their states including the major geographic features.

***Investigations and Projects Masters*, p. 7**

SCORING GUIDE

Interdisciplinary Investigation
(Student Edition, Pages 264–265)

Just "State" The Facts!

Level	Specific Criteria
3 Superior	• Shows a thorough understanding of the concepts of *rounding whole numbers, writing and simplifying fractions,* and *constructing bar graphs.* • Uses appropriate strategies to solve problems. • Computations are correct. • Written explanations are exemplary. • Charts, model, and any statements included are appropriate and sensible. • Goes beyond the requirements of some or all problems.
2 Satisfactory, with minor flaws	• Shows understanding of the concepts of *rounding whole numbers, writing and simplifying fractions,* and *constructing bar graphs.* • Uses appropriate strategies to solve problems. • Computations are mostly correct. • Written explanations are effective. • Charts, model, and any statements included are appropriate and sensible. • Satisfies the requirements of problems.
1 Nearly Satisfactory, with obvious flaws	• Shows understanding of most of the concepts of *rounding whole numbers, writing and simplifying fractions,* and *constructing bar graphs.* • May not use appropriate strategies to solve problems. • Computations are mostly correct. • Written explanations are satisfactory. • Charts, model, and any statements included are appropriate and sensible. • Satisfies the requirements of problems.
0 Unsatisfactory	• Shows little or no understanding of the concepts of *rounding whole numbers, writing and simplifying fractions,* and *constructing bar graphs.* • Does not use appropriate strategies to solve problems. • Computations are incorrect. • Written explanations are not satisfactory. • Charts, model, and any statements included are not appropriate or sensible. • Does not satisfy the requirements of the problems.

© Glencoe/McGraw-Hill   7   *Mathematics: Applications and Connections, Course 1*

You may have groups finish their presentations with a population comparison of their chosen states to their home state. Encourage groups to include visuals such as posters.

Instructional Resources ▶ ▶ ▶
Sample solutions for this investigation are provided in the *Investigations and Projects Masters* on p. 6. The scoring guide for assessing student performance shown at the right is also available on p. 7.

Multiplying and Dividing Fractions

Previewing the Chapter

Overview

In this chapter, students learn to multiply and divide fractions and mixed numbers. Compatible numbers are used to estimate fraction products. Connections include finding the circumference of a circle and changing units within the customary system of measurement. Students learn to solve problems by finding and extending a pattern. The look-for-a-pattern strategy and spreadsheets are used to help recognize and extend sequences.

Lesson (pages)	Lesson Objectives	NCTM Standards 2000	Standardized Tests	State/Local Objectives
7-1 (268–270)	Estimate fraction products using compatible numbers and rounding.	1, 3, 4, 6–10	CTBS, TN	
7-2A (271–272)	Multiply fractions by using a geoboard.	1, 3, 4, 6–8, 10		
7-2 (273–276)	Multiply fractions.	1, 2, 4, 6–10	CAT, CTBS, ITBS, MAT, SAT, TN	
7-3 (277–279)	Multiply mixed numbers.	1–4, 6–9	SAT	
7-4 (280–283)	Find the circumference of circles.	1–4, 6–10		
7-5A (284)	Divide fractions by using a geoboard.	1, 8, 10		
7-5 (285–288)	Divide fractions.	1, 2, 6–10	CAT, CTBS, MAT, SAT, TN	
7-6 (289–291)	Divide mixed numbers.	1, 2, 5–9	CTBS, SAT, TN	
7-7 (292–294)	Change units within the customary system.	1, 2, 4, 6–10	CAT, CTBS, MAT, SAT, TN	
7-7B (295)	Compare weights.	1, 4, 6–9		
7-8A (296–297)	Solve problems by finding and extending a pattern.	1–4, 6–10	CAT, CTBS, ITBS, MAT, SAT, TN	
7-8 (298–300)	Recognize and extend sequences.	1–4, 6–10		
7-8B (301)	Use a spreadsheet to extend sequences.	1–4, 6–9		

CAT = California Achievement Tests, CTBS = Comprehensive Tests of Basic Skills, ITBS = Iowa Tests of Basic Skills, MAT = Metropolitan Achievement Tests, SAT = Stanford Achievement Tests, TN = Terra Nova
For the key to numbering of NCTM Standards 2000, see page T6.

Organizing the Chapter

The **Interactive Lesson Planner** contains all of the blackline masters and transparencies. This CD-ROM also includes an easy-to-use lesson planning calendar.

LESSON PLANNING GUIDE

Lesson	Extra Practice (Student Edition)	BLACKLINE MASTERS (PAGE NUMBERS)										Transparencies A and B
		Study Guide	Practice	Enrichment	Assessment & Evaluation	Classroom Games	Diversity	Hands-On Lab	School to Career	Science and Math Lab Manual	Technology	
7-1	p. 575	49	49	49								7-1
7-2A								51				
7-2	p. 575	50	50	50	183				7			7-2
7-3	p. 575	51	51	51			7					7-3
7-4	p. 576	52	52	52	182, 183			75				7-4
7-5A								52				
7-5	p. 576	53	53	53		19–20					14	7-5
7-6	p. 576	54	54	54	184							7-6
7-7	p. 577	55	55	55								7-7
7-7B								53				
7-8A	p. 577											
7-8	p. 577	56	56	56	184						13	7-8
7-8B												
Study Guide/ Assessment					169–181, 185–187							

OTHER CHAPTER RESOURCES

Student Edition
Chapter Project, pp. 267, 279, 291, 305
Math in the Media, p. 279
Let the Games Begin, p. 276

Technology
 MathPASS CD-ROM

🖳 Interactive Mathematics Tools Software

Teacher's Classroom Resources

Applications
Family Letters and Activities, pp. 13–14
Investigations and Projects Masters, pp. 41–44
Meeting Individual Needs
Transition Booklet, pp. 29–34
Investigations for the Special Education Student, pp. 19–20

Teaching Aids
Answer Key Masters
Block Scheduling Booklet
Lesson Planning Guide
Solutions Manual

Professional Publications
Glencoe Mathematics Professional Series

Planning the Chapter

MindJogger Videoquizzes provide a unique format for reviewing concepts presented in the chapter.

ASSESSMENT RESOURCES

Student Edition

Mixed Review, pp. 270, 276, 279, 283, 288, 291, 294, 300
Mid-Chapter Self Test, p. 283
Math Journal, pp. 275, 290
Study Guide and Assessment, pp. 302–305
Performance Task, p. 305
Portfolio Suggestion, p. 305
Standardized Test Practice, pp. 306–307
Chapter Test, p. 601

Assessment and Evaluation Masters

Multiple-Choice Tests (Forms 1A, 1B, 1C), pp. 169–174
Free-Response Tests (Forms 2A, 2B, 2C), pp. 175–180
Performance Assessment, p. 181
Mid-Chapter Test, p. 182
Quizzes A–D, pp. 183–184
Standardized Test Practice, pp. 185–186
Cumulative Review, p. 187

Teacher's Wraparound Edition

5-Minute Check, pp. 268, 273, 277, 280, 285, 289, 292, 298
Building Portfolios, p. 266
Math Journal, pp. 272, 284, 295, 301
Closing Activity, pp. 270, 276, 279, 283, 288, 291, 294, 297, 300

Technology

Test and Review Software
MindJogger Videoquizzes
CD-ROM Program

MATERIALS AND MANIPULATIVES

Lesson 7-2A
geoboard*†
geobands*†
dot paper

Lesson 7-2
poster board
number cubes*
calculator

Lesson 7-4
tape measure*
calculator
circular objects

Lesson 7-5A
geoboard*†
geobands*†
dot paper

Lesson 7-7B
measuring cups*
containers
water

Lesson 7-8B
computer
spreadsheet software

*Glencoe Manipulative Kit   †Glencoe Overhead Manipulative Resources

PACING CHART

See pages T25–T27 for the Course Planning Calendar.

COURSE	DAY 1	DAY 2	DAY 3	DAY 4	DAY 5	DAY 6	DAY 7
Standard	Chapter Project	Lesson 7-1	Lessons 7-2A & 7-2		Lesson 7-3	Lesson 7-4	Lessons 7-5A & 7-5
Honors	Chapter Project	Lesson 7-1	Lesson 7-2	Lesson 7-3	Lesson 7-4	Lesson 7-5	Lesson 7-6
Block	Chapter Project & Lesson 7-1	Lessons 7-2A & 7-2	Lesson 7-3	Lesson 7-4	Lessons 7-5A & 7-5	Lessons 7-6 & 7-7	Lessons 7-8A & 7-8

The *Transition Booklet* (Skills 13–15) can be used to practice measuring length, capacity, and weight.

Interactive Mathematics:
Activities and Investigations

is an activity-based program that may be used as an enhancement for chapters in *Mathematics: Applications and Connections.*

Unit 11, Activity Four
Use with Lesson 7-3.

Summary Students work in groups to solve multiplication problems in three different clock systems. Then they write about their observations. Each group presents its findings to the class.

Math Connection Students explore the characteristics of multiplication in clock systems, which parallels multiplication of real numbers. Clock multiplication tables allow some students to observe symmetry, patterns, sequences, and the special cases of zero and one. They also may make generalizations about the properties of real numbers.

Unit 12, Pre-Assessment Activity
Use with Lesson 7-7.

Summary Students work in pairs to determine a route and a description using nonstandard units for getting from school to another location. They are to write a brief report and are invited to share their presentations with the class.

Math Connection Students use their knowledge of direction and distance to write instructions for getting from school to another location. Knowledge of customary units of measure is used to complete this activity.

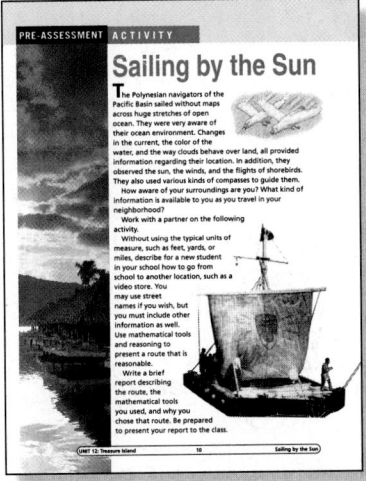

DAY 8	DAY 9	DAY 10	DAY 11	DAY 12	DAY 13	DAY 14	DAY 15
(continue from Day 7)	Lesson 7-6	Lesson 7-7		Lesson 7-8A	Lesson 7-8	Study Guide and Assessment	Chapter Test
Lessons 7-7 & 7-7B		Lesson 7-8A	Lessons 7-8 & 7-8B		Study Guide and Assessment	Chapter Test	
Study Guide and Assessment, Chapter Test							

Enhancing the Chapter

APPLICATIONS

Classroom Games, pp. 19–20

Chapter 7 In-Class Game
(Lesson 7-5)

Mathematical Tennis

Work in two teams.

- The first player on Team A "serves" a "ball" that consists of an expression that involves addition, subtraction, multiplication, division, decimals, fractions, or any combination of them; for example, 6 × 3.
- Within an agreed-upon time limit, the first player on Team B "returns" the ball by stating an expression that is equivalent to the first expression; for example, "half of 36."
- This continues without any repetition of expressions. Each player should try to make his or her expression as complex as possible. An example is, "2 times open parenthesis, 5 squared minus 4 close parenthesis" or "2 thirds times 3 fourths times 36." The value is still 18.
- If a player cannot return the ball within the time limit, the opposing team scores 1 point. If a player repeats an expression or makes an error, the opposing team scores 2 points. The winning team is the first to score 10 points.

24 + 13

14 ÷ 2

7 × 12

8 – 3

Diversity Masters, p. 7

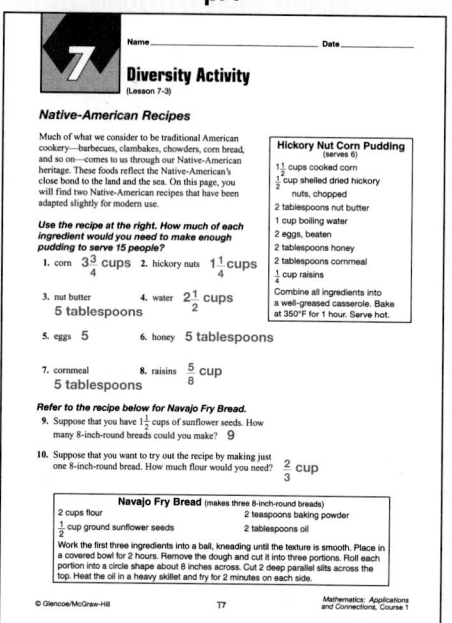

Diversity Activity
(Lesson 7-3)

Native-American Recipes

Much of what we consider to be traditional American cookery—barbecues, clambakes, chowders, corn bread, and so on—comes to us through our Native-American heritage. These foods reflect the Native-American's close bond to the land and the sea. On this page, you will find two Native-American recipes that have been adapted slightly for modern use.

Use the recipe at the right. How much of each ingredient would you need to make enough pudding to serve 15 people?

1. corn $3\frac{3}{4}$ cups   2. hickory nuts $1\frac{1}{4}$ cups
3. nut butter 5 tablespoons   4. water $2\frac{1}{2}$ cups
5. eggs 5   6. honey 5 tablespoons
7. cornmeal 5 tablespoons   8. raisins $\frac{5}{8}$ cup

Hickory Nut Corn Pudding (serves 6)

$1\frac{1}{2}$ cups cooked corn
$\frac{1}{2}$ cup shelled dried hickory nuts, chopped
2 tablespoons nut butter
1 cup boiling water
2 eggs, beaten
2 tablespoons honey
2 tablespoons cornmeal
$\frac{1}{4}$ cup raisins

Combine all ingredients into a well-greased casserole. Bake at 350°F for 1 hour. Serve hot.

Refer to the recipe below for Navajo Fry Bread.

9. Suppose that you have $1\frac{1}{2}$ cups of sunflower seeds. How many 8-inch-round breads could you make? 9

10. Suppose that you want to try out the recipe by making just one 8-inch-round bread. How much flour would you need? $\frac{2}{3}$ cup

Navajo Fry Bread (makes three 8-inch-round breads)

2 cups flour   2 teaspoons baking powder
$\frac{1}{2}$ cup ground sunflower seeds   2 tablespoons oil

Work the first three ingredients into a ball, kneading until the texture is smooth. Place in a covered bowl for 2 hours. Remove the dough and cut it into three portions. Roll each portion into a circle shape about 8 inches across. Cut 2 deep parallel slits across the top. Heat the oil in a heavy skillet and fry for 2 minutes on each side.

School to Career Masters, p. 7

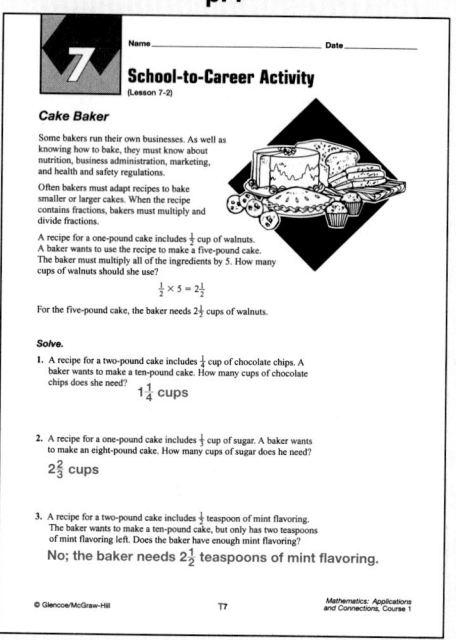

School-to-Career Activity
(Lesson 7-2)

Cake Baker

Some bakers run their own businesses. As well as knowing how to bake, they must know about nutrition, business administration, marketing, and health and safety regulations.

Often bakers must adapt recipes to bake smaller or larger cakes. When the recipe contains fractions, bakers must multiply and divide fractions.

A recipe for a one-pound cake includes $\frac{1}{2}$ cup of walnuts. A baker wants to use the recipe to make a five-pound cake. The baker must multiply all of the ingredients by 5. How many cups of walnuts should she use?

$\frac{1}{2} \times 5 = 2\frac{1}{2}$

For the five-pound cake, the baker needs $2\frac{1}{2}$ cups of walnuts.

Solve.

1. A recipe for a two-pound cake includes $\frac{1}{4}$ cup of chocolate chips. A baker wants to make a ten-pound cake. How many cups of chocolate chips does she need? $1\frac{1}{4}$ cups

2. A recipe for a one-pound cake includes $\frac{1}{3}$ cup of sugar. A baker wants to make an eight-pound cake. How many cups of sugar does he need? $2\frac{2}{3}$ cups

3. A recipe for a two-pound cake includes $\frac{1}{2}$ teaspoon of mint flavoring. The baker wants to make a ten-pound cake, but only has two teaspoons of mint flavoring left. Does the baker have enough mint flavoring? No; the baker needs $2\frac{1}{2}$ teaspoons of mint flavoring.

Family Letters and Activities, pp. 13–14

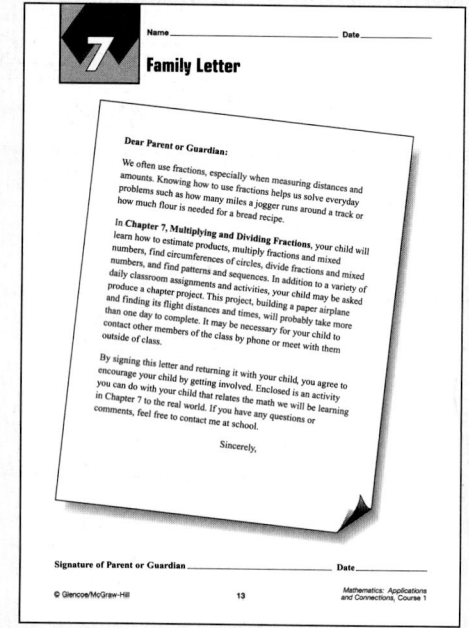

Family Letter

Dear Parent or Guardian:

We often use fractions, especially when measuring distances and amounts. Knowing how to use fractions helps us solve everyday problems such as how many miles a jogger runs around a track or how much flour is needed for a bread recipe.

In **Chapter 7, Multiplying and Dividing Fractions**, your child will learn how to estimate products, multiply fractions and mixed numbers, find circumferences of circles, divide fractions and mixed numbers, and find patterns and sequences. In addition to a variety of daily classroom assignments and activities, your child may be asked to produce a chapter project. This project, building a paper airplane and finding its flight distances and times, will probably take more than one day to complete. It may be necessary for your child to contact other members of the class by phone or meet with them outside of class.

By signing this letter and returning it with your child, you agree to encourage your child by getting involved. Enclosed is an activity you can do with your child that relates the math we will be learning in Chapter 7 to the real world. If you have any questions or comments, feel free to contact me at school.

Sincerely,

Signature of Parent or Guardian _____ Date _____

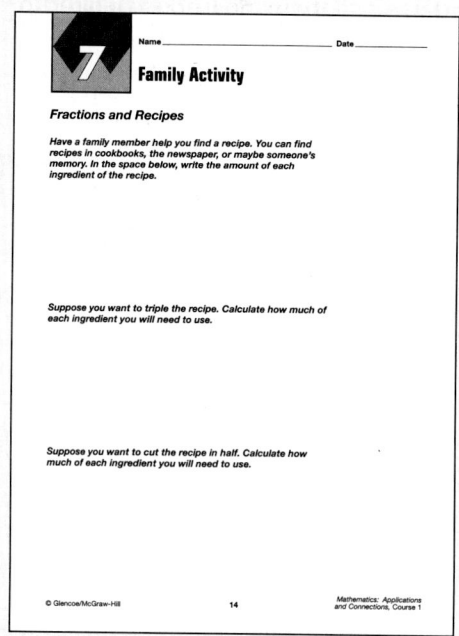

Family Activity

Fractions and Recipes

Have a family member help you find a recipe. You can find recipes in cookbooks, the newspaper, or maybe someone's memory. In the space below, write the amount of each ingredient of the recipe.

Suppose you want to triple the recipe. Calculate how much of each ingredient you will need to use.

Suppose you want to cut the recipe in half. Calculate how much of each ingredient you will need to use.

Hands-On Lab Masters,
p. 75

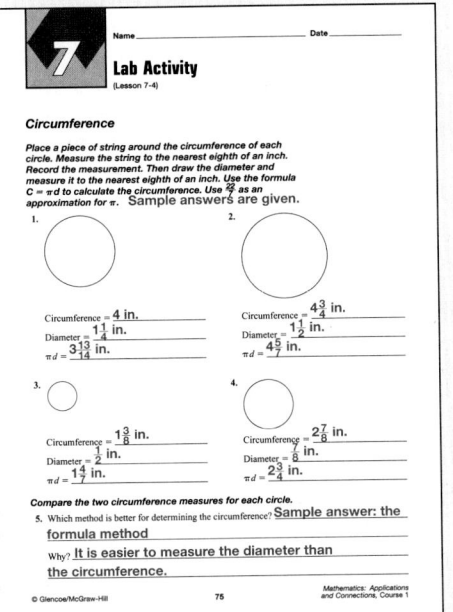

Assessment and Evaluation Masters,
pp. 182–184

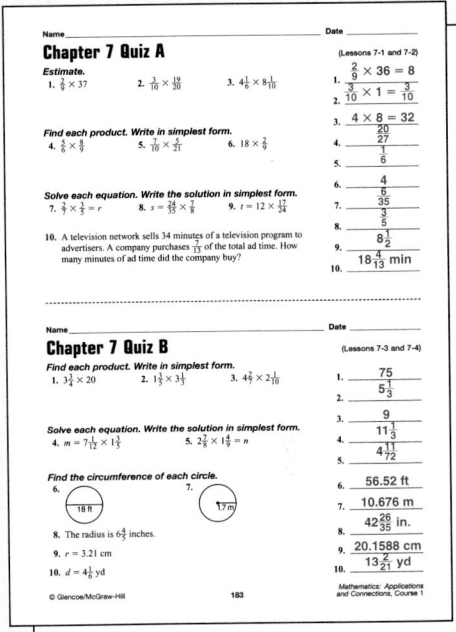

Technology Masters,
pp. 13–14

Investigations for the Special
Education Student, pp. 19–20

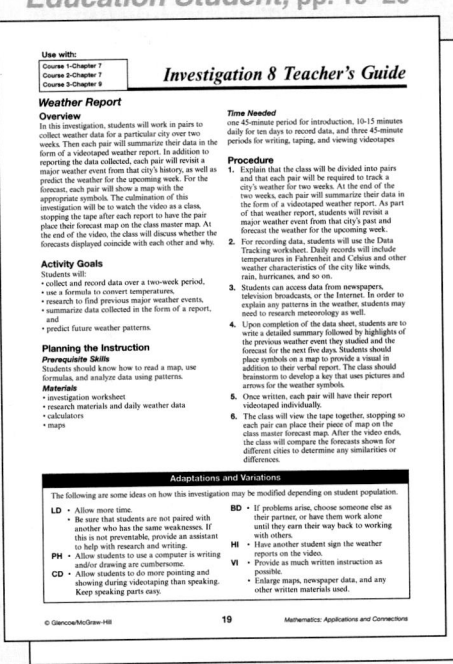

Theme: Flight

Ken Blackburn began to experiment with paper airplanes when he was a child. At age 13, he designed a square-shaped glider that quickly became his favorite plane. Seven years and countless improvements later, Blackburn became the world-record holder for the longest flight by a paper airplane, with a flight of 16.89 seconds. He has since broken his own record twice, most recently in 1994 when his glider stayed airborne for 18.8 seconds. Blackburn has every intention of breaking the 20-second barrier.

Question of the Day Speed equals distance divided by time. If Mitiku's first flight traveled $11\frac{1}{4}$ feet in 2 seconds, how fast did it fly? $5\frac{5}{8}$ ft/s

Assess Prerequisite Skills

Ask students to read through the list of objectives presented in "What you'll learn in Chapter 7." You may wish to ask them what each of the objectives means or if they have used or experienced any of these math concepts before.

 Building Portfolios

Encourage students to revise their portfolios as they study this chapter. They may want to include summaries of what they did in the labs to remind them of relevant applications of fractions.

 Math and the Family

In the *Family Letters and Activities* booklet (pp. 13–14), you will find a letter to the parents explaining what students will study in Chapter 7. An activity appropriate for the whole family is also available.

What you'll learn in Chapter 7

- to multiply and divide fractions and mixed numbers,
- to find the circumference of circles,
- to change units within the customary system,
- to recognize and extend sequences, and
- to solve real-world problems by finding and extending a pattern.

 CD-ROM Program

Activities for Chapter 7
- Chapter 7 Introduction
- Interactive Lesson 7-2
- Extended Activity 7-4
- Assessment Game
- Resource Lessons 7-1 through 7-8

CHAPTER Project

BUILD A PAPER AIRPLANE

In this project, you will use multiplication and division of fractions to help you find flight distances and flight times of a paper airplane. You can create any type of airplane you wish, such as a bomber or a fighter plane.

Getting Started

- Look at the flight table. In which flight did Mitiku's paper airplane travel the farthest?
- Use the table to determine how far Mitiku's plane could have traveled in flight 3 if it had remained in the air for 2 seconds.

Mitiku's Flight and Distance Table

Flight Number	Distance (ft)	Time (s)
1	$11\frac{1}{4}$	2
2	$13\frac{1}{2}$	3
3	$5\frac{3}{4}$	1

- Use a sheet of notebook paper and tape to construct a paper airplane.
  - Throw your airplane three times. Use a tape measure to measure the distance of each flight, in feet, your airplane travels. Use a stopwatch to time each flight. Round to the nearest second. Record your flight results in a table similar to the one above.

Technology Tips

- Use a **spreadsheet** to record your flight results and to find the speed of your airplane.

Research For up-to-date information on paper airplanes, visit the following website.

Data Collection and Comparison To share and compare your data with other students in the U.S., visit:

www.glencoe.com/sec/math/mac/mathnet

Working on the Project

You can use what you'll learn in Chapter 7 to help you find flight distances and flight times of your paper airplane.

Page	Exercise
279	42
291	42
305	Alternative Assessment

Instructional Resources ▶▶▶
A recording sheet to help students organize their data for the Chapter Project is shown at the right and is available in the *Investigations and Projects Masters,* p. 44.

Instructional Resources
- *Study Guide Masters*, p. 49
- *Practice Masters*, p. 49
- *Enrichment Masters*, p. 49
- Transparencies 7-1, A and B

 CD-ROM Program
- Resource Lesson 7-1

Recommended Pacing	
Standard	Day 2 of 15
Honors	Day 2 of 14
Block	Day 1 of 8

1 FOCUS

5-Minute Check
(Chapter 6)

Add or Subtract.

1. $13\frac{2}{5} - 8\frac{1}{3}$ $5\frac{1}{15}$

2. $\frac{1}{8} + \frac{9}{8}$ $1\frac{1}{4}$

3. $\frac{3}{4} + \frac{1}{6}$ $\frac{11}{12}$

4.   9 h 22 min 12 s
   − 6 h 43 min 54 s
   _____
     2 h 38 min 18 s

5. Solve $10\frac{7}{9} = 15 - n$. $4\frac{2}{9}$

 The 5-Minute Check is also available on **Transparency 7-1A** for this lesson.

Motivating the Lesson

Hands-On Activity Give groups of students a handful of small items such as plastic cubes or beans. Ask them to find $\frac{1}{2}$ of the items, then $\frac{1}{5}$ of the items. Have students record their answers and then discuss their methods.

2 TEACH

 Transparency 7-1B contains a teaching aid for this lesson.

Using Manipulatives Each pair of students will need two whole number cubes and two teacher-made fraction cubes with fractions such as $\frac{1}{3}$, $\frac{3}{8}$, and $\frac{6}{7}$. Have them use the cubes to generate two numbers and estimate their product.

268 Chapter 7

What you'll learn

You'll learn to estimate fraction products using compatible numbers and rounding.

When am I ever going to use this?

You'll use estimation to approximate the discount on a sale item.

Word Wise

compatible numbers

Where do you like to study? The circle graph shows where students prefer to study. If there are 16 students in Taylor's class, about how many students prefer to study in their bedrooms?

To solve the problem, you can estimate the product of $\frac{1}{3}$ and 16.

One way to estimate the product is to use **compatible numbers**. Compatible numbers are easy to divide mentally.

Where Students Prefer to Study

Source: Federal National Mortgage Association

$\frac{1}{3} \times 16 = ?$ *$\frac{1}{3} \times 16$ means $\frac{1}{3}$ of 16.*

$\frac{1}{3} \times 15 = ?$ *Think: For 16, the nearest multiple of 3 is 15. 3 and 15 are compatible numbers since $15 \div 3 = 5$.*

$\frac{1}{3} \times 15 = 5$ *Multiplying by $\frac{1}{3}$ is the same as dividing by 3.*

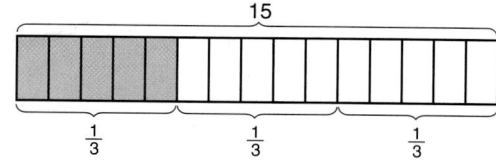

So, the product of $\frac{1}{3}$ and 16 is about 5.

About 5 of the 16 students prefer to study in their bedrooms.

Example **1** Estimate $\frac{5}{8} \times 25$.

$\frac{1}{8} \times 24 = 3$ *For 25, the nearest multiple of 8 is 24. $\frac{1}{8}$ of 24 is 3.*

$\frac{5}{8} \times 24 = 15$ *Since $\frac{1}{8}$ of 24 is 3, it follows that $\frac{5}{8}$ of 24 is 5×3 or 15.*

So, $\frac{5}{8} \times 25$ is about 15.

268 Chapter 7 Multiplying and Dividing Fractions

Cross-Curriculum Cue

Inform the other teachers on your team that your students are studying how to multiply and divide fractions. Suggestions for curriculum integration are:
Music: musical notes
Demographics: statistics
Poetry: verse

You can also estimate products by rounding fractions to 0, $\frac{1}{2}$, or 1.

LOOK BACK
You can refer to Lesson 6-1 for information on rounding fractions.

 Example 2 Estimate $\frac{2}{9} \times \frac{5}{6}$.

Think: $\frac{5}{6}$ is close to 1.

$\frac{2}{9} \times 1 = \frac{2}{9}$ *Round $\frac{5}{6}$ to 1. Any number multiplied by 1 is the number.*

So, $\frac{2}{9} \times \frac{5}{6}$ is about $\frac{2}{9}$.

To estimate the product of mixed numbers, you can round each mixed number to the nearest whole number and then multiply.

 Example 3 **Cooking** Kim needs $3\frac{1}{2}$ batches of cookies. If one recipe calls for $2\frac{1}{4}$ cups of flour, about how many cups of flour are needed?

Real World APPLICATION

You need to estimate $3\frac{1}{2} \times 2\frac{1}{4}$.

$4 \times 2 = 8$ *Round $3\frac{1}{2}$ to 4. Round $2\frac{1}{4}$ to 2.*

So, $3\frac{1}{2} \times 2\frac{1}{4}$ is about 8.

Kim will need about 8 cups of flour.

CHECK FOR UNDERSTANDING

Communicating Mathematics

1–3. See Answer Appendix.

Read and study the lesson to answer each question.

1. *Explain* how you would use rounding to estimate $3\frac{2}{3} \times 9\frac{1}{8}$.

2. *Tell* how the model shows the use of compatible numbers to estimate $\frac{3}{4} \times 9$.

3. *You Decide* Juan says that $8\frac{1}{2} \times 6\frac{1}{4}$ is about 54. Odina says that the product is about 48. Whose estimate is better? Explain your reasoning.

Guided Practice

Round each fraction to 0, $\frac{1}{2}$, or 1 and each mixed number to the nearest whole number.

4. $\frac{1}{8}$ 0

5. $\frac{5}{9}$ $\frac{1}{2}$

6. $7\frac{2}{3}$ 8

Estimate each product.

7. $\frac{1}{8} \times 15$ $\frac{1}{8} \times 16 = 2$

8. $\frac{2}{5} \times \frac{6}{7}$ $\frac{2}{5} \times 1 = \frac{2}{5}$

9. $3\frac{1}{4} \times 8\frac{6}{7}$ $3 \times 9 = 27$

10. *Geometry* Estimate the area of the rectangle. **See margin.**

  $3\frac{3}{4}$ ft

$11\frac{1}{4}$ ft

■ Reteaching the Lesson ■

Activity Have students work in small groups, with each student in the group writing examples of multiplying a fraction and a whole number and multiplying two fractions. For each example, groups should use an appropriate estimation method and then work to find the best estimate.

Additional Answer

10. about 4×11, or 44 ft^2

In-Class Examples

Estimate each product.

For Example 1

a. $\frac{1}{5} \times 11$ $\frac{1}{5} \times 10 = 2$

b. $\frac{3}{7} \times 33$ $\frac{3}{7} \times 35 = 15$

For Example 2

a. $\frac{3}{4} \times \frac{8}{9}$ $\frac{3}{4} \times 1 = \frac{3}{4}$

b. $\frac{7}{8} \times \frac{1}{9}$ $1 \times \frac{1}{9} = \frac{1}{9}$

For Example 3

Takeo painted a mural that was $9\frac{3}{4}$ feet long by $5\frac{1}{3}$ feet wide. Estimate the mural's area, $\ell \times w$. 10 ft $\times 5$ ft $= 50$ ft^2

3 PRACTICE/APPLY

Check for Understanding

If students need additional practice or instruction after completing Exercises 1–10, you may find one of the following options helpful.
- Extra Practice, see p. 575
- Reteaching Activity
- *Study Guide Masters,* p. 49
- *Practice Masters,* p. 49

Study Guide Masters, p. 49

7-1 Study Guide

Name_____ Date_____

Estimating Products

One way to estimate products is using **compatible numbers.**
Compatible numbers are easy to divide mentally.

Example 1 Estimate $\frac{2}{3} \times 9$.

$\frac{1}{3} \times 10 = 2$ *For 9, the nearest multiple of 5 is 10. $\frac{1}{5}$ of 10 is 2.*

$\frac{2}{3} \times 10 = 6$ *Since $\frac{1}{3} \times 10 = 2$, it follows that $\frac{2}{3}$ of 10 is 3×2 or 6.*

So, $\frac{2}{3} \times 9$ is about 6.

You can also estimate products by rounding. Round fractions to 0, $\frac{1}{2}$ or 1.
Round mixed numbers to the nearest whole number.

Examples 2 Estimate $\frac{5}{6} \times \frac{2}{3}$.

$\frac{5}{6} \times \frac{2}{3}$ *Think of a number line.* *$\frac{5}{6}$ rounds to 1.*

$1 \times \frac{2}{3} = \frac{2}{3}$ So, $\frac{5}{6} \times \frac{2}{3}$ is about $\frac{2}{3}$.

3 Estimate $9\frac{9}{11} \times 5\frac{1}{2}$.

$9\frac{9}{11} \times 5\frac{1}{2}$.   *Round $9\frac{9}{11}$ to 10.* *Round $5\frac{1}{2}$ to 5.*

$10 \times 5 = 50$ So, $9\frac{9}{11} \times 5\frac{1}{2}$ is about 50.

Round each fraction to 0, $\frac{1}{2}$ or 1.

1. $\frac{6}{13}$ $\frac{1}{2}$ 2. $\frac{3}{8}$ $\frac{1}{2}$ 3. $\frac{9}{10}$ 1   4. $\frac{1}{9}$ 0

Estimate each product.

5. $\frac{1}{5} \times 24$ 5   6. $7\frac{3}{4} \times 5\frac{1}{4}$ 42   7. $\frac{2}{3} \times 19$ 12   8. $\frac{5}{10} \times \frac{1}{3}$ $\frac{1}{2}$

9. $15 \times \frac{1}{4}$ 4   10. $8\frac{7}{8} \times 2\frac{9}{10}$ 27   11. $\frac{1}{9} \times \frac{1}{12}$ 0   12. $\frac{4}{7} \times 27$ 12

© Glencoe/McGraw-Hill   T49   Mathematics: Applications and Connections, Course 1

4 ASSESS

Family Activity

Have students share their daily situations that involve fractions or mixed numbers. Examples may include cooking, telling time, reading music, or timing sports events. Keep a list on the chalkboard to tally repeats.

Practice Masters, p. 49

EXERCISES

Practice

Family Activity

Ask a family member to help you make a list of situations in your daily life that involve a fraction or a mixed number. Then estimate each number by rounding.

Round each fraction to 0, $\frac{1}{2}$, or 1 and each mixed number to the nearest whole number.

11. $\frac{6}{11}$ $\frac{1}{2}$ **12.** $\frac{4}{5}$ 1 **13.** $\frac{4}{9}$ $\frac{1}{2}$ **14.** $\frac{2}{15}$ 0

15. $6\frac{1}{8}$ 6 **16.** $12\frac{3}{4}$ 13 **17.** $3\frac{1}{2}$ 3 or 4 **18.** $15\frac{2}{9}$ 15

Estimate each product. 19.–27. See Answer Appendix.

19. $\frac{1}{4} \times 31$ **20.** $\frac{3}{5} \times \frac{1}{2}$ **21.** $\frac{1}{7} \times 22$

22. $2\frac{1}{6} \times 5\frac{1}{2}$ **23.** $\frac{1}{6} \times 40$ **24.** $\frac{7}{8} \times 3\frac{1}{4}$

25. $\frac{4}{9} \times 46$ **26.** $\frac{1}{6} \times \frac{7}{8}$ **27.** $7\frac{3}{4} \times 3\frac{1}{8}$

28. Estimate $4\frac{5}{6}$ multiplied by $16\frac{7}{8}$. **5 × 17 = 85**

29. Estimate $14\frac{8}{9} \times 6\frac{3}{5}$. **15 × 7 = 105**

Applications and Problem Solving

30. $\frac{1}{20} \times 100$, or about 5 people

30. *Travel* The circle graph shows when people pack for a vacation. Suppose 96 people were surveyed. About how many people pack the day they leave?

31. *Recreation* There are about 7 million pleasure boats in the United States. About $\frac{2}{3}$ of these boats are motorboats. About how many motorboats are in the United States? $\frac{2}{3} \times 6$, or about 4 million

32. *Critical Thinking* Which point on the number line could be the graph of the product of the numbers graphed at C and D? **point N**

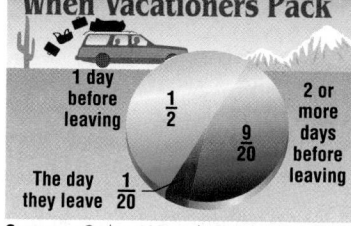
When Vacationers Pack

1 day before leaving | $\frac{1}{2}$ | 2 or more days before leaving | $\frac{9}{20}$
The day they leave $\frac{1}{20}$

Source: Carlson Wagonlit Travel Survey

Mixed Review
33. 1 hr 3 min 51 s
35. 0.498

33. *Measurement* Add 26 min 37 s and 37 min 14 s. *(Lesson 6-7)*

34. Find the prime factorization of 300. *(Lesson 5-2)* **2 · 2 · 3 · 5 · 5**

35. *Measurement* How many kilograms are in 498 grams? *(Lesson 4-9)*

36. *Standardized Test Practice* A bus travels at a speed of 47 miles per hour. About how long will it take the bus to travel 316 miles? *(Lesson 1-3)* **C**

A 4 hours
B 5 hours
C 6 hours
D 8 hours
E 10 hours

For **Extra Practice**, see page 575.

270 Chapter 7 Multiplying and Dividing Fractions

Extending the Lesson

Enrichment Masters, p. 49

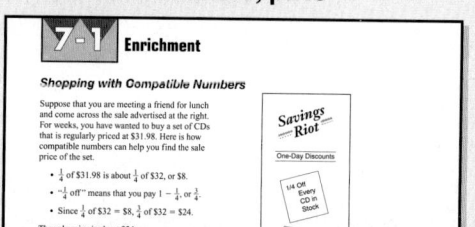

Activity Provide home furnishings catalogs or ask students to bring them from home. Have small groups of students use the catalogs to estimate the cost of window coverings for their classroom windows.

HANDS-ON LAB

COOPERATIVE LEARNING

7-2A Multiplying Fractions

A Preview of Lesson 7-2

You can multiply fractions by using geoboards.

 geoboard
 or dot paper

geobands

TRY THIS

Work with a partner.

❶ Model $\frac{1}{3} \times \frac{1}{2}$ using a geoboard.

Step 1 Place one geoband in a straight line along the bottom of the geoboard to show thirds.

Step 2 Place one geoband perpendicular to the first geoband to show halves.

Step 3 Use geobands to make a rectangle.

Step 4 Place one geoband on the peg as shown. This represents $\frac{1}{3}$.

Step 5 Place one geoband on the peg as shown. This represents $\frac{1}{2}$.

Step 6 Connect the geobands to show a small rectangle.

ON YOUR OWN

1. The area of the small rectangle has an area of 1 square unit. What is the area of the large rectangle? **6 square units**

2. What fraction of the area of the large rectangle is the area of the small rectangle? $\frac{1}{6}$

3. What is $\frac{1}{3} \times \frac{1}{2}$? $\frac{1}{6}$

GET READY

Objective Students multiply fractions by using a geoboard.

Optional Resources
Hands-On Lab Masters
- square dot paper, p. 13
- worksheet, p. 51

Overhead Manipulative Resources
- geoboard
- geobands

Manipulative Kit
- geoboard
- geobands

MANAGEMENT TIPS

Recommended Time
30 minutes

Teaching Tip Each pair of students will need a geoboard and six geobands. If geoboards and geobands are not available, students may draw the figures on square dot paper from the *Hands-On Lab Masters*.

Getting Started Ask students how they would use geoboards to show fractions. Have them illustrate thirds and sixths on their geoboards. Then ask them to determine how they would show $\frac{1}{3} \times \frac{1}{6}$.

Activity 1 uses geobands to represent fractions. Make sure students are counting spaces between pegs, not the pegs themselves. Remind students how to find the area defined by the geobands.

TRY THIS

Work with a partner.

2 Model $\frac{1}{4} \times \frac{1}{3}$ using a geoboard.

Step 1 Place one geoband in a straight line along the bottom of the geoboard to show fourths.

Step 2 Place one geoband perpendicular to the first geoband to show thirds.

Step 3 Use geobands to make a rectangle.

Step 4 Place one geoband on the peg as shown. This represents $\frac{1}{4}$.

Step 5 Place one geoband on the peg as shown. This represents $\frac{1}{3}$.

Step 6 Connect the geobands to show a small rectangle.

ON YOUR OWN

4. The small rectangle has an area of 1 square unit. What is the area of the large rectangle? **12 square units**

5. What fraction of the area of the large rectangle is the area of the small rectangle? $\frac{1}{12}$

6. What is $\frac{1}{4} \times \frac{1}{3}$? $\frac{1}{12}$

7. Write a rule you can use to multiply fractions. **See margin.**

8. *Look Ahead* Use your rule to find $\frac{3}{4} \times \frac{1}{2}$. Check your answer using a geoboard. $\frac{3}{8}$; **See Answer Appendix.**

272 Chapter 7 Multiplying and Dividing Fractions

 Have students write a summary of how they modeled multiplying fractions on their geoboards. Make sure they include any patterns they discovered that will help them multiply fractions in future lessons.

What you'll learn

You'll learn to multiply fractions.

When am I ever going to use this?

Knowing how to multiply fractions can help you make half a batch of chocolate chip cookies.

Did you know? If all of the blood vessels in your body could be laid end to end, they would be about 60,000 miles long.

Do you know your blood type? The human body can contain any one of four different blood types. Suppose the employees of a very large company have the fractions of blood types shown in the table. If $\frac{1}{2}$ of the company's employees donate blood, what fraction will donate type A blood?

Blood Type	Fraction of People With Each Blood Type
A	$\frac{2}{5}$
B	$\frac{1}{10}$
AB	$\frac{1}{20}$
O	$\frac{9}{20}$

You need to find $\frac{2}{5}$ of $\frac{1}{2}$, which means $\frac{2}{5} \times \frac{1}{2}$.

Method 1   Use a model.

Separate a rectangle into halves. Then color $\frac{1}{2}$ of the rectangle blue.

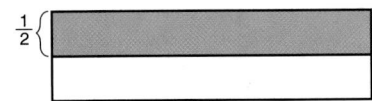

Next, separate the rectangle into fifths, and color $\frac{2}{5}$ of the rectangle yellow.

*2 parts are green.
10 parts in all.*

Since 2 out of 10 parts are green, the product is $\frac{2}{10}$ or $\frac{1}{5}$.

Method 2   Use a rule.

Find the product by multiplying the numerators and multiplying the denominators.

$\frac{2}{5} \times \frac{1}{2} = \frac{2 \cdot 1}{5 \cdot 2}$ *Multiply the numerators.*
Multiply the denominators.

$= \frac{2}{10}$ or $\frac{1}{5}$ *Simplify.*

So, $\frac{1}{5}$ of the company's employees will donate type A blood.

Lesson 7-2 Multiplying Fractions   **273**

Instructional Resources
- *Study Guide Masters*, p. 50
- *Practice Masters*, p. 50
- *Enrichment Masters*, p. 50
- Transparencies 7-2, A and B
- *Assessment and Evaluation Masters*, p. 183
- *School to Career Masters*, p. 7
- CD-ROM Program
  - Resource Lesson 7-2
  - Interactive Lesson 7-2

Recommended Pacing	
Standard	Days 3 & 4 of 15
Honors	Day 3 of 14
Block	Day 2 of 8

1 FOCUS

5-Minute Check
(Lesson 7-1)

Estimate each product.

1. $\frac{3}{5} \times 31$ $\frac{3}{5} \times 30 = 18$
2. $\frac{2}{3} \times 44$ $\frac{2}{3} \times 45 = 30$
3. $\frac{3}{4} \times \frac{1}{3}$ $1 \times \frac{1}{3} = \frac{1}{3}$
4. $\frac{1}{8} \times \frac{25}{28}$ $\frac{1}{8} \times 1 = \frac{1}{8}$
5. $14\frac{1}{8} \times 6\frac{9}{10}$ $14 \times 7 = 98$

The 5-Minute Check is also available on **Transparency 7-2A** for this lesson.

Motivating the Lesson

Problem Solving Ask students how they would determine which group would get the longer length of submarine sandwich.

- Group A will get $\frac{1}{6}$ of the $\frac{3}{4}$-yard submarine sandwich.
- Group B will get $\frac{1}{8}$ of the $\frac{4}{5}$-yard submarine sandwich. **Multiply the fractions; Group A**

Multiple Learning Styles

Logical Have groups of students devise a coded message that requires multiplying by fractions to decode. Let A through Z equal 1 through 26, respectively. Then write a code such as $\frac{2}{3}$X, $\frac{6}{7}$U, 3C, $\frac{13}{2}$D, $\frac{1}{4}$T. This word decodes as "prize." Have students post their coded phrases on a bulletin board. The phrases could be changed daily and the decoding could include additional operations as they are learned.

Transparency 7-2B contains a teaching aid for this lesson.

Using Models You may wish to use pieces of transparencies to create fraction models based on the same rectangular form. Use a permanent black pen to create the whole divided into a particular fractional unit and then use overhead markers to color in the appropriate area. By overlapping the pieces, you can model each multiplication shown in the Examples and Guided Practice.

In-Class Examples

For Example 1
Find $\frac{1}{2} \times \frac{3}{4}$. $\frac{3}{8}$

For Example 2
Find $\frac{1}{8} \times 6$. $\frac{3}{4}$

For Example 3
Find $\frac{2}{3} \times \frac{9}{10}$. $\frac{3}{5}$

For Example 4
Solve $\frac{3}{5} \times \frac{10}{21} = n$. $\frac{2}{7}$

Teaching Tip In Examples 3 and 4, emphasize that the numerator and the denominator must be divided by the same number when simplifying fractions.

3 PRACTICE/APPLY

Check for Understanding

If students need additional practice or instruction after completing Exercises 1–11, you may find one of the following options helpful.
- Extra Practice, see p. 575
- Reteaching Activity, see p. 275
- *Study Guide Masters*, p. 50
- *Practice Masters*, p. 50
- Interactive Mathematics Tools Software

You can use the following rule to multiply fractions.

| **Multiplying Fractions** | To multiply fractions, multiply the numerators. Then multiply the denominators. Simplify if necessary. |

1 Find $\frac{1}{4} \times \frac{2}{3}$.

Method 1   Use a model.

$$\frac{1}{4} \times \frac{2}{3} = \frac{2}{12} \text{ or } \frac{1}{6}$$

Method 2   Use a rule.

$$\frac{1}{4} \times \frac{2}{3} = \frac{1 \cdot 2}{4 \cdot 3} \quad \textit{Multiply.}$$
$$= \frac{2}{12} \text{ or } \frac{1}{6} \quad \textit{Simplify.}$$

Study Hint

Technology You can use a fraction calculator to multiply fractions. For example, to find $\frac{1}{2} \times \frac{3}{4}$, enter

1 / 2 × 3 / 4 = .

2 Find $\frac{2}{5} \times 4$.   *Estimate:* $\frac{1}{2} \times 4 = 2$

$$\frac{2}{5} \times 4 = \frac{2}{5} \times \frac{4}{1} \quad \textit{Express 4 as an improper fraction, } \frac{4}{1}.$$
$$= \frac{2 \cdot 4}{5 \cdot 1} \quad \textit{Multiply.}$$
$$= \frac{8}{5} \text{ or } 1\frac{3}{5} \quad \textit{Simplify. Compare to the estimate.}$$

If the numerator of one fraction and the denominator of another fraction have a common factor, you can simplify *before* you multiply.

3 Find $\frac{5}{9} \times \frac{3}{4}$.   *Estimate:* $\frac{1}{2} \times 1 = \frac{1}{2}$

Simplify before multiplying.

$$\frac{5}{9} \times \frac{3}{4} = \frac{5 \cdot \overset{1}{\cancel{3}}}{\underset{3}{\cancel{9}} \cdot 4} \quad \textit{The GCF of 3 and 9 is 3. So, divide both the numerator and the denominator by 3.}$$
$$= \frac{5}{12}$$

INTEGRATION

LOOK BACK
Refer to Lesson 5-3 for information on GCF.

4 **Algebra** Solve $\frac{3}{10} \times \frac{4}{9} = n$.

$$\frac{3}{10} \times \frac{4}{9} = n$$
$$\frac{\overset{1}{\cancel{3}} \cdot \overset{2}{\cancel{4}}}{\underset{5}{\cancel{10}} \cdot \underset{3}{\cancel{9}}} = n \quad \textit{The GCF of 4 and 10 is 2. The GCF of 3 and 9 is 3. So, divide both the numerator and the denominator by 2 and then by 3.}$$
$$\frac{2}{15} = n$$

The solution is $\frac{2}{15}$.

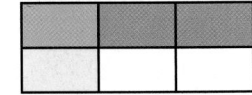

CHECK FOR UNDERSTANDING

Communicating Mathematics

Read and study the lesson to answer each question. 1–3. See margin.

1. **Explain** how the model shows the product of $\frac{1}{3}$ and $\frac{1}{2}$.

2. **Draw** a model to show that $\frac{2}{3} \times \frac{1}{5} = \frac{2}{15}$.

3. **Write** how to find the product of any two fractions.

Guided Practice

Find each product. Write in simplest form.

4. $\frac{1}{6} \times \frac{1}{2}$ $\frac{1}{12}$

5. $\frac{3}{5} \times \frac{1}{4}$ $\frac{3}{20}$

6. $\frac{1}{5} \times \frac{5}{7}$ $\frac{1}{7}$

7. $\frac{2}{3} \times \frac{1}{5}$ $\frac{2}{15}$

Solve each equation. Write the solution in simplest form.

8. $14 \times \frac{2}{7} = a$ **4**

9. $w = \frac{3}{4} \times \frac{4}{9}$ $\frac{1}{3}$

10. $\frac{6}{7} \times \frac{5}{12} = x$ $\frac{5}{14}$

11. **Life Science** About $\frac{7}{10}$ of the human body is water. If a person weighs 150 pounds, how many pounds are water? **about 105 pounds**

EXERCISES

Practice

Find each product. Write in simplest form.

12. $\frac{1}{3} \times \frac{3}{5}$ $\frac{1}{5}$

13. $\frac{8}{9} \times \frac{1}{3}$ $\frac{8}{27}$

14. $\frac{7}{8} \times \frac{3}{4}$ $\frac{21}{32}$

15. $\frac{2}{3} \times \frac{1}{6}$ $\frac{1}{9}$

16. $\frac{2}{3} \times 5$ $3\frac{1}{3}$

17. $\frac{3}{5} \times \frac{2}{9}$ $\frac{2}{15}$

18. $6 \times \frac{5}{8}$ $3\frac{3}{4}$

19. $\frac{7}{9} \times \frac{6}{7}$ $\frac{2}{3}$

20. $\frac{1}{2} \times \frac{8}{9}$ $\frac{4}{9}$

21. $\frac{2}{3} \times \frac{5}{9}$ $\frac{10}{27}$

22. $\frac{3}{4} \times \frac{8}{9}$ $\frac{2}{3}$

23. $\frac{1}{9} \times \frac{2}{3}$ $\frac{2}{27}$

Solve each equation. Write the solution in simplest form.

24. $x = \frac{5}{12} \times \frac{3}{7}$ $\frac{5}{28}$

25. $10 \times \frac{2}{3} = h$ $6\frac{2}{3}$

26. $y = \frac{5}{8} \times \frac{2}{3}$ $\frac{5}{12}$

27. $m = \frac{5}{16} \times \frac{4}{15}$ $\frac{1}{12}$

28. $\frac{1}{2} \times \frac{4}{9} = b$ $\frac{2}{9}$

29. $d = \frac{5}{6} \times \frac{8}{15}$ $\frac{4}{9}$

30. $c = \frac{7}{10} \times \frac{5}{14}$ $\frac{1}{4}$

31. $18 \times \frac{7}{12} = a$ $10\frac{1}{2}$

32. $p = \frac{9}{13} \times \frac{8}{9}$ $\frac{8}{13}$

33. **Algebra** Evaluate mn if $m = \frac{1}{3}$ and $n = \frac{12}{15}$. $\frac{4}{15}$

Applications and Problem Solving

34. **Broadcasting** A television network sells 16 minutes of air time to advertisers. A company purchases $\frac{3}{8}$ of the total ad time. How many minutes of ad time did the company buy?
6 minutes

■ **Reteaching the Lesson** ■

Activity Have students use counters to model problems such as $\frac{1}{4} \times \frac{3}{5}$. Give students 20 counters. Have them divide the counters into piles representing $\frac{3}{5}$ and $\frac{2}{5}$. Have them divide the $\frac{3}{5}$ pile into fourths. How many counters are in one-fourth? Write this as a fraction. $\frac{3}{20}$

MathPASS CD-ROM

This CD-ROM offers a complete, self-paced mathematics curriculum. Each lesson includes a pretest, tutorial, guided practice, and posttest. MathPASS Lesson 21 is corrlated to this Student Edition lesson.
For Windows & Macintosh

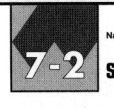

Closing Activity

Writing Have students determine how they would use fraction multiplication to solve the following problem. *What fraction of your classmates have both a first and a last name that begins with a letter from A to M?* Ask them to write out the steps and provide an answer to the problem.

Chapter 7, Quiz A (Lessons 7-1 and 7-2) is available in the *Assessment and Evaluation Masters,* p. 183.

35. *Algebra* The expression 3^2 means 3×3, or 9.
  a. If $m = \frac{3}{8}$, what is the value of m^2? $\frac{9}{64}$
  b. Evaluate h^2 if $h = \frac{4}{5}$. $\frac{16}{25}$

36. *Critical Thinking* Find $\frac{1}{2} \times \frac{2}{3} \times \frac{3}{4} \times \frac{4}{5} \times \ldots \times \frac{99}{100}$. $\frac{1}{100}$

Mixed Review

37. Estimate the product of $\frac{3}{4}$ and 37. *(Lesson 7-1)* $\frac{3}{4} \times 36 = 27$

38. *Algebra* Solve the equation $x - \frac{11}{12} = \frac{5}{12}$. *(Lesson 6-3)* $\frac{16}{12}$ or $1\frac{1}{3}$

39. Determine whether 786 is divisible by 2, 3, 5, 6, 9, or 10. **2, 3, 6**
(Lesson 5-1)

 40. **Standardized Test Practice** Hayley works 8 hours a week baby-sitting and earns $22.40. How much does she earn per hour? *(Lesson 4-5)* **D**
  A $3.20   **B** $2.50   **C** $3.40   **D** $2.80   **E** Not Here

For **Extra Practice,** see page 575.

 Let the **Games** Begin

Multiplication Mania

Get Ready This game is for any number of players.

  ☐ poster board 🎲 2 number cubes 📟 calculator

Math Skill
Multiplying Fractions

Get Set On a poster board, draw a large game board similar to the one shown at the right.

Go
- Place the game board on the floor.
- Each player rolls the number cubes. The person with the highest total starts.
- The first player rolls the number cubes onto the game board. If a number cube rolls off the game board or lands on a line, roll it again. The player then multiplies the two numbers on which the number cubes land and simplifies the product. Use a calculator to determine whether the answer is correct. Each correct answer is worth 1 point.
- The first player to score 10 points wins.

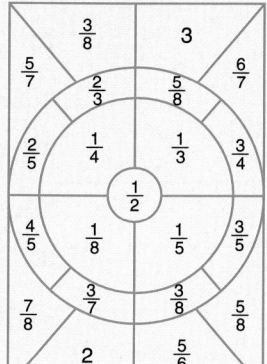

interNET CONNECTION Visit www.glencoe.com/sec/math/mac/mathnet for more games.

276 Chapter 7 Multiplying and Dividing Fractions

Practice Masters, p. 50

7-2 Practice

Multiplying Fractions

Find each product. Write in simplest form.

1. $\frac{3}{4} \times \frac{1}{2}$ $\frac{3}{8}$ 2. $\frac{1}{3} \times \frac{5}{6}$ $\frac{5}{18}$ 3. $\frac{2}{7} \times \frac{3}{5}$ $\frac{6}{35}$

4. $\frac{3}{8} \times 10$ $3\frac{3}{4}$ 5. $\frac{1}{6} \times \frac{3}{5}$ $\frac{1}{10}$ 6. $\frac{1}{4} \times \frac{2}{7}$ $\frac{1}{14}$

7. $\frac{2}{3} \times \frac{5}{8}$ $\frac{5}{12}$ 8. $\frac{9}{10} \times \frac{4}{5}$ $\frac{18}{25}$ 9. $\frac{7}{9} \times \frac{1}{4}$ $\frac{7}{36}$

10. $16 \times \frac{5}{12}$ $6\frac{2}{3}$ 11. $\frac{4}{9} \times \frac{1}{4}$ $\frac{1}{9}$ 12. $\frac{5}{6} \times \frac{7}{10}$ $\frac{7}{12}$

13. $\frac{1}{5} \times \frac{15}{16}$ $\frac{3}{16}$ 14. $\frac{1}{10} \times \frac{4}{7}$ $\frac{2}{35}$ 15. $\frac{5}{9} \times 18$ **10**

Solve each equation. Write the solution in simplest form.

16. $a = \frac{9}{5} \times \frac{4}{5}$ $\frac{4}{9}$ 17. $\frac{9}{5} \times \frac{14}{15} = s$ $\frac{2}{3}$ 18. $\frac{7}{18} \times \frac{3}{14} = p$ $\frac{1}{12}$

19. $r = \frac{2}{3} \times \frac{9}{10}$ $\frac{3}{5}$ 20. $28 \times \frac{5}{8} = x$ $17\frac{1}{2}$ 21. $\frac{5}{6} \times \frac{4}{7} = m$ $\frac{10}{21}$

22. $d = \frac{4}{9} \times \frac{15}{16}$ $\frac{5}{12}$ 23. $\frac{3}{10} \times \frac{5}{8} = k$ $\frac{3}{16}$ 24. $h = \frac{3}{7} \times 35$ **15**

25. $n = \frac{5}{20} \times \frac{5}{6}$ $\frac{1}{8}$ 26. $\frac{9}{14} \times \frac{7}{12} = z$ $\frac{3}{8}$ 27. $f = \frac{5}{12} \times \frac{4}{15}$ $\frac{1}{9}$

28. $\frac{3}{14} \times \frac{2}{9} = c$ $\frac{1}{21}$ 29. $\frac{3}{4} \times \frac{8}{9} = t$ $\frac{2}{3}$ 30. $y = 15 \times \frac{3}{10}$ $4\frac{1}{2}$

31. Find the product of $\frac{4}{5}$ and 30. **24**

32. Evaluate xy if $x = \frac{2}{3}$ and $y = \frac{3}{4}$. $\frac{1}{2}$

© Glencoe/McGraw-Hill   T50   *Mathematics: Applications and Connections, Course 1*

■ Extending the Lesson ■

Enrichment Masters, p. 50

7-2 Enrichment

Word Sums

Can one sixth plus one third equal one? It is possible if the fractions are fractions of *words!* Here is an example.

  Find the last one sixth of the word TOMATO: O
  Find the middle one third of the word FINEST: NE
  Add the letters O + NE = ONE!

Match each word sum in the first column with its definition in the second column.

1. the first one fourth of CHECKERS + the last one half of AFFAIR   h   a. purchased

 Let the **Games** Begin

Another variation for Multiplication Mania is to use 3 number cubes. To also use this game in Lesson 7-5 for division of fractions, students could drop the number cubes one at a time and divide the first fraction by the second.
*Additional resources for this game can be found on page 43 of the **Classroom Games**.*

7-3 Multiplying Mixed Numbers

What you'll learn

You'll learn to multiply mixed numbers.

When am I ever going to use this?

Knowing how to multiply mixed numbers can help you determine the ingredients needed to make a cake.

LOOK BACK

You can refer to Lesson 5-5 for information on improper fractions.

A dot following a musical note (○ ·) means that the note gets $1\frac{1}{2}$ times as many beats as the same note without a dot (○). If a whole note gets four beats, how many beats would a dotted whole note get?

You need to find $1\frac{1}{2}$ of 4, or $1\frac{1}{2} \times 4$. To multiply mixed numbers, express the mixed numbers as improper fractions and then multiply as with fractions.

$$1\frac{1}{2} \times 4 = \frac{3}{2} \times \frac{4}{1} \quad \textit{Express the mixed numbers as improper fractions.}$$

$$= \frac{3 \cdot 4}{2 \cdot 1} \quad \textit{Multiply the numerators. Multiply the denominators.}$$

$$= \frac{12}{2} \text{ or } 6 \quad \textit{Simplify.}$$

A dotted whole note gets 6 beats.

Examples

1 Find $\frac{1}{3} \times 3\frac{3}{8}$. *Estimate:* $\frac{1}{3} \times 3 = 1$

$$\frac{1}{3} \times 3\frac{3}{8} = \frac{1}{3} \times \frac{27}{8} \quad \textit{Express } 3\frac{3}{8} \textit{ as an improper fraction.}$$

$$= \frac{1 \cdot \overset{9}{27}}{\underset{1}{3} \cdot 8} \quad \textit{Divide 27 and 3 by the GCF, 3. Then multiply.}$$

$$= \frac{9}{8} \text{ or } 1\frac{1}{8} \quad \textit{Compare with your estimate.}$$

INTEGRATION

2 **Algebra** If $m = 2\frac{2}{5}$ and $n = 1\frac{7}{8}$, what is the value of mn?

$$mn = 2\frac{2}{5} \cdot 1\frac{7}{8} \quad \textit{Replace m with } 2\frac{2}{5} \textit{ and n with } 1\frac{7}{8}.$$

$$\textit{Estimate: } 2 \times 2 = 4$$

$$= \frac{12}{5} \cdot \frac{15}{8} \quad \textit{Express the mixed numbers as improper fractions.}$$

$$= \frac{\overset{3}{12} \cdot \overset{3}{15}}{\underset{1}{5} \cdot \underset{2}{8}} \quad \begin{array}{l}\textit{Divide 12 and 8 by the GCF, 4.}\\ \textit{Divide 15 and 5 by the GCF, 5.}\end{array}$$

$$\textit{Then multiply.}$$

$$= \frac{9}{2} \text{ or } 4\frac{1}{2} \quad \textit{Compare with your estimate.}$$

Lesson 7–3 Multiplying Mixed Numbers **277**

MathPASS CD-ROM

This CD-ROM offers a complete, self-paced mathematics curriculum. Each lesson includes a pretest, tutorial, guided practice, and posttest. MathPASS Lesson 22 is correlated to this Student Edition lesson.

For Windows & Macintosh

Motivating the Lesson

Communication Bring in a blueberry muffin recipe that makes 12 muffins. Discuss with the class how they might increase the recipe to make enough muffins for everybody in the class.

$2\frac{1}{2}$ times for a class of 30 students

7-3 Lesson Notes

Instructional Resources

- *Study Guide Masters*, p. 51
- *Practice Masters*, p. 51
- *Enrichment Masters*, p. 51
- Transparencies 7-3, A and B
- *Diversity Masters*, p. 7
- CD-ROM Program
  - Resource Lesson 7-3

Recommended Pacing	
Standard	Day 5 of 15
Honors	Day 4 of 14
Block	Day 3 of 8

1 FOCUS

5-Minute Check
(Lesson 7-2)

Find each product. Write in simplest form.

1. $\frac{1}{4} \times \frac{3}{7}$ $\frac{3}{28}$

2. $8 \times \frac{3}{4}$ 6

3. $\frac{2}{3} \times \frac{9}{14}$ $\frac{3}{7}$

Solve each equation. Write the solution in simplest form.

4. $m = \frac{3}{5} \times \frac{1}{9}$ $\frac{1}{15}$

5. $\frac{4}{9} \times \frac{27}{32} = t$ $\frac{3}{8}$

 The 5-Minute Check is also available on **Transparency 7-3A** for this lesson.

2 TEACH

 Transparency 7-3B contains a teaching aid for this lesson.

Using Models Represent mixed numbers with models as we did fractions. For example, model $3\frac{3}{8} \times \frac{1}{3}$ as shown and write out as $\frac{8}{24} + \frac{8}{24} + \frac{8}{24} + \frac{3}{24} = \frac{27}{24}$, or $1\frac{1}{8}$.

Lesson 7-3 277

3 PRACTICE/APPLY

Check for Understanding

If students need additional practice or instruction after completing Exercises 1–13, you may find one of the following options helpful.
- Extra Practice, see p. 575
- Reteaching Activity
- *Study Guide Masters*, p. 51
- *Practice Masters*, p. 51

Assignment Guide
Core: 15–41 odd, 43–48
Enriched: 14–40 even, 41, 43–48

Study Guide Masters, p. 51

CHECK FOR UNDERSTANDING

Communicating Mathematics

Read and study the lesson to answer each question.

1. **Tell** how to multiply mixed numbers. **1–2. See Answer Appendix.**

2. **Explain** to a classmate how to find the product of $3\frac{1}{2}$ and $1\frac{1}{2}$. What is the product?

Guided Practice

Express each mixed number as an improper fraction.

3. $6\frac{1}{3}$ $\frac{19}{3}$ 4. $2\frac{5}{8}$ $\frac{21}{8}$ 5. $5\frac{3}{4}$ $\frac{23}{4}$

Find each product. Write in simplest form.

6. $6 \times 2\frac{1}{4}$ $13\frac{1}{2}$ 7. $\frac{2}{3} \times 5\frac{2}{5}$ $3\frac{3}{5}$ 8. $2\frac{4}{5} \times 3\frac{3}{4}$ $10\frac{1}{2}$

Solve each equation. Write the solution in simplest form.

9. $12 \times 3\frac{1}{6} = n$ **38**   10. $a = 2\frac{4}{5} \times 3\frac{1}{8}$ $8\frac{3}{4}$ 11. $1\frac{1}{4} \times \frac{8}{9} = x$ $1\frac{1}{9}$

12. **Algebra** Evaluate the expression st if $s = 2\frac{2}{3}$ and $t = 4\frac{2}{3}$. $12\frac{4}{9}$

13. **Music** Refer to the beginning of the lesson.
   a. If an eighth note gets half of a beat, how many beats would a dotted eighth note get? $\frac{3}{4}$
   b. A sixteenth note gets one-fourth of a beat. How many beats would a dotted sixteenth note get? $\frac{3}{8}$

EXERCISES

Practice

Express each mixed number as an improper fraction.

14. $4\frac{1}{2}$ $\frac{9}{2}$ 15. $7\frac{2}{3}$ $\frac{23}{3}$ 16. $3\frac{1}{4}$ $\frac{13}{4}$ 17. $4\frac{2}{3}$ $\frac{14}{3}$

18. $5\frac{5}{7}$ $\frac{40}{7}$ 19. $6\frac{3}{5}$ $\frac{33}{5}$ 20. $1\frac{5}{8}$ $\frac{13}{8}$ 21. $8\frac{3}{4}$ $\frac{35}{4}$

Find each product. Write in simplest form.

22. $1\frac{4}{5} \times 3$ $5\frac{2}{5}$ 23. $1\frac{7}{9} \times 3\frac{3}{4}$ $6\frac{2}{3}$ 24. $12\frac{1}{2} \times \frac{1}{5}$ $2\frac{1}{2}$

25. $4\frac{3}{8} \times 2\frac{2}{5}$ $10\frac{1}{2}$ 26. $4 \times \frac{2}{5}$ $1\frac{3}{5}$ 27. $3\frac{3}{8} \times 1\frac{4}{9}$ $4\frac{7}{8}$

28. $\frac{5}{11} \times 6\frac{2}{7}$ $2\frac{6}{7}$ 29. $7\frac{7}{8} \times 5\frac{1}{3}$ **42**   30. $3\frac{5}{8} \times 4$ $14\frac{1}{2}$

Solve each equation. Write the solution in simplest form.

31. $6 \times 3\frac{1}{2} = y$ **21**   32. $h = \frac{1}{3} \times 2\frac{1}{4}$ $\frac{3}{4}$ 33. $k = 3\frac{1}{6} \times 2\frac{4}{7}$ $8\frac{1}{7}$

34. $j = \frac{5}{12} \times 1\frac{4}{5}$ $\frac{3}{4}$ 35. $2\frac{3}{4} \times 2\frac{2}{3} = d$ $7\frac{1}{3}$ 36. $8 \times 1\frac{5}{6} = c$ $14\frac{2}{3}$

37. **Algebra** What is the value of $\frac{2}{3} a$ if $a = 45$? **30**

38. **Algebra** Evaluate ab if $a = \frac{2}{3}$ and $b = 3\frac{1}{2}$. $2\frac{1}{3}$

Reteaching the Lesson

Activity Have students use grid paper to model mixed numbers. $5\frac{7}{8}$ would use 6 columns of 8 boxes. Shade in 5 whole columns and 7 boxes in the last column. How many boxes are shaded? **47** Since each box represents $\frac{1}{8}$, there are $\frac{47}{8}$ shaded.

Error Analysis

Watch for students who combine whole numbers and then fractions when multiplying mixed numbers.
Prevent by reinforcing the fact that mixed numbers are rewritten as improper fractions *before* multiplying.

39. *Algebra* If $x = \frac{9}{10}$ and $y = 8\frac{1}{3}$, find the value of xy. $7\frac{1}{2}$

Applications and Problem Solving

Real World

40. *Cooking* A recipe for a two-layer, 8-inch cake calls for a box of cake mix, 2 eggs, and $1\frac{1}{3}$ cups of water. How much of each ingredient is needed to make a three-layer, 8-inch cake? $1\frac{1}{2}$ **boxes of cake mix, 3 eggs, 2 cups of water**

41. *Geometry* To find the area of a parallelogram, you can use the formula, $A = b \times h$, where b is the length of the base and h is the height. Find the area of the parallelogram. $8\frac{1}{4}$ **sq ft**

$2\frac{3}{4}$ ft

3 ft

42. *Working on the* **CHAPTER Project** Refer to the table on page 267.

   a. In flight 2, Mitiku's airplane flew $13\frac{1}{2}$ feet in 3 seconds. How far would his airplane travel if it remained in the air for 1 minute? Find the distance the other two airplanes would travel in 1 minute. **270 ft; $337\frac{1}{2}$ ft; 345 ft**

   b. For each of your flights, find the distance the plane would travel in 1 minute. **See students' work.**

43. *Critical Thinking* Is $2\frac{2}{3} \times 4\frac{1}{2}$ more or less than 10? Explain how you know without actually multiplying. **more; $2\frac{2}{3} \times 4\frac{1}{2} \approx 3 \times 4$ or 12**

Mixed Review

44. **Standardized Test Practice** Evaluate ab if $a = \frac{7}{8}$ and $b = \frac{2}{3}$. *(Lesson 7-2)* **D**

   A $\frac{72}{83}$ **B** $\frac{21}{16}$ **C** $\frac{9}{11}$ **D** $\frac{7}{12}$ **E** Not Here

45. Find $7\frac{1}{6} - 3\frac{3}{4}$. Write the answer in simplest form. *(Lesson 6-6)* $3\frac{5}{12}$

46. Round $\frac{8}{11}$ to the nearest half. *(Lesson 6-1)* **1**

47. *Money Matters* Mr. Maldonado kept track of the phone calls each of his four children made during the month of September. Make a bar graph for the set of data. *(Lesson 2-3)* **See margin.**

Name	Number of Calls
Luis	45
Lorena	40
Diana	25
Mirna	25

For **Extra Practice**, see page 575.

48. Evaluate the expression $12 - 8 \div 2 + 1$. *(Lesson 1-4)* **9**

MATH IN THE MEDIA

1. Explain why the comic is funny. **See students' work.**

2. Suppose Sally multiplies $4\frac{1}{2}$ by $6\frac{5}{8}$. What is the product? $29\frac{13}{16}$

Peanuts

■ Extending the Lesson ■

Enrichment Masters, p. 51

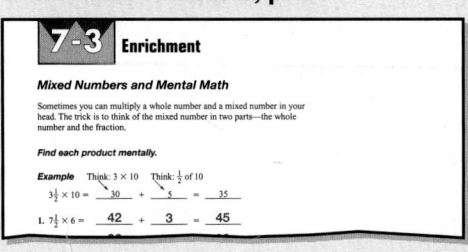

7-3 Enrichment

Mixed Numbers and Mental Math

Sometimes you can multiply a whole number and a mixed number in your head. The trick is to think of the mixed number in two parts—the whole number and the fraction.

Find each product mentally.

Example Think: 3×10 Think: $\frac{1}{2}$ of 10

$3\frac{1}{2} \times 10 = \underline{30} + \underline{5} = \underline{35}$

1. $7\frac{1}{2} \times 6 = \underline{42} + \underline{3} = \underline{45}$

MATH IN THE MEDIA

Begin a class discussion/debate by asking the same question Sally asks: "Why should I learn that?" Encourage students to look for or to create other comics that involve fractions.

CHAPTER Project

Exercise 42 asks students to advance to the next stage of work on the Chapter Project. You may ask the class to set up an algebraic expression to answer Exercise 42b.

4 ASSESS

Closing Activity

Modeling Bring in or obtain a variety of boxes that have mixed numbers as lengths and widths. Have pairs of students choose a box and determine the area of one of its sides by multiplying length × width.

Additional Answer

47.

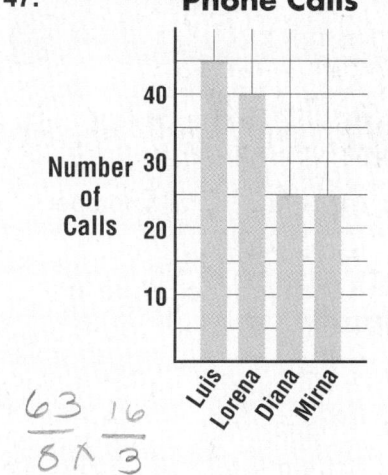

Phone Calls

Number of Calls

40

30

20

10

Luis Lorena Diana Mirna

Practice Masters, p. 51

Name _____ Date _____

7-3 Practice

Multiplying Mixed Numbers

Express each mixed number as an improper fraction.

1. $2\frac{4}{5}$ $\frac{14}{5}$ 2. $6\frac{3}{4}$ $\frac{27}{4}$ 3. $8\frac{6}{7}$ $\frac{62}{7}$

4. $5\frac{2}{9}$ $\frac{47}{9}$ 5. $9\frac{5}{6}$ $\frac{59}{6}$ 6. $3\frac{1}{12}$ $\frac{37}{12}$

Find each product. Write in simplest form.

7. $3\frac{1}{3} \times \frac{3}{4}$ $2\frac{2}{5}$ 8. $9 \times 4\frac{2}{3}$ 42   9. $2\frac{5}{6} \times 4\frac{1}{2}$ $12\frac{3}{4}$

10. $\frac{4}{9} \times 3\frac{1}{2}$ $1\frac{7}{9}$ 11. $1\frac{3}{8} \times 2\frac{2}{7}$ $3\frac{1}{7}$ 12. $4\frac{1}{6} \times \frac{9}{10}$ $3\frac{3}{4}$

13. $3\frac{1}{3} \times 2\frac{1}{4}$ $7\frac{1}{2}$ 14. $\frac{8}{9} \times 5\frac{1}{4}$ $4\frac{4}{7}$ 15. $2\frac{5}{8} \times 6$ $15\frac{3}{4}$

16. $3\frac{1}{2} \times 2\frac{3}{5}$ $10\frac{1}{2}$ 17. $\frac{5}{7} \times 4\frac{3}{8}$ $3\frac{1}{8}$ 18. $20 \times 1\frac{2}{5}$ 28

Solve each equation. Write the solution in simplest form.

19. $2\frac{2}{3} \times \frac{6}{11} = s$ $1\frac{1}{3}$ 20. $p = 1\frac{1}{6} \times 3\frac{3}{7}$ $3\frac{6}{7}$ 21. $\frac{4}{9} \times 2\frac{5}{12} = x$ $2\frac{1}{14}$

22. $d = 14 \times 1\frac{3}{4}$ $24\frac{1}{2}$ 23. $5\frac{2}{3} \times \frac{6}{7} = t$ $4\frac{4}{5}$ 24. $3\frac{1}{3} \times 2\frac{2}{5} = a$ 8

25. $r = 1\frac{4}{5} \times 3\frac{4}{9}$ $6\frac{3}{7}$ 26. $n = \frac{7}{9} \times 5\frac{1}{6}$ $3\frac{4}{9}$ 27. $1\frac{1}{14} \times \frac{7}{9} = y$ $1\frac{3}{16}$

28. $k = 2\frac{3}{8} \times 16$ 38   29. $5\frac{1}{4} \times 2\frac{1}{3} = b$ $12\frac{1}{4}$ 30. $m = \frac{7}{9} \times 5\frac{5}{8}$ $4\frac{3}{8}$

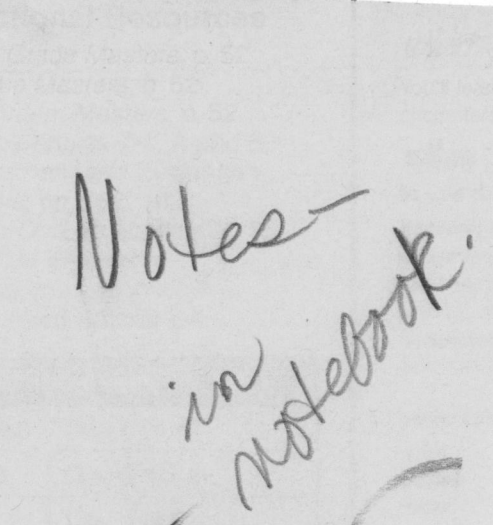

Notes — in notebook.

Instructional Resources

1 FOCUS

5-Minute Check
(Lesson 7-3)

1. Express $3\frac{5}{7}$ as an improper fraction. $\frac{26}{7}$

Find each product. Write in simplest form.

2. $\frac{2}{5} \times 6\frac{1}{4}$ $2\frac{1}{2}$

3. $6 \times 3\frac{5}{12}$ $20\frac{1}{2}$

4. Solve $n = 4\frac{1}{2} \times 3\frac{4}{9}$. $15\frac{1}{2}$

5. A farm co-op donates $\frac{1}{8}$ of its harvest to a local pantry. How much of $2\frac{2}{3}$ tons of vegetables will go to the pantry? $\frac{1}{3}$ ton

 The 5-Minute Check is also available on **Transparency 7-4A** for this lesson.

Motivating the Lesson
Problem Solving Ask students how they would determine the dimensions of a basketball.

$\frac{1}{8} \times \frac{8}{3}$

7-4

Integration: Geometry
Circles and Circumference

The first African-American woman to win an Olympic gold medal was Alice Coachman. She received a gold medal for the high jump in the 1948 Olympics. An Olympic medal is a model of a circle.

A **circle** is a set of points in a plane, all of which are the same distance from a fixed point in the plane called the **center**.

The distance from the center to any point on the circle is called the **radius (r)**. The distance across the circle through its center is called the **diameter (d)**. The diameter of a circle is twice the length of its radius. The **circumference (C)** is the distance around the circle.

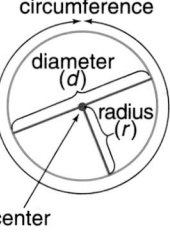
circumference
diameter (d)
radius (r)
center

Circumference and diameter are related in a special way.

MINI-LAB

Work with a partner. tape measure calculator

 circular objects

Try This

- Wrap a tape measure around the circumference of one of the circular objects. Record the measurement. It is the circumference of the object.

... diameter of the object.

... circumference by the diameter.

1. The ... close ...

2. The ... of a ... a littl... three... diam...

Quick Quiz

Write on Board. ←

... a piece of string, a ruler, ... find a length representing the circumference. They measure the string and the diameter of the circle in both metric and customary units. We calculate the ratio of circumference to diameter to estimate π."

Marilyn L. McNamara, Teacher
Walter T. Bergen Middle School
Bloomingdale, NJ

In the Mini-Lab, you discovered that the circumference of a circle is always a little more than three times its diameter. The exact number of times is represented by the Greek letter π (pi).

| **Circumference** | **Words:** | The circumference of a circle is equal to π times its diameter or π times twice its radius. |
| | **Symbols:** $C = \pi d$
 or
 $C = 2\pi r$ | **Model:** 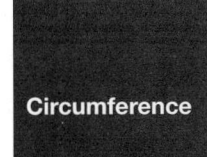 |

The decimal 3.14 and the fraction $\frac{22}{7}$ are used as approximations for π.

Examples

① Find the circumference of a circle with a diameter of $1\frac{1}{2}$ feet.

$C = \pi d$

$\approx \frac{22}{7} \cdot 1\frac{1}{2}$ *Replace π with $\frac{22}{7}$ and d with $1\frac{1}{2}$.*

$\approx \frac{22}{7} \cdot \frac{3}{2}$ *Write $1\frac{1}{2}$ as an improper fraction.*

$\approx \frac{\overset{11}{22}}{7} \cdot \frac{3}{\underset{1}{2}}$ *Divide 2 and 22 by the GCF, 2.*

$\approx \frac{33}{7}$ or $4\frac{5}{7}$ *Simplify.*

The circumference of the circle is $4\frac{5}{7}$ feet.

APPLICATION

② **Inventions** The first Ferris wheel was built for the 1893 World's Columbian Exposition in Chicago. It had a radius of 125 feet, weighed 1,200 tons, and held about 2,100 people. For 50 cents, fairgoers could ride the Ferris wheel for twenty minutes. How far did the passengers travel on each revolution?

You need to find the circumference of the Ferris wheel. The radius of the wheel is 125 feet.

$C = 2\pi r$

$\approx 2 \cdot 3.14 \cdot 125$ *Replace π with 3.14 and r with 125.*

2 ⊠ 3.14 ⊠ 125 ⊟ 785

The passengers traveled about 785 feet on each revolution.

Lesson 7-4 Integration: Geometry Circles and Circumference **28**

 Transparency 7-4B contains a teaching aid for this lesson.

Using the Mini-Lab Review the importance of accuracy when using measuring instruments. Suggest that students record their measurements in a four-column table with headings *Object*, *Circumference*, *Diameter*, and $\frac{Circumference}{Diameter}$.

In-Class Examples

For Example 1
Find the circumference of a circle with a diameter of $2\frac{3}{4}$ feet. $8\frac{9}{14}$ ft

For Example 2
A radio telescope, located at Jodrell Bank in Great Britain, has a radius of 38.1 meters. Find the circumference of the Jodrell Bank radio dish rounded to the nearest tenth. **about 239.3 m**

Teaching Tip Show students how $\pi d = 2\pi r$ by including an extra

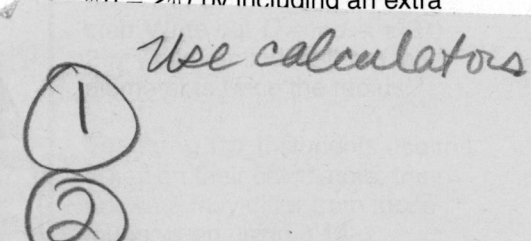

3 PRACTICE/APPLY

Check for Understanding

If students need additional practice or instruction after completing Exercises 1–8, you may find one of the following options helpful.
- Extra Practice, see p. 576
- Reteaching Activity
- *Study Guide Masters*, p. 52
- *Practice Masters*, p. 52

Assignment Guide

Core: 9–21 odd, 23–26
Enriched: 10–20 even, 21–26
All: Self Test, 1–10

Additional Answers

1. Sample answer: Multiply 2 by π by 3.

2. If the diameter or radius of a circle is a fraction, use $\frac{22}{7}$ for π. If the diameter or radius is a whole number or decimal, use 3.14 for π.

Study Guide Masters, p. 52

7-4 Study Guide

Name_____ Date_____

Integration: Geometry
Circles and Circumferences

A **circle** is all of the points in a plane that are the same distance from a point called the **center**. The **diameter** (d) is the distance across the circle through its center. The **radius** (r) is the distance from the center to any point on the circle. The **circumference** (C) is the distance around the circle.

Examples 1 Find the circumference of a circle with a diameter of 7.5 inches.
$C = \pi d$ *Formula for circumference*
$\approx 3.14 \cdot 7.5$ *Replace π with 3.14 and d with 7.5.*
$3.14 \times 7.5 = 23.55$
The circumference of the circle is about 23.55 inches.

2 Find the circumference of a circle with a radius of 21 meters.
$C = 2\pi r$ *Formula for circumference*
$= 2 \cdot \frac{22}{7} \cdot 21$ *Replace π with $\frac{22}{7}$ and r with 21.*
$= \frac{2}{1} \cdot \frac{22}{7} \cdot \frac{21}{1}$ *Divide 7 and 21 by the GCF, 7.*
$= \frac{132}{1}$ or 132   *Simplify.*
The circumference of the circle is about 132 meters.

Find the circumference of each circle to the nearest tenth.
Use $\frac{22}{7}$ or 3.14 for π.

1. 25 ft	2. $2\frac{1}{2}$ cm	3. 10 m	4. 1.5 in.
157 ft	**7.9 cm**	**62.8 m**	**4.7 in.**
5. $d = 11$ km	6. $r = 24$ mi	7. $d = 12$ m	8. $r = 30\frac{3}{4}$ ft
34.5 km	**150.7 mi**	**37.7 m**	**193$\frac{2}{7}$ ft**
9. $r = 4\frac{2}{3}$ yd	10. $d = 15$ km	11. $r = 50$ ft	12. $d = 4.1$ m
29$\frac{1}{3}$ yd	**47.1 km**	**314 ft**	**12.9 m**

© Glencoe/McGraw-Hill   T52   *Mathematics: Applications and Connections, Course 1*

---

282   Chapter 7

CHECK FOR UNDERSTANDING

Communicating Mathematics

Read and study the lesson to answer each question. 1–2. See margin.

1. *Write*, in your own words, how to find the circumference of a circle with a radius of 3 centimeters.

2. *Tell* how you know when to use either $\frac{22}{7}$ or 3.14 for π.

HANDS-ON **MATH**

3. *Locate* two circular objects in your home. Measure the circumference and diameter of each object. How does the quotient of each circumference and its diameter compare to π? **See students' work.**

Guided Practice

Find the circumference of each circle shown or described. Use $\frac{22}{7}$ or 3.14 for π. Round decimal answers to the nearest tenth.

4. **87.9 ft**

14 ft

5.

$2\frac{1}{2}$ yd
$\pi = \frac{22}{7}$;
$7\frac{6}{7}$ yd

6. $d = \frac{7}{8}$ yd $\pi = \frac{22}{7}$;
$2\frac{3}{4}$ yd

7. Find the circumference of a circle with a radius of 0.95 meter. **6.0 m**

8. *Earth Science* Scientists in Goldstone, California, use a radio telescope to search for signs of life in space. This radio telescope has a circular dish with a diameter of 112 feet. What is the circumference of the radio dish? $\pi = \frac{22}{7}$; **352 ft**

EXERCISES

Practice

Answers are calculated using 3.14 and then rounded unless otherwise noted.

Find the circumference of each circle shown or described. Use $\frac{22}{7}$ or 3.14 for π. Round decimal answers to the nearest tenth.

9. **12.6 in.**

4 in.

10.
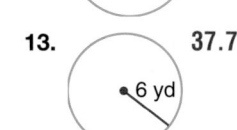
$1\frac{3}{4}$ ft
$\pi = \frac{22}{7}$;
11 ft

11.

$2\frac{1}{3}$ in.
$\pi = \frac{22}{7}$;
$7\frac{1}{3}$ in.

12.
4.3 ft
13.5 ft

13. **37.7 yd**
6 yd

14.
$3\frac{1}{2}$ ft
$\pi = \frac{22}{7}$;
22 ft

16. $\pi = \frac{22}{7}$; **29$\frac{1}{3}$ in.**

15. $d = 8$ ft **25.1 ft**

16. $r = 4\frac{2}{3}$ in.

17. $d = 3.1$ yd **9.7 yd**

18. Find the circumference of a circle with a radius of 9.6 inches. **60.3 in.**

19. Find the measure of the circumference of a circle that has a diameter of 16.8 centimeters. **52.8 cm**

20. The radius of a circle measures $5\frac{1}{4}$ feet. What is the measure of its circumference? **33.0 ft**

282   Chapter 7 Multiplying and Dividing Fractions

Reteaching the Lesson

Activity Provide small groups of students with objects such as paper plates, plastic lids, or CDs. First they should measure the diameter to figure out the circumference of each object. Then they should check their results by measuring the circumference.

Error Analysis

Watch for students who confuse the radius and diameter in a circle.
Prevent by reminding them that the word *radius* is shorter than the word *diameter*. So the radius is the shorter segment.

21. *Transportation* A certain model of a "penny-farthing" bicycle had a large front wheel with a radius of $2\frac{1}{2}$ feet. How far would the bicycle travel on each rotation of the wheel?

21. $\pi = \frac{22}{7}$; $15\frac{5}{7}$ ft

22. *Entertainment* The tallest Ferris wheel in the United States today is the Texas Star Ferris wheel at Fair Park in Dallas, Texas. Its diameter is about 212 feet. What is the difference between the circumference of this Ferris wheel and the Ferris wheel described in Example 2 on page 281? **about 119 feet**

23. The circumference is twice as long.

23. *Critical Thinking* Tell how the circumference of two circles compare if the diameter of one is twice as long as the diameter of the other.

Mixed Review

24. Find $1\frac{5}{7} \times 2\frac{5}{8}$. Write in simplest form. *(Lesson 7-3)* $4\frac{1}{2}$

25. *Algebra* Solve $x - \frac{1}{12} = \frac{5}{12}$. Write the solution in simplest form. *(Lesson 6-3)* $\frac{1}{2}$

26. *Standardized Test Practice* In July, an average of 209 books were checked out each day at the Strongville Public Library. Which is the best estimate for the number of books checked out for the whole month of July? *(Lesson 1-3)* **D**

A 2,000 **B** 4,000 **C** 5,000 **D** 6,000 **E** 8,000

For **Extra Practice**, see page 576.

CHAPTER 7 — Mid-Chapter Self Test

Estimate each product. *(Lesson 7-1)*

1. $17 \times \frac{3}{4}$ $16 \times \frac{3}{4} = 12$

2. $3\frac{4}{5} \times 6\frac{1}{7}$ $4 \times 6 = 24$

3. $2\frac{3}{4} \times \frac{2}{5}$ $3 \times \frac{1}{2} = 1\frac{1}{2}$

Find each product. *(Lessons 7-2 and 7-3)*

4. $\frac{1}{6} \times \frac{4}{5}$ $\frac{2}{15}$

5. $\frac{3}{10} \times \frac{5}{6}$ $\frac{1}{4}$

6. $\frac{1}{3} \times 4\frac{2}{7}$ $1\frac{3}{7}$

7. $2\frac{5}{8} \times 1\frac{2}{7}$ $3\frac{3}{8}$

Find the circumference of each circle shown or described. Use $\frac{22}{7}$ or 3.14 for π. Round decimal answers to the nearest tenth. *(Lesson 7-4)*

8.

$1\frac{2}{5}$ yd

$\pi = \frac{22}{7}$; $8\frac{4}{5}$ yd

9. $d = 13.6$ cm **42.7 cm**

10. *Pets* If a hamster wheel has a radius of 4 inches, how far does the hamster run in one rotation of the wheel? *(Lesson 7-4)* **25.1 in.**

Extending the Lesson

Enrichment Masters, p. 52

Activity Have pairs of students research the history of π. Have them find out, for example, how π came to be used and how the introduction of decimals in the 1600s affected its value.

GET READY

Objective Students divide fractions by using a geoboard.

Optional Resources
Hands-On Lab Masters
• square dot paper, p. 13
• worksheet, p. 52

Overhead Manipulative Resources
• geoboard
• geobands

Manipulative Kit
• geoboard
• geobands

MANAGEMENT TIPS

Recommended Time
30 minutes

Getting Started Review using geoboards to multiply fractions by having students model $\frac{1}{8} \times \frac{1}{2}$. Then ask them how they would model $\frac{1}{2} \div \frac{1}{8}$.

The **Activity** uses a geoboard and geobands to model dividing fractions. After students have modeled the activity, ask the following questions.
• What is the area of the rectangle? **16 square units**
• How does the area relate to the fractions being divided? **16 is a multiple of 4 and 8.**
• Can you use other shapes to model division with fractions? **A rectangle with an area of 8 square units also could be used.**

ASSESS

After students complete Exercises 1–4, have pairs of students write a sentence or two explaining how geoboards can be used to model division with fractions.

Use Exercise 5 to determine whether students understand dividing fractions.

COOPERATIVE LEARNING

HANDS-ON LAB

7-5A Dividing Fractions

A Preview of Lesson 7-5

In Lesson 7-2A, you learned how to use a geoboard to multiply fractions. You can also use a geoboard to divide fractions.

geoboard or dot paper

geobands

TRY THIS

Work with a partner.

Step 1 Use geobands to make a rectangle as shown at the right. This rectangle represents 1.

Step 2 Use geobands to show fourths. There are four $\frac{1}{4}$'s in 1. Therefore, $1 \div \frac{1}{4} = 4$.

Step 3 Use geobands to show eighths. There are eight $\frac{1}{8}$'s in 1. Therefore, $1 \div \frac{1}{8} = 8$.

Examine the geoboard. What is $\frac{1}{4} \div \frac{1}{8}$? *Think: $\frac{1}{4} \div \frac{1}{8}$ means: How many $\frac{1}{8}$'s are in $\frac{1}{4}$?*

ON YOUR OWN

Use a geoboard and geobands to find each quotient.

1. $1 \div \frac{1}{2}$ **2** **2.** $\frac{1}{2} \div \frac{1}{8}$ **4** **3.** $\frac{2}{3} \div \frac{1}{6}$ **4** **4.** $\frac{3}{4} \div \frac{1}{8}$ **6**

1–4. See Answer Appendix for geoboard models.

5. *Look Ahead* Find the quotient of $\frac{1}{3}$ and $\frac{1}{6}$ without using a geoboard. **2**

Have students write a paragraph explaining how to divide fractions using a geoboard.

Dividing Fractions

What you'll learn

You'll learn to divide fractions.

When am I ever going to use this?

Knowing how to divide fractions can help you decide how much food to order for a party.

Word Wise
reciprocal

Dan ordered 5 large pepperoni pizzas for his birthday party. There will be 16 guests at the party. He estimates that each guest will eat about $\frac{1}{4}$ of a pizza. Did Dan order enough pizza?

You need to find the number of $\frac{1}{4}$ servings that are in 5 pizzas.

The model shows $5 \div \frac{1}{4}$.

The dashed lines show that each pizza contains four $\frac{1}{4}$-pizza servings. Five pizzas contain 5 times 4, or 20 servings of pizza. That is, $5 \div \frac{1}{4} = 20$. So, Dan will have enough pizza.

$5 \div \frac{1}{4} = 20 \Leftrightarrow 5 \times 4 = 20$ *Dividing by $\frac{1}{4}$ gives the same result as multiplying by 4.*

The numbers $\frac{1}{4}$ and 4 have a special relationship. Their product is 1.

$$\frac{1}{4} \times 4 = 1$$

Any two numbers whose product is 1 are called **reciprocals**.

Examples

Find the reciprocal of each number.

① 6

Since $6 \times \frac{1}{6} = 1$,

the reciprocal of 6 is $\frac{1}{6}$.

② $\frac{3}{8}$

Since $\frac{3}{8} \times \frac{8}{3} = 1$,

the reciprocal of $\frac{3}{8}$ is $\frac{8}{3}$.

Study Hint

Mental Math The reciprocal of a number is found by "inverting" the fraction. That is, the numerator and the denominator are interchanged.

You can use reciprocals to divide fractions.

Dividing Fractions	To divide by a fraction, multiply by its reciprocal.

Lesson 7-5 Dividing Fractions   **285**

Instructional Resources

- *Study Guide Masters*, p. 53
- *Practice Masters*, p. 53
- *Enrichment Masters*, p. 53
- Transparencies 7-5, A and B
- *Classroom Games*, pp. 19–20
- *Technology Masters*, p. 14
- CD-ROM Program
  - Resource Lesson 7-5

Recommended Pacing	
Standard	Days 7 & 8 of 15
Honors	Day 6 of 14
Block	Day 5 of 8

1 FOCUS

5-Minute Check
(Lesson 7-4)

Find the circumference of each circle described. Use $\frac{22}{7}$ or 3.14 for π. Round decimal answers to the nearest tenth.

1. $d = 4.2$ ft **13.2 ft**
2. $r = 3\frac{7}{8}$ in. **$24\frac{5}{14}$ in.**
3. $d = 12.8$ cm **40.2 cm**
4. $r = 5.7$ yd **35.8 yd**
5. $d = 7\frac{3}{11}$ ft **$22\frac{6}{7}$ ft**

The 5-Minute Check is also available on **Transparency 7-5A** for this lesson.

Motivating the Lesson

Hands-On Activity Have students work in small groups using measuring cups and water to determine:

- the number of $\frac{1}{2}$-cup servings in 3 cups of punch, **6**
- the number of $\frac{1}{4}$-cup servings in $\frac{7}{8}$-cup of sour cream. **$3\frac{1}{2}$**

Multiple Learning Styles

Interpersonal Make a list of division examples and corresponding multiplication examples. Give the multiplication examples to small groups of students. Write the division examples, one at a time, on the overhead projector. Have the group with the corresponding multiplication example find the product.

MathPASS CD-ROM

This CD-ROM offers a complete, self-paced mathematics curriculum. Each lesson includes a pretest, tutorial, guided practice, and posttest. MathPASS Lesson 24 is correlated to this Student Edition lesson.
For Windows & Macintosh

Closing Activity

Writing Have students write directions for a person who needs to divide $\frac{3}{4}$ of a pound of cheese into $\frac{1}{16}$-pound slices.

---

32. If you divide $\frac{5}{6}$ by $\frac{1}{4}$, what is the quotient? $3\frac{1}{3}$

Solve each equation. Write the solution in simplest form.

33. $\frac{2}{3} \div \frac{3}{4} = m$ $\frac{8}{9}$ **34.** $k = \frac{3}{4} \div 12$ $\frac{1}{16}$ **35.** $\frac{1}{5} \div \frac{3}{10} = z$ $\frac{2}{3}$

36. $d = \frac{1}{4} \div \frac{1}{8}$ 2 **37.** $\frac{3}{4} \div \frac{5}{6} = v$ $\frac{9}{10}$ **38.** $a = \frac{1}{3} \div \frac{1}{2}$ $\frac{2}{3}$

39. $\frac{8}{9} \div 4 = h$ $\frac{2}{9}$ **40.** $x = \frac{5}{9} \div \frac{2}{3}$ $\frac{5}{6}$ **41.** $3 \div \frac{6}{7} = w$ $3\frac{1}{2}$

42. *Algebra* Find the value of $a \div b$ if $a = \frac{1}{2}$ and $b = 9$. $\frac{1}{18}$

Applications and Problem Solving

43. *Money Matters* Mr. Barojas parked his car at a 4-hour parking meter. If each half-hour of parking costs 25 cents, how many quarters does he need for 4 hours of parking? **8 quarters**

44. *Geography* The table lists the continents' approximate sizes relative to Earth's total landmass.

   a. About how many times larger is North America than South America? $1\frac{1}{3}$

   b. About how many times larger is Asia than North America? $1\frac{4}{5}$

   c. About how many times larger is Asia than Africa? $1\frac{1}{2}$

Continent	Fraction of Earth's Landmass
Asia	$\frac{3}{10}$
Africa	$\frac{1}{5}$
North America	$\frac{1}{6}$
South America	$\frac{1}{8}$
Antarctica	$\frac{1}{10}$
Europe	$\frac{1}{16}$
Australia	$\frac{1}{20}$

45. *Critical Thinking* Solve mentally.

   a. $\frac{6,978}{3,012} \times \frac{11}{10} \div \frac{6,978}{3,012}$ $\frac{11}{10}$

   b. $\frac{6,978}{10} \times \frac{11}{3,012} \div \frac{6,978}{3,012}$ $\frac{11}{10}$

Mixed Review

46. *Geometry* Find the circumference of a circle with a radius of 4 meters. *(Lesson 7-4)* **25.1 m**

For **Extra Practice**, see page 576.

47. Express $\frac{7}{9}$ as a decimal. Use bar notation to show a repeating decimal. *(Lesson 5-10)* **$0.\overline{7}$**

48. **Standardized Test Practice** Warren's dog weighs 25.9 kilograms. How many grams does the dog weigh? *(Lesson 4-9)* **A**
   A 25,900 g   **B** 0.0259 g
   C 1025.9 g   **D** 259,000 g

inter NET CONNECTION
For the latest weather statistics, visit: www.glencoe.com/sec/math/mac/mathnet

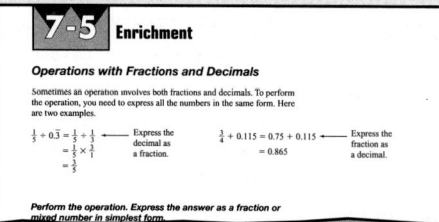

49. *Statistics* The average annual precipitation in Georgia is 48.61 inches. About how many inches of precipitation does Georgia average each month? *(Lesson 4-5)* **about 4 inches**

50. Add 15.783 and 390.81. *(Lesson 3-6)* **406.593**

Practice Masters, p. 53

Extending the Lesson

Enrichment Masters, p. 53

7-5 Enrichment

Operations with Fractions and Decimals

Activity Using two different colors of fraction cubes, have pairs of students take turns rolling the cubes. Using one color as the divisor and the other color as the dividend, students should write out and solve the expression. They should continue until they get a whole number quotient or until a predetermined time runs out.

Dividing Mixed Numbers

What you'll learn

You'll learn to divide mixed numbers.

When am I ever going to use this?

Knowing how to divide mixed numbers can help you find the average speed you travel on a trip.

A tsunami, (soo-NAH-mee), or tidal wave, can travel from one side of the Pacific Ocean to the other in less than a day. If a tsunami traveled 1,400 miles from a point in the Pacific Ocean to the Alaskan coastline in $2\frac{1}{2}$ hours, how many miles per hour did it travel?

You need to find $1,400 \div 2\frac{1}{2}$.
To divide mixed numbers, express each mixed number as an improper fraction. Then divide as with fractions.

$$1,400 \div 2\frac{1}{2} = \frac{1,400}{1} \div \frac{5}{2} \quad \textit{Express each mixed number as an improper fraction.}$$

$$= \frac{1,400}{1} \times \frac{2}{5} \quad \textit{Multiply by the reciprocal.}$$

$$= \frac{\overset{280}{1,400}}{1} \times \frac{2}{5} \quad \textit{Divide 5 and 1,400 by the GCF, 5.}$$

$$= 560$$

The tsunami traveled 560 miles per hour.

Examples

1 Find $4\frac{1}{2} \div 3\frac{3}{4}$. *Estimate: $4 \div 4 = 1$*

$$4\frac{1}{2} \div 3\frac{3}{4} = \frac{9}{2} \div \frac{15}{4} \quad \textit{Express each mixed number as an improper fraction.}$$

$$= \frac{9}{2} \times \frac{4}{15} \quad \textit{Multiply by the reciprocal.}$$

$$= \frac{\overset{3}{9}}{2} \times \frac{\overset{2}{4}}{\underset{5}{15}} \quad \textit{Divide 9 and 15 by the GCF, 3. Divide 2 and 4 by the GCF, 2.}$$

$$= \frac{6}{5} \text{ or } 1\frac{1}{5} \quad \textit{Simplify. Compare with your estimate.}$$

INTEGRATION **2** **Algebra** Solve $w = 2\frac{4}{5} \div \frac{7}{8}$. *Estimate: $3 \div 1 = 3$*

$$w = \frac{14}{5} \div \frac{7}{8} \quad \textit{Express each mixed number as an improper fraction.}$$

$$w = \frac{\overset{2}{14}}{5} \times \frac{8}{\underset{1}{7}} \quad \textit{Multiply by the reciprocal. Divide 7 and 14 by the GCF, 7.}$$

$$w = \frac{16}{5} \text{ or } 3\frac{1}{5} \quad \textit{Simplify. Compare with your estimate.}$$

Lesson 7-6 Dividing Mixed Numbers **289**

Multiple Learning Styles

Intrapersonal Have students write about any difficulties they have when dividing mixed numbers. Encourage them to include examples of their own experiences of dealing with fractions and what would make it easier for them.

Motivating the Lesson

Problem Solving Ask students how they would solve the following problem. *A square brownie has an area of $1\frac{1}{2}$ square inches. How many brownies could be made in a pan having an area of $114\frac{3}{4}$ square inches?* $76\frac{1}{2}$ **brownies**

Instructional Resources

- *Study Guide Masters*, p. 54
- *Practice Masters*, p. 54
- *Enrichment Masters*, p. 54
- Transparencies 7-6, A and B
- *Assessment and Evaluation Masters*, p. 184
- CD-ROM Program
  - Resource Lesson 7-6

Recommended Pacing	
Standard	Day 9 of 15
Honors	Day 7 of 14
Block	Day 6 of 8

1 FOCUS

5-Minute Check
(Lesson 7-5)

1. Find the reciprocal of $\frac{4}{5}$. $\frac{5}{4}$

Find each quotient. Write in simplest form.

2. $\frac{3}{4} \div \frac{1}{5}$ $3\frac{3}{4}$

3. $\frac{1}{6} \div \frac{2}{3}$ $\frac{1}{4}$

4. $5 \div \frac{1}{4}$ 20

5. Evaluate $r \div s$, if $r = \frac{3}{5}$ and $s = 6$. $\frac{1}{10}$

The 5-Minute Check is also available on **Transparency 7-6A** for this lesson.

2 TEACH

Transparency 7-6B contains a teaching aid for this lesson.

Thinking Algebraically Some students may make the connection that dividing and multiplying are inverse operations. Give them a simple equation such as $\frac{a}{2} = 6$ and ask them to find a. Show them that $\frac{a}{2} = 6$ is the same as $a \cdot \frac{1}{2} = 6$, which can also be expressed as the related equation $a = 6 \div \frac{1}{2}$.

3 PRACTICE/APPLY

Check for Understanding

If students need additional practice or instruction after completing Exercises 1–13, you may find one of the following options helpful.
• Extra Practice, see p. 576
• Reteaching Activity
• *Study Guide Masters*, p. 54
• *Practice Masters*, p. 54

Study Guide Masters, p. 54

7-6 Study Guide

Dividing Mixed Numbers

To divide mixed numbers, express each mixed number as an improper fraction. Then divide as with fractions.

Example Solve $m = 2\frac{5}{8} \div 1\frac{3}{4}$. *Estimate:* $2 \div 2 = 1$

$m = 2\frac{5}{8} \div \frac{7}{4}$ *Express each mixed number as an improper fraction.*

$m = \frac{21}{8} \times \frac{4}{7}$ *Multiply by the reciprocal. Divide 21 and 7 by the GCF, 7. Divide 4 and 8 by the GCF, 4.*

$m = \frac{3}{2} \times \frac{1}{1}$ *Simplify.*

$m = \frac{3}{2}$ or $1\frac{1}{2}$ *Compare with your estimate.*

Find each quotient. Write in simplest form.

1. $2\frac{1}{4} \div \frac{2}{3}$ $3\frac{3}{8}$
2. $1\frac{2}{3} \div 1\frac{1}{4}$ $1\frac{1}{3}$
3. $5 \div 1\frac{3}{7}$ $3\frac{1}{2}$
4. $2\frac{1}{3} \div \frac{7}{9}$ 3
5. $5\frac{2}{5} \div \frac{9}{10}$ 6
6. $7\frac{1}{2} \div 1\frac{2}{3}$ $4\frac{1}{2}$

Solve each equation. Write the solution in simplest form.

7. $n = 10\frac{1}{2} \div \frac{7}{10}$ 15
8. $3\frac{1}{3} \div 10 = p$ $\frac{9}{25}$
9. $r = 6\frac{2}{3} \div 2\frac{1}{3}$ 3
10. $15 \div 3\frac{1}{3} = t$ $4\frac{1}{2}$
11. $6\frac{2}{3} \div 1\frac{2}{3} = c$ 4
12. $h \div 2\frac{1}{12} \div 5$ $\frac{5}{12}$
13. $m = 18 \div \frac{9}{11}$ 22
14. $r = 4\frac{4}{5} \div \frac{8}{15}$ 9
15. $6\frac{3}{4} \div 1\frac{1}{8} = k$ 6

© Glencoe/McGraw-Hill   T54   *Mathematics: Applications and Connections, Course 1*

Communicating Mathematics

1–3. See Answer Appendix.

Math Journal

Guided Practice

CHECK FOR UNDERSTANDING

Read and study the lesson to answer each question.

1. *Explain* to a classmate how to find the reciprocal of $4\frac{5}{8}$.

2. *Tell* whether $4 \div \frac{1}{2}$ is more or less than 4. Explain your reasoning.

3. *Write*, in your own words, the steps to follow when finding the quotient of 12 and $2\frac{2}{3}$.

Write each mixed number as an improper fraction. Then write its reciprocal.

4. $2\frac{1}{4}$ $\frac{9}{4}, \frac{4}{9}$

5. $7\frac{2}{3}$ $\frac{23}{3}, \frac{3}{23}$

6. $6\frac{1}{3}$ $\frac{19}{3}, \frac{3}{19}$

Find each quotient. Write in simplest form.

7. $8 \div 2\frac{1}{2}$ $3\frac{1}{5}$

8. $9\frac{1}{2} \div 4\frac{3}{4}$ 2

9. $3\frac{3}{4} \div \frac{5}{6}$ $4\frac{1}{2}$

Solve each equation. Write the solution in simplest form.

10. $6\frac{1}{4} \div \frac{1}{2} = g$ $12\frac{1}{2}$

11. $5\frac{1}{3} \div 4\frac{2}{3} = n$ $1\frac{1}{7}$

12. If $9\frac{1}{2}$ is divided by $\frac{1}{2}$, what is the quotient?   **19**

13. *Food* Mrs. Golubec needs to cut a zucchini into slices that measure $\frac{3}{8}$ inch thick. If the zucchini measures $13\frac{1}{2}$ inches long, how many slices can she cut? **36 slices**

EXERCISES

Practice

Write each mixed number as an improper fraction. Then write its reciprocal.

14. $4\frac{1}{2}$ $\frac{9}{2}, \frac{2}{9}$

15. $6\frac{2}{5}$ $\frac{32}{5}, \frac{5}{32}$

16. $1\frac{3}{8}$ $\frac{11}{8}, \frac{8}{11}$

17. $2\frac{4}{5}$ $\frac{14}{5}, \frac{5}{14}$

18. $5\frac{5}{6}$ $\frac{35}{6}, \frac{6}{35}$

19. $3\frac{3}{4}$ $\frac{15}{4}, \frac{4}{15}$

20. $7\frac{1}{2}$ $\frac{15}{2}, \frac{2}{15}$

21. $9\frac{1}{4}$ $\frac{37}{4}, \frac{4}{37}$

Find each quotient. Write in simplest form.

22. $7\frac{1}{3} \div 6$ $1\frac{2}{9}$

23. $4\frac{3}{4} \div \frac{5}{8}$ $7\frac{3}{5}$

24. $5\frac{1}{4} \div 3\frac{1}{2}$ $1\frac{1}{2}$

25. $10\frac{1}{2} \div \frac{7}{8}$ 12

26. $1\frac{5}{9} \div 2\frac{1}{3}$ $\frac{2}{3}$

27. $5 \div 6\frac{1}{4}$ $\frac{4}{5}$

28. $2\frac{4}{5} \div 5\frac{3}{5}$ $\frac{1}{2}$

29. $10 \div 2\frac{2}{7}$ $4\frac{3}{8}$

30. $13 \div 2\frac{3}{5}$ 5

Solve each equation. Write the solution in simplest form.

31. $3 \div 4\frac{1}{2} = t$ $\frac{2}{3}$

32. $a = 1\frac{3}{8} \div 2\frac{3}{4}$ $\frac{1}{2}$

33. $6\frac{1}{2} \div \frac{1}{4} = m$ 26

34. $y = 4\frac{4}{7} \div 2\frac{2}{3}$ $1\frac{5}{7}$

35. $\frac{4}{5} \div 1\frac{1}{5} = q$ $\frac{2}{3}$

36. $c = 5\frac{1}{3} \div 4$ $1\frac{1}{3}$

■Reteaching the Lesson■

Activity Have two pairs of students play "Check." Have Team 1 give Team 2 a mixed number division problem to solve. Have Team 1 use estimation and a fraction calculator to check Team 2's answer. When the answer checks, Team 2 then gives Team 1 a problem, and so on.

MathPASS CD-ROM

This CD-ROM offers a complete, self-paced mathematics curriculum. Each lesson includes a pretest, tutorial, guided practice, and posttest. MathPASS Lessons 25 and 26 are correlated to this Student Edition lesson.
For Windows & Macintosh

39a. $\frac{7}{10}$; $5\frac{11}{12}$; $9\frac{5}{8}$

39b. $\frac{1}{10}$; $\frac{7}{12}$; $6\frac{3}{8}$

39c. $\frac{3}{25}$; $8\frac{2}{3}$; 13

39d. $1\frac{1}{3}$; $1\frac{7}{32}$; $4\frac{12}{13}$

37. *Algebra* What is the value of $m \div n$ if $m = 6\frac{2}{3}$ and $n = \frac{4}{5}$? $8\frac{1}{3}$

38. *Algebra* Evaluate $p \div q$ if $p = 9$ and $q = 3\frac{3}{5}$. $2\frac{1}{2}$

39. Find the following for each pair of fractions.

$\frac{2}{5}$ and $\frac{3}{10}$, $3\frac{1}{4}$ and $2\frac{2}{3}$, 8 and $1\frac{5}{8}$

  a. sum   **b.** difference

  c. product   **d.** quotient in simplest form

Applications and Problem Solving

40. *Statistics* The table shows how many hours Tiarri watched cartoons each day after school. What is the mean number of hours Tiarri watched cartoons in the 5 days? $1\frac{1}{10}$ h

Day	Hours
Monday	$1\frac{1}{4}$
Tuesday	$\frac{1}{2}$
Wednesday	$1\frac{1}{2}$
Thursday	$\frac{1}{2}$
Friday	$1\frac{3}{4}$

41. *Measurement* Marnee is working on her history project. She wants to place photographs of people from various countries in one vertical row on a poster board that is $17\frac{1}{2}$ inches long. If each photograph is $2\frac{3}{4}$ long, how many photographs can Marnee place on the poster board? **6 photographs**

42. *Working on the CHAPTER Project* Refer to the table on page 267.
  a. Use the information from Mitiku's first flight to determine how long it would take his airplane to fly 100 miles. **about 26 hours**
  b. Use the information from your first flight to determine how long it would take your airplane to fly 100 miles. **See students' work.**

43. *Critical Thinking* Tell whether $\frac{8}{10} \div \frac{2}{3}$ is greater than or less than $\frac{8}{10} \div \frac{3}{4}$ without solving. Explain your reasoning. **Greater than; $\frac{2}{3}$ is less than $\frac{3}{4}$.**

Mixed Review

44. Find $\frac{3}{7} \div \frac{3}{5}$. Write in simplest form. *(Lesson 7-5)* $\frac{5}{7}$

45. Find $\frac{5}{7} \times \frac{2}{3}$. Write in simplest form. *(Lesson 7-2)* $\frac{10}{21}$

46. *Algebra* Solve $y - \frac{7}{12} = \frac{5}{12}$. *(Lesson 6-3)* $\frac{12}{12}$ **or 1**

47. **Standardized Test Practice** What is the GCF of 96 and 172? *(Lesson 5-3)* **B**

  A 2   **B** 4   **C** 24   **D** 43

48. *Geometry* What is the area of a rectangle with a length of 12.8 feet and a width of 7.4 feet? *(Lesson 4-4)* **94.7 sq ft**

49. *Life Science* A 150-pound human body contains about 0.2 ounce of iron, 0.07 ounce of zinc, and 0.004 ounce of copper. Write each of these decimals in words. *(Lesson 3-1)* **See margin.**

For **Extra Practice**, see page 576.

50. *Technology* Bob's answering machine can record fifty 30-second messages. How many minutes of tape does his machine have? *(Lesson 1-1)* **25 minutes**

Lesson 7-6 Dividing Mixed Numbers **291**

Extending the Lesson

Enrichment Masters, p. 54

7-6 Enrichment

Modeling Division of Fractions on a Ruler

How many half-inch lengths are in 4 inches? When you look at a ruler, it is easy to see that the answer is 8.

So this diagram is also a model for the division $4 \div \frac{1}{2} = 8$.

Write the division that is modeled in each diagram.

Activity Ask students to design a shipping crate for a floppy disk case that is $4\frac{1}{8}$ in. long by 2 in. wide by $4\frac{5}{8}$ in. high. Use these guidelines: (1) The wood used for the crate will be $5\frac{1}{4}$ in. wide, $\frac{1}{4}$ in. thick, and 8 ft long; (2) The design must have a minimum amount of waste; (3) The crate must hold 12 cases.

---

4 ASSESS

Closing Activity

Modeling Have students work in pairs to illustrate a division problem with blocks, a geoboard, or dot paper and colored pencils.

Chapter 7, Quiz C (Lessons 7-5 and 7-6) is available in the *Assessment and Evaluation Masters*, p. 184.

Additional Answer

49. two tenths; seven hundredths; four thousandths

Practice Masters, p. 54

7-6 Practice

Dividing Mixed Numbers

Write each mixed number as an improper fraction. Then write its reciprocal.

1. $8\frac{3}{4}$ $\frac{35}{4}$, $\frac{4}{35}$ 2. $9\frac{6}{7}$ $\frac{69}{7}$, $\frac{7}{69}$ 3. $7\frac{5}{6}$ $\frac{47}{6}$, $\frac{6}{47}$

4. $3\frac{5}{12}$ $\frac{41}{12}$, $\frac{12}{41}$ 5. $1\frac{7}{16}$ $\frac{23}{16}$, $\frac{16}{23}$ 6. $6\frac{7}{8}$ $\frac{55}{8}$, $\frac{8}{55}$

Find each quotient. Write in simplest form.

7. $4 \div 2\frac{2}{5}$ $1\frac{2}{3}$ 8. $3\frac{1}{4} \div 1\frac{3}{8}$ $2\frac{4}{11}$ 9. $\frac{8}{9} \div 5\frac{1}{3}$ $\frac{1}{6}$

10. $2\frac{1}{2} \div 4\frac{2}{7}$ $\frac{7}{12}$ 11. $3\frac{1}{9} \div 7$ $\frac{4}{9}$ 12. $6\frac{3}{4} \div 4\frac{1}{2}$ $1\frac{7}{18}$

13. $2\frac{1}{7} \div \frac{3}{14}$ 10   14. $3\frac{3}{5} \div 2\frac{1}{4}$ $1\frac{2}{5}$ 15. $9 \div 3\frac{3}{7}$ $2\frac{5}{8}$

16. $1\frac{7}{9} \div 1\frac{5}{8}$ $\frac{2}{3}$ 17. $\frac{7}{10} \div 2\frac{5}{8}$ $\frac{4}{15}$ 18. $3\frac{1}{3} \div 1\frac{7}{9}$ $1\frac{4}{15}$

19. $1\frac{3}{4} \div 14$ $\frac{1}{8}$ 20. $2\frac{7}{15} \div 3\frac{8}{9}$ $\frac{3}{5}$ 21. $2\frac{1}{10} \div \frac{7}{12}$ $2\frac{2}{5}$

22. $6\frac{3}{4} \div 1\frac{7}{20}$ 5   23. $18 \div 1\frac{1}{8}$ 16   24. $4\frac{1}{6} \div 1\frac{3}{7}$ $2\frac{11}{12}$

Solve each equation. Write the solution in simplest form.

25. $\frac{5}{12} \div 2\frac{1}{2} = p$ $\frac{1}{6}$ 26. $s = 2\frac{2}{3} \div 1\frac{5}{6}$ $1\frac{5}{11}$ 27. $a = 1\frac{3}{4} \div 6$ $\frac{3}{10}$

28. $k = 2\frac{1}{3} \div 1\frac{7}{9}$ $1\frac{7}{20}$ 29. $1\frac{1}{6} \div \frac{7}{18} = x$ $4\frac{1}{5}$ 30. $1\frac{3}{5} \div 3\frac{4}{7} = x$ $\frac{56}{125}$

Evaluate each expression.

31. $f \div g$, if $f = 5\frac{1}{4}$ and $g = 1\frac{3}{8}$ $3\frac{3}{8}$ 32. $w \div z$, if $w = 9$ and $z = 2\frac{1}{4}$ $4\frac{1}{5}$

33. $t \div v$, if $t = 6\frac{1}{2}$ and $v = 1\frac{7}{8}$ $3\frac{7}{15}$ 34. $j \div k$, if $j = 12$ and $k = 2\frac{3}{4}$ $4\frac{4}{7}$

© Glencoe/McGraw-Hill   T54   *Mathematics: Applications and Connections, Course 1*

Lesson 7-6   **291**

Integration: Measurement
Changing Customary Units

Instructional Resources

- *Study Guide Masters*, p. 55
- *Practice Masters*, p. 55
- *Enrichment Masters*, p. 55
- Transparencies 7-7, A and B

 CD-ROM Program
- Resource Lesson 7-7

Recommended Pacing	
Standard	Days 10 & 11 of 15
Honors	Days 8 & 9 of 14
Block	Day 6 of 8

1 FOCUS

5-Minute Check
(Lesson 7-6)

Find each quotient. Write in simplest form.

1. $5 \div 2\frac{1}{3}$ $2\frac{1}{7}$

2. $\frac{14}{15} \div 1\frac{2}{3}$ $\frac{14}{25}$

3. $6\frac{2}{5} \div 3\frac{1}{3}$ $1\frac{23}{25}$

Solve each equation. Write the solution in simplest form.

4. $3\frac{5}{6} \div \frac{1}{3} = v$ $11\frac{1}{2}$

5. $x = 4\frac{2}{3} \div 5\frac{1}{4}$ $\frac{8}{9}$

The 5-Minute Check is also available on **Transparency 7-7A** for this lesson.

Motivating the Lesson

Communication Ask students to read the opening paragraph of the lesson. Ask the following questions:
- What units of measure are mentioned? **quarts and gallons**
- Can you think of goods around your house that come in quarts or gallons? **Sample answers: ice cream, laundry detergent, oil, milk, paint**

What you'll learn
You'll learn to change units within the customary system.

When am I ever going to use this?
You'll often need to change customary units when you are comparing labels in the grocery store.

Word Wise

fluid ounce	gallon
cup	ounce
pint	pound
quart	ton

Kijana (meaning "little boy" in Swahili) is the first African elephant since 1984 to survive birth in captivity. His mother rejected him so the keepers at the Oakland Zoo in California decided to raise him. Kijana drinks about 25 quarts of formula a day. How many gallons of formula does he drink each day?

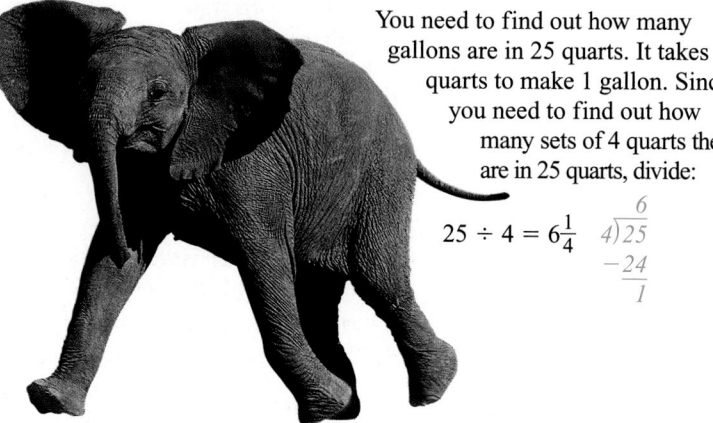

You need to find out how many gallons are in 25 quarts. It takes 4 quarts to make 1 gallon. Since you need to find out how many sets of 4 quarts there are in 25 quarts, divide:

$$25 \div 4 = 6\frac{1}{4} \qquad \begin{array}{r} 6 \\ 4\overline{)25} \\ -24 \\ \hline 1 \end{array}$$

Kijana drinks $6\frac{1}{4}$ gallons of formula a day.

The most commonly used customary units of capacity are the **fluid ounce**, **cup**, **pint**, **quart**, and **gallon**.

1 cup (c) = 8 fluid ounces (fl oz)
1 pint (pt) = 2 cups
1 quart (qt) = 2 pints
1 gallon (gal) = 4 quarts

The most commonly used customary units of weight are **ounce**, **pound**, and **ton**.

1 pound (lb) = 16 ounces (oz)
1 ton (T) = 2,000 pounds

To change customary units of capacity and weight,

1. Determine whether you are changing from smaller to larger units or from larger to smaller units.

2. To change from smaller to larger units, divide. To change from larger to smaller units, multiply.

 MathPASS CD-ROM

This CD-ROM offers a complete, self-paced mathematics curriculum. Each lesson includes a pretest, tutorial, guided practice, and posttest. MathPASS Lesson 27 is correlated to this Student Edition lesson.
For Windows & Macintosh

To solve Example 1, you can use the ratio of 2 cups to 1 pint.

1 **5 pt = _?_ c**   *Think: Each pint equals 2 cups.*

$5 \times 2 = 10$ *Multiply to change from a larger unit (pt) to smaller unit (c)*

5 pt = 10 c

2 **5,000 lb = _?_ T**   *Think: It takes 2,000 pounds to make 1 ton.*

$5,000 \div 2,000 = 2\frac{1}{2}$ *Divide to change from smaller units (lb) to larger units (T).*

$5,000 \text{ lb} = 2\frac{1}{2} \text{ T}$

3 **9 gal = _?_ pt**   *Think: Each gallon equals 4 quarts. Each quart equals 2 pints. You need to multiply twice.*

$9 \times 4 = 36$ *Multiply to change from gallons to quarts.*

$36 \times 2 = 72$ *Multiply to change from quarts to pints.*

9 gal = 72 pt

CONNECTION **4** **Life Science** Miquel estimates that the finches eat 8 ounces of bird seed a day at his feeder. If he buys a 25-pound bag of bird seed, about how many days will it last?

Explore   You know how much the finches eat each day. You need to find how many days a 25-pound bag of bird seed will last.

Plan   First, find the total number of ounces in 25 pounds. Then find how many sets of 8 ounces there are in the 25-pound bag of bird seed.

Solve   25 lb = _?_ oz   *Think: Each pound equals 16 ounces.*
$25 \times 16 = 400$ *Multiply to change from pounds to ounces.*
There are 400 ounces in a 25-pound bag of bird seed.
$400 \div 8 = 50$
So, the bag of bird seed will last about 50 days.

Examine   To see if your answer makes sense, think $8 \times 50 = 400$. So, 50 days is a reasonable answer.

CHECK FOR UNDERSTANDING

Communicating Mathematics

Read and study the lesson to answer each question.

1. *List* the common customary units of capacity and weight. **See margin.**
2. *Tell* how to change 3 tons to pounds. **Multiply 3 by 2,000.**

Lesson 7-7 Integration: Measurement   Changing Customary Units   **293**

■ Reteaching the Lesson ■

Activity Have pairs of students fill containers with water and measure the contents in fluid ounces, cups, pints, quarts, or gallons as appropriate. Have them record their findings in a chart. Use a scale and a similar recording method to weigh various sized objects in ounces and pounds.

Additional Answer
1. fluid ounce, cup, pint, quart, gallon, ounce, pound, and ton

---

 Transparency 7-7B contains a teaching aid for this lesson.

Reading Mathematics Students need to readily recognize the symbol for each unit of measurement when reading problems. Part of the understanding of these units should be to determine which unit is smaller than the other.

In-Class Examples

For Example 1
3 gal = _?_ qt **12**

For Example 2
96 oz = _?_ lb **6**

For Example 3
5 qt = _?_ c **20**

For Example 4
Lamont is bringing refreshments to a reception for 200 people. He estimates one cup of drink for each person. How many gallons of juice should Lamont buy? $12\frac{1}{2}$ **gal**

Study Guide Masters, p. 55

7-7 Name_____ Date_____
Study Guide

Integration: Measurement
Changing Customary Units

Customary Units	
Weight	**Liquid Capacity**
1 pound (lb) = 16 ounces (oz) 1 ton (T) = 2,000 pounds	1 cup (c) = 8 fluid ounces (fl oz) 1 pint (pt) = 2 cups 1 quart (qt) = 2 pints 1 gallon (gal) = 4 quarts

To change from larger units to smaller units, multiply.

Example 1 $4\frac{1}{2}$ lb = _____ oz   *Think: Each pound equals 16 ounces.*
$4\frac{1}{2} \times 16 = 72$ *Multiply to change from pounds to ounces.*
$4\frac{1}{2}$ lb = 72 oz

To change from smaller units to larger units, divide.

Example 2 700 qt = _____ gal   *Think: It takes 4 quarts to make 1 gallon.*
$700 \div 4 = 175$ *Divide to change from quarts to gallons.*
700 qt = 175 gal

Complete.

1. 2 lb = _____ oz **32**   2. 3 T = _____ lb **6,000**   3. 5 c = _____ fl oz **40**

4. 1.5 lb = _____ oz **24**   5. 10 pt = _____ qt **5**   6. 12 qt = _____ gal **3**

7. 12 fl oz = _____ c $1\frac{1}{2}$ 8. 24 oz = _____ lb $1\frac{1}{2}$ 9. 7 c = _____ fl oz **56**

10. 2.5 pt = _____ c **5**   11. 1.5 gal = _____ qt **6**   12. 3.5 qt = _____ pt **7**

13. 48 oz = _____ lb **3**   14. 8,000 lb = _____ T **4**   15. 2 pt = _____ c **4**

© Glencoe/McGraw-Hill   T55   Mathematics: Applications and Connections, Course 1

3 PRACTICE/APPLY

Check for Understanding

If students need additional practice or instruction after completing Exercises 1–9, you may find one of the following options helpful.

- Extra Practice, see p. 577
- Reteaching Activity, see p. 293
- *Transition Booklet*, pp. 29–34
- *Study Guide Masters*, p. 55
- *Practice Masters*, p. 55

Assignment Guide

Core: 11–27 odd, 29–33
Enriched: 10–26 even, 27–33

4 ASSESS

Closing Activity

Writing Have students work in pairs to create word problems that involve changing units of measure within the customary system. Have them exchange their problems with others to solve.

Practice Masters, p. 55

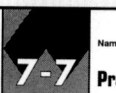

7-7 Practice

Name_____ Date_____

Integration: Measurement Changing Customary Units

Complete.

1. 6 pt = __12__ c
2. 20 qt = __5__ gal
3. 64 oz = __4__ lb
4. 7 c = __56__ fl oz
5. 12 qt = __24__ pt
6. 12,000 lb = __6__ T
7. 8 gal = __32__ qt
8. 9 lb = __144__ oz
9. 72 fl oz = __9__ c
10. 4 T = __8,000__ lb
11. 14 c = __7__ pt
12. 26 pt = __13__ qt
13. 10 qt = __2½__ gal
14. 2 T = __64,000__ oz
15. 18 pt = __36__ c
16. 3½ c = __28__ fl oz
17. 128 c = __8__ gal
18. 96 oz = __6__ lb
19. 21 qt = __42__ pt
20. 750 lb = __0.375__ T
21. 3 qt = __96__ fl oz
22. 15 pt = __7½__ c
23. 7 T = __14,000__ lb
24. 2 gal = __32__ c
25. 19 c = __9½__ pt
26. 4 qt = __16__ c
27. 5¼ lb = __84__ oz
28. 6 gal = __24__ qt
29. 104 fl oz = __13__ c
30. 64 pt = __8__ gal

© Glencoe/McGraw-Hill   T55   Mathematics: Applications and Connections, Course 1

---

294   Chapter 7

Guided Practice

Complete.

3. 2 gal = _?_ qt **8**
4. 14 c = _?_ pt **7**
5. 64 oz = _?_ lb **4**
6. $3\frac{1}{2}$ T = _?_ lb **7,000**
7. 32 fl oz = _?_ pt **2**
8. 4 T = _?_ oz **128,000**

9. *Life Science* Kijana, the baby elephant, will weigh about $6\frac{1}{2}$ tons when fully grown. About how many pounds will he weigh? **about 13,000 lb**

EXERCISES

Practice

Complete.

10. 8 qt = _?_ pt **16**
11. 24 qt = _?_ gal **6**
12. 7 c = _?_ pt **$3\frac{1}{2}$**
13. 9 lb = _?_ oz **144**
14. 6 gal = _?_ qt **24**
15. 16 fl oz = _?_ c **2**
16. 10 pt = _?_ qt **5**
17. 5 c = _?_ fl oz **40**
18. 500 lb = _?_ T **$\frac{1}{4}$**
19. $2\frac{1}{4}$ T = _?_ lb **4,500**
20. $4\frac{1}{2}$ pt = _?_ c **9**
21. $2\frac{1}{2}$ qt = _?_ c **10**
22. 32 c = _?_ gal **2**
23. 12 pt = _?_ gal **$1\frac{1}{2}$**
24. 12 c = _?_ qt **3**

25. How many tons are in 80,000 pounds? **40**

26. Find how many quarts there are in 40 fluid ounces. **$1\frac{1}{4}$ qt**

Applications and Problem Solving

27. *Geography* Giant clams live along the Great Barrier Reef off the coast of Australia. They measure up to 6 feet long and weigh as much as 0.25 ton. How many pounds is this? **500 pounds**

28. *Money Matters* Tashauna rides her moped from her home in Connecticut to her ballet lessons in New York. She uses about 3 quarts of gasoline a week. How much will she save a year in taxes if she buys her gasoline in New York rather than Connecticut? **$6.75**

Gasoline Taxes

gasoline taxes in cents per gallon:

Lowest state		Highest state	
Florida	12.5¢	New York	21.7¢
Georgia	7.5¢	Connecticut	39.0¢
Alaska	8.0¢	Rhode Island	29.0¢

Source: Federation of Tax Administrators

For **Extra Practice**, see page 577.

29. *Critical Thinking* What can you divide by to change 256 cups directly to gallons? **16**

Mixed Review

30. Find $2\frac{3}{5} \div 1\frac{2}{3}$. Write the quotient in simplest form. *(Lesson 7-6)* **$1\frac{14}{25}$**

31. State whether 405 is divisible by 2, 3, 5, 6, 9, or 10. *(Lesson 5-1)* **3, 5, 9**

32. 12.237 liters

32. *Measurement* Change 12,237 milliliters to liters. *(Lesson 4-9)*

33. **Standardized Test Practice** Frank purchased $13.72 worth of gasoline. He gives the gas station attendant a $20 bill. How much change should he receive? *(Lesson 3-6)* **E**

   A $7.72   **B** $7.58   **C** $7.28   **D** $6.72   **E** Not Here

---

Extending the Lesson

Enrichment Masters, p. 55

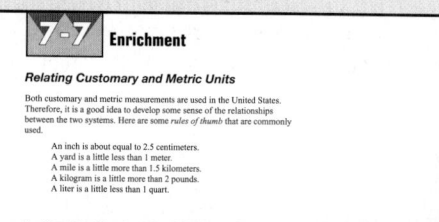

7-7 Enrichment

Relating Customary and Metric Units

Both customary and metric measurements are used in the United States. Therefore, it is a good idea to develop some sense of the relationships between the two systems. Here are some *rules of thumb* that are commonly used.

An inch is about equal to 2.5 centimeters.
A yard is a little less than 1 meter.
A mile is a little more than 1.5 kilometers.
A kilogram is a little more than 2 pounds.
A liter is a little less than 1 quart.

Activity Have small groups of students interview professionals such as chemists, building contractors, chefs, or meteorologists to determine the system of measurement they use in their work. Encourage students to ask why they use that system and how it is used in their profession.

HANDS-ON LAB

COOPERATIVE LEARNING

7-7B Measurement

A Follow-Up of Lesson 7-7

measuring cups

containers

water

Have you ever dreamed of visiting another planet or the moon? You would discover many things to be different, even your weight!

Planets' Weight Factors

| Sun 28 | Mercury $\frac{1}{3}$ | Venus $\frac{9}{10}$ | Earth 1 | Moon $\frac{1}{6}$ | Mars $\frac{3}{8}$ | Jupiter 3 |

TRY THIS

Work with a partner.

Step 1 Choose a work station. Record the name of the planet and its weight factor relative to Earth.

Step 2 Fill the 1-cup measuring cup with water. This represents the weight of one cup of water on Earth. Pour this amount into the container labeled *Earth.*

Step 3 Use the planet's weight factor to fill as many measuring cups with water as needed to represent the weight of one cup of water on this planet. For example, Jupiter's weight factor is 3 times that of the Earth's. So, empty 3 cups of water into the container labeled *Jupiter.* Record your results.

Step 4 Repeat Steps 1–3 at each work station.

4. Sample answer: A 126-pound student would weigh 21 pounds.

ON YOUR OWN

1. Analyze your results. Is the weight of 1 cup of water on each planet more or less than the weight of one cup of water on Earth? more or less than one cup of water on Jupiter? Record your results. **1–2. See Answer Appendix.**

2. Which planet's container weighs the most? Explain your reasoning.

3. How much would a 22-pound dog weigh on Jupiter? **66 pounds**

4. How much would you weigh on the moon?

5. *Reflect Back* On Earth, a certain object weighs 1 pound. How many ounces would the same object weigh on Mars? **6 ounces**

Math Journal

Have students write a paragraph about comparing weights on different planets and how astronauts are affected by these changes. Have them include a description of how working with fractions applies to this activity.

GET READY

Objective Students compare weights.

Optional Resources
Hands-On Lab Masters
• worksheet, p. 53
Manipulative Kit
• measuring cups

MANAGEMENT TIPS

Recommended Time
45 minutes

Getting Started Ask students to read the opening sentences of the lesson. Then ask: *How are astronauts affected by changes in weight in our solar system?*

Prepare work stations that have a measuring cup, water, a container labeled Earth, and one labeled Moon or one of the other planets. Ask students to pour the water back into its original container before moving on to the next station.

Teaching Tip Encourage students to use approximate measures at the Venus and Moon stations. Ask questions such as: *Of all the containers at each station, which one weighs the least? How do you know?*

ASSESS

After students complete Exercises 1–4, have pairs of students write and solve word problems about the weight of an object on a different planet.

Use Exercise 5 to determine whether students understand how to compare weights.

Objective Students solve problems by finding and extending a pattern.

Recommended Pacing	
Standard	Day 12 of 15
Honors	Day 10 of 14
Block	Day 7 of 8

1 FOCUS

Getting Started Ask students how they would solve this problem. *Once Jenny started making pizzas, she couldn't stop. She made one pizza on Monday, two pizzas on Tuesday, four pizzas on Wednesday, and eight pizzas on Thursday. If this pattern continues, how many pizzas will Jenny make on Sunday?* **64 pizzas**

2 TEACH

Teaching Tip To help students understand how patterns are relevant to their everyday lives, have them list three activities in their daily lives that follow a pattern. Then ask them to create a problem using one of the activities.

In-Class Example

The Mayan numbering system used symbols that were combined to give different values. The chart shows some of the numbers. Draw the Mayan symbols for 4 and 13.

1	■
2	■■
5	▬
6	▬
10	▬
4	■■■■
13	▬

7-8A Look for a Pattern

A Preview of Lesson 7-8

Kerri and her brother Eric are at the museum. They are learning about the history and culture of the Hopi Indians. Let's listen in!

It says here that the Hopi Indians began making pottery about 1,500 years ago. Wow, that's a long time ago!

Here is one of the designs they used to decorate the pottery. It appears that they liked to use geometric shapes in the designs.

I wonder what the design would look like if the pattern was continued to the right.

Well, since the Hopi Indians liked to use geometric shapes, maybe the design would include circles and triangles.

I disagree. The beauty of the design is in the pattern. I think that the same pattern is probably continued to the right.

Eric

THINK ABOUT IT

Work with a partner. **1–2. See students' work.**

1. **Compare and contrast** Kerri's and Eric's thinking. Whose thinking do you think is accurate? Explain your reasoning.

2. **Describe** the pattern the Hopi Indians used in the design.

3. **Draw** the next three segments to the right in the pattern. **See Answer Appendix.**

4. **Apply** the **look for a pattern** strategy to find the next two numbers in each pattern below.
   a. 3, 6, 9, 12, _?_ , _?_ **15,18**
   b. 5, 10, 20, 40, _?_ , _?_ **80,160**

■ Reteaching the Lesson ■

Activity Have students create a pattern with fractions. Have them write the beginning of their pattern on an overhead transparency. Then have the class ask yes-and-no questions such as "Did you use addition?" to try to guess the pattern.

For **Extra Practice**, see page 577.

ON YOUR OWN

5. The third step of the 4-step plan for problem solving asks you to *solve* the problem. ***Tell*** how you can use the look for a pattern strategy to help you solve a problem. **See margin.**

6–7. See students' work.

6. ***Write a Problem*** in which you would use the look for a pattern strategy to solve. Then ask a classmate to describe the pattern and solve the problem.

7. ***Look Ahead*** Explain how you could use the look for a pattern strategy to find the next number in the sequence in Exercise 17 on page 300.

MIXED PROBLEM SOLVING

STRATEGIES

Look for a pattern.
Solve a simpler problem.
Act it out.
Guess and check.
Draw a diagram.
Make a chart.
Work backward.

Solve. Use any strategy.

8. ***Fashion*** Matthew is choosing a shirt and a pair of jeans to wear. He has black, blue, and stonewashed jeans, and blue, gray, and white shirts. How many different combinations of jeans and shirts are possible? **9 combinations**

9. ***Food*** Richard eats half of a ham sandwich at 1:00 P.M. At 3:00 P.M., he eats half of what was left of his sandwich from lunch. At 5:00 P.M., he eats half of what was left from his ham sandwich.

  a. If Richard continues eating at this rate for four more hours, how much of the sandwich has been eaten? **See margin.**

  b. At this rate, will Richard ever eat the entire sandwich? Explain. **No; see margin.**

10. ***Measurement*** What is the missing measurement in the pattern?
$\ldots, \underline{\ ?\ }, \frac{1}{4}$ in., $\frac{1}{8}$ in., $\frac{1}{16}$ in., $\ldots$
See margin.

11. 1,476 sq cm

11. ***Geometry*** Find the area of the figure.

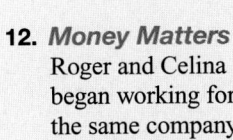

45 cm
20 cm
18 cm
32 cm

12. ***Money Matters*** Roger and Celina began working for the same company in 1997. Celina earned $18,000 per year, and Roger earned $14,500. Each year Roger received a $1,500 raise, and Celina received a $1,000 raise.

  a. In what year will they earn the same amount of money? **2004**

  b. What will be their annual salary in that year? **$25,000**

13. ***Standardized Test Practice*** At Hershal Middle School, the bell rings at 8:55, 9:40, 10:25, and 11:10 each morning. If this pattern continues, when would the next bell ring? **C**

  A 11:50 A.M.
  B 11:45 A.M.
  C 11:55 A.M.
  D 10:40 A.M.

Lesson 7-8A THINKING **LAB** **297**

Check for Understanding
Have students work through Exercises 1–4. Use the results from Exercise 4 to determine whether students comprehend how to extend patterns.

Extra Practice If students need additional practice in problem solving, extra practice is available on the following pages.
- Look for a Pattern, see p. 577
- Mixed Problem Solving, see pp. 593–594.

Assignment Guide

All: 5–13

Closing Activity
Modeling Have groups of students design new patterns using manipulatives or pictures. Then ask them to trade the designs with other groups and look for patterns.

Additional Answers
5. **Sample answer: Once you identify the pattern, then you can continue the pattern to solve the problem.**

9a. $\frac{31}{32}$

9b. **Richard will not finish the sandwich, but the amount will be so small that it will be like he did eat it all.**

10. $\frac{1}{2}$ in.

Extending the Lesson

Activity Have small groups of students look for patterns in history. For example, they could research the population of their community for the past 50 years. Ask them to record their findings in a graph. Have them determine whether they can make a prediction for the future.

Sample problem: *U.S. presidential elections follow a pattern. If there were elections in 1988, 1992, and 1996, when are the next three elections?* **2000, 2004, 2008**

Instructional Resources
- *Study Guide Masters*, p. 56
- *Practice Masters*, p. 56
- *Enrichment Masters*, p. 56
- Transparencies 7-8, A and B
- *Assessment and Evaluation Masters*, p. 184
- *Technology Masters*, p. 13
- CD-ROM Program
  - Resource Lesson 7-8

Recommended Pacing	
Standard	Day 13 of 15
Honors	Days 11 & 12 of 14
Block	Day 7 of 8

1 FOCUS

5-Minute Check
(Lesson 7-7)

Complete.
1. 6 gal = _?_ qt **24**
2. 14 c = _?_ pt **7**
3. 4 T = _?_ lb **8,000**
4. 2 T = _?_ oz **64,000**
5. A jar of salsa weighs 12 oz. How many pounds will 48 jars of salsa weigh? **36 lb**

 The 5-Minute Check is also available on **Transparency 7-8A** for this lesson.

2 TEACH

 Transparency 7-8B contains a teaching aid for this lesson.

Reading Mathematics Write the words *sequence* and *reciprocal* on the chalkboard and pronounce them. Give an example of a sequence such as $\frac{1}{2}, \frac{1}{4}, \frac{1}{8}$, and $\frac{1}{16}$. Then write $\frac{2}{1}, \frac{4}{1}, \frac{8}{1}$, and $\frac{16}{1}$, and have students match the reciprocals. Ask students to use the words in sentences.

7-8

What you'll learn

You'll learn to recognize and extend sequences.

When am I ever going to use this?

You can use sequences to determine the cost of a long-distance phone call.

Word Wise
sequence

Study Hint

Mental Math
Add 32 because
$32 - 0 = 32$,
$64 - 32 = 32$,
$96 - 64 = 32$,
and $128 - 96 = 32$.

Integration: Patterns and Functions
Sequences

On Earth, gravity causes all falling objects to accelerate at 32 ft/s². This means that if gravity is the only force acting on a falling object, its speed will increase about 32 feet per second each second.

The table shows the effect of gravity. What will the speed of the object be after 5 seconds?

Seconds After Object is Dropped	0	1	2	3	4	5
Speed of Object (ft/s)	0	32	64	96	128	?

The numbers 0, 32, 64, 96, and 128 form a **sequence**. A sequence is a list of numbers in a specific order.

In the sequence, notice that 32 is added to each number.

$$0, \quad 32, \quad 64, \quad 96, \quad 128$$
$$+32 \quad +32 \quad +32 \quad +32$$

The next number in the sequence is 128 + 32, or 160. So, after 5 seconds, the speed of the object will be 160 ft/s.

Examples

Find the next number in each sequence.

1 18, 24, 30, 36, . . .
$$+6 \quad +6 \quad +6$$

In this sequence, 6 is added to each number. The next number is 36 + 6, or 42.

2 21, $18\frac{1}{2}$, 16, $13\frac{1}{2}$, . . .
$$-2\frac{1}{2} \quad -2\frac{1}{2} \quad -2\frac{1}{2}$$

In this sequence, $2\frac{1}{2}$ is subtracted from each number. The next number is $13\frac{1}{2} - 2\frac{1}{2}$ or 11.

Another type of sequence is one where the numbers are found by multiplying by the same number.

298 Chapter 7 Multiplying and Dividing Fractions

Motivating the Lesson
Hands-On Activity Bring in or obtain copies of simple sheet music. Have students work in small groups to look for patterns in the musical arrangements.

Find the next number in each sequence.

3 2, 8, 32, 128,...

$\times 4 \quad \times 4 \quad \times 4$

Each number in the sequence is multiplied by 4. The next number is 128×4, or 512.

4 243, 81, 27, 9,...

$\times \frac{1}{3} \quad \times \frac{1}{3} \quad \times \frac{1}{3}$

Each number in the sequence is multiplied by $\frac{1}{3}$. The next number is $9 \times \frac{1}{3}$, or 3.

 APPLICATION **5** **Carpentry** A roof rafter of a building is to be braced as shown. The length of braces A, B, and C are $10\frac{1}{2}$ inches, 21 inches, and $31\frac{1}{2}$ inches, respectively. Find the lengths of braces D and E.

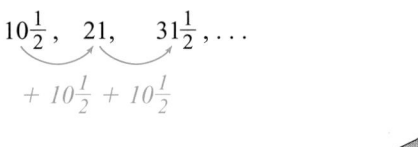

$10\frac{1}{2}$, 21, $31\frac{1}{2}$,...

$+ 10\frac{1}{2} + 10\frac{1}{2}$

In the sequence, $10\frac{1}{2}$ is added to each number.
The length of brace D is $31\frac{1}{2} + 10\frac{1}{2}$, or 42 inches.
The length of brace E is $42 + 10\frac{1}{2}$, or $52\frac{1}{2}$ inches.

CHECK FOR UNDERSTANDING

Communicating Mathematics

Read and study the lesson to answer each question. 1–2. See margin.

1. *Write*, in your own words, a definition for sequence.

2. *Tell* how the numbers are related in the sequence $16, 4, 1, \frac{1}{4}$.

3. *You Decide* Janet says that the next number in the sequence $5, 7\frac{1}{2}, 10, 12\frac{1}{2}$, is 14. Joshua says the next number is 15. Who is correct? Explain your reasoning. **Joshua; see Answer Appendix for explanations.**

Guided Practice

Find the next two numbers in each sequence.

4. 6, 18, 54, 162,... **486, 1,458**   5. 45, 38, 31, 24,... **17, 10**

Find the missing number in each sequence.

6. 2, _?_, 9, $12\frac{1}{2}$,... $5\frac{1}{2}$ 7. _?_, 25, 5, 1,... **125**

8. *Geometry* Draw the next two figures in the sequence.

■ **Reteaching the Lesson** ■

Activity Give a group of students a "rule" by which they will create a sequence. Have them roll a number cube or select a random number to begin the sequence. Each person in the group names the next number in the sequence.

Additional Answers
1. Sample answer: A sequence is a list of numbers in a specific order.
2. Each number in the sequence is multiplied by $\frac{1}{4}$.

---

3 PRACTICE/APPLY

Check for Understanding
If students need additional practice or instruction after completing Exercises 1–8, you may find one of the following options helpful.
- Extra Practice, see p. 577
- Reteaching Activity
- *Study Guide Masters*, p. 56
- *Practice Masters*, p. 56
- Interactive Mathematics Tools Software

Study Guide Masters, p. 56

interNET **CONNECTION**

Chapter Review **For additional lesson-by-lesson review, visit:**
www.glencoe.com/sec/math/mac/mathnet

Vocabulary

After completing this chapter, you should be able to define each term, concept, or phrase and give an example or two of each.

Number and Operations
compatible numbers (p. 268)
reciprocals (p. 285)

Geometry
center (p. 280)
circle (p. 280)
circumference (p. 280)
diameter (p. 280)
radius (p. 280)

Problem Solving
look for a pattern (p. 296)

Measurement
cup (p. 292)
fluid ounce (p. 292)
gallon (p. 292)
ounce (p. 292)
pint (p. 292)
pound (p. 292)
quart (p. 292)
ton (p. 292)

Patterns and Functions
sequence (p. 298)

10. When changing from smaller units to larger units, divide. When changing from larger units to smaller units, multiply.

Understanding and Using the Vocabulary

Choose the letter of the term that best matches each phrase.

1. 2,000 pounds k
2. the distance across a circle through the center e
3. 2 cups i
4. the distance from the center of a circle to any point on the circle c
5. 8 fluid ounces h
6. a list of numbers in a specific order g
7. the distance around a circle f
8. any two numbers whose product is 1 a
9. the set of all points in a plane that are the same distance from a given point d

a. reciprocals
b. center
c. radius
d. circle
e. diameter
f. circumference
g. sequence
h. cup
i. pint
j. gallon
k. ton

In Your Own Words

10. *Explain* how you would change customary units of capacity such as cups to gallons or tons to pounds.

302 Chapter 7 Multiplying and Dividing Fractions

MindJogger Videoquizzes

MindJogger Videoquizzes provide an alternative review of concepts presented in this chapter. Students work in teams to answer questions, gaining points for correct answers. The questions are presented in three rounds.
Round 1 Concepts–5 questions
Round 2 Skills–4 questions
Round 3 Problem Solving–4 questions

45. Statistic
find out h
participat
students,
play. How
in the play

46. Geomet
perimeter
you can u
$P = 4s$, v
length of
square. F
of the squ

47. Food A
cider for
1-cup ser
(Lesson

Objectives & Examples

Upon completing this chapter, you should be able to:

● estimate fraction products using compatible numbers and rounding *(Lesson 7-1)*

Estimate $\frac{4}{5} \times 11$.

For 11, the nearest multiple of 5 is 10.
$\frac{4}{5}$ *of 10 is 8.*

So, $\frac{4}{5} \times 11$ is about 8.

● multiply fractions *(Lesson 7-2)*

$\frac{5}{9} \times \frac{3}{10} = \frac{\overset{1}{5} \cdot \overset{1}{3}}{\underset{3}{9} \cdot \underset{2}{10}}$ *Divide by the GCF.*

$= \frac{1}{6}$

● multiply mixed numbers *(Lesson 7-3)*

$3\frac{1}{2} \times 4\frac{2}{3} = \frac{7}{2} \times \frac{\overset{7}{14}}{3}$

$= \frac{49}{3}$ or $16\frac{1}{3}$

● find the circumference of circles *(Lesson 7-4)*

$C = 2\pi r$
$C \approx 2 \cdot 3.14 \cdot 2.4$
$C \approx 15.072$

The circumference of the circle is about 15.1 meters.

Review Exercises

Use these exercises to review and prepare for the chapter test.

Estimate each product.

11. $10 \times 2\frac{3}{4}$ **12.** $4\frac{1}{7} \times 5\frac{4}{5}$

13. $\frac{5}{6} \times 13$ **14.** $\frac{7}{8} \times \frac{1}{2}$

15. $\frac{2}{3} \times 19$ **16.** $7\frac{3}{4} \times \frac{1}{4}$

11–16. See Answer Appendix.

Find each product. Write in simplest form.

17. $\frac{7}{8} \times \frac{4}{5}$ $\frac{7}{10}$ **18.** $\frac{14}{15} \times \frac{10}{21}$ $\frac{4}{9}$

Solve each equation. Write the solution in simplest form.

19. $y = 12 \times \frac{5}{8}$ $7\frac{1}{2}$ **20.** $\frac{4}{5} \times \frac{3}{8} = t$ $\frac{3}{10}$

Find each product. Write in simplest form.

21. $3\frac{3}{4} \times 1\frac{1}{5}$ $4\frac{1}{2}$ **22.** $3\frac{2}{3} \times 6$ 22

Solve each equation. Write the solution in simplest form.

23. $7\frac{1}{5} \times 1\frac{7}{8} = x$ $13\frac{1}{2}$ **24.** $w = 3\frac{1}{8} \times 2\frac{2}{5}$ $7\frac{1}{2}$

26. 51.5 cm   **27.** $\pi = \frac{22}{7}$; $5\frac{1}{2}$ yd

Find the circumference of each circle shown or described. Use $\frac{22}{7}$ or 3.14 for π. Round decimal answers to the nearest tenth.

25.
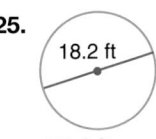
18.2 ft

57.1 ft

26. $r = 8.2$ cm

27. $d = 1\frac{3}{4}$ yd

Objectives & Examples

This section reviews the skills and concepts of the chapter and shows completely worked examples.

Review Exercises

These exercises provide practice for the corresponding objectives.

Assessment and Evaluation Masters, pp. 171–172

7   Name_____ Date_____

Chapter 7 Test, Form 1B

1. Estimate $\frac{1}{3} \times 17$.
   A. 8   B. 60   C. 5   D. 6   **1. ___D___**

2. Estimate $\frac{9}{10} \times \frac{7}{16}$.
   A. $\frac{9}{10}$ B. $\frac{4}{8}$ C. 0   D. 1   **2. ___B___**

3. Estimate $5\frac{7}{8} \times 3\frac{1}{6}$.
   A. 15   B. 20   C. 18   D. 24   **3. ___C___**

4. Find $\frac{12}{15} \times \frac{3}{21}$. Write in simplest form.
   A. $\frac{2}{33}$ B. $\frac{4}{7}$ C. $\frac{4}{14}$ D. $\frac{120}{336}$ **4. ___C___**

5. Solve $18 \times \frac{5}{6} = n$. Write the solution in simplest form.
   A. 15   B. $\frac{5}{108}$ C. $\frac{5}{6}$ D. $21\frac{3}{5}$ **5. ___A___**

6. A foot of metal pipe sells for $9. How much will $\frac{2}{3}$ foot cost?
   A. $\frac{9}{27}$ B. $13.50   C. $3   D. $6   **6. ___D___**

7. Find $7\frac{1}{2} \times 4\frac{1}{2}$. Write in simplest form.
   A. $28\frac{7}{25}$ B. 30   C. $\frac{1}{30}$ D. $7\frac{1}{12}$ **7. ___B___**

8. Solve $2\frac{7}{16} \times 1\frac{3}{5} = x$. Write the solution in simplest form.
   A. $3\frac{1}{2}$ B. $2\frac{9}{80}$ C. $2\frac{1}{21}$ D. $1\frac{47}{128}$ **8. ___A___**

9. Find the area of a room that is $5\frac{1}{2}$ yards long by $3\frac{1}{3}$ yards wide.
   A. $8\frac{5}{6}$ yd²   B. $18\frac{1}{3}$ yd²   C. $15\frac{5}{6}$ yd²   D. $3\frac{1}{2}$ yd²   **9. ___B___**

10. Find the circumference of a circle with a radius of 18 feet. Use 3.14 for π.
    A. 113.04 ft   B. 56.52 ft   C. 36 ft   D. 9 ft   **10. ___A___**

11. Find the circumference of the circle.
    A. 40.82 m   B. 163.28 m
    C. 8,164 m   D. 81.64 m   26 m   **11. ___D___**

12. Find the circumference of a circle with a diameter of $24\frac{1}{2}$ inches.
    A. $77\frac{5}{35}$ in.   B. $152\frac{34}{35}$ in.   C. $76\frac{6}{35}$ in.   D. $75\frac{5}{35}$ in.   **12. ___C___**

13. Find $18 \div \frac{1}{3}$. Write in simplest form.
    A. $\frac{1}{54}$ B. 54   C. 6   D. $\frac{1}{6}$ **13. ___B___**

14. Solve $\frac{6}{7} \div \frac{3}{7} = x$. Write the solution in simplest form.
    A. $1\frac{1}{9}$ B. $2\frac{1}{2}$ C. $\frac{9}{10}$ D. $\frac{2}{7}$ **14. ___A___**

© Glencoe/McGraw-Hill   171   *Mathematics: Applications and Connections, Course 1*

7   **Chapter 7 Test, Form 1B (continued)**

15. Evaluate $a \div b$ if $a = \frac{7}{18}$ and $b = 3$.
    A. $\frac{8}{21}$ B. $\frac{7}{54}$ C. $10\frac{4}{5}$ D. $\frac{5}{6}$ **15. ___B___**

16. Find $3\frac{7}{16} \div 2$. Write in simplest form.
    A. $6\frac{7}{8}$ B. $\frac{8}{55}$ C. $1\frac{23}{32}$ D. $\frac{32}{33}$ **16. ___C___**

17. Solve $2\frac{7}{16} \div 1\frac{3}{4} = m$. Write the solution in simplest form.
    A. $\frac{64}{245}$ B. $3\frac{31}{64}$ C. $\frac{4}{5}$ D. $1\frac{1}{4}$ **17. ___D___**

18. Divide $5\frac{1}{4}$ by $1\frac{1}{6}$.
    A. $\frac{2}{9}$ B. $\frac{87}{24}$ C. $4\frac{1}{2}$ D. $5\frac{1}{24}$ **18. ___C___**

19. Complete: 5 T = __?__ lb.
    A. 5,000   B. 10,000   C. 80   D. 1,000   **19. ___B___**

20. Complete: 80 oz = __?__ lb.
    A. 5   B. 1,280   C. 8   D. $6\frac{2}{3}$ **20. ___A___**

21. Find the next number in the sequence 200, 100, 50, 25, ...
    A. 10   B. 20   C. 12.5   D. 12   **21. ___C___**

22. Find the next number in the sequence 640, 565, 490, 415, ...
    A. 365   B. 75   C. 340   D. 400   **22. ___C___**

23. Find the next number in the sequence $\frac{1}{5}$, $\frac{1}{15}$, $\frac{1}{45}$, $\frac{1}{135}$, ...
    A. $\frac{1}{405}$ B. $\frac{1}{270}$ C. $\frac{1}{180}$ D. 405   **23. ___A___**

24. Keisha needs 12 gallons of water for a science project. The largest container she can find is a quart milk carton. How many times will she need to fill the quart carton to get 12 gallons?
    A. 3   B. 48   C. 24   D. 6   **24. ___B___**

25. Rashaan was measuring the speed of a dropped ball for science class. At 1 second, the speed was 32.16 ft/s. At 2 seconds, it was 64.32 ft/s. At 3 seconds, it was 96.48 ft/s. What will it be after 7 seconds?
    A. 192.96 ft/s   B. 32.16 ft/s
    C. 225.12 ft/s   D. 160.8 ft/s   **25. ___C___**

© Glencoe/McGraw-Hill   172   *Mathematics: Applications and Connections, Course 1*

Additi
Open
● **Mult**
● **To n**
  dou
  drin
  $2\frac{1}{2}$ c
  crea

Open Enc

Suppose you
make one bat
science proje

1 T oil

$2\frac{1}{2}$ c water

2 pkg. soft dr

How will you
ingredient ne
the dough? S

Suppose you
dough. How
you need? S

A practice test
provided on pa

● Assessment and Evaluation

Six forms of Chapter 7 Test are available in the *Assessment and Evaluation Masters* as shown in the chart.

Chapter 7 Test, Form 1B, is shown at the right. Chapter 7 Test, Form 2B, is shown on the next page.

1A	Multiple Choice	Honors
1B	Multiple Choice	Average
1C	Multiple Choice	Basic
2A	Free Response	Honors
2B	Free Response	Average
2C	Free Response	Basic

The Standardized Test Practice may be used to help students prepare for standardized tests. The test items are written in the same style as those in state proficiency tests and standardized tests like CAT, CTBS, ITBS, MAT, SAT, and Terra Nova. The test items cover skills and concepts covered up to this point in the text.

The pages can be used as an overnight assessment. After students have completed the pages, discuss how each problem can be solved, or provide copies of the solutions from the *Solutions Manual*.

Assessment and Evaluation Masters, p. 187

Section One: Multiple Choice

There are twelve multiple-choice questions in this section. Choose the best answer. If a correct answer is *not here*, mark the letter for Not Here.

1. What are the next two numbers in the sequence 1,024, 256, 64, 16, . . . ? **C**
   A 8, 4
   B 8, 2
   C 4, 1
   D 4, 0

2. What is the area of the rectangle? **F**

   4.6 ft
   3.5 ft

   F 16.1 sq ft
   G 14.0 sq ft
   H 12.3 sq ft
   J 12.0 sq ft

3. Jamonte's room is 8 feet wide. How many inches is this? **B**
   A 92 inches
   B 96 inches
   C 20 inches
   D 44 inches

4. Evaluate $p \div m - 4$ if $p = 10$ and $m = 2$. **F**
   F 1
   G 0
   H 5
   J 2

5. Express $3 \times 4 \times 4 \times 4 \times 5$ in exponential notation. **B**
   A $3^2 \times 4^2 \times 5$
   B $3 \times 4^3 \times 5$
   C $3 \times 4^2 \times 5$
   D $3 \times 4^4 \times 5$

Please note that Questions 6–12 have five answer choices.

6. How many 1-foot square tiles are needed to cover the floor of a kitchen that is 13 feet by 10 feet? **G**
   F 13
   G 130
   H 1,300
   J 13,000
   K 130,000

7. A sign at The Gift Gallery reads:

   Clearance Sale
   $2.99
   to
   $9.99

   Suppose a customer purchases four items that are on sale. What is a reasonable total cost of the items, without tax? **B**
   A $5
   B $30
   C $50
   D $10
   E $75

8. A car travels at an average speed of 64 miles per hour. At this rate, how many hours will it take to travel 384 miles? **J**
   F 2 hours
   G 4 hours
   H 3 hours
   J 6 hours
   K 5 hours

◄◄◄Instructional Resources
Another cumulative review is shown at the left and is available in the *Assessment and Evaluation Masters*, p. 187.

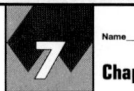

Name_____

7 Chapt...

Estimate.
1. $\frac{1}{5} \times 29$
2. $\frac{11}{12} \times \frac{3}{8}$
3. $5\frac{5}{8} \times 3\frac{1}{6}$
4. $\frac{9}{10} \times 6\frac{1}{6}$

Find each product. Write in si...
5. $\frac{4}{5} \times \frac{1}{4}$
6. $28 \times \frac{4}{7}$
7. $1\frac{1}{16} \times \frac{4}{5}$
8. $\frac{7}{10} \times 1\frac{9}{14}$

Find the circumference of eac...
9. The radius is $4\frac{1}{2}$ inches.

10. 0.5 m

11. The diameter is 8 meters.

Find each quotient. Write in s...
12. $\frac{15}{32} \div \frac{5}{8}$
13. $\frac{9}{20} \div 18$
14. $\frac{21}{40} \div \frac{7}{20}$
15. $2\frac{2}{9} \div 5$
16. $8\frac{1}{10} \div 1\frac{4}{5}$
17. $2\frac{1}{12} \div 1\frac{7}{8}$

© Glencoe/McGraw-Hill

---

7 Chapter

Find the next two numbers in...
18. 15, $17\frac{1}{2}$, 20, $22\frac{1}{2}$, . . .
19. 729, 243, 81, 27, . . .
20. $2\frac{1}{2}$, $12\frac{1}{2}$, $62\frac{1}{2}$, $312\frac{1}{2}$, . . .
21. 112, 56, 28, 14, . . .

Solve each equation. Write th...
22. $y = 12 \div 1\frac{1}{3}$
23. $\frac{3}{5} \div \frac{7}{15} = a$
24. $z = 11 \div 1\frac{5}{6}$
25. $\frac{4}{9} \div \frac{9}{14} = c$
26. $3\frac{2}{3} \times 2\frac{1}{3} = n$
27. $4\frac{1}{2} \times 1\frac{1}{3} = m$

Complete.
28. 80 oz = ? lb
29. 9 T = ? lb
30. 40 c = ? gal
31. 64 fl oz = ? qt

32. Eight bricks are laid end to en... Each brick is $8\frac{1}{2}$ inches long...

33. Constance is writing a diary in... 15 minutes the first day, 20 mi... third, and 30 minutes the fourt... how many minutes will she w...

© Glencoe/McGraw-Hill

Name_____ Date_____

7 Cumulative Review, Chapters 1–7

Estimate. (Lessons 1-3, 4-1, 6-2, and 7-1)
1. 3,510 ÷ 7
2. 68.3 × 2.73
3. $\frac{9}{10} + \frac{11}{12}$
4. $7\frac{7}{8} \times 4\frac{1}{12}$

Solve each equation. Simplify if necessary. (Lessons 4-3, 1-6, 6-5, and 3-6)
5. $a = 3.4 \times 3.4$
6. $h = 3^3$
7. $m = \frac{15}{16} - \frac{1}{16}$
8. $x = 30 - 2.37$

Express each fraction as a decimal. (Lessons 3-1 and 5-10)
9. $\frac{99}{10,000}$
10. $\frac{4}{9}$

Order from least to greatest. (Lessons 3-3 and 5-8)
11. 3.9, 3.005, 3.0009, 3.55

12. $\frac{1}{8}$, $\frac{2}{3}$, $\frac{11}{24}$, $\frac{5}{16}$

13. Elsa made the following bowling scores: 108, 120, 108, 141, 130. What is the median of her bowling scores? (Lesson 2-7)

14. What is the area of a room with a length of 18 feet and a width of 13 feet? (Lesson 4-4)

15. Evaluate 16^4. (Lesson 1-6)

16. What is the GCF of 32 and 40? (Lesson 5-3)

17. What is the LCM of 16 and 40? (Lesson 5-7)

Complete. (Lessons 4-9 and 7-7)
18. 1.4 ℓ = ? mL

19. 20,000 lb = ? T

Perform the indicated operation. Write the answer in simplest form. (Lessons 6-4, 7-2, 7-5, 7-6, and 7-3)
20. $\frac{1}{12} + \frac{4}{9}$
21. $9\frac{1}{2} - 3\frac{2}{3}$
22. $\frac{9}{16} \times \frac{5}{8}$
23. $\frac{5}{11} + \frac{4}{7}$
24. $20 \div 3\frac{1}{3}$
25. $2\frac{1}{2} \times 3\frac{3}{8}$

1.	3,500 ÷ 7 = 500
2.	70 × 3 = 210
3.	1 + 1 = 2
4.	8 × 4 = 32
5.	11.56
6.	27
7.	$\frac{7}{8}$
8.	27.63
9.	0.0099
10.	0.44
11.	3.0009, 3.005, 3.55, 3.9
12.	$\frac{5}{16}$, $\frac{11}{24}$, $\frac{2}{3}$
13.	120
14.	234 ft²
15.	65,536
16.	8
17.	80
18.	1,400 mL
19.	10 T
20.	$\frac{5}{6}$
21.	$5\frac{23}{24}$
22.	$\frac{9}{16}$
23.	$\frac{8}{11}$
24.	6
25.	$7\frac{5}{16}$

© Glencoe/McGraw-Hill   187

Mathematics: Applications and Connections, Course 1

9. Suppose a car is traveling at a speed of 51 miles per hour. Which is a good estimate for the number of hours it will take to travel 248 miles? **D**

   A 2 h

   B 3 h

   C 4 h

   D 5 h

   E 6 h

10. Mrs. Alvarez bought groceries for $19.58. How much change should she receive from a $20 bill? **G**

    F $1.42

    G $0.42

    H $1.52

    J $0.52

    K Not Here

11. Mr. Meuser is planning to travel from Dallas to New York. The flight will take about 3 hours. It is time to leave, but the flight has been delayed for $2\frac{1}{2}$ hours. About how long will it be before he arrives in New York? **A**

    A $5\frac{1}{2}$ hours

    B $6\frac{1}{2}$ hours

    C $4\frac{1}{2}$ hours

    D 5 hours

    E Not Here

12. Mrs. Miles purchased a ham that weighed $6\frac{1}{4}$ pounds and a turkey that weighed $11\frac{1}{2}$ pounds. How many pounds of meat did she purchase? **H**

    F $17\frac{1}{2}$ pounds   **G** $18\frac{1}{4}$ pounds

    H $17\frac{3}{4}$ pounds   **J** $16\frac{1}{4}$ pounds

    K Not Here

Test-Taking Tip THE PRINCETON REVIEW

If you're working on a group of questions and find that the questions are getting too difficult, quickly read through the rest of the questions in the section and answer the ones that you know. Then come back to the ones you skipped.

Section Two: Free Response

This section contains six questions for which you will provide short answers. Write your answers on your paper.

13. Jamaal works 22 hours a week and earns $111.10. How much money does he earn per hour? **$5.05**

14. Order the fractions $\frac{2}{7}, \frac{1}{3}, \frac{2}{9}, \frac{2}{5}, \frac{4}{1}$ from greatest to least. **See margin.**

15. Andrea had purchased $6\frac{1}{2}$ yards of material to make curtains for her dining room. If she used 6 yards of material to make the curtains, how much of the material was not used? $\frac{1}{2}$ **yd**

16. How many fluid ounces are in 3 quarts? **96**

17. Draw the next figure in the sequence.

18. Four dogs have weights of 17, 24, 18, and 25 pounds. What is the average weight of the dogs? **21 pounds**

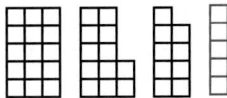

interNET CONNECTION Test Practice For additional test practice questions, visit:

www.glencoe.com/sec/math/mac/mathnets

Additional Answer

14. $\frac{4}{1}, \frac{2}{5}, \frac{1}{3}, \frac{2}{7}, \frac{2}{9}$

Instructional Resources ▶▶▶

Additional standardized test practice is shown at the right and is available in the *Assessment and Evaluation Masters,* pp. 185–186.

Assessment and Evaluation Masters, pp. 185–186

Name_____ Date_____

7 **Chapter 7 Standardized Test Practice**

1. Juliana would like $\frac{1}{4}$ of the money in the miscellaneous fund to be budgeted for outdoor lighting. If the fund has $595, about how much will be budgeted for outdoor lighting?
   A. $500   **B.** $100   **C.** $175   **D.** $150
   1. ___ D

2. The diameter of Earth is 7,927 miles. What is the circumference of Earth, rounded to the nearest ten?
   A. 49,780 miles   **B.** 24,910 miles
   C. 24,890 miles   **D.** 25,000 miles
   2. ___ C

3. How many times must you run around a $\frac{1}{4}$-mile track to run $2\frac{1}{2}$ miles?
   A. 12   **B.** $2\frac{1}{2}$ **C.** 8   **D.** 10
   3. ___ D

4. An elephant weighing 4.7 tons weighs about how many more pounds than a 2.8-ton rhinoceros?
   A. 3,800 lb   **B.** 4,200 lb   **C.** 6,000 lb   **D.** 1,900 lb
   4. ___ A

5. Fatima is reading about the metric system and discovers that 1 meter is equivalent to 39.37 inches. If Fatima is 1.31 meters tall, how many inches tall is she to the nearest hundredth?
   A. 51.57 in.   **B.** 40.68 in.   **C.** 30.05 in.   **D.** 51.575 in.
   5. ___ D

6. Logan is working at the grocery store unloading trucks. One truck has sacks of potatoes on it. What unit would the sacks be measured in?
   A. milligram   **B.** gram   **C.** kilogram   **D.** liter
   6. ___ C

7. Tom and Trish went out to eat. Tom's dinner was $9.95. Trish's dinner was $7.95. They each had a soft drink for $0.99. They wanted to leave a tip of about $4. What was a reasonable total amount for them to pay?
   A. $20   **B.** $26   **C.** $22   **D.** $24
   7. ___ D

8. 1 nautical mile equals 1.852 kilometers. Write the decimal in words.
   A. one thousand eight hundred fifty-two
   B. one point eight-five-two thousandths
   C. one and eight hundred fifty-two thousandths
   D. one and eight hundred and fifty-two thousands
   8. ___ C

9. Mrs. Klaus purchased 4 chairs that cost $59 each. She gave the cashier five $50 bills. How much change did she receive?
   A. $250   **B.** $236   **C.** $14   **D.** $9
   9. ___ C

© Glencoe/McGraw-Hill   185   Mathematics: Applications and Connections, Course 1

---

7 **Chapter 7 Standardized Test Practice (continued)**

10. Mr. Carter has a class of 27 students. He wants to separate the class into groups of 3. Which expression would help him solve this problem?
    A. $27 \div x = 3$ **B.** $x + 27 = 3$
    C. $x \div 3 = 27$ **D.** none of these
    10. ___ A

11. Use the bar graph to find how many more points were scored by Sims than by Juarez.

    Points Scored
    Abbott, Sims, Cole, Juarez
    0 4 8 12 16 20

    A. 4   **B.** 5   **C.** 18   **D.** 13
    11. ___ B

12. Cameron has to make a stem-and-leaf plot of the data in the graph in Question 11. What stems would he use?
    A. 1   **B.** 3, 4, 6, 8
    C. 0, 1, 2   **D.** none of these
    12. ___ A

13. The average depth of the Atlantic Ocean is 12,254 feet. Rounded to the nearest yard, how many yards is this?
    A. 1,021 yd   **B.** 4,085 yd
    C. 340 yd   **D.** none of these
    13. ___ B

14. The Statue of Liberty in New York harbor is about 110 feet tall. Its right arm is 42 feet long. If a 55-inch tall statue were built to the same proportion, how long would its arm be?
    A. 144 in.   **B.** 84 in.   **C.** 21 in.   **D.** 27 in.
    14. ___ C

15. The condor has an average wingspan of 9 feet. The Kalong fruit bat has an average wingspan of $5\frac{7}{12}$ feet. What is the difference in wingspans?
    A. $4\frac{5}{12}$ ft   **B.** $3\frac{5}{12}$ ft   **C.** $4\frac{5}{12}$ ft   **D.** $3\frac{5}{12}$ ft
    15. ___ D

16. Captain James Gallagher flew the first non-stop flight around the world in $3\frac{11}{12}$ days. Dick Rutan and Jeana Yeager flew the first non-stop, non-refueled flight around the world in 9 days. How much longer did the Rutan and Yeager flight take than the Gallagher flight?
    A. $6\frac{1}{12}$ days   **B.** $5\frac{1}{12}$ days
    C. $12\frac{11}{12}$ days   **D.** none of these
    16. ___ B

© Glencoe/McGraw-Hill   186   Mathematics: Applications and Connections, Course 1

Exploring Ratio, Proportion, and Percent

Previewing the Chapter

Overview

In this chapter, students learn to express ratios and rates as fractions and to solve proportions by using cross products. Then, using their knowledge of ratios, students find actual lengths from scale drawings. Students explore the relationship among fractions, decimals, and percents as well as find the percent of a number. Students also learn to solve problems by drawing a diagram.

Lesson (pages)	Lesson Objectives	NCTM Standards 2000	Standardized Tests	State/Local Objectives
8-1A (310–311)	Use tangram pieces to explore ratios and the relationship between ratio and area.	1, 3, 6–8, 10		
8-1 (312–315)	Express ratios and rates as fractions.	1, 3, 4, 6–10	CAT, ITBS, MAT	
8-1B (316)	Explore ratios and probability.	1, 5–10		
8-2 (317–320)	Solve proportions by using cross products.	1–4, 6–10	MAT	
8-2B (321)	Use spreadsheets to solve problems involving proportions.	1–4, 6–10		
8-3A (322–323)	Solve problems by drawing diagrams.	1–4, 6–10	CTBS, MAT, SAT, TN	
8-3 (324–327)	Find actual length from a scale drawing.	1–4, 6–10	CTBS, MAT, SAT, TN	
8-4A (329)	Illustrate the meaning of percent using models.	1, 6–10	CTBS, TN	
8-4 (330–333)	Express percents as fractions and vice versa.	1, 2, 5–10	CTBS, ITBS, TN	
8-5 (334–336)	Express percents as decimals and vice versa.	1–10	CTBS, ITBS, TN	
8-6 (337–339)	Estimate the percent of a number.	1, 2, 5–10	CTBS, ITBS, TN	
8-7 (340–343)	Find the percent of a number.	1–10	CTBS, ITBS, TN	

CAT = California Achievement Tests, CTBS = Comprehensive Tests of Basic Skills, ITBS = Iowa Tests of Basic Skills, MAT = Metropolitan Achievement Tests, SAT = Stanford Achievement Tests, TN = Terra Nova
For the key to numbering of NCTM Standards 2000, see page T6.

The **Interactive Lesson Planner** contains all of the blackline masters and transparencies. This CD-ROM also includes an easy-to-use lesson planning calendar.

LESSON PLANNING GUIDE

Lesson	Extra Practice (Student Edition)	BLACKLINE MASTERS (PAGE NUMBERS)										Transparencies A and B
		Study Guide	Practice	Enrichment	Assessment & Evaluation	Classroom Games	Diversity	Hands-On Lab	School to Career	Science and Math Lab Manual	Technology	
8-1A								54				
8-1	p. 578	57	57	57								8-1
8-1B								55				
8-2	p. 578	58	58	58	211					8		8-2
8-2B												
8-3A	p. 578											
8-3	p. 579	59	59	59							16	8-3
8-4A								56				
8-4	p. 579	60	60	60	210, 211							8-4
8-5	p. 579	61	61	61						81–84		8-5
8-6	p. 580	62	62	62	212		8	76		85–88		8-6
8-7	p. 580	63	63	63	212	21–22					15	8-7
Study Guide/ Assessment					197–209, 213–215							

OTHER CHAPTER RESOURCES

Student Edition

Chapter Project, pp. 309, 315, 327, 333, 347
School to Career, p. 328
Let the Games Begin, p. 343

Technology

 MathPASS CD-ROM

Interactive Mathematics Tools Software

Teacher's Classroom Resources

Applications
Family Letters and Activities, pp. 15–16
Investigations and Projects Masters, pp. 45–48
Meeting Individual Needs
Investigations for the Special Education Student, pp. 21–28

Teaching Aids
Answer Key Masters
Block Scheduling Booklet
Lesson Planning Guide
Solutions Manual

Professional Publications
Glencoe Mathematics Professional Series

Planning the Chapter

MindJogger Videoquizzes provide a unique format for reviewing concepts presented in the chapter.

ASSESSMENT RESOURCES

Student Edition

Mixed Review, pp. 315, 320, 327, 333, 336, 339, 343

Mid-Chapter Self Test, p. 327

➡ Math Journal, pp. 313, 338

Study Guide and Assessment, pp. 344–347

Performance Task, p. 347

📁 Portfolio Suggestion, p. 347

Standardized Test Practice, pp. 348–349

Chapter Test, p. 602

Assessment and Evaluation Masters

Multiple-Choice Tests (Forms 1A, 1B, 1C), pp. 197–202

Free-Response Tests (Forms 2A, 2B, 2C), pp. 203–208

Performance Assessment, p. 209

Mid-Chapter Test, p. 210

Quizzes A–D, pp. 211–212

Standardized Test Practice, pp. 213–214

Cumulative Review, p. 215

Teacher's Wraparound Edition

5-Minute Check, pp. 312, 317, 324, 330, 334, 337, 340

📁 Building Portfolios, p. 308

➡ Math Journal, pp. 311, 316, 321, 329

Closing Activity, pp. 315, 320, 323, 327, 333, 336, 339, 343

Technology

💾 Test and Review Software

📼 MindJogger Videoquizzes

💿 CD-ROM Program

MATERIALS AND MANIPULATIVES

Lesson 8-1A
patty paper
scissors*

Lesson 8-1
grid paper†
ruler*

Lesson 8-1B
spinner*

Lesson 8-2
pattern blocks*

Lesson 8-2B
computer
spreadsheet software

Lesson 8-4A
grid paper†
colored pencils

Lesson 8-4
wastebasket
coin
grid paper†
colored pencils

Lesson 8-7
index cards
scissors*

*Glencoe Manipulative Kit   †Glencoe Overhead Manipulative Resources

PACING CHART

See pages T25–T27 for the Course Planning Calendar.

COURSE	DAY 1	DAY 2	DAY 3	DAY 4	DAY 5	DAY 6	DAY 7
Standard	Chapter Project	Lessons 8-1A & 8-1			Lesson 8-2	Lesson 8-3A	Lesson 8-3
Honors	Chapter Project	Lessons 8-1 & 8-1B		Lessons 8-2 & 8-2B		Lesson 8-3A	Lesson 8-3
Block	Chapter Project & Lessons 8-1A & 8-1		Lessons 8-2 & 8-3A	Lessons 8-3 & 8-4A	Lessons 8-4 & 8-5	Lessons 8-6 & 8-7	Study Guide and Assessment, Chapter Test

Interactive Mathematics:
Activities and Investigations

is an activity-based program that may be used as an enhancement for chapters in *Mathematics: Applications and Connections.*

Unit 12, Activity Two
Use with Lesson 8-2.

Summary Students work in groups to make a map of a variety of locations in the school, using the paces of two members of the group as unit measures. They develop a key comparing a number of paces with a specific distance.

Math Connection Students compare units of measure and use proportions. They draw maps based on nonstandard units of measure. They then determine distances on the map using a standard unit of measure.

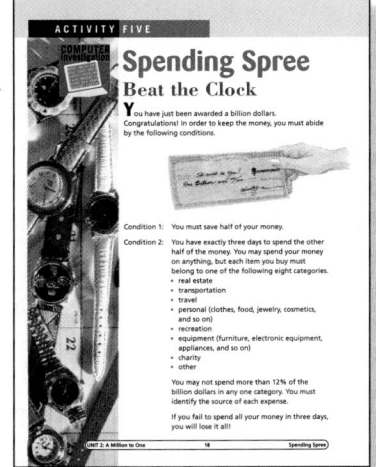

Unit 2, Activity Five
Use with Lesson 8-7.

Summary Students use spreadsheets to investigate how to spend one billion dollars under certain regulations. Students write a report on their findings, explaining their expenditures.

Math Connection Students use a computer and spreadsheet software to organize their spending into categories. Because students must stay within 12% of the entire budget in each category, they need to find percents of whole numbers.

DAY 8	DAY 9	DAY 10	DAY 11	DAY 12	DAY 13	DAY 14	DAY 15
Lessons 8-4A & 8-4		Lesson 8-5	Lesson 8-6	Lesson 8-7	Study Guide and Assessment	Chapter Test	
Lesson 8-4	Lesson 8-5	Lesson 8-6	Lesson 8-7	Study Guide and Assessment	Chapter Test		

APPLICATIONS

Classroom Games, pp. 21–22

Diversity Masters, p. 8

School to Career Masters, p. 8

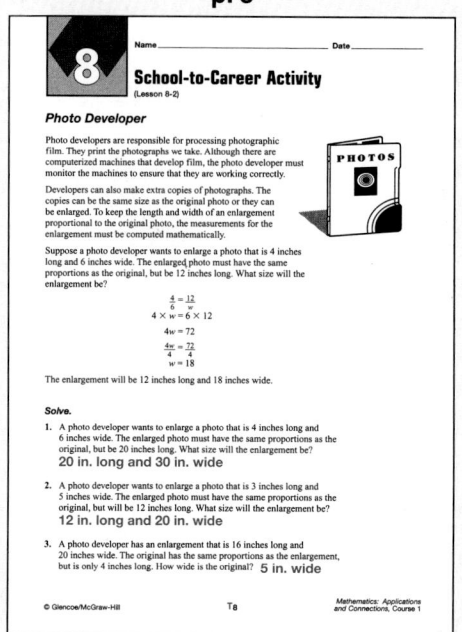

Family Letters and Activities, pp. 15–16

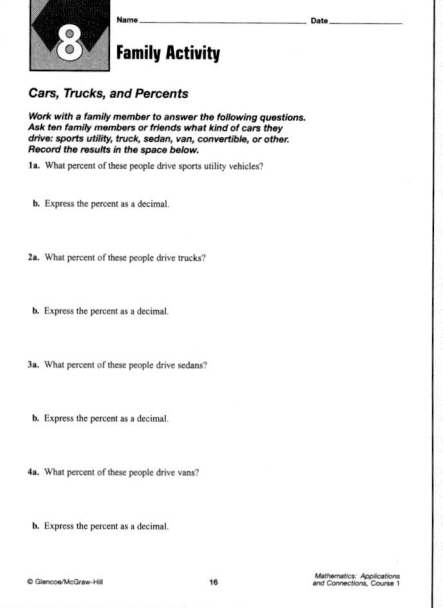

Science and Math Lab Manual, pp. 81–88

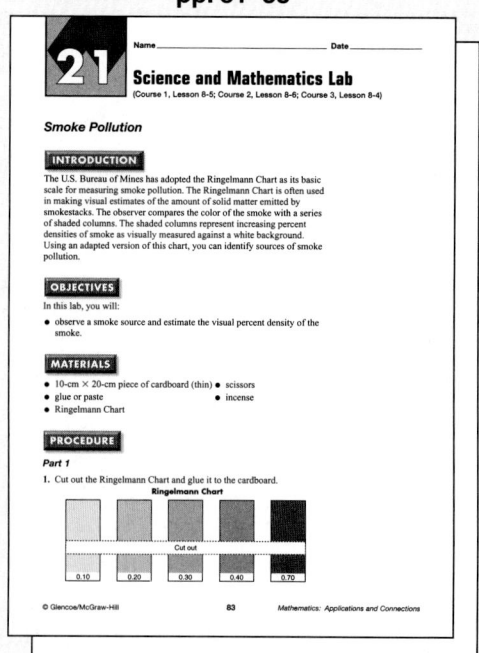

MANIPULATIVES/MODELING

Hands-On Lab Masters, p. 76

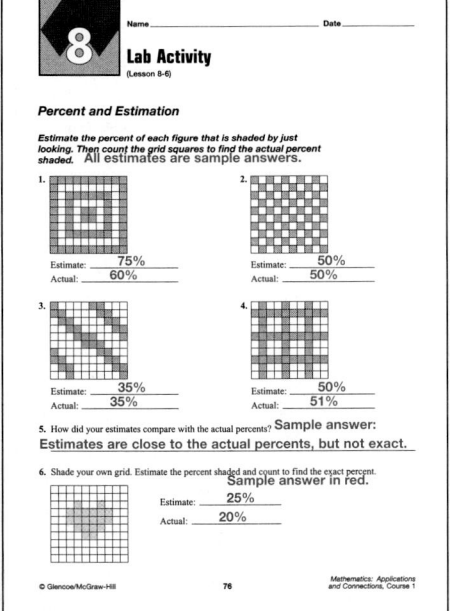

8 Lab Activity
(Lesson 8-6)

Name _____ Date _____

Percent and Estimation

Estimate the percent of each figure that is shaded by just looking. Then count the grid squares to find the actual percent shaded. All estimates are sample answers.

1.
Estimate: 75%
Actual: 60%

2.
Estimate: 50%
Actual: 50%

3.
Estimate: 35%
Actual: 35%

4.
Estimate: 50%
Actual: 51%

5. How did your estimates compare with the actual percents? Sample answer:
Estimates are close to the actual percents, but not exact.

6. Shade your own grid. Estimate the percent shaded and count to find the exact percent. Sample answer in red.
Estimate: 25%
Actual: 20%

© Glencoe/McGraw-Hill   76   Mathematics: Applications and Connections, Course 1

ASSESSMENT/EVALUATION

Assessment and Evaluation Masters, pp. 210–212

8 Chapter 8 Mid-Chapter Test
(Lessons 8-1 through 8-4)

Name _____ Date _____

1. Write the ratio in three different ways: 7 out of 23 M & M's are brown.
   1. $\frac{7}{23}$; 7:23; 7 out of 23

Express each ratio as a fraction in simplest form.
2. 22 games won out of 44 games played
   2. $\frac{1}{2}$
3. 15 sheep out of 55 animals
   3. $\frac{3}{11}$

Express each ratio as a rate.
4. 360 miles in 6 hours
   4. 60 mph
5. 4 tapes for $23.96
   5. $5.99 per tape

Use cross products to determine whether each pair of ratios forms a proportion.
6. $\frac{9}{20}$, $\frac{18}{42}$ 6. no
7. $\frac{5}{10}$, $\frac{4}{8}$ 7. yes

Solve each proportion.
8. $\frac{5}{20} = \frac{6}{c}$ 8. 60
9. $\frac{6}{c} = \frac{18}{30}$ 9. 10
10. $\frac{x}{16} = \frac{6}{4}$ 10. 27

11. Leslie is setting up a singles tennis tournament. She wants each player to play every other player one time. If 4 players enter, how many games will Leslie need to set up?   11. 6 games

Scale drawings were made of four famous structures. The scale for each drawing is 1 cm = 30 m. The given measurement is the size of the drawing to the nearest centimeter. Find the actual height of each structure.
12. Statue of Liberty, New York City, 3 cm   12. 90 m
13. Washington Monument, Washington, D.C., 5 cm   13. 150 m
14. Gateway Arch, St. Louis, Missouri, 6 cm   14. 180 m

If you were to make a scale drawing for the following structures with a scale of 1 in. = 50 ft, what would be the measurement of the drawing?
15. a skyscraper 500 ft tall   15. 10 in.
16. a space shuttle 125 ft long   16. 2.5 in.

Express each percent as a fraction in simplest form.
17. 56%   17. $\frac{14}{25}$
18. 143%   18. $1\frac{43}{100}$

Express each fraction as a percent.
19. $\frac{2}{5}$ 19. 40%
20. $\frac{9}{50}$ 20. 18%

© Glencoe/McGraw-Hill   210   Mathematics: Applications and Connections, Course 1

Name _____ Date _____

Chapter 8 Quiz A
(Lessons 8-1 and 8-2)

Express each ratio as a fraction in simplest form.
1. 45 people out of 60   1. $\frac{3}{4}$
2. 12 red marbles out of 28 marbles   2. $\frac{3}{7}$

Express each ratio as a rate.
3. 178 feet in 2 seconds   3. 89 ft per s
4. 12 muffins for $3   4. $0.25 per muffin
5. 24 cans of soft drink for $4.99   5. $0.21 per can

Solve each proportion.
6. $\frac{18}{m} = \frac{50}{100}$ 6. 36
7. $\frac{27}{36} = \frac{x}{16}$ 7. 12
8. $\frac{45}{60} = \frac{60}{y}$ 8. 80

9. Use cross products to determine if $\frac{9}{16}$ and $\frac{3}{4}$ form a proportion.   9. no
10. Use cross products to determine if $\frac{3}{11}$ and $\frac{14}{21}$ form a proportion.   10. yes

---

Name _____ Date _____

Chapter 8 Quiz B
(Lessons 8-3 and 8-4)

Solve by drawing a diagram.
1. The Hys choose mirror squares that are 16 inches by 16 inches to cover a wall that is 8 feet tall and 4 feet wide. How many mirror squares are needed?   1. 18
2. The distance between two cities on a map is $3\frac{1}{2}$ inches. The scale reads "1 in. = 24 mi." What is the actual distance between the cities?   2. 90 miles

Express each fraction as a percent.
3. $\frac{23}{25}$ 3. 92%
4. $\frac{13}{20}$ 4. 65%
5. $\frac{7}{8}$ 5. 87.5%
6. $\frac{7}{20}$ 6. 35%

Express each percent as a fraction.
7. 95%   7. $\frac{19}{20}$
8. 15%   8. $\frac{3}{20}$
9. 24%   9. $\frac{6}{25}$
10. 58%   10. $\frac{29}{50}$

© Glencoe/McGraw-Hill   211   Mathematics: Applications and Connections, Course 1

TECHNOLOGY/MULTIMEDIA

Technology Masters, pp. 15–16

8 Calculator Activity
(Lesson 8-7)

Name _____ Date _____

The Percent Key

Most calculators have a special key to work with percents.

Example   Find 25.5% of 82.
Enter: 82 ⊠ 25.5 [2nd] [%] ⊟ 20.91
The solution is 20.91.

Find the percent of each number.
1. 80% of 40   32
2. 16% of 18   2.88
3. 7% of 35   2.45
4. 12% of 42   5.04
5. 1.8% of 14   0.252
6. 0.5% of 30   0.15
7. 120% of 18   21.6
8. 33% of 300   99
9. 99% of 200   198
10. 25% of 412   103
11. 8.4% of 17   1.428
12. 213% of 241   513.33
13. 0.01% of 120   0.012
14. 0.12% of 310   0.372
15. 0.15% of 114   0.171
16. 114% of 18.2   20.748
17. 3.1% of 30.5   0.9455
18. 5.2% of 92.4   4.8048
19. 9.25% of 12.4   1.147
20. 122% of 0.055   0.0671

© Glencoe/McGraw-Hill   T15   Mathematics: Applications and Connections, Course 1

---

8 Graphing Calculator Activity
(Lesson 8-3)

Name _____ Date _____

Scale Drawings

You can use a graphing calculator to draw geometric shapes and scale drawings. First, clear all lists by pressing [2nd] [MEM] 4 [ENTER].

Example   An architect was given a floor plan with corners at $A(0, 0)$, $B(2, 0)$, $C(2, 1)$, $D(3, 1)$, $E(3, 4)$, and $F(0, 4)$. Graph the scale drawing of the floor plan that has a scale of 1 to 2.

Step 1   Press [STAT] [ENTER] and enter the x-coordinates in column L1 and the y-coordinates in column L2. Repeat the first entry in each column at the end of each column.

Step 2   To graph a scale drawing with a scale factor of 2, multiply each coordinate in the ordered pairs by 2. Enter the new coordinates in columns L3 and L4.

Step 3   You must turn on the two point plots.
Enter: [2nd] [STAT PLOT] [ENTER] [ENTER] ▼ ▶
[ENTER] ▲ ▲ ▶ [ENTER] ▼ ▶
[ENTER] ▼ [2nd] [L3] ▼ [2nd] [L4]

Step 4   Press [WINDOW] and make entries to match the settings shown.

Step 5   Press [GRAPH].

Use a graphing calculator to draw the polygons and their scale drawings. (Reset [WINDOW] so that Xmax = 20 and Ymax = 20.) Sketch the drawings. Label the vertices and coordinates of each polygon.

1. $A(1, 2)$; $B(3, 4)$; $C(4, 3)$
   scale: 1 to 5
2. $A(4, 8)$; $B(16, 16)$; $C(12, 4)$
   scale: 4 to 1
3. $A(1, 6)$; $B(6, 4)$; $C(4, 2)$
   scale: 1 to 3
4. $A(1, 1)$; $B(1, 3)$; $C(3, 3)$; $D(3, 1)$
   scale: 1 to 4
5. $A(1.8, 9)$; $B(12, 9)$; $C(6, 18)$; $D(21, 18)$
   scale: 3 to 1
6. Why did the upper right-hand corner of Exercise 5 not show on the screen?
   The x-coordinate of a vertex is 21. This is greater than the Xmax setting.

© Glencoe/McGraw-Hill   T16   Mathematics: Applications and Connections, Course 1

MEETING INDIVIDUAL NEEDS

Investigations for the Special Education Student, pp. 21–28

Use with:
Course 1-Chapter 10
Course 2-Chapter 11
Course 3-Chapter 9

Investigation 9 Teacher's Guide

Park It!

Overview
Students will work in groups of four to design a park according to preset criteria. During this investigation, students will experience firsthand how measurement, proportions, and decimal operations are necessary for careers that involve design. Each student is responsible for a certain job in the group: engineer, draftsperson, finance officer, or public relations person. The culminating point of the investigation is a videotaped, oral presentation of the designs.

Activity Goals
Students will:
• design a park to scale using proportions,
• use decimal operations for budgeting, and
• work cooperatively and responsibly with a group.

Planning the Instruction
Prerequisite Skills
Students should have a significant amount of practice measuring, solving proportions, using scales, and computing with decimals.
Materials
• investigation worksheets
• calculators
• rulers, measuring tape
• drawing paper
• crayons, colored pencils, markers
• video camera and videotape

Time Needed
ten 45-minute periods

Procedure
1. Discuss the investigation with the class. Explain that their task is to design a park to scale that will fit on a 200-foot by 300-foot piece of land. The investigation will end with a videotaped, oral presentation to the class.
2. Brainstorm with the entire class a list of features they would like to include in their designs.
3. Set up student groups.
4. Have each group meet and compile their own list of features, using ideas from the class list.
5. Describe the different jobs to the class. Then have the groups discuss and sign the Group Job Contract worksheet according to their responsibilities.
6. Have students begin their designated jobs according to their Job Specification worksheets.
7. Monitor student progress through observations and group meetings. In addition, be available to answer questions when necessary.
8. Set a date for the presentations.
9. Conduct and videotape presentations while students evaluate each other.
10. Collect evaluations and have students view the recorded presentations.

Adaptations and Variations
The following are some ideas on how this investigation may be modified depending on student population.

LD • Allow more time.
• If measuring is difficult, allow students to use nonstandard units such as their hands.
• If converting measurements is difficult using scale factors and proportions, allow students to convert using nonstandard scale units such as one paper clip in drawing length.

PH • For students who have trouble drawing, allow them to use computer graphics.

CD • If a communically-troubled student should choose to be the public relations person, have each group member say several lines of the speech.

BD • Assign job specification tasks one at a time, with a reward system in place for each one completed in an appropriate manner.

HI • Have another student sign each presentation.

VI • Have students give a detailed description of their designs when presenting.

© Glencoe/McGraw-Hill   21   Mathematics: Applications and Connections

Theme: Toys

For many years toys were created by individual craftspeople. However, in the twentieth century, manufacturing processes made it possible for millions of children to own the exact same toy. One of the most popular manufactured toys is a miniature toy car, created in 1947 by Leslie and Rodney Smith. Another popular toy is a teen fashion doll, created by Ruth Handler in 1959.

Question of the Day Original miniature toy cars have a 1:75 scale. This means 1 inch on the model equals 75 inches on the actual car. If an original miniature toy bus is $2\frac{1}{4}$ inches long, how long is an actual bus, to the nearest foot? **14 ft**

Assess Prerequisite Skills

Ask students to read through the list of objectives presented in "What you'll learn in Chapter 8." You may wish to ask them what each of the objectives means or if they have experienced or used any of these math concepts before.

Building Portfolios

Encourage students to revise their portfolios as they study this chapter. Have them include work that illustrates their growing understanding of ratios, proportions, and percents.

 Math and the Family

In the *Family Letters and Activities* booklet (pp. 15–16), you will find a letter to the parents explaining what students will study in Chapter 8. An activity appropriate for the whole family is also available.

Exploring Ratio, Proportion, and Percent

What you'll learn in Chapter 8

- to express ratios and rates as fractions,
- to solve proportions by using cross products,
- to solve problems by drawing a diagram,
- to find actual length from a scale drawing,
- to express percents as fractions and as decimals, and
- to find the percent of a number.

308 Chapter 8 Exploring Ratio, Proportion, and Percent

 CD-ROM Program

Activities for Chapter 8

- Chapter 8 Introduction
- Interactive Lessons 8-1, 8-2, 8-6, 8-7
- Extended Activity 8-4
- Assessment Game
- Resource Lessons 8-1 through 8-7

CHAPTER Project

THE WONDERFUL WORLD OF TOYS

Many toys are small replicas of actual objects. For example, Matchbox cars are small replicas of cars. In this project, you will use ratios and proportions to find and compare the size of toys and the actual size of the objects that they represent. You will then make a poster to illustrate your findings.

Getting Started

- Look at the drawings of the two race cars. What is the length of stock car 88? What is the height of stock car 16?
- How could you use these dimensions to calculate the actual length and height of the stock cars that they represent?

Stock Car 88 Scale:
1 cm = 144 cm

3.6 cm

1.1 cm

|←1.5 cm→|

Stock Car 16 Scale:
1 cm = 64 cm

2.3 cm

3.0 cm

|←——— 7.7 cm ———→|

Technology Tips

- Use a **spreadsheet** to record the measurements of toys and actual objects and to calculate measurements.
- Use **publishing software** to make parts of your poster such as graphs, tables, and drawings.
- Use a **calculator** to help you find the actual dimensions of the stock cars.

interNET
CONNECTION For up-to-date information on toy cars, visit:
www.glencoe.com/sec/math/mac/mathnet

Working on the Project

You can use what you'll learn in Chapter 8 to help you make your poster.

Page	Exercise
315	35
327	11
333	37
347	Alternative Assessment

CHAPTER Project
N O T E S

Objectives Students should
- use ratios and proportions to find and compare the size of toys and the actual size of the objects that they represent.
- make a poster to illustrate their findings.

Project Pointer You may suggest that students begin a *Project Folder* to keep their work as they complete each stage of the Chapter Project. The completed project may also be added to their portfolios.

Suggest that students give an oral presentation explaining the results of their comparison. Then have them display their posters in the classroom.

Using the Diagrams Have students explain in their own words what the diagrams represent. Ask them why they think it would be important to draw diagrams to scale. Then have them describe how ratios and proportions can be used to make toy cars.

Investigations and Projects Masters, p. 48

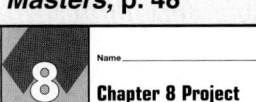

---

interNET
CONNECTION

Instructional Resources ▶▶▶
A recording sheet to help students organize their data for the Chapter Project is shown at the right and is available in the *Investigations and Projects Masters,* p. 48.

GET READY

Objective Students use tangram pieces to explore ratios and the relationship between ratio and area.

Optional Resources
Hands-On Lab Masters
• worksheet, p. 54
• tangram, p. 15
Manipulative Kit
• scissors

MANAGEMENT TIPS

Recommended Time
30 minutes

Getting Started Patty paper can be purchased at restaurant supply stores. If patty paper is not available, squares of waxed paper can be used.
Prepare a tangram to be displayed on the overhead. Show how the pieces may be reconfigured to form many creative, different shapes. Show that a tangram always has seven pieces—five triangles, a square, and a rhombus.

The **Activity** leads students through five steps of cutting and folding to make a tangram. At Steps 1, 3, 4, and 5, students can use their tangram pieces to verify the given ratios.

HANDS-ON LAB

COOPERATIVE LEARNING

8-1A Ratios

A Preview of Lesson 8-1

◇ 2 sheets of patty paper

✂ scissors

Have you ever put together a tangram? The tangram was first developed in China and was very popular in the 1800s. In this lab, you will construct a tangram and use ratios to compare the areas of the tangram pieces. Recall that a ratio is a comparison of two numbers by division.

TRY THIS

Work with a partner.

Step 1 Using one sheet of patty paper, fold the top left corner to the bottom right corner. Crease the paper and unfold the square. Cut along the fold.

The ratio 1 to 2 compares the area of one of the triangles to the area of the uncut square.

Step 2 Using one of the triangles, fold the bottom left corner to the bottom right corner. Make a crease and unfold the triangle. Cut along the fold. Label the triangles A and B.

Step 3 Using the other triangle, fold the bottom left corner to the bottom right corner as shown. Make a crease and unfold the triangle. Then fold the top corner to the bottom edge along the crease. Crease and cut on this second crease line. Label the small triangle C.

The ratio 1 to 3 compares the area of triangle C to the area of the remaining piece.

Step 4 Cut on the crease of the remaining piece as shown. Using the piece on the left, fold the bottom left corner to the bottom right corner. Make a crease and unfold. Cut on this fold. Label the triangle D and the square E.

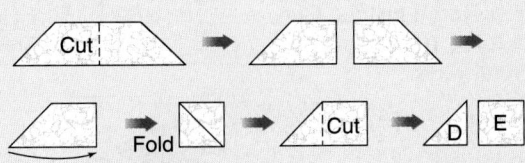

The ratio 1 to 6 compares the area of triangle D to the area of the original figure in this step. The ratio 1 to 3 compares the area of square E to the area of the original figure.

Step 5 Using the remaining piece, fold the bottom left corner to the top right corner. Make a crease and unfold. Cut along the fold. Label the triangle F and the other figure G.

The ratio 1 to 3 compares the area of triangle F to the area of the original figure in this step.

1a. $\frac{1}{2}$ square unit   1b. Triangle C is $\frac{1}{2}$ the size of triangle B.

2a. $\frac{1}{4}$ square unit   2b. Triangle F is $\frac{1}{4}$ the size of triangle B.

3a. $\frac{1}{2}$ 3b. $\frac{1}{4}$ 3c. 1 3d. $\frac{2}{1}$ 3e. $\frac{1}{2}$ 3f. $\frac{1}{2}$

ON YOUR OWN

1a. If the area of triangle B is 1 square unit, what is the area of triangle C?

  b. How does the area of triangle C compare to the area of triangle B?

2a. If the area of triangle B is 1 square unit, what is the area of triangle F?

  b. How does the area of triangle F compare to the area of triangle B?

3. Write a ratio that compares the areas of the tangram pieces. Express each ratio as a fraction.

  a. C to A
  b. F to A
  c. A to B
  d. B to C
  e. D to E
  f. F to G

4. Look Ahead Write a ratio that compares the number of yellow squares to the total number of squares. Express the ratio as a fraction in simplest form. $\frac{1}{3}$

Lesson 8-1A HANDS-ON **LAB** 311

Math Journal Suggest that students create interesting figures using tangrams and include them, or drawings of them, in their journals.

Hands-On Lab 8-1A **311**

Instructional Resources

- *Study Guide Masters*, p. 57
- *Practice Masters*, p. 57
- *Enrichment Masters*, p. 57
- Transparencies 8-1, A and B
- CD-ROM Program
  - Resource Lesson 8-1
  - Interactive Lesson 8-1

Recommended Pacing	
Standard	Days 2–4 of 14
Honors	Days 2 & 3 of 13
Block	Days 1 & 2 of 7

1 FOCUS

5-Minute Check
(Chapter 7)

1. Write the product of $2\frac{1}{3}$ and $\frac{3}{4}$ in simplest form. $1\frac{3}{4}$

2. Find the circumference of an apple pie with an 8-inch diameter. Use 3.14 for π. 25.12 in.

3. Find the next two numbers in the sequence 15, $12\frac{3}{4}$, $10\frac{1}{2}$, $8\frac{1}{4}$. 6, $3\frac{3}{4}$

4. Write the quotient of $3\frac{1}{5}$ and $\frac{3}{10}$ in simplest form. $10\frac{2}{3}$

5. Complete: $3\frac{1}{2}$ lb = ? oz. 56

 The 5-Minute Check is also available on **Transparency 8-1A** for this lesson.

Motivating the Lesson

Hands-On Activity Have students choose a short paragraph of reading material. Then ask questions such as:
- How many total words are there?
- How many of the words contain the letter r?
- How would you express the relationship of the words with the letter r to the total number of words?

What you'll learn

You'll learn to express ratios and rates as fractions.

When am I ever going to use this?

Knowing how to express ratios as fractions can help you determine better buys in a grocery store.

Word Wise

rate

The table shows the cards in a card game. Notice that 24 out of the 108 cards are purple.

You can compare these two numbers by using a ratio. Recall that the ratio that compares 24 to 108 can be written in several ways.

Type of Card	Amount
Heart	24
Yellow	24
Purple	24
Green	24
Wild Draw	10
Extra Cards	2

24 to 108   24:108

24 out of 108 $\frac{24}{108}$

A common way to express a ratio is as a fraction in simplest form.

$$\frac{24}{108} = \frac{2}{9}$$

The GCF of 24 and 108 is 12. Divide the numerator and the denominator by the GCF, 12. ($\div 12$)

So, $\frac{2}{9}$ of the cards are purple.

The ratio can also be expressed as 2 to 9, 2:9, or 2 out of 9.

Example ➊ Express the ratio that compares the number of strawberries to the total number of berries as a fraction in simplest form.

strawberries → $\frac{4}{10} = \frac{2}{5}$ *The GCF of 4 and 10 is 2.*
berries →   *Divide the numerator and the denominator by the GCF, 2.* ($\div 2$)

The ratio in simplest form is $\frac{2}{5}$.

If the two quantities that you are comparing have different units of measure, the ratio is called a **rate**. For example, $\frac{125 \text{ miles}}{2 \text{ hours}}$ compares the number of miles traveled to the number of hours the trip took.

Rate	A rate is a ratio of two measurements that have different units.

 Investigations for the Special Education Student

This blackline master booklet helps you plan for the needs of your special education students by providing long-term projects along with teacher notes. Investigation 9, *Park It!*, may be used with this chapter.

Rates are usually expressed in a *per unit* form, where the number in the denominator is 1.

Examples

② **Express the ratio *7 inches of rain in 28 days* as a rate.**

$$\frac{7 \text{ inches}}{28 \text{ days}} = \frac{0.25 \text{ inch}}{1 \text{ day}}$$
┌ ÷ 28 ┐
└ ÷ 28 ┘

Divide the numerator and denominator by 28 to get a denominator of 1.

The total rainfall is equivalent to 0.25 inch each day.

APPLICATION

③ **Money Matters** Dhara purchased a 14.5-ounce bag of chips for $3.19. What was the cost per ounce?

Explore You know that the 14.5-ounce bag of chips costs $3.19. You need to find the cost per ounce.

Plan Use a rate to compare the cost to the weight.

Solve
$$\frac{\$3.19}{14.5 \text{ ounces}} = \frac{\$0.22}{1 \text{ ounce}}$$
┌ ÷ 14.5 ┐
└ ÷ 14.5 ┘

Divide the numerator and denominator by 14.5 to get a denominator of 1.
$3.19 ÷ 14.5 = 0.22$

The cost is 22 cents per ounce.

Examine $0.22 × 14.5 = $3.19

So, the answer is correct.

CHECK FOR UNDERSTANDING

Communicating Mathematics

Read and study the lesson to answer each question. 1–3. See margin.

1. **Explain** the difference between a ratio and a rate.

2. **Draw** a picture in which the ratio of blue circles to the total number of circles is $\frac{3}{5}$.

3. **Write** about a situation in which rates would be helpful.

Guided Practice
4–7. See margin.

Write each ratio in three different ways.

4. 7 carnations out of 24 flowers

5. 15 mint chip cookies in a bag of 34 cookies

Express each ratio as a fraction in simplest form.

6. 16 beagles out of 24 dogs   7. 10 emeralds out of 25 gems

Express each ratio as a rate.

8. 120 words in 3 minutes   9. 5 soft drinks for $3.25

8. 40 words per minute

9. $0.65 per soft drink

10. 40 miles per hour

10. **Life Science** The fastest running bird is the ostrich. An ostrich can run 240 miles in 6 hours. What is the average speed of an ostrich?

Lesson 8-1 Ratios and Rates   **313**

Reteaching the Lesson

Activity Give small groups of students a set of assorted items. Then have them make and complete a chart such as the following:

	Red	Blue
Number of each type	2	3
Total number	14	14
Ratio	1:7	3:14

Error Analysis

Watch for students who write ratios as number of items of one type compared to remaining items.

Prevent by reminding students that the denominator in a ratio is the *total* number of items being considered.

Check for Understanding

If students need additional practice or instruction after completing Exercises 1–10, one of these options may be helpful.
- Extra Practice, see p. 578
- Reteaching Activity, see p. 313
- *Study Guide Masters,* p. 57
- *Practice Masters,* p. 57
- 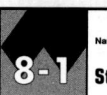 Interactive Mathematics Tools Software

Assignment Guide

Core: 11–33 odd, 36–40
Enriched: 12–30 even, 31–34, 36–40

Study Guide Masters, p. 57

8-1 Study Guide

Ratios and Rates

You can compare numbers with the same unit of measure using a ratio. A ratio is a comparison of two numbers.

Example 1 There were 52 animals in the ugly pet show. 24 of them were dogs.

The ratio can be written as follows.
24 to 52   24:52   24 out of 52 $\frac{24}{52}$

24 and 52 have 4 as a common factor.
The ratio can be simplified as $\frac{6}{13}$.

$$\frac{24}{52} = \frac{6}{13}$$

A **rate** is a ratio that compares two different units of measure.

Example 2 Julie entered 40 pages of data into her computer in 5 hours.

$\frac{40 \text{ pages}}{5 \text{ hours}} = \frac{8 \text{ pages}}{1 \text{ hour}}$ Compare the number of pages to the number of hours.
Simplify to find the unit rate, the number of pages entered in 1 hour.
Julie entered data at the rate of 8 pages per hour.

Express each ratio as a fraction in simplest form.

1. 12 out of 25 people $\frac{12}{25}$
2. 8 out of 10 bicycles $\frac{4}{5}$
3. 9 wins in 12 games $\frac{3}{4}$
4. 14 station wagons out of 40 vehicles $\frac{7}{20}$
5. 10 out of 15 days $\frac{2}{3}$
6. 18 baseball caps out of 36 hats $\frac{1}{2}$

Express each ratio as a rate.

7. $18 for 6 tickets $3 per ticket
8. 30 km in 6 hours 5 km per hour
9. $42 for 7 books $6 per book
10. $28 for 4 hours $7 per hour

Use the letters in the word "WORLDWIDE." Write the ratios comparing the numbers of letters in simplest form.

11. W to D 1:1
12. R to W 1:2
13. vowels to consonants 1:2

© Glencoe/McGraw-Hill   157   Mathematics: Applications and Connections, Course 1

Practice

11–16. Sample answers are given.
11. 9 out of 16, 9 to 16, 9:16
12. 13 to 16, 13:16, $\frac{13}{16}$
13. 18 out of 29, 18 to 29, 18:29
14. $\frac{11}{15}$, 11:15, 11 out of 15
15. 23 out of 25, 23 to 25, 23:25
16. 7:19, 7 out of 19, $\frac{7}{19}$

Write each ratio in three different ways.

11. 9 pairs of boots out of 16 are yellow.
12. 13 bikes out of 16 bikes have combination locks.
13. 18 out of 29 centimeter cubes are pink.
14. 11 brownies out of 15 brownies contain walnuts.
15. 23 out of 25 ants are red.
16. 7 out of 19 days were cloudy.

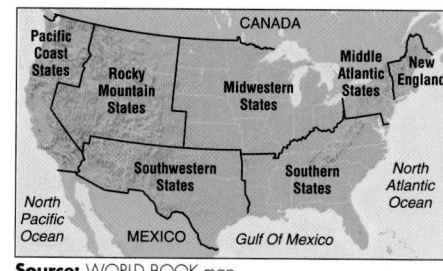

Express each ratio as a fraction in simplest form.

17. 19 games won out of 57 games played $\frac{1}{3}$
18. 25 brick houses out of 45 houses $\frac{5}{9}$
19. 14 tabby cats out of 18 cats $\frac{7}{9}$
20. 16 states visited out of 50 states $\frac{8}{25}$
21. 32 cows out of 72 animals $\frac{4}{9}$
22. 10 drums out of 75 instruments $\frac{2}{15}$

Express each ratio as a rate.   23–29. See margin.

23. 395 kilometers in 5 hours
24. 3 CDs for $41.91
25. 4 tickets for $35
26. 63 million albums in 7 years
27. $1.32 for a dozen eggs
28. 79.8 miles on 3 gallons of gas

29. Write the ratio *13 quarters out of 24 coins* in three different ways.

30. Express the ratio *ten oranges for two dollars* as a rate. **$0.20 per orange**

Applications and Problem Solving

Real World

31a. $\frac{2}{25}$

32d. $\frac{1}{3}, \frac{1}{3}, \frac{1}{9}$;

The ratio that compares the length of the sides times the ratio that compares the perimeters equals the ratio that compares the areas.

31. *Geography* Refer to the map.
   a. Write the ratio that compares the number of states in the Southwestern States region to the total number of states.
   b. Write the ratio that compares the number of states in the Midwestern States to the total number of states. $\frac{6}{25}$

32. *Geometry* Draw a 1-by-1 unit square and a 2-by-2 unit square on grid paper. Then write the ratio that compares each of the following.
   a. the length of the side of the small square to the length of the side of the large square $\frac{1}{2}$
   b. the perimeter of the small square to the perimeter of the large square $\frac{1}{2}$
   c. the area of the small square to the area of the large square $\frac{1}{4}$
   d. Draw a 3-by-3 unit square. Compare the same measures between the 1-by-1 unit square and the 3-by-3 unit square. Describe the relationship that exists between the ratios of the sides, perimeters, and areas.

314   Chapter 8 Exploring Ratio, Proportion, and Percent

Additional Answers

23. 79 kilometers per hour
24. $13.97 per CD
25. $8.75 per ticket
26. 9 million albums per year
27. $0.11 per egg
28. 26.6 miles per gallon
29. Sample answer: 13 out of 24; 13 to 24; 13:24

MathPASS CD-ROM

This CD-ROM offers a complete, self-paced mathematics curriculum. Each lesson includes a pretest, tutorial, guided practice, and posttest. MathPASS Lesson 28 is correlated to this Student Edition lesson.
For Windows & Macintosh

33. Life Science Scientists say that a pterodactyl could fly 75 miles in three hours. How far could a pterodactyl travel in one hour? **25 miles**

34. The 16-ounce bag costs $0.16 per ounce. The 32-ounce bag costs $0.11 per ounce. So, the better buy is the 32-ounce bag.

34. Money Matters At the supermarket, the cost of a 16-ounce bag of gum balls is $2.56. A 32-ounce bag costs $3.52. Which is the better buy? Explain.

35b. $\frac{1}{64}$

35. Working on the CHAPTER Project Refer to page 309.
   a. Write the ratio that compares the size of the toy stock car 88 to the actual size of the race car as a fraction. $\frac{1}{144}$
   b. Write the ratio that compares the size of the toy stock car 16 to the actual size of the race car as a fraction.
   c. Find three toys that represent real-life objects. Measure the height and width of each toy to the nearest centimeter. Then find out the actual height and width of the objects that the toys represent. Write the ratios that compare the height, width, and length of each toy to the actual height, width, and length of each real object as a fraction in simplest form. **See students' work.**

36. Critical Thinking Mr. Sarmiento stated that 18 out of 24 students in his class scored 85% or higher on the last test. He instructed the class to write a ratio comparing the number of students scoring below 85% to the total number of students. Explain why each answer is incorrect.
   a. 18:24   b. 24:6   c. 24:18 **See Answer Appendix.**

Mixed Review

37. Patterns Find the missing number in the sequence $3\frac{7}{8}$, $4\frac{1}{4}$, _?_ , 5, $5\frac{3}{8}$. *(Lesson 7-8)* $4\frac{5}{8}$

38. Geometry What is the circumference of a circle that has a diameter of 13.4 centimeters? *(Lesson 7-4)* **42.1 cm**

interNET CONNECTION
For the latest agricultural statistics, visit: www.glencoe.com/sec/math/mac/mathnet

39. Agriculture Refer to the graph. *(Lesson 3-6)*
   a. How many more pounds of potatoes were harvested in Washington than in Colorado and North Dakota? **6.6 billion lb**
   b. Find the total amount of potatoes harvested in these eight states. **34.1 billion lb**

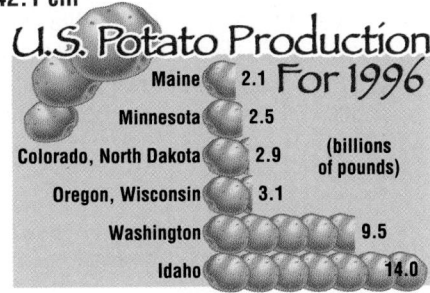

U.S. Potato Production For 1996

Maine	2.1
Minnesota	2.5
Colorado, North Dakota	2.9	(billions of pounds)
Oregon, Wisconsin	3.1
Washington	9.5
Idaho	14.0

Source: U.S. Agriculture Department

40. Standardized Test Practice Find the next figure in the pattern. *(Lesson 1-2)* **C**

A   B   C   D

For **Extra Practice**, see page 578.

Lesson 8-1 Ratios and Rates **315**

4 ASSESS

Closing Activity
Writing Have students explain in writing how a rate is different from a ratio in lowest terms.

Practice Masters, p. 57

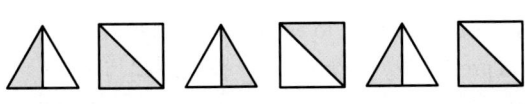

Practice

Ratios and Rates

Write each ratio in three different ways.
1. 11 out of 32 students have blue eyes. **11 to 32; 11: 32; $\frac{11}{32}$**
2. 4 out of 7 vacation days were sunny. **4 to 7; 4:7; $\frac{4}{7}$**
3. 19 out of 20 thank-you notes were written. **19 to 20; 19: 20; $\frac{19}{20}$**
4. 8 out of 45 jelly beans are black. **8 to 45; 8:45; $\frac{8}{45}$**

Express each ratio in simplest form.
5. read 75 pages out of 90 $\frac{5}{6}$
6. 8 blueberry muffins in $1\frac{1}{2}$ dozen muffins $\frac{4}{9}$
7. 4 aces in a deck of 52 playing cards $\frac{1}{13}$
8. 36 black keys out of 88 piano keys $\frac{9}{22}$
9. 9 caramels in a box of 48 chocolates $\frac{3}{16}$
10. score 24 points out of 72 points in basketball $\frac{1}{3}$
11. 325 full-sized cars out of 500 cars $\frac{13}{20}$
12. 42 pairs of hi-tops out of 56 pairs of sneakers $\frac{3}{4}$
13. 16 male teachers out of 40 teachers $\frac{2}{5}$
14. 35 sopranos in an 84-member chorus $\frac{5}{12}$
15. exercise 45 out of 63 minutes $\frac{5}{7}$
16. 18 goldfish in a tank of 48 fish $\frac{3}{8}$

Express each ratio as a rate.
17. 105 words typed in 3 minutes **35 words per minute**
18. 10 pounds lost in 4 weeks **2.5 pounds per week**
19. 2,800 miles driven in 7 days **400 miles per day**
20. $38 for 2 sweaters **$19 per sweater**
21. $375 saved in 5 years **$75 per year**
22. 72 hits in 24 baseball games **3 hits per game**

Using the letters of the phrase "STATE OF MASSACHUSETTS," write the ratios comparing the numbers of letters.
23. A to T $\frac{3}{4}$
24. M to E $\frac{1}{2}$
25. E to S $\frac{2}{5}$
26. F to A $\frac{1}{3}$
27. vowels to consonants $\frac{7}{13}$
28. T to S $\frac{4}{5}$
29. H to T $\frac{1}{4}$
30. E to A $\frac{2}{3}$

© Glencoe/McGraw-Hill   T 57   *Mathematics: Applications and Connections, Course 1*

Extending the Lesson

Enrichment Masters, p. 57

Enrichment

Ratios and Rectangles
1. Use a centimeter ruler to measure the width and the length of each rectangle. Then express the ratio of the width to the length as a fraction in simplest form.

C: width = 4 cm
length = 6 cm
ratio = $\frac{2}{3}$

A: width = 2 cm

B: width = 3 cm
length = 5 cm

Activity Food coloring, water, cotton swabs, paper, paper cups, and droppers or measuring spoons will be needed. Using these materials, have students develop ratios of food coloring and water for creating certain colors. Ask them to make a chart that shows their colors and the required ratios.

Lesson 8-1 **315**

GET READY

Objective Students explore ratios and probability.

Optional Resources

Hands-On Lab Masters
• spinners, p. 20
• worksheet, p. 55

Overhead Manipulative Resources
• spinners

Manipulative Kit
• spinners

MANAGEMENT TIPS

Recommended Time
30 minutes

Getting Started Have students read the introduction to the lab. Display a spinner divided into 4 sections. Ask students what the possibilities are for labeling sections as "make" or "miss." Ask them whether the order of the sections would make any difference in the results of spinning.

Activities 1 and 2 use spinners to generate experimental data for 100 free throws. In both activities, the resulting number of baskets is written as a fraction over 100 and as a decimal. Point out to students that if a player makes 1 out of every 2 free throws, half of the throws are good. Thus, the probability is $\frac{1}{2}$.

ASSESS

Have students complete Exercises 1–4. Make sure students realize that the fraction is formed as the number of "makes" over the number of tries or spins.

Use Exercise 5 to check that students set up ratios correctly and can express the probability as a decimal.

HANDS-ON LAB

COOPERATIVE LEARNING

8-1B Ratios and Probability

A Follow-Up of Lesson 8-1

◈ spinner

Suppose the probability that a basketball player makes a basket from the free throw line is 0.75. Since the decimal 0.75 means seventy-five hundredths, the probability can also be expressed as the ratio $\frac{75}{100}$. This means that the player makes a free throw 75 out of 100 times. In this lab, you will explore ratios and probability. *You can refer to Lesson 5-4B to review experimental probability.*

TRY THIS

Work with a partner.

❶
• Make a spinner with four equal sections.
• Mark one section of the spinner "make" and the other sections "miss". Each section represents the player making or missing a basket.
• Spin the spinner 100 times. Record the number of baskets made as the ratio $\frac{baskets\ made}{100}$. Write the ratio as a decimal. What is the probability that the player makes a basket from the free throw line?

❷
• Mark three sections of the spinner "make" and one section "miss". Again, each section represents the player making or missing a basket.
• Spin the spinner 100 times. Record the number of baskets made as the ratio $\frac{baskets\ made}{100}$. Write the ratio as a decimal. What is the probability that the player makes a basket from the free throw line?

ON YOUR OWN

1. Write a ratio that compares the area of each region marked "make" to the total area of the circle for each spinner. $\frac{1}{4}$; $\frac{3}{4}$

2. What is the probability of making a basket on each spinner? Express the probability as a decimal. **0.25; 0.75**

3. Compare your results from the activity to each probability in Exercise 2. **See margin.**

4. Describe how ratio and probability are related. **See margin.**

5. *Look Back* A player makes a basket every 50 out of 80 times. What is the probability that he will make a basket on his next attempt? Express the probability as a decimal. **0.625**

316 **Chapter 8** Exploring Ratio, Proportion, and Percent

Additional Answers

3. Sample answer: The results are about the same.

4. Sample answer: Probability is the ratio of the number of times an event occurs to the total number of possible outcomes.

Have students write a paragraph about why their results with the spinners might not be exactly the same as the expected probabilities.

Solving Proportions

Have you ever played dominoes? In the standard set of dominoes, 7 out of 28 tiles, or one-fourth of the tiles, are doubles.

The ratios $\frac{7}{28}$ and $\frac{1}{4}$ are equivalent. That is, $\frac{7}{28} = \frac{1}{4}$. The equation $\frac{7}{28} = \frac{1}{4}$ is an example of a **proportion**.

| **Proportion** | **Words:** | A proportion is an equation that shows that two ratios are equivalent. |
| | **Symbols:** | $\frac{a}{b} = \frac{c}{d}, b \neq 0, d \neq 0$ |

In the following Mini-Lab, you will use pattern blocks to explore ratios that are equivalent and ratios that are not equivalent.

HANDS-ON MINI-LAB

Work with a partner.

 pattern blocks

Try This

Use the triangle pattern block as the unit of measure.

1. Build a shape that has a ratio equivalent to each ratio shown.

a.
   See margin.

b.
   See margin.

2. Build a shape that has a ratio *not* equivalent to each ratio shown.

a.
   See students' work.

b.
   See students' work.

Talk About It

3. How did you find the equivalent ratios?

4. How did you know when two ratios were not equivalent?

3. Sample answer: write a proportion.

4. Sample answer: If you first make the ratios equivalent, then add or subtract a triangle to one numerator or denominator, the resulting ratios will not be equivalent

Additional Answers for the Mini-Lab

1a.

1b.

MathPASS CD-ROM

This CD-ROM offers a complete, self-paced mathematics curriculum. Each lesson includes a pretest, tutorial, guided practice, and posttest. MathPASS Lesson 29 is correlated to this Student Edition lesson.
For Windows & Macintosh

Recommended Pacing	
Standard	Day 6 of 14
Honors	Day 6 of 13
Block	Day 3 of 7

1 FOCUS

Getting Started Ask students to discuss how a drawing or diagram can help to solve a problem. Ask for eight volunteers to perform handshakes in the manner described at the beginning of the lab. As they do so, ask another student to keep a record of the handshakes on the chalkboard.

2 TEACH

Teaching Tip Some students may be hesitant to draw diagrams. Encourage them to draw diagrams to help them understand and picture the information before attempting to solve the problem.

In-Class Example

The stops on Toya, Amy, and Zoe's subway line are 1st St., 2nd St., and so on. Amy gets off 1 stop before Toya. Zoe gets off 6 stops after Amy. If Toya gets off on 3rd St., what are Amy's and Zoe's stops? **2nd St., 8th St.**

Additional Answers

1.

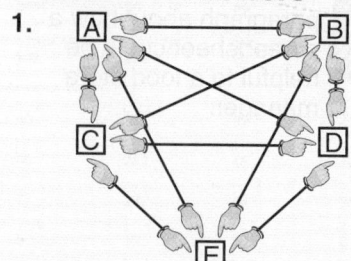

2. The number of handshakes increases by 2, 3, 4, and so on.

⟨THINKING⟩ LAB — PROBLEM SOLVING

8-3A Draw a Diagram

A Preview of Lesson 8-3

Alison and Ben are the first guests to arrive at Cindy's party. They are discussing how many handshakes there will be if every guest at the party shakes hands with everyone else once. Let's listen in!

If we shake hands, then there would be one handshake. **Alison**

If Cindy joined us, then she would shake hands with you and me. That's two, a total of three.

Let's draw a diagram to picture the situation.

Ben

 2 guests 1 handshake · 3 guests 3 handshakes 4 guests 6 handshakes

For five people, we can add the handshakes for the fifth person. Add four more handshakes. A total of 10!

Wow! We can use this method to find the number of handshakes for any number of people.

THINK ABOUT IT

Work with a partner. 1–2. See margin.

1. **Draw a diagram** to illustrate the number of handshakes with five guests.

2. **Describe** the pattern that exists between the number of guests and the number of handshakes.

3. **Extend** the pattern to predict how many handshakes there will be with six guests. **15 handshakes**

4. **Apply** the **draw a diagram** strategy to solve the following problem.

   Kayla lives in Littleton and works in Parker. There is no direct route from Littleton to Parker, so Kayla goes through either Stoney Creek or Castle Rock. There is one road between Stoney Creek and Castle Rock. How many different ways can Kayla drive to work? **4 ways**

322 Chapter 8 Exploring Ratio, Proportion, and Percent

■ Reteaching the Lesson ■

Activity Have students work with a partner to draw a diagram that helps find the solution to the following problem. *If tiles measuring 2 feet by 2 feet are used to cover a 16 foot by 12 foot floor, how many tiles are needed?* **48**

9. *History* During World War II, America's main strategic weapon was the B-17 Flying Fortress. This aircraft has a length of about 80 feet and a wingspan of about 104 feet. If a scale model of the airplane is built with a wingspan of 26 feet, what will be its length? **20 feet**

10. *School* An original 5-inch by 8-inch photograph must be reduced to $1\frac{1}{4}$ by 2 inches to fit in the school yearbook. What is the scale of the reduced photograph to the original in simplest form? **1 in. = 4 in.**

11a. length: 5.18 m; width: 2.16 m; height: 1.58 m

11b. length: 4.93 m; width: 1.92 m; height: 1.47 m

11. *Working on the* **CHAPTER Project** Refer to the drawings on page 309.
   a. The drawing of stock car 88 has a scale of 1 cm = 144 cm. Find the length, width, and height of the actual stock car 88 race car.
   b. The drawing of stock car 16 has a scale of 1 cm = 64 cm. Find the length, width, and height of the actual stock car 16 race car.
   c. For each of the three toys that you selected, write a scale that can be used to compare the size of the toy to the actual size of the object. **See students' work.**

For **Extra Practice,** see page 579.

12. *Critical Thinking* If you were asked to make a scale drawing of the Statue of Liberty, which scale would you use: 1 cm = 1 m or 1 cm = 1 mm? Explain. **1 cm = 1 m; The other scale would make the statue smaller than the drawing.**

Mixed Review 13. Solve $\frac{7.3}{h} = \frac{14.6}{10.8}$. *(Lesson 8-2)* **5.4**

14. *Standardized Test Practice* Valerie purchased $40.06 worth of groceries. She gives the cashier a $50 bill. How much change should she receive? *(Lesson 3-6)* **C**

   A $9.84   **B** $9.34   **C** $9.94   **D** $10.84   **E** Not Here

---

CHAPTER 8

Mid-Chapter Self Test

Write each ratio in three different ways. *(Lesson 8-1)* **1–2. See margin.**

1. 11 rulers out of 19 are blue.
2. 7 students out of 39 are boys.

Express each ratio as a fraction in simplest form. *(Lesson 8-1)*

3. 12 parrots out of 28 birds $\frac{3}{7}$
4. 15 green apples out of 48 apples $\frac{5}{16}$

Express each ratio as a rate. *(Lesson 8-1)*

5. 270 miles in 4.5 hours **60 mph**
6. 8 kiwis for $1.00 **12.5 cents per kiwi**

Solve each proportion. *(Lesson 8-2)*

7. $\frac{8}{9} = \frac{w}{108}$ **96**
8. $\frac{m}{17} = \frac{35}{42.5}$ **14**
9. $\frac{1.3}{h} = \frac{5.2}{11.2}$ **2.8**

10. *Geography* On a map, the distance between the towns of Gorden and Florin measures $\frac{3}{4}$ inch. Suppose the map has a scale of $\frac{1}{4}$ inch = 10 miles. What is the actual distance between the two towns? *(Lesson 8-3)* **30 miles**

Extending the Lesson

Enrichment Masters, p. 59

8-3 Enrichment

Planning a Room

Before moving furniture into a room, many people plan an arrangement by making a scale drawing. This makes it possible to find the best arrangement for the room without actually moving heavy furniture.

For each piece of furniture, actual measurements are given. Compute scale measurements using the scale $\frac{1}{2}$ inch = 1 foot.

1. bed: $6\frac{1}{2}$ feet long, 3 feet wide $3\frac{1}{4}$ **inches long, $1\frac{1}{2}$ inches wide**
2. bedside table: $1\frac{1}{2}$ feet long, $1\frac{1}{2}$ feet wide $\frac{3}{4}$ **inch long, $\frac{3}{4}$ inch wide**
3. bookcase: $3\frac{1}{2}$ feet long, 1 foot wide $1\frac{3}{4}$ **inches long, $\frac{1}{2}$ inch wide**

Activity Have students work in pairs to draw a scale drawing of the school playground, the basketball court, or the athletic field. They may wish to use centimeter grid paper.

---

4 ASSESS

Closing Activity

Speaking Tell students that the wingspan of a Boeing 747-400 is 213 feet. Ask: *How long would the wingspan be in a scale drawing if the scale were 1 inch = 71 feet?* **3 in.**

Mid-Chapter Self Test

The Mid-Chapter Self Test reviews concepts in Lessons 8-1 through 8-3. Lesson references are given so students can review concepts not yet mastered.

Additional Answers for the Self Test

1–2. Sample answers are given.

1. 11 to 19, $\frac{11}{19}$, 11:19
2. 7 out of 39, 7:39, $\frac{7}{39}$

Practice Masters, p. 59

Motivating Students

Students learned about toy scale models in the Chapter Project on page 309. Students may be interested in toymaking or a related career. Professional doll makers strive for precision in proportions and carefully crafted details. To begin a discussion of toy making, ask students these questions.

- Have you ever owned a homemade toy? What made it different from a manufactured toy? **Answers will vary.**
- What should a toy maker consider when designing a new toy? **Sample answer: the age for which the toy is intended, the educational value of the toy, safety**

Making the Math Connection

To make dolls or other toys, a craftsperson needs a thorough knowledge of scale, the ability to measure accurately and perform calculations involving measurements, and an understanding of geometric principles such as perimeter, area, and volume.

Working on *Your Turn*

Have students prepare questions in advance and interview craftspeople in groups. Then have groups write a paragraph summarizing the information they gathered during the interview.

An additional School to Career activity is available on page 8 of the School to Career Masters.

SCHOOL to CAREER

Arts and Crafts

Carol Larsen
DOLL MAKER

Carol Larsen, mother of nine children, has turned her hobby of doll collecting into a career. In addition to designing and making her own dolls, she also sews the clothing for the dolls, and teaches classes on doll making.

There are various types of crafts in the arts and crafts industry. The skills that you will need depend on the type of craft that you would like to make. To design and make dolls or any other toys, you need to have a good understanding of mathematics. Having a good knowledge of proportions and scale drawings will enable you to create finished products that have the correct dimensions.

For more information:
Toy Manufacturers of
  America, Inc.
200 5th Avenue, Suite 740
New York, NY 10010

inter NET
CONNECTION
www.glencoe.com/sec/math/mac/mathnet

Someday, I'd like to design and create toys.

Your Turn
Interview a person in your community that is involved in the arts and crafts industry. Find out how they began their career and how they use mathematics when making their craft.

328 Chapter 8 Exploring Ratio, Proportion, and Percent

More About Carol Larsen

- Carol Larsen lives on a farm in west central Iowa. She has been sewing since she was a young girl, but she did not take up doll making until her own children were grown.

- Ms. Larsen makes porcelain dolls by pouring the liquid porcelain into molds and firing it in a kiln. Then she paints the faces and sews each doll a special outfit. She enjoys designing dolls for meaningful occasions and often dresses her dolls in wedding or christening gowns.

COOPERATIVE LEARNING

8-4A Modeling Percents

A Preview of Lesson 8-4

 grid paper

 colored pencils

You know that a 10 × 10 grid can be used to represent hundredths. Since the word *percent* means *out of one hundred,* you can also use a 10 × 10 grid to model percents.

TRY THIS

Work with a partner.

❶ Model 25%.

Shade 25 of the 100 squares.

25% means "25 out of 100". By shading 25 out of 100 squares, you can show 25%. What decimal does the model represent?

❷ Shade two fifths of the 10 × 10 grid. What percent have you modeled?

Separate the model into fifths. Shade two of the fifths.

There are 40 squares shaded, so 40% is modeled. Two fifths is equivalent to 40%.

ON YOUR OWN

1. Draw five 10 × 10 squares on a sheet of grid paper. Shade a 10 × 10 grid to represent each percent. **1–3. See Answer Appendix.**

   a. 1%   **b.** 75%   **c.** 30%   **d.** 100%   **e.** 60%

2. Draw five more 10 × 10 squares on another sheet of grid paper. Shade a 10 × 10 grid to represent each fraction or number.

   a. 0.3   **b.** $\frac{1}{100}$ **c.** 0.75   **d.** 1   **e.** $\frac{3}{5}$

3. How do the two sets of shaded 10 × 10 grids compare?

4. *Look Ahead* Express 36% as a fraction in simplest form. Use a model if necessary. $\frac{9}{25}$

Have students write a paragraph explaining how $\frac{3}{4}$ and 75% are related. Have them include a grid to model this percent and fraction.

GET READY

Objective Students illustrate the meaning of percent using models.

Optional Resources
Hands-On Lab Masters
• grid paper, p. 11
• worksheet, p. 56
Overhead Manipulative Resources
• decimal models
• grid paper

MANAGEMENT TIPS

Recommended Time
30 minutes

Getting Started Review using 10 × 10 grids to write decimals as fractions. For example, ask students to write 0.83 as a fraction by showing it first on a grid.

Activity 1 produces a model for 25% by shading 25 out of 100 squares on a 10 × 10 grid. What fraction does the model represent? $\frac{1}{4}$

Activity 2 requires students to divide the 10 × 10 grid into 5 sections, shade 2 sections, and then recognize that 40 out of 100 squares have been shaded. Follow up by asking how students would model $\frac{1}{25}$.

ASSESS

Have students complete Exercises 1–3. Watch for students who have difficulty comparing the percents in Exercise 1 with the numbers in Exercise 2. Remind students what *percent* means.

Use Exercise 4 to determine whether students comprehend the concept of percent.

Instructional Resources

- *Study Guide Masters*, p. 60
- *Practice Masters*, p. 60
- *Enrichment Masters*, p. 60
- Transparencies 8-4, A and B
- *Assessment and Evaluation Masters*, pp. 210, 211

 CD-ROM Program
- Resource Lesson 8-4
- Extended Activity 8-4

Recommended Pacing	
Standard	Days 8 & 9 of 14
Honors	Day 8 of 13
Block	Day 5 of 7

1 FOCUS

5-Minute Check
(Lesson 8-3)

The floor plan shown has a scale of 1 cm = 2 m. Compute the actual measurement of each room.

	Drawing (cm)		Actual (m)	
	ℓ	w	ℓ	w
Foyer	3	2	6	4
Office A	4	2	8	4
Office B	2	2	4	4
Office C	2	2	4	4
Bathroom	2	1	4	2

 The 5-Minute Check is also available on **Transparency 8-4A** for this lesson.

What you'll learn

You'll learn to express percents as fractions and vice versa.

When am I ever going to use this?

Knowing how to express a number in a different form can help you interpret a monthly budget.

Word Wise

percent

> **Study Hint**
> Reading Math The symbol % means percent.

Did you know that the word pasta is an Italian term meaning dough? Pasta comes in more than 100 shapes and sizes. What is your favorite type of pasta: spaghetti, ravioli, vermicelli, or possibly gnocchi? According to the results of a survey, 10% of people eat lasagna at least once every two weeks.

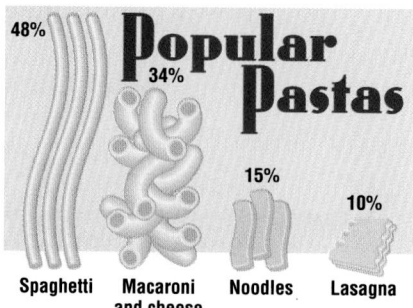

Popular Pastas

48% Spaghetti · 34% Macaroni and cheese · 15% Noodles · 10% Lasagna

Source: National Pasta Association

A **percent** is a ratio that compares a number to 100. All of the percents in the graph can be expressed as fractions. To express a percent as a fraction, follow these steps.
- Express the percent as a fraction with a denominator of 100.
- Simplify.

> **Examples**

Express each percent as a fraction in simplest form.

1 28%

28% means "28 out of 100."

$28\% = \dfrac{28}{100}$ *Express the percent as a fraction with a denominator of 100.*

$= \dfrac{\overset{7}{\cancel{28}}}{\underset{25}{\cancel{100}}}$ *Simplify. Divide the numerator and the denominator by 4, the GCF of 28 and 100.*

$= \dfrac{7}{25}$

28%

2 118%

118% means "118 out of 100."

$118\% = \dfrac{118}{100}$ *Express the percent as a fraction with a denominator of 100.*

$= 1\dfrac{18}{100}$ or $1\dfrac{9}{50}$ *Simplify.*

118%

Classroom Vignette

"I have groups of students count, by color, the number of M&Ms in a bag. They write fractions for each color and then change those fractions to percents. We apply the percents to making circle graphs and display the results around the room. It's a big and fun project!"

Mary Schirm

Mary Schirm, Teacher
Summerour Middle School
Norcross, GA

❸ **Health** Refer to the graph. What fraction of teen-age boys always or often use sunscreen before going out into the sun?

From the graph, you can see that 30% of teen-age boys use sunscreen before going into the sun.

How regularly teenagers use sunscreen

36% 21% 34% 33% 30% 46%

Boys Girls | Boys Girls | Boys Girls
Rarely/never | **Sometimes** | **Always/often**

Source: Sovereign Research for Seventeen, Nivea, and the American Academy of Dermatology

$$30\% = \frac{30}{100}$$

$$= \frac{3}{10}$$

So, $\frac{3}{10}$ of teen-age boys always or often use sunscreen.

You can also express fractions as percents.

 HANDS-ON **MINI-LAB**

Work in groups of four. paper ▽ wastebasket

Try This
- Stand behind a line 15 feet from a wastebasket.
- Have each person throw a wadded paper ball into the basket. Each person will have five tries.
- Have one group member record a ratio for the total number of baskets made out of the total number of tries.
- Calculate the percent of baskets made for the group.

Talk About It **2. See students' work.**
1. How did you find the percent? **See margin.**
2. How does your group's percent compare to the other groups?

To express a fraction as a percent, write a proportion and solve it.

Examples

❹ Express $\frac{1}{5}$ as a percent.

$$\frac{1}{5} = \frac{n}{100} \quad \textit{Set up a proportion.}$$
$$1 \times 100 = 5 \times n \quad \textit{Find the cross}$$
$$100 = 5n \qquad \textit{products.}$$
$$100 \div 5 = 5n \div 5 \quad \textit{Divide.}$$
$$20 = n$$

So, $\frac{1}{5}$ is equivalent to 20%.

❺ Express $\frac{9}{4}$ as a percent.

$$\frac{9}{4} = \frac{c}{100}$$
$$9 \times 100 = 4 \times c$$
$$900 = 4c$$
$$900 \div 4 = 4c \div 4$$
$$225 = c$$

So, $\frac{9}{4}$ is equivalent to 225%.

Study Hint

Mental Math When changing $\frac{1}{5}$ to a percent, think of finding $\frac{1}{5}$ of 100 parts. $\frac{1}{5} = 20\%$.

Lesson 8-4 Percents and Fractions **331**

Additional Answer for the Mini-Lab
1. number of shots made ÷ number of tries × 100

🪩 **MathPASS CD-ROM**

This CD-ROM offers a complete, self-paced mathematics curriculum. Each lesson includes a pretest, tutorial, guided practice, and posttest. MathPASS Lesson 30 is correlated to this Student Edition lesson.
For Windows & Macintosh

Motivating the Lesson
Communication Have students work in small groups. Give each group $100 in play money to budget on entertainment, food, savings, and so on. Ask students how they could use fractions and percents to describe their budgets.

2 TEACH

Transparency 8-4B contains a teaching aid for this lesson.

In-Class Examples
Express each percent as a fraction in simplest form.

For Example 1
40% $\frac{2}{5}$

For Example 2
125% $\frac{5}{4}$

For Example 3
Refer to the graph on page 331. What fraction of teenage girls always or often uses sunscreen before going out into the sun?
$\frac{23}{50}$

Teaching Tip Before Example 2, tell students that percents can be greater than 100%.

Using the Mini-Lab You may wish to have the groups complete this activity simultaneously by having each group use a different wastebasket.

In-Class Examples
Express each fraction as a percent.

For Example 4
$\frac{3}{10}$ 30%

For Example 5
$\frac{7}{2}$ 350%

Check for Understanding

If students need additional practice or instruction after completing Exercises 1–10, one of these options may be helpful.
- Extra Practice, see p. 579
- Reteaching Activity
- *Study Guide Masters*, p. 60
- *Practice Masters*, p. 60

Assignment Guide

Core: 11–35 odd, 38–43
Enriched: 12–34 even, 35, 36, 38–43

Study Guide Masters, p. 60

8-4 Study Guide

Percents and Fractions

A **percent** is a ratio that compares a number to 100.
To express a percent as a fraction, write it as a fraction with a denominator of 100 and then simplify.

Example 1 $48\% = \frac{48}{100}$
$= \frac{12}{25}$ *Divide the numerator and denominator by 4.*

To express a fraction as a percent, first set up a proportion. Then solve the proportion using cross products.

Example 2 Express $\frac{13}{20}$ as a percent.
$\frac{13}{20} = \frac{k}{100}$ *Set up a proportion.*
$13 \times 100 = 20 \times k$ *Find the cross products.*
$1,300 = 20k$
$1,300 \div 20 = 20k \div 20$ *Divide each side by 20.*
$65 = k$
$\frac{13}{20} = \frac{65}{100}$ or 65%

Express each percent as a fraction in simplest form.

1. 60% $\frac{3}{5}$ 2. 75% $\frac{3}{4}$ 3. 50% $\frac{1}{2}$ 4. 99% $\frac{99}{100}$
5. 12% $\frac{3}{25}$ 6. 45% $\frac{9}{20}$ 7. 54% $\frac{27}{50}$ 8. 5% $\frac{1}{20}$

Express each shaded section as a fraction and as a percent.

9. $\frac{2}{5}$, 40% 10. $\frac{3}{4}$, 75% 11. $\frac{3}{10}$, 30%

Express each fraction as a percent.

12. $\frac{17}{100}$ 17% 13. $\frac{4}{5}$ 80% 14. $\frac{1}{4}$ 25% 15. $\frac{8}{20}$ 40%
16. $\frac{1}{50}$ 2% 17. $\frac{7}{10}$ 70% 18. $\frac{5}{24}$ 24% 19. $\frac{1}{10}$ 10%

© Glencoe/McGraw-Hill   T60   Mathematics: Applications and Connections, Course 1

Communicating Mathematics

Read and study the lesson to answer each question.

1. *Identify* the percent that is represented by each model shown.

a. 25%
b. 47%
c. 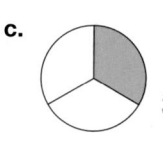 $33\frac{1}{3}\%$
d. 80%
e. 50%
f. $66\frac{2}{3}\%$

2. *Tell* what fraction is equivalent to 75%. $\frac{3}{4}$

HANDS-ON MATH

3. Toss a coin 50 times. Record the number of times the coin shows heads. Then calculate the percent that represents the number of times the coin showed heads. **See students' work.**

Guided Practice

Express each percent as a fraction in simplest form.

4. 2% $\frac{1}{50}$ 5. 55% $\frac{11}{20}$ 6. 120% $1\frac{1}{5}$

Express each fraction as a percent.

7. $\frac{34}{100}$ 34%   8. $\frac{13}{20}$ 65%   9. $\frac{5}{4}$ 125%

10. *Technology* According to a survey, 36% of consumers prefer to buy a personal computer at an electronics store. What fraction of consumers is this? $\frac{9}{25}$

EXERCISES

Practice

11. $\frac{7}{50}$ 12. $\frac{9}{10}$
13. $\frac{1}{100}$ 14. $\frac{13}{20}$
15. $1\frac{3}{10}$ 16. $\frac{24}{25}$
17. $1\frac{1}{20}$ 18. $\frac{33}{50}$
19. $\frac{17}{100}$ 20. $1\frac{3}{25}$

Express each percent as a fraction in simplest form.

11. 14%   12. 90%   13. 1%   14. 65%   15. 130%
16. 96%   17. 105%   18. 66%   19. 17%   20. 112%

Use a 10 × 10 grid to shade the amount stated in each fraction. Then express each fraction as a percent. 21–24. For grids, see Answer Appendix.

21. $\frac{4}{5}$ 80%   22. $\frac{4}{10}$ 40%   23. $\frac{9}{20}$ 45%   24. $\frac{13}{50}$ 26%

Express each fraction as a percent.

25. $\frac{63}{100}$ 63%   26. $\frac{1}{20}$ 5%   27. $\frac{3}{2}$ 150%   28. $\frac{12}{25}$ 48%

29. $\frac{37}{50}$ 74%   30. $\frac{17}{20}$ 85%   31. $\frac{19}{25}$ 76%   32. $\frac{17}{10}$ 170%

33. How is forty-five hundredths written as a percent? 45%

34. Express eighty-five percent as a fraction in simplest form. $\frac{17}{20}$

Reteaching the Lesson

Activity Have students separate into groups according to the months in which they were born. Then have each group figure out what percent of the class their group represents. Have students express their results in both fraction and percent form.

Error Analysis

Watch for students who are confused by percents greater than 100.
Prevent by reviewing the steps in changing improper fractions to mixed numbers and vice versa.

35. *Travel* The graph shows why RV owners like to travel in an RV.

a. What percent of those surveyed believe that traveling in a recreational vehicle is the best way to see the United States? **48%**

b. What percent of those surveyed have other reasons why they like to travel in an RV? **9%**

Traveling in an RV

Best way to see the USA	12/25
Cost-efficient travel	7/25
Spend time with family/friends	3/20
Other	9/100

Source: Allstate Motor Club Survey of 400 RV owners

36. *Money Matters* The circle graph shows the monthly budget for the Balint family.

36a. $\frac{7}{20}$ 36b. $\frac{7}{25}$

a. What fraction, in simplest form, represents the portion of the family budget that is spent on rent?

b. What fraction, in simplest form, represents the portion of the family budget that is spent on food and utilities?

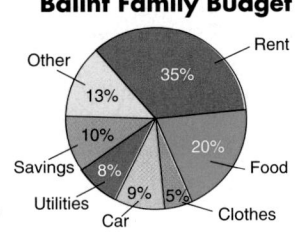

Balint Family Budget

Other 13%, Rent 35%, Food 20%, Clothes 5%, Car 9%, Utilities 8%, Savings 10%

37. *Working on the* **CHAPTER Project** Refer to Exercise 35 on page 315.

37a. $\frac{1}{144}$, 0.01, 1%

37b. $\frac{1}{64}$, 0.02, 2%

37c. See students' work.

a. Express the ratio in part a as a fraction, decimal, and as a percent.

b. Express the ratio in part b as a fraction, decimal, and as a percent.

c. Express each ratio in part c as a fraction, decimal, and as a percent.

38. *Critical Thinking* A woman made a will leaving $\frac{1}{2}$ of her fortune to her sister, $\frac{1}{3}$ to her brother, $\frac{1}{7}$ to her nephew, and the remainder to her cat. What percent of the woman's fortune was left to the cat? Round to the nearest whole percent. **about 2%**

Mixed Review

39. *Geography* A map has a scale of 1 inch = 20 miles. The distance from Hartville to Dixon is $2\frac{3}{4}$ inches. What is the actual distance between these two cities? *(Lesson 8-3)* **55 miles**

40. *Measurement* Painters used 170 gallons of white topcoat to paint the famous Hollywood sign. How many quarts are in 170 gallons? *(Lesson 7-7)* **680 quarts**

41. Find $\frac{3}{8} + \frac{7}{8}$. *(Lesson 6-3)* $1\frac{1}{4}$

42. **Standardized Test Practice** What is the perimeter of the figure? *(Lesson 4-4)* **B**

A 74.3 m
B 73.2 m
C 72.2 m
D 75.3 m

21.4 m, 15.6 m, 12.5 m, 23.7 m

For **Extra Practice**, see page 579.

43. *Algebra* Evaluate $gh + j$ if $g = 4$, $h = 7$, and $j = 2$. *(Lesson 1-5)* **30**

Lesson 8-4 Percents and Fractions **333**

Extending the Lesson

Enrichment Masters, p. 60

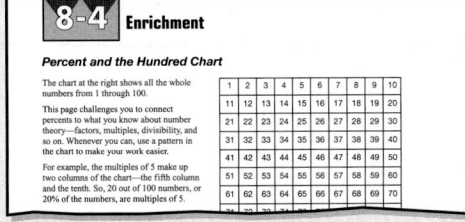

8-4 Enrichment

Percent and the Hundred Chart

The chart at the right shows all the whole numbers from 1 through 100.

This page challenges you to connect percents to what you know about number theory—factors, multiples, divisibility, and so on. Whenever you can, use a pattern in the chart to make your work easier.

For example, the multiples of 5 make up two columns of the chart—the fifth column and the tenth. So, 20 out of 100 numbers, or 20% of the numbers, are multiples of 5.

1	2	3	4	5	6	7	8	9	10
11	12	13	14	15	16	17	18	19	20
21	22	23	24	25	26	27	28	29	30
31	32	33	34	35	36	37	38	39	40
41	42	43	44	45	46	47	48	49	50
51	52	53	54	55	56	57	58	59	60
61	62	63	64	65	66	67	68	69	70

Activity Have students use spreadsheet software to create a bar graph. Ask them to use the graph to create problems about writing percents as fractions. Then have them display the graph and the problems on the bulletin board for others to solve.

CHAPTER Project

Exercise 37 asks students to advance to the next stage of work on the Chapter Project. You may wish to have students work in pairs to express the ratios as fractions, decimals, and percents.

4 ASSESS

Closing Activity

Act It Out Have students work in groups to determine what fraction and percent of their group is left-handed.

Chapter 8, Quiz B (Lessons 8-3 and 8-4) is available in the *Assessment and Evaluation Master,* p. 211.

Mid-Chapter Test (Lessons 8-1 through 8-4) is available in the *Assessment and Evaluation Masters,* p. 210.

Practice Masters, p. 60

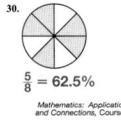

8-4 Practice

Name _____ Date _____

Percents and Fractions

Express each percent as a fraction in simplest form.

1. 24% $\frac{6}{25}$ 2. 98% $\frac{49}{50}$ 3. 35% $\frac{7}{20}$ 4. 7% $\frac{7}{100}$

5. 120% $\frac{6}{5}$ 6. 54% $\frac{27}{50}$ 7. 76% $\frac{19}{25}$ 8. 5% $\frac{1}{20}$

9. 82% $\frac{41}{50}$ 10. 130% $\frac{13}{10}$ 11. 19% $\frac{19}{100}$ 12. 175% $\frac{7}{4}$

Use a 10 × 10 grid to shade the amount stated in each fraction. Then express each fraction as a percent.

13. $\frac{1}{10}$ 10% 14. $\frac{1}{20}$ 5% 15. $\frac{1}{50}$ 2%

Express each fraction as a percent.

16. $\frac{47}{100}$ 47% 17. $\frac{8}{25}$ 32% 18. $\frac{9}{10}$ 90% 19. $\frac{13}{50}$ 26%

20. $\frac{11}{20}$ 55% 21. $\frac{7}{5}$ 140% 22. $\frac{3}{100}$ 3% 23. $\frac{21}{25}$ 84%

24. $\frac{7}{10}$ 70% 25. $\frac{3}{20}$ 15% 26. $\frac{31}{50}$ 62% 27. $\frac{5}{4}$ 125%

Express each shaded area as a fraction and as a percent.

28. $\frac{2}{5}$ = 40% 29. $\frac{4}{4}$ = 100% 30. $\frac{5}{8}$ = 62.5%

© Glencoe/McGraw-Hill   T 60   Mathematics: Applications and Connections, Course 1

Instructional Resources

- *Study Guide Masters*, p. 61
- *Practice Masters*, p. 61
- *Enrichment Masters*, p. 61
- Transparencies 8-5, A and B
- *Science and Math Lab Manual*, pp. 81–84

CD-ROM Program
- Resource Lesson 8-5

Recommended Pacing	
Standard	Day 10 of 14
Honors	Day 9 of 13
Block	Day 5 of 7

1 FOCUS

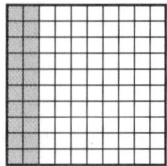

5-Minute Check
(Lesson 8-4)

Express each percent as a fraction in simplest form.

1. 55% $\frac{11}{20}$ 2. 72% $\frac{18}{25}$

3. Use a 10 × 10 grid to shade $\frac{1}{5}$ of the model. Then express the fraction as a percent. **20%**

Express each fraction as a percent.

4. $\frac{3}{5}$ 60%   5. $\frac{24}{21}$ 114%

The 5-Minute Check is also available on **Transparency 8-5A** for this lesson.

Motivating the Lesson

Hands-On Activity Have groups of students divide 100 pennies equally, putting any extra pennies aside. Then have them express the amount they received as a percent and as a decimal of the whole.

What you'll learn
You'll learn to express percents as decimals and vice versa.

When am I ever going to use this?
Knowing how to express a percent as a decimal can help you determine the amount of sales tax paid on a dollar.

Five years after it opened, a theme park became France's top tourist attraction. The graph shows where the 11.7 million visitors came from. What part of the visitors came from Italy? *This problem will be solved in Example 3.*

Theme Park Visitors

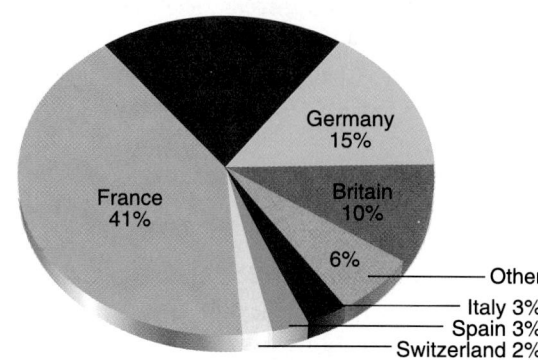

Germany 15%
France 41%
Britain 10%
6%
Other
Italy 3%
Spain 3%
Switzerland 2%

Notice that the sections of the graph are labeled as percents. In Lesson 8-4, you learned how to express percents as fractions. Percents can also be written as decimals. To express a percent as a decimal, follow these steps.

- Rewrite the percent as a fraction with a denominator of 100.
- Express the fraction as a decimal.

Examples

Study Hint

Mental Math To express a percent as a decimal, you can use this shortcut. Move the decimal point two places to the left, which is the same as dividing by 100.

Express each percent as a decimal.

1 65%

$65\% = \frac{65}{100}$ *Rewrite the percent as a fraction with a denominator of 100.*

$= 0.65$ *Express the fraction as a decimal.*

2 0.5%

$0.5\% = \frac{0.5}{100}$ *Rewrite the percent as a fraction with a denominator of 100.*

$= \frac{5}{1,000}$ $\frac{0.5}{100} \times \frac{10}{10} = \frac{5}{1,000}$

$= 0.005$ *Express the fraction as a decimal.*

Classroom Vignette

"After distributing baseball cards, I ask students to find averages and ratios that aren't listed on them and write them as decimals and percents. Students would find slugging and on-base averages for hitters and win and strikeout ratios for pitchers."

Betty Fulton, Teacher
Clearmount Elementary School
North Canton, OH

Example **3**

Example
INTEGRATION

3 **Statistics** Refer to the beginning of the lesson. What part of the visitors came from Italy? Express the answer as a decimal.

From the graph, you can see that 3% of the visitors came from Italy.

$3\% = \dfrac{3}{100}$

$= 0.03$

The graph shows that 0.03 of the visitors came from Italy.

To express a decimal as a percent, follow these steps.

- Express the decimal as a fraction.
- Express the fraction as a percent.

Examples

Express each decimal as a percent.

Study Hint

Mental Math To express a decimal as a percent you can use another shortcut. Move the decimal point two places to the right, which is the same as multiplying by 100.

4 **0.72**

$0.72 = \dfrac{72}{100}$ *Express the decimal as a fraction.*

$= 72\%$ *Express the fraction as a percent.*

5 **0.257**

$0.257 = \dfrac{257}{1,000}$ *Express the decimal as a fraction.*

$= \dfrac{25.7}{100}$ $\dfrac{257 \div 10}{1,000 \div 10} = \dfrac{25.7}{100}$

$= 25.7\%$ *Express the fraction as a percent.*

CHECK FOR UNDERSTANDING

Communicating Mathematics

Read and study the lesson to answer each question. 1–3. See Answer Appendix.

1. **Draw** a model that shows the decimal equivalent of 36%.

2. **Explain** how to express 0.008 as a percent.

3. **You Decide** Kellile says that the decimal 3.78 is less than 100%. Betty says that the decimal is more than 100%. Who is correct? Explain your reasoning.

Guided Practice

Express each percent as a decimal.

4. 46% **0.46**   5. 81% **0.81**   6. 7% **0.07**   7. 0.8% **0.008**

Express each decimal as a percent.

8. 0.52 **52%**   9. 0.9 **90%**   10. 0.175 **17.5%**   11. 0.02 **2%**

12. **Life Science** About 95% of all species of fish have skeletons made of bone. Express 95% as a decimal. **0.95**

Lesson 8-5 Percents and Decimals   **335**

■**Reteaching the Lesson**■

Activity Have students solve this problem. *George Brett was the batting champion in 1980 and again in 1990. His batting average was 39% in 1980 and 32.8% in 1990. How would you express Brett's batting averages in decimals?* **0.390; 0.328**

 MathPASS CD-ROM

This CD-ROM offers a complete, self-paced mathematics curriculum. Each lesson includes a pretest, tutorial, guided practice, and posttest. MathPASS Lesson 31 is correlated to this Student Edition lesson.
For Windows & Macintosh

---

2 TEACH

 Transparency 8-5B contains a teaching aid for this lesson.

Reading Mathematics Reading a fraction or decimal correctly can help students understand place value. Fractions and decimals are read the same way. For example, $19\frac{3}{10}$ and 19.3 are both read as *nineteen and three tenths.*

In-Class Examples

Express each percent as a decimal.

For Example 1
23% **0.23**

For Example 2
0.8% **0.008**

For Example 3
Refer to the graph on page 334. What part of the visitors came from Germany? Express the answer as a decimal. **0.15**

Express each decimal as a percent.

For Example 4
0.64 **64%**

For Example 5
0.519 **51.9%**

Study Guide Masters, p. 61

8-5 **Study Guide**

Name_____ Date_____

Percents and Decimals

To express a percent as a decimal, rewrite the percent as a fraction with a denominator of 100. Then express the fraction as a decimal.

Examples Express each percent as a decimal.

$1\ 29\% = \frac{29}{100}$ $2\ 0.7\% = \frac{0.7}{100}$ $3\ 145\% = \frac{145}{100}$
$= 0.29$ $= \frac{7}{1,000}$ $= 1.45$
$= 0.007$

To express a decimal as a percent, first express the decimal as a fraction with a denominator of 100. Then express the fraction as a percent.

Examples Express each decimal as a percent.

$4\ 0.09 = \frac{9}{100}$ $5\ 0.005 = \frac{5}{1,000}$ $6\ 1.8 = \frac{18}{10}$
$= 9\%$ $= \frac{0.5}{100}$ $= \frac{180}{100}$
$= 0.5\%$ $= 180\%$

Express each percent as a decimal.

1. 97%   2. 6%   3. 15%   4. 0.8%
0.97   **0.06**   **0.15**   **0.008**

5. 362%   6. 62.3%   7. 3.5%   8. 708%
3.62   **0.623**   **0.035**   **7.08**

Express each decimal as a percent.

9. 0.66   10. 0.08   11. 0.75   12. 0.001
66%   **8%**   **75%**   **0.1%**

13. 1.19   14. 0.72   15. 0.136   16. 4.02
119%   **72%**   **13.6%**   **402%**

© Glencoe/McGraw-Hill   T61   *Mathematics: Applications and Connections, Course 1*

Check for Understanding

If students need additional practice or instruction after completing Exercises 1–12, one of these options may be helpful.
- Extra Practice, see p. 579
- Reteaching Activity, see p. 335
- *Study Guide Masters,* p. 61
- *Practice Masters,* p. 61

Assignment Guide

Core: 13–41 odd, 42–47
Enriched: 14–38 even, 40–47

4 ASSESS

Closing Activity

Modeling Ask students to look through magazine ads or newspaper articles to find uses of percents. Have them use 10 × 10 grids to express each percent as a decimal.

Practice Masters, p. 61

EXERCISES

Practice

Express each percent as a decimal.

13. 32% **0.32**	14. 84% **0.84**	15. 1% **0.01**	16. 0.9% **0.009**
17. 6% **0.06**	18. 17% **0.17**	19. 0.3% **0.003**	20. 63% **0.63**
21. 39% **0.39**	22. 3.5% **0.035**	23. 4% **0.04**	24. 26% **0.26**

Express each decimal as a percent.

25. 0.96 **96%**	26. 0.1 **10%**	27. 0.364 **36.4%**	28. 0.27 **27%**
29. 0.716 **71.6%**	30. 0.66 **66%**	31. 0.07 **7%**	32. 0.5 **50%**
33. 0.08 **8%**	34. 0.104 **10.4%**	35. 0.2 **20%**	36. 0.03 **3%**

37. How is eighteen thousandths written as a percent? **1.8%**

38. Write two and four tenths percent as a decimal. **0.024**

39. Express each number as a:
   a. decimal: $\frac{321}{10,000}, \frac{3}{25}, 9\%, 26\frac{1}{2}$ **0.0321, 0.12, 0.09, 26.5**
   b. fraction: 0.07, 1.129, 3%, 47 $\frac{7}{100}, 1\frac{129}{1,000}, \frac{3}{100}, \frac{47}{1}$
   c. percent: 0.04, 0.538, $\frac{12}{20}, \frac{3}{8}$ **4%, 53.8%, 60%, 37.5%**

Applications and Problem Solving

40. *Taxes* In 1997, the residents of the state of Texas paid a 8.25% sales tax on purchases.
   a. Express 8.25% as a decimal. **0.0825**
   b. On each dollar, how much money did Texans pay in sales tax? **8.25 cents**

41. *Media* Refer to the graph.
   a. What percent of those surveyed spend more than an hour reading the Sunday paper? **18%**
   b. What percent of those surveyed do *not* spend more than an hour reading the Sunday paper? **82%**

TIME SPENT READING THE
Sunday Paper 1998

0.46
0.18
0.12
0.24

More than an hour | **26-60 minutes** | **25 minutes or less** | **None**

Source: Impact Resources

42a. 2.34, 23.4%, 20.34%, 0.0234

42b. 40%, 0.6, $\frac{7}{5}$, $2\frac{1}{4}$, 2.75

42. *Critical Thinking* Arrange the following groups of numbers.
   a. from greatest to least: 23.4%, 2.34, 0.0234, 20.34%
   b. from least to greatest: $2\frac{1}{4}$, 0.6, 2.75, 40%, $\frac{7}{5}$

Mixed Review

43. Express 156% as a fraction in simplest form. *(Lesson 8-4)* $1\frac{14}{25}$

44. *Money Matters* Ahmik purchased a package of four mechanical pencils for $6.48. How much does each pencil cost? *(Lesson 8-1)* **$1.62**

45. **Standardized Test Practice** What number is missing from the sequence 14, 56, ? , 896, 3,584? *(Lesson 7-8)* **D**
   A 284   B 194   C 334   D 224

For **Extra Practice,** see page 579.

46. *Measurement* How many inches are in $2\frac{1}{2}$ yards? *(Lesson 5-6)* **90 inches**

47. Round 64.35 ÷ 12 to the nearest tenth. *(Lesson 4-5)* **5.4**

Extending the Lesson

Enrichment Masters, p. 61

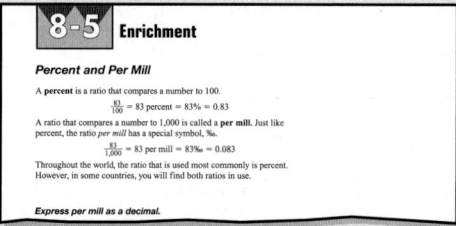

Activity Have students in small groups discuss how changing percents to decimals and vice versa might be useful in a job setting. Have students make a list of professions they think might use this skill. You may wish to have the groups compare their lists to see how similar they are.

Estimating with Percents

You'll learn to estimate the percent of a number.

When am I ever going to use this?

Knowing how to estimate the percent of a number can help you determine the tip at a restaurant.

The Watch Store is having a sale on watches. Every watch is on sale for 60% of the regular price. About how much would you pay for a watch that normally sells for $34.99? *This problem will be solved in Example 3.*

The word *about* tells you that an exact answer is not needed. So, you can estimate the answer. When you estimate with percents, you should round the percent to a fraction that is easy to multiply. The chart shows some commonly-used percents and their fraction equivalents.

$20\% = \frac{1}{5}$	$25\% = \frac{1}{4}$	$12\frac{1}{2}\% = \frac{1}{8}$	$16\frac{2}{3}\% = \frac{1}{6}$
$40\% = \frac{2}{5}$	$50\% = \frac{1}{2}$	$37\frac{1}{2}\% = \frac{3}{8}$	$33\frac{1}{3}\% = \frac{1}{3}$
$60\% = \frac{3}{5}$	$75\% = \frac{3}{4}$	$62\frac{1}{2}\% = \frac{5}{8}$	$66\frac{2}{3}\% = \frac{2}{3}$
$80\% = \frac{4}{5}$	$100\% = 1$	$87\frac{1}{2}\% = \frac{7}{8}$	$83\frac{1}{3}\% = \frac{5}{6}$

Examples

Study Hint

Problem Solving You can also make a model to help you estimate 22% of 197.

Estimate each percent.

1 22% of 197

22% is close to 20% or $\frac{1}{5}$.

Round 197 to 200.

$\frac{1}{5} \times 200 = \frac{1}{5} \times \frac{\overset{40}{\cancel{200}}}{1}$

$= 40$

So, 22% of 197 is about 40.

2 50% of 1,512

50% is $\frac{1}{2}$.

Round 1,512 to 1,500.

$\frac{1}{2} \times 1,500 = \frac{1}{2} \times \frac{\overset{750}{\cancel{1,500}}}{1}$

$= 750$

So, 50% of 1,512 is about 750.

APPLICATION

3 **Money Matters** Refer to the beginning of the lesson. About how much would you pay for a watch that normally sells for $34.99?

Express 60% as a fraction. $60\% = \frac{60}{100} = \frac{3}{5}$ *Simplify.*

Then estimate the product of the fraction and the price.

$\frac{3}{5} \times 35 = \frac{3}{5} \times \frac{35}{1}$ *Think: $34.99 is close to $35.*

$= \frac{3}{5} \times \frac{\overset{7}{\cancel{35}}}{1}$ *Divide 5 and 35 by their GCF, 5.*

$= 21$ *Multiply.*

You will pay about $21 for the watch.

Lesson 8-6 Estimating with Percents **337**

Multiple Learning Styles

Intrapersonal Ask students how much they would save buying a $29.95 pair of jeans at 50% off. Have them write a paragraph answering the following questions. *How did you figure the savings? Are you more comfortable working with decimals or fractions?*

Motivating the Lesson

Problem Solving Ask students how they would determine which pair of boots costs less.
- a $69 pair at 35% off
- a $79 pair at 50% off
- a $79 pair at 50% off

Sometimes you need to estimate a percent.

 Example ➍ **Estimate the percent of the figure that is shaded.**

13 out of 15 squares are shaded.
$\frac{13}{15}$ is about $\frac{12}{15}$ or $\frac{4}{5}$.
$\frac{4}{5} = 80\%$
So, about 80% of the figure is shaded.

CHECK FOR UNDERSTANDING

Communicating Mathematics

Read and study the lesson to answer each question.

1. *Explain* how you would estimate 75% of 1,976. **See Answer Appendix.**
2. *Draw* a figure in which the percent of the figure that is shaded is about 60%. **See students' work.**
3. *Write* about a situation in which you would use estimating to find the percent of a number. **See students' work.**

Math Journal

Guided Practice

4. $\frac{1}{5} \times 35 = 7$

5. $\frac{1}{4} \times 200 = 50$

6. $\frac{1}{10} \times 15 = 1.5$

Estimate each percent. 4–6. Sample answers are given.

4. 17% of 34   5. 25% of 208   6. 8% of 15

Estimate the percent of each figure that is shaded.

7. Sample answer: 50%

8. Sample answer: 25%

9. *Money Matters* When the Chou family went out to dinner, their bill was $35.98. Mrs. Chou wants to leave a 20% tip. About how much money should she leave? **Sample answer:** $\frac{1}{5} \times \$35 = \$7$

EXERCISES

Practice

10. $\frac{3}{4} \times 40 = 30$

11. $\frac{1}{3} \times 60 = 20$

12. $\frac{1}{10} \times 90 = 9$

13. $\frac{1}{2} \times 50 = 25$

14. $\frac{4}{5} \times 125 = 100$

15. $\frac{2}{5} \times 100 = 40$

Estimate each percent.   10–24. Sample answers are given.

10. 77% of 39   11. 34% of 60   12. 9% of 91
13. 47% of 52   14. 80% of 123   15. 38% of 104
16. 66% of 89   17. 97% of 302   18. 24% of 276
16–18. See Answer Appendix.

Estimate the percent of each figure that is shaded.

19. 75%   20. 60%   21. $66\frac{2}{3}\%$

Reteaching the Lesson

Activity Write the example 21% of 249 on an overhead transparency. Then ask the following questions. *What is 21% expressed as a fraction? What is 249 rounded to the nearest ten? Is 21% of 249 about $\frac{1}{3}$ of 200 or about $\frac{1}{5}$ of 250?* Continue with other examples. $\frac{1}{5}$, 250, $\frac{1}{5}$ of 250

Error Analysis

Watch for students who make errors when multiplying fractions and whole numbers.
Prevent by giving these students additional practice exercises and reviewing multiplying fractions and whole numbers.

22.
25%

23. 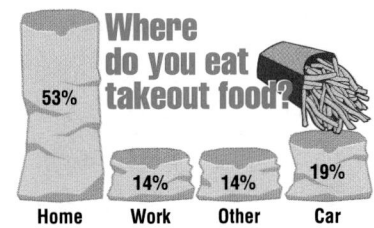 100%

24. $66\frac{2}{3}\%$

25. Estimate 37.5% of 50. **Sample answer:** $\frac{3}{8} \times 48 = 18$

26. *True* or *false*? 26% of 1,400 is about 350. Explain. **See margin.**

27. About how much is one and two tenths percent of ten?
Sample answer: $\frac{1}{100} \times 10 = \frac{1}{10}$

28. Sample answer:
$\frac{1}{8} \times 2,400 = 300$

Applications and Problem Solving

28. *Life Science* According to a survey, 13% of gardeners plant geraniums in their flowerbed. If 2,450 gardeners participated in the survey, about how many can be expected to plant geraniums in their flowerbed?

29. *Food* Refer to the graph. Suppose 5,012 people participated in the fast food survey. About how many more people can be expected to eat takeout food in their home than in their car? **See margin.**

Where do you eat takeout food?
53% 14% Home 14% Work 19% Other Car

Source: Beef Industry Council

30. *Money Matters* The Bike Shop is having their annual bike sale. Every 15-speed bicycle is on sale for 75% of the regular price, and every mountain bicycle is on sale for 80% of the regular price.

30b. Sample answer:
$\frac{4}{5} \times \$200 = \$160$;
$\$200 - \$160 = \$40$

  a. About how much would you pay for a 15-speed bicycle that usually sells for $125? **Sample answer:** $\frac{3}{4} \times \$120$ or $\$90$

  b. About how much would you save if you purchased a mountain bike that normally sells for $196?

31. *Critical Thinking* Which percent problem does not belong? Explain.
  a. 50% of 22   **b.** 22% of 50   **c.** $\frac{1}{2}\%$ of 22
  c; because a and b equal 11 while c equals 0.11.

Mixed Review

32. *Statistics* According to a survey, 56% of people brush their teeth after eating snacks. Express 56% as a decimal. *(Lesson 8-5)* **0.56**

33. *Geometry* Find the area of the rectangle. *(Lesson 4-4)* **23.04 m²**
9.6 m

2.4 m

34. *Standardized Test Practice* Shalana is buying a jean shirt for $35.95, a pair of jeans for $25.98, and a T-shirt for $11.50. Find the total cost of the items not including tax. *(Lesson 3-6)* **B**
  A $68.93   **B** $73.43   **C** $70.63   **D** $72.83   **E** Not Here

For **Extra Practice,** see page 580.

35. *Statistics* Find the mean of 14, 73, 25, 25, and 53. *(Lesson 2-7)* **38**

Lesson 8-6 Estimating with Percents   **339**

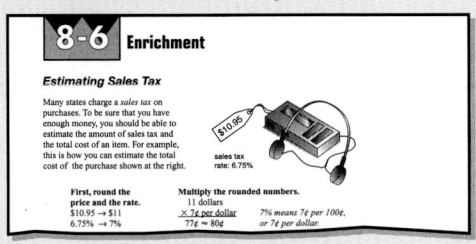
Activity Ask students how percents are used in developing a budget. Discuss what may be involved in developing a budget for their school. What items need to be included, and from where does the funding come? Compare this budget to the state and national budget.

4 ASSESS

Closing Activity

Writing Have students work in pairs to write an explanation of how to estimate the percent of a number for a new employee in a department store.

Chapter 8, Quiz C (Lessons 8-5 and 8-6) is available in the *Assessment and Evaluation Masters,* p. 212.

Additional Answers

26. True; 26% is close to 25%.
$25\% = \frac{1}{4}$; $\frac{1}{4} \times 1,400 = 350$

29. Sample answer:
$50\% \times 5,000 = 2,500$
$20\% \times 5,000 = 1,000$
$2,500 - 1,000 = 1,500$

Lesson 8-6   339

Percent of a Number

Instructional Resources

- *Study Guide Masters*, p. 63
- *Practice Masters*, p. 63
- *Enrichment Masters*, p. 63
- Transparencies 8-7, A and B
- *Assessment and Evaluation Masters*, p. 212
- Classroom Games, pp. 21–22
- *Technology Masters*, p. 15

 CD-ROM Program
- Resource Lesson 8-7
- Interactive Lesson 8-7

Recommended Pacing	
Standard	Day 12 of 14
Honors	Day 11 of 13
Block	Day 6 of 7

1 FOCUS

5-Minute Check
(Lesson 8-6)

Estimate each percent.

1. 18% of 34 $\frac{1}{5} \times 35 = 7$
2. 72% of 95 $\frac{3}{4} \times 100 = 75$
3. 43% of 68 $\frac{2}{5} \times 70 = 28$
4. 17% of 41 $\frac{1}{5} \times 40 = 8$
5. Of the 675 types of toys in the Fun-R-We toystore, 17% are games. About how many of the toys are games? **135 toys**

 The 5-Minute Check is also available on **Transparency 8-7A** for this lesson.

Motivating the Lesson

Communication Have students analyze and discuss the graph at the beginning of the lesson. Ask them these questions.
- Why are percents used instead of whole numbers? **easier to compare statistics**
- Why would retailers be interested in graphs like this one? **get an idea of consumer needs**
- What other information can be represented as a percent? **any measure that is part of a whole unit**

What you'll learn
You'll learn to find the percent of a number.

When am I ever going to use this?
Knowing how to find the percent of a number can help you determine the sale price of a skateboard.

According to the graph, 20% of parents buy shoes for their children every four to five months. If 2,500 parents were surveyed, how many said that they purchase shoes for their children every four to five months?

Source: Opinion Research for Payless Shoe Source

To find 20% of 2,500, you can change the percent to a fraction or to a decimal, and then multiply it by the number. You can also use a model or a calculator.

Method 1 Change the percent to a fraction.

$20\% = \frac{20}{100}$ or $\frac{1}{5}$

$\frac{1}{5}$ of 2,500 $= \frac{1}{5} \times 2,500$

$= 500$

Method 2 Change the percent to a decimal.

$20\% = \frac{20}{100}$ or 0.2

0.2 of 2,500 $= 0.2 \times 2,500$

$= 500$

Method 3 Use a model.

Since 20% $= \frac{1}{5}$, separate a rectangle into fifths. Label the top and bottom in equal intervals as shown.

0%	20%	40%	60%	80%	100%

0   500   1,000   1,500   2,000   2,500

20% of 2,500 is 500.

Method 4 Use a calculator.

20 [2nd] [%] [×] 2,500 [=] *500*

500 out of 2,500 parents surveyed buy shoes for their children every four to five months.

Example **1** Find 24% of 250 by changing the percent to a fraction.

$24\% = \frac{24}{100}$ or $\frac{6}{25}$ *Change the percent to a fraction.*

$\frac{6}{25} \times 250 = \frac{6}{25} \times \frac{\overset{10}{250}}{1}$ *Divide 25 and 250 by the GCF, 25.*

$= 60$

24% of 250 is 60.

② Find 9% of 105 by changing the percent to a decimal.

$9\% = \dfrac{9}{100}$ or 0.09 *Change the percent to a decimal.*

$0.09 \times 105 = 9.45$ *Multiply 0.09 by 105.*

9% of 105 is 9.45.

③ Find 75% of 256 by using a model.

Since $75\% = \dfrac{3}{4}$, separate a rectangle into fourths.

0%	25%	50%	75%	100%

```
0      64     128    192    256
```

75% of 256 is 192.

④ Find 0.5% of 188 by using a calculator.

0.5 [2nd] [%] [×] 188 [=] *0.94*

0.5% of 188 is 0.94.

APPLICATION

⑤ **Travel** According to a survey, 31% of parents named "road construction and traffic" when asked what they'd like to avoid on a family vacation. If 3,000 parents were surveyed, how many said they'd like to avoid road construction and traffic?

Things to avoid on a family vacation

- 2% Other/don't know
- 7% Stress of too much togetherness
- 14% Looking for place to eat/sleep
- 23% Getting lost
- 24% Kids complaining of boredom
- 31% Road construction /traffic

Source: Travel Industry Association, Amtrak

Explore   You need to know the number of parents, out of 3,000, who said to avoid road construction and traffic.

Plan   Multiply 31% by the number of parents surveyed, 3,000.

Estimate: 31% is close to 30% or $\dfrac{3}{10}$.

$\dfrac{3}{10} \times 3,000 = 900$

Solve   Change 31% to a decimal. Then multiply it by 3,000.

$31\% = \dfrac{31}{100}$ or 0.31

0.31 of $3,000 = 0.31 \times 3,000$
$\qquad\qquad\qquad = 930$

930 out of 3,000 parents said they'd like to avoid road construction and traffic.

Examine   Check the answer by comparing it to the estimate. 930 is close to the estimate. So, the answer is correct.

Lesson 8-7 Percent of a Number   **341**

2 TEACH

Transparency 8-7B contains a teaching aid for this lesson.

Using Problem Solving Have students use all four methods to solve the following problem, and then discuss advantages and disadvantages of each method. *Rick Barry retired from the NBA with a 90% free throw percentage. In his career, he attempted 4,243 free throws. How many did he make?* **3,819 free throws**

In-Class Examples

For Example 1
Find 36% of 375 by changing the percent to a fraction. **135**

For Example 2
Find 47% of 211 by changing the percent to a decimal. **99.17**

For Example 3
Find 25% of 132 by using a model. **33**

For Example 4
Find 0.9% of 80 by using a calculator. **0.72**

For Example 5
Refer to the graph on page 341. If 4,200 parents were surveyed, how many answered "getting lost"? **966**

Teaching Tip Tell students that in everyday life, they may use the method with which they are most comfortable. However, it is helpful to understand each method for finding the percent of a number.

Multiple Learning Styles

Logical A daily recommended diet requires about 2,000–2,500 Calories. Of this daily intake, 600–750 Calories should be fat, 58% of the daily Calorie intake should be carbohydrates, and 240–300 Calories should be proteins. What percent of the daily caloric intake should be fat? **30%** How many Calories should be carbohydrates? **1,160–1,450** What percent of the daily caloric intake should be proteins? **12%**

Check for Understanding

If students need additional practice or instruction after completing Exercises 1–8, one of these options may be helpful.
- Extra Practice, see p. 580
- Reteaching Activity
- *Study Guide Masters,* p. 63
- *Practice Masters,* p. 63

Assignment Guide

Core: 9–25 odd, 27–30
Enriched: 10–24 even, 25–30

Additional Answer

1. Sample answer:
   Method 1: Change the percent to a fraction. First, change the percent to a fraction. Then multiply the number by the fraction.

   Method 2: Change the percent to a decimal. First, change the percent to a decimal. Then multiply the number by the decimal.

   Method 4: Use a calculator. First, enter the percent by entering the number [2nd] [%]. Then press [×] and the number by which you are multiplying. Press [=].

Study Guide Masters, p. 63

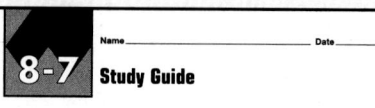

CHECK FOR UNDERSTANDING

Communicating Mathematics

3. Kosey is correct. 125% = 1.25. 1.25 × 150 = 187.5. So, 125% of 150 is 187.5.

Read and study the lesson to answer each question.

1. *Describe* the steps in three of the four methods for finding the percent of a number. **See margin.**
2. *Tell* what number the shaded portion of the model shows. **570**

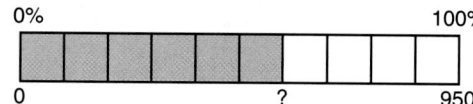

3. *You Decide* Arturo says that 125% of 150 is 18.75. Kosey disagrees. He says that 125% of 150 is 187.5. Who is correct? Explain your reasoning.

Guided Practice

Find the percent of each number.

4. 40% of 65 **26**   5. 8% of 84 **6.72**   6. 0.3% of 500 **1.5**

7. What is 98% of 6? **5.88**

8. *Sports* The Fitch High School softball team won 88% of their games. If they played 25 games, how many games did they win? **22**

EXERCISES

Practice

Find the percent of each number.

9. 25% of 72 **18**   10. 7% of 7 **0.49**   11. 80% of 115 **92**
12. 3% of 156 **4.68**   13. 15% of 40 **6**   14. 33% of 390 **128.7**
15. 101% of 98 **98.98**   16. 0.5% of 85 **0.425**   17. 125% of 145 **181.25**
18. 0.4% of 20 **0.08**   19. 100% of 137 **137**   20. 0.1% of 250 **0.25**

21. What is 60% of 365? **219**   22. Find 22% of 55. **12.1**
23. What is eight-tenths percent of eight hundred? **6.4**
24. A test had 64 problems. Anika got 48 correct.
    a. What percent were correct? **75%**
    b. What percent were incorrect? **25%**
    c. If Maria got 81.25% correct, how many problems did she get correct? **52**

Applications and Problem Solving

25. *Money Matters* Ali paid $31.50 for an item that was reduced by 30%.
    a. What was the original price? **$45.00**
    b. If the original price was reduced by 25%, what is the sale price? **$33.75**
26. *Technology* Rachel is using her computer to decode a secret message. The table shows the results of the scan. Suppose the secret message contains 1,500 vowels.
    a. How many of the vowels are a? **375**
    b. How many of the vowels are o? **300**
    c. How many of the vowels are e? **450**

Vowel	Occurred (%)
A	25%
E	30%
I	20%
O	20%
U	5%

■ Reteaching the Lesson ■

Activity Have students mark off 10 squares on centimeter grid paper strips. Ask them to shade 30%. Ask: *Could you use the strip to show 30% of 100? of 45?* Have students practice finding percents of different numbers.

MathPASS CD-ROM

This CD-ROM offers a complete, self-paced mathematics curriculum. Each lesson includes a pretest, tutorial, guided practice, and posttest. MathPASS Lesson 32 is correlated to this Student Edition lesson.
For Windows & Macintosh

27. *Critical Thinking* Solve each problem.
   a. 14 is what percent of 70? **20%**
   b. What is 35% of 240? **84**
   c. 45 is 15% of what? **300**

Mixed Review
28. Sample answer:
$\frac{2}{5} \times 900$ or 360

28. *Hobbies* The graph shows how much readers are willing to spend on a book. Suppose 932 readers participated in the survey. About how many of those surveyed are willing to spend between $5 and $14.99? *(Lesson 8-6)*

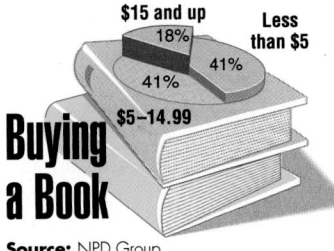
$15 and up
18%
Less than $5
41%
41%
$5–14.99
Buying a Book
Source: NPD Group

29. $\frac{3}{8} \times 64 = 24$

29. Estimate $\frac{3}{8} \times 65$. *(Lesson 7-1)*

 30. *Standardized Test Practice* What is the greatest common factor of 35, 56, and 63? *(Lesson 5-3)* **D**

A 6   **B** 9   **C** 8   **D** 7

For **Extra Practice**, see page 580.

Let the **Games** Begin

Fishin' for Matches

Get Ready This game is for two to four players.

 24 index cards   ✂ scissors

Math Skill
Equivalent Fractions, Decimals, and Percents

Get Set Cut two index cards in half. On one half, write a percent. On the other halves, write its decimal equivalent, its fraction equivalent, and its fraction equivalent in simplified form. If the fraction cannot be simplified, write the fraction on two cards. For example, $\frac{3}{4}$ cannot be simplified. So, $\frac{3}{4}$ will be written on two cards. Continue until you have 12 sets of cards.

25%

Go ● Shuffle the cards and deal 7 cards to each player. Place the remaining cards face down on the table.

0.25

● The first player requests a matching card from any player. If a match is made, that player sets the match aside and it becomes the next player's turn. If a match is not made, the player chooses one card without looking from the remaining cards. If a match is made, the player sets the match aside, and it is the next player's turn.

$\frac{25}{100}$

● The game continues until a player runs out of cards to match. The player with the most matches wins.

$\frac{1}{4}$

interNET CONNECTION Visit www.glencoe.com/sec/math/mac/mathnet for more games.

Lesson 8-7 Percent of a Number **343**

■ **Extending the Lesson** ■

Enrichment Masters, p. 63

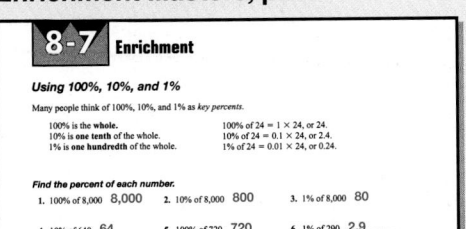

8-7 **Enrichment**

Using 100%, 10%, and 1%

Many people think of 100%, 10%, and 1% as *key percents*.

100% is the **whole**.   100% of 24 = 1 × 24, or 24.
10% is **one tenth** of the whole.   10% of 24 = 0.1 × 24, or 2.4.
1% is **one hundredth** of the whole.   1% of 24 = 0.01 × 24, or 0.24.

Find the percent of each number.
1. 100% of 8,000 **8,000**   2. 10% of 8,000 **800**   3. 1% of 8,000 **80**
4. 10% of 640 **64**   5. 100% of 720 **720**   6. 1% of 290 **2.9**

Let the **Games** Begin

The cards could be used to practice writing fractions, decimals, and percents in other forms. Players could challenge each other to draw a card and write that number in as many equivalent ways as they can in a set amount of time.

Practice Masters, p. 63

8-7 **Practice**

Name_____ Date_____

Percent of a Number

Find the percent of each number.
1. 75% of 52 **39**   2. 40% of 65 **26**   3. 15% of 80 **12**
4. 30% of 24 **7.2**   5. 62.5% of 96 **60**   6. 9% of 20 **1.8**
7. 28% of 75 **21**   8. 95% of 60 **57**   9. 70% of 15 **10.5**
10. 12% of 300 **36**   11. 85% of 48 **40.8**   12. 125% of 16 **20**
13. 0.6% of 5 **0.03**   14. 36% of 175 **63**   15. 48% of 50 **24**
16. 160% of 90 **144**   17. 65% of 120 **78**   18. 87.5% of 56 **49**
19. 5% of 85 **4.25**   20. 90% of 18 **16.2**   21. 0.4% of 150 **0.6**
22. 120% of 70 **84**   23. 37.5% of 104 **39**   24. 52% of 25 **13**
25. 80% of 40 **32**   26. 45% of 200 **90**   27. 2.5% of 4 **0.1**
28. 34% of 30 **10.2**   29. 55% of 95 **52.25**   30. 150% of 110 **165**

31. Gina read 35% of her 140-page book. How many pages did she read? **49**

32. Larry delivered 75% of his 120 newspapers. How many papers did he deliver? **90**

© Glencoe/McGraw-Hill   T63   *Mathematics: Applications and Connections, Course 1*

Lesson 8-7 **343**

Additional Answers

15. Sample answer: Express the percent as a fraction with a denominator of 100 and then simplify.
16. $\frac{3}{5}$
17. $\frac{11}{20}$

CHAPTER 8

Study Guide and Assessment

Chapter Review For additional lesson-by-lesson review, visit:
www.glencoe.com/sec/math/mac/mathnet

Vocabulary

After completing this chapter, you should be able to define each term, concept, or phrase and give an example or two of each.

Number and Operations
cross products (p. 318)
percent (p. 330)
proportion (p. 317)
rate (p. 312)

Geometry
scale drawing (p. 324)

Problem Solving
draw a diagram (p. 322)

Understanding and Using the Vocabulary

State whether each sentence is *true* or *false*. If false, replace the underlined word or number to make a true sentence.

1. A ratio is a comparison of two numbers by <u>multiplication</u>. **false; division**
2. The simplest form of the ratio $\frac{12}{28}$ is $\frac{3}{7}$. **true**
3. A <u>rate</u> is a ratio of two measurements that have different units. **true**
4. Three tickets for $7.50 expressed as a rate is <u>$1.50</u> per ticket. **false; $2.50**
5. A <u>percent</u> is an equation which shows that two ratios are equivalent. **false; proportion**
6. The model shown represents <u>85%</u>. **false; 73%**
7. The cross products of a proportion are <u>equal</u>. **true**
8. 8% can be expressed as <u>0.008</u>. **false; 0.08**
9. $\frac{3}{25}$ can be expressed as <u>12%</u>. **true**
10. 38% of 40 is <u>1,520</u>. **false; 15.2**
11. A <u>scale drawing</u> shows an object exactly as it looks, but it is generally larger or smaller. **true**
12. A percent is a ratio that compares a number to <u>10</u>. **false; 100**
13. The decimal 0.346 can be expressed as <u>3.46%</u>. **false; 34.6%**
14. $62\frac{1}{2}\%$ can be expressed as the fraction $\frac{5}{8}$. **true**

In Your Own Words

15. *Explain* how to change a percent to a fraction. **See margin.**

MindJogger Videoquizzes

MindJogger Videoquizzes provide an alternative review of concepts presented in this chapter. Students work in teams to answer questions, gaining points for correct answers. The questions are presented in three rounds.
Round 1 Concepts–5 questions
Round 2 Skills–4 questions
Round 3 Problem Solving–4 questions

Objectives & Examples

Upon completing this chapter, you should be able to:

● express ratios and rates as fractions *(Lesson 8-1)*

Express the ratio 3 winners out of 12 competitors as a fraction in simplest form.

$$\frac{3 \text{ winners}}{12 \text{ competitors}} = \frac{1 \text{ winner}}{4 \text{ competitors}}$$
$\div 3$ ... $\div 3$

● solve proportions by using cross products *(Lesson 8-2)*

Solve the proportion $\frac{9}{12} = \frac{g}{8}$.

$9 \times 8 = 12 \times g$ *Write cross products.*
$72 = 12g$ *Multiply.*
$\frac{72}{12} = \frac{12g}{12}$ *Divide.*
$6 = g$

● find actual length from a scale drawing *(Lesson 8-3)*

6 units
11 units

The drawing of the room has a scale of 1 unit = 2 feet. What is the actual length of the room?

$drawing \rightarrow$ $\frac{1 \text{ unit}}{2 \text{ feet}} = \frac{11 \text{ units}}{d \text{ feet}}$ $\leftarrow drawing$
$actual \rightarrow$ ... $\leftarrow actual$

$1 \times d = 2 \times 11$
$d = 22$

The actual length is 22 feet.

Review Exercises

Use these exercises to review and prepare for the chapter test.

Express each ratio as a fraction in simplest form. 16–17. See margin.

16. 18 out of 30 babies are girls.

17. 11 potatoes out of 20 are rotten.

Express each ratio as a rate.

18. 3 inches of rain in 6 months

19. 189 pounds of garbage in 12 weeks

18. 0.5 inch per month

19. 15.75 pounds per week

Use cross products to determine whether each pair of ratios forms a proportion.

20. $\frac{4}{11}, \frac{7}{22}$ **no** **21.** $\frac{3}{9}, \frac{12}{36}$ **yes**

Solve each proportion.

22. $\frac{7}{11} = \frac{m}{33}$ **21** **23.** $\frac{12}{20} = \frac{15}{k}$ **25**

24. $\frac{g}{20} = \frac{9}{12}$ **15** **25.** $\frac{10}{12} = \frac{25}{h}$ **30**

Refer to the scale drawing at the left.

26. What is the actual width of the room? **12 feet**

27. Suppose that the doorway to the room is actually 3 feet wide. How wide will the doorway be on the drawing? **1.5 units**

28. *Geography* On a map, the measure from Baxter to Sidney is 2 inches. Suppose that the map has a scale of $\frac{3}{4}$ inch = 30 miles. What is the actual distance between the two cities? **80 miles**

Chapter 8 Study Guide and Assessment **345**

Objectives & Examples

This section reviews the skills and concepts of the chapter and shows completely worked examples.

Review Exercises

These exercises provide practice for the corresponding objectives.

Assessment and Evaluation Masters, pp. 199–200

Assessment and Evaluation

Six forms of Chapter 8 Test are available in the *Assessment and Evaluation Masters* as shown in the chart.

Chapter 8 Test, Form 1B, is shown at the right. Chapter 8 Test, Form 2B, is shown on the next page.

1A	Multiple Choice	Honors
1B	Multiple Choice	Average
1C	Multiple Choice	Basic
2A	Free Response	Honors
2B	Free Response	Average
2C	Free Response	Basic

Assessment and Evaluation Masters, pp. 205–206

Objectives & Examples

● express percents as fractions and vice versa
(Lesson 8-4)

Express $\frac{3}{10}$ as a percent.

$$\frac{3}{10} \gtreqless \frac{n}{100}$$
$$3 \times 100 = 10 \times n$$
$$300 = 10n$$
$$300 \div 10 = 10n \div 10$$
$$30 = n$$

So, $\frac{3}{10}$ is equivalent to 30%.

● express percents as decimals and vice versa
(Lesson 8-5)

Express 21% as a decimal.

$$21\% = \frac{21}{100}$$
$$= 0.21$$

● estimate the percent of a number
(Lesson 8-6)

Estimate 33% of 60.

33% is close to $33\frac{1}{3}\%$ or $\frac{1}{3}$.

$$\frac{1}{3} \times 60 = \frac{1}{3} \times \frac{\overset{20}{\cancel{60}}}{\underset{1}{1}}$$
$$= 20$$

So, 33% of 60 is about 20.

● find the percent of a number
(Lesson 8-7)

Find 20% of 50.

$$20\% = \frac{20}{100} \text{ or } \frac{1}{5}$$
$$\frac{1}{5} \times 50 = 10$$

20% of 50 is 10.

Review Exercises

Express each percent as a fraction in simplest form.

29. 3% $\frac{3}{100}$ **30.** 17% $\frac{17}{100}$
31. 150% $1\frac{1}{2}$ **32.** 48% $\frac{12}{25}$

Express each fraction as a percent.

33. $\frac{3}{5}$ 60%   **34.** $\frac{9}{10}$ 90%
35. $\frac{11}{20}$ 55%   **36.** $\frac{5}{25}$ 20%

37. How is five hundredths written as a percent? 5%

Express each percent as a decimal.
38. 2.2% **0.022**   **39.** 38% **0.38**
40. 140% **1.4**   **41.** 66% **0.66**

Express each decimal as a percent.
42. 0.003 **0.3%**   **43.** 1.3 **130%**
44. 0.65 **65%**   **45.** 0.591 **59.1%**

**46–50. Sample answer given.
Estimate each percent.**
46. 19% of 99 $\frac{1}{5} \times 100 = 20$
47. 27% of 82 $\frac{1}{4} \times 80 = 20$
48. 48% of 48 $\frac{1}{2} \times 50 = 25$
49. 41% of 243 $\frac{2}{5} \times 240 = 96$

50. Estimate the percent of the figure that is shaded. **30%**

Find the percent of each number.
51. 18% of 89 **16.02**
52. 40% of 150 **60**
53. 5% of 340 **17**
54. 0.8% of 132 **1.056**
55. What is one-tenth percent of 162? **0.162**
56. Find two hundred thirty-six percent of 42. **99.12**

346   Chapter 8 Exploring Ratio, Proportion, and Percent

Test and Review Software

You may use this software, a combination of an item generator and item bank, to create your own tests or worksheets. Types of items include free response, multiple choice, short answer, and open ended.

CD-ROM Program

The CD-ROM Program contains an Assessment Game whose questions review the concepts in this chapter.

Applications & Problem Solving

57. Travel Tatanka drove 300 miles in 6 hours. How many miles did he drive per hour? *(Lesson 8-1)* **50 mph**

58. Statistics According to a survey, 37% of Americans feel that public libraries will become the place to go to use computers. If 1,500 people participated in the survey, how many said that libraries would become the place to use computers? *(Lesson 8-2)* **555**

59. Draw a Diagram A store manager displays 36 cans of cat food in a triangular shape. The display is one can deep. How many cans are on the bottom row? *(Lesson 8-3A)* **8 cans**

60. School Nick's class is planning a fund-raiser. The results of a class vote show that 75% of the students want to sell candy, 15% of the students want to sell wrapping paper, and 10% of the students want to sell calendars. *(Lessons 8-4 and 8-7)*

   a. What fraction of the class wants to sell calendars? $\frac{1}{10}$

   b. What fraction of the class wants to sell candy? $\frac{3}{4}$

   c. If there are 40 students in the class, how many voted to sell candy? **30**

Alternative Assessment

Open Ended

Suppose your teacher assigns you to make a scale drawing of your school. What information would you need to collect? What decisions would you need to make? **See margin.**

Suppose your school is rectangular-shaped with a length of 220 feet and a width of 90 feet. You want to make the length of the school on the scale drawing 11 inches. Find the scale and the width of the school on the map.

1 inch = 20 feet; 4.5 inches

Completing the CHAPTER Project

Use the following checklist to make sure your poster is complete.

☑ A sketch of each toy is included.

☑ The dimensions of each toy are labeled, and the dimensions of the actual objects are listed.

☑ For each sketch, include a scale that can be used to compare the size of the toy to the actual size of the object.

Add any finishing touches to make your poster unique.

 PORTFOLIO Select an item from the chapter that you found to be challenging. Place it in your portfolio and write a paragraph that explains why you found the item to be challenging.

A practice test for Chapter 8 is provided on page 602.

Additional Answer for the Open Ended item

You would need to know the dimensions of the school. You would need to decide how much detail to show, such as the parking lot, playground, classroom locations, etc. You would also have to decide on what scale to use.

 ### Performance Assessment

Additional performance assessment tasks for this chapter are included in the *Assessment and Evaluation Masters* on page 209. A scoring guide is also provided on page 221.

This section provides additional practice in solving real-world problems that involve the skills of this chapter.

Alternative Assessment

The *Open Ended* section provides students with a performance assessment opportunity to evaluate their work and understanding.

 CHAPTER Project

Students should complete the final stages of their project and prepare a class demonstration of their results. A scoring guide for the project is available in the *Investigations and Projects Masters*, p. 47.

 PORTFOLIO Students should add to their portfolios at this time.

Assessment and Evaluation Masters, p. 209

8

Name _____ Date _____

Chapter 8 Performance Assessment

Instructions: Demonstrate your knowledge by giving a clear, concise solution to each problem. Be sure to include all relevant drawings and justify your answers. You may show your solutions in more than one way or investigate beyond the requirements of the problems.

1. a. Tell in your own words the meaning of *ratio*.

   b. Give an example of a ratio. Write the ratio in four ways.

   c. Tell in your own words the meaning of *rate*. Give two examples of rates.

   d. Tell in your own words the meaning of *proportion*.

   e. Write a word problem that uses proportions. Include a scale drawing.

   f. Solve the word problem in part e. Explain each step.

2. Matthew is in charge of marking merchandise down for the back-to-school sale. Clothing is to be marked down 30%. School supplies are to be on sale for $\frac{1}{4}$ off, and sporting goods prices will be reduced 20%.

   a. Tell how to express a percent as a fraction and as a decimal.

   b. Find the sale price of a $35 basketball in two ways.

   c. Estimate the sale price of a jacket regularly priced $40. Explain your reasoning.

   d. Find the sale price of the jacket in part c.

   e. Tell how to express a fraction as a percent.

   f. Express $\frac{1}{4}$ as a percent. Show your work.

   g. On which item would a customer save more money, the $35 basketball or a $32 book for school? Explain your reasoning.

© Glencoe/McGraw-Hill   209   *Mathematics: Applications and Connections, Course 1*

The Standardized Test Practice may be used to help students prepare for standardized tests. The test items are written in the same style as those in state proficiency tests and standardized tests like CAT, CTBS, ITBS, MAT, SAT, and Terra Nova. The test items cover skills and concepts covered up to this point in the text.

The pages can be used as an overnight assessment. After students have completed the pages, discuss how each problem can be solved, or provide copies of the solutions from the *Solutions Manual*.

Assessment and Evaluation Masters, p. 215

Section One: Multiple Choice

There are thirteen multiple-choice questions in this section. Choose the best answer. If a correct answer is *not here*, choose the letter for Not Here.

1. How could you estimate a 20% tip for a $23.25 restaurant bill? **C**

   A Find $\frac{1}{2}$ of $23.25.

   B Find $\frac{1}{4}$ of $23.00.

   C Find $\frac{1}{5}$ of $23.00.

   D Find $\frac{1}{20}$ of $24.00.

2. Rogelio is 1.6 meters tall. How many centimeters is this? **H**

   F 0.016 cm   **G** 16 cm

   H 160 cm   **J** 1,600 cm

3. The stem-and-leaf plot shows the speeds in miles per hour for the fastest birds in the world. What is the mean speed? **A**

Stem	Leaf
6	5 5 8
7	0 2 7
8	0 8
9	5
10	6

   8|8 = 88 mph

   A 78.6 mph   **B** 74.5 mph

   C 75.6 mph   **D** 77.8 mph

4. Round $3\frac{3}{5}$ to the nearest half. **H**

   F $3\frac{1}{5}$ **G** 3

   H $3\frac{1}{2}$ **J** 4

5. Find the value of $132 \div 6 + 4 \times 3$. **D**

   A 36   **B** 78

   C 68   **D** 34

Please note that Questions 6–13 have five answer choices.

6. The table shows the cost for 4 brands of tennis shoes at two different stores.

Brand	Sporting Goods Store	Department Stores
R	$49.99	$45.65
S	$67.98	$65.00
T	$37.50	$37.95
U	$75.97	$72.98

At the department store, how much more is brand S than brand R? **J**

   F $20.45

   G $19.45

   H $20.35

   J $19.35

   K $19.25

7. Use the table in Question 6. Connie purchases brand T and brand R from the sporting goods store. What is the total cost before sales tax is added? **D**

   A $87.39

   B $90.59

   C $88.99

   D $87.49

   E $86.59

8. Tickets to Splash City cost $10 for adults and $8 for children. If 12 people paid a total of $102, how many were adults, and how many were children? **H**

   F 7 adults, 4 children

   G 5 adults, 6 children

   H 3 adults, 9 children

   J 6 adults, 6 children

   K 4 adults, 8 children

◄◄◄ Instructional Resources

Another cumulative review is shown at the left and is available in the *Assessment and Evaluation Masters*, p. 215.

9. Solve $\frac{16}{25} = \frac{x}{100}$. **D**

 A 4

 B 10

 C 16

 D 64

 E Not Here

10. Yoruba bought 6 packages of hot dogs for a picnic. Each package weighs 1.15 pounds. What is the total weight of the packages? **G**

 F 7.15 lb

 G 6.90 lb

 H 8.40 lb

 J 6.55 lb

 K Not Here

11. Find the sum of 12.675 and 7.081. **C**

 A 18.996

 B 19.566

 C 19.756

 D 18.796

 E Not Here

12. A bicycle costs $159, a helmet costs $59, and bike shorts cost $24. What is the cost of these items before tax is added? **G**

 F $280   G $242

 H $220   J $275

 K Not Here

13. $3\frac{3}{4} \times 2\frac{2}{5} =$ **D**

 A $6\frac{9}{20}$ B $8\frac{1}{2}$

 C $7\frac{2}{5}$ D $9\frac{3}{4}$

 E Not Here

 Test Practice For additional test practice questions, visit:

www.glencoe.com/sec/math/mac/mathnet

 Test-Taking Tip THE PRINCETON REVIEW

Remember that, on most tests, you get as much credit for correctly answering the easy questions as you do for the difficult ones. Answer the easy ones first and then spend time on the more challenging questions.

Section Two: Free Response

This section contains seven questions for which you will provide short answers. Write your answers on your paper.

14. What is the value of $3c - 4d$ if $c = 8$ and $d = 3$? **12**

15. Two-fifths of the registered voters voted in the town election. What percent of the voters did not vote? **60%**

16. Estimate 39% of 70. **See margin.**

17. To the nearest eighth of an inch, what is the length of the line segment shown? **See margin.**

⊢―――――⊣

18. Find the value of the expression $76 - 16 \div 4 \times 3 + 12$. **76**

19. Dawit sells small bouquets of flowers at his flower shop for $2.75 each. On Saturday, he made $57.75 in sales from the bouquets. How many bouquets of flowers did he sell? **21**

20. Add a number to the following set of data so that the mode, median, and mean of the new set of data are the same as those for the original set of data: 91, 93, 93, 95, 95, 98, 100. **95**

Additional Answers

16. Sample answer: 40% of 70 = 28

17. $1\frac{3}{8}$ inches

Instructional Resources ▶▶▶

Additional standardized test practice is shown at the right and is available in the *Assessment and Evaluation Masters*, pp. 213–214.

Assessment and Evaluation Masters, pp. 213–214

Name_____ Date_____

8 **Chapter 8 Standardized Test Practice**

1. An average camel can drink 114 liters in 10 minutes. Express this ratio as a rate.   1. B
   A. 114 liters   B. 11.4 liters per minute
   C. 10 minutes per liter   D. none of these

2. Alex used a proportion to convert between feet and inches. He knows that 1 foot = 12 inches. He is 56 inches tall. Solve the proportion $\frac{12}{1} = \frac{56}{x}$ to determine Alex's height in feet.   2. C
   A. 5 ft 6 in.   B. 5.6 ft   C. $4\frac{2}{3}$ ft   D. $4\frac{1}{3}$ ft

3. Oxygen makes up 65% of the chemical elements in the human body. Express this percent as a decimal.   3. C
   A. $\frac{65}{100}$ B. 65.0   C. 0.65   D. 6.5

4. Five of the first 25 presidents were born in March. What percent of the first 25 presidents were born in March?   4. A
   A. 20%   B. $\frac{1}{5}$ C. $\frac{5}{25}$ D. 25%

5. In music, putting a flag on the stem of a note halves the value of the note. If you start with a quarter note and add a flag, what note results?   5. C
   A. half note   B. quarter note
   C. eighth note   D. sixteenth note

6. Josiah is making dip for a party. The recipe calls for $\frac{1}{2}$ teaspoon of lemon juice. He wants to make $2\frac{1}{2}$ times the recipe. How much lemon juice does Josiah need?   6. A
   A. $1\frac{1}{4}$ tsp   B. $2\frac{1}{4}$ tsp   C. $\frac{1}{4}$ tsp   D. none of these

7. Mrs. Smith is ordering pizzas for her class as a reward. She has decided that she needs $4\frac{1}{4}$ pizzas to feed her class. How many pizzas should she order?   7. C
   A. 4   B. $4\frac{1}{2}$ C. 5   D. none of these

8. If $\frac{2}{9}$ of the marbles in a bag are red and $\frac{6}{9}$ of the marbles are white, what portion of the marbles are neither red nor white?   8. D
   A. $\frac{7}{9}$ B. $\frac{1}{9}$ C. 2   D. $\frac{2}{9}$

9. Eight presidents out of 41 were born in Virginia. Express this ratio as a decimal rounded to the nearest thousandth.   9. B
   A. $\frac{8}{41}$ B. 0.195   C. 5.125   D. 19.5

© Glencoe/McGraw-Hill   213   Mathematics: Applications and Connections, Course 1

---

8 **Chapter 8 Standardized Test Practice (continued)**

10. Joy wanted to bundle by weight the newspapers collected for recycling by each of the three classes in the sixth grade. The classes collected 22 pounds, 55 pounds, and 44 pounds. Joy used the greatest common factor of these numbers for the weight of each newspaper bundle. That way no class would have unbundled newspapers left over. How many pounds did each bundle weigh?   10. A
   A. 11 lb   B. 5 lb   C. 7 lb   D. none of these

11. An average mountain lion weighs 77 kilograms. What is this weight in grams?   11. C
   A. 0.077 g   B. 77 g   C. 77,000 g   D. 7,700 g

12. Solve 3 × 12,541 = a using the distributive property.   12. B
   A. 4,180   B. 37,623   C. 3,762   D. none of these

13. The cubit is an old unit of length. The Roman cubit is 0.444 meter. The Greek cubit is 0.463 meter. The Assyrian cubit is 0.469 meter. The Egyptian short cubit is 0.450 meter. Put these decimals in order from least to greatest.   13. A
   A. 0.444, 0.450, 0.463, 0.469   B. 0.469, 0.463, 0.450, 0.444
   C. 0.450, 0.469, 0.463, 0.444   D. none of these

14. One square meter is equivalent to 1.196 square yards. Round the square yards to the nearest hundredth.   14. B
   A. 2.0   B. 1.20   C. 1.0   D. none of these

15. Mrs. Overbeck's math class had the following scores on a test: 75, 90, 85, 90, 80, 52, 95, 83, 90. What is the best measure of central tendency to describe this data?   15. D
   A. range   B. mode   C. mean   D. median

16. Susie started taking piano lessons. The first week she practiced 2 hours, the second week she practiced $2\frac{1}{2}$ hours, the third week she practiced 3 hours, and the fourth week she practiced $3\frac{1}{2}$ hours. If she continues this pattern, how many hours will she practice the sixth week?   16. B
   A. 4 hours   B. $4\frac{1}{2}$ hours   C. 5 hours   D. $5\frac{1}{2}$ hours

© Glencoe/McGraw-Hill   214   Mathematics: Applications and Connections, Course 1

Geometry: Investigating Patterns

Previewing the Chapter

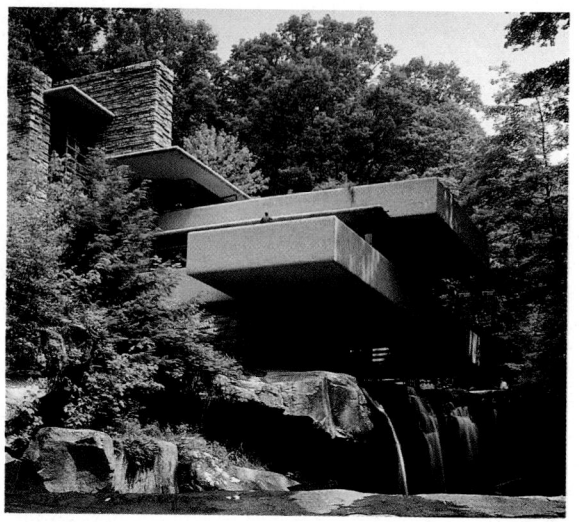

Overview

This chapter explores geometry and its many applications. Students learn to classify, measure, and draw angles; to construct congruent segments and angles; and to bisect line segments and angles. Students investigate two-dimensional figures by describing and defining lines of symmetry and by determining congruence and similarity. Students learn to solve problems by using logical reasoning.

Lesson (pages)	Lesson Objectives	NCTM Standards 2000	Standardized Tests	State/Local Objectives
9-1 (352–355)	Classify and measure angles.	1, 3, 4, 6–10	CAT, CTBS, ITBS, SAT, TN	
9-1B (356–357)	Solve problems by using logical reasoning.	1–3, 6–10		
9-2 (358–361)	Draw angles and estimate measures of angles.	1, 3–10		
9-3A (362–363)	Construct congruent segments and angles.	1, 3, 4, 6–8, 10	CTBS, TN	
9-3 (364–366)	Bisect line segments and angles.	1, 3, 4, 6–10	CAT	
9-4A (368–369)	Classify triangles and quadrilaterals.	3, 6–8, 10	CAT, ITBS	
9-4 (370–373)	Name two-dimensional figures.	1–4, 6–10	CAT, ITBS	
9-4B (374)	Make a net and use it to wrap a cube.	3, 6–8, 10		
9-5 (375–378)	Describe and define lines of symmetry.	1, 3, 6–10	CTBS, SAT, TN	
9-6 (379–383)	Determine congruence and similarity.	1, 3, 4, 6–10	CTBS, TN	
9-6B (384–385)	Create Escher-like drawings by using translations.	2, 3, 6–8, 10		

CAT = California Achievement Tests, CTBS = Comprehensive Tests of Basic Skills, ITBS = Iowa Tests of Basic Skills,
MAT = Metropolitan Achievement Tests, SAT = Stanford Achievement Tests, TN = Terra Nova
For the key to numbering of NCTM Standards 2000, see page T6.

The **Interactive Lesson Planner** contains all of the blackline masters and transparencies. This CD-ROM also includes an easy-to-use lesson planning calendar.

LESSON PLANNING GUIDE

Lesson	Extra Practice (Student Edition)	BLACKLINE MASTERS (PAGE NUMBERS)										Transparencies A and B
		Study Guide	Practice	Enrichment	Assessment & Evaluation	Classroom Games	Diversity	Hands-On Lab	School to Career	Science and Math Lab Manual	Technology	
9-1	p. 580	64	64	64							18	9-1
9-1B	p. 581											
9-2	p. 581	65	65	65	239				9		17	9-2
9-3A								57				
9-3	p. 581	66	66	66	238, 239							9-3
9-4A								58				
9-4	p. 582	67	67	67		23–26	9					9-4
9-4B								59				
9-5	p. 582	68	68	68	240			77				9-5
9-6	p. 582	69	69	69	240					13–16		9-6
9-6B								60				
Study Guide/ Assessment					225–237, 241–243							

OTHER CHAPTER RESOURCES

Student Edition

Chapter Project, pp. 351, 361, 373, 382, 389
Math in the Media, p. 382
School to Career, p. 367
Let the Games Begin, p. 383

Technology

 MathPASS CD-ROM

 Interactive Mathematics Tools Software

Teacher's Classroom Resources

Applications
Family Letters and Activities, pp. 17–18
Investigations and Projects Masters, pp. 49–52

Meeting Individual Needs
Investigations for the Special Education Student, p. 29

Teaching Aids
Answer Key Masters
Block Scheduling Booklet
Lesson Planning Guide
Solutions Manual

Professional Publications
Glencoe Mathematics Professional Series

Planning the Chapter

MindJogger Videoquizzes provide a unique format for reviewing concepts presented in the chapter.

ASSESSMENT RESOURCES

Student Edition

Mixed Review, pp. 355, 361, 366, 373, 378, 382
Mid-Chapter Self Test, p. 373
Math Journal, p. 360
Study Guide and Assessment, pp. 386–389
Performance Task, p. 389
Portfolio Suggestion, p. 389
Standardized Test Practice, pp. 390–391
Chapter Test, p. 603

Assessment and Evaluation Masters

Multiple-Choice Tests (Forms 1A, 1B, 1C), pp. 225–230
Free-Response Tests (Forms 2A, 2B, 2C), pp. 231–236
Performance Assessment, p. 237
Mid-Chapter Test, p. 238
Quizzes A–D, pp. 239–240
Standardized Test Practice, pp. 241–242
Cumulative Review, p. 243

Teacher's Wraparound Edition

5-Minute Check, pp. 352, 358, 364, 370, 375, 379
Building Portfolios, p. 350
Math Journal, pp. 363, 369, 374, 385
Closing Activity, pp. 355, 357, 361, 366, 373, 378, 382

Technology

Test and Review Software
MindJogger Videoquizzes
CD-ROM Program

MATERIALS AND MANIPULATIVES

Lesson 9-1
protractor*†

Lesson 9-2
protractor*†
straightedge*†
paper plate
scissors*

Lesson 9-3A
straightedge*†
compass*†

Lesson 9-3
straightedge*†
ruler*†
protractor*†
compass*†

Lesson 9-4A
geoboards*†
geobands*†
dot paper†
scissors*

Lesson 9-4B
scissors*
cube*

Lesson 9-5
geomirror*
tracing paper
scissors*

Lesson 9-6
scissors*
tracing paper
grid paper†
geoboard*†
geobands*†

Lesson 9-6B
grid paper†
colored pencils

*Glencoe Manipulative Kit

†Glencoe Overhead Manipulative Resources

PACING CHART

See pages T25–T27 for the Course Planning Calendar.

COURSE	DAY 1	DAY 2	DAY 3	DAY 4	DAY 5	DAY 6	DAY 7
Standard	Chapter Project	Lesson 9-1	Lesson 9-1B	Lesson 9-2	Lessons 9-3A & 9-3		Lessons 9-4A & 9-4
Honors	Chapter Project	Lesson 9-1	Lesson 9-1B	Lesson 9-2	Lesson 9-3	Lessons 9-4 & 9-4B	
Block	Chapter Project & Lesson 9-1	Lessons 9-1B & 9-2	Lessons 9-3A & 9-3	Lessons 9-4A & 9-4	Lesson 9-5	Lesson 9-6	Study Guide and Assessment, Chapter Test

Interactive Mathematics:
Activities and Investigations

is an activity-based program that may be used as an enhancement for chapters in *Mathematics: Applications and Connections.*

Unit 12, Activity One
Use before Lesson 9-1.

Summary Students make their own protractors by folding paper and labeling the angles. Using their protractors, they draw angles of varying sizes and justify their measurements. Then they use nonstandard measuring devices to measure length. Students then design a map.

Math Connection Students identify angles of 90°, 180°, 270°, and 360° and then use them to find the measures of other angles. They also measure angles and lengths without the use of standard measuring tools, and use map scale and angle measurements to give directions.

Unit 4, Activity Two
Use with Lesson 9-5.

Summary Students work in groups using a geomirror to test if each logo found in the Data Bank has symmetry and where the line of symmetry is located. Then they complete six drawings on a recording sheet by using symmetry.

Math Connection Students investigate line symmetry using a geomirror.

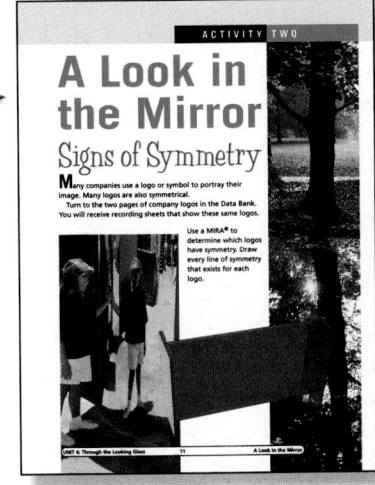

DAY 8	DAY 9	DAY 10	DAY 11	DAY 12	DAY 13	DAY 14	DAY 15
(continue from Day 7)		Lesson 9-5	Lesson 9-6		Study Guide and Assessment	Chapter Test	
Lesson 9-5	Lessons 9-6 & 9-6B		Study Guide and Assessment	Chapter Test			

APPLICATIONS

Classroom Games, pp. 23–26

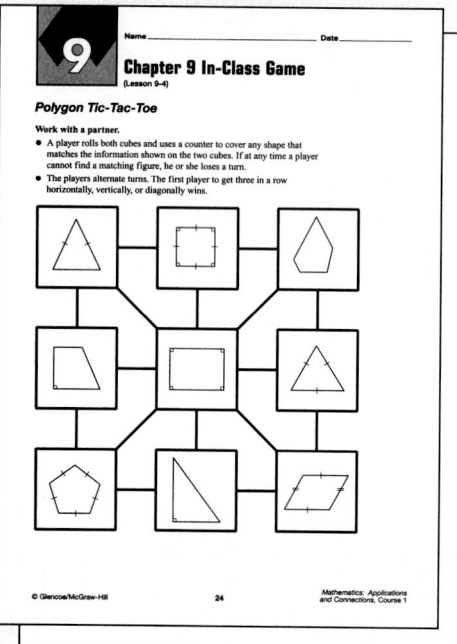

Diversity Masters, p. 9

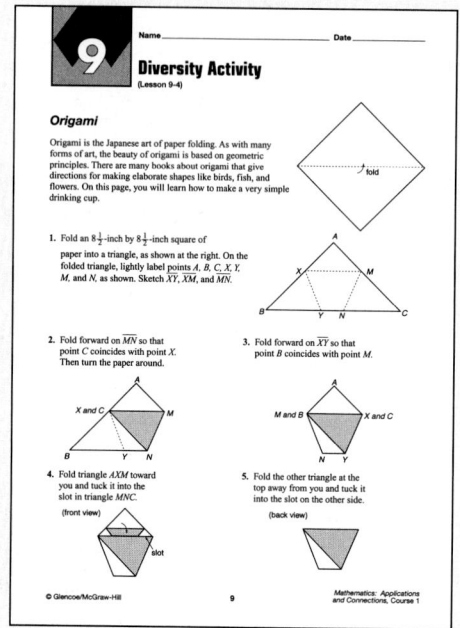

School to Career Masters, p. 9

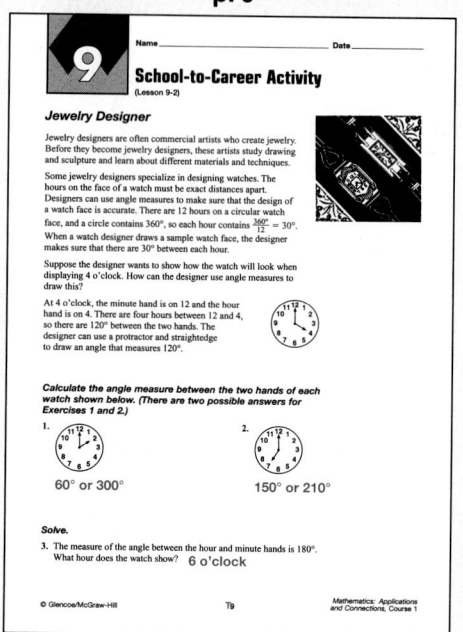

Family Letters and Activities, pp. 17–18

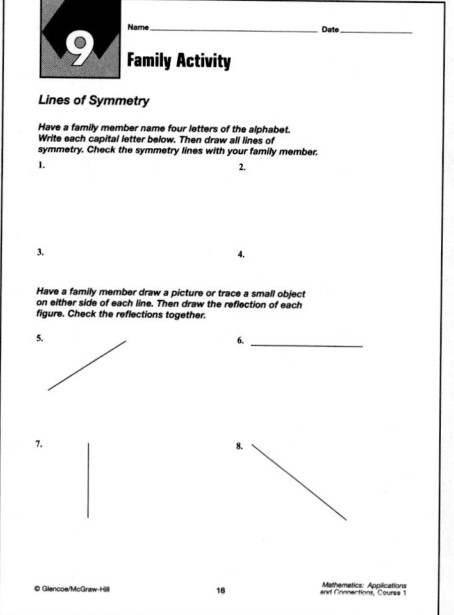

Science and Math Lab Manual, pp. 13–16

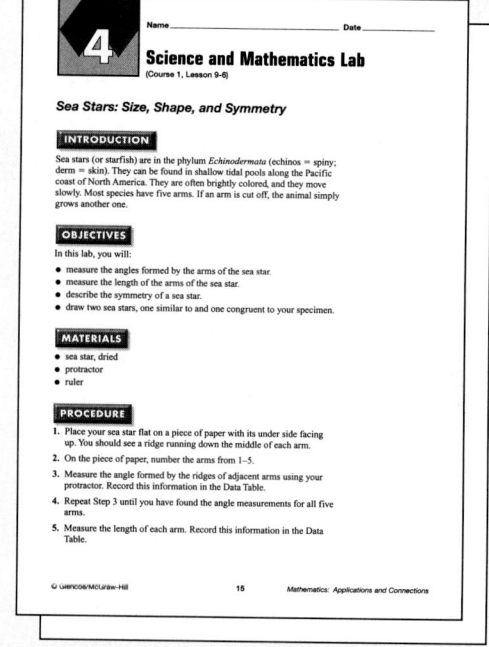

Hands-On Lab Masters, p. 77

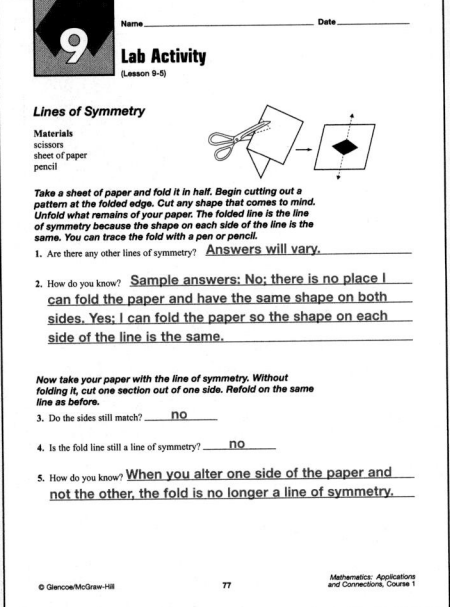

Assessment and Evaluation Masters, pp. 238–240

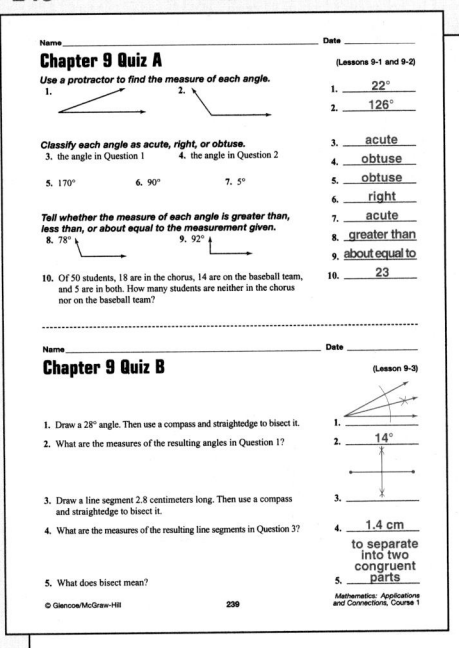

Technology Masters, pp. 17–18

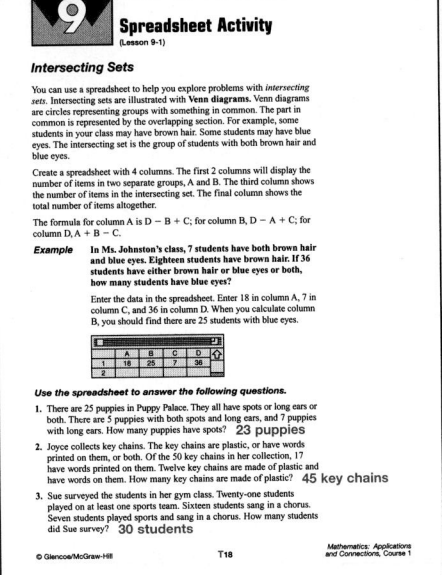

Investigations for the Special Education Student, p. 29

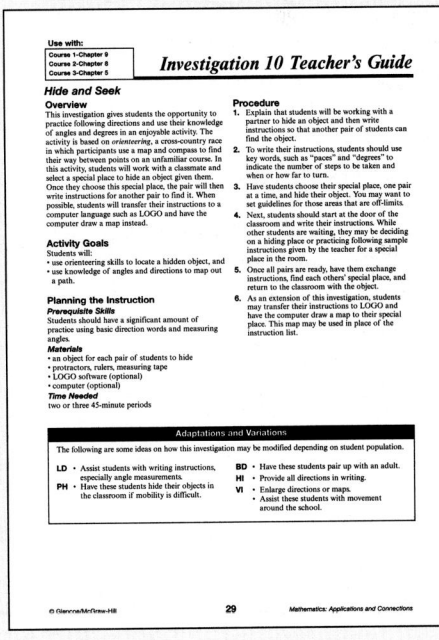

Geometry: Investigating Patterns

Theme: Architecture

Architects often redefine the American "dream" house. In the mid-twentieth century, simple designs with plenty of rooms and modern appliances were considered the ideal. By the end of the twentieth century, "dream" was defined as luxury with many specialized rooms added to houses built both for comfort and for the spectacular views they afforded.

Question of the Day How many lines of symmetry does the shape formed by the exterior walls of the dream house have? **8**

Assess Prerequisite Skills

Ask students to read through the list of objectives presented in "What you'll learn in Chapter 9." You may wish to ask them what each of the objectives means or if they have experienced or used any of these math concepts before.

 Building Portfolios

Encourage students to revise their portfolios as they study this chapter. Suggest that students add work to their portfolios that demonstrates progression as their math knowledge increases.

 Math and the Family

In the *Family Letters and Activities* booklet (pp. 17–18), you will find a letter to the parents explaining what students will study in Chapter 9. An activity appropriate for the whole family is also available.

What you'll learn in Chapter 9

- to classify and measure angles,
- to solve problems by using logical reasoning,
- to bisect segments and angles,
- to name two-dimensional figures, and
- to determine congruence and similarity.

CD-ROM Program

Activities for Chapter 9
- Chapter 9 Introduction
- Interactive Lessons 9-2, 9-5
- Extended Activity 9-6
- Assessment Game
- Resource Lessons 9-1 through 9-6

CHAPTER Project

DESIGNING A DREAM HOUSE

In this project, you will use geometry to find the actual angle measures and the actual lengths of the walls of the dream house shown. You will need a ruler and a protractor to complete this project.

Getting Started

- Look at the floor plan shown. What shape is the house?

$\frac{1}{8}$ in. = $2\frac{1}{4}$ ft

Technology Tips

- Use geometry or drawing **software** to design a dream house.
- Surf the **Internet** for more information on designing houses.
- Use a **spreadsheet** to convert from inches to feet.

inter NET CONNECTION Research For up-to-date information on houses, visit:

www.glencoe.com/sec/math/mac/mathnet

Working on the Project

You can use what you'll learn in Chapter 9 to help you design a dream house.

Page	Exercise
361	27
373	27
382	19
389	Alternative Assessment

CHAPTER Project
N O T E S

Objectives Students use a scale drawing to find
- angle measures.
- wall lengths.

Project Pointer You may suggest that students begin a *Project Folder* to keep their work as they complete each stage of the Chapter Project. The completed project may also be added to their portfolios.

In addition to the Chapter Project, have students add their own design for a dream house to their portfolios.

Using the Diagram Make sure students understand which lines represent walls and how doorways are indicated by line breaks. Have them look at the diagram from the entry point of view and visualize what the dream house looks like.

Investigations and Projects Masters, p. 52

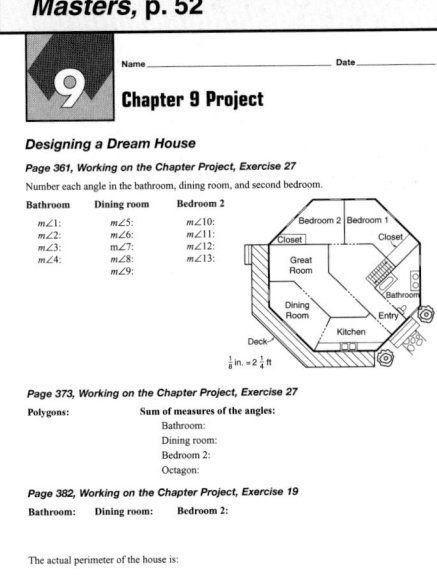

Instructional Resources ▶▶▶
A recording sheet to help students organize their data for the Chapter Project is shown at the right and is available in the *Investigations and Projects Masters*, p. 52.

Instructional Resources

- *Study Guide Masters*, p. 64
- *Practice Masters*, p. 64
- *Enrichment Masters*, p.64
- Transparencies 9-1, A and B
- *Technology Masters*, p. 18
- CD-ROM Program
  - Resource Lesson 9-1

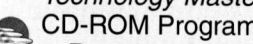

Recommended Pacing	
Standard	Day 2 of 14
Honors	Day 2 of 12
Block	Day 1 of 7

1 FOCUS

5-Minute Check
(Chapter 8)

1. Solve the proportion $\frac{5}{6} = \frac{x}{18}$.
   $\frac{5}{6} = \frac{15}{18}$

2. Express $\frac{14}{25}$ as a percent.
   56%

3. Express 2.8% as a fraction and as a decimal. $\frac{7}{250}$, 0.028

4. Express 7.3 as a percent.
   730%

5. Find 36% of 92. **33.12**

The 5-Minute Check is also available on **Transparency 9-1A** for this lesson.

Motivating the Lesson

Hands-On Activity Have students read the beginning of the lesson and work in pairs to identify angles in the classroom. Then have them order the angles from least measure to greatest.

2 TEACH

Transparency 9-1B contains a teaching aid for this lesson.

Reading Mathematics Have students discuss how the non-mathematical meanings of *acute* and *obtuse* relate to the mathematical meanings. Also, point out that *complementary* is spelled with an "e," not an "i."

9-1 Angles

What you'll learn
You'll learn to classify and measure angles.

When am I ever going to use this?
Knowing how to classify and measure angles helps a carpenter build houses.

Word Wise
edges
vertex
angle
degree
protractor
acute angle
obtuse angle
right angle
complementary
supplementary

Study Hint
Reading Math The measurement 0° is read as zero degrees.

Have you ever watched a magician place a person in a box and then "saw the box in half?" The **edges** of the front of the box look like two lines that meet at a point called the **vertex**.

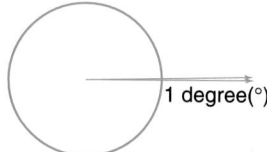

Vertices and edges of the box form **angles**.

The most common unit of measure for angles is the **degree**. A circle can be separated into 360 equal-sized parts. Each part would make up a one-degree (1°) angle as shown.

1 degree(°)

You can use a **protractor** to measure angles.

Step 1 Place the center of the protractor on the vertex of the angle with the straightedge along one side.

Step 2 Use the scale that begins with 0° on the side of the angle. Read the angle measure where the other side crosses the same scale. Extend the sides if needed.

The angle measures 140°.

Notice the arrows on the sides of the angles. These tell you that you can extend the sides.

Angles can be classified according to their measure.

This mark indicates a right angle.

Acute angles
measure between 0° and 90°.

Obtuse angles
measure between 90° and 180°.

Right angles
measure 90°.

Cross-Curriculum Cue

Inform the teachers on your team that your students are studying shapes and angles. Suggestions for curriculum integration are:
History: historical monuments
Industrial Technology: molding, trim
Physical Education: playing fields
Art: sculpture, painting, pottery

Study Hint

Problem Solving Lay a corner of your notebook paper on top of the given angle to determine whether an angle is acute, right, or obtuse.

① Use a protractor to find the measure of each angle. Then classify the angle as acute, right, or obtuse.

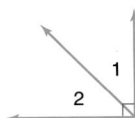

0° on one side

center of protractor

The angle measures 65°. It is an acute angle.

②

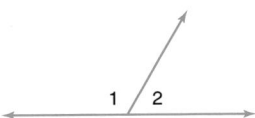

The angle measures 135°. It is an obtuse angle.

Some pairs of angles are **complementary** or **supplementary**. If the sum of the measures of two angles is 90°, the angles are complementary. If the sum of the measures of two angles is 180°, the angles are supplementary.

Study Hint

Reading Math The symbol $m\angle 1$ is read as the measure of angle 1.

complementary angles
$m\angle 1 + m\angle 2 = 90°$

supplementary angles
$m\angle 1 + m\angle 2 = 180°$

③ Algebra The angles shown are complementary. If $m\angle X = 36°$, what is $m\angle Y$?

$m\angle X + m\angle Y = 90°$ *complementary angles*

$36 + m\angle Y = 90$ *Replace $m\angle X$ with 36.*

$m\angle Y = 54$ *You know that $36 + 54 = 90$.*

The measure of the angle is 54°.

CHECK FOR UNDERSTANDING

Communicating Mathematics

Read and study the lesson to answer each question.

1. *Draw* an obtuse angle. Then write the steps describing how to use a protractor to measure your obtuse angle. **See Answer Appendix.**

2. *Tell* how you can determine whether two angles are complementary or supplementary. **See margin.**

Lesson 9-1 Angles **353**

Teaching Tip To help students remember the types of angles, encourage them to develop mnemonic devices, such as "a cute" animal is usually small, such as a puppy or a kitten.

In-Class Examples

Use a protractor to find the measure of each angle. Classify each angle as *acute*, *right,* or *obtuse*.

For Example 1

80°; acute

For Example 2

155°; obtuse

For Example 3
The angles shown are supplementary. If $m\angle X = 48°$, what is $m\angle Y$? **132°**

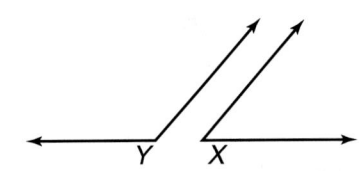

Teaching Tip Before Example 3, remind students that the sum of two numbers minus one of the numbers equals the other number.

---

3 PRACTICE/APPLY

Check for Understanding
If students need additional practice or instruction after completing Exercises 1–9, one of these options may be helpful.
- Extra Practice, see p. 580
- Reteaching Activity
- *Study Guide Masters,* p. 64
- *Practice Masters,* p. 64

Additional Answer
2. If the sum of the two angles is 90°, the angles are complementary. If the sum of the angles is 180°, the angles are supplementary.

Reteaching the Lesson

Activity Open the classroom door to form a right angle. Have pairs of students use masking tape on the floor to mark the right angle formed. Then have them open and close the door to show an acute angle and an obtuse angle. Have students measure the angles with a large classroom protractor.

Error Analysis
Watch for students who make errors measuring angles with protractors.
Prevent by reminding them to align one side with 0° and follow along the scale to see where the other side lands.

Guided Practice

Use a protractor to find the measure of each angle. Then classify the angle as *acute, right,* or *obtuse.*

3.

50°; acute

4.

135°; obtuse

Classify each angle measure as *acute, right,* or *obtuse.*

5. 140° **obtuse**   6. 17° **acute**   7. 86° **acute**

8. Classify the angles shown as complementary, supplementary, or neither. **complementary**

9. *Algebra* Angles A and B are supplementary. If $m\angle B = 106°$, find $m\angle A$. **74°**

EXERCISES

Practice

Use a protractor to find the measure of each angle. Then classify the angle as *acute, right,* or *obtuse.*

10.

20°; acute

11.

65°; acute

12.

110°; obtuse

13.

135°; obtuse

14.

63°; acute

15.

15°; acute

Classify each angle measure as *acute, right,* or *obtuse.*

16. 74° **acute**   17. 90° **right**   18. 28° **acute**   19. 174° **obtuse**
20. 168° **obtuse**   21. 54.6° **acute**   22. 137.5° **obtuse** 23. 4° **acute**

Classify each pair of angles as *complementary, supplementary,* or *neither.*

24.

complementary

25.

neither

26.

supplementary

27. An angle measures 89.9°. Is it an acute angle or a right angle? **acute**

28. If an angle measures 90.4°, is it an obtuse angle or a right angle? **obtuse**

29. *Algebra* Angles J and K are complementary angles. Find $m\angle K$ if $m\angle J = 72°$. **18°**

354   Chapter 9 Geometry: Investigating Patterns

Study Guide Masters, p. 64

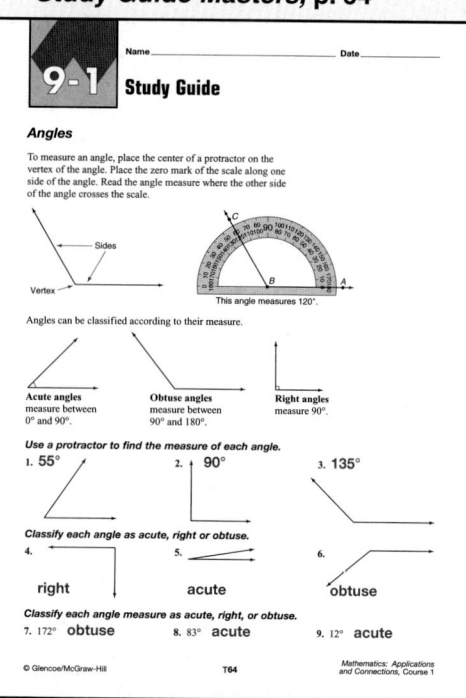

Investigations for the Special Education Student

This blackline master booklet helps you plan for the needs of special education students by providing long-term projects along with teacher notes. Investigation 10, *Hide and Seek,* may be used with this chapter.

30. *Algebra* Angles M and N are supplementary angles. If angle M measures $119°$, what is the measure of angle N? **61°**

31. *Carpentry* A carpenter joins two pieces of molding as shown. What types of angles can you identify and where? Explain. **See margin.**

32. *Geometry* The geometric figure shown is a regular pentagon. Are the angles inside a regular pentagon acute, right, or obtuse?

obtuse

140°

33. *Critical Thinking* Truck drivers find it difficult to accelerate when the grade of a hill is steep.
   a. How would you change the grade so that it is not so steep? **See margin.**
   b. Would the obtuse angle with the ground become larger or smaller? **larger**

Mixed Review

34. Estimate 1.5% of $127,500. *(Lesson 8-6)* **See margin.**

35. $0.76 = \frac{19}{25}$;
$0.15 = \frac{3}{20}$;
$0.09 = \frac{9}{100}$

35. *Statistics* Eight out of 10 mountain bicyclists have been injured at least once while riding their mountain bike. The graph shows where accidents occur. Express each decimal as a fraction in simplest form. *(Lesson 5-9)*

Mountain Bike Accidents

Downhill 0.76
Flat 0.15
0.09
Uphill

Source: *Acute Injuries from Mountain Biking,* by T. Chow, M. Bracker, K. Patrick, M.D.'s

36. *Standardized Test Practice* The table shows the results of a cost comparison for three compact discs at different stores. Which statement is true? *(Lesson 3-3)* **A**

Compact Disc	Music Store	Department Store	Discount Store
X	$13.95	$18.95	$11.95
Y	$15.95	$14.50	$13.50
Z	$16.50	$14.98	$15.98

   A Compact disc X costs the most at the department store.
   B The discount store has the best price for any of the three compact discs.
   C Compact disc Y costs the most at the department store.
   D The least expensive place to get compact disc Z is at the discount store.

For **Extra Practice**, see page 580.

37. *Algebra* Evaluate $3 + xy - 5$ if $x = 6$ and $y = 9$. *(Lesson 1-5)* **52**

38. Round 108 to the nearest ten. *(Lesson 1-3)* **110**

Extending the Lesson

Enrichment Masters, p. 64

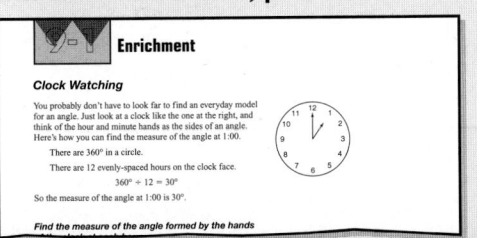

Enrichment

Clock Watching

You probably don't have to look far to find an everyday model for an angle. Just look at a clock like the one at the right, and think of the hour and minute hands as the sides of an angle. Here's how you can find the measure of the angle at 1:00.

There are 360° in a circle.

There are 12 evenly-spaced hours on the clock face.

$360° ÷ 12 = 30°$

So the measure of the angle at 1:00 is 30°.

Find the measure of the angle formed by the hands

Activity Have students work in pairs to determine how they can use Computer Aided Design (CAD) to measure and copy angles. Have them produce angles of various sizes if the software is available.

Practice Masters, p. 64

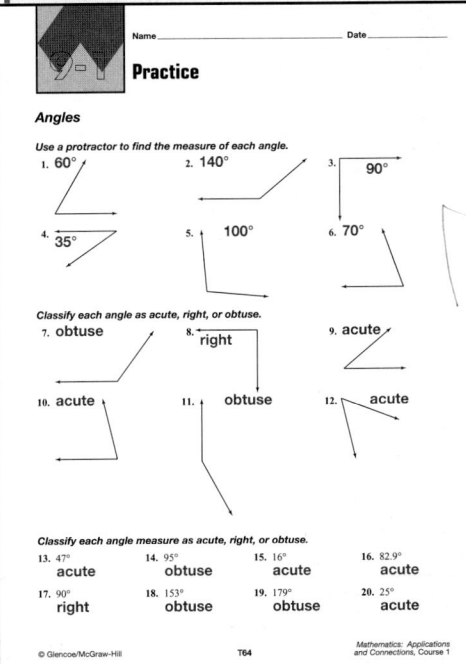

Name _____ Date _____

Practice

Angles

Use a protractor to find the measure of each angle.
1. 60° 2. 140° 3. 90°
4. 35° 5. 100° 6. 70°

Classify each angle as acute, right, or obtuse.
7. obtuse 8. right 9. acute
10. acute 11. obtuse 12. acute

Classify each angle measure as acute, right, or obtuse.
13. 47° acute 14. 95° obtuse 15. 16° acute 16. 82.9° acute
17. 90° right 18. 153° obtuse 19. 179° obtuse 20. 25° acute

© Glencoe/McGraw-Hill   T64   Mathematics: Applications and Connections, Course 1

THINKING

Objective Students solve problems by using logical reasoning.

Recommended Pacing	
Standard	Day 3 of 14
Honors	Day 3 of 12
Block	Day 2 of 7

1 FOCUS

Getting Started Have students act out the situation presented at the beginning of the lesson using smaller numbers. Have them put the Venn diagram on the chalkboard. Then have them work in pairs to answer Exercises 1–3. After the class discusses the results, have them solve Exercise 4.

2 TEACH

Teaching Tip To help students solve Exercise 4b, suggest that they draw 24 boxes to represent students. Write *LB* in 7 boxes for both lunch bags and backpacks. Then mark *L* in enough boxes so $L + LB = 12$ and *B* in enough boxes so $B + LB = 10$. The number of boxes with no letters answers Exercise 4b.

In-Class Example

A survey of 83 students showed that 56 chose books by author, 23 chose books by subject, and 15 chose books both by author and by subject. How many students used other methods to choose books? **19 students**

9-1B Use Logical Reasoning

A Follow-Up of Lesson 9-1

Jesse and Estella are standing in front of the sign-up board for extra-curricular activities. There are 55 students who play sports, 60 who are involved in clubs, and 33 who are involved in both sports and clubs. They are trying to find out how many students participate only in sports. Let's listen in!

I made a Venn diagram using the information from the sign-up sheets.

What's a Venn diagram?

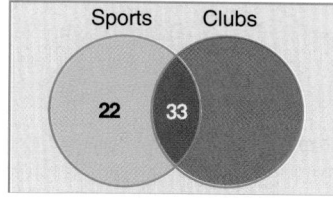

Jesse

Sports   Clubs

22   33

You can use a Venn diagram to solve the problem. The circle on the left represents sports. The circle on the right represents clubs. The overlapping region represents both sports and clubs and the region outside the circles represents neither sports nor clubs.

Estella

I see! There are 55 students who play sports and 33 who are involved in both sports and clubs. 55 − 33 = 22. So, 22 students participate only in sports.

THINK ABOUT IT

Work with a partner.   1. See margin.   2. 27 students

1. *Analyze* the information in the *Venn diagram*. Do you agree or disagree with Estella's and Jesse's thinking? Explain your reasoning.

2. *Use logical reasoning* to find the number of students who are involved only in clubs.

3. *Find* the total number of students who participate in extracurricular activities by **using logical reasoning**. **82 students**

4. *Apply* the logical reasoning strategy to solve the following problem.

   In a line of 24 students waiting to go on a field trip, 12 have lunch bags, 10 have backpacks, and 7 have both lunch bags and backpacks.

   a. *How many students have only lunch bags?* **5 students**

   b. *How many have neither a lunch bag nor a backpack?* **9 students**

356 Chapter 9 Geometry: Investigating Patterns

■ Reteaching the Lesson ■

Activity Have students draw a Venn diagram outline and use it to group various manipulatives. For example, use colored three-dimensional solids and group red figures, circular figures, and red and circular figures. Have students write out the situation as a word problem.

Additional Answer

1. Sample answer: Jesse's and Estella's thinking does make sense because 22 + 33 = 55, the number of students who play sports.

For **Extra Practice**, see page 581.

ON YOUR OWN

5. The last step of the 4-step plan for problem solving asks you to *examine* the solution. *Explain* how you can use the solution in Exercise 4 to verify the number of students who are going on the field trip. **See margin.**

6. *Write a Problem* that can be solved by using logical reasoning. Then ask a classmate to solve the problem. **See Answer Appendix.**

7. *Reflect back* Explain how you can use logical reasoning to answer Exercise 28 on page 354. **See margin.**

MIXED PROBLEM SOLVING

STRATEGIES
Look for a pattern.
Solve a simpler problem.
Act it out.
Guess and check.
Draw a diagram.
Make a chart.
Work backward.

Solve. Use any strategy.

8. *Communication* Lisa places a long distance phone call to Jason and talks for 33 minutes at a rate of 17 cents per minute. Did she spend about $4 or $6 for the call? **about $6**

9. *Patterns* What is the missing number in the pattern? . . ., 234, 345, _?_, 567, . . . **456**

10. *School* Of the 150 students at Washington Middle School, 55 are in the orchestra, 75 are in marching band, and 25 are in both orchestra and marching band. How many students are in neither orchestra nor marching band? **45 students**

11. *Patterns* The Sweepstakes Prize Company is having a contest. To enter the contest, you need to draw the next figure in the pattern.

a. Draw a sample entry. **See margin.**
b. Explain why your entry would be the next figure in the pattern. **See margin.**

12. *Enrico*

12. *Careers* Enrico, Angela, and Marcus are all engineers. Their specialties are electrical, mechanical, and civil engineering, but not in that particular order. The civil engineer and Enrico played golf together on Friday. Marcus, who works for the power company, is married to the civil engineer. Who is the mechanical engineer?

13. *Standardized Test Practice* The Venn diagram shows the relationship between the members in Moesha's scout troop.

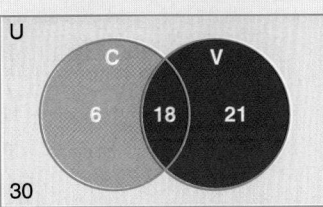

U = set of all members in Moesha's scout troop
C = set of members who have a camping badge
V = set of members who have a volunteer badge
Which of the following is *not* true? **C**

A 30 scouts do not have a camping badge or a volunteer badge.

B 21 scouts have only a volunteer badge.

C 63 students have at least one badge.

D There are more scouts with a camping badge than those who have only a volunteer badge.

E 6 students have only a camping badge.

Lesson 9-1B THINKING **LAB** **357**

■ **Extending the Lesson** ■

Activity Have students look for logic problems in various sources, such as crossword puzzle books and juvenile magazines. Have them solve the problems and then present their favorites for the class to solve.

Check for Understanding
Use the results from Exercise 4 to determine whether students comprehend how to solve problems by using logical thinking.

Extra Practice If students need additional practice in problem solving, extra practice is available on the following pages.
- Use Logical Reasoning, see p. 581
- Mixed Problem Solving, see pp. 593–594

Assignment Guide

All: 5–13

4 ASSESS

Closing Activity
Writing Have small groups of students develop a quiz on logical reasoning for the rest of the class. Have them include at least one of each type of problem used in the lesson.

Additional Answers
5. You found that 5 students have only lunch bags, 10 have only backpacks, and 9 have neither a lunch bag nor a backpack. 5 + 10 + 9 = 24. So, there are 24 students going on the trip.

7. A right angle measures 90°. The measure of the angle given is 90.4°. Since 90.4° is greater than 90°, it is only logical that the angle is an obtuse angle.

11a. Sample answer:

11b. Each figure has one more side than the previous figure, so the next figure must have six sides.

Instructional Resources

- *Study Guide Masters*, p. 65
- *Practice Masters*, p. 65
- *Enrichment Masters*, p. 65
- Transparencies 9-2, A and B
- *Assessment and Evaluation Masters*, p. 239
- *School to Career Masters*, p. 9
- *Technology Masters*, p. 17

 CD-ROM Program
  - Resource Lesson 9-2
  - Interactive Lesson 9-2

Recommended Pacing	
Standard	Day 4 of 14
Honors	Day 4 of 12
Block	Day 2 of 7

1 FOCUS

5-Minute Check
(*Lesson 9-1*)

Use a protractor to find the measure of the angle. Then classify the angle as *acute*, *right*, or *obtuse*.

1.

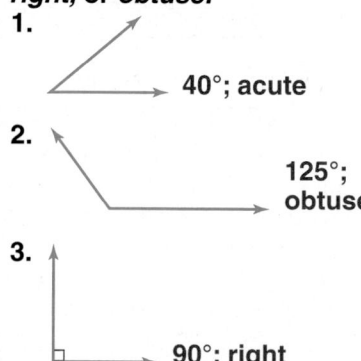

40°; acute

2.

125°; obtuse

3.

90°; right

Classify each angle measure as *acute*, *right*, or *obtuse*.

4. 176° obtuse
5. 34° acute

 The 5-Minute Check is also available on **Transparency 9-2A** for this lesson.

Motivating the Lesson

Communication Ask students if they think a protractor could be used to draw an angle with a certain measure. Have them suggest ways they could draw a specific angle.

9-2 Using Angle Measures

***What* you'll learn**

You'll learn to draw angles and estimate measures of angles.

***When* am I ever going to use this?**

Knowing how to use angle measures helps a sailor navigate a boat.

Word Wise

straightedge

> **Study Hint**
>
> **Problem Solving** You can use the draw-a-diagram strategy to help you with angle measures.

Many people enjoy the relaxation of sailing. Others enjoy the excitement of sailboat racing. To determine their direction when sailing, sailors can use a compass.

If a sailboat traveling east increases its directional angle by 45°, in what direction is it now sailing? (*Hint*: The directional angle is measured clockwise from magnetic north.)

East (E) has a directional angle of 90° measured from the north (N). By increasing this angle by 45°, the new directional angle is 90° + 45°, or 135°. The sailboat is now traveling southeast (SE).

You can use a protractor and a straightedge to draw an angle.

Step 1 Draw one side of the angle. Then mark the vertex and draw an arrow.

Step 2 Place the protractor along the side as you would to measure an angle. On the protractor, find the number of degrees needed for the angle you are drawing and make a pencil mark as shown.

Step 3 A **straightedge** is a ruler or any object with a straight side, which can be used to draw a line. With a straightedge, draw the side that connects the vertex and the pencil mark. Draw an arrow on the end of the other side.

The angle drawn is a 150° angle.

Example ❶ Draw a 68° angle.

| Draw one side. Mark the vertex and draw an arrow. | Find 68° on the appropriate scale. Make a pencil mark. | Draw the side that connects the vertex and the pencil mark. |

You can estimate the measure of an angle by comparing it to an angle whose measure you know.

HANDS-ON MINI-LAB

Work with a partner. ⬭ paper plate ╱ straightedge
✂ scissors ⌓ protractor

Try This
- Find and mark the center of a paper plate by folding it in half twice.
- Measure and cut wedges of 180°, 90°, and 45° from the plate. Write the measure on each wedge.

- Have one partner draw any angle on a piece of paper. The other partner should use the wedges to estimate the measure of the angle.
- Repeat for several different angles.

Talk About It
1. Explain how you could estimate the measure of an angle without using the wedges. **Compare the angle with a right angle.**
2. What is the measure of the angle of the remaining wedge? **45°**

Example ❷ Estimate the measure of the angle.

You can estimate the measure of the angle by using the angle wedges from the Mini-Lab. The angle shown is about the same as the 90° angle wedge and the 45° angle wedge. So, the measure of the angle is about 90° + 45°, or 135°.

 Transparency 9-2B contains a teaching aid for this lesson.

In-Class Example
For Example 1
Draw a 75° angle.

Using the Mini-Lab You may wish to use wedges cut from color transparencies to model the activity with students on the overhead projector. Encourage students to use several different wedges to determine the closest estimate. Students can also form 45° angles by folding a 90° wedge in half.

In-Class Example
For Example 2
Estimate the measure of the angle shown.

Sample answer: about 80°

Multiple Learning Styles

 Verbal/Linguistic Have pairs of students use geoboards and geobands to estimate the measure of angles. Have one student in each pair tell the other student an angle measure or a type of angle. The other student then creates the angle on the geoboard. Students should measure the angle with a protractor for accuracy. Have them switch roles and repeat.

3 PRACTICE/APPLY

Check for Understanding

If students need additional practice or instruction after completing Exercises 1–9, one of these options may be helpful.
- Extra Practice, see p. 581
- Reteaching Activity
- *Study Guide Masters*, p. 65
- *Practice Masters*, p. 65
- Interactive Mathematics Tools Software

Study Guide Masters, p. 65

Example **3**
INTEGRATION

Statistics The circle graph shows the results of a survey of music preference among sixth-graders at Pine Middle School. Use the measures of the angles to order the types of music from most preferred to least preferred.

Music Preference

Explore You need to order the types of music from most preferred to least preferred.

Plan Use a protractor to measure the angles that are too close to estimate. Then order the measures from greatest to least.

Solve Oldies is shown by the smallest angle. It is least preferred. Country is shown by the largest angle. It is most preferred. The measure of the angle for rock is 85°. The measure of the angle for rap is 90°.

So, the sixth-graders prefer country, rap, rock, and oldies, in that order.

Examine Find the measure of each angle. Then add. The total should be 360°.

$$140° + 90° + 85° + 45° = 360°$$

CHECK FOR UNDERSTANDING

Communicating Mathematics

Read and study the lesson to answer each question.   1–2. See students' work

1. *Explain* to a classmate how to draw a 145° angle.

2. *Show* an angle of about 120° using two pencils as the sides.

3. *Write* a sentence explaining how to use paper folding to show an angle of 45°. **See margin.**

Guided Practice

Use a protractor and a straightedge to draw angles having the following measurements. 4–6. See Answer Appendix.

4. 120°   5. 25°   6. 43°

Estimate the measure of each angle. 7–8. Sample answers are given.

7. about 120°   8. about 90°

9. Is the measure of angle *ABC* greater than, less than, or about equal to 155°? **about equal to**

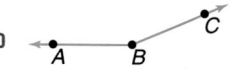

360   Chapter 9 Geometry: Investigating Patterns

Practice

Use a protractor and a straightedge to draw angles having the following measurements. **10–17. See Answer Appendix.**

10. 165°   11. 90°   12. 85°   13. 8°
14. 95°   15. 145°   16. 32°   17. 66°

Estimate the measure of each angle. **18–23. Sample answers are given.**

18. **about 60°**   19. **about 40°**   20. **about 90°**

21. **about 55°**   22. **about 135°**   23. **about 70°**

24. Is the angle shown greater than, less than, or about equal to 79°? **less than**

Applications and Problem Solving

25. *Navigation* A pilot is flying northeast (45° east of north). He increases the directional angle of the plane by 135°.
   a. In which direction is the plane now traveling? **south**
   b. How many degrees from north is the plane now traveling? **180°**

26. *Life Science* The branches on young trees should be spread to form angles of at least 60° with the tree trunk. This strengthens the branches and allows for more air circulation and light. Which branches on the tree shown need to be spread? **A, D, E**

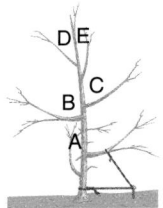

27. *Working on the* **CHAPTER Project** Refer to page 351. Trace the floor plan onto your paper. Use a protractor to measure each angle of the bathroom, the dining room, and the second bedroom. Then label the measures of the angles on your diagram. Save your diagram for use in other lessons. **See Answer Appendix.**

28. *Critical Thinking* The sum of the measures of a triangle is 180°. Find the measure of all the angles of a right triangle if one angle measures 10°.
   10°, 90°, 80°

Mixed Review

29. *Geometry* Classify the angle shown as *acute, right,* or *obtuse.* *(Lesson 9-1)* **acute**

30. *Standardized Test Practice* If an airplane travels 438 miles per hour, how many miles will it travel in 5 hours? *(Lesson 8-2)* **D**
   A 2,050 mi   B 2,090 mi   C 2,150 mi   D 2,190 mi   E Not Here

31. Find the LCM of 24 and 30. *(Lesson 5-7)* **120**

32. *Measurement* How many milliliters are in 2.14 liters? *(Lesson 4-9)*
   2,140 mL

For **Extra Practice,** see page 581.

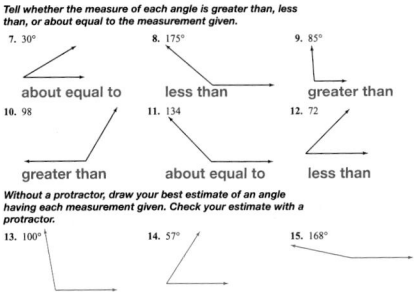

Extending the Lesson

Activity Have small groups of students determine how pilots use their knowledge of angles to fly an airplane. Have them look for information about the angle required for takeoff and how angles are used in navigation.

HANDS-ON LAB

COOPERATIVE LEARNING

9-3A Constructing Congruent Segments and Angles

A Preview of Lesson 9-3

straightedge

compass

A *line segment* is a straight path between two endpoints. To indicate line segment *JK*, write $\overline{JK}$. Line segments that have the same length are called *congruent segments*.

You can construct congruent segments using a straightedge and a compass. A compass is used to draw circles or circular arcs and to measure distances.

TRY THIS

Work with a partner.

❶ To construct a line segment congruent to $\overline{JK}$, follow these steps.

• Draw $\overline{JK}$. Then use a straightedge to draw a line segment longer than $\overline{JK}$. Label it $\overline{LM}$.

• Place the compass point at *J* and adjust the compass setting so that the pencil is on point *K*. The compass setting equals the length of $\overline{JK}$.

• Use this compass setting and place the compass point at *L*. Draw an arc that intersects $\overline{LM}$ at *P*. $\overline{LP}$ is congruent to $\overline{JK}$.

ON YOUR OWN

Trace each segment. Then construct a segment congruent to it. 1–3. See Answer Appendix.

1. *A* ____ *B*   2. *S* ____ *T*   3. *X* ____ *Y*

4. **Look Ahead** The length of $\overline{MN}$ is 38 millimeters. If $\overline{MN}$ is separated into two congruent parts, what will be the length of each part? **19 mm**

M ___ 38 mm ___ *N*

362 Chapter 9 Geometry: Investigating Patterns

The symbol ∠ is used to indicate an angle. The angle shown can be named in two ways, ∠JKL or ∠LKJ. The middle letter is always the vertex.

You can also use a straightedge and a compass to construct congruent angles. *Congruent angles* are angles that have the same measure.

TRY THIS

Work with a partner.

❷ To construct an angle congruent to ∠JKL, follow these steps.
- Draw ∠JKL. Then use a straightedge to draw side $\overrightarrow{BA}$. $\overrightarrow{BA}$ means ray BA. A ray is a path that extends infinitely from one point in a certain direction.

- With the compass point at K, draw an arc that intersects the sides of ∠JKL. Label the intersections M and N.

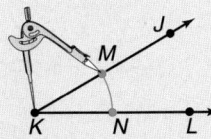

- With the same compass setting, move to side BA. Place the compass point at B and draw an arc that intersects side $\overrightarrow{BA}$. Label this intersection P.

- On ∠JKL, set the compass at points M and N as shown. With that setting, go to side $\overrightarrow{BA}$. Place the compass point at P, and draw an arc that intersects the larger arc you drew before. Label the intersection Q.

- Use a straightedge to draw side $\overrightarrow{BQ}$. ∠QBA is congruent to ∠JKL.

ON YOUR OWN

Trace each angle. Then construct an angle congruent to it. 5–7. See Answer Appendix.

5.

6.

7.

8. **Look Ahead** The measure of an angle is 113°. If the angle is divided into two congruent angles, what will be the measure of each angle? **56.5°**

Lesson 9-3A HANDS-ON **LAB** 363

Have students write the procedures for constructing congruent line segments and angles. Suggest that they include an illustration of each.

Activity 2 has students construct an angle congruent to a given angle. Have students repeat the activity with various angles.

ASSESS

Have students complete Exercises 1–3 and 5–7. After students construct congruent segments and angles, have them check their answers by cutting one out and laying it on top of the other one. Students may hold their papers up to the light to check their accuracy.

Use Exercises 4 and 8 to determine whether students understand constructing congruent segments and angles.

Hands-On Lab Masters, p. 57

Hands-On Lab 9-3A 363

- *Study Guide Masters*, p. 66
- *Practice Masters*, p. 66
- *Enrichment Masters*, p. 66
- Transparencies 9-3, A and B
- *Assessment and Evaluation Masters*, pp. 238, 239

 CD-ROM Program
- Resource Lesson 9-3

Recommended Pacing	
Standard	Days 5 & 6 of 14
Honors	Day 5 of 12
Block	Day 3 of 7

1 FOCUS

5-Minute Check
(Lesson 9-2)

Use a protractor and a straightedge to draw angles having the following measurements.

1. 160°

2. 25°

3. 95°

Estimate the measure of each angle.

4.

Sample answer: about 65°

5.

Sample answer: about 135°

 The 5-Minute Check is also available on **Transparency 9-3A** for this lesson.

Motivating the Lesson

Problem Solving Ask students how they would determine the midpoint of a piece of ribbon that is $3\frac{11}{16}$ inches long.

364 Chapter 9

9-3 Constructing Bisectors

EVCLIDE MEGARENS

What you'll learn
You'll learn to bisect line segments and angles.

When am I ever going to use this?
Knowing how to find bisectors helps a carpenter make miter cuts.

Word Wise
bisect

The Greek mathematician Euclid answered the following problem more than 2,000 years ago.

Given a line segment of any length, find a geometric method for dividing the line segment into two equal parts.

To **bisect** something means to separate it into two congruent parts.

 MINI-LAB

Work with a partner. ruler

Try This

- Draw $\overline{AB}$ using a straightedge.
- Fold point A onto point B and make a crease as shown. The crease bisects $\overline{AB}$. Label the intersection point C.

Talk About It It is halfway between point A and B.
Measure $\overline{AC}$ and $\overline{CB}$. What can you say about point C?

You can also use a straightedge and a compass to bisect a line segment.

Example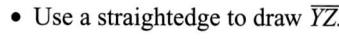

1 Use a straightedge and a compass to bisect $\overline{YZ}$.

- Use a straightedge to draw $\overline{YZ}$.

- Place the compass point at Y. Set the compass to more than half the length of $\overline{YZ}$. Draw two arcs as shown.

- With the same compass setting, place the compass point at Z and draw two arcs as shown. These arcs should intersect the first arc at W and V.

- With a straightedge, draw $\overline{WV}$. $\overline{WV}$ bisects $\overline{YZ}$ at P. So, $\overline{PY}$ and $\overline{PZ}$ are congruent.

When segments meet to form right angles, they are perpendicular. You can say that $\overline{WV}$ is a perpendicular bisector of $\overline{YZ}$.

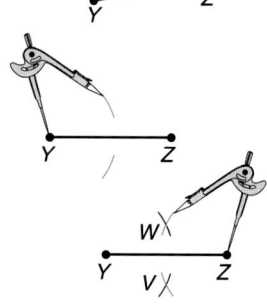

In the previous Mini-Lab and in Example 1, you learned how to bisect a line segment. You can also bisect an angle.

MINI-LAB

Work with a partner. straightedge protractor

Try This

- Draw ∠*ABC* using a straightedge.
- Fold side $\overline{BA}$ onto side $\overline{BC}$. Make a crease. The crease bisects ∠*ABC*.

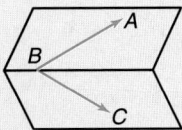

Talk About It They have the same measure.
Use a protractor to compare the measures of the two angles formed by the crease. What can you say about the two angles?

You can also use a straightedge and a compass to bisect an angle.

Example 2

Use a straightedge and a compass to bisect ∠*DEF*.

- Draw ∠*DEF* using a straightedge.

- Place the compass point at *E* and draw an arc that intersects both sides of the angle. Label these points *G* and *H*.

- Place the compass point at *G* and draw an arc as shown.

- With the same compass setting, place the compass point at *H* and draw an arc that intersects the one drawn in the previous step. Label the intersection *J*.

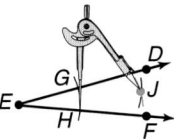

- Using a straightedge, draw $\overrightarrow{EJ}$. Side $\overrightarrow{EJ}$ bisects ∠*DEF*. So, ∠*DEJ* and ∠*JEF* are congruent.

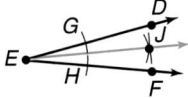

Lesson 9-3 Constructing Bisectors **365**

Check for Understanding

If students need additional practice or instruction after completing Exercises 1–7, one of these options may be helpful.
- Extra Practice, see p. 581
- Reteaching Activity, see p. 365
- *Study Guide Masters,* p. 66
- *Practice Masters,* p. 66

Assignment Guide
Core: 9–17 odd, 19–22
Enriched: 8–16 even, 17–22

Closing Activity

Modeling Have one student draw a line segment equal to the width of his or her hand. Another draws an angle equal to the angle formed by the index and middle fingers spread apart. Then have them bisect each figure.

Chapter 9, Quiz B (Lesson 9-3) is available in the *Assessment and Evaluation Masters,* p. 239.

Mid-Chapter Test (Lessons 9-1 through 9-3) is available in the *Assessment and Evaluation Masters,* p. 238.

Practice Masters, **p. 66**

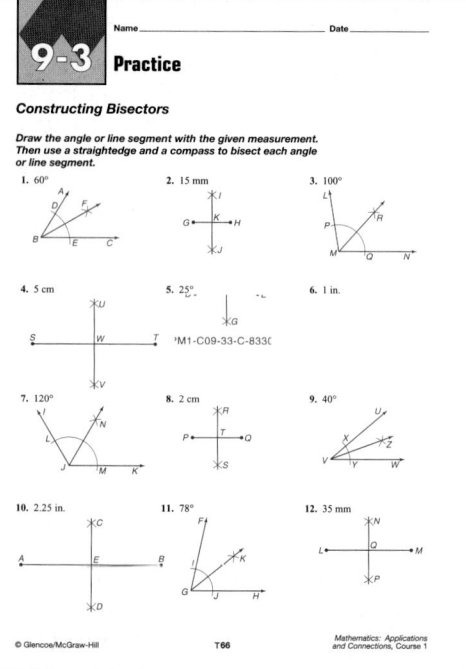

CHECK FOR UNDERSTANDING

Communicating Mathematics

Read and study the lesson to answer each question. 1–3. See Answer Appendix.

1. *Explain* the meaning of the word *bisect*.

2. *Tell* how to bisect a line segment using a straightedge and a compass.

HANDS-ON MATH 3. *Draw* an angle on a sheet of paper. Then fold the paper through the vertex of the angle so that the sides of the angle match. Make a crease and unfold the paper. What can you say about the crease?

Guided Practice

Draw the angle or line segment with the given measurement. Then use a straightedge and a compass to bisect each angle or line segment.

4–7. See Answer Appendix.

4. 4 in.   5. 65°   6. 7 cm

7. Draw a 119° angle. Then bisect the angle. What is the measure of each angle?

EXERCISES

Practice

Draw the angle or line segment with the given measurement. Then use a straightedge and a compass to bisect each angle or line segment.

8–15. See Answer Appendix.

8. 120°   9. 75°   10. 5 cm   11. 30°
12. 25 mm   13. 9 cm   14. 108°   15. 3 in.

16. In the figure shown, name the side that appears to bisect ∠MNP.   **side $\vec{NB}$**

Applications and Problem Solving

17–18. See Answer Appendix.

17. *Geometry* Copy the figure. Use a protractor to measure each angle formed by one side of the square and a diagonal. What can you say about the diagonals of a square?

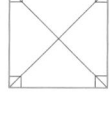

18. *Design* Draw a circle that is 6 inches in diameter. Draw a diameter. Construct a second diameter that bisects the first one. Construct two more diameters that bisect the angles of the intersection.

19. *Critical Thinking* Explain how to construct the following using a compass and straightedge. **See student constructions.**
   a. an equilateral triangle   b. an equilateral triangle
   c. a perpendicular bisector of a line segment
   d. a line passing through a given point and perpendicular to a given line

For **Extra Practice**, see page 581.

Mixed Review

20. Sample answer: about 30°

20. *Geometry* Estimate the measure of the angle. *(Lesson 9-2)*

21. Express 0.74 as a fraction in simplest form. *(Lesson 5-9)* $\frac{37}{50}$

22. **Standardized Test Practice** Three people bought pens for $11.55. How much did each person pay if they shared the price equally? *(Lesson 4-5)* **D**
   A $3.25   B $3.45   C $3.65   D $3.85   E $3.55

Extending the Lesson

Enrichment Masters, **p. 66**

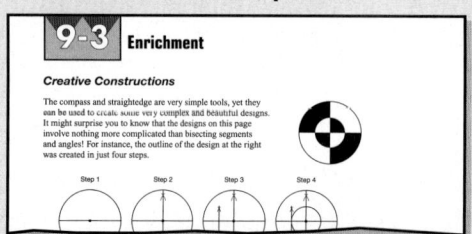

Activity Have small groups of students use a protractor to draw a triangle whose three angles are all 60°. Then have them bisect each angle using their compasses. Ask students to discuss what they have observed.

Architecture

Maya Ying Lin
Architect

When Maya Ying Lin designed the *Vietnam Veterans Memorial* in 1980, she became the first woman to design a major Washington, D.C., monument. Since then she has designed other memorials including the *Civil Rights Memorial* in Montgomery, Alabama.

To be an architect, you'll need at least a bachelor's degree in architecture and three years of practical experience. In addition to organizational skills and computer skills, math skills are needed to determine the dimensions of a design and to draw blue prints. Architects design shopping centers, schools, homes, museums, office buildings, and sports arenas, to name a few.

For more information:
American Institute of Architects
1735 New York Avenue, NW
Washington, DC 20006

interNET CONNECTION
www.glencoe.com/sec/math/mac/mathnet

Someday, I'd like to design memorials and monuments like Maya Lin.

Your Turn
Research architecture as a career. Then write a report that describes the benefits of a career in architecture.

Motivating Students
When visitors arrive in a city, the first thing they see is the city's skyline—its tallest buildings. Ideally, these structures are built artistically to please the eye; however, they must also be practical. Architects must consider the safety, comfort, and efficiency of each structure they design. To start a discussion about this profession, ask students questions about architectural designs.

- What three shapes are most often used for buildings? **squares, rectangles, and spheres**
- How can an architect design a building to make use of solar energy? **Include many large windows or walls made of glass.**

Making the Math Connection
As students learned in the Chapter Project on page 351, designing a house requires a floor plan. An architect must draw the building plans to scale, which means the size of each part of the drawing must be directly proportional to the size of that part of the actual building.

Working on *Your Turn*
Remind students that most architects work for an architectural firm. Many specialize in designing certain types of buildings, such as commercial offices or houses.

More About Maya Lin
- Maya Lin was a 21-year-old student at Yale University when she won the architectural competition to design the *Vietnam Veterans Memorial.*
- Originally from Athens, Ohio, Maya Lin now works as an architect in New York City.

*An additional School to Career activity is available on page 9 of the **School to Career Masters.***

COOPERATIVE LEARNING

9-4A Triangles and Quadrilaterals

A Preview of Lesson 9-4

geoboard

geobands

dot paper

scissors

Polygons are simple closed figures formed by three or more line segments. The line segments, or sides, intersect at their endpoints. These points of intersection are called *vertices* (plural of vertex).

In this lab, you will classify *triangles* and *quadrilaterals*. A triangle is a polygon with three sides. A quadrilateral is a polygon with four sides.

TRY THIS

Work with a partner.

❶ Use geobands to make a triangle. A sample triangle is shown.

• Draw the triangle on dot paper and cut it out.
• Repeat these steps until you have ten different triangles.
• Every triangle has at least two acute angles. The triangle shown has two acute angles. Since the third angle is obtuse, the triangle is an obtuse triangle.
• Sort your triangles into three groups, based on the third angle. Name the groups acute, right, and obtuse triangles.

ON YOUR OWN

Classify each triangle as *acute, right,* or *obtuse.*

1.

acute

2.

obtuse

3.

right

4. *Look Ahead* Write a definition for each type of triangle. **See margin.**

Additional Answer
4. An acute triangle is a triangle that has 3 acute angles. A right triangle is a triangle that has one right angle. An obtuse triangle is a triangle that has one obtuse angle.

Triangles can be classified by the type of angles they have while quadrilaterals are classified by the characteristics of their sides and angles.

Have students complete Exercises 1–3 and 5–7. Make sure students correctly differentiate between the shapes.

Use Exercises 4 and 8 to determine whether students can recognize types of triangles and quadrilaterals.

TRY THIS

Work with a partner.

❷ Use geobands to make a quadrilateral. Several samples are shown.

- Draw the quadrilateral on dot paper and cut it out.
- Repeat these steps until you have ten different quadrilaterals.
- You can classify quadrilaterals according to the characteristics of their sides and angles. The first quadrilateral shown can be classified as a quadrilateral with four congruent sides and four right angles.
- Sort your quadrilaterals into three groups, based on any characteristic you choose. Write a description of the quadrilaterals in each group.

Additional Answers

5. **Sample answer: The quadrilateral has two sides that are congruent.**

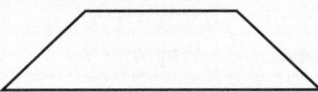

6. **Sample answer: The opposite sides of the quadrilateral are congruent.**

7. **Sample answer: The opposite sides of the quadrilateral are parallel.**

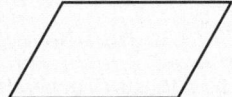

ON YOUR OWN

Write a sentence that describes one characteristic of each quadrilateral. Then draw a different quadrilateral that has the same characteristic. 5–8. See margin.

5.   6.   7.

8. *Look Ahead* Draw a quadrilateral that has two obtuse angles and exactly one pair of opposite sides congruent.

Lesson 9-4A HANDS-ON **LAB** **369**

Hands-On Lab Masters, p. 58

Math Journal Have students write a paragraph about the different types of triangles and quadrilaterals. Have them include illustrations and examples of everyday objects that fit the categories.

Additional Answer
8. Sample answer:

Hands-On Lab 9-4A **369**

Instructional Resources
- *Study Guide Masters*, p. 67
- *Practice Masters*, p. 67
- *Enrichment Masters*, p. 67
- Transparencies 9-4, A and B
- *Classroom Games*, pp. 23–26
- *Diversity Masters*, p. 9

 CD-ROM Program
- Resource Lesson 9-4

Recommended Pacing	
Standard	Days 7–9 of 14
Honors	Days 6 & 7 of 12
Block	Day 4 of 7

1 FOCUS

 5-Minute Check
(Lesson 9-3)

Draw the angle or line segment with the given measurement. Then use a straightedge and compass to bisect each angle or line segment. See students' work.
1. 35 mm   2. 5 in.
3. 74°   4. 128°

The 5-Minute Check is also available on **Transparency 9-4A** for this lesson.

Motivating the Lesson
Hands-On Activity Have students read the introduction to the lesson and the discussion of polygons. Then have students choose items in the room and determine what types of polygons they represent.

2 TEACH

 Transparency 9-4B contains a teaching aid for this lesson.

Reading Mathematics The word *polygon* and each of the names of polygons have their meanings hidden in their root words from Latin and Greek. *Poly-* means many, and *-gon* means sides. So a polygon has many sides. Have students use a dictionary to look up the root meaning of each of the polygon names.

What you'll learn
You'll learn to name two-dimensional figures.

When am I ever going to use this?
Knowing how to name two-dimensional figures can help you identify the shapes of traffic signs.

Word Wise
polygon
triangle
quadrilateral
pentagon
hexagon
octagon
decagon
regular polygon
parallel
parallelogram
equilateral triangle

Powwows are American Indian celebrations of heritage. Dancing, games, and parades are all part of the festivities. The colorful headdress shown is an example of what an American Indian may wear to a powwow. The figures on the headdress are examples of polygons.

A **polygon** is a simple closed figure formed by three or more sides. The number of sides determines the name of the polygon.

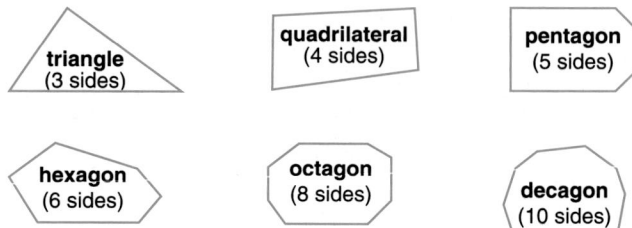

Any polygon with all sides congruent and all angles congruent is called a **regular polygon**. Some examples of common regular polygons are shown below.

Examples

Study Hint
Reading Math The red slash marks show congruent sides. The red arcs show congruent angles.

Name each polygon. Then tell if the polygon is a regular polygon.

❶   ❷   ❸

The polygon is a pentagon. The sides and angles are congruent so it is a regular polygon.

The polygon is a triangle. The sides and angles are not congruent so it is not a regular polygon.

The polygon is a quadrilateral. The sides are not all congruent so it is not a regular polygon.

Certain types of quadrilaterals have special characteristics.

 square

- All sides are congruent.
- All angles are right angles.
- Opposite sides are **parallel**. If you extend the lengths of the sides, the opposite sides will never meet.

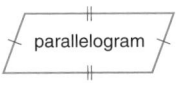 parallelogram

- Opposite sides are congruent.
- Opposite sides are parallel.

 rectangle

- Opposite sides are congruent.
- All angles are right angles.
- Opposite sides are parallel.

Example ❹ Explain how a rectangle and a parallelogram are alike and how they are different.

A rectangle and a parallelogram are alike because they
- have four sides.
- have opposite sides parallel.
- have opposite sides congruent.

They are different because a rectangle has four right angles and a parallelogram does not necessarily have four right angles.

A triangle with three congruent sides is called an **equilateral triangle**.

Example ❺ **Public Safety** The traffic sign shown is a yield sign.

a. What shape is a yield sign?
b. What is the perimeter of the sign?

36 in.
YIELD
36 in. 36 in.

LOOK BACK

You can refer to Lesson 4-4 to review perimeter.

a. A yield sign is shaped like an equilateral triangle.
b. The perimeter is the sum of the lengths of the sides.

$$36 + 36 + 36 = 108$$

So, the perimeter of the yield sign is 108 inches.

Check for Understanding

If students need additional practice or instruction after completing Exercises 1–10, one of these options may be helpful.

- Extra Practice, see p. 582
- Reteaching Activity
- *Study Guide Masters,* p. 67
- *Practice Masters,* p. 67

Assignment Guide

Core: 11–25 odd, 28–32
Enriched: 12–24 even, 25, 26, 28–32
All: Self Test, 1–10

Additional Answers

3. Jonathan: all squares are parallelograms since both sets of opposite sides of a square are parallel.
Victoria is incorrect. Some parallelograms are not squares since some parallelograms do not have right angles.

6. Alike: quadrilaterals, opposite sides parallel, four right angles, opposite sides congruent
Different: a square must have four congruent sides; a rectangle may not have four congruent sides.

Study Guide Masters, p. 67

CHECK FOR UNDERSTANDING

Communicating Mathematics

1–2. See Answer Appendix.

Read and study the lesson to answer each question.

1. *Identify* two different polygons that you see in your classroom.
2. *Draw* a triangle that has exactly one pair of congruent sides.
3. *You Decide* Victoria says that all parallelograms are squares. Jonathan says that all squares are parallelograms. Who is correct? Explain your reasoning. **See margin.**

Guided Practice

Name each polygon. Then tell if the polygon is a regular polygon.

4. hexagon; no
5. equilateral triangle; yes

Explain how each pair of figures is alike and how each pair is different.

6.
7.

See margin.   See margin.

Draw an example of each polygon. Mark any congruent sides, congruent angles, and right angles. 8–9. See Answer Appendix.

8. parallelogram
9. regular hexagon

10. *Design* Winona needs to design a table that will seat six people with equal comfort and work space. What shape should she make the table? **hexagon**

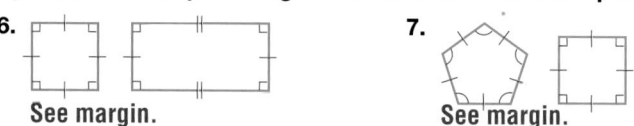

EXERCISES

Practice

11. pentagon; yes
12. hexagon; no
13. square; yes
14. quadrilateral; no

15–17. See Answer Appendix.

25. hexagon, pentagon

Name each polygon. Then tell if the polygon is a regular polygon.

11.   12.   13.   14.

Explain how each pair of figures is alike and how each pair is different.

15.   16.   17.

Draw an example of each polygon. Mark any congruent sides, congruent angles, and right angles. 18–23. See Answer Appendix.

18. quadrilateral
19. pentagon
20. equilateral triangle
21. regular octagon
22. triangle
23. rectangle

24. How many sides does a regular decagon have? **10**

Applications and Problem Solving

25. *Sports* The most popular game in the world is soccer. A soccer ball is shown. Which two polygons make up the pattern on a soccer ball?

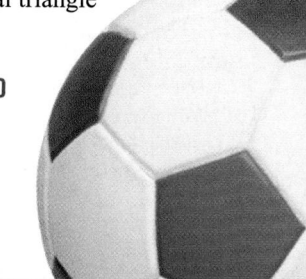

■ Reteaching the Lesson ■

Activity Have students make a chart listing all of the polygons named in this lesson. For each polygon, they should identify the number of angles and tell whether the sides are parallel or congruent.

Additional Answer

7. Alike: all sides congruent, all angles congruent
Different: pentagon has five sides and square has four sides.

27a. quadrilaterals, pentagons, hexagons, octagons

27b. 360°; 540°; 360°; 1,080°; See students' explanations.

26. *Carpentry* A clubhouse is shaped like a regular pentagon. If the perimeter of the floor is 30 feet long, how long is each wall? **6 feet**

27. *Working on the* Refer to page 351.

    a. Name the different types of polygons in the floor plan.

    b. Find the sum of the measures of the angles of the bathroom, the dining room, and the second bedroom. What is the sum of the measures of the angles of an octagon? Explain.

28. *Critical Thinking* A point is in the *interior* of a polygon if it lies on the inside of the polygon and does not lie on the polygon itself. A point is in the *exterior* if it lies outside the polygon and does not lie on the polygon itself. Tell whether each point is in the interior of the polygon, the exterior of the polygon, or neither.

For **Extra Practice**, see page 582.

  a.

    •*x*

    exterior

  b.

    •*X*

    neither

  c.

    •*x*

    interior

Mixed Review

29. *Geometry* Trace $\overline{CD}$. Use a compass and straightedge to bisect it. *(Lesson 9-3)* **See Answer Appendix.**

    C   *D*

30. Find 84% of 24. *(Lesson 8-7)* **20.16**

31. **Standardized Test Practice** Dr. Rodriguez drove 384.2 miles on 17 gallons of fuel. How many miles per gallon did his car get? *(Lesson 8-1)* **B**

    A 22.5 mpg **B** 22.6 mpg **C** 126 mpg **D** 226 mpg **E** Not Here

32. Express 2.375 as a fraction. *(Lesson 5-9)* $2\frac{3}{8}$

CHAPTER 9

Mid-Chapter Self Test

Use a protractor to find the measure of each angle. Then classify each angle as *acute, right,* or *obtuse.* *(Lesson 9-1)*

1. 125°; obtuse

2. 40°; acute

3. 90°; right

Estimate the measure of each angle. *(Lesson 9-2)* **4–6. Sample answers are given.**

4. about 120°

5. about 30°

6. about 110°

Draw the angle or line segment with the given measurement. Then use a straightedge and compass to bisect each angle or line segment. *(Lesson 9-3)* **7–9. See Answer Appendix.**

7. 75°   **8.** 7 cm   **9.** 117°

10. *Architecture* The gazebo at Jefferson Park is shaped like a regular hexagon. If each side is 7 feet long, what is the perimeter of the gazebo? *(Lesson 9-4)* **42 feet**

Lesson 9-4 Two-Dimensional Figures **373**

Extending the Lesson

Enrichment Masters, p. 67

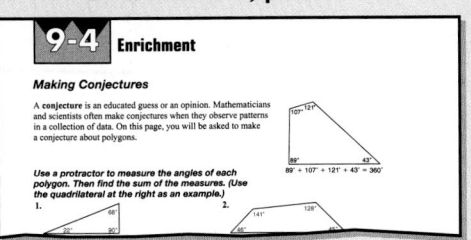

Activity Have students design a creature with squares, parallelograms, pentagons, hexagons, and equilateral triangles so that at least one side of each polygon touches another polygon. Use cardboard models of the polygons to construct the creatures.

CHAPTER Project

Exercise 27 asks students to advance to the next stage of work on the Chapter Project. You may wish to have students make a chart listing angle measure sums for different polygons.

4 ASSESS

Closing Activity

Writing Ask students to draw two different polygons. Have them exchange their drawings with others and then write an explanation of how they are alike and how they are different.

Mid-Chapter Self Test

The Mid-Chapter Self Test reviews the concepts in Lessons 9-1 through 9-4. Lesson references are given so students can review concepts not yet mastered.

Practice Masters, p. 67

HANDS-ON LAB Notes

GET READY

Objective Students make a net and use it to wrap a cube.

Optional Resources
Hands-On Lab Masters
• cube pattern, p. 24
• worksheet, p. 59
Manipulative Kit
• centimeter cube
• scissors

MANAGEMENT TIPS

Recommended Time
30 minutes

Getting Started Have students read the opening paragraph of the lesson and then ask the following questions. *Have you ever wrapped a box? How did you do it? How do you think a net is different from the material you used for wrapping?*

The **Activity** has students make a net by tracing the faces of a cube. Ask students if it matters which face they trace. **No; all six sides are congruent.** Make sure that students' nets have six squares.

ASSESS

Have students complete Exercises 1–3. Make sure students check their nets for coverability. Save any nets that don't work to discuss with the class.

Use Exercise 4 to determine whether students have discovered what is required to make a net.

 Have students use their findings to write a conclusion about the requirements of a net for wrapping a box. Encourage them to include diagrams of various nets.

HANDS-ON LAB

COOPERATIVE LEARNING

9-4B Using Nets to Wrap a Cube

A Follow-Up of Lesson 9-4

 scissors

cube

In this lab, you will make a figure called a *net* and use it to wrap a cube. The faces of the cube are shaped like squares.

TRY THIS

Work with a partner.

Step 1 Count the number of faces of the cube.

Step 2 Place the cube on the paper as shown and draw a square.

Step 3 Continue drawing squares to make a figure like the one shown. This figure is called a net.

Step 4 Cut out the net and try to wrap the cube.

Step 5 Repeat Step 3 to make a net like the one shown. Cut out the net and try to wrap the cube.

ON YOUR OWN

1. *Tell* if both nets covered the cube. If not, explain why the net or nets did not cover the cube. **See margin.**
2. *Find* three other nets of six squares that will cover the cube. Look for a pattern. **See Answer Appendix.**
3. *Write* three sentences describing the net patterns you found. **See Answer Appendix.**
4. *Reflect Back* Give an example of a net that can be used to cover a box whose faces are shaped like rectangles. **See margin.**

374 Chapter 9 Geometry: Investigating Patterns

Additional Answers

1. The second net did not cover the cube. The "top" and "bottom" covers are on the same side of the cube.

4. Sample answer:

Lines of Symmetry

What you'll learn

You'll learn to describe and define lines of symmetry.

When am I ever going to use this?

Knowing how to describe lines of symmetry can help you design and build a kite.

Word Wise

line of symmetry

reflection

More than 2,000 years ago, the Chinese military used kites for military purposes. They attached bamboo pipes to kites and flew them over the enemy at night. As wind passed through the pipes, the whistling noise caused the enemy to flee.

If you draw a line down the center of a diamond-shaped kite, the two halves match. When this happens, the line is called a **line of symmetry**. Lines of symmetry can be found in certain figures.

Examples

Draw all lines of symmetry for each figure.

❶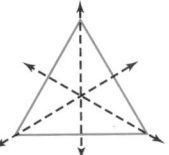

An equilateral triangle has 3 lines of symmetry.

❷

This quadrilateral has 1 line of symmetry.

❸

The letter F has no lines of symmetry.

CONNECTION ❹ **Geography** The flag of Jamaica is shown. How many lines of symmetry does the flag have?

Explore   You know the design of the Jamaican flag. You need to find all of the lines of symmetry.

Plan   To find the lines of symmetry, you can draw them.

Solve

There are 2 lines of symmetry.

Examine   Imagine folding the flag in half vertically, horizontally, and diagonally. Since the sides and patterns match exactly when it is folded vertically and horizontally, it has 2 lines of symmetry.

Lesson 9-5 Lines of Symmetry   **375**

Multiple Learning Styles

Interpersonal Separate students into small cooperative groups.
Each group should use geoboards and geobands to design pictures or figures that have symmetry. When all of the designs are complete, have groups present their designs to each other.

Motivating the Lesson

Communication Display a diamond-shaped kite that has a non-symmetric pattern on it. Ask students how many lines of symmetry the kite has. Point out that the figure itself has one line of symmetry. However, by looking at the figure with the design, the two halves do not match.

Instructional Resources

- *Study Guide Masters*, p. 68
- *Practice Masters*, p. 68
- *Enrichment Masters*, p. 68
- Transparencies 9-5, A and B
- *Assessment and Evaluation Masters*, p. 240
- *Hands-On Lab Masters*, p. 77
- CD-ROM Program
  - Resource Lesson 9-5
  - Interactive Lesson 9-5

Recommended Pacing	
Standard	Day 10 of 14
Honors	Day 8 of 12
Block	Day 5 of 7

1 FOCUS

5-Minute Check
(Lesson 9-4)

Name each polygon. Then tell if the polygon is a regular polygon.

1.   2.

decagon, yes; triangle, yes

3. In what ways are the triangle and the pentagon alike? In what ways are they different?

Alike: polygons with congruent sides
Different: number of sides

Draw an example of each polygon. Mark any congruent sides, congruent angles, and right angles. See students' work.

4. square

5. octagon

 The 5-Minute Check is also available on **Transparency 9-5A** for this lesson.

Transparency 9-5B contains a teaching aid for this lesson.

In-Class Examples

Draw all lines of symmetry for each figure.

For Example 1

For Example 2

For Example 3

For Example 4
A Texas flag (1510–1685) is shown. How many lines of symmetry does the flag have? Explain.

None; the design would not match exactly when folded horizontally, vertically, or diagonally.

Tell whether the figure shows a reflection. Write *yes* or *no*.

For Example 5

yes

For Example 6

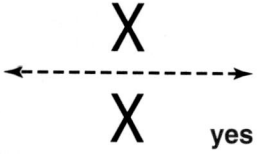

yes

The capital letter M has one line of symmetry. Notice that the right half is a **reflection** of the left half. A reflection is a mirror image of a figure across a line of symmetry. You can use a geomirror to draw reflections.

 geomirror   tracing paper

Work with a partner.

1a–c. See students' work.

Try This
1. Trace each figure shown. Then place the geomirror on the dashed line of each figure and draw its reflection.

   a.   b.   c.

Talk About It 2. mirror image
2. How did the reflection look on the other side of the geomirror?
3. What would you call the dashed line with respect to the figure and its reflection? **line of reflection**

Examples

Tell whether the figure shows a reflection.

5

Since the figure on the right is a mirror image of the figure on the left, it is a reflection.

6

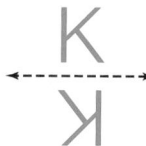

The figure on the bottom is not a mirror image of the figure on the top. So, it is not a reflection.

CHECK FOR UNDERSTANDING

Communicating Mathematics

Read and study the lesson to answer each question.
1. *Draw* a figure that has exactly four lines of symmetry. **See students' work.**
2. *Tell* which figure does not have at least one line of symmetry. **C**

   A   B   C   D

Classroom Vignette

"I have my students construct an art project using line symmetry. I have had them use both the computer and manual drawing techniques. This helps them to see and appreciate mathematics in artwork and other designs."

Deanna Gallagher, Teacher
Nathan Hale Middle School
Northvale, NJ

Deanna Gallagher

HANDS-ON MATH

3. *Draw* and cut out a rectangle and a square. How many ways can you fold each figure so that one half matches the other half? How many lines of symmetry does each figure have? **See students' work.**

Guided Practice

Tell whether the dashed line is a line of symmetry. Write *yes* or *no*.

4.
no

5.
yes

6.
no

Trace each figure. Draw all lines of symmetry.

7.

8.
none

9.

Tell whether the figure shows a reflection. Write *yes* or *no*.

10.
no

11.
yes

12. *Life Science* How many lines of symmetry does the starfish shown have?
5

Using the Mini-Lab If a geomirror or a similar reflector is not available, any reflective surface may be used, for example, mirrored glass tiles or pancake turners.

3 PRACTICE/APPLY

Check for Understanding

If students need additional practice or instruction after completing Exercises 1–12, one of these options may be helpful.
- Extra Practice, see p. 582
- Reteaching Activity
- *Study Guide Masters*, p. 68
- *Practice Masters*, p. 68

Assignment Guide
Core: 13–37 odd, 38–43
Enriched: 14–34 even, 36–43

EXERCISES

Tell whether the dashed line is a line of symmetry. Write *yes* or *no*.

13.
yes

14.
no

15.
yes

16.
yes

17.
yes

18.
yes

19.
no

20.
yes

Trace each figure. Draw all lines of symmetry.

21.

22.
none

23.

24.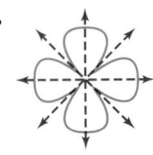

Study Guide Masters, p. 68

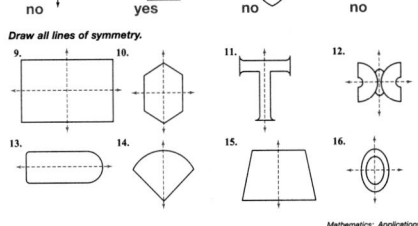

Reteaching the Lesson

Activity Have students play a game like "Concentration." Use sets of cards with one-half of a symmetrical shape on each card. Have players place all of the cards in front of them. Then have them take turns trying to match the halves of each shape.

Error Analysis
Watch for students who draw lines of symmetry between all of the vertices in a multi-sided figure.
Prevent by reminding students that a symmetrical shape may have only one line of symmetry.

Closing Activity

Modeling Have students work in pairs to draw an object that has three lines of symmetry. Have them exchange their drawings and draw the lines of symmetry.

Chapter 9, Quiz C (Lessons 9-4 and 9-5) is available in the *Assessment and Evaluation Masters,* p. 240.

Trace each figure. Draw all lines of symmetry.

25.
26.
27.
28.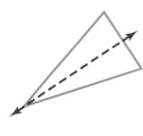

Tell whether the figure shows a reflection. Write *yes* or *no*.

29. **yes**
30. **no**
31. **no**
32. **no**
33. **yes**
34. 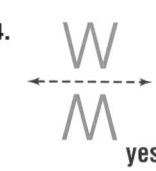 **yes**

Applications and Problem Solving

35. How many lines of symmetry does a stop sign have? **8**

36. *Geography* Switzerland is located in the Alps mountains in central Europe. How many lines of symmetry does the flag of Switzerland have? **4**

37. *Life Science* There are more than 20,000 different types of bees. The mining bee is known for making its nest in loose ground. How many lines of symmetry does the mining bee shown at the left have? **1**

38. *Critical Thinking* Copy the figure shown. Then shade enough squares so that the figure has a diagonal line of symmetry. **Sample answer:**

Mixed Review

39. *Geometry* Draw an example of an octagon. *(Lesson 9-4)*

39. See students' work.

40. **Standardized Test Practice** Three-fifths of the sixth-grade students went on the class trip. What percent of the sixth-grade students did *not* go on the class trip? *(Lesson 8-4)* **A**

   A 40%   **B** 45%   **C** 50%   **D** 60%

41. *Algebra* If $x = 1\frac{2}{3}$, and $y = 3\frac{4}{5}$, what is the value of xy? *(Lesson 7-3)* $6\frac{1}{3}$

42. Express 0.84 as a fraction in simplest form. *(Lesson 5-9)* $\frac{21}{25}$

For **Extra Practice,** see page 582.

43. *Entertainment* The graph shows the number of visitors who toured the Rock and Roll Hall of Fame in Cleveland on a Saturday. How many visitors altogether toured the Rock and Roll Hall of Fame before 1:00 P.M.? *(Lesson 2-3)* **525 people**

Rock and Roll Hall of Fame

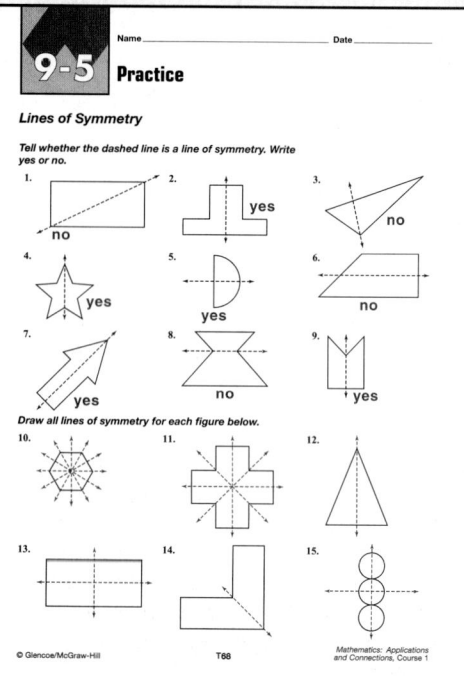
Extending the Lesson

Enrichment Masters, p. 68

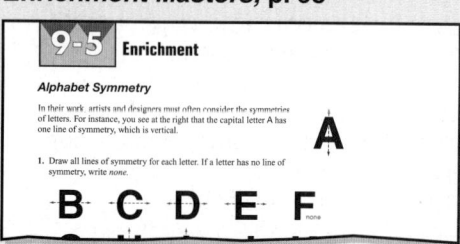

Activity Ask small groups of students to go to the library to find pictures of works of art that have symmetry or pictures of state or country flags that show symmetry. Have groups present their findings to the class.

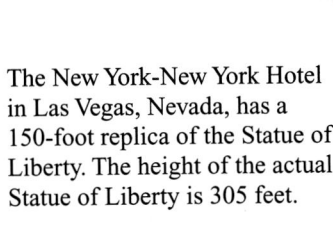

9-6 Size and Shape

What you'll learn
You'll learn to determine congruence and similarity.

When am I ever going to use this?
Knowing how to determine congruence and similarity helps an architect design statues.

Word Wise
similar figures
congruent figures

The New York-New York Hotel in Las Vegas, Nevada, has a 150-foot replica of the Statue of Liberty. The height of the actual Statue of Liberty is 305 feet.

Figures that have the same shape and angles, but different size are called **similar figures**. The symbol ~ means *is similar to*.

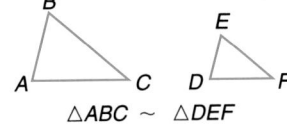

△ABC ~ △DEF

Suppose the replica was 305 feet tall. The statues would be the same size and shape.

Figures that are the same size and shape are called **congruent figures**. The symbol ≅ means *is congruent to*.

△MNP ≅ △RST

In the following lab, you will explore some characteristics of congruent figures and similar figures.

Study Hint

Reading Math The symbol △ABC is read as *triangle ABC*.

1. yes; The figures in choice b.
2. In choice a, the angles are congruent. In choice b, the angles and sides are congruent.
3. yes; the figures in choice a

Did you know? The length of the Statue of Liberty's nose is about 0.04 of her height.

 HANDS - ON
MINI-LAB

Work with a partner. scissors ✂ tracing paper

Try This
• Trace each pair of figures and cut them out.

 a.

b.

• Try to match each pair of figures.

Talk About It
1. Congruent figures are exact matches. Did either pair of figures match? If so, name the congruent figures.
2. Compare the angles and segments of each pair of figures. How are they alike? How are they different?
3. Did either pair of figures not match? A pair of figures may be similar without being congruent. Name the similar figures.

Lesson 9-6 Size and Shape **379**

Multiple Learning Styles

 Intrapersonal Have students write a paragraph about ways to estimate angle measures and determine if figures are similar or congruent. Have them include a description of reminders or shortcuts that help them.

MathPASS CD-ROM

This CD-ROM offers a complete, self-paced mathematics curriculum. Each lesson includes a pretest, tutorial, guided practice, and posttest. MathPASS Lesson 33 is correlated to this Student Edition lesson.
For Windows & Macintosh

9-6 Lesson Notes

Instructional Resources
• *Study Guide Masters*, p. 69
• *Practice Masters*, p. 69
• *Enrichment Masters*, p. 69
• Transparencies 9-6, A and B
• *Assessment and Evaluation Masters*, p. 240
• *Science and Math Lab Manual*, pp. 13–16
 CD-ROM Program
  • Resource Lesson 9-6
  • Extended Activity 9-6

Recommended Pacing	
Standard	Days 11 & 12 of 14
Honors	Days 9 & 10 of 12
Block	Day 6 of 7

1 FOCUS

5-Minute Check
(Lesson 9-5)

Tell whether the dashed line is a line of symmetry. Write *yes* or *no*.

1. yes
2. no

Copy each figure. Draw all lines of symmetry.

3.
4.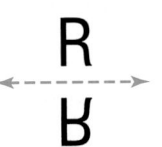

5. Does the figure show a reflection?

 yes

The 5-Minute Check is also available on **Transparency 9-6A** for this lesson.

Motivating the Lesson
Problem Solving Have students read the opening paragraphs of the lesson. Then hand out magazines and ask students to look for similar and congruent shapes. Have them cut out the shapes and identify them as similar, congruent, or neither.

Lesson 9-6 **379**

Transparency 9-6B contains a teaching aid for this lesson.

Using the Mini-Lab Point out that all congruent figures are similar but not all similar figures are congruent. You may use an overhead projector to model the activity.

In-Class Examples

Tell whether each triangle is congruent or similar to the triangle shown.

For Example 1

 congruent

For Example 2

 neither congruent nor similar

For Example 3

 similar

For Example 4
△*ABC* is congruent to △*DEF*.

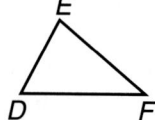

a. What side of △*DEF* corresponds to side $\overline{AC}$? $\overline{DF}$
b. What is the perimeter of △*DEF*? **97 ft**

Teaching Tip Explain to students that congruent figures are like exact photocopies. Similar figures are like photocopies made using the zoom feature.

---

3 PRACTICE/APPLY

Check for Understanding

If students need additional practice or instruction after completing Exercises 1–7, one of these options may be helpful.
• Extra Practice, see p. 582
• Reteaching Activity
• *Study Guide Masters*, p. 69
• *Practice Masters*, p. 69

Examples

Tell whether each quadrilateral is congruent or similar to the quadrilateral shown.

① The quadrilaterals have the same shape and angles, but not the same size. They are similar.

② The quadrilaterals are the same size and shape. They are congruent.

③ The quadrilaterals are not the same shape or size. They are neither congruent nor similar.

INTEGRATION ④ **Geometry** △*MNP* is congruent to △*RST*.

a. What side of △*RST* corresponds to side $\overline{MN}$?

b. What is the perimeter of △*RST*?

a. Side $\overline{RS}$ corresponds to side $\overline{MN}$.

b. The perimeter of △*MNP* is 25 + 48 + 47, or 120 centimeters. Since △*MNP* and △*RST* are congruent, they have the same size and shape. So, the perimeter of △*RST* is also 120 centimeters.

CHECK FOR UNDERSTANDING

Communicating Mathematics

Read and study the lesson to answer each question. 2–3. See students' work.

1. **Tell** why the two figures shown are similar. **See margin.**

2. **Draw** two similar triangles.

HANDS-ON MATH 3. **Use** a geoboard and geobands to make two similar figures and two congruent figures. Then write a sentence explaining the difference between similarity and congruence.

Guided Practice

Tell whether each pair of polygons is *congruent*, *similar*, or *neither*.

4. neither
5. congruent

6. **Geometry** Quadrilateral *ABCD* is congruent to quadrilateral *EFGH*.
a. What is the measure of side $\overline{AD}$? **4 m**
b. What side corresponds to side $\overline{BC}$? $\overline{FG}$

380 Chapter 9 Geometry: Investigating Patterns

■ **Reteaching the Lesson** ■

Activity Have students use geoboards and geobands to make similar and congruent figures. If geoboards are unavailable, dot paper may be substituted. Have students take turns making figures and asking others to make a similar or congruent figure.

Additional Answer

1. **The angles are congruent, they have the same shape, and they are different sizes.**

7. Geography The flag of the state of North Carolina is shown. How many pairs of congruent quadrilaterals are there? **3**

EXERCISES

Practice **Tell whether each pair of polygons is *congruent*, *similar*, or *neither*.**

8. **similar**

9. **neither**

10. **congruent**

11. **neither**

12. **similar**

13. 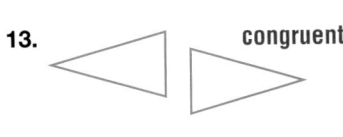 **congruent**

14. Which pair of polygons are neither similar nor congruent? **b.**

a. b. c.

15. The triangles shown are acute triangles and $\triangle DEF \cong \triangle LMN$. **a. 2.5 m b. $\overline{NM}$**
    a. What is the measure of side $\overline{DF}$?
    b. What side corresponds to side $\overline{FE}$?

16. Quadrilateral *MNOP* is congruent to quadrilateral *WXYZ*.
    a. Find the perimeter of quadrilateral *WXYZ*. **18 in.**
    b. What side corresponds to side $\overline{MP}$? **$\overline{WZ}$**

Applications and Problem Solving

Real World

17. *Puzzles* A tangram is a Chinese puzzle consisting of seven geometric shapes. The diagram shows how the pieces of the puzzle can form a square. Which of the geometric shapes in a tangram are similar? **See margin.**

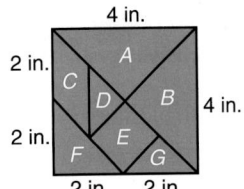

Lesson 9-6 *Size and Shape* **381**

Assignment Guide

Core: 9–17 odd, 20–23
Enriched: 8–16 even, 17, 18, 20–23

Additional Answer
17. **A and D; A and F; A and G; B and D; B and F; B and G; F and D; A and B; D and G; F and G**

Study Guide Masters, p. 69

Lesson 9-6 **381**

4 ASSESS

Closing Activity

Speaking Have students explain how to tell whether two figures are congruent or similar. Suggest that they demonstrate their explanations by using toothpicks or drinking straws to make congruent and similar figures.

Chapter 9, Quiz D (Lesson 9-6) is available in the *Assessment and Evaluation Masters*, p. 240.

18. **Technology** A photocopier can make copies that are reduced or enlarged. At 50%, a photocopier makes a copy that is 50%, or one-half, of the original length and width. Nina needs to photocopy a picture that is 7 inches long and 5 inches wide. **b. similar**

    a. Draw a diagram that shows the dimensions of the original picture and the dimensions of the copy reduced by 50%. **See Answer Appendix.**

    b. Are the two pictures similar or congruent?

19. **Working on the CHAPTER Project**

    Refer to the floor plan on page 351. Use the given scale to find the actual length of each wall of the bathroom, dining room, and the second bedroom. Then find the actual perimeter of the house. Label each length on your diagram. **See Answer Appendix.**

20. yes; They all have 4 right angles and 4 congruent sides.

Mixed Review

20. **Critical Thinking** Are all squares similar? Explain your reasoning.

21. **Standardized Test Practice** Which figure does *not* have at least one line of symmetry? *(Lesson 9-5)* **B**

    A   B   C   D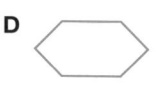

For **Extra Practice**, see page 582.

22. **Money Matters** One fourth of the 417 students in the sixth grade owe the library for fines. About how many sixth grade students owe the library for fines? *(Lesson 7-2)* **about 100 students**

23. Find $7\frac{1}{2} - 1\frac{3}{4}$. *(Lesson 6-6)* $5\frac{3}{4}$

MATH IN THE MEDIA

Peanuts

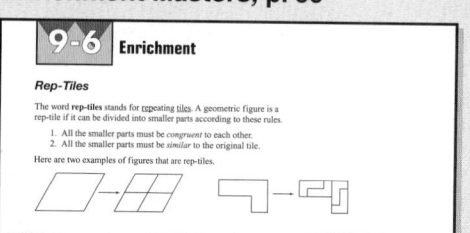

1. What does it mean to be congruent to? **equal in size and shape**

2. *Draw* two octagons that are congruent. **See students' work.**

382 Chapter 9 Geometry: Investigating Patterns

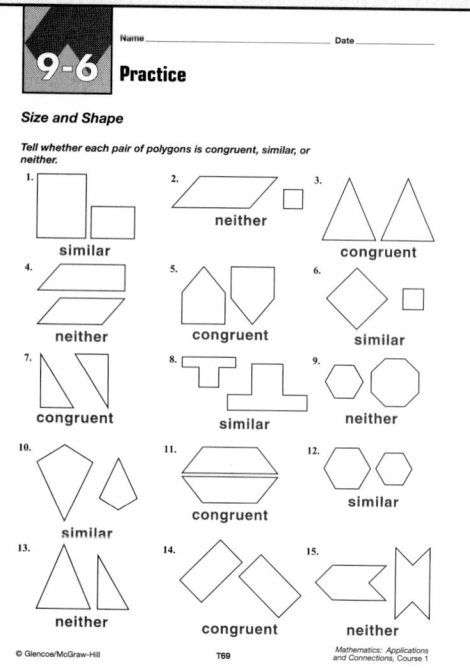
■ Extending the Lesson ■

MATH IN THE MEDIA

Have students practice drawing the symbols for *congruent* and *similar*. Discuss meanings of other symbols that students use in math or in other areas, such as addition or subtraction symbols and recycling or traffic symbols.

Pento

Get Ready   This game is for two players.

   grid paper

Get Set   A *pento* is a game piece made of five squares. Some sample pentos are shown. Two *pentos* are alike if they can be rotated so that they exactly match each other when stacked. They are different if they do not match when stacked or if they must be flipped over in order to match.

alike   **different**   **different**

Go   • **Round 1:** Each player has 1 minute to draw as many different *pentos* as possible on grid paper. Each player scores 1 point for every *pento* drawn. Two points are scored for each *pento* found by only one of the players.

• **Round 2:** Cut out all of the *pentos* from round 1. Then choose one *pento* as a model. Using any four different *pentos*, each player builds a similar figure where the length of each side is twice the length of the side in the model. Sketch the results on grid paper.

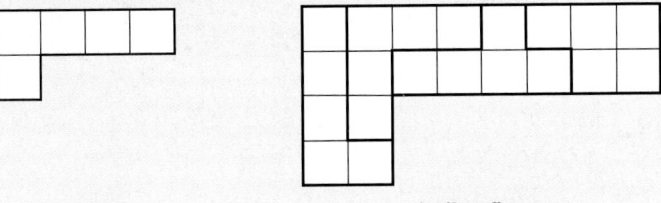

model   **similar figure**

Continue this round for 2 minutes. Each player scores 3 points for each similar figure drawn. The player with the most total points wins.

 Visit www.glencoe.com/sec/math/mac/mathnet for more games.

Let the Games Begin Pento   **383**

In Round 1, make sure students check carefully for duplicates. Some additional original pentos are shown.

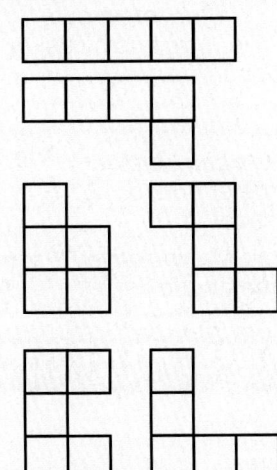

Another possible solution for Round 2 is below.

COOPERATIVE LEARNING

9-6B Translations and Escher Drawings

A Follow-Up of Lesson 9-6

grid paper

colored pencils

M. C. Escher (1898-1972), a Dutch artist, was famous for his unusual artwork. His most famous pieces were created by using congruent figures shaped as birds, reptiles, or fish that fit together to cover the entire surface of the artwork. You can create an Escher-like drawing by using a *translation*. When you do a translation, you slide a figure from one location to another.

TRY THIS

Work with a partner.

1 To create an Escher-like drawing using a translation, follow these steps.
   • Draw a square. Then draw a triangle on the top of the square as shown.
   • Translate, or slide, the triangle to the opposite side of the square. The pattern unit for our Escher-like drawing is formed.
   • Repeat the pattern unit you made in the steps above to create an Escher-like drawing on grid paper. Use colored pencils to decorate your drawing.

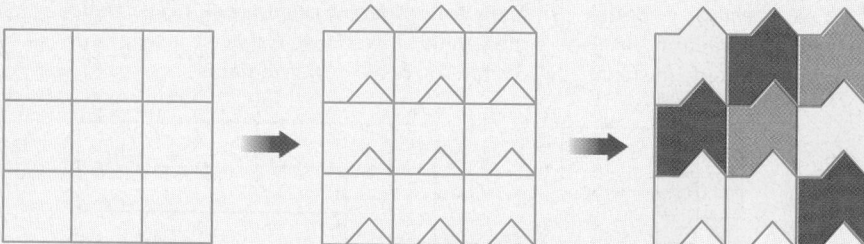

ON YOUR OWN

Create an Escher-like drawing for each pattern unit shown. 1–3. See Answer Appendix.

1.

2.

3. ![pattern unit 3]

4. *Reflect Back* Are the pattern units in your Escher-like drawing congruent? **yes**

384 Chapter 9 Geometry: Investigating Patterns

You can also create an Escher-like drawing using two translations.

Work with a partner.

2 To create an Escher-like drawing using two translations, follow these steps.

- Draw a square. Then draw a rectangle on the top of the square as shown. Next, translate the rectangle to the opposite side of the square.

- Draw a triangle on the left side and translate the triangle to the right side.

- Repeat the pattern unit you made above to create an Escher-like drawing on grid paper. Use colored pencils to decorate your drawing.

Create an Escher-like drawing for each pattern unit shown. 5-7. See Answer Appendix.

5.   6.   7.

8. *Reflect Back* Why do the pieces fit together exactly? **They are congruent.**

Activity 2 has students use two translations to create the drawings. Emphasize to students that the order of translations doesn't matter as long as they perform both.

Have students complete Exercises 1–3 and 5–7. Watch for students who forget to make the translation before repeating the pattern.

Use Exercises 4 and 8 to determine whether students understand how to create Escher-like drawings by using translations.

Hands-On Lab Masters, p. 60

Name_____ Date_____

9

Hands-On Lab
(Lesson 9-6B)

Translations and Escher Drawings

On Your Own

1.   2. 3.

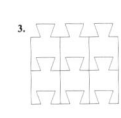

4. **Reflect Back** Are the pattern units in your drawings congruent? _____ yes

5.   6. 7.

8. **Reflect Back** Why do the pieces fit together exactly? **They are congruent.**

© Glencoe/McGraw-Hill   60   *Mathematics: Applications and Connections, Course 1*

Math Journal Have students write a few sentences describing how translations can be used to make an Escher-like drawing. Encourage them to include designs they have created.

Vocabulary

This section provides a listing of the new terms, properties, and phrases that were introduced in this chapter. Have students define each term and provide an example or two of it, if appropriate.

Understanding and Using the Vocabulary

These exercises check students' understanding of the terms by using a variety of verbal formats including matching, completion, and true/false.

Glossaries A complete glossary of terms appears on pages 642–648. The glossary also appears in Spanish on pages 649–656.

Additional Answer

11. An acute angle is less than 90°, a right angle is 90°, and an obtuse angle is greater than 90°.

Vocabulary

After completing this chapter, you should be able to define each term, concept, or phrase and give an example or two of each.

Geometry

acute angle (p. 352)
angle (p. 352)
bisect (p. 364)
complementary (p. 353)
congruent angles (p. 363)
congruent figures (p. 379)
congruent segments (p. 362)
decagon (p. 370)
degree (p. 352)
edges (p. 352)
equilateral triangle (p. 371)

hexagon (p. 370)
line of symmetry (p. 375)
line segment (p. 362)
net (p. 374)
obtuse angle (p. 352)
octagon (p. 370)
parallel (p. 371)
parallelogram (p. 371)
pentagon (p. 370)
polygon (pp. 368, 370)
protractor (p. 352)
quadrilateral (pp. 368, 370)
ray (p. 363)

rectangle (p. 371)
reflection (p. 376)
regular polygon (p. 370)
right angle (p. 352)
similar figures (p. 379)
square (p. 371)
straightedge (p. 358)
supplementary (p. 353)
translation (p. 384)
triangle (pp. 368, 370)
vertex (p. 352)

Problem Solving

use logical reasoning (p. 356)

Understanding and Using the Vocabulary

Choose the letter of the term that best matches each phrase.

1. a line dividing a shape into two matching halves **f**
2. a six-sided figure **i**
3. a polygon with all sides and all angles congruent **a**
4. a quadrilateral with opposite sides parallel **j**
5. a simple closed figure formed by three or more sides **e**
6. a ruler or any object with a straight side **c**
7. the point where two edges of a polygon intersect **b**
8. the most common unit of measure for an angle **h**
9. an angle whose measure is between 0° and 90° **d**
10. an angle whose measure is between 90° and 180° **g**

a. regular polygon
b. vertex
c. straightedge
d. acute angle
e. polygon
f. line of symmetry
g. obtuse angle
h. degree
i. hexagon
j. parallelogram

In Your Own Words

11. *Explain* how to classify an angle as acute, right, or obtuse. **See margin.**

MindJogger Videoquizzes

MindJogger Videoquizzes provide an alternative review of concepts presented in this chapter. Students work in teams to answer questions, gaining points for correct answers. The questions are presented in three rounds.
Round 1 Concepts–5 questions
Round 2 Skills–4 questions
Round 3 Problem Solving–4 questions

Objectives & Examples

Upon completing this chapter, you should be able to:

- classify and measure angles *(Lesson 9-1)*

  The angle is an acute angle since it measures between 0° and 90°.

  The angle is a right angle since it measures 90°.

  The angle is an obtuse angle since it measures between 90° and 180°.

- draw angles and estimate measures of angles *(Lesson 9-2)*

  You can use a protractor and a straightedge to draw an angle.

  The angle drawn is a 47° angle.

- bisect line segments and angles *(Lesson 9-3)*

  To *bisect* something means to divide it into two congruent parts. You can use paper folding or a straightedge and a compass to bisect a line segment or an angle.

Review Exercises

Use these exercises to review and prepare for the chapter test.

Use a protractor to find the measure of each angle. Then classify the angle as *acute*, *right*, or *obtuse*.

12. 90°; right

13. 42°; acute

Classify each angle measure as *acute*, *right*, or *obtuse*.

14. 147° obtuse

15. 38.5° acute

16. 93° obtuse

17. 12.2° acute

Use a protractor and a straightedge to draw angles having the following measurements. 18–19. See Answer Appendix.

18. 36°

19. 127°

Estimate the measure of each angle.

20. about 120°

21. about 90°

Draw the angle or line segment with the given measurement. Then use a straightedge and a compass to bisect each angle or line segment. 22–25. See Answer Appendix.

22. 5 in.

23. 100°

24. 35°

25. 7 cm

Chapter 9 Study Guide and Assessment   387

Objectives & Examples

This section reviews the skills and concepts of the chapter and shows completely worked examples.

Review Exercises

These exercises provide practice for the corresponding objectives.

Assessment and Evaluation Masters, pp. 227–228

Assessment and Evaluation

Six forms of Chapter 9 Test are available in the *Assessment and Evaluation Masters* as shown in the chart.

Chapter 9 Test, Form 1B, is shown at the right. Chapter 9 Test, Form 2B, is shown on the next page.

1A	Multiple Choice	Honors
1B	Multiple Choice	Average
1C	Multiple Choice	Basic
2A	Free Response	Honors
2B	Free Response	Average
2C	Free Response	Basic

Assessment and Evaluation Masters, pp. 233–234

Objectives & Examples

● name two-dimensional figures *(Lesson 9-4)*

Name each polygon. Then tell if the polygon is a regular polygon.

The polygon is an octagon. The sides and angles are congruent so it is a regular polygon.

The polygon is a quadrilateral. The sides and angles are not congruent so it is not a regular polygon.

● describe and define lines of symmetry *(Lesson 9-5)*

Draw all lines of symmetry for each figure.

A square has 4 lines of symmetry.

The letter R has no lines of symmetry.

● determine congruence and similarity *(Lesson 9-6)*

Tell whether each pair of polygons is congruent, similar, or neither.

congruent   similar   neither

Review Exercises

Name each polygon. Then tell if the polygon is a regular polygon.

26.   27.

square; yes   pentagon; no

Draw an example of each polygon. Mark any congruent sides and right angles.

28. pentagon
29. equilateral triangle
28–29. See Answer Appendix.

Tell whether the dashed line is a line of symmetry. Write *yes* or *no*.

30. 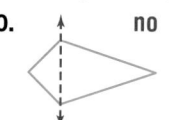 no   31. yes

Trace each figure. Draw all lines of symmetry.

32.   33.

Tell whether each pair of polygons is congruent, similar, or neither.

34.   35.

congruent   similar

Test and Review Software

You may use this software, a combination of an item generator and item bank, to create your own tests or worksheets. Types of items include free response, multiple choice, short answer, and open ended.

CD-ROM Program

The CD-ROM Program contains an Assessment Game whose questions review the concepts in this chapter.

Applications & Problem Solving

36. Use Logical Reasoning There are 32 students in Mr. Miyar's literature class. Of these, 12 take Spanish, 15 take tennis, and 8 take both Spanish and tennis. How many take neither Spanish nor tennis? *(Lesson 9-1B)* **13 students**

37. Geometry Kurano drew the figure shown as a design on a round tablecloth. She wants to draw three more stripes from the center that will bisect the three angles. Copy her design and bisect the angles to show what the new design will look like. *(Lesson 9-3)* **See Answer Appendix.**

38. Remodeling A kitchen floor is to be covered with vinyl flooring. The pattern of the flooring is a square surrounded by four regular octagons. Draw a section of the flooring. Mark any congruent sides and angles. *(Lesson 9-4)* **See Answer Appendix.**

39. School The student council voted to have a contest to design a school flag. The flag may be of any shape but must have at least one line of symmetry. Use any shapes, letters, objects, and colors to design a flag. *(Lesson 9-5)* **See students' work.**

Alternative Assessment

● **Open Ended**

Suppose that you are a graphic designer. A client has asked you to make a sign for the grand opening of her store, The Sports Store. Design a logo that displays line symmetry. Use two-dimensional figures in the design of your sign.

Identify the types of angles in your design. Explain how your design meets all of the requirements. **See students' work.**

A practice test for Chapter 9 is provided on page 603.

● **Completing the CHAPTER Project**

Use the following checklist to make sure the design of the house is complete.

☑ The angle measures of the dining room, bathroom, and second bedroom are correct.

☑ The measurements of the walls of the dining room, bathroom, and second bedroom are correct.

☑ The floor plans of the house's actual angle measures and actual lengths are included.

 PORTFOLIO Select one of the assignments from this chapter and place it in your portfolio. Attach a note to it explaining why you selected it.

 Performance Assessment

Additional performance assessment tasks for this chapter are included in the *Assessment and Evaluation Masters* on page 237. A scoring guide is also provided on page 249.

Applications & Problem Solving

This section provides additional practice in solving real-world problems that involve the skills of this chapter.

Alternative Assessment

The **Open Ended** section provides students with a performance assessment opportunity to evaluate their work and understanding.

CHAPTER Project

Students should complete the final stages of their project and prepare a class demonstration of their results. A scoring guide for the project is available in the *Investigations and Projects Masters*, p. 51.

 PORTFOLIO Students should add to their portfolios at this time.

***Assessment and Evaluation Masters*, p. 237**

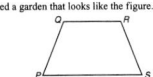

Name _____ Date _____

Chapter 9 Performance Assessment

Instructions: Demonstrate your knowledge by giving a clear, concise solution to each problem. Be sure to include all relevant drawings and justify your answers. You may show your solutions in more than one way or investigate beyond the requirements of the problems.

1. Taylor planted a garden that looks like the figure.

   a. Name the shape of the garden. Explain your reasoning.

   b. Name each of the angles as acute, obtuse, or right. Explain your reasoning and estimate the measures of each angle.

   c. She wishes to bury a pipe for a sprinkler along the bisector of ∠QPS. Use a compass and straightedge to bisect ∠QPS. Explain each step.

   d. If Taylor wants her garden to be symmetrical, where could she draw lines of symmetry in her garden?

   e. Taylor decides that she wants a smaller garden that is exactly like her large garden. Tell the term that describes that other garden and explain what parts must be the same.

© Glencoe/McGraw-Hill   237   *Mathematics: Applications and Connections, Course 1*

The Standardized Test Practice may be used to help students prepare for standardized tests. The test items are written in the same style as those in state proficiency tests and standardized tests like CAT, CTBS, ITBS, MAT, SAT, and Terra Nova. The test items cover skills and concepts covered up to this point in the text.

The pages can be used as an overnight assessment. After students have completed the pages, discuss how each problem can be solved, or provide copies of the solutions from the *Solutions Manual*.

Section One: Multiple Choice

There are twelve multiple-choice questions in this section. Choose the best answer. If a correct answer is *not here,* mark the letter for Not Here.

1. What is the measure of the line segment shown? **C**

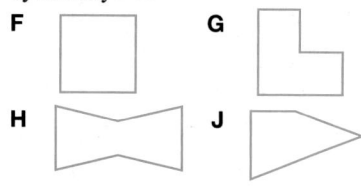

- **A** 60 km
- **B** 60 m
- **C** 60 mm
- **D** 60 cm

2. Which figure has only two lines of symmetry? **H**

F   G

H   J

3. A pedometer measures the number of miles a person has walked. Which list shows the pedometer readings in order from least to greatest? **D**
- **A** 4.75, 4.7, 4.04, 4.17
- **B** 4.17, 4.75, 4.7, 4.04
- **C** 4.04, 4.7, 4.17, 4.75
- **D** 4.04, 4.17, 4.7, 4.75

4. Which point is in the exterior of quadrilateral *WXYZ*? **H**

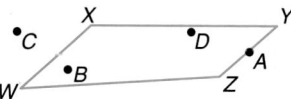

- **F** point *A*
- **G** point *B*
- **H** point *C*
- **J** point *D*

Please note that Questions 5–12 have five answer choices.

5. Four students are 15, 11, 12, and 14 years old. What is an average age of the four students? **A**
- **A** 13   **B** 10
- **C** 14   **D** 12
- **E** 15

6. $\triangle MNP \cong \triangle RST$. Which of the following is a true statement? **J**

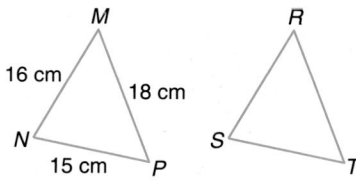

- **F** The perimeter of $\triangle RST$ is 59 centimeters.
- **G** The measure of side *RT* is 16 centimeters.
- **H** The measures of angles *M* and *T* are equal.
- **J** The measures of sides *RS* and *MN* are equal.
- **K** The measure of side *RS* is equal to 18 centimeters.

7. The lights on a street sign blink 5 times every 6 seconds. How many times do they blink in 3 minutes? **B**
- **A** 900   **B** 150
- **C** 75   **D** 30
- **E** 450

8. Which is a reasonable remainder when a number is divided by 8? **J**
- **F** 10   **G** 8
- **H** 11   **J** 7
- **K** 9

Assessment and Evaluation Masters, p. 243

◀◀◀ **Instructional Resources**

Another cumulative review is shown at the left and is available in the *Assessment and Evaluation Masters,* p. 243.

9. Find the product of $\frac{3}{4}$ and $\frac{4}{5}$. **A**

A $\frac{3}{5}$

B $\frac{15}{16}$

C $1\frac{2}{5}$

D 12

E Not Here

10. Teisha works 17 hours a week and earns $99.45. How much money does she earn each hour? **H**

F $5.65

G $4.75

H $5.85

J $4.95

K Not Here

11. The students at Glenwood Middle School sold 1,808 magazine subscriptions. The students at Center Middle School sold 2,046 subscriptions. How many more subscriptions did the students at Center Middle School sell than the students at Glenwood Middle School? **C**

A 148

B 242

C 238

D 762

E Not Here

12. Solve $m = 26 \div 3.25$. **J**

F 0.008

G 0.08

H 0.8

J 8

K Not Here

Test-Taking Tip
THE PRINCETON REVIEW

You can improve your chances of doing well on a test by keeping your test anxiety under control. Getting a good night's sleep will help. Right before the test, take deep breaths and focus on doing well. Panicking or getting overly worried about a test can keep you from doing your best.

Section Two: Free Response

This section contains six questions for which you will provide short answers. Write your answers on your paper.

13. A dog is on a 20-foot leash attached to a stake in the ground. If the dog walks in a circle at the end of the leash, how far can he walk before returning to his starting point? Round to the nearest foot. **126 feet**

14. Determine whether 708 is divisible by 2, 3, 5, 6, 9, or 10. **2, 3, 6**

15. Write the decimal 0.125 as a fraction in simplest form. $\frac{1}{8}$

16. Evaluate $a + b$ if $a = 4\frac{1}{2}$ and $b = 7\frac{1}{4}$. $11\frac{3}{4}$

17. Brenda keeps her turtle in an aquarium that is 14 inches wide and 18 inches long. She buys a new aquarium that is 12 inches wider, but is the same length as the other cage. What are the dimensions of the new aquarium? **26 inches by 18 inches**

18. Angles C and D are supplementary angles. If angle C measures 101.3°, what is the measure of angle D? **78.7°**

interNET CONNECTION Test Practice **For additional test practice questions, visit:**

www.glencoe.com/sec/math/mac/mathnet

Instructional Resources ▶▶▶
Additional standardized test practice is shown at the right and is available in the *Assessment and Evaluation Masters,* pp. 241–242.

Test-Taking Tip
Tell students that other ways to reduce test anxiety include waking up early to avoid being rushed, eating a healthy breakfast for energy, and making a checklist to remember what to bring to the test.

Assessment and Evaluation Masters, pp. 241–242

---

9 Name_____ Date_____

Chapter 9 Standardized Test Practice

1. Three road blinkers are turned on at the same time. One blinks every 6 seconds, another every 10 seconds, and the third every 12 seconds. How many times per hour do they blink at once?
   A. 72   B. 60   C. 30   D. 36   **1. B**

2. Dale bought a package of meat weighing 0.88 pound. Express this decimal as a fraction in lowest terms.
   A. $\frac{22}{25}$ B. $\frac{88}{100}$ C. $\frac{44}{50}$ D. $1\frac{1}{12}$ **2. A**

3. Therese took 10 karate lessons. She spent a total of $7\frac{1}{2}$ hours in instruction. How long was each lesson?
   A. $\frac{2}{3}$ hour   B. $\frac{3}{4}$ hour   C. $17\frac{1}{2}$ hours   D. 1 hour   **3. B**

4. Madison rents an apartment for $725 a month. Each year the monthly rent is expected to increase $14.75. What will the monthly rent be at the end of six years?
   A. $815.30   B. $798.75   C. $813.50   D. $828.25   **4. C**

5. A movie company made a large model of a domino. The actual width of a domino is 15 millimeters. If the scale is 1 m = 2.5 mm, what is the width of the model?
   A. 6 m   B. 37.5 m   C. 17.5 m   D. 12.5 m   **5. A**

6. The local appliance center purchases their vacuum cleaners for $129. When they sell the vacuum cleaners, they mark the price up 43%. What is the final cost of a vacuum cleaner?
   A. $55.47   B. $129   C. $184.47   D. $73.53   **6. C**

7. Elena found a cone from a Scotch pine that was $1\frac{1}{6}$ inches long and a cone from a white pine that was $4\frac{5}{8}$ inches long. Estimate how much longer the cone from the white pine is than the cone from the Scotch pine.
   A. 3 in.   B. $4\frac{1}{4}$ in.   C. 5 in.   D. $3\frac{1}{2}$ in.   **7. D**

8. Jamie spent $\frac{3}{8}$ of her free time on Tuesday morning and $\frac{1}{6}$ of her free time on Tuesday afternoon at the pool. What fraction of her free time did Jamie spend at the pool on Tuesday?
   A. $\frac{5}{24}$ B. $\frac{13}{24}$ C. $\frac{4}{14}$ D. none of these   **8. B**

9. Miranda has 27 CDs. She gave g CDs to her friend Charmaine. She has 21 CDs left. Which equation represents the situation?
   A. $g - 21 = 27$ B. $27 + 21 = g$ C. $27 - g = 21$ D. none of these   **9. C**

© Glencoe/McGraw-Hill 241 *Mathematics: Applications and Connections, Course 1*

---

9 **Chapter 9 Standardized Test Practice (continued)**

10. The owner of the Pachyderm Press Bookstore is reviewing her sales records for the past six months. She wants to make a graph to more easily compare her results. Which type of graph should she use?
    A. bar graph   B. number line   C. circle graph   D. stem-and-leaf plot   **10. A**

11. Jackie walked 3.8 kilometers on Monday, 2.1 kilometers on Tuesday, 3.4 kilometers on Wednesday, 2.8 kilometers on Thursday, and 3.4 kilometers on Friday. Estimate the total distance she walked that week.
    A. 13 km   B. 15 km   C. 17 km   D. none of these   **11. B**

12. A class of 40 students went to a museum. The trip cost $294.40, which included bus rental of $156.40. How much was each student's museum ticket?
    A. $7.36   B. $3.45   C. $3.91   D. $5.00   **12. B**

13. Macauley's dad bought a new lawn chair. Macauley decided to practice his math skills and measure the chair at each of the settings. He made a drawing of the most comfortable setting. Use a protractor to measure the angle.

    A. 19°   B. 109°   C. 161°   D. 172°   **13. C**

14. Mandy and Jenny went to the art museum. They were looking at a modern sculpture similar to the figure at the right. How many lines of symmetry does the figure have?
    A. 0   B. 1   C. 2   D. 4   **14. C**

15. Andre and Darrell were drawing two-dimensional figures, but they couldn't remember how many sides a parallelogram has. How many sides does a parallelogram have?
    A. 3   B. 4   C. 5   D. 6   **15. B**

16. Tyree made a drawing of his dad's office and included a bird's eye view of two desks as shown. Tell whether the shapes are congruent, similar, or neither.
    A. congruent   B. similar   C. neither   D. both A & B   **16. A**

© Glencoe/McGraw-Hill 242 *Mathematics: Applications and Connections, Course 1*

GET READY

This optional investigation is designed to be completed by a group of 3 or 4 students over several days or several weeks.

Mathematical Overview

This investigation utilizes the mathematical skills and concepts presented in Chapters 7–9.
- multiplying and dividing fractions and mixed numbers
- changing customary units
- exploring ratios, percents, and fractions

Time Management	
Gathering Data	45 minutes
Calculations	30 minutes
Creating Graphs	30 minutes
Summarizing Data	30 minutes
Presentation	10 minutes

Instructional Resources
- *Investigations and Projects Masters*, pp. 9–12

Investigations and Projects Masters, p. 12

THAT IS ONE HUMONGOUS PIE!

Did you know that the largest pie ever made weighed almost 38,000 pounds? The largest milkshake ever made was 2,000 gallons. Imagine the amount of each ingredient needed to make a record-setting food.

What You'll Do

In this investigation, you will write a recipe for a giant-sized food and determine the cost of making this food.

Materials
 a copy of a book of world records

 cookbooks

 supermarket advertisements

 calculator

Procedure

1. Work in groups of 3 or 4. Find a record-setting food in a book of world records. Then find a recipe for that food in a cookbook. Make sure that the recipe has at least 6 ingredients and that at least 3 of the ingredients have measurements that are given as fractions or mixed numbers.

2. Tell how many times the recipe would need to be increased to make a record-setting food. Express this relationship as a ratio. Explain your reasoning. Then find the amount of each ingredient needed to make the record-setting food. Organize the information in a table.

3. Research the cost of each ingredient in your recipe. Which ingredient costs the most? Find the total cost of the ingredients.

4. Use your data to find the percent of the total cost that each ingredient represents. Make a graph of your data.

5. Make a booklet or brochure that contains your recipe, the costs, the graphs, and any other information on your project.

Technology Tips

- Use a **spreadsheet** to calculate the amount of each ingredient needed and the total cost of the ingredients.

- Use **graphing software** to display the data.

- Use **publishing software** to help make your booklet or brochure.

◀◀◀Instructional Resources

A recording sheet to help students organize their data for this investigation is shown at the left and is available in the *Investigations and Projects Masters*, p. 12.

 Cooperative Learning

This investigation offers an excellent opportunity for using cooperative learning groups. For more information on cooperative learning strategies and group management, see *Cooperative Learning in the Mathematics Classroom.*

Making the Connection

Use the data collected about your record-setting food as needed to help in these investigations.

Language Arts

Suppose you want to make a record-setting food to put your school in a book of world records. Write a newspaper article convincing people to donate to your project. Use the data that you gathered in the investigation. Be creative and describe the cost involved.

Health

Find the number of Calories in one serving of your record-setting food, and also in the whole food.

Social Studies

Research the history of a book of world records. When and why was the first book published?

Go Further

- Estimate the area and perimeter of your record-setting food. Mark off an area in your school or on the school grounds to demonstrate the size of the food. How does the perimeter of the record-setting food compare to its area?

- How many people could have a serving of your record-setting food? Determine how much money you should charge for a serving so that enough is made to pay for the project.

 Research **For current information on recipes, visit:**
www.glencoe.com/sec/math/mac/mathnet

 You may want to place your work on this investigation in your portfolio.

MANAGEMENT TIPS

Working in Teams Have the teams decide which recipe to use and the amount of increase. Each team member should be responsible for a specific ingredient and should present a different part of the investigation if they do an oral presentation.

Making the Connection
You may wish to alert other teachers on your team that your students may need their assistance in this investigation.
Language Arts Students may need to research different styles of newspaper articles and reporting.
Health Students need to know about how many Calories their bodies need in a day.
Social Studies Students may wish to research the importance of record keeping in society.

ASSESS

You may wish to have students do an oral presentation. If so, they should make large graphs and cost tables on posterboard to accompany their discussion.

Investigations and Projects Masters, p. 11

Instructional Resources ▶ ▶ ▶
Sample solutions for this investigation are provided in the *Investigations and Projects Masters* on p. 10. The scoring guide for assessing student performance shown at the right is also available on p. 11.

SCORING GUIDE

Interdisciplinary Investigation
(Student Edition, Pages 392–393)

That Is One Humongous Pie!

Level	Specific Criteria
3 Superior	• Shows a thorough understanding of the concepts of *multiplying fractions, multiplying mixed numbers, and changing customary units.* • Uses appropriate strategies to solve problems. • Computations are correct. • Written explanations are exemplary. • Charts, model, and any statements included are appropriate and sensible. • Goes beyond the requirements of some or all problems.
2 Satisfactory, with minor flaws	• Shows understanding of the concepts of *multiplying fractions, multiplying mixed numbers, and changing customary units.* • Uses appropriate strategies to solve problems. • Computations are mostly correct. • Written explanations are effective. • Charts, model, and any statements included are appropriate and sensible. • Satisfies the requirements of problems.
1 Nearly Satisfactory, with obvious flaws	• Shows understanding of most of the concepts of *multiplying fractions, multiplying mixed numbers, and changing customary units.* • May not use appropriate strategies to solve problems. • Computations are mostly correct. • Written explanations are satisfactory. • Charts, model, and any statements included are appropriate and sensible. • Satisfies the requirements of problems.
0 Unsatisfactory	• Shows little or no understanding of the concepts of *multiplying fractions, multiplying mixed numbers, and changing customary units.* • Does not use appropriate strategies to solve problems. • Computations are incorrect. • Written explanations are not satisfactory. • Charts, model, and any statements included are not appropriate or sensible. • Does not satisfy the requirements of the problems.

© Glencoe/McGraw-Hill   11   *Mathematics: Applications and Connections, Course 1*

CHAPTER 10

Geometry: Understanding Area and Volume

Previewing the Chapter

Overview

In this chapter, students learn to find the areas of parallelograms, triangles, and circles and to construct circle graphs. Students identify and draw three-dimensional figures. They find the surface area and volume of rectangular prisms, both with and without using a spreadsheet. Students learn to solve problems by making models.

Lesson (pages)	Lesson Objectives	NCTM Standards 2000	Standardized Tests	State/Local Objectives
10-1A (396–397)	Find the areas of irregular shapes.	1, 3, 4, 6–10	CAT, MAT, SAT	
10-1 (398–401)	Find the area of parallelograms.	1–4, 6–10	CAT, MAT, SAT	
10-2 (402–405)	Find the area of triangles.	1–4, 6–10	CAT, MAT, SAT	
10-3 (406–409)	Find the area of circles.	1–4, 6–10	CAT, MAT, SAT	
10-3B (410–411)	Construct circle graphs.	1, 3–10	CTBS, TN	
10-4 (412–414)	Identify three-dimensional figures.	1, 3, 4, 6–10	MAT	
10-4B (415)	Draw three-dimensional figures.	3, 6–8, 10		
10-5A (416–417)	Solve problems by making models.	1–4, 6–10	CTBS, MAT, TN	
10-5 (418–420)	Find the volume of rectangular prisms.	1–4, 6–10	ITBS, MAT	
10-6 (421–424)	Find the surface area of rectangular prisms.	1, 3, 4, 6–10	MAT	
10-6B (425)	Use spreadsheets to find the surface area and volume of rectangular prisms.	1–4, 6–9		

CAI = California Achievement Tests, CTBS = Comprehensive Tests of Basic Skills, ITBS = Iowa Tests of Basic Skills, MAT = Metropolitan Achievement Tests, SAT = Stanford Achievement Tests, TN = Terra Nova
For the key to numbering of NCTM Standards 2000, see page T6.

Organizing the Chapter

The **Interactive Lesson Planner** contains all of the blackline masters and transparencies. This CD-ROM also includes an easy-to-use lesson planning calendar.

LESSON PLANNING GUIDE

Lesson	Extra Practice (Student Edition)	BLACKLINE MASTERS (PAGE NUMBERS)										
		Study Guide	Practice	Enrichment	Assessment & Evaluation	Classroom Games	Diversity	Hands-On Lab	School to Career	Science and Math Lab Manual	Technology	Transparencies A and B
10-1A								61				
10-1	p. 583	70	70	70							20	10-1
10-2	p. 583	71	71	71	267			78		17–20		10-2
10-3	p. 583	72	72	72	266, 267	27–28					19	10-3
10-3B								62				
10-4	p. 584	73	73	73			10					10-4
10-4B								63				
10-5A	p. 584											
10-5	p. 584	74	74	74	268							10-5
10-6	p. 585	75	75	75	268					10		10-6
10-6B												
Study Guide/ Assessment					253–265, 269–271							

OTHER CHAPTER RESOURCES

Student Edition
Chapter Project, pp. 395, 420, 424, 429
Let the Games Begin, p. 409

Technology
 MathPASS CD-ROM
 Interactive Mathematics Tools Software

Teacher's Classroom Resources

Applications
Family Letters and Activities, pp. 19–20
Investigations and Projects Masters, pp. 53–56
Meeting Individual Needs
Investigations for the Special Education Student, pp. 43–44

Teaching Aids
Answer Key Masters
Block Scheduling Booklet
Lesson Planning Guide
Solutions Manual

Professional Publications
Glencoe Mathematics Professional Series

Planning the Chapter

MindJogger Videoquizzes provide a unique format for reviewing concepts presented in the chapter.

ASSESSMENT RESOURCES

Student Edition

Mixed Review, pp. 401, 405, 409, 414, 420, 424

Mid-Chapter Self Test, p. 414

Math Journal, pp. 413, 423

Study Guide and Assessment, pp. 426–429

Performance Task, p. 429

Portfolio Suggestion, p. 429

Standardized Test Practice, pp. 430–431

Chapter Test, p. 604

Assessment and Evaluation Masters

Multiple-Choice Tests (Forms 1A, 1B, 1C), pp. 253–258

Free-Response Tests (Forms 2A, 2B, 2C), pp. 259–264

Performance Assessment, p. 265

Mid-Chapter Test, p. 266

Quizzes A–D, pp. 267–268

Standardized Test Practice, pp. 269–270

Cumulative Review, p. 271

Teacher's Wraparound Edition

5-Minute Check, pp. 398, 402, 406, 412, 418, 421

Building Portfolios, p. 394

Math Journal, pp. 397, 411, 415, 425

Closing Activity, pp. 401, 405, 409, 414, 417, 420, 424

Technology

Test and Review Software

MindJogger Videoquizzes

CD-ROM Program

MATERIALS AND MANIPULATIVES

Lesson 10-1A
centimeter grid paper*†
ruler*

Lesson 10-1
grid paper*†
scissors*
ruler*

Lesson 10-2
plain paper
scissors*
ruler*

Lesson 10-3
paper plate
scissors*
counters*†
felt squares
markers
compass*†

Lesson 10-3B
colored pencils
ruler*
compass*†
protractor*†
calculator

Lesson 10-4B
isometric dot paper†
ruler*

Lesson 10-5
centimeter cubes*

Lesson 10-6
centimeter grid paper*†
scissors*
ruler*
tape
calculator

Lesson 10-6B
computer
spreadsheet software

*Glencoe Manipulative Kit   †Glencoe Overhead Manipulative Resources

PACING CHART

See pages T25–T27 for the Course Planning Calendar.

COURSE	DAY 1	DAY 2	DAY 3	DAY 4	DAY 5	DAY 6	DAY 7
Standard	Chapter Project	Lessons 10-1A & 10-1		Lesson 10-2	Lesson 10-3		Lesson 10-4
Honors	Chapter Project	Lesson 10-1	Lesson 10-2	Lessons 10-3 & 10-3B		Lessons 10-4 & 10-4B	
Block	Chapter Project & Lesson 10-1A	Lessons 10-1 & 10-2	Lesson 10-3	Lesson 10-4	Lessons 10-5A & 10-5	Lesson 10-6	Study Guide and Assessment, Chapter Test

Interactive Mathematics:
Activities and Investigations

is an activity-based program that may be used as an enhancement for chapters in *Mathematics: Applications and Connections.*

Activities and Investigations

Unit 3, Activity Six, Menu E
Use with Lesson 10-5.

Summary Students use cubes to build various larger cubes for the given edge lengths. They record the number of cubes for each figure and graph the relationship between the edge length and the volume. They look for a pattern among the graphed points and write a function describing the graphed relationship.

Math Connection Students graph data and look for patterns created by modeling cubes of different edge lengths. They express the relationship between the edge length of a cube and its volume in terms of a function.

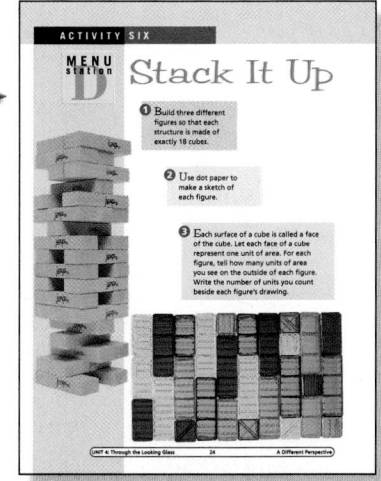

Unit 4, Activity Six, Menu D
Use with Lesson 10-6.

Summary Students use blocks to build three 3-dimensional structures composed of 18 cubes. They make a sketch of each one using dot paper. Then students determine the surface area of each figure.

Math Connection Students build 3-dimensional structures and explore the concept of surface area. They create isometric drawings of their structures. Isometric dot paper is dot paper in which each dot is equidistant from the dots around it, thus allowing for lengths to be preserved. Angle measures are not preserved in such drawings.

DAY 8	DAY 9	DAY 10	DAY 11	DAY 12	DAY 13	DAY 14	DAY 15
(continue from Day 7)	Lesson 10-5A	Lesson 10-5	Lesson 10-6	Study Guide and Assessment	Chapter Test		
Lesson 10-5A	Lesson 10-5	Lessons 10-6 & 10-6B		Study Guide and Assessment	Chapter Test		

Enhancing the Chapter

APPLICATIONS

Classroom Games,
pp. 27–28

Diversity Masters,
p. 10

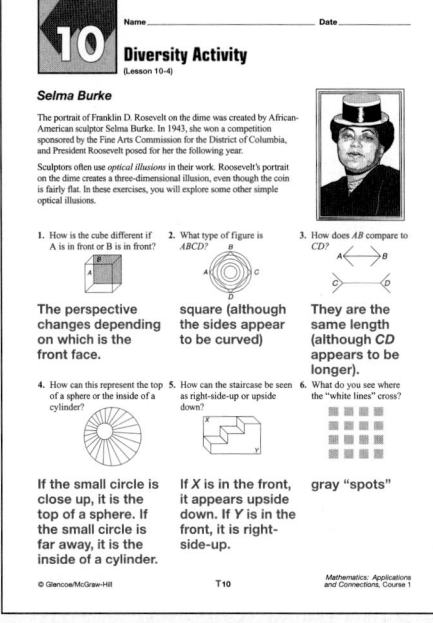

School to Career Masters,
p. 10

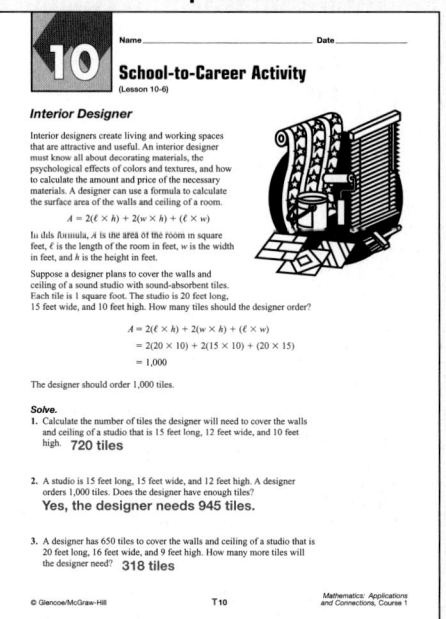

Family Letters and Activities,
pp. 19–20

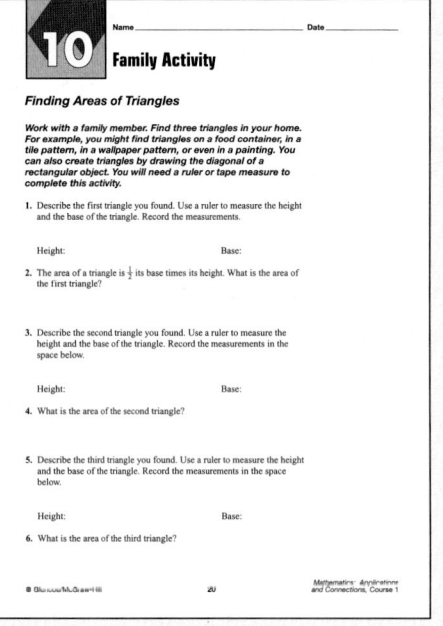

Science and Math Lab Manual,
pp. 17–20

Hands-On Lab Masters, p. 78

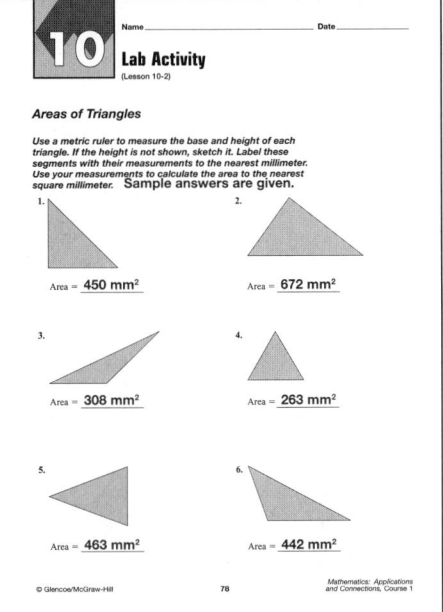

Assessment and Evaluation Masters, pp. 266–268

Technology Masters, pp. 19–20

Investigations for the Special Education Student, pp. 43–44

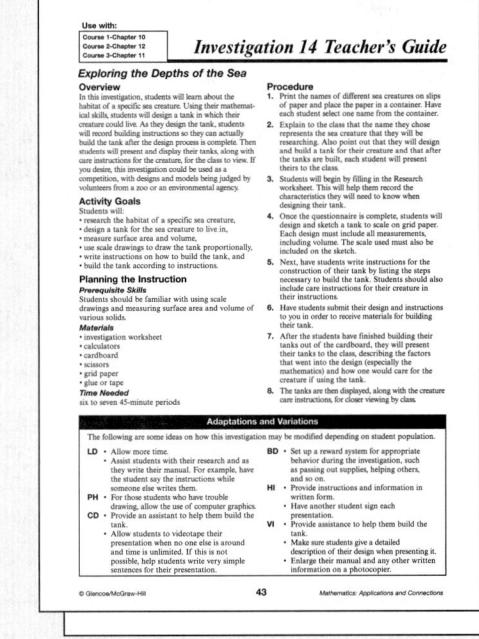

Geometry: Understanding Area and Volume

Theme: Measurement

The United States does not use the metric system. The Metric Program at the National Institute of Standards and Technology is encouraging voluntary conversion from the customary system to the metric system.

Question of the Day What is the volume in cubic inches of a cube whose edge is 1 foot long? **1,728 in³**

Assess Prerequisite Skills

Ask students to read through the list of objectives presented in "What you'll learn in Chapter 10." You may wish to ask them what each of the objectives means or if they have experienced or used any of these math concepts before.

 Building Portfolios

Encourage students to revise their portfolios as they study this chapter. Have them choose examples of their work that show improvement. Have students include an explanation of how each example demonstrates increased understanding of math concepts.

 Math and the Family

In the *Family Letters and Activities* booklet (pp. 19–20), you will find a letter to the parents explaining what students will study in Chapter 10. An activity appropriate for the whole family is also available.

What you'll learn in Chapter 10

- to estimate the areas of irregular figures,
- to find the areas of parallelograms, triangles, and circles,
- to construct circle graphs,
- to identify and draw three-dimensional figures,
- to solve problems by making a model, and
- to find the surface area and volume of rectangular prisms.

394 Chapter 10 Geometry: Understanding Area and Volume

 CD-ROM Program

Activities for Chapter 10

- Chapter 10 Introduction
- Interactive Lessons 10-1, 10-2, 10-5, 10-6
- Extended Activity 10-4
- Assessment Game
- Resource Lessons 10-1 through 10-6

CHAPTER Project

MEASURING UP

You are familiar with inches, feet, yards, centimeters, and meters. In this project, you will design your own system of measure. You will take measurements using your system and compare your system to a standard system. You will present your findings in a poster.

Getting Started

- Early measurement systems in many cultures were based on readily available objects. For example, the cubit is one of the oldest units. A cubit is the length of your forearm from the point of your elbow to the tip of your middle finger. The table shows some other early units of measure.

Early Units of Measure	
Unit	**Measure**
girth	distance around the waist
span	length from tip of thumb to little finger of outstretched hand
fathom	distance between finger tips when arms are outstretched
grain	weight of one seed of grain
Sun or moon	time in one day

Select a unit of length to use for your project. You may choose a historical unit such as your span, or make your own unit from something you have close by. Some units could be the length of a pen, your little brother's height, or the length of your foot.

Technology Tips

- Use a **spreadsheet** to calculate areas and volumes using your own measurement system.
- Use an **electronic encyclopedia** to research historical or unusual measurements.
- Use a **word processor** to create all or part of your poster.

 interNET CONNECTION Research For up-to-date information on the history of mathematics, visit:

www.glencoe.com/sec/math/mac/mathnet

Working on the Project

You can use what you'll learn in Chapter 10 to help you make a poster about your system of measurement.

Page	Exercise
420	17
424	22
429	Alternative Assessment

interNET CONNECTION

Glencoe has made every effort to ensure that the website links for *Mathematics: Applications and Connections* at **www.glencoe.com/sec/math/mac/mathnet** are current and contain appropriate content. However, these website links are not under Glencoe's control.

CHAPTER Project
NOTES

Objectives Students should
- develop a new system of measure.
- compare their system with a standard system.

Project Pointer You may suggest that students begin a *Project Folder* to keep their work as they complete each stage of the Chapter Project. The completed project may also be added to their portfolios.

Make sure students choose a unit of length that is accessible and easy to use. Encourage them to use their system to measure many objects before comparing it to a standard system of measure.

Using the Table Make sure students realize that the units listed were used because no standard system of measure existed. Point out that measurements based on the human body would be defined differently by each person using them. Demonstrate how your fathom compares to a student's fathom.

Investigations and Projects Masters, p. 56

Instructional Resources ▶▶▶
A recording sheet to help students organize their data for the Chapter Project is shown at the right and is available in the *Investigations and Projects Masters,* p. 56.

---

10 Name_____ Date_____

Chapter 10 Project

Measuring Up

Page 420, Working on the Chapter Project, Exercise 17

Object Chosen:	Length	Width	Height	Volume
Standard Unit				
Nonstandard Unit				

Page 424, Working on the Chapter Project, Exercise 22

Object Chosen:	Surface Area
Standard Unit	
Nonstandard Unit	

© Glencoe/McGraw-Hill   56   *Mathematics: Applications and Connections, Course 1*

COOPERATIVE LEARNING

10-1A Area of Irregular Shapes

A Preview of Lesson 10-1

GET READY

Objective Students find the areas of irregular shapes.

Optional Resources
Hands-On Lab Masters
• centimeter grid, p. 12
• worksheet, p. 61

Overhead Manipulative Resources
• centimeter grid

Manipulative Kit
• ruler

centimeter
grid paper

ruler

In Chapter 4, you learned how to find the area of a rectangle. You can also find the areas of irregular shapes. There are two different methods you might use.

MANAGEMENT TIPS

Recommended Time
45 minutes

Getting Started Use a centimeter grid overhead transparency to review finding the area of a rectangle. Ask students to determine how they would use centimeter grid paper to find the area of a leaf.

Activity 1 on page 396 directs students to trace their hand onto a grid. Have students make two columns to record their numbers—one for whole squares and the other for partial squares. They could then add a third column for total number of squares. Students may want to mark or shade squares they have counted so they don't miss any.

Activity 2 on page 397 directs students to draw freehand an irregular shape. Encourage them to make the shape very irregular. Have them use the same table as in Activity 1. Suggest that they redo each activity using the other method and compare results.

TRY THIS

Work with a partner.

1 Find the mean.
• Place your hand on a sheet of centimeter grid paper so that your fingers and thumb are close together. Then draw an outline.

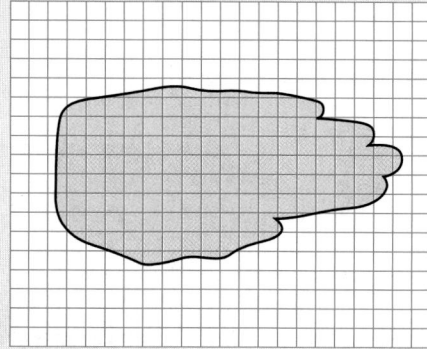

• Count the number of whole squares inside of your outline. Record the number.
• Count the number of squares that have the outline running through them. Add this number to the number of whole squares that you recorded. Then record this number.

ON YOUR OWN

1. Find the mean of the two numbers that you recorded to estimate the area of your hand. *Refer to Lesson 2-7 for information on finding the mean.* **Answers will vary.**

2. Can you think of another way to find the approximate area of your hand? Explain your answer. **See margin.**

Additional Answer
2. Sample answer: Draw two rectangles to enclose the hand outline. Find the area of each rectangle. Then add the two areas to find the total area of the hand.

TRY THIS

Work with a partner.

❷ Use a rectangle.

• Draw an outline of an irregular shape like the one at the right on a piece of centimeter grid paper.

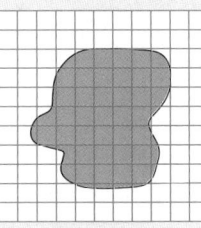

• Use the grid lines to draw a rectangle that encloses most of the figure.
• Count squares to find the length of the rectangle.
• Then count squares to find the width of the rectangle.

ON YOUR OWN

3–5. See students' work.

3. Find the area of the rectangle you drew to estimate the area of the irregular figure.

4. Use the method in the first activity to estimate the area of the irregular figure.

5. Which estimation method do you think is more accurate? Explain your reasoning.

Estimate the area of each figure. Use whichever method you prefer. 6–10. Sample answers given.

6.

$9\frac{1}{2}$ square units

7. 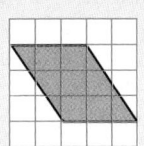 **5 square units**

8. **9 square units**

9.

$4\frac{1}{2}$ square units

10. 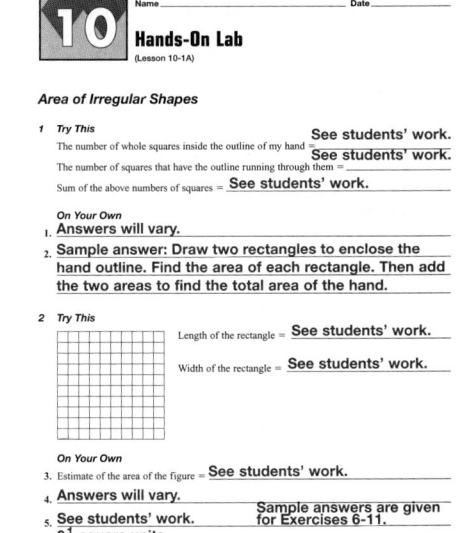 **48,600 square miles**

VIRGINIA

one square = 900 sq mi

11. **Look Ahead** Compare the area of the figure in Exercise 8 to the area of a square with sides 3 units long. What do you observe? **The areas are the same.**

Math Journal Have students write a paragraph about the accuracy of each method and how to determine when to use each method. Have them describe how to find the area of the top surface of a skateboard.

Have students complete Exercises 1–10. You may want to have students work in pairs for Exercises 6–10 and have each partner use a different method. Have students compare the methods and the answers. Ask if it is possible to get an exact answer using either method.

Use Exercise 11 to determine whether students understand finding the area of an irregular shape.

Hands-On Lab Masters, p. 61

Hands-On Lab
(Lesson 10-1A)

Name _____ Date _____

Area of Irregular Shapes

1 *Try This*
The number of whole squares inside the outline of my hand = **See students' work.**
The number of squares that have the outline running through them = **See students' work.**
Sum of the above numbers of squares = **See students' work.**

On Your Own
1. **Answers will vary.**
2. **Sample answer: Draw two rectangles to enclose the hand outline. Find the area of each rectangle. Then add the two areas to find the total area of the hand.**

2 *Try This*
Length of the rectangle = **See students' work.**
Width of the rectangle = **See students' work.**

On Your Own
3. Estimate of the area of the figure = **See students' work.**
4. **Answers will vary.**
5. **See students' work.** Sample answers are given for Exercises 6–11.
6. **$9\frac{1}{2}$ square units** 7. **5 square units** 8. **9 square units**
9. **$4\frac{1}{2}$ square units** 10. **48,600 square miles**
11. Look Ahead **The areas are the same.**

© Glencoe/McGraw-Hill 61 *Mathematics: Applications and Connections, Course 1*

Hands-On Lab 10-1A 397

- *Study Guide Masters*, p. 70
- *Practice Masters*, p. 70
- *Enrichment Masters*, p. 70
- Transparencies 10-1, A and B
- *Technology Masters*, p. 20

 CD-ROM Program
- Resource Lesson 10-1
- Interactive Lesson 10-1

Recommended Pacing	
Standard	Days 2 & 3 of 13
Honors	Day 2 of 13
Block	Day 2 of 7

1 FOCUS

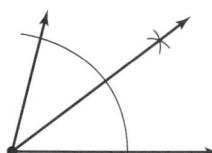

5-Minute Check
(Chapter 9)

1. Draw a 74° angle. Then use a straightedge and compass to bisect it.

2. Tell whether the polygons are *congruent*, *similar*, or *neither*. **neither**

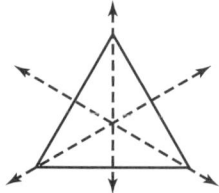

3. Name the polygons in Question 2. **octagon, decagon**

4. Draw an equilateral triangle and show any lines of symmetry.

 The 5-Minute Check is also available on **Transparency 10-1A** for this lesson.

10-1   Area of Parallelograms

 you'll learn

You'll learn to find the area of parallelograms.

When am I ever going to use this?

Knowing how to find the area of a parallelogram can help you determine the amount of wood needed to build a deck.

Word Wise

base
height

LOOK BACK
Refer to Lesson 4-4 for information on the area of rectangles.

If you watched the Olympic Games in Atlanta, you probably remember the way the United States women's basketball team rolled over the competition to win the gold medal.

A basketball court is rectangular, with a length of 94 feet and a width of 50 feet. Because the court is rectangular, you can find its area by multiplying the length and the width.

$$A = \ell \times w$$
$$A = 94 \times 50 \quad \textit{Replace } \ell \textit{ with 94 and w with 50.}$$
$$A = 4{,}700$$

The area of a basketball court is 4,700 square feet.

A rectangle is a special type of parallelogram. A parallelogram is a quadrilateral with two pairs of parallel sides. The **base** of a parallelogram is any one of its sides. The shortest distance from the base to the opposite side is the **height** of the parallelogram.

height (*h*)

base (*b*)

In the Mini-Lab, you will compare the area of a parallelogram to the area of a rectangle with the same height and base.

 MINI-LAB

Work with a partner. grid paper   scissors   ruler

Try This
- Draw a parallelogram on a sheet of grid paper.
- Cut out the parallelogram.
- Draw a straight line to represent the height of the parallelogram. Then cut along the line.

• Reassemble the pieces to form a rectangle as shown.

Talk About It

1. How do the areas of the parallelogram and the rectangle compare? **They are the same.**

2. What part of the rectangle is the same as the height of the parallelogram? What part is the same as the parallelogram's base? **height; base**

3. Use what you observed to write a formula for the area of a parallelogram. *A = bh*

Area of a Parallelogram	**Words:** The area (*A*) of a parallelogram equals the product of its base (*b*) and height (*h*). **Symbols:** *A = bh* **Model:**

Examples

Find the area of each parallelogram to the nearest tenth.

①

$A = bh$

$A = 5 \cdot 8$

$A = 40$

The area is 40 square units.

②

$A = bh$

$A = 3.7 \cdot 16.2$

$3.7 \times 16.2 = 59.94$

The area is 59.9 square meters.

Lesson 10-1 Area of Parallelograms **399**

Motivating the Lesson

Hands-On Activity Use a centimeter grid overhead transparency. Ask a student to draw a rectangle on it. Then, on another transparency, draw a parallelogram with the same base and height as the rectangle. Have students estimate the area of each by counting the number of squares to see if they are the same size.

2 TEACH

Transparency 10-1B contains a teaching aid for this lesson.

Using the Mini-Lab Have students share tasks. Ask them whether the method used would work for all parallelograms. Have students explain their answers, drawing additional parallelograms if necessary.

In-Class Examples

Find the area of each parallelogram to the nearest tenth.

For Example 1

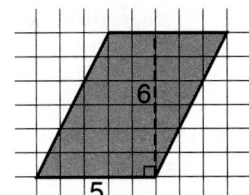

30 square units

For Example 2

24.4 m²

Teaching Tip For Example 3, remind students how to multiply mixed numbers by changing them to improper fractions and how to change the answer back to a mixed number.

Multiple Learning Styles

Kinesthetic Have pairs of students cut a rectangle out of grid paper. The area of the rectangle should be 20 square units. Have one partner draw a diagonal through the rectangle to form two triangles and then cut along the line. Then have the other partner arrange the two pieces to form a parallelogram. The area is still 20 square units. Repeat the activity several times with students trading roles each time. Challenge students to see how many different parallelograms they can model that have an area of 20 square units.

3 PRACTICE/APPLY

Example APPLICATION

3 Manufacturing A company in Dallas, Texas, makes ceramic tile that is used to cover floors or walls. Find the area of a ceramic tile that needs to be glazed if it is shaped like a parallelogram with a height of $4\frac{1}{2}$ inches and a base of $6\frac{3}{4}$ inches.

Use the formula for the area of a parallelogram to find the area of the top of the tile.

$A = bh$

$A = \left(6\frac{3}{4}\right)\left(4\frac{1}{2}\right)$ *Replace b with $6\frac{3}{4}$ and h with $4\frac{1}{2}$.*

$A = \left(\frac{27}{4}\right)\left(\frac{9}{2}\right)$ $6\frac{3}{4} = \frac{27}{4}$, and $4\frac{1}{2} = \frac{9}{2}$

$A = \frac{243}{8}$ or $30\frac{3}{8}$ The area of the tile is $30\frac{3}{8}$ square inches.

CHECK FOR UNDERSTANDING

Communicating Mathematics

Read and study the lesson to answer each question. 1–3. See margin.

1. *State* why the formula for finding the area of a rectangle is related to the formula for finding the area of a parallelogram.

2. *Explain* why a rectangle is a parallelogram, but a parallelogram may not be a rectangle.

HANDS-ON MATH

3. *Draw* a rectangle and a parallelogram that have the same area. Explain how you know they have the same area.

Guided Practice

Find the area of each parallelogram to the nearest tenth. 4. 48 square units

4.

5. 13.6 m²

interNET CONNECTION

To investigate the shapes in other flags, visit: www.glencoe.com/sec/math/mac/mathnet

6. **Flags** The flag of Brunei Darussalam has white and black parallelograms on a field of yellow. If a flag is 40 inches wide and the white and black parallelograms each have an area of 240 square inches, how long is the base of each parallelogram? **6 inches**

EXERCISES

Practice

Find the area of each parallelogram. Round decimal answers to the nearest tenth.

7. 54 in²

8. 35 units²

9. 38.8 cm²

10.
$6\frac{7}{8}$ in. **$48\frac{7}{8}$ in²**
$5\frac{3}{4}$ in. $8\frac{1}{2}$ in.

11.
9 m 7 m
10 m
70 m²

12.
40.4 mm 22.6 mm
16.2 mm
366.1 mm²

13. Find the area of a parallelogram that is 5.4 centimeters wide and 7.9 centimeters high to the nearest tenth. **42.7 cm²**

14. The area of a parallelogram is $20\frac{7}{12}$ square yards. What is the length of the parallelogram if the base is $3\frac{1}{4}$ yards long? **$6\frac{1}{3}$ yards**

15. *Sports* Some alpine snowboards resemble parallelograms. Estimate the area of a snowboard if it is 29 centimeters wide and 159 centimeters long. **4,611 cm²**

16. *Crafts* The quilt pattern at the right is called the Lone Star pattern.

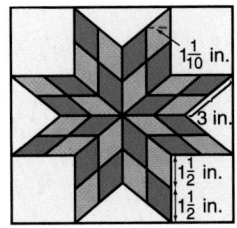
$1\frac{1}{10}$ in.
3 in.
$1\frac{1}{2}$ in.
$1\frac{1}{2}$ in.

  a. Find the area of one of the smallest parallelograms. **1.65 in²**

  b. If the fabric chosen is 36 inches wide, how long should the piece be to have enough to make all of the pieces for a quilt square? **about 3 inches**

17. *Critical Thinking* Suppose you double the height of a parallelogram.

  a. How does the area change? **The area doubles.**

  b. What happens to the area if you double the base as well as the height? **The area is increased four times.**

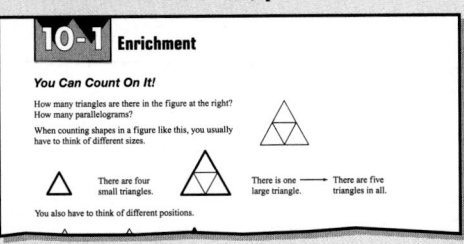
Mixed Review

18. **Standardized Test Practice** Which best describes the two triangles? *(Lesson 9-6)* **C**
2 in. 4 in.
4 in.
  A symmetrical
  B congruent
  6 in. 3 in.
  C similar
  D regular
  6 in.
  E reflections

For **Extra Practice**, see page 583.

19. State whether 708 is divisible by 2, 3, 5, 6, 9, or 10 using divisibility rules. *(Lesson 5-1)* **2, 3, 6**

Lesson 10-1 Area of Parallelograms **401**

▬▬▬ **Extending the Lesson** ▬▬▬

Enrichment Masters, p. 70

10-1 Enrichment

You Can Count On It!

How many triangles are there in the figure at the right?
How many parallelograms?

When counting shapes in a figure like this, you usually
have to think of different sizes.

There are four small triangles. There is one large triangle. There are five triangles in all.

You also have to think of different positions.

Activity Have students look for everyday items that have parallelograms as faces. Remind them that rectangles are special parallelograms. Ask students to make a scale drawing of one item.

---

4 ASSESS

Closing Activity

Modeling Have each student draw a parallelogram and its dimensions on one index card and write its area on another index card. Mix up the cards and have students match the drawing cards to the area cards.

Practice Masters, p. 70

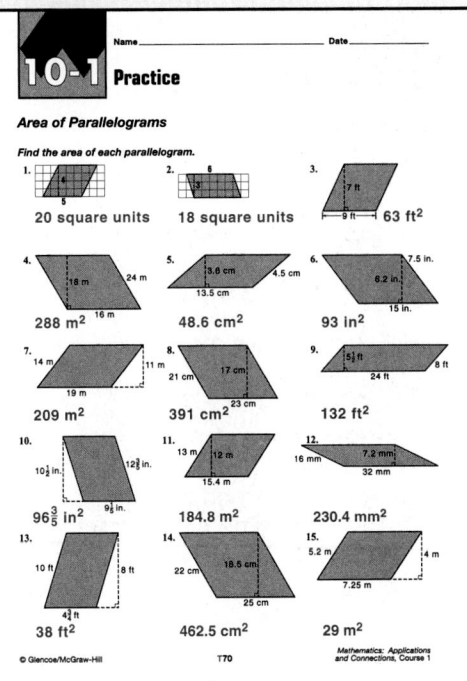

10-1 Practice

Area of Parallelograms

Find the area of each parallelogram.

1. **20 square units** 2. **18 square units** 3. 7 ft / 9 ft **63 ft²**

4. 18 m / 24 m **288 m²** 5. 3.6 cm / 4.5 cm / 13.5 cm **48.6 cm²** 6. 7.5 in. / 6.2 in. / 15 in. **93 in²**

7. 14 m / 11 m / 19 m **209 m²** 8. 21 cm / 17 cm / 23 cm **391 cm²** 9. $5\frac{1}{2}$ ft / 8 ft / 24 ft **132 ft²**

10. $10\frac{1}{2}$ in. / $12\frac{3}{8}$ in. **$96\frac{3}{8}$ in²** 11. 13 m / 12 m / 15.4 m **184.8 m²** 12. 16 mm / 7.2 mm / 32 mm **230.4 mm²**

13. 10 ft / 8 ft / $4\frac{3}{4}$ ft **38 ft²** 14. 22 cm / 18.5 cm / 25 cm **462.5 cm²** 15. 5.2 m / 4 m / 7.25 m **29 m²**

© Glencoe/McGraw-Hill T70 Mathematics: Applications and Connections, Course 1

Lesson 10-1 401

- *Study Guide Masters*, p. 71
- *Practice Masters*, p. 71
- *Enrichment Masters*, p. 71
- Transparencies 10-2, A and B
- *Assessment and Evaluation Masters*, p. 267
- *Hands-On Lab Masters*, p. 78
- *Science and Math Lab Manual*, pp. 17–20

 CD-ROM Program
- Resource Lesson 10-2
- Interactive Lesson 10-2

Recommended Pacing	
Standard	Day 4 of 13
Honors	Day 3 of 13
Block	Day 2 of 7

1 FOCUS

5-Minute Check
(Lesson 10-1)

Find the area of each parallelogram.

1. base: 13 cm
height: 8 cm 104 cm²

2. base: 7 ft
height: 9 ft 63 ft²

3.

6 in.   9 in.
5 in.

30 in²

4.

5 m   3 m
2 m

6 m²

 The 5-Minute Check is also available on **Transparency 10-2A** for this lesson.

Motivating the Lesson

Communication Ask students to find the area of a triangle using the method they learned in Hands-On Lab 10-1A. Ask them if this method would work to get an exact answer.

10-2 Area of Triangles

What you'll learn

You'll learn to find the area of triangles.

When am I ever going to use this?

You can use the area of a triangle to solve problems in navigation and architecture.

Sailors have told stories of unusual occurrences in the area known as The Bermuda Triangle. This imaginary triangle has Melbourne, Florida; Bermuda; and Puerto Rico as its vertices as shown in the diagram. What is the area enclosed by the Bermuda Triangle? *You will solve this problem in Example 3.*

To answer this and other questions, you need to discover a formula for the area of a triangle. In the Mini-Lab, you will compare the area of a triangle to the area of a parallelogram.

Bermuda Triangle
Atlantic Ocean
Bermuda

1,150 miles
 950 miles
756 miles
Florida

950 miles

 Puerto Rico

HANDS-ON MINI-LAB

Work with a partner.   ☐ plain paper   ✂ scissors   📏 ruler

Try This

- Trace two triangles like the one at the right on a sheet of paper.
- Cut out both triangles.
- Place the triangles together to form a parallelogram.

X Y
Z

Talk About It 1–3. See margin.

1. How does the area of one of the triangles compare to the area of the parallelogram?
2. What part of the parallelogram is the same as the height of the triangle? What part is the same as the triangle's base?
3. Write a formula for finding the area of a triangle.
4. Rearrange the triangles into a different parallelogram. Does your formula still hold true? **See students' work.; yes**

✳ Cross-Curriculum Cue

Inform the other teachers on your team that your students are studying triangles. Suggestions for curriculum integration are:

Health: food pyramid
Social Studies: sails and navigation
Physical Science: velocity

A parallelogram can be formed by two congruent triangles. You know that the area of a parallelogram is $A = bh$. The triangles have the same area. So, the area of a triangle is one-half the area of the parallelogram, or $A = \frac{1}{2}bh$.

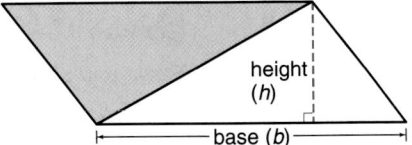

The base of a triangle is any one of its sides. The height of the triangle is the distance from a base to the opposite vertex.

Area of a Triangle	**Words:** The area (A) of a triangle equals half of the product of the length of the base (b) and the height (h).	
	Symbols: $A = \frac{1}{2}bh$	**Model:**

Examples

Find the area of each triangle.

①

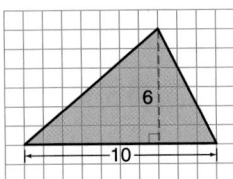

$A = \frac{1}{2}bh$

$A = \frac{1}{2} \cdot 10 \cdot 6$ *Replace b with 10 and h with 6.*

$A = 5 \cdot 6$ or 30

The area is 30 square units.

②

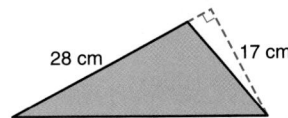

The base is 28 cm, and the height is 17 cm.

$A = \frac{1}{2}bh$

$A = \frac{1}{2} \cdot 28 \cdot 17$

$0.5 \boxed{\times} 28 \boxed{\times} 17 \boxed{=} \; 238$

$A = 238$

The area is 238 square centimeters.

CONNECTION **③** **Geography** Refer to the beginning of the lesson. Find the area of the Bermuda Triangle.

Let the base be the distance from Melbourne to Bermuda, which is 1,150 miles long. Then the height will be 756 miles. So, $b = 1,150$ and $h = 756$.

$A = \frac{1}{2}bh$

$A = \frac{1}{2} \cdot 1,150 \cdot 756$

$A = 434,700$ $0.5 \boxed{\times} 1150 \boxed{\times} 756 \boxed{=} \; 434700$

The area of the Bermuda Triangle is 434,700 square miles.

 Transparency 10-2B contains a teaching aid for this lesson.

Using the Mini-Lab If necessary, review the formula for finding the area of a parallelogram. Ask students whether this formula works for any two triangles. Have students repeat the activity with triangles they draw.

Teaching Tip Before Example 1, point out that the formula $A = \frac{1}{2}bh$ is the same as $A = \frac{bh}{2}$.

In-Class Examples

Find the area of each triangle.

For Example 1

18 in²

For Example 2

336 m²

For Example 3
Twila, Julie, and Renata are making school pennants. The height of each pennant is 18 inches. The base is 6 inches. Find the area of each pennant.
54 in²

Investigations for the Special Education Student

This blackline master booklet helps you plan for the needs of your special education students by providing long-term projects along with teacher notes. Investigation 14, *Exploring the Depths of the Sea,* may be used with this chapter.

Additional Answers for the Mini-Lab

1. The area of the parallelogram is twice the area of the triangle.

2. height; base

3. $A = \frac{1}{2}bh$

Check for Understanding

If students need additional practice or instruction after completing Exercises 1–8, one of these options may be helpful.
• Extra Practice, see p. 583
• Reteaching Activity
• *Study Guide Masters*, p. 71
• *Practice Masters*, p. 71

Assignment Guide

Core: 9–23 odd, 24–27
Enriched: 10–18 even, 20–27

Additional Answer

3. Ebony is correct. If 5.8 is used as the height, then the base is the length of the side to which the height is drawn, the 7-inch side.

Study Guide Masters, p. 71

CHECK FOR UNDERSTANDING

Communicating Mathematics

Read and study the lesson to answer these questions.

1. *Tell* why the area of a triangle can be defined as half the area of a parallelogram. **Two congruent triangles form a parallelogram.**

2. *Develop* a way to remember the formulas for finding the area of a parallelogram and a triangle. **See students' work.**

3. *You Decide* Ebony says that for the triangle at the right, $A = \frac{1}{2} \cdot 7 \cdot 5.8$. Dália says that $A = \frac{1}{2} \cdot 8 \cdot 5.8$. Who is correct and why? **See margin.**

Guided Practice   **Find the area of each triangle.**

4.
27 units²

5.
35 mm²

6.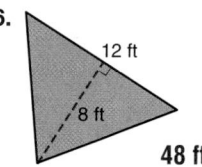
48 ft²

7. What is the area of a triangle with a height of 40 meters and a base 56.8 meters long? **1,136 m²**

8. *Architecture* The Rock and Roll Hall of Fame in Cleveland opened to fans in 1995. Part of the hall is a pyramid covered in glass. Each of the four sides of the pyramid is a triangle with a base of 241 feet and a height of 165 feet. How much glass was used to cover the entire pyramid? **79,530 ft²**

EXERCISES

Practice   **Find the area of each triangle. Round decimal answers to the nearest tenth.**

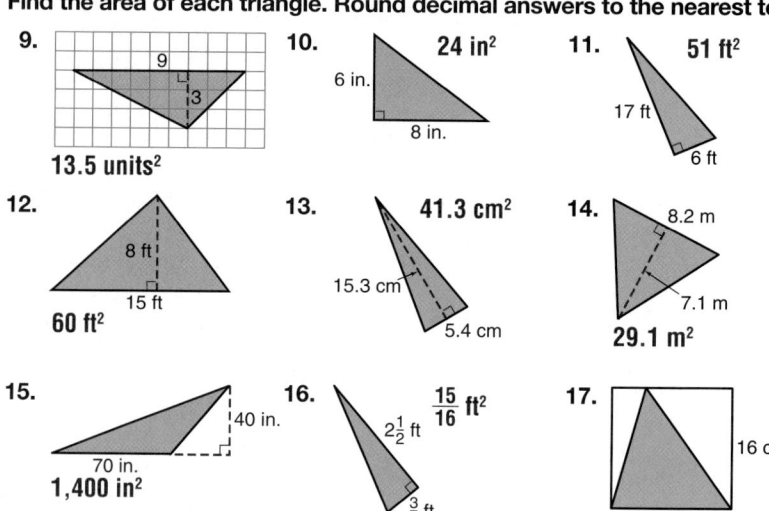

9. **13.5 units²**

10. **24 in²**

11. **51 ft²**

12. **60 ft²**

13. **41.3 cm²**

14. **29.1 m²**

15. **1,400 in²**

16. $\frac{15}{16}$ **ft²**

17. **128 cm²**

404   Chapter 10   Geometry: Understanding Area and Volume

Reteaching the Lesson

Activity Have each partner of a student pair draw a triangle on centimeter grid paper. Then have the partners estimate the area of each other's triangle. Have them use the formula learned in this lesson to find the area of the triangles.

Error Analysis

Watch for students who multiply both the base and the height by $\frac{1}{2}$.

Prevent by reminding students that in a multiplication problem, each factor is used only once.

18. Find the area of a triangle with a base of 42 inches and a height of 35 inches. **735 in²**

19. Find the area and perimeter of the figure at the right. **14 ft²; 16 ft**

2 ft
5 ft
4 ft
5 ft

Applications and Problem Solving

20. 355.3 square feet

20. *Sailing* When comparing sailboats, sailors often consider the sail area. The sail area is the total of the areas of all the sails used on the boat. On a Precision 28, the jib sail is a triangle with a base of 10 feet 6 inches and a height of 31 feet. The base of the triangular mainsail is 11 feet 7 inches and the height is 33 feet 3 inches. What is the sail area of the boat?

21. *Life Science* African elephants have large ears that are roughly triangular in shape. They help the elephant to keep cool in the hot climate. Research the ways that the ears cool an elephant in a reference book or on the Internet. **See margin.**

22. *Sports* The triangular wing of a hang glider has an area of 27 square feet. If the wingspread is 9 feet, what is the height of the wing? **6 ft**

23. *Write a Problem* that can be solved by finding the area of a triangle. **See students' work.**

24. *Critical Thinking* Draw two different triangles that have areas of 18 square feet. **See margin.**

Mixed Review

25. *Geometry* Find the area of the parallelogram at the right. *(Lesson 10-1)* **320 mm²**

16 mm
20 mm

26. *Standardized Test Practice* At Langley High School, 19% of the 2,200 students walk to school. How many students walk to school? *(Lesson 8-7)* **B**

A 400   **B** 418   **C** 428   **D** 476

For **Extra Practice**, see page 583.

27. *Waste* Every person in the U.S. is responsible for about 2.9 pounds of waste that is disposed of per day. How many ounces is that? *(Lesson 7-7)* **46.4 ounces**

Lesson 10-2 Area of Triangles **405**

Extending the Lesson

Enrichment Masters, p. 71

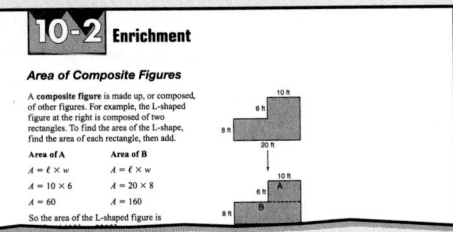

Activity Give students the area and one dimension of a triangle and have them find the other dimension. For example, ask: *What is the base of a triangle with an area of 32 square meters and a height of 16 meters?* **4 meters**

---

4 ASSESS

Closing Activity

Modeling Have pairs of students use geoboards and geobands to make triangles of different sizes. Ask them to find the area of each triangle in square units.

Chapter 10, Quiz A (Lessons 10-1 and 10-2) is available in the *Assessment and Evaluation Masters*, p. 267.

Additional Answers

21. Sample answer: An elephant's ears expand its overall surface area, allowing it more space to release heat and cool itself.

24. Sample answers: a triangle with a base 9 feet long and a height of 4 feet; a triangle with a base of 6 feet and a height of 6 feet

Practice Masters, p. 71

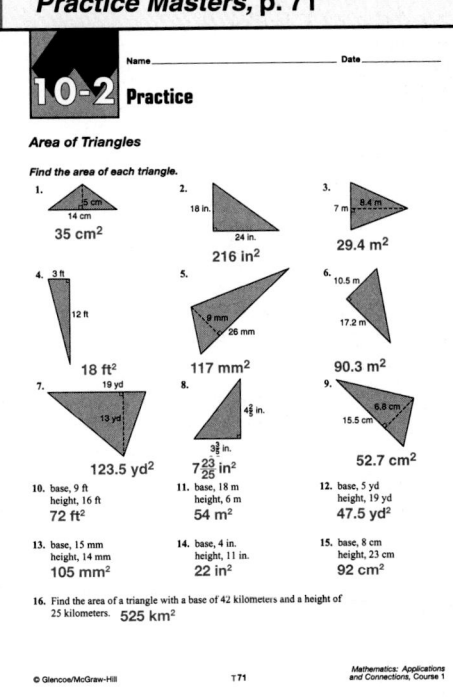

Instructional Resources

- *Study Guide Masters*, p. 72
- *Practice Masters*, p. 72
- *Enrichment Masters*, p. 72
- Transparencies 10-3, A and B
- *Assessment and Evaluation Masters*, pp. 266, 267
- *Classroom Games*, pp. 27–28
- *Technology Masters*, p. 19

CD-ROM Program
- Resource Lesson 10-3

Recommended Pacing	
Standard	Days 5 & 6 of 13
Honors	Days 4 & 5 of 13
Block	Day 3 of 7

1 FOCUS

5-Minute Check
(Lesson 10-2)

Find the area of each triangle. Round decimal answers to the nearest tenth.

1. base = 14 cm
   height = 22 cm **154 cm²**
2. base = 9 m
   height = 6.3 m **28.4 m²**

3. 18 in.
   3 in.
   27 in²

4. 4.1 m
   3.2 m
   6.6 m²

The 5-Minute Check is also available on **Transparency 10-3A** for this lesson.

Motivating the Lesson

Problem Solving Ask students how they would solve this problem. *Antonio's Pizzeria sells a 12-inch pizza for $8.75 and a 14-inch pizza for $10.25. Which pizza costs less per square inch?*

10-3 Area of Circles

What you'll learn

You'll learn to find the area of circles.

When am I ever going to use this?

You can use the area of a circle to find the area of your yard covered by a sprinkler.

The people of Kobe, Japan, were awakened at 5:46 the morning of January 17, 1995 by one of the most destructive earthquakes in history. The epicenter of the quake was near the island of Awaji-shima. Damage extended as far as Osaka, 27 miles away. What is the area of the region affected by the earthquake? *This problem will be solved in Example 3.*

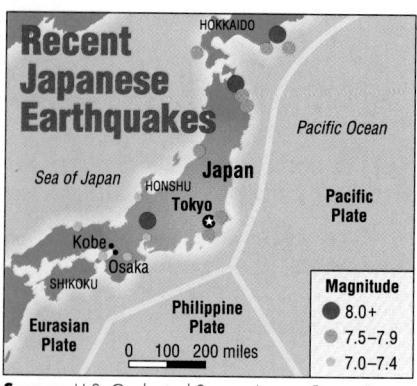

Source: U.S. Geological Survey, Agence France Presse

You need a formula for the area of a circle to answer this question. In the Mini-Lab, you will find the area of a circle by forming a parallelogram.

HANDS-ON MINI-LAB

Work with a partner. paper plate scissors

Try This
- Fold your paper plate into eighths.
- Unfold the plate and cut along the creases.
- Arrange the pieces to form a "parallelogram" as shown below.

Talk About It
1. What is the height of the parallelogram?
2. What is the length of the parallelogram's base?
3. How would you find the area of the parallelogram?

1. the radius of the circle
2. half of the circumference of the circle
3. base × height

LOOK BACK
Refer to Lesson 7-4 for information on the formula for circumference of a circle.

The shape of the figure you formed in the Mini-Lab is nearly a parallelogram. The length of its base is one-half of the circumference of the circle, $\frac{1}{2}C$. So $b = \frac{1}{2}C$. Its height is the radius of the circle, r. So $h = r$.

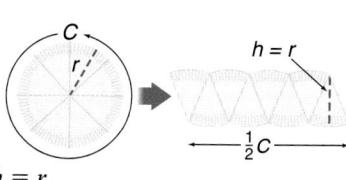

406 Chapter 10 Geometry: Understanding Area and Volume

Multiple Learning Styles

Auditory/Musical Drums come in many sizes, each with a circular head. Have pairs of students make three drums of different sizes. Have them find the area of each drumhead. After sounding each drum, discuss how the sound is affected by the size of the drum.

$$A = bh \qquad \textit{Formula for the area of a parallelogram}$$
$$A = \left(\tfrac{1}{2}C\right)r \qquad \textit{Replace b with } \tfrac{1}{2}C \textit{ and h with r.}$$
$$A = \tfrac{1}{2}(2\pi r)r \qquad \textit{Replace C with } 2\pi r.$$
$$A = \pi \cdot r \cdot r \qquad \textit{Simplify. } \tfrac{1}{2} \cdot 2 = 1$$
$$A = \pi r^2 \qquad \textit{Simplify. } r \cdot r = r^2$$

Area of a Circle	**Words:** The area (*A*) of a circle equals the product of π and the square of the radius (*r*).
	Symbols: $A = \pi r^2$ **Model:** 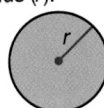

Examples

Find the area of each circle. Use 3.14 for π.

①

16 ft

$$A = \pi r^2$$
$$A = \pi(16)^2$$
3.14 $\boxed{\times}$ 16 $\boxed{x^2}$ $\boxed{=}$ *803.84*

The area is about 804 ft².

②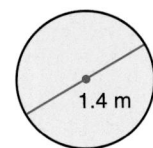

1.4 m

The diameter is 1.4 meters. So the radius is 1.4 ÷ 2 or 0.7 m.
$$A = \pi(0.7)^2$$
$$A \approx 1.5386 \quad \textit{Use a calculator.}$$
The area is about 1.54 m².

CONNECTION **③** **Earth Science** Refer to the beginning of the lesson. Find the area of the region affected by the earthquake.

The radius of the circular region affected was 27 miles.
$$A = \pi r^2$$
$$A = \pi(27)^2$$
3.14 $\boxed{\times}$ 27 $\boxed{x^2}$ $\boxed{=}$ *2289.06*
$$A \approx 2,289$$

The area of the region is about 2,289 square miles.

CHECK FOR UNDERSTANDING

Communicating Mathematics

Read and study the lesson to answer each question.

1. *Explain* how the area of a parallelogram is related to the area of a circle. **See margin.**

2. *Tell* why you can estimate the area of a circle by multiplying the square of the radius by 3. **π is close to 3, so $3r^2$ is close to the area of a circle.**

Lesson 10-3 Area of Circles **407**

 Transparency 10-3B contains a teaching aid for this lesson.

Using the Mini-Lab Lightweight paper plates will be needed for folding and cutting. Students may want to use a ruler to compare the height of the "parallelogram" with the radius of the plate. Repeat the activity with each wedge cut into two congruent wedges (16 slices). Does this figure look more like a parallelogram?

In-Class Examples
Find the area of each circle. Use 3.14 for π.

For Example 1

6 cm

113.0 cm²

For Example 2

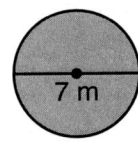

7 m

38.5 m²

For Example 3
The world's largest cylindrical sundial is in Orlando, Florida. Arata Isozaki of Tokyo, Japan, designed it. The face of the sundial has a diameter of 122 feet. What is the area of the face? Round to the nearest whole number. 11,690 ft²

Teaching Tip Remind students to notice whether the measurement given is the radius or the diameter of the circle before finding the area.

Additional Answer
1. A circle can be cut and arranged into a figure like a parallelogram to find the area.

Check for Understanding

If students need additional practice or instruction after completing Exercises 1–8, one of these options may be helpful.
- Extra Practice, see p. 583
- Reteaching Activity
- *Study Guide Masters,* p. 72
- *Practice Masters,* p. 72

Assignment Guide

Core: 9–23 odd, 25–28
Enriched: 10–22 even, 23–28

Study Guide Masters, p. 72

---

3. *Find* an object with a circular face such as a jar lid or the bottom of a mug. Then find the area of the circular region. **See students' work.**

Guided Practice   Find the area of each circle to the nearest tenth. Use 3.14 for π.

4. **78.5 in²**

5. **254.3 m²**

6. radius, 3.7 millimeters **43.0 mm²**   **7.** diameter, $1\frac{1}{3}$ feet **1.4 ft²**

8. *Gardening* The Roundabout water sprinkler can be adjusted to spray up to 25 feet. If the spray is in a circular pattern, what is the area watered by the sprinkler? **1,962.5 ft²**

EXERCISES

Practice   Find the area of each circle to the nearest tenth. Use 3.14 for π.

9. **28.3 in²**   **10.** **201.0 m²**   **11.** **615.4 ft²**

12. **907.5 cm²**   **13.** **95.0 in²**   **14.** **72.3 m²**

15. radius, 11 inches **379.9 in²**   **16.** radius, 23 centimeters **1,661.1 cm²**

17. radius, 4.5 meters **63.6 m²**   **18.** diameter, 16 inches **201.0 in²**

19. diameter, 22 millimeters **379.9 mm²**   **20.** diameter, $6\frac{2}{3}$ yards **34.9 yd²**

21. A circle has a radius 5.5 meters long. Find the area of the circle. **95.0 m²**

22. What is the area of a circle with a diameter of $32\frac{1}{2}$ feet? **829.2 ft²**

Applications and Problem Solving

23. *Physical Therapy* A therapy pool in the Central High School training room is in the shape of a circle. The diameter is 9 meters. The coach would like to have a cover made to conserve energy when the pool is not in use. How much material is needed to cover the pool? **about 63.6 m²**

Reteaching the Lesson

Activity Have students use a compass to draw circles of different diameters. Then have them measure each diameter, find the radius, and use a calculator to find the area.

Error Analysis
Watch for students who use the diameter rather than the radius when finding the area of a circle.
Prevent by stressing that the area formula $A = \pi r^2$ uses only the radius.

24. Sports American Matt Ghaffari captured a silver medal in 286-pound Greco-Roman wrestling at the Atlanta Olympics. Wrestling uses a 12-by-12 meter mat with a circular ring inside. The ring has an inside radius of 4.5 meters and a width of 10 centimeters.

Matt Ghaffari

    a. Draw and label a diagram of a wrestling mat and ring. **a, c. See margin.**

b. about 63.62 m²

    b. What is the area inside a wrestling ring?

    c. What is the area of the ring itself? *(Hint:* Subtract the area of the inside circle from that of the outside circle.)

25. Critical Thinking If you double the radius of a circle, how is the area affected? **The area is multiplied by 4.**

Mixed Review

26. What is the area of a triangle with a base 8 meters long and a height of 14 meters? *(Lesson 10-2)* **56 m²**

27. Standardized Test Practice A recipe calls for $1\frac{2}{3}$ cups water, $\frac{1}{3}$ cup oil, and $2\frac{1}{3}$ cups milk. How much liquid is used? *(Lesson 6-3)* **A**

  A $4\frac{1}{3}$ cups   **B** $3\frac{1}{3}$ cups   **C** 3 cups   **D** $2\frac{3}{3}$ cups   **E** Not Here

For **Extra Practice**, see page 583.

28. Change 3,400 centimeters to meters. *(Lesson 4-9)* **34 m**

Let the Games Begin

Tiddlywink Target

Get Ready This game is for 2 or 3 players. ⬤ counters

🗂 felt squares ✏ markers ✐ compass

Math Skill
Area

Get Set Draw three circles on a felt square to make a target like the one at the right. Give each player five counters of one color and a felt piece.

Go ● To shoot a counter, place it on a felt piece and press with a second counter. Slowly slide off the edge to shoot the counter onto the target. The score is the number in the area where most of the counter lands.

● Shoot counters toward the target in turns. A counter may be bumped off the target by another counter. Any counter that lands off of the target is out of play.

● After each player shoots four counters, the winner is the player with the highest total score.

💻**interNET CONNECTION** Visit www.glencoe.com/sec/math/mac/mathnet for more games.

■ Extending the Lesson ■

Enrichment Masters, p. 72

Let the Games Begin

If a player's counter lands partially in one area and partially in another, have students see how much of the counter is resting in each area. The player is awarded the points allotted to the area where most of the counter lies.

*Additional resources for this game can be found on page 44 of the **Classroom Games.***

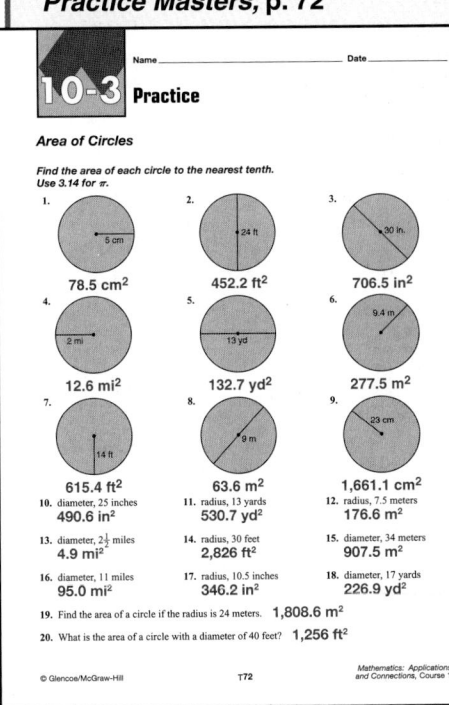

GET READY

Objective Students construct circle graphs.

Optional Resources
Hands-On Lab Masters
• circle graph template, p. 29
• protractor, p. 22
• worksheet, p. 62

Overhead Manipulative Resources
• compass
• protractor

Manipulative Kit
• ruler
• compass
• protractor

MANAGEMENT TIPS

Recommended Time
45 minutes

Getting Started Review reading circle graphs from Chapter 2, pages 60–63. Ask students how circle graphs show that one part of the whole is less than, greater than, or about equal to another. Then ask them how they think circle graphs are constructed.

The **Activity** demonstrates how to construct a circle graph. Remind students that percents in a circle graph must add up to 100% and that the degrees must add up to 360°. Discuss the possibility that this may not always happen due to rounding. Students may then need to round up or down to get 360°.

COOPERATIVE LEARNING

10-3B Making Circle Graphs

A Follow-Up of Lesson 10-3

 colored pencils

 ruler

 compass

 protractor

calculator

Sun tops the list of things Americans look for in a vacation spot. The graph shows how people answered the question "How important is sunny weather in a vacation location?"

Circle graphs are used to compare parts of a whole. Usually the information is expressed in percents as in the circle graph at the right.

Vacation Sun

Important 69%
Not very important 16%
Not at all important 15%

Source: *Opinion Research Corp.*

TRY THIS

Work with a partner.

The chart shows the percent of toys that are sold in several price ranges. Use the information to make a circle graph.

Price	Percent of Toys
Under $4.00	47%
$4.00–$7.99	21%
$8.00 and above	32%

Source: The TMI Report

Step 1 Find the number of degrees for each price range. To do this, multiply the decimal equivalent of each percent by 360°, which is the total number of degrees in a circle. For example, for "Under $4.00," find the number of degrees as follows.

0.47 ☒ 360 ☐ *169.2*

The section of the circle graph for this price range should be about 169°.

Step 2 Use a compass to draw a circle. Then draw a radius of the circle with the ruler.

Step 3 Draw the angle for "Under $4.00" using your protractor. Repeat this step for each price range.

Step 4 Use the colored pencils to color each section of the graph. Label the sections. Then give the graph a title.

410 **Chapter 10** Geometry: Understanding Area and Volume

Classroom Vignette

"Another way to create a circle graph is to have students cut a strip of paper 100 cm long. Have them mark the strip into sections so that each section represents a given percent of the graph (1 cm = 1%). Join the ends of the strip to form a circle and use the marks to define each section."

Gail Burrill, Teacher
Whitnall High School
Hales Corners, WI

ON YOUR OWN

1. Compare the graph you made to the chart. Which do you think displays the data more clearly? Explain your reasoning.

2. Why were you able to display the data on toy prices in a circle graph? **The data show the relative proportions.**

3. What type of information *cannot* be displayed in a circle graph? How could you display this type of data?

4. *Hobbies* Say cheese! A camera film maker surveyed customers about how often they take pictures. Make a circle graph of the data. **See Answer Appendix.**

How Long Does Film Spend in Your Camera Before Being Developed?					
2 weeks or less	2–4 weeks	1–3 months	3–12 months	more than a year	don't know
40%	19%	19%	12%	3%	7%

5. *Population* The table below shows the approximate percent of the population of Earth living in each region. Make a circle graph of the data. **See Answer Appendix.**

Region	Percent of Population
Asia	59.39%
Africa	12.68%
Europe	8.78%
Latin America and the Caribbean	8.47%
Former USSR	5.07%
North America	5.11%
Oceania and Australia	0.50%

Source: Bureau of the Census

6. *Entertainment* Do you like to play video games? According to a sports magazine survey, 90% of kids do! The graph shows the amount of time kids who play video games spend playing each day.

   a. How much time do most of the kids surveyed spend playing video games each day? **less than 1 hour**

   b. How much time do 15% of the video players spend each day? **2 hours**

   c. What percent of those surveyed spend one hour or less on video games each day? **72%**

7. *Reflect Back* How is the area of a circle related to making a circle graph? **The area of the circle is divided into parts to represent the portion of the whole for each category.**

Time for Video Games

Source: Sports Illustrated

1. **Sample answer: The circle graph, because it allows a visual comparison of the proportions.**

3. **Sample answers: data that doesn't equal 100%; a bar or line graph**

Lesson 10-3B HANDS-ON **LAB** 411

Have students write a paragraph about the uses of circle graphs. Encourage them to include a description of the limitations.

Have students complete Exercises 1–4. Discuss with students how they could make a circle graph with information that is not given in percents. Make sure they understand that only information that can be shown as a part of a whole should be shown in a circle graph.

Use Exercises 5–7 to determine whether students understand how to construct and analyze a circle graph.

Hands-On Lab Masters, p. 62

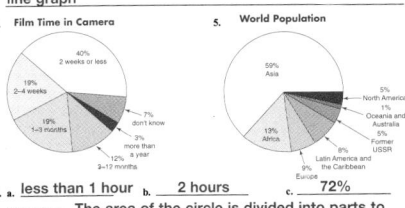

Instructional Resources
- *Study Guide Masters*, p. 73
- *Practice Masters*, p. 73
- *Enrichment Masters*, p. 73
- Transparencies 10-4, A and B
- *Diversity Masters*, p. 10
- CD-ROM Program
  - Resource Lesson 10-4
  - Extended Activity 10-4

Recommended Pacing	
Standard	Days 7 & 8 of 13
Honors	Days 6 & 7 of 13
Block	Day 4 of 7

1 FOCUS

5-Minute Check
(Lesson 10-3)

Find the area of each circle to the nearest tenth. Use 3.14 for π.

1. 6 ft

2. 5.62 cm

   113.0 ft²   **24.8 cm²**

3. radius, 32 m **3,215.4 m²**
4. diameter, 4 ft **12.6 ft²**
5. Find the area of a circle if the diameter is 24 cm. **452.2 cm²**

 The 5-Minute Check is also available on **Transparency 10-4A** for this lesson.

Motivating the Lesson
Hands-On Activity Use a variety of objects such as cans, boxes, marbles, and party hats or use wooden geometric solids. Pass them around and have students identify the flat and curved surfaces. Discuss how the shapes could be named.

10-4 Three-Dimensional Figures

What you'll learn
You'll learn to identify three-dimensional figures.

When am I ever going to use this?
Knowing how to identify three-dimensional figures will help you to solve problems in social studies and earth science.

Word Wise
three-dimensional figure
face
edge
vertex (vertices)
prism
base
rectangular prism
pyramid
square pyramid
cone
cylinder
sphere
center

You can find Captain Eddie's Flying Circus Kite Team in competitions all year. A stunt kite like the team uses is a two-dimensional object. Other kites, like box kites, are three-dimensional objects.

A **three-dimensional figure** encloses a part of space. The flat surfaces of a three-dimensional figure are called **faces**. The **edges** are the segments formed by intersecting faces. The edges intersect at the **vertices**.

Boxes are examples of **prisms**. A prism has at least three lateral faces that are shaped like rectangles. The faces on the top and bottom are the **bases** and are parallel. The shape of the bases tells the name of the prism. Because its bases are rectangles, a cereal box is a **rectangular prism**.

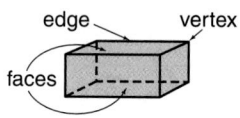

A rectangular prism has 12 edges and 8 vertices.

This pyramid has 8 edges and 5 vertices.

A **pyramid**, like the Egyptian pyramids, has only one base. The base can be shaped like any polygon. The shape of the base gives the pyramid its name. For example, a pyramid with a square base is called a **square pyramid**. The other faces of the pyramid are triangles.

> **Example**
> **CONNECTION**

Geography How many faces, edges, and vertices are there in the Great Pyramid of Khufu?

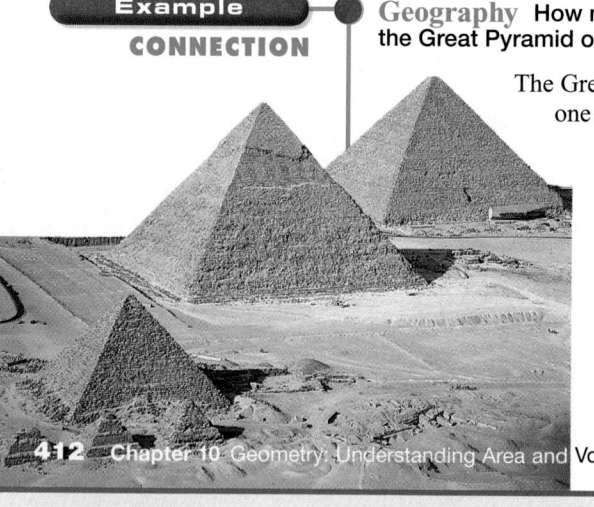

The Great Pyramid of Khufu is a square pyramid. It has one square face and four triangular faces. So there are five faces in all.

There are four edges where the side faces meet the base. Four more edges are formed where the side faces meet each other. So, there are eight edges in the pyramid.

There are four vertices of the square base and the vertex where the other faces meet. So there are five vertices in the pyramid.

Classroom Vignette

"In the spring, students construct three-dimensional tetrahedron kites using straws, string, and tissue paper. Then we go outside and attempt to fly the kites."

Kathy Bessette, Teacher
Dover Middle School
Dover, NH

Jan Wickboldt

There are three-dimensional figures that have curved surfaces. One of these figures is a **cone**. Like a pyramid, a cone has one base. Its base is a circle.

A cone has one vertex, but no edges.

A cylinder has no vertices and no edges.

Another figure with a curved surface is a **cylinder**. A soup can is a model of a cylinder. A cylinder has two circular bases.

A basketball is a model of a sphere. A **sphere** is a three-dimensional figure with no faces, bases, edges, or vertices. All of the points on a sphere are the same distance from a given point called the **center**.

center

A sphere has no vertices or edges.

Study Hint

Reading Math In diagrams of three-dimensional figures, dashed lines are used to indicate edges that are hidden from view.

CHECK FOR UNDERSTANDING

Communicating Mathematics

Read and study the lesson to answer each question.

1. *Tell* what type of pyramid is shown at the right. **square pyramid**

2. *Explain* the difference between a two-dimensional and a three-dimensional figure. **See Answer Appendix.**

3. *List* each type of three-dimensional figure in this lesson. Then give an example of a real-world object with that shape. **See students' work.**

Guided Practice

Name each figure.

4. **triangular pyramid**

5. **cone**

State the number of faces, edges, and vertices in each figure.

6. rectangular prism **6; 12; 8**

7. triangular prism **5; 9; 6**

8. *Hobbies* What type of three-dimensional figure is the base for the box kite shown on page 412? **rectangular prism**

EXERCISES

Practice

Name each figure.

9. **cylinder**

10. **sphere**

11. 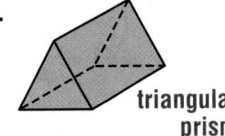 **triangular prism**

Lesson 10-4 Three-Dimensional Figures **413**

---

2 TEACH

Transparency 10-4B contains a teaching aid for this lesson.

Reading Mathematics Have students use a dictionary to look up the words in the Word Wise list. Suggest that they read all of the definitions for each word and pick out the mathematical one to copy. Then discuss their lists of definitions and make sure they understand what each term means. Emphasize that "vertices" is plural for "vertex."

In-Class Example

For the Example

a. How many faces, edges, and vertices are there in a triangular pyramid? **4, 6, 4**

b. How many faces, edges, and vertices are there in a shoebox? **6, 12, 8**

3 PRACTICE/APPLY

Check for Understanding

If students need additional practice or instruction after completing Exercises 1–8, one of these options may be helpful.

- Extra Practice, see p. 584
- Reteaching Activity
- *Study Guide Masters*, p. 73
- *Practice Masters*, p. 73

***Study Guide Masters*, p. 73**

Reteaching the Lesson

Activity Draw the figures shown in this lesson on an overhead transparency and have students identify them. Trace the edges and vertices of each figure as students count them. Then display an object or block and have students identify and count the faces.

Error Analysis

Watch for students who have difficulty interpreting three-dimensional drawings. **Prevent by** suggesting they focus on one face of the object at a time.

Lesson 10-4 **413**

4 ASSESS

Closing Activity

Speaking Separate students into pairs. Ask one partner to verbally describe an object in the room including the number of faces, edges, and vertices. Have the other partner guess the identity of the object. Then have them reverse roles.

Mid-Chapter Self Test

The Mid-Chapter Self Test reviews the concepts in Lessons 10-1 through 10-4. Lesson references are given so students can review concepts not yet mastered.

Practice Masters, p. 73

Family Activity

Write a list of three-dimensional figures. Then challenge family members to a scavenger hunt to see who can find the most items that match the figures on the list.

Name each figure.   12. rectangular prism

12.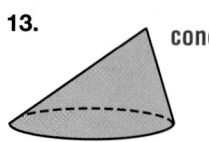

13. cone

14. hexagonal prism

Copy and complete the chart for the numbers of faces, edges, and vertices in each figure.

	Figure	Faces	Edges	Vertices
15.	triangular pyramid	4	6	4
16.	cylinder	none	none	none
17.	sphere	none	none	none
18.	hexagonal pyramid	7	12	7
19.	hexagonal prism	8	18	12

Applications and Problem Solving

20. **Number Theory** Swiss mathematician Leonard Euler (pronounced OY ler) found that in three-dimensional figures that have no curved surfaces $E = F + V - 2$ for the number of faces F, edges E, and vertices, V. Does this formula agree with what you found in Exercises 15, 18, and 19? **Sample answer: yes**

21. **Earth Science** A crystal of alum is in the form of two square pyramids sharing the same base.1
   a. How many faces, edges, and vertices are in the crystal? **8; 12; 6**
   b. Does your answer to part a agree with Euler's formula above? **yes**

22. **Critical Thinking** A pyramid has four faces. What type of pyramid must it be? **triangular**

23. 1,519.76 in²

Mixed Review

23. Find the area of a circle with a radius of 22 inches. *(Lesson 10-3)*

24. How many lines of symmetry are there in a square? *(Lesson 9-5)* **4 lines**

25. **Standardized Test Practice** If you work 22 hours a week and earn $139.70, how much money do you earn per hour? *(Lesson 8-2)* **B**
   A $6.50   **B** $6.35   **C** $6.05   **D** $5.85   **E** Not Here

For **Extra Practice,** see page 584.

CHAPTER 10

Mid-Chapter Self Test

1. Find the area of a parallelogram with a base 50 feet long and a height of 77 feet. *(Lesson 10-1)*

2. What is the area of a triangle with a 21-inch base and a height of 15 inches? *(Lesson 10-2)*

3. What is the area of a circle with a 2-inch radius? *(Lesson 10-3)* **12.6 in²**

4. The diameter of a circle is 88 meters. Find the area of the circle. *(Lesson 10-3)* **6,079.0 m²**

5. A stack of compact discs is a model of what three-dimensional figure? *(Lesson 10-4)* **cylinder**

1. 3,850 ft²   2. 157.5 in²

Extending the Lesson

Enrichment Masters, p. 73

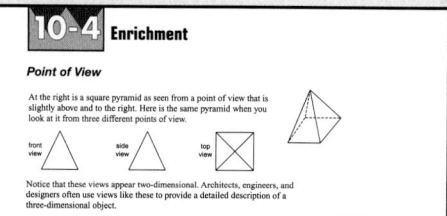

Activity Have groups of students write a brief report on famous examples of various types of three-dimensional buildings such as the Egyptian pyramids. Ask them to look for information such as when and how the buildings were constructed.

COOPERATIVE LEARNING

10-4B Three-Dimensional Figures

A Follow-Up of Lesson 10-4

 isometric
dot paper

ruler

Sometimes it helps to draw a sketch of a three-dimensional figure when you are trying to solve a problem. You can use isometric dot paper to help you draw a three-dimensional figure.

TRY THIS

Work with a partner.

A rectangular prism has a length of 3 units, a height of 4 units, and a width of 2 units. Use isometric dot paper to sketch the prism.

The rectangular surfaces of the prism are drawn as parallelograms to give a three-dimensional appearance.

Step 1 Draw a parallelogram with sides of 3 units and 2 units. This represents the top of the prism.

Step 2 Place your pencil at one of the vertices of the parallelogram. Then draw a line passing through four dots. Repeat for the other three vertices, drawing the hidden edges as dashed lines.

Step 3 Finally, connect the ends of the lines to complete the prism.

ON YOUR OWN

1. In the prism that you drew, which faces are the bases of the prism?

2. If you turned the drawing on its side, would the figure appear different? **yes**

3. Explain how to draw a prism with a hexagonal base. **See margin.**
1. the sides that are rectangles 3 units long and 2 units wide
Use isometric dot paper to draw a sketch of each figure. 4–5. See Answer Appendix.

4. a rectangular prism 4 units long, 2 units high, and 2 units wide

5. cube that is 3 units long, 3 units high, and 3 units wide

6. *Reflect Back* Do you think this method would work well for sketching a sphere? Explain. **Sample answer: No; because the sphere has no faces to draw.**

Lesson 10-4B HANDS-ON **415**

 Have students write a description of how to use isometric dot paper to draw a three-dimensional figure.

HANDS-ON
10-4B LAB Notes

GET READY

Objective Students draw three-dimensional figures.

Optional Resources
Hands-On Lab Masters
• isometric dot paper, p. 14
• worksheet, p. 63

Overhead Manipulative Resources
• isometric dot paper

Manipulative Kit
• ruler
• rubber stamp (isometric dot paper)

MANAGEMENT TIPS

Recommended Time
30 minutes

Getting Started Discuss with students the differences between two-dimensional and three-dimensional drawings. Have students try to sketch a simple box freehand. Discuss what would make this task easier.

The **Activity** demonstrates drawing a three-dimensional figure using isometric dot paper. Make sure students use the same number of units for parallel sides.

ASSESS

Have students complete Exercises 1–5. Watch for students who have difficulty connecting the points. Remind them that the bases of a prism match.

Use Exercise 6 to determine whether students understand drawing three-dimensional figures.

Additional Answer
3. Draw the hexagonal base first. Then for each vertex, draw a line to represent depth. Then connect the ends of the segments.

Hands-On Lab 10-4B 415

Objective Students solve problems by making models.

Recommended Pacing	
Standard	Day 9 of 13
Honors	Day 8 of 13
Block	Day 5 of 7

1 FOCUS

Getting Started Give students centimeter cubes and have them form various size "squares." Have them record how many cubes it takes to make each square.

2 TEACH

Teaching Tip Have students duplicate Emilio and Terrence's model with small blocks. Have them try the activity with other numbers of cubes.

In-Class Example

Charles has 24 cubes. Which structure can he make?

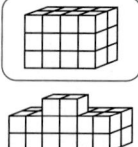

10-5A Make a Model

A Preview of Lesson 10-5

Emilio and Terrence work at Brooks Sporting Goods. The store has just received a shipment of 72 basketballs packaged in 18-inch cubes. The store manager asked Emilio and Terrence to use as many of them as possible to build a pyramid with the boxes in the display window. Let's listen in as they plan.

Emilio

You know, Terrence, there are an awful lot of boxes here. Let's make sure we have a plan that will work before we start to build.

Terrence

You're right. Let's build a model with these smaller baseball boxes over here. The base of the pyramid should be a square. Then each layer above it can be a smaller square.

That sounds good. If the bottom layer is a 4-by-4 square, it will take 16 boxes.

The next layer would be 3 by 3, or 9 boxes. Then 2 by 2 or 4 boxes in the next layer. And 1 box on top.

That's 16 + 9 + 4 + 1 or 30 boxes. Since we have 72 boxes to use, we can probably add another layer.

OK. Then we'd start with a 5-by-5 layer. So we'd use 25 boxes in the first layer and 30 in the ones above it, for a total of 55 boxes.

Great! That leaves 72 − 55 or 17 boxes left over. 17 isn't enough for a 6-by-6 layer, so it will work.

Grab a box and let's go!

■ Reteaching the Lesson ■

Activity Have students work in pairs to create word problems that can be solved by making a model. Have them exchange their problems with others to solve. Be sure they check each other's models.

For **Extra Practice**, see page 584.

THINK ABOUT IT

Work with a partner.

1. **Tell** how making a model helped Terrence and Emilio plan their pyramid. **See margin.**

2. **Describe** another way that Terrence and Emilio could have displayed the basketballs. **See margin.**

ON YOUR OWN

3. **See margin.**
3. The last step of the 4-step plan for problem solving is to *examine* the solution. How did Emilio and Terrence examine the solution?

4. **Write** a list of real-life situations where it would be helpful to **make a model** to solve a problem. **Answers will vary.**

5. **Look Ahead** If you built a model of Emilio and Terrence's pyramid with cubes that are 1 cubic inch each, how many cubic inches would there be in the model? **55 cubic inches**

8. Suzy—volleyball; Benito—soccer; Vicky—basketball

MIXED PROBLEM SOLVING

STRATEGIES

Look for a pattern.
Solve a simpler problem.
Act it out.
Guess and check.
Draw a diagram.
Make a chart.
Work backward.

Solve. Use any strategy.

6. **Patterns** A number is doubled and then 9 is subtracted. If the result is 15, what was the original number? **12**

7. **Sales** Karen is making a pyramid-shaped display of laundry detergent. Each box is a rectangular prism. The bottom layer of the pyramid has six boxes. If there is one less box in each layer and there are five layers in the pyramid, how many boxes will Karen need to make the display? **20 boxes**

8. **Sports** Vicky, Benito, and Suzy play volleyball, soccer, and basketball. One of the girls is Benito's next door neighbor. No person's sport begins with the same letter as their first name. Benito's neighbor plays volleyball. Which sport does each person play?

9. **Geometry** A rectangular prism is made of exactly 8 cubes. Find the length, width, and height of the prism. **Sample answer: 4 by 2 by 1**

10. **Geometry** Find the area of the shaded region. Round to the nearest tenth. **7.7 m²**

11. **Number Theory** What is the least positive number that you can divide by 7 and get a remainder of 4, divide by 8 and get a remainder of 5, and divide by 9 and get a remainder of 6? **501**

12. **Standardized Test Practice** An equilateral triangle has a base of 10 inches and a height of 8.7 inches. If you arranged six triangles like this into a hexagon as shown, what is the area of the hexagon? **D**

    A 600 in²   B 522 in²
    C 300 in²   D 261 in²

■ Extending the Lesson ■

Activity Ask students what other shapes besides cubes could be useful for making models. Have them look at the lists they made in Exercise 4 of On Your Own and determine for which situations other shapes may be needed to build accurate models.

Check for Understanding
Use the results from Exercises 1–2 to determine whether students understand how to solve a problem by modeling.

Extra Practice If students need additional practice in problem solving, extra practice is available on the following pages.
- Make a Model, see p. 584
- Mixed Problem Solving, see pp. 593–594

Assignment Guide
All: 3–12

4 ASSESS

Closing Activity
Writing Have students write an explanation of how a model could be used to decide how to build storage units for a closet.

Additional Answers
1. Sample answer: It allowed them to first build a small pyramid with easy-to-move boxes.

2. Sample answer: They could have built a prism that was 3 boxes long, 3 boxes wide, and 8 boxes tall.

3. Emilio made sure that the number of boxes they planned to use was the most possible for the type of pyramid they were building.

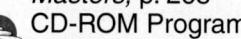

10-5 Lesson Notes

Instructional Resources

- *Study Guide Masters,* p. 74
- *Practice Masters,* p. 74
- *Enrichment Masters,* p. 74
- Transparencies 10-5, A and B
- *Assessment and Evaluation Masters,* p. 268

 CD-ROM Program
- Resource Lesson 10-5
- Interactive Lesson 10-5

Recommended Pacing	
Standard	Day 10 of 13
Honors	Day 9 of 13
Block	Day 5 of 7

1 FOCUS

5-Minute Check
(Lesson 10-4)

Name each figure.

1.   **2.**

pyramid   cylinder

State the number of faces, edges, and vertices for each figure.

3. cone no faces, no edges, 1 vertex

4. triangular pyramid 4 faces, 6 edges, 4 vertices

5. rectangular prism 6 faces, 12 edges, 8 vertices

 The 5-Minute Check is also available on **Transparency 10-5A** for this lesson.

2 TEACH

 Transparency 10-5B contains a teaching aid for this lesson.

Using the Mini-Lab You may suggest that students make up dimensions for a fourth prism and predict the number of cubes that would be needed to build the prism.

10-5 Volume of Rectangular Prisms

What you'll learn
You'll learn to find the volume of rectangular prisms.

When am I ever going to use this?
Knowing how to find the volume of a rectangular prism will help you find the amount of water needed to fill an aquarium.

Word Wise
volume

7. The volume of a rectangular prism is the product of its length, width, and height.

The amount of space inside a three-dimensional figure is called its **volume**. You can investigate the volume of a rectangular prism by building models.

MINI-LAB

Work with a partner.   centimeter cubes

Try This

1. Build rectangular prism A so that it is 3 units long, 2 units wide, and 4 units high. **See student's work.**
2. Count the number of cubes that you used to build the prism. **24**
3. Find the product of the length, width, and height of the prism. **24**
4. Copy the table below. Complete the first row. **See below.**

Prism	Length	Width	Height	Number of Cubes	Length × Width × Height
A	3	2	4	24	24
B	3	4	4	48	48
C	4	1	3	12	12

Talk About It

5. In prism A, how does the number of cubes compare to the product of its length, width, and height? **They are the same.**
6. Build prisms B and C with the dimensions given. Record the results in your table. **See above.**
7. Write a sentence about how the volume of a prism is related to the length, width, and height.

From the Mini-Lab, we can conclude that the volume of a rectangular prism is directly related to its dimensions.

	Words:	The volume (V) of a rectangular prism equals the product of its length (ℓ), its width (w), and its height (h).
Volume of a Rectangular Prism	Symbols:	$V = \ell w h$ Model:

Volume is expressed in cubic units. For example, if the length, width, and height are measured in feet, the volume will be written in cubic feet, or ft^3.

Motivating the Lesson

Communication Review Lessons 4-8 and 7-7. Have students compare capacity and volume. Discuss the different units that are used for volume.

 MathPASS CD-ROM

This CD-ROM offers a complete, self-paced mathematics curriculum. Each lesson includes a pretest, tutorial, guided practice, and posttest. MathPASS Lesson 36 is correlated to this Student Edition lesson.
For Windows & Macintosh

① Find the volume of the rectangular prism.

$\ell = 4$ cm

$w = 6$ cm

$h = 10$ cm

$V = \ell wh$

$V = 4 \times 6 \times 10$

$V = 240$

The volume is 240 cm³.

APPLICATION **②** **Money Matters** Firewood is sold in units called *cords*. A cord of wood is 8 feet long, 4 feet wide, and 4 feet high. If you buy a stack of wood that is 8 feet long, 2 feet wide, and 8 feet high, is it equivalent to a cord?

Explore You know the dimensions of a cord. You need to know if a stack that is 8 feet long, 2 feet wide, and 8 feet high is equivalent to a cord.

Plan If the volume of your stack is equal to the volume of a cord, then your stack is equivalent to a cord. Find the volume of your stack and of a cord. Then compare.

Solve

Volume of your stack	Volume of a cord
$V = \ell wh$	$V = \ell wh$
$V = 8 \times 2 \times 8$	$V = 8 \times 4 \times 4$
$V = 128$ ft³	$V = 128$ ft³

The volumes are equal. So the 8-by-2-by-8 foot stack is equivalent to a cord.

Examine Use cubes to build a rectangular prism that is 8 units long, 4 units wide, and 4 units high. Rearrange the cubes to verify that they can make a prism 8 units long, 2 units wide, and 8 units high.

CHECK FOR UNDERSTANDING

Communicating Mathematics

Read and study the lesson to answer each question. 1–2. See margin.

1. *State* why volume is expressed in cubic units.

2. *You Decide* Maise says that when you find the volume of a prism, the order in which you multiply the length, width, and height does not matter. Craig disagrees. Who is correct and why?

HANDS-ON MATH 3. *Build* a rectangular prism that has a volume of 18 cm³ using centimeter cubes.
Sample answer: a prism 1 cm high, 2 cm wide, and 9 cm long

Lesson 10-5 Volume of Rectangular Prisms **419**

■ **Reteaching the Lesson** ■

Activity Have students work in pairs using centimeter cubes to construct models. Ask them to build a model, sketch it, find its volume with a calculator, and then take it apart and count the cubes to check their answer.

Additional Answers

1. Each of the three dimensions being multiplied is expressed in a unit of measure.

2. Maise is correct. Because multiplication is commutative, the order in which the numbers are multiplied is not important.

CHAPTER Project

Exercise 17 asks students to advance to the next stage of work on the Chapter Project. You may want to have students use a piece of string or paper to make a model of their unit of length. They can use this model when taking their measurements.

4 ASSESS

Closing Activity

Speaking Have students make up dimensions for rectangular prisms and then find their volumes. Ask them to explain their work.

Chapter 10, Quiz C (Lessons 10-4 and 10-5) is available in the *Assessment and Evaluation Masters*, p. 268.

Practice Masters, p. 74

Guided Practice   Find the volume of each rectangular prism.

4.   **600 ft³**   5.   **588 cm³**

6. Find the volume of a rectangular prism 15 meters long, 22 meters wide, and 26 meters tall. **8,580 m³**

EXERCISES

Practice   Find the volume of each rectangular prism to the nearest tenth.   9. 1,536 ft³

7.   **14,400 in³**   8.   **240 m³**   9.   12 ft, 8 ft, 16 ft

10.   5½ ft, 6½ ft, 4 ft   **143 ft³**   11.   24 m, 18.4 m, 6.2 m   **2,737.9 m³**   12.   3.1 cm, 3.1 cm, 3.1 cm   **29.8 cm³**

13. Find the volume of a rectangular prism that is 5 mm wide, 3 mm high, and 6 mm long. **90 mm³**

14. What is the volume of a rectangular prism 15 by 12 by 3 feet? **540 ft³**

Applications and Problem Solving

Real World

15. *Sports* An Olympic-sized pool is 25 meters wide, 50 meters long, and 3 meters deep.
   a. What is the pool's volume? **3,750 m³**
   b. A liter of water occupies 0.001 cubic meter. How many liters of water are needed to fill an Olympic-sized pool? **3,750,000 liters**

16. *World Records* Popcorn lovers in Albermarle, North Carolina, made the largest box of popcorn ever in the United States. The box was 52 feet 7¼ inches wide and 10 feet 1½ inches long. The average depth of the popcorn was 10 feet 2½ inches! What was the volume of the popcorn? Round to the nearest cubic foot. **5,437 ft³**

For **Extra Practice**, see page 584.

17. *Working on the* **CHAPTER Project** Use your unit of length and a standard unit such as feet to measure the length, width, and height of a rectangular prism such as your classroom. Then find the volume of your prism using each cubic unit. **See students' work.**

18. Sample answer: 2 in. × 12 in. × 12 in

18. *Critical Thinking* A mailing box in the shape of a rectangular prism has a volume of 288 in³. What are the possible dimensions of the box?

Mixed Review

19. *Standardized Test Practice* The base of a cone is a — *(Lesson 10-4)* **B**
   A triangle.   **B** circle.   **C** radius.   **D** rectangle.

20. *Patterns* Find the next two numbers in the sequence 160, 80, 40, 20, ... *(Lesson 7-8)* **10, 5**

Extending the Lesson

Enrichment Masters, p. 74

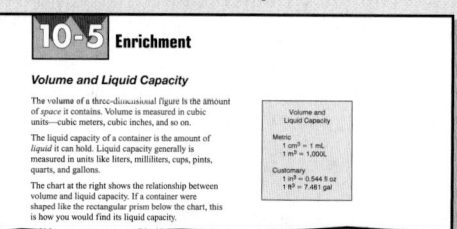

Activity In energy-efficient classrooms, experts recommend 15 ft³ of fresh air per minute for every student. Ask students how much fresh air should be pumped into their classroom every minute. Have them find the percent this is of all the air in the room.

10-6 Surface Area of Rectangular Prisms

What you'll learn

You'll learn to find the surface area of rectangular prisms.

When am I ever going to use this?

Knowing how to find the surface area of a rectangular prism will help you find the amount of paint needed to complete a room.

Word Wise

surface area

Just imagine! The NBA changes the rules so that a basketball is a cube! Dribbling, passing, shooting . . . everything would be different. The current NBA ball uses about 284 square inches of material. Would they use more or less material to make a basketball that is shaped like a $9\frac{1}{4}$-inch cube? *This problem will be solved in Example 3.*

Lumpy Gravy *by John Long*

IT'S TIME TO MAKE BASKETBALL MORE OF A CHALLENGE

The **surface area** of a three-dimensional object is the total area of its faces and curved surfaces. In the Mini-Lab, you will construct a rectangular prism and find its surface area.

HANDS-ON MINI-LAB

Work with a partner. ruler   centimeter grid paper

scissors   calculator   tape

Try This

- Use the measurements shown to draw a pattern like this on a sheet of grid paper.
- Cut out the pattern along the dark lines.
- Fold the pattern along the dashed lines to form a rectangular prism. Tape the edges.

Talk About It

1. Find the area of each face of the prism.
2. What is the sum of the areas, or the surface area, of the prism?
3. What do you observe about the opposite sides of the prism? How could this simplify finding the surface area? **See margin.**

1. top and bottom: 40 cm²; front and back: 24 cm²; sides: 15 cm²
2. 158 cm²

Additional Answer for the Mini-Lab

3. **They have the same dimensions. You can find the area of each unique shape once and multiply by 2 to find the total.**

Motivating the Lesson

Problem Solving Ask students how they would determine which package will require more wrapping paper.
- a rectangular box that is 2 inches high, 12 inches long, and 8 inches wide
- a square box with 8-inch sides

Instructional Resources

- *Study Guide Masters*, p. 75
- *Practice Masters*, p. 75
- *Enrichment Masters*, p. 75
- Transparencies 10-6, A and B
- *Assessment and Evaluation Masters*, p. 268
- *School to Career Masters*, p. 10
- CD-ROM Program
  - Resource Lesson 10-6
  - Interactive Lesson 10-6

Recommended Pacing	
Standard	Day 11 of 13
Honors	Days 10 & 11 of 13
Block	Day 6 of 7

1 FOCUS

5-Minute Check
(Lesson 10-5)

1. A filing cabinet is 42 inches high, 30 inches wide, and 19 inches deep. What is the volume of the cabinet? **23,940 in³**

Find the volume of each rectangular prism to the nearest tenth.

2.
   6 cm, 6 cm, 3 cm   **108 cm³**

3.
   2 ft, 8 ft, 12 ft   **192 ft³**

4. length = 16 mm
   width = 7 mm
   height = 4 mm   **448 mm³**

5. Find the volume of a rectangular prism whose length is 9 inches, width is 6 inches, and height is 14 inches. **756 in³**

 The 5-Minute Check is also available on **Transparency 10-6A** for this lesson.

Transparency 10-6B contains a teaching aid for this lesson.

Using the Mini-Lab Since the pattern will cover almost a full sheet of paper, have students start their drawing at the top of the paper. Designate one student as the model maker and the other as the recorder.

Teaching Tip Have students review the formula for finding the area of a rectangle.

In-Class Examples

Find the surface area of each rectangular prism to the nearest tenth.

For Example 1

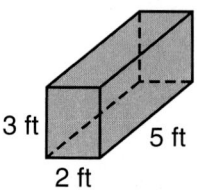

3 ft, 5 ft, 2 ft

62 ft²

For Example 2

3.2 cm, 1.4 cm, 4.1 cm

46.7 cm²

For Example 3
Jesse is making enclosed storage cubes for his room. Each cube has faces that are $1\frac{3}{4}$ feet on each side. He has three 32 square-foot sheets of plywood. How many storage containers can he make?
5 containers

Examples

Find the surface area of each rectangular prism to the nearest tenth.

①

7 ft, 6 ft, 8 ft

Did you know Physical Education Instructor James Naismith dreamed up the game of basketball in 1891. Volleyball and basketball are the only popular sports invented by Americans.

In a rectangular prism, opposite sides have the same dimensions.

top and bottom
$8 \times 6 = 48 \text{ ft}^2$

front and back
$8 \times 7 = 56 \text{ ft}^2$

right and left sides
$7 \times 6 = 42 \text{ ft}^2$

Add the areas.
$2(48) + 2(56) + 2(42) = 292$

The surface area is 292 ft².

②

2.1 cm, 4.4 cm, 3.5 cm

Opposite sides have the same dimensions.

top and bottom
$3.5 \times 4.4 = 15.4 \text{ cm}^2$

front and back
$2.1 \times 3.5 = 7.35 \text{ cm}^2$

right and left sides
$2.1 \times 4.4 = 9.24 \text{ cm}^2$

Find the total of the areas.

2 ⊠ 15.4 ⊞ 2 ⊠ 7.35 ⊞ 2 ⊠ 9.24 ⊟ *63.98*

The surface area is about 64.0 cm².

APPLICATION ③

Real World

Sports Refer to the beginning of the lesson. Would the cube-shaped basketball require more or less material than the current professional basketball?

Explore You know the surface area of the spherical ball. You need to determine whether the surface area of the cube is larger or smaller.

Plan First, find the surface area of the cube. Then compare it with the surface area of the sphere.

Solve All six faces of the cube are squares that are $9\frac{1}{4}$ inches on each side. So the surface area of the cube is 6 times the area of one face.

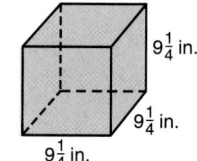
$9\frac{1}{4}$ in., $9\frac{1}{4}$ in., $9\frac{1}{4}$ in.

Area of a face: $9\frac{1}{4} \times 9\frac{1}{4} = \frac{37}{4} \times \frac{37}{4} = \frac{1,369}{16} \text{ in}^2$

Surface area: $6 \times \frac{1,369}{16} = \frac{8,214}{16}$ or $513\frac{3}{8} \text{ in}^2$

The surface area of the spherical ball is about 284 in². The cube's surface area is greater. It would use more material to make a cube-shaped basketball.

Examine Find the surface areas of several different cubes with edges between 9 and 10 inches long to verify that the solution is reasonable.

422 Chapter 10 Geometry: Understanding Area and Volume

Reteaching the Lesson

Activity Give each group of four students a box such as a shoe box. Ask three of the students to each write their initials on two opposite sides and find the area of each. Have the fourth student use a calculator to find the surface area.

Error Analysis
Watch for students who overlook a face when finding the surface area of a rectangular prism.
Prevent by having students check to make sure they have six numbers before adding.

Communicating Mathematics

Read and study the lesson to answer each question. 2–3. See margin.

1. *Identify* the relevant dimension as length, area, or volume.
   a. the perimeter of a rectangle **length**
   b. the number of tiles needed to tile a floor **area**
   c. the capacity of a swimming pool **volume**
   d. the height of a flagpole **length**
   e. the capacity of a pitcher **volume**
   f. the garden space to be planted **area**

2. *Tell* why you can find the surface area of a rectangular prism after finding the area of just three faces.

3. *Describe* a situation when you would have to find the surface area of a rectangular solid.

Guided Practice

Find the surface area of each rectangular prism.

4. 20 in. 24 in. 30 in.
3,600 in²

5. 7 cm 5 cm 3 cm **142 cm²**

6. length = 2 mm
   width = 7 mm
   height = 5 mm
   118 mm²

7. *Manufacturing* A cereal package is a rectangular prism 12 inches high, 8 inches wide, and 3 inches deep. How many square inches did the label designer have to cover on the package? **312 in²**

Practice

Find the surface area of each rectangular prism to the nearest tenth.

8. 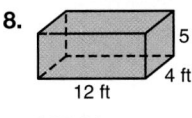 5 ft 4 ft 12 ft
256 ft²

9. 5 m 7 m 9 m
286 m²

10. 3 in. 4 in. 6 in.
108 in²

11. 4 cm 4 cm 4 cm
96 cm²

12. 10.2 mm 8.7 mm 16.1 mm
786.1 mm²

13. 6 ft $16\frac{1}{2}$ ft 10 ft
648 ft²

14. length = 7 in.
    width = 5 in.
    height = $12\frac{1}{2}$ in.
    370 in²

15. length = 15.5 m
    width = 10 m
    height = 8 m
    718 m²

16. length = 2.4 cm
    width = 0.8 cm
    height = 6.6 cm
    46.1 cm²

Lesson 10-6 Surface Area of Rectangular Prisms **423**

Additional Answers

2. Opposite sides have the same dimensions. So you can find the area of three different-shaped faces. Then add each area to the total twice to account for each face.

3. Sample answers: determining the correct amount of paint for a room; choosing enough wrapping paper for a package

---

3 PRACTICE/APPLY

Check for Understanding

If students need additional practice or instruction after completing Exercises 1–7, one of these options may be helpful.
- Extra Practice, see p. 585
- Reteaching Activity, see p. 422
- *Study Guide Masters*, p. 75
- *Practice Masters*, p. 75

Assignment Guide

Core: 9–21 odd, 23–26
Enriched: 8–18 even, 20, 21, 23–26

Study Guide Masters, p. 75

4 ASSESS

Closing Activity

Writing Have students work in pairs to create word problems about containers that can be solved by finding the surface area.

Chapter 10, Quiz D (Lesson 10-6) is available in the *Assessment and Evaluation Masters,* p. 268.

Practice Masters, p. 75

---

17. What is the surface area of a rectangular prism that is 10 inches long, 14 inches wide, and 20 inches high? **1,240 in²**

18. Find the volume of a rectangular prism with base 15 inches, height 25 inches, and width 30 inches. For the same rectangular prism, find its surface area. **11,250 in³; 3,150 in²**

19. *Write a Problem* involving a rectangular prism with a surface area of 720 in². **See students' work.**

Applications and Problem Solving

20. *Sports* Wallyball is a variation of volleyball invented in the 1970s. A wallyball court is 20 feet wide, 40 feet long, and 20 feet high. If a gallon of paint will cover 400 square feet, how many gallons will be needed to cover the walls, ceiling, and floor of a wallyball court? **10 gallons**

21. *Life Science* The shark petting tank at Nauticus, in Norfolk, Virginia, is 20 feet long, 8 feet wide, and 3 feet deep. Sometimes the tanks must be resurfaced to prevent leakage. What is the area to be resurfaced if the top of the shark petting tank is open? **328 ft²**

22. *Working on the* **CHAPTER Project**
Choose an object shaped like a rectangular prism such as a cabinet or your classroom. Find the surface area of the object using your unit of length and a standard unit such as square feet or square meters. **See students' work.**

23. *Critical Thinking* In a certain cube, the measure of the surface area is the same as the measure of its volume. What are its dimensions? **6 units on each side**

Mixed Review

24. *Standardized Test Practice* A rectangular fish tank measures 34 inches by 22 inches by 18 inches. If the tank is filled to a height of 15 inches, what is the volume of water in the tank? *(Lesson 10-5)* **B**
   A 13,464 in³
   B 11,220 in³
   C 9,180 in³
   D 5,940 in³

25. On December 19, the sunrise was at 7:19 A.M., and the sunset was at 4:28 P.M. How many hours of daylight were there? *(Lesson 6-7)* **9 hours 9 minutes**

For **Extra Practice,** see page 585.

26. *Statistics* What scale would you use in making a frequency table for the following set of data? 21, 79, 11, 9, 55, 38, 111, 92 *(Lesson 2-2)* **0 to 120**

424 Chapter 10 Geometry: Understanding Area and Volume

Extending the Lesson

Enrichment Masters, p. 75

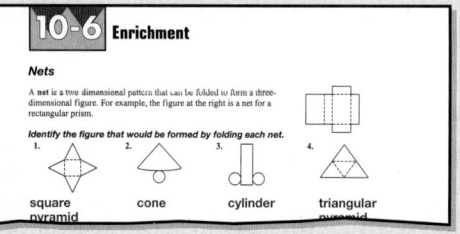

Activity Have several students write to manufacturers for information on how they design their packaging. Encourage students to ask for information on how marketing information, shipping requirements, and materials affect the design.

SPREADSHEETS

10-6B Surface Area and Volume

A Follow-Up of Lesson 10-6

- computer
- spreadsheet software

The spreadsheet below can be used to find the volume and surface area of a rectangular prism. To use the spreadsheet, you enter the length, width, and height of the prism. Then the computer finds the volume and the surface area.

The formula in cell D2 tells the computer to multiply the values in cells A2, B2, and C2 together.

	A	B	C	D	E
1	LENGTH	WIDTH	HEIGHT	VOLUME	SURFACE AREA
2	A2	B2	C2	= A2*B2*C2	= 2*A2*B2 + 2*A2*C2 + 2*B2*C2
3	A3	B3	C3	= A3*B3*C3	= 2*A3*B3 + 2*A3*C3 + 2*B3*C3
4	A4	B4	C4	= A4*B4*C4	= 2*A4*B4 + 2*A4*C4 + 2*B4*C4
5	A5	B5	C5	= A5*B5*C5	= 2*A5*B5 + 2*A5*C5 + 2*B5*C5
6	A6	B6	C6	= A6*B6*C6	= 2*A6*B6 + 2*A6*C6 + 2*B6*C6
7	A7	B7	C7	= A7*B7*C7	= 2*A7*B7 + 2*A7*C7 + 2*B7*C7

TRY THIS

Work with a partner.

The result of using the spreadsheet to find the surface area and volume of the rectangular prism in row 2 is shown below.

	A	B	C	D	E
1	LENGTH	WIDTH	HEIGHT	VOLUME	SURFACE AREA
2	3	3	7	63	102
3	10.2	4.1	1.6	66.912	129.4
4	4	4	4	64	96
5	8	4	4	128	160
6	8	8	4	256	256
7	8	8	8	512	384

ON YOUR OWN

1. Use the spreadsheet to determine the volume and surface area for the rectangular prisms in rows 3, 4, 5, 6, and 7. Print or record your results. **See above**.

2. What does the formula in cell E2 tell the computer to do? **2. Find the surface area of the prism using the quantities in cells A2, B2, and C2.**

3. Show how to modify the spreadsheet to find the area and perimeter of a rectangle. **See margin.**

4. How do the dimensions of the prisms in rows 5, 6, and 7 compare to those of the prism in row 4? **See margin.**

5. Describe the pattern of volumes for prisms in rows 4, 5, 6, and 7. **5–6. See Answer Appendix.**

6. Describe the pattern of surface areas of prisms in rows 4, 5, 6, and 7.

Lesson 10-6B TECHNOLOGY **LAB** **425**

Additional Answers

3. Delete the height column. Change "volume" to "area" and change the formulas in column D to A2*B2, A3*B3, and so on. Change "surface area" to "perimeter." Change the formulas in column E to 2*A2 + 2*B2, 2*A3 + 2*B3, and so on.

4. The dimensions of prism 5 are the same as those for prism 4 with the length doubled. The dimensions of prism 6 are the same as those for prism 4 with the length and width doubled. The dimensions of prism 7 are the same as those for prism 4 with the length, width, and height doubled.

TECHNOLOGY
10-6B **LAB** Notes

GET READY

Objective Students use spreadsheets to find the surface area and volume of rectangular prisms.

Technology Resources
Suggested spreadsheet software:
- *Lotus 1·2·3*
- *ClarisWorks*
- *Microsoft Excel*

MANAGEMENT TIPS

Recommended Time
30 minutes

Getting Started Remind students how each cell of a spreadsheet is named. Also review how formulas using cell names are entered into the spreadsheet.

Using a Calculator If spreadsheet software is not available, have groups of students create the table on paper and use a calculator to find the values.

ASSESS

Lead a class discussion on the answers for Exercises 4–6. Have students give examples of other series of prisms that would show a similar pattern. **any series where the dimensions increased by a factor of two**

Math Journal — Have students write a description of how the spreadsheet was used to compare surface area and volume.

Vocabulary

This section provides a listing of the new terms, properties, and phrases that were introduced in this chapter. Have students define each term and provide an example or two of it, if appropriate.

Understanding and Using the Vocabulary

These exercises check students' understanding of the terms by using a variety of verbal formats including matching, completion, and true/false.

Glossaries A complete glossary of terms appears on pages 642–648. The glossary also appears in Spanish on pages 649–656.

Additional Answer

10. Find the area of the two rectangular bases, the rectangular front and back, and the rectangular right and left sides. Add these areas to find the surface area.

 Chapter Review For additional lesson-by-lesson review, visit:
www.glencoe.com/sec/math/mac/mathnet

Vocabulary

After completing this chapter, you should be able to define each term, concept, or phrase and give an example or two of each.

Measurement
surface area (p. 421)
volume (p. 418)

Geometry
base (pp. 398, 412)
center (p. 413)
cone (p. 413)
cylinder (p. 413)
edge (p. 412)
face (p. 412)

height (p. 398)
prism (p. 412)
pyramid (p. 412)
rectangular prism (p. 412)
sphere (p. 413)
square pyramid (p. 412)
three-dimensional figure (p. 412)
vertex (p. 412)

Problem Solving
make a model (p. 416)

Understanding and Using the Vocabulary

Choose the correct term or number to complete each sentence.

1. The (<u>height</u>, edge) of a parallelogram is the distance from the base to the opposite side.
2. The flat surfaces of a three-dimensional figure are called (<u>faces</u>, vertices).
3. The faces of three-dimensional figures intersect in (bases, <u>edges</u>).
4. A (<u>pyramid</u>, cylinder) is a three-dimensional figure with one base where all other faces are triangles that meet at one point.
5. A (<u>sphere</u>, cone) is a three-dimensional figure with no faces, bases, edges, or vertices.
6. A three-dimensional figure with two circular bases is a (cone, <u>cylinder</u>).
7. The amount of space that a three-dimensional figure contains is called its (area, <u>volume</u>).
8. A rectangular prism with length 3 meters, width 4 meters, and height 2 meters has a volume of (14, <u>24</u>) cubic meters.
9. The total area of a three-dimensional object's faces and curved surfaces is called its (<u>surface area</u>, volume).

In Your Own Words

10. *Explain* how to find the surface area of the rectangular prism. **See margin.**

3 ft
6 ft
2 ft

 ## MindJogger Videoquizzes

MindJogger Videoquizzes provide an alternative review of concepts presented in this chapter. Students work in teams to answer questions, gaining points for correct answers. The questions are presented in three rounds.
Round 1 Concepts–5 questions
Round 2 Skills–4 questions
Round 3 Problem Solving–4 questions

Objectives & Examples

Upon completing this chapter, you should be able to:

- find the area of parallelograms *(Lesson 10-1)*

  Find the area.

  $A = bh$

  $A = 6 \times 5$

  $A = 30$

  5 in.

  6 in.

  The area of the parallelogram is 30 in².

- find the area of triangles *(Lesson 10-2)*

  Find the area.

  $A = \frac{1}{2}bh$

  $A = \frac{1}{2}(150 \times 50)$

  $A = 3,750$

  150 m

  50 m

  The area of the triangle is 3,750 m².

- find the area of circles *(Lesson 10-3)*

  What is the area of the circle?

  Use 3.14 for π.

  $A = \pi r^2$

  $A = \pi \cdot 7^2$

  $A = \pi \cdot 49$

  $A \approx 153.9 \text{ cm}^2$

  7 cm

  The area is about 153.9 cm².

Review Exercises

Use these exercises to review and prepare for the chapter test. **12. $48\frac{1}{8}$ in²**

Find the area of each parallelogram.

11. 2 m, 3 m, 7 m

14 m²

12. $5\frac{1}{2}$ in., $7\frac{5}{8}$ in., $8\frac{3}{4}$ in.

13. Find the area of a parallelogram that is 12.5 centimeters wide and 7 centimeters high. **87.5 cm²**

Find the area of each triangle. Round decimals to the nearest tenth.

14. 99 in², 11 in., 18 in.

15. 72 cm², 12 cm, 12 cm

16. 3.4 m, 3.1 m **5.3 m²**

17. $18\frac{1}{2}$ ft, 17 ft, $6\frac{3}{4}$ ft **$62\frac{7}{16}$ ft²**

Find the area of each circle to the nearest tenth. Use 3.14 for π. 19. 153.9 in²

18. 11 m **379.9 m²**

19. 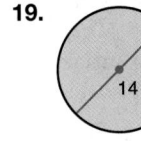 14 in.

20. radius, 1.5 km **7.1 km²**

21. diameter, $7\frac{1}{6}$ in. **40.3 in²**

Objectives & Examples

This section reviews the skills and concepts of the chapter and shows completely worked examples.

Review Exercises

These exercises provide practice for the corresponding objectives.

Assessment and Evaluation Masters, pp. 255–256

Name_____ Date_____

10 **Chapter 10 Test, Form 1B**

1. Find the area of the parallelogram shown at the right.
   A. 18 square units
   B. 24 square units
   C. 30 square units
   D. 27 square units
   1. ___B___

2. Find the area of a parallelogram if the base is 18 centimeters and the height is 25 centimeters.
   A. 430 cm²   B. 86 cm²   C. 450 cm²   D. none of these
   2. ___C___

3. Find the area of the parallelogram shown at the right.
   A. 245 ft²   B. 196 ft²   C. 69 ft²   D. none of these
   3. ___B___

4. Find the area of the triangle shown at the right.
   A. 49 cm²   B. 12.25 cm²   C. 24.5 cm²   D. none of these
   4. ___C___

5. What is the area of a triangle with a base of 64 feet and a height of 36 feet?
   A. 1,152 ft²   B. 100 ft²   C. 2,304 ft²   D. none of these
   5. ___A___

6. Find the area of the triangle shown at the right.
   A. 20.6 in²   B. 50.84 in²   C. 101.68 in²   D. none of these
   6. ___B___

7. Find the area of the circle shown at the right. Use 3.14 for π.
   A. 28.26 in²   B. 254.34 in²   C. 2,289.06 in²   D. none of these
   7. ___B___

8. Find the area of a circle with a diameter of 4.2 centimeters. Use 3.14 for π.
   A. 13.188 cm²   B. 13.8474 cm²   C. 6.594 cm²   D. none of these
   8. ___B___

9. State the number of edges in a square pyramid.
   A. 4   B. 3   C. 5   D. none of these
   9. ___D___

10. Name the figure shown at the right.
    A. cone   B. rectangular prism   C. square pyramid   D. sphere
    10. ___B___

© Glencoe/McGraw-Hill   255   *Mathematics: Applications and Connections, Course 1*

10 **Chapter 10 Test, Form 1B (continued)**

11. State the number of faces in a rectangular prism.
    A. 6   B. 12   C. 8   D. none of these
    11. ___A___

12. Which pattern can be folded to form a box shaped like a rectangular prism?
    A.   B.   C.   D.
    12. ___B___

13. How many different rectangular prisms can be formed by using exactly 15 cubes?
    A. 1   B. 2   C. 3   D. none of these
    13. ___B___

14. Find the volume of the rectangular prism shown at the right.
    A. 48 mm³   B. 1,536 mm³   C. 4,096 mm³   D. none of these
    14. ___C___

15. A box is 26 inches long by 15 inches wide by 12 inches high. What is the volume of the box?
    A. 53 in³   B. 4,680 in³   C. 1,764 in³   D. none of these
    15. ___B___

16. Find the volume of the rectangular prism described at the right. length, 10.5 ft; width, 8.5 ft; height, 5 ft
    A. 223.125 ft³   B. 446 ft³   C. 89.25 ft³   D. none of these
    16. ___D___

17. Find the surface area of the rectangular prism shown at the right.
    A. 26 m²   B. 576 m²   C. 432 m²   D. none of these
    17. ___C___

18. Find the surface area of the rectangular prism described at the right. length, 17 in.; width, 13 in.; height, 8 in.
    A. 922 in²   B. 461 in²   C. 1,768 in²   D. none of these
    18. ___A___

19. A circular tabletop has a radius of 30 inches. What is the area of the tabletop? Use 3.14 for π.
    A. 94.2 in²   B. 2,826 in²   C. 188.4 in²   D. none of these
    19. ___B___

20. How much paper would it take to cover a box that is 32 centimeters by 20 centimeters by 10 centimeters if there is no overlap?
    A. 62 cm²   B. 6,400 cm²   C. 1,160 cm²   D. none of these
    20. ___D___

© Glencoe/McGraw-Hill   256   *Mathematics: Applications and Connections, Course 1*

 Assessment and Evaluation

Six forms of Chapter 10 Test are available in the *Assessment and Evaluation Masters* as shown in the chart.

Chapter 10 Test, Form 1B, is shown at the right. Chapter 10 Test, Form 2B, is shown on the next page.

1A	Multiple Choice	Honors
1B	Multiple Choice	Average
1C	Multiple Choice	Basic
2A	Free Response	Honors
2B	Free Response	Average
2C	Free Response	Basic

Additional Answers
22. triangular pyramid
23. rectangular prism

Assessment and Evaluation Masters, pp. 261–262

10 **Chapter 10 Test, Form 2B**

Name_____ Date_____

Find the area of each figure. Use 3.14 for π.

1. 48 mm / 84 mm   1. _4,116 mm²_

2. 20 m   2. _1,256 m²_

3. 14 cm / 24 cm   3. _168 cm²_

4. 5 cm / 5.1 cm / 9 cm   4. _45 cm²_

5. 54 ft   5. _2,289.06 ft²_

6. 5.8 cm / 12 cm   6. _34.8 cm²_

7. A circular tablecloth has a diameter of 50 inches. What is the area of the tablecloth? Use 3.14 for π.   7. _1,962.5 in²_

Name each figure.
8.   8. _sphere_

9.   9. _square pyramid_

10. State the number of edges for the figure in Question 9.   10. _8_

© Glencoe/McGraw-Hill   261   Mathematics: Applications and Connections, Course 1

10 **Chapter 10 Test, Form 2B (continued)**

Find the surface area of each rectangular prism.
11. 13 mm / 51 mm / 8 mm   11. _3,188 mm²_

12. 4.5 ft / 15 ft / 6 ft   12. _369 ft²_

13. length, 42 in.; width, 30 in.; height, 12 in.   13. _4,248 in²_

14. length, 33 cm; width, 24 cm; height, 8 cm   14. _2,496 cm²_

Find the volume of each rectangular prism.
15. 13 mm / 51 mm / 8 mm   15. _5,304 mm³_

16. 6 ft / 18 ft / 8.5 ft   16. _918 ft³_

17. length, 36 in.; width, 22 in.; height, 17 in.   17. _13,464 in³_

18. length, 29 cm; width, 20 cm; height, 11 cm   18. _6,380 cm³_

19. A rectangular aquarium is 20 inches long by 12 inches wide by 10 inches deep. What is the volume of the aquarium?   19. _2,400 in³_

20. How many different rectangular prisms can be formed by using exactly 12 cubes?   20. _4_

© Glencoe/McGraw-Hill   262   Mathematics: Applications and Connections, Course 1

● identify three-dimensional figures
(*Lesson 10-4*)

 rectangular prism   cylinder   pyramid

cone   sphere

● find the volume of rectangular prisms
(*Lesson 10-5*)

Find the volume.

$V = \ell wh$

$V = 8 \times 4 \times 5$

$V = 160 \text{ in}^3$

The volume is 160 cubic inches.

 5 in. / 8 in. / 4 in.

● find the surface area of rectangular prisms
(*Lesson 10-6*)

What is the surface area of the prism above?

top and bottom: $8 \times 4 = 32 \text{ in}^2$
front and back: $8 \times 5 = 40 \text{ in}^2$
sides: $4 \times 5 = 20 \text{ in}^2$

Surface area = $2(32) + 2(40) + 2(20)$
                  = $64 + 80 + 40$ or 184

The surface area is 184 square inches.

Name each figure. 22–23. See margin.

22.   23.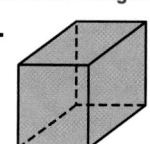

State the number of faces, edges, and vertices in each figure.

24. triangular pyramid **4; 6; 4**
25. square prism **6; 12; 8**

26. **96 m³**
Find the volume of each rectangular prism.

26. 4 m / 3 m / 8 m   27. 2 yd / $9\frac{3}{8}$ yd / $5\frac{1}{2}$ yd
                                                            $103\frac{1}{8}$ yd³

28. A rectangular prism has a length of 3.6 meters, a height of 4.1 meters, and a width of 8.2 meters. What is the volume of the prism to the nearest tenth? **121.0 m²**

Find the surface area of each rectangular prism.

29. 56 m / 32 m / 21 m   30. 7 in. / 7 in. / 6 in.
    7,280 m²   **266 in²**

31. length = 2 mm
    width = 2.5 mm
    height = 1.7 mm **25.3 mm²**

32. length = $20\frac{1}{3}$ yd
    width = 4 yd
    height = $5\frac{2}{3}$ yd **$438\frac{4}{9}$ yd²**

 Test and Review Software

You may use this software, a combination of an item generator and item bank, to create your own tests or worksheets. Types of items include free response, multiple choice, short answer, and open ended.

 CD-ROM Program

The CD-ROM Program contains an Assessment Game whose questions review the concepts in this chapter.

Applications & Problem Solving

33. Architecture Each year, the Corn Palace in Mitchell, South Dakota, is covered in grain murals. Suppose one mural is as shown below. *(Lessons 10-1 and 10-2)*

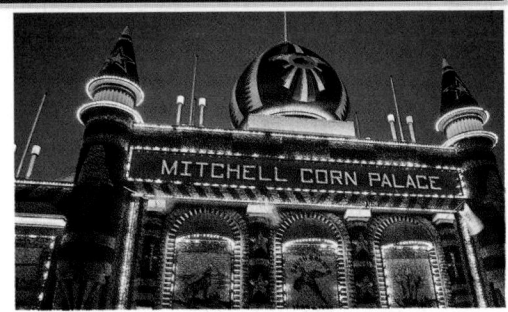

a. What is the area to be covered in dark grain? **See margin.**

b. If a bushel of grain covers 25 square feet, how many bushels of dark grain are needed? **4 bushels**

34. Gift Wrapping Mauna Loa of Honolulu, Hawaii, sells gift boxes of macadamia nuts. The 15-pound box is 18 inches long, 8 inches wide, and 5 inches high. Not counting overlap, how much wrapping paper is needed for each 15-pound box? *(Lesson 10-6)* **548 in²**

35. Plumbing A plumber digs a rectangular hole in the ground to install water pipes. The hole is dug straight down and has parallel sides. If the hole is 3 meters deep, 1.5 meters wide, and 2 meters long, what volume of dirt must be removed? *(Lesson 10-5)* **9 m³**

36. Make a Model The outside of a cube made of 27 small cubes is painted. Find the number of small cubes that are unpainted. *(Lesson 10-5A)* **1**

Alternative Assessment

● **Open Ended**

Suppose you are planning to remodel your family room. The rectangular room is 12 feet wide, 10 feet long, and 8 feet high. How can you determine the number of square feet of carpet, wall paint, and ceiling paint needed? Find these amounts. **See margin.**

If carpet costs $5 per square foot and paint costs $15 per gallon (which is enough to cover 400 square feet), how much will these supplies cost? **carpet, $600; paint, $30; remodeling, $630**

A practice test for Chapter 10 is provided on page 604.

● **Completing the CHAPTER Project**

Use the following checklist to make sure your poster is complete.

☑ Describe your unit of measure. Include it or an equivalent length of string.

☑ Show how you found the volume and surface area of your prisms.

☑ Explain why you think measurement systems are now standardized.

● Draw examples of the three-dimensional figures you studied in this chapter. Label the faces, edges, and vertices, or center. Place these diagrams in your portfolio.

Additional Answer
33a. $85\frac{2}{3}$ ft²

Additional Answer for the Open Ended item
Find the area of the floor, ceiling, and walls: floor, 120 ft²; walls, 352 ft²; ceiling, 120 ft²

Performance Assessment

Additional performance assessment tasks for this chapter are included in the *Assessment and Evaluation Masters* on page 265. A scoring guide is also provided on page 277.

Applications & Problem Solving

This section provides additional practice in solving real-world problems that involve the skills of this chapter.

Alternative Assessment

The **Open Ended** section provides students with a performance assessment opportunity to evaluate their work and understanding.

CHAPTER Project

Students should complete the final stages of their project and prepare a class demonstration of their results. A scoring guide for the project is available in the *Investigations and Projects Masters*, p. 55.

 Students should add to their portfolios at this time.

Assessment and Evaluation Masters, p. 265

---

10 Name_____ Date_____

Chapter 10 Performance Assessment

Instructions: Demonstrate your knowledge by giving a clear, concise solution to each problem. Be sure to include all relevant drawings and to justify your answers. You may show your solutions in more than one way or investigate beyond the requirements of the problems.

1. Diana and her mother are making some flags of the states and territories for a report in social studies class. Diana needs to find the amount of material to buy.

a. How many square inches of material will be needed to make the Alaska flag?

b. How many square inches of blue material will be needed to make the rectangular Virginia flag? How many square inches of white material will be needed to make the circle in the middle? Assume no material will be wasted. Show your work. Use 3.14 for π.

c. Tell in your own words how to find the area of a triangle.

d. Find the amount of white material needed to make the triangular part of the American Samoa flag. Show your work.

e. Tell in your own words how to find the area of a parallelogram.

f. Find the area of the white parallelogram in the Arkansas flag. Show your work.

g. Diana's mother made a Wyoming flag. How would you estimate the area of the buffalo in the center?

2. Write a word problem that involves finding the surface area and volume of a rectangular prism. Draw an illustration for your word problem.

© Glencoe/McGraw-Hill   265   *Mathematics: Applications and Connections, Course 1*

The Standardized Test Practice may be used to help students prepare for standardized tests. The test items are written in the same style as those in state proficiency tests and standardized tests like CAT, CTBS, ITBS, MAT, SAT, and Terra Nova. The test items cover skills and concepts covered up to this point in the text.

The pages can be used as an overnight assessment. After students have completed the pages, discuss how each problem can be solved, or provide copies of the solutions from the *Solutions Manual.*

Assessment and Evaluation Masters, p. 271

CHAPTERS 1–10

Standardized Test Practice
Assessing Knowledge & Skills

Section One: Multiple Choice

There are ten multiple choice questions in this section. Choose the best answer. If a correct answer is *not here,* choose the letter for Not Here.

1. Name the percent shaded on the base-ten model. **A**

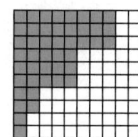

   A 45%
   B 55%
   C 68%
   D 72%

2. Find the area of the parallelogram. **H**
   F 22.826 cm²
   G 62.0 cm²
   H 91.53 cm²
   J 163.62 cm²

   20.2 cm   11.3 cm   8.1 cm

3. Two figures that are the same size and shape are — **B**

   A similar.
   B congruent.
   C neither similar nor congruent.
   D bisectors.

4. Find the area of the triangle. **G**
   F $\frac{15}{8}$ in²
   G $\frac{15}{16}$ in²
   H $\frac{30}{8}$ in²
   J 2 in²

   $2\frac{1}{2}$ in.
   $\frac{3}{4}$ in.

430 Chapters 1–10 Standardized Test Practice

Please note that Questions 5–10 have five answer choices.

5. Lenora bought pencils that cost 29¢ each and pens that cost 89¢ each. What do you need to know to find out how much she spent? **D**
   A the cost of each pen and pencil
   B how much money she has
   C how much change she received
   D how many pens and pencils she bought
   E how much tax is in her area

6. Which is a reasonable remainder when a number is divided by 8? **H**
   F 8
   G 9
   H 7
   J 12
   K 10

7. Which is the best estimate for the weight of a 1-year old child? **B**
   A 8 g
   B 8 kg
   C 60 kg
   D 60 g
   E 60 mg

8. A map has a scale of 1 cm = 20 km. The map distance from Rawson to Delta is 7.2 cm. How far is it from Rawson to Delta? **H**
   F 720 km
   G 27.2 km
   H 144 km
   J 20 km
   K Not Here

◄◄◄ **Instructional Resources**
Another cumulative review is shown at the left and is available in the *Assessment and Evaluation Masters,* p. 271.

9. The graph shows the number of boys and girls who signed up for Moosehead Camp. **A**

Moosehead Camp

Which is a reasonable conclusion that can be drawn from the information in the graph?

A The percent of campers who are girls increased every year after 1993.

B Girls are less interested in camp than boys.

C The number of boys who signed up for camp went down each year.

D More girls than boys signed up for camp in 1995.

E More people signed up for camp in 1996 than any other year.

10. The figure shows a triangle in the interior of a rectangle. **H**

Which method would you use to find the area of the shaded region?

F perimeter of the rectangle minus perimeter of the triangle

G perimeter of the rectangle plus perimeter of the triangle

H area of the rectangle minus area of the triangle

J area of the rectangle plus area of the triangle

K area of the triangle minus area of the rectangle

Test-Taking Tip THE PRINCETON REVIEW

Make sure you know what the rules are for the type of test you are taking. If you are familiar with the method of scoring and the different types of instructions, you may increase your score.

Section Two: Free Response

This section contains six questions for which you will provide short answers. Write your answers on your paper.

11. Dave, Judy, and Marco bought a large submarine sandwich for $19.05. How much did each pay if they shared the price of the submarine equally? **$6.35**

12. Which difference is greater, $28\frac{1}{7} - 6\frac{3}{4}$ $28\frac{1}{7} - 6\frac{3}{4}$ or $30\frac{1}{8} - 8\frac{3}{4}$? **$28\frac{1}{7} - 6\frac{3}{4}$ is greater.**

13. Name the number of faces, edges, and vertices of a triangular pyramid. **4; 6; 4**

14. Find the volume of the rectangular prism. **2,737.92 m³**

18.4 m
24 m
6.2 m

15. Find the surface area of a rectangular solid with a length of 8 ft, a width of 10 ft, and a height of $15\frac{1}{2}$ ft. **718 ft²**

16. Each serving of pizza is $\frac{1}{16}$ of a pizza. If $\frac{3}{4}$ of the pizza is left, how many servings are left? **12 servings**

inter NET CONNECTION   Test Practice   **For additional test practice questions, visit:**

www.glencoe.com/sec/math/mac/mathnet

Instructional Resources ▶▶▶

Additional standardized test practice is shown at the right and is available in the *Assessment and Evaluation Masters*, pp. 269–270.

Test-Taking Tip

Before students begin the test, suggest they skim through it to check the length and the types of problems it includes. Make sure they know ahead of time whether this particular type of test penalizes them for wrong answers.

Assessment and Evaluation Masters, pp. 269–270

Algebra: Investigating Integers

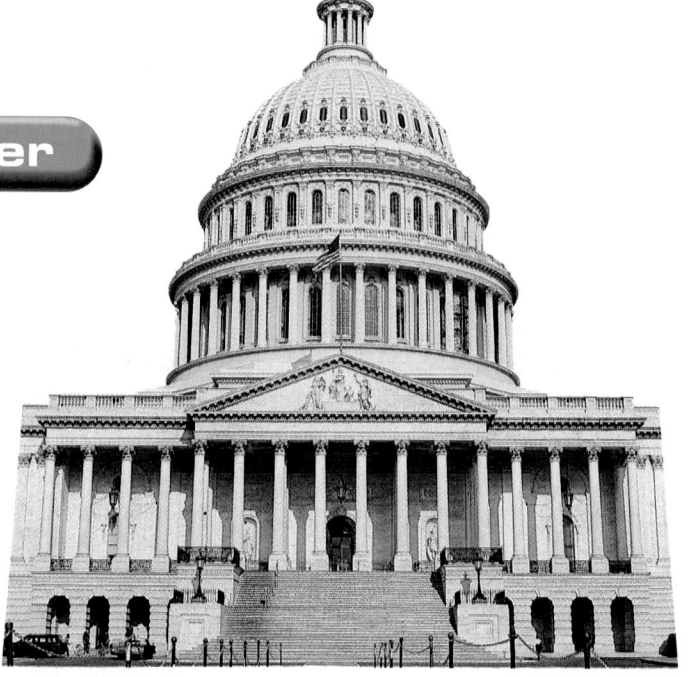

Previewing the Chapter

Overview

In this chapter, students use models and patterns to compare, order, add, subtract, multiply, and divide integers. Through graphing ordered pairs and transformations, students become familiar with the coordinate system. Students learn to solve problems by working backward.

Lesson (pages)	Lesson Objectives	NCTM Standards 2000	Standardized Tests	State/Local Objectives
11-1 (434–436)	Identify, name, and graph integers.	1–10	MAT	
11-2 (437–439)	Compare and order integers.	1, 2, 5–10	CAT, CTBS, ITBS, MAT, SAT, TN	
11-3A (440)	Model integers using counters.	1, 2, 6–8, 10	CTBS, MAT, TN	
11-3 (441–444)	Add integers using models.	1, 2, 6–10	MAT	
11-4 (445–448)	Subtract integers using models.	1–3, 6–10	MAT	
11-5 (449–452)	Multiply integers using models.	1, 2, 4, 6–10	MAT	
11-6A (454–455)	Solve problems by working backward.	1, 2, 6–9	MAT	
11-6 (456–458)	Divide integers using models and patterns.	1–3, 5–10	MAT	
11-7 (459–461)	Graph ordered pairs of numbers on a coordinate grid.	1–10	MAT	
11-8A (462–463)	Find transformations by using patty paper.	2, 3, 6–8, 10		
11-8 (464–467)	Graph transformations on a coordinate grid.	1–4, 6–10	MAT	

CAT = California Achievement Tests, CTBS = Comprehensive Tests of Basic Skills, ITBS = Iowa Tests of Basic Skills,
MAT = Metropolitan Achievement Tests, SAT = Stanford Achievement Tests, TN = Terra Nova
For the key to numbering of NCTM Standards 2000, see page T6.

Organizing the Chapter

 The **Interactive Lesson Planner** contains all of the blackline masters and transparencies. This CD-ROM also includes an easy-to-use lesson planning calendar.

LESSON PLANNING GUIDE

| Lesson | Extra Practice (Student Edition) | BLACKLINE MASTERS (PAGE NUMBERS) | | | | | | | | | | Transparencies A and B |
		Study Guide	Practice	Enrichment	Assessment & Evaluation	Classroom Games	Diversity	Hands-On Lab	School to Career	Science and Math Lab Manual	Technology	
11-1	p. 585	76	76	76								11-1
11-2	p. 585	77	77	77	295				11			11-2
11-3A								64				
11-3	p. 586	78	78	78		29–32						11-3
11-4	p. 586	79	79	79	294, 295							11-4
11-5	p. 586	80	80	80						89–92		11-5
11-6A	p. 587											
11-6	p. 587	81	81	81	296		11				21	11-6
11-7	p. 587	82	82	82				79			22	11-7
11-8A								65				
11-8	p. 588	83	83	83	296							11-8
Study Guide/ Assessment					281–293, 297–299							

OTHER CHAPTER RESOURCES

Student Edition
Chapter Project, pp. 433, 436, 444, 461, 471
School to Career, p. 453
Let the Games Begin, p. 444

Technology
 MathPASS CD-ROM

Interactive Mathematics Tools Software

Teacher's Classroom Resources

Applications
Family Letters and Activities, pp. 21–22
Investigations and Projects Masters, pp. 57–60

Teaching Aids
Answer Key Masters
Block Scheduling Booklet
Lesson Planning Guide
Solutions Manual

Professional Publications
Glencoe Mathematics Professional Series

Planning the Chapter

MindJogger Videoquizzes
provide a unique format for reviewing concepts presented in the chapter.

ASSESSMENT RESOURCES

Student Edition

Mixed Review, pp. 436, 439, 444, 448, 452, 458, 461, 467
Mid-Chapter Self Test, p. 452
Math Journal, pp. 435, 458
Study Guide and Assessment, pp. 468–471
Performance Task, p. 471
Portfolio Suggestion, p. 471
Standardized Test Practice, pp. 472–473
Chapter Test, p. 605

Assessment and Evaluation Masters

Multiple-Choice Tests (Forms 1A, 1B, 1C), pp. 281–286
Free-Response Tests (Forms 2A, 2B, 2C), pp. 287–292
Performance Assessment, p. 293
Mid-Chapter Test, p. 294
Quizzes A–D, pp. 295–296
Standardized Test Practice, pp. 297–298
Cumulative Review, p. 299

Teacher's Wraparound Edition

5-Minute Check, pp. 434, 437, 441, 445, 449, 456, 459, 464
Building Portfolios, p. 432
Math Journal, pp. 440, 463
Closing Activity, pp. 436, 439, 444, 448, 452, 455, 458, 461, 467

Technology

Test and Review Software
MindJogger Videoquizzes
CD-ROM Program

MATERIALS AND MANIPULATIVES

Lesson 11-3A
counters*†
integer mat*†

Lesson 11-3
counters*†
integer mat*†
number cubes*

Lesson 11-4
counters*†
integer mat*†

Lesson 11-5
counters*†
integer mat*†

Lesson 11-6
counters*†
integer mat*†

Lesson 11-8A
patty paper
scissors*
notebook paper†

Lesson 11-8
grid paper†
scissors*
geomirror*

*Glencoe Manipulative Kit   †Glencoe Overhead Manipulative Resources

PACING CHART

See pages T25–T27 for the Course Planning Calendar.

COURSE	DAY 1	DAY 2	DAY 3	DAY 4	DAY 5	DAY 6	DAY 7
Standard	Chapter Project	Lesson 11-1	Lesson 11-2		Lessons 11-3A & 11-3		Lesson 11-4
Honors	Chapter Project	Lesson 11-1	Lesson 11-2	Lesson 11-3	Lesson 11-4	Lesson 11-5	Lesson 11-6A
Block	Chapter Project & Lesson 11-1	Lessons 11-2 & 11-3A	Lessons 11-3 & 11-4	Lesson 11-5	Lessons 11-6A & 11-6	Lesson 11-7	Lessons 11-8A & 11-8

CHAPTER Project

YOU WIN SOME, YOU LOSE SOME

In this project, you will draw a map of the United States and use the map to visually show how the number of members in the House of Representatives has changed for each state. You will also make a line plot and write a paragraph about these changes. You will display your map, line plot, and paragraph on a poster or in a brochure.

Getting Started

- The number of members in the House of Representatives for each state varies according to its population. As a result of the 1990 census, Florida gained 4 members to the House of Representatives, and Pennsylvania lost 2 members. Research how the number of representatives for each state changed after the last census.
- Draw or trace a map of the United States showing each state.
- Color all of the states that lost members in the House of Representatives red. Color all of the states that gained members in the House of Representatives blue. Leave the states that did not change the number of representatives white.

Technology Tips

- Use the **Internet** to find out which states gained and lost members in the House of Representatives.
- Use a **spreadsheet** to keep track of the data you collect.
- Use a **word processor** to write your paragraph about the changes.

interNET
CONNECTION For up-to-date information on the House of Representatives, visit:

www.glencoe.com/sec/math/mac/mathnet

Working on the Project

You can use what you'll learn in Chapter 11 to help you keep track of the changes in the House of Representatives.

Page	Exercise
436	41
444	34
461	34
471	Alternative Assessment

Communicating Mathematics

Rea...

1.

2.

3.

Guided Practice

Dra... num...

4.

Wri...

7.

8.

Wri...

9.

12. See Answer Appendix.

12.

13.

CHAPTER Project
N O T E S

Objectives Students should
- show changes in numbers of members in the House of Representatives for each state.
- make a line plot of the changes.

Project Pointer You may suggest that students begin a *Project Folder* to keep their work as they complete each stage of the Chapter Project. The completed project may also be added to their portfolios.

Explain to students that each citizen of the United States is represented equally in the House of Representatives. To achieve this, census numbers are used to determine the population of each state. The state is then divided into districts, each containing approximately the same number of people. One member of the House of Representatives is elected from each district. When shifts in population occur, the states that lost people are divided into fewer districts, and the states that gained people are divided into more districts.

Investigations and Projects Masters, p. 60

11

Name _____ Date _____

Chapter 11 Project

You Win Some, You Lose Some
Page 433, Getting Started
Page 436, Working on the Chapter Project, Exercise 41

Page 444, Working on the Chapter Project, Exercise 34
My state:
Surrounding States:

Sum:
Gained: Lost:
Page 461, Working on the Chapter Project, Exercise 34

-3 -2 -1 0 1 2 3 4 5 6 7

© Glencoe/McGraw-Hill   60   Mathematics: Applications and Connections, Course 1

■ Reteachin...

Activity Identify o... a negative cube ar... positive. Starting a... have students take... cube and moving t... right. After five turr... they are in relation...

interNET
CONNECTION

Glencoe has made every effort to ensure that the website links for *Mathematics: Applications and Connections* at **www. glencoe.com/sec/math/mac/mathnet** are current and contain appropriate content. However, these website links are not under Glencoe's control.

Instructional Resources ▶▶▶

A recording sheet to help students organize their data for the Chapter Project is shown at the right and is available in the *Investigations and Projects Masters,* p. 60.

Instructional Re...

- *Study Guide Mast...*
- *Practice Masters*, p...
- *Enrichment Master...*
- Transparencies 11-...
- CD-ROM Program
- Resource Lesson...

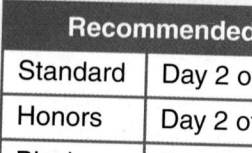

Recommended...	
Standard	Day 2 of...
Honors	Day 2 of...
Block	Day 1 of...

1 FOCU...

5-Minute C...
(Chapter 10)

Find the area of eac...
the nearest tenth.

1.

3 m   4 m
8 m

2.
63.6 cr
9 cm

3.

6.8 ft
4 ft
2.9 ft
5 ft

4. Find the surface ar...
rectangular prism w...
length of 16 inches,...
of 8 inches, and a h...
12 inches. **832 in²**

5. Find the volume of t...
rectangular prism in...
Exercise 4. **1,536 i...**

The 5-Minute Check is...
available on **Transpar...**
for this lesson.

Motivating the Less...

Hands-On Activity Sho...
students that a thermome...
measures temperature in...
separated increments. Ha...
use a thermometer to rea...
temperature inside and o...
classroom. Tell students t...
learning to read a thermo...
just one skill in everyday l...
involves integers.

434 Chapter 11

---

3 PRACTICE/APPLY

Check for Understanding

If students need additional practice or instruction after completing Exercises 1–13, one of these options may be helpful.

- Extra Practice, see p. 585
- Reteaching Activity, see p. 435
- *Study Guide Masters*, p. 76
- *Practice Masters*, p. 76

Assignment Guide

Core: 15–39 odd, 42–47
Enriched: 14–38 even, 39, 40, 42–47

CHAPTER Project

Exercise 41 asks students to advance to the next stage of work on the Chapter Project. Have students place their work in their Project Folders.

4 ASSESS

Closing Activity

Modeling Have pairs of students use a thermometer to measure the temperature of hot, warm, and cold water. Then have them show the temperatures and their opposites on a number line.

Practice Masters, p. 76

436 Chapter 11

Practice

Draw a number line from −10 to 10. Graph each integer on the number line. 14–21. **See Answer Appendix.**

14. +4	**15.** −1	**16.** 0	**17.** −6
18. −8	**19.** 3	**20.** 7	**21.** −2

Write an integer to describe each situation.

22. A token is moved back 6 spaces on a game board. **−6**

23. A helicopter rises 75 feet. **+75**

24. A withdrawal of $45 is made from a bank account. **−45**

25. A submarine is 100 meters below the surface of the water. **−100**

26. The value of a stock decreases by $1. **−1**

27. An employee receives a $100 bonus. **+100**

Write the opposite of each integer.

28. −35 **+35**	**29.** +23 **−23**	**30.** −1 **+1**	**31.** 45 **−45**
32. −250 **+250**	**33.** 77 **−77**	**34.** −52 **+52**	**35.** −110 **+110**

36. Graph the opposite of 12. **36–38. See Answer Appendix.**

37. Graph −6, −8, 0, 3, and 5 on the same number line.

38. Graph 7, −3, 4, and 0 on the same number line.

Applications and Problem Solving

Real World

39. *Earth Science* The temperature of the center of Earth is estimated to be 7,000°C. Express this number as an integer. **+7,000**

40. *Geography* Jacksonville, Florida, is at sea level. Express the elevation of Jacksonville as an integer. **0**

41. *Working on the* **CHAPTER Project** Refer to the map of the United States you made on page 433. In each state, write an integer that represents how the number of members to the House of Representatives has changed for that state. **See students' work.**

42. *Critical Thinking* Compare a number line to a thermometer. How are they alike? How are they different? **See Answer Appendix.**

Mixed Review

43. **Standardized Test Practice** Juana is going to wrap a present shaped like a rectangular prism with dimensions 27 inches by 14 inches by 5 inches. What is the minimum amount of wrapping paper Juana will need? *(Lesson 10-6)* **C**
   A 46 in²   **B** 583 in²   **C** 1,166 in²   **D** 1,890 in²

44. *Geometry* Name the polygon by the number of sides. *(Lesson 9-4)* **octagon**

45. Express 1.35 as a percent. *(Lesson 8-5)* **135%**

46. Find $6\frac{2}{3} - 4\frac{3}{5}$ in simplest form. *(Lesson 6-5)* **$2\frac{1}{15}$**

For **Extra Practice**, see page 585.

47. Round 673.018 to the nearest tenth. *(Lesson 3-4)* **673.0**

Extending the Lesson

Enrichment Masters, p. 76

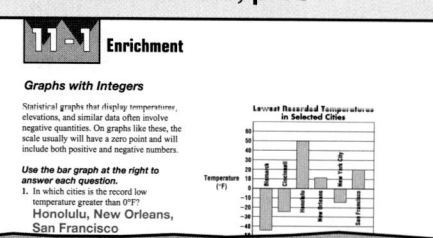

Activity Ask students the following questions. *Can each integer be written as a fraction?* **yes** *Can the set of integers be considered a subset of the set of fractions?* **yes**

11-2 Comparing and Ordering Integers

What you'll learn
You'll learn to compare and order integers.

When am I ever going to use this?
Knowing how to compare integers can help you compare temperatures.

LOOK BACK
You can refer to Lesson 3-3 to review the symbols < and >.

History books use timelines to show the order of events. This timeline shows the establishment of various cities.

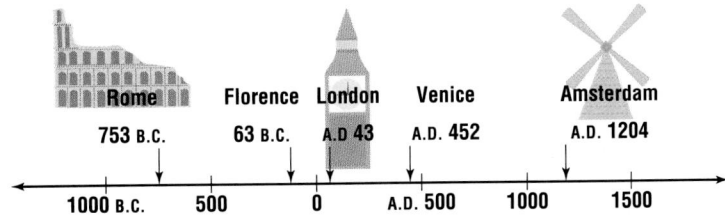

| Rome | Florence | London | Venice | Amsterdam |
| 753 B.C. | 63 B.C. | A.D 43 | A.D. 452 | A.D. 1204 |

1000 B.C.   500   0   A.D. 500   1000   1500

On a timeline, an event depicted to the left always occurred before an event to the right. So, Florence was established after Rome, but before London.

You can use a number line to compare numbers. On a number line, the number to the left is always less than the number to the right.

$$-7\ -6\ -5\ -4\ -3\ -2\ -1\ 0\ 1\ 2\ 3\ 4\ 5\ 6\ 7$$

Notice that -7 is to the left of -3. Therefore, $-7 < -3$. Also, $-3 > -7$ since -3 is to the right of -7.

Examples

Replace each ● with $<$, $>$, or $=$ to make a true sentence.

1 -5 ● -2

Graph -5 and -2 on a number line.

$$-7\ -6\ -5\ -4\ -3\ -2\ -1\ 0\ 1\ 2\ 3\ 4\ 5\ 6\ 7$$

-5 is to the left of -2, so $-5 < -2$.

2 0 ● -5

Graph 0 and -5 on a number line.

$$-7\ -6\ -5\ -4\ -3\ -2\ -1\ 0\ 1\ 2\ 3\ 4\ 5\ 6\ 7$$

0 is to the right of -5, so $0 > -5$.

Big Ben

Lesson 11-2 Comparing and Ordering Integers **437**

11-2 Lesson Notes

Instructional Resources
- *Study Guide Masters*, p. 77
- *Practice Masters*, p. 77
- *Enrichment Masters*, p. 77
- Transparencies 11-2, A and B
- *Assessment and Evaluation Masters*, p. 295
- *School to Career Masters*, p. 11
- CD-ROM Program
  - Resource Lesson 11-2
  - Interactive Lesson 11-2

Recommended Pacing	
Standard	Days 3 & 4 of 15
Honors	Day 3 of 13
Block	Day 2 of 8

1 FOCUS

5-Minute Check
(Lesson 11-1)

Draw a number line from -10 to 10. Graph each integer on the number line.
1. -4 2. 7

-10 -5 0   5   10

3. Write an integer to describe 13 degrees below zero. -13

Write the opposite of each integer.
4. 26 -26 5. -11 11

The 5-Minute Check is also available on **Transparency 11-2A** for this lesson.

2 TEACH

Transparency 11-2B contains a teaching aid for this lesson.

Reading Mathematics Have students locate a timeline in a newspaper, magazine, or history book. Ask them to read the events listed to the class, indicating whether each event occurred before or after the last event mentioned. Ask students how they can tell which event occurred first.

Multiple Learning Styles

Visual/Spatial Have pairs of students look up results from golf tournaments in newspapers or sports magazines. Then have them graph the final scores on a number line. Use "0" for par. Ask students to identify the players with the lowest and highest number of strokes.

Motivating the Lesson

Communication Draw a number line on the chalkboard, placing a 0 in the middle. Have volunteers label $+1$, -1, $+4$, and -3. Ask: *Which is the greatest number?* $+4$ *the least?* -3 *Where might you see a number line like this?* **thermometer**

438 Chapter 11

 Examples ——● **3** Order the integers −4, 3, 0, and −5 from least to greatest.

Graph each number on a number line first.

−7 −6 −5 −4 −3 −2 −1 0 1 2 3 4 5 6 7

Then, write the integers as they appear on the number line from left to right.   −5, −4, 0, and 3 are in order from least to greatest.

APPLICATION

Real World

LOOK BACK
You can refer to Lesson 2-7 to review median.

4 **Weather** The record cold temperatures for five states are recorded on the map. Find the median of these temperatures.

List the temperatures in order from least to greatest.

−80, −70, −52, −2, 12

The median is the middle number when the numbers are arranged in order. So the median of these low temperatures is −52.

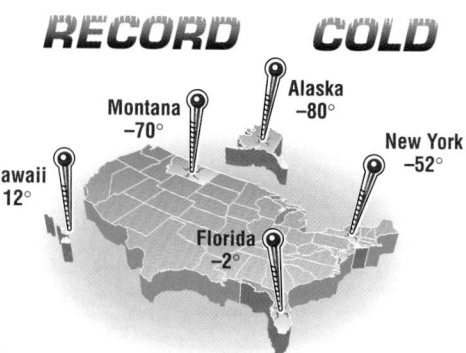

RECORD COLD

Montana −70°
Alaska −80°
Hawaii 12°
New York −52°
Florida −2°

Source: *The USA Today Weather Almanac*

CHECK FOR UNDERSTANDING

Communicating Mathematics

Read and study the lesson to answer each question.   1–3. See Answer Appendix.

1. *Explain* how a number line can be used to order integers.

2. *Write a Problem* where integers would be compared or ordered.

3. *You Decide* Amy says that 5 is greater than 3, and therefore, −5 > −3. Cordelia disagrees. Who is correct? Explain your reasoning.

Guided Practice

Replace each ● with < , > , or = to make a true sentence.

4. +3 ● −1   >   5. −8 ● −4   <   6. 0 ● −2   >

7. Order −3, 5, 0, and −2 from least to greatest.   −3, −2, 0, 5

8. 4 feet below sea level; on a number line −5 is to the left of −4.

8. *Geography* Which is higher, 5 feet below sea level or 4 feet below sea level? Explain.

EXERCISES

Practice

Replace each ● with < , > , or = to make a true sentence.

9. +3 ● −4   >   10. −10 ● −100   >   11. −3 ● 0   <
12. +32 ● −32   >   13. 0 ● +5   <   14. −6 ● −7   >
15. −82 ● −85   >   16. −44 ● −33   <   17. −200 ● +123   <

438 Chapter 11 Algebra: Investigating Integers

---

19. 41, 10, 3, 0, −10, −20

18. Order 4, −5, 6, and −7 from least to greatest. **−7, −5, 4, 6**

19. Order 0, 41, 3, −20, −10, and 10 from greatest to least.

20. Which is greater, −45 or −42? **−42**

21. Which is least, 0, −3, −17, or −8? **−17**

22. Is zero greater than, less than, or equal to negative ten? **greater than**

Applications and Problem Solving

23a. −458, −435, −361, −38, 450, 1,542, 1,763, 1,947, 2,795

23. *Physical Science* The table shows the melting point of some common elements. As the temperature rises above the melting point, the element changes from a solid to a liquid.
  a. List the melting points from least to greatest.
  b. The average annual temperature in the interior of Antarctica is −71°F. Would mercury be a solid or a liquid at this temperature? **solid**
  c. Find the median of the melting points. **450**

Element	Melting Point (°F)
Calcium	1,542
Gold	1,947
Helium	−458
Hydrogen	−435
Iron	2,795
Mercury	−38
Oxygen	−361
Silver	1,763
Tin	450

24. *Life Science* Some sea creatures live near the surface while others live in the depths of the ocean. Make a drawing showing the relative habitats of the following creatures. **See Answer Appendix.**

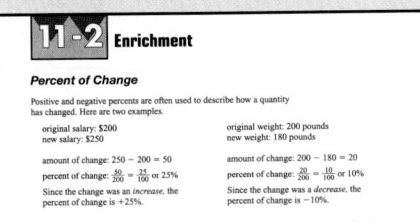

- ribbon fish: 600 to 3,300 feet below the surface
- blue marlin: 0 to 600 feet below the surface
- brittle stars: 13,200 to 19,800 feet below the surface
- lantern fish: 3,300 to 13,200 feet below the surface

Brittle Star

25. *Critical Thinking* Why is any negative integer less than any positive integer? **See margin.**

Mixed Review

26. *Geography* New Orleans is 8 feet below sea level. Express this elevation as an integer. *(Lesson 11-1)* **−8**

27. *Standardized Test Practice* Fred had an equilateral triangle with an area of 3 square feet. He traced the triangle several times to make a hexagon. What is the area of the hexagon? *(Lesson 10-2)* **C**

Area = 3 ft²

  A 8 ft²   **B** 12 ft²
  C 18 ft²   **D** 22 ft²

For **Extra Practice**, see page 585.

28. Find the GCF of 120 and 150. *(Lesson 5-3)* **30**

Lesson 11-2 Comparing and Ordering Integers **439**

Extending the Lesson

Enrichment Masters, p. 77

11-2 Enrichment

Percent of Change

Positive and negative percents are often used to describe how a quantity has changed. Here are two examples.

original salary: $200
new salary: $250

original weight: 200 pounds
new weight: 180 pounds

amount of change: 250 − 200 = 50
percent of change: $\frac{50}{200} = \frac{25}{100}$ or 25%
Since the change was an *increase*, the percent of change is +25%.

amount of change: 200 − 180 = 20
percent of change: $\frac{20}{200} = \frac{10}{100}$ or 10%
Since the change was a *decrease*, the percent of change is −10%.

Activity Separate students into groups to research the following questions. *How do temperature extremes on Mercury or Mars compare with those on Earth? How deep are the craters on the moon?* Have groups show their findings on a number line.

Assignment Guide

Core: 9–23 odd, 25–28
Enriched: 10–22 even, 23–28

4 ASSESS

Closing Activity

Modeling Write each integer from −5 to 5 on an index card. Give one card to each of 11 students and ask them to form a human number line, holding the cards in front of them. Ask each student to name one integer greater than and one less than his or her card. Then have students in the line pass their cards to 11 other students and see how quickly they can form a new line. Continue with questions and discussion.

Chapter 11, Quiz A (Lessons 11-1 and 11-2) is available in the *Assessment and Evaluation Masters*, p. 295.

Additional Answer

25. All negative integers are to the left of 0 on a number line while all positive integers are to the right. The number to the left is always less than the number to the right.

Practice Masters, p. 77

11-2 Practice

Comparing and Ordering Integers

Fill in each ◯ with <, >, or =.

1. −9 ◯ 8 **<**
2. 0 ◯ −1 **>**
3. −14 ◯ −15 **>**
4. +26 ◯ 26 **=**
5. −32 ◯ 23 **<**
6. −148 ◯ 148 **<**
7. 19 ◯ −91 **>**
8. −67 ◯ −60 **<**
9. 245 ◯ −254 **>**
10. −971 ◯ 791 **<**
11. −830 ◯ −803 **<**
12. −64 ◯ −64 **=**
13. −57 ◯ −75 **>**
14. −33 ◯ 3 **<**
15. 169 ◯ −196 **>**
16. −200 ◯ −201 **>**

Order each set of integers from least to greatest.

17. −6, 16, −26
    −26, −6, 16
18. −213, −231, 132
    −231, −213, 132
19. 5, −3, −11, 9, −7
    −11, −7, −3, 5, 9
20. 8, −6, 4, −10, −2
    −10, −6, −2, 4, 8
21. −36, 28, −4, −17, −59
    −59, −36, −17, −4, 28
22. −84, 95, −71, −103, −62
    −103, −84, −71, −62, 95
23. 21, −34, 65, −12, 43, 0, −56
    −56, −34, −12, 0, 21, 43, 65
24. −22, 2, 0, 202, 22, −222, −2
    −222, −22, −2, 0, 2, 22, 202
25. −3, −33, 36, −66, 63, −6, 0
    −66, −33, −6, −3, 0, 36, 63
26. 0, −172, 1, −127, 7, −171, −117
    −172, −171, −127, −117, 0, 1, 7

27. Which is greater, negative 21 or negative 22? **−21**

28. Which is greater, 8 degrees above zero or 9 degrees below zero? **8 degrees above zero**

29. Which is less, a checkbook balance of −30 dollars or a balance of −25 dollars? **−30 dollars**

30. Which is greater, negative 98 or positive 89? **+89**

© Glencoe/McGraw-Hill 77 Mathematics: Applications and Connections, Course 1

Lesson 11-2 **439**

COOPERATIVE LEARNING

11-3A Zero Pairs

A Preview of Lesson 11-3

GET READY

Objective Students model integers using counters.

Optional Resources

Hands-On Lab Masters
• counters, p. 6
• integer mat, p. 9
• worksheet, p. 64

Overhead Manipulative Resources
• counters
• integer mat

Manipulative Kit
• counters

MANAGEMENT TIPS

Recommended Time
30 minutes

Getting Started The concept of *zero pair* is very important in modeling not only addition of integers, but other operations as well. It is also used in modeling solving equations and modeling polynomials. Have students practice the zero pair concept by pairing positive and negative counters from a large pile of counters.

The **Activity** has students model +3 + (−3). You may want to model the activity on an overhead transparency or on the chalkboard with colored chalk. If counters are not available, have students cut counters from construction paper.

ASSESS

Have students complete Exercises 1–6. Watch for students who don't understand the meaning of *zero pair*.

Use Exercise 7 to determine whether students understand how to use counters to model integers.

counters of two colors

integer mat

You can use counters to help you understand integers. Yellow counters represent positive integers, and red counters represent negative integers. When you pair one counter of each color, the result is zero. We call this pair of counters a *zero pair*.

TRY THIS

Work with a partner.

Step 1 Place three yellow counters on the mat to represent the integer +3.

Step 2 Place three red counters on the same mat to represent the integer −3.

Step 3 Pair the positive and negative counters. Remove as many zero pairs as possible.

+3 + (−3) = ?

ON YOUR OWN

1. How many counters do you have on the mat? **none**
2. What is the sum of +3 + (−3)? **0**
3. How are +3 and −3 related? **They are opposites.**
4. What is the sum of any pair of opposites? **0**
5. What is the value of a zero pair? **0**
6. If you removed a zero pair from the mat, what effect does it have on the value of the counters left on the mat? **none**
7. *Look Ahead* How do you think you could use counters to find the sum of +4 and −3? **See margin.**

440 Chapter 11 Algebra: Investigating Integers

Additional Answer

7. **Place 4 yellow counters on the mat to represent +4. Place 3 red counters on the mat to represent −3. Remove as many zero pairs as possible. The 1 yellow counter left represents the sum (+1).**

Math Journal

Have students write a paragraph on how to use zero pairs to find the sum of +6 and −6.

Adding Integers

11-3 Lesson Notes

What you'll learn
You'll learn to add integers using models.

When am I ever going to use this?
Knowing how to add integers can help you keep score in games.

Word Wise
zero pair

Remember that yellow counters represent positive integers and red counters represent negative integers.

Monsa and Victor are playing a board game. In the game, each player rolls a number cube and moves a token. Some squares on the game board have further instructions.

- Monsa starts at 0 and rolls a 5.
- The fifth square tells him to roll again. He rolls a 6.
- His token lands on a square that tells him to move back 3 spaces.

How many spaces from the start is Monsa's token?

To find the location of Monsa's token, you will need to add integers. You can add integers using models.

Use yellow counters to represent positive integers and red counters to represent negative integers.

Step 1 Use 5 positive counters to represent Monsa's first roll (+5). Use 6 positive counters to represent Monsa's second roll (+6). Place all of the counters on a mat.

$$+5 + (+6) = +11$$

Step 2 Use 3 negative counters to represent the 3 spaces backward. Place the 3 negative counters on the mat with the 11 positive counters.

$$+11 + (-3)$$

Step 3 Pair the positive and negative counters. Remove as many **zero pairs** as possible since it does not change the value on the mat.

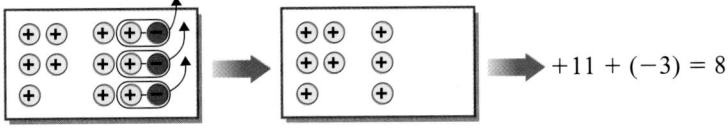

$$+11 + (-3) = 8$$

There are a total of 8 positive counters left on the mat. Monsa's token is 8 spaces from the starting point.

Lesson 11-3 Adding Integers **441**

Instructional Resources
- *Study Guide Masters*, p. 78
- *Practice Masters*, p. 78
- *Enrichment Masters*, p. 78
- Transparencies 11-3, A and B
- *Classroom Games*, pp. 29–32
- CD-ROM Program
  - Resource Lesson 11-3
  - Interactive Lesson 11-3

Recommended Pacing	
Standard	Days 5 & 6 of 15
Honors	Day 4 of 13
Block	Day 3 of 8

1 FOCUS

 5-Minute Check
(Lesson 11-2)

Replace each ● with <, >, or = to make a true sentence.
1. 14 ● −26 **>**
2. −285 ● −42 **<**
3. 0 ● −12 **>**
4. Which is greater, −37 or −9? **−9**
5. Is zero greater than, less than, or equal to negative two? **greater than**

 The 5-Minute Check is also available on **Transparency 11-3A** for this lesson.

Motivating the Lesson
Hands-On Activity Give small groups of students a random number of red (negative) and yellow (positive) counters. Ask them to remove as many zero pairs as possible. Then ask them to name the integer that describes the remaining counters.

Classroom Vignette

"To help students picture adding integers on a number line, we call it 'dancing' up and down the number line. We physically move up and down a number line, which is displayed around the perimeter of my classroom."

Karen Shevnock Jamieson, Teacher
Thurman White Middle School
Henderson, NV

Karen Shevnock Jamieson

Transparency 11-3B contains a teaching aid for this lesson.

Using Problem Solving Have students solve the following problem. *In the game "Treadmill," you go backward if you spin an odd number and forward if you spin an even number. What would be your position if you started at 0 and spun 1, 3, 4, and 4?* **+4**

In-Class Examples

For Example 1
Use counters to find −8 + 5.
−3

For Example 2
Use counters to find −6 + (−6).
−12

For Example 3
A computer consultant earns $2,600.00 in the first month she runs her own company. She spends $3,100.00 to set up her office. How much money does she have at the end of the month? **−$500.00**

Teaching Tip After Example 3, review the four possible sign combinations of adding integers: negative plus positive, negative plus negative, positive plus positive, and positive plus negative.

---

1 Use counters to find −4 + 3.

Step 1 Place 4 negative counters on the mat to represent −4. Place 3 positive counters on the same mat to represent adding 3.

Step 2 Pair the positive and negative counters. Remove as many zero pairs as possible.

Step 3 Count the counters left on the mat. There is 1 negative counter. This represents −1. So, −4 + 3 = −1.

2 Use counters to find −2 + (−2).

Step 1 Place 2 negative counters on the mat to represent −2. Place 2 more negative counters on the same mat to represent adding −2.

Step 2 Since there are no positive counters, you cannot remove any zero pairs.

Step 3 Count the counters on the mat. There are 4 negative counters. This represents −4. So −2 + (−2) = −4.

You can also use a number line to add integers.

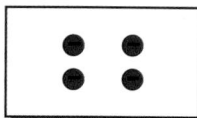

3 **Game Shows** On a popular TV game show, a contestant has 200 points and then loses 500 points. What is the contestant's score?

You need to find the sum of 200 + (−500). Consider a number line. Start at 0 and go 200 in the positive direction (right).

From that point, go 500 in the negative direction (left).

You end at −300. So, 200 + (−500) = −300.

Communicating Mathematics

Read and study the lesson to answer each question.

1. *Write* an addition sentence represented by the model. **−5 + 2 = −3**

2. *Model* −3 + 2 and 2 + (−3) using counters. Compare and contrast these two problems. **See margin.**

Guided Practice

State whether each sum is *positive*, *negative*, or *zero*.

3. −5 + 3 **negative**   4. −3 + 7 **positive**

Find each sum. Use counters or a number line if necessary.

5. 3 + (−1) **2**   6. −4 + (−8) **−12** 7. 0 + (−2) **−2**   8. 4 + (−6) **−2**

9. Find the sum of −4, 8, and −12. **−8**

10. *Football* The Centerville Middle School football team has the ball on the 20-yard line. The team is heading towards the 50-yard line. On the first play, the team gains 6 yards. On the next play, the team loses 8 yards. Where is the ball after the second play? **18 yard line**

EXERCISES

Practice

State whether each sum is *positive*, *negative*, or *zero*.

11. 3 + (−5) **negative**   12. −2 + (−7) **negative** 13. 6 + 3 **positive**
14. −4 + 6 **positive**   15. −3 + (−3) **negative** 16. −10 + 10 **zero**

Find each sum. Use counters or a number line if necessary.

17. **−9**

25. **−8**

17. −3 + (−6)   18. 3 + (−8) **−5** 19. −12 + 12 **0** 20. 3 + 0 **3**
21. −3 + 0 **−3**   22. −5 + 4 **−1** 23. 6 + (−2) **4** 24. −4 + 10 **6**
25. −4 + (−4)   26. −5 + 5 **0**   27. 13 + (−3) **10** 28. −11 + (−18)
−29

29. Find the sum of −18, 6, and 20. **8**

30. What is −3 plus −6 plus 4? **−5**

32a. −21 + 12

31. *Algebra* Find the value of $a + b$ if $a = -9$ and $b = 6$. **−3**

Applications and Problem Solving

32. *Scuba Diving* A scuba diver dived 21 feet below sea level. Then the diver went up 12 feet.
  a. Write an addition statement representing the dive.
  b. What integer represents the diver's location with respect to sea level? **−9**

33. *Earth Science* At night, the average temperature on the surface of Saturn is −150°C. During the day, the temperature rises 27°C. What is the average temperature on the planet's surface during the day? **−123°C**

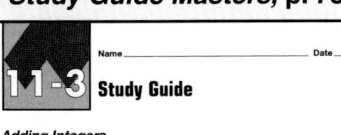

Reteaching the Lesson

Activity Use a standard deck of playing cards with the face cards removed to add integers. Groups of students will need 10 cards. Use red cards to represent negative integers and black cards to represent positive integers.

Error Analysis

Watch for students who are having difficulty understanding whether the sum of a positive integer and a negative integer is positive or negative.

Prevent by telling students to use counters to model the problem.

Check for Understanding

If students need additional practice or instruction after completing Exercises 1–10, one of these options may be helpful.
- Extra Practice, see p. 586
- Reteaching Activity
- *Study Guide Masters,* p. 78
- *Practice Masters,* p. 78
- Interactive Mathematics Tools Software

Assignment Guide

Core: 11–33 odd, 35–39
Enriched: 12–30 even, 32, 33, 35–39

Additional Answer

2. See Answer Appendix for art. One has 3 negative counters on the mat and adds 2 positive counters. The other has 2 positive counters and adds 3 negative counters. Both result in 2 zero pairs with just one negative counter left on the mat. The answer to both problems is −1.

Study Guide Masters, p. 78

Exercise 34 asks students to advance to the next stage of work on the Chapter Project. You may have students add integers for another region. Then have students place their work in their Project Folders.

4 ASSESS

Closing Activity

Modeling Have pairs of students use counters and a mat to find sums of examples such as $-4 + 6$. Then have them add another integer to the sum so that the new sum will be the opposite of the original sum.
$2; 2 + (-4) = -2$

Additional Answer

37. Sample answer:

Practice Masters, p. 78

---

34. **Working on the** Refer to the map of the United States you made on page 433. Write the integers for your state and each state that touches your state. Find the sum of the integers. Has your area of the country gained or lost members in the House of Representatives? **See students' work.**

35. **Critical Thinking** Write an addition sentence that satisfies each statement. **a. Sample answer:** $-2 + (-3) = -5$
    a. All addends are negative integers, and the sum is -5.
    b. One addend is zero, and the sum is -5.
    c. At least one addend is a positive integer, and the sum is -5.

35b. Sample answer: $0 + (-5) = -5$

35c. Sample answer: $-8 + 3 = -5$

Mixed Review

36. Which is greater, -66 or -75? *(Lesson 11-2)* **-66**

37. **Geometry** Draw a rectangular prism. *(Lesson 10-4)* **See margin.**

38. **Algebra** Evaluate ab if $a = \frac{3}{8}$ and $b = \frac{7}{15}$. *(Lesson 7-2)* $\frac{7}{40}$

39. **Standardized Test Practice** Before sales tax, what is the total cost of three CDs selling for $13.98 each? *(Lesson 4-1)* **D**
    A $13.98   **B** $20.97   **C** $27.96   **D** $41.94   **E** $48.93

For **Extra Practice**, see page 586.

Falling Off the Ends

Math Skill
Adding Integers

Get Ready   This game is for two players.

   two different colored number cubes

⬤   two different colored counters

Get Set   Draw a game board as shown below.

| -6 | -5 | -4 | -3 | -2 | -1 | 0 | 1 | 2 | 3 | 4 | 5 | 6 |

Go
- Let one number cube represent positive integers, and the other represent negative integers.
- Each player places a counter on zero.
- One player rolls the number cubes and adds the numbers shown. The player then moves his or her counter the number of spaces in the direction indicated by the sum.
- Players take turns rolling the number cubes and moving the counters.
- The first player to go off the board in either direction wins the game.

 Visit www.glencoe.com/sec/math/mac/mathnet for more games.

■ Extending the Lesson ■

Enrichment Masters, p. 78

Let the **Begin**

Students can use the game to practice the addition of integers. Suggest that students challenge each others' answers if they think a sum is incorrect. The player who supplies the correct answer then moves his or her counter.
*Additional resources for this game can be found on page 45 of the **Classroom Games**.*

Subtracting Integers

11-4 Lesson Notes

What you'll learn

You'll learn to subtract integers using models.

When am I ever going to use this?

Knowing how to subtract integers can help you to compare elevations when studying geography.

A parade had 18 helium balloons. Five of the balloons were making their first appearance in the parade. How many of the balloons had been in the parade before?

To answer this question, you must find 18 − 5. You can model this subtraction problem using counters.

Step 1 Place 18 positive counters on a mat to represent the 18 balloons.

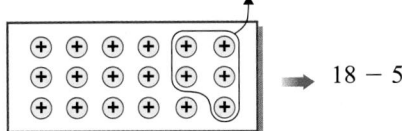

→ 18

Step 2 Since subtraction is the opposite of addition, remove 5 of the positive counters from the mat to represent subtracting 5.

→ 18 − 5

Step 3 Count the counters remaining on the mat.

→ 18 − 5 = 13

There are 13 positive counters. This represents 13. So, 18 − 5 = 13. There were 13 balloons that had been in the parade previously.

Lesson 11-4 Subtracting Integers **445**

Instructional Resources
- *Study Guide Masters,* p. 79
- *Practice Masters,* p. 79
- *Enrichment Masters,* p. 79
- Transparencies 11-4, A and B
- *Assessment and Evaluation Masters,* pp. 294, 295
- CD-ROM Program
  - Resource Lesson 11-4
  - Interactive Lesson 11-4

Recommended Pacing	
Standard	Day 7 of 15
Honors	Day 5 of 13
Block	Day 3 of 8

1 FOCUS

5-Minute Check
(Lesson 11-3)

State whether each sum is *positive, negative,* or *zero*.

1. −8 + 12 **positive**

2. −2 + (−6) **negative**

Find each sum. Use counters or a number line if necessary.

3. −6 + 2 **−4**

4. 9 + (−4) **5**

5. −7 + −8 **−15**

The 5-Minute Check is also available on **Transparency 11-4A** for this lesson.

Motivating the Lesson

Problem Solving Ask students how they would solve this problem: *A bird is perched on a cliff 12 feet above a lake, watching a fish swim 5 feet underwater. What is the difference between their locations?* **17 feet**

Transparency 11-4B contains a teaching aid for this lesson.

In-Class Examples

For Example 1
Use counters to find
$-14 - (-4)$. **−10**

For Example 2
Use counters to find $-8 - 3$.
−11

For Example 3
Abraham was born on January 20, 1989. The temperature was +15°F. The temperature on his birthday this year was −6°F. Find the difference in temperatures. **21°F**

Teaching Tip After Example 2, show students that $-5 - 4$ could also be written as $-5 - (+4)$ or $-5 + (-4)$. The answer is the same in all cases.

Using Discussion After working through the examples with students, ask them to discuss the relationship between the subtraction of and the addition of integers.

You can also use counters to model subtraction problems involving negative integers.

Example ➊ Use counters to find $-5 - (-2)$.

Step 1 Place 5 negative counters on the mat to represent -5.

Step 2 Remove 2 negative counters from the mat to represent subtracting -2.

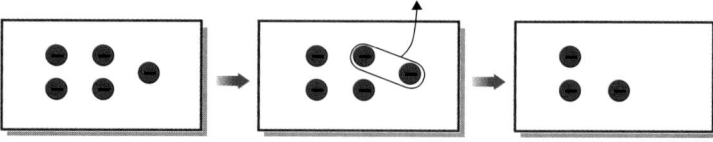

Step 3 Count the counters remaining on the mat. There are 3 negative counters. This represents -3. So, $-5 - (-2) = -3$.

Sometimes, you need to add zero pairs in order to subtract. When you add zero pairs, the value of the integers on the mat does not change.

Examples ➋ Use counters to find $-5 - 4$.

Step 1 Place 5 negative counters on the mat to represent -5.

Step 2 To subtract 4, you must remove 4 positive counters. But you cannot remove 4 positive counters because there are none on the mat. You must add 4 zero pairs to the mat. Then you can remove 4 positive counters.

Step 3 Count the counters remaining on the mat. There are 9 negative counters. This represents -9. So, $-5 - 4 = -9$.

APPLICATION ➌ **Weather** One morning when Melissa awoke, the temperature outside was -5°F. By noon, the temperature was 10°F. Find the change in temperature.

Explore You know the starting and ending temperatures. You want to know the change in the temperature.

Plan To find the change in temperature, subtract the starting temperature (-5) from the ending temperature (10). Use counters to find $10 - (-5)$.

Classroom Vignette

"I use students holding a positive or negative sign instead of using counters. Students take turns in front of the room displaying their signs. Those at their seats write the sentence shown by the human counters. Those students remaining after the zero pairs sit down represent the answer."

Sandra J. Hart, Teacher
Emporia Middle School
Emporia, KS

Solve Place 10 positive counters on the mat to represent +10. To subtract −5, you must remove 5 negative counters. But you cannot remove 5 negative counters because there are none on the mat. You must first add 5 zero pairs to the mat. Then you can remove 5 negative counters.

Count the counters remaining on the mat. There are 15 positive counters. This represents 15. So, 10 − (−5) = 15. The change in temperature is 15°F.

Examine Let a vertical number line represent a thermometer. Locate the starting and ending temperatures. The number line indicates the change in temperature is 15°F. The answer is correct.

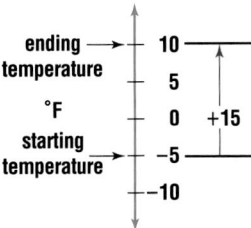

Study Hint

Problem Solving The strategy of drawing a diagram is used in the examine step.

CHECK FOR UNDERSTANDING

Communicating Mathematics

Read and study the lesson to answer each question.

1. *Write* a subtraction sentence represented by the model. **4 − (−2) = 6**

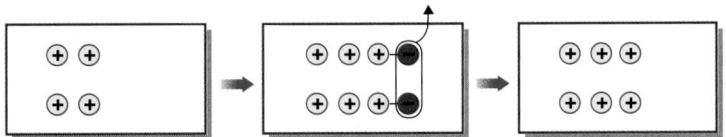

2. You need zero pairs when there are not enough positive or negative counters to remove from the mat.

2. *Explain* when it is necessary to use zero pairs to model subtraction.

3. *You Decide* Andy says that you cannot subtract 8 from 5. Donnell disagrees. Who is correct? Explain. **Donnell; you can subtract 8 from 5 by using negative integers. 5 − 8 = −3**

Guided Practice

Find each difference. Use counters or a number line if necessary.

4. 3 − (−1) **4**   5. −4 − (−4) **0**   6. −2 − 5 **−7**   7. 6 − 8 **−2**

8. *Games* Mai-Lin and Jamal are playing *Mother, May I.* They start by standing next to each other. Mai-Lin moves 4 steps forward and Jamal moves 2 steps backward. How many steps separate the two children? **6 steps**

Lesson 11-4 Subtracting Integers **447**

3 PRACTICE/APPLY

Check for Understanding

If students need additional practice or instruction after completing Exercises 1–8, one of these options may be helpful.
- Extra Practice, see p. 586
- Reteaching Activity
- *Study Guide Masters*, p. 79
- *Practice Masters*, p. 79

Study Guide Masters, p. 79

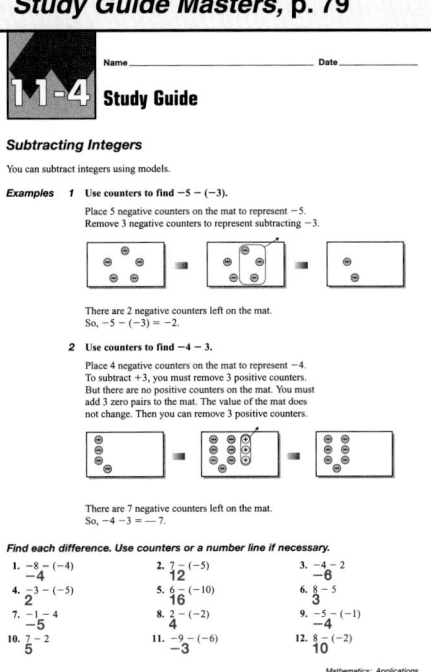

Reteaching the Lesson

Activity Have pairs of students work together to decide if the answers to these problems are positive or negative: 3 − (−5); −11 − (−9); 10 − (−8); −13 − 7. Then assign a student tutor to each group to check the answers and explain how to work each problem.

Error Analysis

Watch for students who have difficulty understanding how the difference can be greater than the minuend when subtracting integers.

Prevent by using a number line to show that they are finding the distance between two points.

4 ASSESS

Closing Activity

Writing Have pairs of students use the chart to create word problems that can be solved by subtracting integers.

Average January Temperatures in Four Canadian Cities	
Winnipeg	−2°F
Dawson	−18°F
Quebec	9°F
Toronto	25°F

Chapter 11, Quiz B (Lessons 11-3 and 11-4) is available in the *Assessment and Evaluation Masters,* p. 295.

Mid-Chapter Test (Lessons 11-1 through 11-4) is available in the *Assessment and Evaluation Masters,* p. 294.

Practice Masters, p. 79

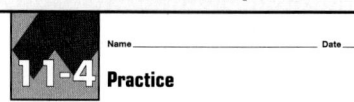

EXERCISES

Practice **Find each difference. Use counters or a number line if necessary.**

9. $2 - 4$ **−2** **10.** $4 - 2$ **2** **11.** $0 - 5$ **−5** **12.** $0 - (-5)$ **5**

13. $-3 - (-6)$ **3** **14.** $3 - (-8)$ **11** **15.** $-12 - 12$ **−24** **16.** $-7 - (-5)$ **−2**

17. $6 - (-2)$ **8** **18.** $-4 - 10$ **−14** **19.** $-7 - (-7)$ **0** **20.** $5 - (-5)$ **10**

21. Use counters to find $3 + (-6) - (-3)$. **See Answer Appendix; 0.**

22. *Algebra* Find the value of $x - y$ if $x = 9$ and $y = 16$. **−7**

Applications and Problem Solving

23. *Geography* About one third of the Netherlands is below sea level. The map shows approximate elevations for parts of the country.
   a. What is the difference in elevation between Prins Alexander Polder and Leiden? **18 ft**
   b. What is the difference in elevation between Leiden and a location in the Dunes that is 15 feet above sea level? **19 ft**

24. *Communications* Javier lives in Santa Barbara, California. At 10:00 A.M., he called his grandmother in Orlando, Florida. She told him that it was 1:00 P.M. in Orlando. If we use the number 0 to represent time in Orlando, then what integer would represent the time in Santa Barbara? **−3**

25. *Critical Thinking* When you subtract a lesser number from a greater number, will the answer always be positive? Give examples to support your answer. **Yes; sample examples: 8 − 3 = 5, 0 − (−2) = 2, and −3 − (−5) = 2.**

Mixed Review

26. *Algebra* Find the value of $x + y$ if $x = 7$ and $y = -12$. *(Lesson 11-3)* **−5**

27. Express the ratio, 2 student council representatives out of 28 students in the class, as a fraction in simplest form. *(Lesson 8-1)* $\frac{1}{14}$

28. **Standardized Test Practice** There are $18\frac{2}{3}$ cups of jellybeans to be divided among a group of children. If each child gets $\frac{2}{3}$ cup of jellybeans, how many children are there? *(Lesson 7-6)* **D**
   A 25
   B 26
   C 27
   D 28
   E Not Here

For **Extra Practice**, see page 586.

448 Chapter 11 Algebra: Investigating Integers

Extending the Lesson

Enrichment Masters, p. 79

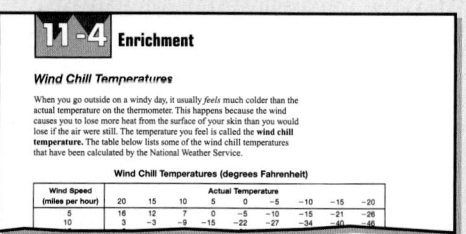

Activity Have students find the value of each pair of expressions.
   a. $3 - (-9)$ **+12** $3 + 9$ **+12**
   b. $-14 - (-5)$ **−9** $-14 + 5$ **−9**
   c. $-2 - (-10)$ **+8** $-2 + 10$ **+8**
   d. $+6 - (-6)$ **+12** $6 + 6$ **+12**

Then ask students to write rules for finding sums and differences of integers.

11-5

Multiplying Integers

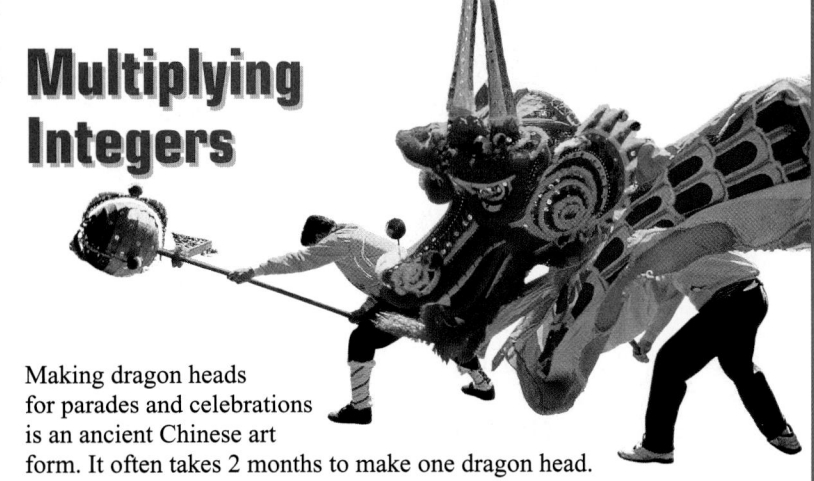

What you'll learn

You'll learn to multiply integers using models.

When am I ever going to use this?

Knowing how to multiply integers can help you solve problems involving repeated addition with integers.

Cultural Kaleidoscope

A dragon head can weigh over 26 pounds. A dragon can be as long as 300 feet and require about 60 dancers to manipulate.

Making dragon heads for parades and celebrations is an ancient Chinese art form. It often takes 2 months to make one dragon head. At this rate, how long does it take to make 5 dragon heads?

To answer this question, you must multiply 5×2. Remember that multiplication is repeated addition. Therefore, 5×2 means $2 + 2 + 2 + 2 + 2$. You can model this multiplication problem using counters.

Step 1 5×2 means to *put in* 5 sets of 2 positive counters. Place these counters on the mat.

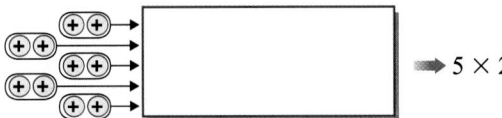

$\Rightarrow 5 \times 2$

Step 2 Count the counters on the mat.

$\Rightarrow 5 \times 2 = 10$

There are 10 positive counters. This represents 10. So, $5 \times 2 = 10$. It will take 10 months to make the dragon heads.

Example

1 Use counters to find $4 \times (-2)$.

Step 1 $4 \times (-2)$ means to *put in* 4 sets of 2 negative counters. Place these counters on the mat.

Step 2 Count the counters on the mat. There are 8 negative counters. This represents -8. So, $4 \times (-2) = -8$.

Lesson 11-5 Multiplying Integers **449**

Multiple Learning Styles

Interpersonal Have students work in small groups to create a board game that is played by adding, subtracting, and multiplying integers. The title and illustrations should have a theme that relates to integers, such as weather, exercise, or elevation. Then have groups play each others' games.

---

1 FOCUS

5-Minute Check
(Lesson 11-4)

Find each difference. Use counters or a number line if necessary.

1. $5 - (-7)$ **12**
2. $-6 - 4$ **−10**
3. $-8 - (-3)$ **−5**
4. $9 - 3$ **6**
5. When Jasmine went to bed, the temperature was 3°F. When she woke up the next morning, the temperature was −6°F. How many degrees did the temperature drop during the night? **9°F**

The 5-Minute Check is also available on **Transparency 11-5A** for this lesson.

Motivating the Lesson

Problem Solving Use a geoboard on the overhead to find 4×3 and 2×5. Ask students how they could model multiplication of negative numbers.

Transparency 11-5B contains a teaching aid for this lesson.

Thinking Algebraically Point out that 6 × 2 is equivalent to 2 × 6. Tell students that this is an example of the commutative property for the multiplication of real numbers. This property is one of the basic rules of algebra.

Teaching Tip Have students compare the models of 4 × (−2), −2 × 4, −4 × 2, and 2 × (−4). What patterns do they notice?

In-Class Examples

For Example 1
Use counters to find 5 × (−3). **−15**

For Example 2
Use counters to find −4 × 2. **−8**

For Example 3
Use counters to find −3(−2). **6**

For Example 4
If the average daily temperature decreased by 2° F each day for a week, how much did the temperature change? **−14°F**

Teaching Tip After going over the examples, ask students to explain to each other what each model shows. Encourage questions and written demonstrations on the chalkboard.

To multiply a positive integer times another number, you *put in* that many sets. To multiply a negative integer times another number, you do the opposite or *remove* that many sets.

Examples

2 Use counters to find −2 × 3.

Step 1 Since −2 is the opposite of 2, −2 × 3 means to *remove* 2 sets of 3 positive counters. But you cannot remove counters because there are none to remove. You must first add 2 sets of 3 zero pairs. Then you can remove 2 sets of 3 positive counters.

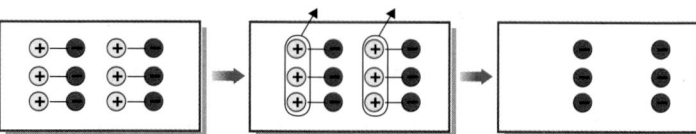

Step 2 Count the counters remaining on the mat. There are 6 negative counters. This represents −6. So, −2 × 3 = −6.

3 Use counters to find −4(−3).

Step 1 Since −4 is opposite of 4, −4(−3) means to *remove* 4 sets of 3 negative counters. But you cannot remove counters because there are none to remove. You must first add 4 sets of 3 zero pairs. Then you can remove 4 sets of 3 negative counters.

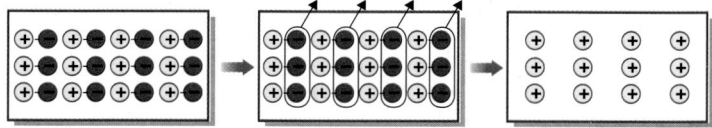

Step 2 Count the counters remaining on the mat. There are 12 positive counters. This represents 12. So, −4(−3) = 12.

CONNECTION **4** **Earth Science** The temperature drops about 7°C for each kilometer above Earth. If the temperature at ground level is 0°C, find the temperature 3 kilometers above Earth.

Explore You know the temperature drop per kilometer above Earth and the temperature at ground level. You want to know the temperature 3 kilometers above Earth.

Plan To find the temperature, multiply 3 times the amount of change per kilometer (−7).

Solve $3(-7)$ means to *put in* 3 sets of 7 negative ounters. Place these counters on the mat.

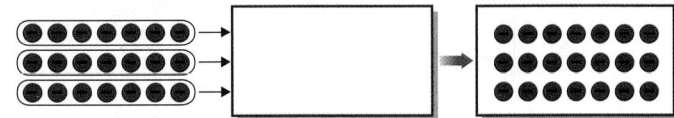

You have 21 negative counters on the mat. This represents -21. So, $3(-7) = -21$. The temperature is $-21°C$.

Examine Let a vertical number line represent a thermometer. Start at zero. Mark 3 drops of 7°. The number line indicates that the temperature will be $-21°C$. The answer is correct.

CHECK FOR UNDERSTANDING

Communicating Mathematics

Read and study the lesson to answer each question.

1. *Write* a multiplication sentence represented by the model. $-2 \times (-2) = 4$

2. *Model* -2×6 and $6 \times (-2)$. Compare and contrast these two problems. **See margin.**

Guided Practice **Find each product. Use counters or a number line if necessary.**

3. $3 \times (-1)$ **-3** 4. $-4 \times (-8)$ **32** 5. $4(-4)$ **-16** 6. $-2(5)$ **-10**

7. Find the product of -3 and -7. **21**

8. *Oceanography* A submarine is at the surface of the water. It starts to descend at a rate of 4 meters per second. How far below the surface will the submarine be after 5 seconds? **20 m below the surface**

EXERCISES

Practice **Find each product. Use counters or a number line if necessary.**

9. $-3 \times (-6)$ **18** 10. $3 \times (-8)$ **-24** 11. 7×4 **28** 12. 3×0 **0**

13. $-3(0)$ **0** 14. $5(4)$ **20** 15. $6(-3)$ **-18** 16. $9(-3)$ **-27**

17. $8(-3)$ **-24** 18. $3(-3)$ **-9** 19. $5(-5)$ **-25** 20. $7(-5)$ **-35**

Lesson 11-5 Multiplying Integers **451**

■ **Reteaching the Lesson** ■

Activity Ask students to use a number line to solve the following problem.
Alyssa has decided to have her long hair cut in stages. On each of her next 4 visits to the salon, she will have 3 inches cut. What is the total length that will be cut?
12 in.

3 PRACTICE/APPLY

Check for Understanding

If students need additional practice or instruction after completing Exercises 1–8, one of these options may be helpful.

• Extra Practice, see p. 586
• Reteaching Activity
• *Study Guide Masters*, p. 80
• *Practice Masters*, p. 80

Additional Answer

2. **See Answer Appendix for models. In -2×6, you place 2 groups of 6 zero pairs and remove 2 groups of 6 positive counters. In $6 \times (-2)$, you add 6 groups of 2 negative counters. In both problems, there are 12 negative counters on the mat at the end. The answer for both problems is -12.**

Study Guide Masters, p. 80

Lesson 11-5 **451**

4 ASSESS

Closing Activity

Writing Have pairs of students write an explanation of how they would solve the following problem. Encourage them to include drawings of counters. *A leaky faucet wastes 2 pints of water each day. How much water is wasted in 2 weeks?*

Mid-Chapter Self Test

The Mid-Chapter Self Test reviews the concepts in Lessons 11-1 through 11-5. Lesson references are given so students can review concepts not yet mastered.

Practice Masters, p. 80

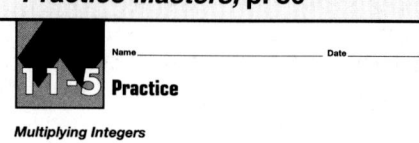

21. Find the product of 7 and −6. **−42**

22. Evaluate.
   a. −4(5 + (−9)) **16**
   b. 3(−4 − 7) **−33**

Applications and Problem Solving

Real World

23. *Pet Care* Sam is a black Labrador retriever who weighs 80 pounds. Her owner puts her on a diet.
   a. If Sam loses 3 pounds each month, how much will she lose in 4 months? **12 lb**
   b. What will Sam weigh at the end of the 4 months? **68 lb**

24. *Time* Suppose you had a watch that loses 2 minutes each day.
   a. How many minutes will it lose in a week? **14 min**
   b. How many minutes will it lose in the month of April? **60 min**

25. *Critical Thinking* The product of 1 times any number is the number itself. What is the product of −1 times any number? **the number's opposite**

Mixed Review

26. *Algebra* Find the value of $s − t$ if $s = 6$ and $t = −5$. *(Lesson 11-4)* **11**

27. *Geometry* Draw a line segment that is $2\frac{1}{2}$ inches long, and then bisect it using a straightedge and compass. *(Lesson 9-3)* **See Answer Appendix.**

28. *Standardized Test Practice* If a can of green beans weighs 13 ounces, how many pounds will a case of 24 cans weigh? *(Lesson 7-7)* **C**
   A 1.5 lb
   B 15 lb
   C 19.5 lb
   D 312 lb
   E Not Here

For **Extra Practice,** see page 586.

CHAPTER 11 — Mid-Chapter Self Test

1. *Geography* Death Valley, California, has the lowest altitude in the United States. Its elevation is 282 feet below sea level. Express the elevation of Death Valley as an integer. *(Lesson 11-1)* **−282**

Replace each ● with < , > , or = to make a true sentence. *(Lesson 11-2)*

2. +3 ● −2 **>**

3. −7 ● −3 **<**

4. 0 ● −2 **>**

Find each sum, difference, or product. Use counters or a number line if necessary. *(Lessons 11-3, 11-4, and 11-5)*

5. −4 + (−6) **−10**

6. −7 + 12 **5**

7. −9 − (−5) **−4**

8. 6 − (−5) **11**

9. −9 × 2 **−18**

10. −8(−5) **40**

452 Chapter 11 Algebra: Investigating Integers

Extending the Lesson

Enrichment Masters, p. 80

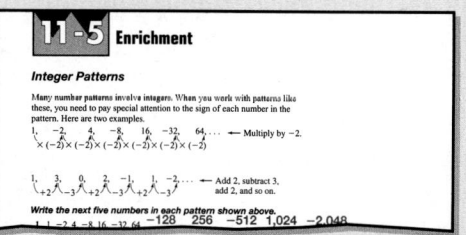

Activity Place small stacks of pennies, nickels, and dimes on your desk in the front of the classroom. Tell students the number of coins in any given stack. Ask them to calculate how many cents each stack of coins is worth. Point out that multiplying integers is a skill used in everyday life, and encourage students to name situations that use the skill.

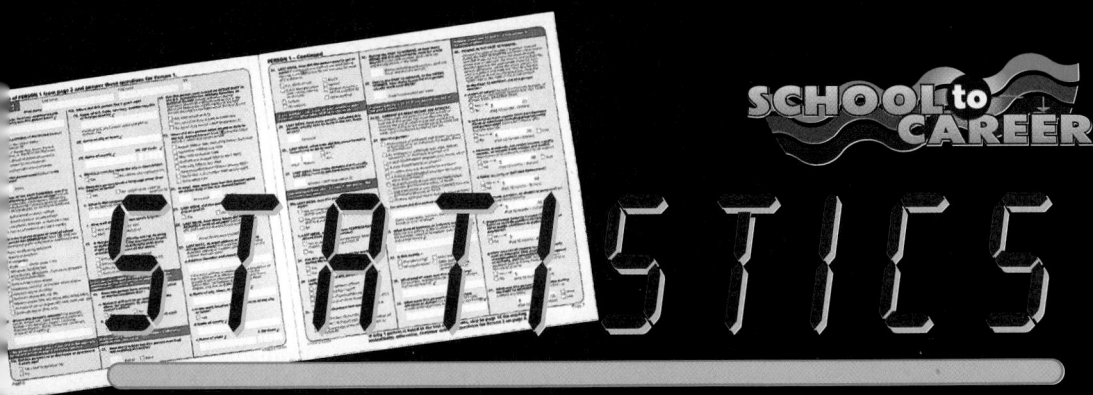

STATISTICS

SCHOOL to CAREER

Robert W. Cleveland
SURVEY STATISTICIAN

Robert Cleveland is a survey statistician for the Bureau of the Census. In the Bureau of the Census, census takers interview people and that information is given to the statisticians. Robert Cleveland works for the Income Statistics Branch of the Bureau of the Census. Each year, he works on the March Current Population Survey. This report includes information about people's jobs, income, and health.

To become a statistician, you will need at least a bachelor's degree. If you would like to become a statistician, you should take as many mathematics and computer courses as possible.

For more information:
American Statistical Association
1429 Duke Street
Alexandria, VA 22314

 inter NET
CONNECTION
www.glencoe.com/sec/
math/mac/mathnet

Someday, I'd like to study and interpret data like Robert Cleveland.

Your Turn
Find the results of a survey in a newspaper. Write a paragraph describing the data and explaining why it is important.

School to Career: Statistics **453**

Motivating Students
Statisticians work in a wide variety of industries, including consumer marketing, politics, medical research, and education. Ask students the following questions.
• Where have you seen statistics used? **sports section of a newspaper, weather data on local television newscasts, public opinion polls**
• Why would a statistician need to understand integers? **to add and subtract numerical data**

Making the Math Connection
Statisticians use math skills on a daily basis. They interpret numerical data using addition, subtraction, multiplication, and division. Often they express a given number as a percent to show how it relates to the other numbers in a set. In addition, statisticians make conclusions based on the mathematical operations they perform.

Working on *Your Turn*
Remind students that statisticians usually work with a large collection of data. Be sure the survey they select to describe contains enough information to analyze. Have students add and subtract survey results to explain the significance of the data. Encourage them to look for trends.

More About Robert W. Cleveland

• Robert Cleveland has been a survey statistician for the Bureau of the Census since 1975. In addition to writing reports, he writes computer programs for evaluating data.
• Cleveland became a statistician because he liked math and found college courses in statistics "quite interesting."

*An additional School to Career activity is available on page 11 of the **School to Career Masters.***

Objective Students solve problems by working backward.

Recommended Pacing	
Standard	Day 9 of 15
Honors	Day 7 of 13
Block	Day 5 of 8

1 FOCUS

Getting Started Have students act out the situation presented at the beginning of the lesson. Have them use a calendar to verify the dates. Then have them work in pairs to answer Exercises 1 and 2. Have the class discuss the results. Then have them solve Exercise 3.

2 TEACH

Teaching Tip Encourage students to make a diagram of their steps as they work backward through a problem. It will help keep them organized.

In-Class Example

Kyoto is 2 inches shorter than Mike. Mike is 3 inches taller than Amie and 2 inches shorter than Maren. Maren is the tallest. Amie is 53 inches tall. How tall is Maren? **58 in.**

Additional Answers

1. Callie and Nora used a calendar to locate April 15. Then they counted backward from that date the number of weeks they wanted to spend on each activity.

2. Sample answer: They could add the minimum number of weeks for each activity and then count back that number of weeks to find the latest they could start preparations. They could add the maximum number of weeks for each activity and then count back that number of weeks to find the earliest they could start preparations.

THINKING LAB

PROBLEM SOLVING

11-6A Work Backward

A Preview of Lesson 11-6

Callie and Nora want to get ready for the summer softball season that starts June 15. Before the season starts, they plan to spend 3 to 4 weeks hitting and fielding balls. Before hitting and fielding balls, they plan to spend 6 to 8 weeks running and exercising. The girls are trying to determine the latest and earliest dates to start getting ready for the season. Let's listen in!

Look at a calendar. Three weeks before June 15 is May 25 and 4 weeks before June 15 is May 18.

That means the latest we can begin hitting and fielding is May 25. The earliest we should begin is May 18.

Callie

Six weeks before May 25 is April 13. The latest we can start getting ready for the season is April 13.

Nora

Eight weeks before May 18 is March 23. We could start getting ready as early as March 23.

THINK ABOUT IT

Work with a partner. 1–2. See margin.

1. **Discuss** how using a calendar and **working backward** helped Callie and Nora plan their preparation for the softball season.

2. **Explain** how Callie and Nora could solve their problem differently.

3. **Apply** the work backward strategy to solve this problem.

   Chris and Dani volunteer at the food bank at 9:00 A.M. on Saturday mornings. It takes 30 minutes to get from Dani's house to the food bank. Chris picks up Dani, but it takes him 15 minutes to get to Dani's house. If it takes Chris 45 minutes to get ready in the morning, what is the latest Chris should get out of bed? **7:30 A.M.**

454 Chapter 11 Algebra: Investigating Integers

■ Reteaching the Lesson ■

Activity Give students index cards with a beginning number, an ending number, and several operations (add 5, multiply by 2). Have them start with the ending number and arrange the operation cards in order to get the desired beginning number.

For **Extra Practice**, see page 587.

ON YOUR OWN

4. The fourth step of the 4-step plan for problem solving tells you to *examine* your answer. *Tell* how you can check an answer to a problem solved by working backward.
4–6. See margin.

5. *Write a Problem* in which an effective strategy to solve it would be to work backward.

6. *Look Ahead* You know $-4 \times (-3) = 12$. Explain how the work-backward strategy could be used to find $12 \div (-3)$.

MIXED PROBLEM SOLVING

STRATEGIES

Look for a pattern.
Solve a simpler problem.
Act it out.
Guess and check.
Draw a diagram.
Make a chart.
Work backward.

Solve. Use any strategy.

7. *Sales* Books Galore bookstore arranges its best sellers in the front window. In how many different orders can they arrange 4 best sellers? **24 ways**

8. *Education* A multiple choice test has 10 questions. A student receives $+3$ for each question answered correctly, -1 for each question answered incorrectly, and 0 for each question not answered. **a. 19 points**

  a. Joe answered 7 questions correctly and 2 questions incorrectly. He did not answer 1 question. What is his score on the test?

  b. Mary scored 23 points on the test. How many did she answer correctly? How many did she answer incorrectly? **See margin.**

9. *Geometry* The area of a square is 49 square feet. **a. 7 ft**

  a. Find the length of each side of the square.

  b. Find the perimeter of the square. **28 ft**

10. *Life Science* A certain bacteria doubles its population every 12 hours. After 3 full days, there are 1,600 bacteria. How many bacteria were there at the beginning of the first day? **25 bacteria**

11. *Puzzles* In a magic square, each row, column, and diagonal have the same sum. Copy and complete the magic square.

-2	? 3	?-4
-3	-1	1
? 2	?-5	? 0

12. about 488 times

12. *Geography* The area of Rhode Island is 1,212 square miles. The area of Alaska is 591,004 square miles. About how many times larger is Alaska than Rhode Island?

13. *Money Matters* Gloria bought some watercolor paints and brushes. She spent $3.75 on brushes and 5 times that on paint. After paying for the items, she had $6.89 left. How much money did she have before she went shopping? **$29.39**

14. *Standardized Test Practice* Which problem does *not* have -8 as its answer? **C**

  A $-5 + (-3)$

  B $2 - 10$

  C $-4(-2)$

  D $-6 - 2$

---

3 PRACTICE/APPLY

Check for Understanding
Use the results from Exercise 3 to determine whether students understand how to solve problems by working backward.

Extra Practice If students need additional practice in problem solving, extra practice is available on the following pages.
• Work Backward, see p. 587
• Mixed Problem Solving, see pp. 593–594

Assignment Guide
All: 4–14

4 ASSESS

Closing Activity
Writing Have students write a brief explanation of how to solve a problem by working backward for a student who missed the lesson.

Additional Answers
4. Start with the answer and then work forward. If the final result checks with the problem, the answer is correct.

5. Sample answer: Sue has a dental appointment at 3:30 P.M. She wants to get there 10 minutes early. If it takes 40 minutes to drive to the dentist's office, what time should she leave her house for the appointment?

6. Division is the opposite of multiplication. Therefore, if $-4 \times (-3) = 12$, $12 \div (-3) = -4$.

8b. 8 questions; 1 question

▪ Extending the Lesson ▪

Activity Have small groups of students use the results of Olympic games to create word problems that can be solved by working backward. Ask them to display their problems with illustrations or photographs on the bulletin board. Suggested sources for statistics are magazines and almanacs.

Instructional Resources

- *Study Guide Masters*, p. 81
- *Practice Masters*, p. 81
- *Enrichment Masters*, p. 81
- Transparencies 11-6, A and B
- *Assessment and Evaluation Masters*, p. 296
- *Diversity Masters*, p. 11
- *Technology Masters*, p. 21

 CD-ROM Program
- Resource Lesson 11-6

Recommended Pacing	
Standard	Day 10 of 15
Honors	Day 8 of 13
Block	Day 5 of 8

1 FOCUS

 5-Minute Check
(Lesson 11-5)

Find each product. Use counters or a number line if necessary.

1. $4 \times (-6)$ **−24**
2. $-7 \times (-4)$ **28**
3. $-5(3)$ **−15**
4. $-2(-9)$ **18**
5. $-5(5)$ **−25**

The 5-Minute Check is also available on **Transparency 11-6A** for this lesson.

Motivating the Lesson

Problem Solving Remind students that $6 \div 3 = 2$ because $2 \times 3 = 6$. Have them write related sentences for these problems:
$15 \div 3 \qquad 24 \div 6 \qquad 36 \div 2$
$5 \times 3 = 15 \quad 4 \times 6 = 24 \quad 18 \times 2 = 36$

2 TEACH

 Transparency 11-6B contains a teaching aid for this lesson.

Using Connections
Review the inverse operations of multiplication and division. Then ask students what multiplication expression can help them find the quotient $12 \div (-6)$. $-2 \times (-6) = 12$

Dividing Integers

11-6

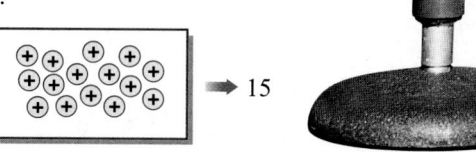

What you'll learn
You'll learn to divide integers using models and patterns.

When am I ever going to use this?
Knowing how to divide integers can help you to find the mean of data with negative integers.

A radio station plans to play 15 minutes of music with no interruptions. How many 3-minute recordings can be played during this time?

To answer this question, you must divide 15 by 3. You can model this division problem using counters.

Step 1 Place 15 positive counters on the mat to represent 15.

 → 15

Step 2 Separate the 15 counters into 3 equal-sized groups.

 → $15 \div 3 = 5$

There are 3 groups of 5 positive counters each. So, $15 \div 3 = 5$. The station can play 5 recordings during the 15 minutes.

You can use counters to divide a negative integer by a positive integer.

Example **1** Use counters to find $-20 \div 5$.

Step 1 Place 20 negative counters on the mat to represent -20.

Step 2 Separate the 20 counters into 5 equal-sized groups.

There are 5 groups of 4 negative counters each. So, $-20 \div 5 = -4$.

You can also divide integers by *working backward*. For example, to find $56 \div 7$, think "what number times 7 equals 56?"

$8 \times 7 = 56$, so $56 \div 7 = 8$. *The quotient is positive.*

Examples

2 Find $-10 \div (-2)$.

$5 \times (-2) = -10$, so $-10 \div (-2) = 5$. *The quotient is positive.*

3 Find $18 \div (-6)$.

$-3 \times (-6) = 18$, so $18 \div (-6) = -3$. *The quotient is negative.*

4 Find $-28 \div 7$.

$-4 \times 7 = -28$, so $-28 \div 7 = -4$. *The quotient is negative.*

Do you notice any patterns in Examples 1–4? Notice that when you divide two positive integers or two negative integers, the quotient is positive. When you divide a negative integer and a positive integer, the quotient is negative.

Example 5

Sports For each lap of a race, Angeleila was farther behind Paloma. Angeleila finished the race 12 meters behind Paloma. Both runners ran 4 laps. On average, how many meters did Angeleila fall behind each lap?

Represent Angeleila's final position with respect to Paloma as -12. You need to find $-12 \div 4$.

$-3 \times 4 = -12$, so $-12 \div 4 = -3$.

Angeleila lost 3 meters per lap.

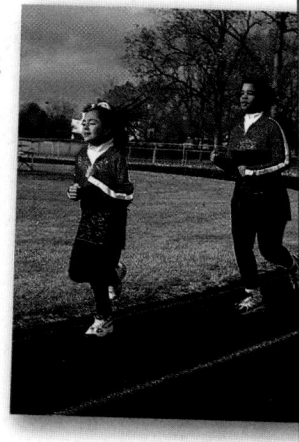

Did you know? A male sprinter can run about 22 miles per hour. An African elephant can run 25 miles per hour, and a cheetah can run 62 miles per hour.

Teaching Tip Before Example 1, review the signs of the products when multiplying two integers.

In-Class Examples

For Example 1
Use counters to find $-18 \div 3$.
-6

For Example 2
Find $-16 \div (-4)$. **4**

For Example 3
Find $9 \div (-3)$. **-3**

For Example 4
Find $-25 \div 5$. **-5**

For Example 5
The Bobcat football team was given penalties for a total loss of 20 yards. What was the yardage lost on each penalty if 4 equal penalties were called on the Bobcats? **-5**

---

3 PRACTICE/APPLY

Check for Understanding

If students need additional practice or instruction after completing Exercises 1–8, one of these options may be helpful.
- Extra Practice, see p. 587
- Reteaching Activity
- *Study Guide Masters*, p. 81
- *Practice Masters*, p. 81

Study Guide Masters, p. 81

CHECK FOR UNDERSTANDING

Communicating Mathematics

1. $-9 \div 3 = -3$

2. a positive number

Read and study the lesson to answer each question.

1. **Write** a division sentence represented by the model.

2. **Describe** the quotient of two negative integers.

Lesson 11-6 Dividing Integers **457**

■ Reteaching the Lesson ■

Activity Have pairs of students use counters and integer mats to make up word problems dealing with division of integers. Suggest that problems can involve temperature, time, distance, or money to include positive and negative integers. Have pairs exchange and complete each others' problems.

Assignment Guide

Core: 9–23 odd, 25–28
Enriched: 10–22 even, 23–28

4 ASSESS

Closing Activity

Modeling Have students work in small groups. Review factors. Then ask them to divide 24 negative counters into 3 equal groups and write the division sentence. Continue with other factors of 24.

Chapter 11, Quiz C (Lessons 11-5 and 11-6) is available in the *Assessment and Evaluation Masters*, p. 296.

Additional Answers

3a. Sample answer: $-5 \times (-3) = 15$; $15 \div (-5) = -3$ and $15 \div (-3) = -5$

3b. Sample answer: $4 \times (-6) = -24$; $-24 \div 4 = -6$ and $-24 \div (-6) = 4$

Practice Masters, p. 81

11-6 Practice

Dividing Integers

Find each quotient. Use counters or patterns if necessary.

1. $56 \div (-7)$ **−8**	2. $-45 \div 9$ **−5**	3. $-72 \div (-6)$ **12**
4. $60 \div (-4)$ **−15**	5. $-38 \div 2$ **−19**	6. $-51 \div (-3)$ **17**
7. $48 \div (-8)$ **−6**	8. $-80 \div 5$ **−16**	9. $-91 \div (-7)$ **13**
10. $36 \div (-9)$ **−4**	11. $-42 \div 3$ **−14**	12. $-54 \div (-6)$ **9**
13. $110 \div (-10)$ **−11**	14. $-126 \div 7$ **−18**	15. $-35 \div (-5)$ **7**
16. $-27 \div 9$ **−3**	17. $104 \div (-8)$ **−13**	18. $-32 \div (-16)$ **2**
19. $-68 \div 4$ **−17**	20. $-120 \div (-8)$ **15**	21. $-84 \div (-6)$ **14**
22. $132 \div (-11)$ **−12**	23. $49 \div (-7)$ **−7**	24. $-18 \div 2$ **−9**
25. $30 \div (-3)$ **−10**	26. $-75 \div (-15)$ **5**	27. $-28 \div 14$ **−2**
28. $-116 \div (-29)$ **4**	29. $256 \div (-32)$ **−8**	30. $-144 \div 24$ **−6**

© Glencoe/McGraw-Hill   T81   *Mathematics: Applications and Connections, Course 1*

458 Chapter 11

Math Journal

3a. *Write* a multiplication sentence with two negative factors. Then, write two related division sentences. **See margin.**

b. *Write* a multiplication sentence with one positive factor and one negative factor. Then, write two related division sentences. **See margin.**

Guided Practice

Find each quotient. Use counters or patterns if necessary.

4. $16 \div 2$ **8**   **5.** $18 \div (-9)$ **−2**   **6.** $-27 \div 3$ **−9**   **7.** $-81 \div (-9)$ **9**

8. descent of 4 meters per second

8. *Oceanography* In an undersea exhibition, a self-contained module started at sea level. It descended to a depth of 24 meters. If this descent took 6 seconds, what was the rate of descent?

EXERCISES

Practice

Find each quotient. Use counters or patterns if necessary.

9. $12 \div 6$ **2**   **10.** $24 \div (-8)$ **−3**   **11.** $-36 \div 9$ **−4**   **12.** $-8 \div (-2)$ **4**
13. $-35 \div 7$ **−5**   **14.** $32 \div (-4)$ **−8**   **15.** $-15 \div (-5)$ **3**   **16.** $-12 \div (-2)$ **6**
17. $45 \div (-5)$ **−9**   **18.** $-40 \div 8$ **−5**   **19.** $36 \div (-6)$ **−6**   **20.** $-42 \div (-7)$ **6**

21. Evaluate.

   a. $\dfrac{(-3 + (-7))}{2}$ **−5**   **b.** $\dfrac{(4 + (-6))(-1 + 7)}{-3}$ **4**

22. *Algebra* Find the value of $r \div n$ if $r = -12$ and $n = -6$. **2**

Applications and Problem Solving

interNET CONNECTION

For the latest air pollution statistics, visit: www.glencoe.com/sec/math/mac/mathnet

23. *Football* The Madison Middle School football team lost 12 yards in 3 plays. If the team lost an equal amount on each play, how many yards were lost on each play? **loss of 4 yd per play**

24. *Environment* The graph shows the change of the concentration of pollutants and small particles in the air. What is the mean percent change of these pollutants and particles? **−3%**

Change in Pollutants

−2% Nitrogen dioxide   +2% Ozone   −3% Particulate matter   −11% Lead   −1% Sulfur dioxide

Source: EPA

25. Sample answers: $14 \div (-2) = -7$, $-21 \div 3 = -7$, $28 \div (-4) = -7$, $-35 \div 5 = -7$

25. *Critical Thinking* Write four different division problems with a quotient of -7.

Mixed Review

26. Standardized Test Practice A diver is descending at the rate of 4 meters per minute. How far below the surface will the diver be in 8 minutes? *(Lesson 11-5)* **D**

   A 2 m   **B** 4 m   **C** 12 m   **D** 32 m

For **Extra Practice,** see page 587.

27. Estimate 31% of 15. *(Lesson 8-6)* **Sample answer: 5**

28. Find the value of ten plus five divided by five. *(Lesson 1-4)* **11**

458 Chapter 11 Algebra: Investigating Integers

Extending the Lesson

Enrichment Masters, p. 81

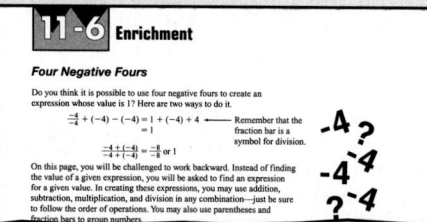

11-6 Enrichment

Four Negative Fours

Do you think it is possible to use four negative fours to create an expression whose value is 1? Here are two ways to do it.

$\dfrac{-4}{-4} + (-4) - (-4) = 1 + (-4) + 4$ ← Remember that the fraction bar is a symbol for division.
$= 1$

$\dfrac{-4 + (-4)}{-4 + (-4)} = \dfrac{-8}{-8}$ or 1

On this page, you will be challenged to work backward. Instead of finding the value of a given expression, you will be asked to find an expression for a given value. In creating these expressions, you may use addition, subtraction, multiplication, and division in any combination—just be sure to follow the order of operations. You may also use parentheses and fraction bars to group numbers.

Activity Have students solve the following problem. *A steel drill bit was attached to the end of 30-ft sections of steel to drill for oil. About how many sections were needed to drill 23,077 feet below the surface of the Pacific Ocean?* **770 sections**

Integration: Geometry
The Coordinate System

What you'll learn

You'll learn to graph ordered pairs of numbers on a coordinate grid.

When am I ever going to use this?

Knowing how to locate points on a coordinate grid can help you locate places on maps.

Word Wise

coordinate system
coordinate grid
origin
x-axis
y-axis
quadrants
ordered pairs
x-coordinate
y-coordinate

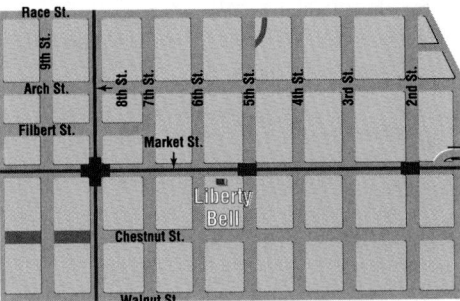

Patrick is studying the map of Philadelphia, Pennsylvania. He wants to take the subway to visit the Liberty Bell. He notices that there is a subway station located at the intersection of Market Street and 5th Street.

Similarly, points can be located on a coordinate system.

A **coordinate system**, or **coordinate grid**, consists of a horizontal number line and a vertical number line that intersect at their zero points. The point of intersection is called the **origin**. The horizontal line is called the **x-axis**, and the vertical line is called the **y-axis**.

The *x*-axis and *y*-axis divide the coordinate system into four **quadrants**. Point *P* is located in the fourth quadrant. It can be named by the **ordered pair** $(3, -5)$. The first number in the ordered pair is the **x-coordinate**, and the second number is the **y-coordinate**.

Example

LOOK BACK
You can refer to Lesson 2-9 to review graphing ordered pairs in the first quadrant.

1 Name the ordered pair for point *A* and identify its quadrant.

- Start at 0. Move left along the *x*-axis until you are directly under point *A*. Since you moved four units to the left, the first coordinate of the ordered pair is -4.

- Now, move up parallel to the *y*-axis until you reach point *A*. Since you moved up 3 units, the second coordinate of the ordered pair is 3.

- The ordered pair for point *A* is $(-4, 3)$. Point *A* is in the second quadrant.

Lesson 11-7 Integration: Geometry   The Coordinate System   **459**

Multiple Learning Styles

Kinesthetic Have each group of three students use sidewalk chalk to draw a coordinate system outdoors. Have two students stand on the grid while the third names their locations with ordered pairs. Then have the third student name two ordered pairs and the other two students find those locations. Switch roles.

MathPASS CD-ROM

This CD-ROM offers a complete, self-paced mathematics curriculum. Each lesson includes a pretest, tutorial, guided practice, and posttest. MathPASS Lesson 38 is correlated to this Student Edition lesson.
For Windows & Macintosh

Instructional Resources

- *Study Guide Masters*, p. 82
- *Practice Masters*, p. 82
- *Enrichment Masters*, p. 82
- Transparencies 11-7, A and B
- *Hands-On Lab Masters*, p. 79
- *Technology Masters*, p. 22
- CD-ROM Program
  - Resource Lesson 11-7
  - Extended Activity 11-7

Recommended Pacing	
Standard	Day 11 of 15
Honors	Day 9 of 13
Block	Day 6 of 8

1 FOCUS

5-Minute Check
(Lesson 11-6)

Find each quotient. Use counters or patterns if necessary.

1. $39 \div (-3)$ -13
2. $-42 \div 6$ -7
3. $-22 \div (-2)$ 11
4. $27 \div (-9)$ -3
5. $-32 \div 8$ -4

The 5-Minute Check is also available on **Transparency 11-7A** for this lesson.

Motivating the Lesson

Communication Ask students to determine whether each set of numbers is positive or negative.

- *y*-coordinates above the *x*-axis? **positive**
  below the *x*-axis? **negative**
- *x*-coordinates right of the *y*-axis? **positive**
  left of the *y*-axis? **negative**

2 TEACH

Transparency 11-7B contains a teaching aid for this lesson.

Reading Mathematics Have students translate ordered pairs into verbal directions to locate a point. For example, $(-2, 3)$ means "from the origin, go 2 units left and 3 units up."

Lesson 11-7   459

You can also graph a point on a coordinate grid. To graph a point means to place a dot at the point named by an ordered pair.

Examples

2 Graph *B*(−3, −4).
• Start at 0. Move 3 units to the left on the *x*-axis.
• Then move 4 units down parallel to the *y*-axis to locate the point.
• Place a dot and label the dot *B*.

3 Graph *C*(0, 1), *D*(5, 1), *E*(3, −2), and *F*(−2, −2).
a. Draw $\overline{CD}$, $\overline{DE}$, $\overline{EF}$, and $\overline{FC}$.
b. Describe the figure formed.

a. Locate the points and draw the segments.
b. The figure formed looks like a parallelogram.

CHECK FOR UNDERSTANDING

Communicating Mathematics

Read and study the lesson to answer each question.

1. **Tell** how to graph the ordered pair (−3, 6). **See margin.**
2. **Draw** a coordinate grid. **a–b. See Answer Appendix.**
   a. **Identify** the portion(s) of the grid where the points are named by coordinates that are both negative. Color the portion(s) blue.
   b. **Identify** the portion(s) of the grid where the points are named by coordinates with one negative number and one positive number. Color the portion(s) red.

Guided Practice

Name the ordered pair for each point.
3. *P* **(3, 1)**   4. *Q* **(0, 2)**
5. *R* **(−3, −2)**   6. *S* **(4, −2)**

Graph and label each point. 7–9. See Answer Appendix.
7. *T*(1, −4)   8. *U*(−3, −2)   9. *V*(−4, 5)

10. **Maps** Refer to the map at the beginning of the lesson. If the location of the station at Market Street and 8th Street is at (0, 0), what are the coordinates of the station nearest the Liberty Bell? **(3, 0)**

▪ Reteaching the Lesson ▪

Activity Display a grid with the following points graphed and labeled: *A*(−4, 4), *B*(−4, 2), *C*(−2, 1), *D*(1, 2), *E*(3, 3), *F*(−2, −2), *G*(−3, −4), *H*(3, −2), and *I*(4, −3). Give students clues to help them name the points. For example, for point *D*, "Both of the coordinates are positive. The *y*-coordinate is not 3."

Additional Answer

1. Start at 0. Move 3 units to the left on the *x*-axis. Then move 6 units up parallel to the *y*-axis to locate the point. Place a dot at this location and label the point.

EXERCISES

Practice

Name the ordered pair for each point.

11. A $(-3, 1)$ **12.** B $(1, 1)$ **13.** C $(4, -3)$

14. D $(1, -4)$ **15.** E $(2, 3)$ **16.** F $(0, 3)$

17. G $(0, -2)$ **18.** H $(-4, -2)$ **19.** I $(-2, -3)$

20. J $(-2, 0)$ **21.** K $(-4, 4)$ **22.** M $(-2, -1)$

Graph and label each point. 23–30. See Answer Appendix.

23. $N(2, -2)$ **24.** $P(5, 2)$ **25.** $Q(-5, -5)$ **26.** $R(0, 4)$

27. $S(-2, 3)$ **28.** $T(-1, -5)$ **29.** $V(-5, 0)$ **30.** $W(1, 3)$

31a. See Answer Appendix.

31. a. Graph $X(-1, -5)$, $Y(0, -2)$, and $Z(1, 1)$ on the same coordinate grid.
  b. Are points X, Y, and Z in the same line? **yes**

Applications and Problem Solving

32a. See students' work.

32b. yes; on the Equator just south and west of Nigeria in the Atlantic Ocean

34. See students' work; 0.

32. *Geography* Longitude and latitude are used to locate places on a map.
  a. Find the longitude and latitude of the place where you live.
  b. Is there a place with a longitude of 0 and a latitude of 0? If so, where is it?

33. *Weather* Use the chart to form ordered pairs where the day is the x-coordinate and the temperature is the y-coordinate. Graph the point named by each ordered pair. **(1, −5), (2, −3), (3, 0), (4, 5), (5, 8); See Answer Appendix.**

Day	1	2	3	4	5
Temperature (°F)	−5	−3	0	5	8

34. *Working on the* CHAPTER *Project* Refer to the map of the United States you made on page 433. For each state that had a change in the number of members to the House of Representatives, represent the data on a line plot showing positive and negative integers. What is the total change in the number of members in the House of Representatives?

35a–d. See Answer Appendix.

35. *Critical Thinking* On a coordinate grid, graph and label each point.
  a. $A\left(2\frac{1}{2}, 3\frac{3}{4}\right)$ **b.** $B\left(4\frac{1}{4}, \frac{1}{2}\right)$ **c.** $C(0.5, 1.8)$ **d.** $D(-2.3, -1.5)$

Mixed Review

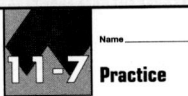

36. Solve $-24 \div 8 = t$. *(Lesson 11-6)* **−3**

37. Standardized Test Practice Is an angle that measures $92°$ *acute*, *right*, *obtuse*, or *straight*? *(Lesson 9-1)* **C**
  A acute   **B** right
  C obtuse   **D** straight

38. Sample answer: 22

38. Estimate $18\frac{3}{16} + 4\frac{1}{9}$. *(Lesson 6-2)*

39. *Statistics* Find Rita's mean golf score for the season if she played 9 times and her scores were 84, 88, 78, 79, 84, 84, 86, 83, and 81. *(Lesson 2-7)* **83**

For **Extra Practice**, see page 587.

CHAPTER Project

Exercise 34 asks students to advance to the next stage of work on the Chapter Project. You may wish to have students work in groups to complete their line plots.

4 ASSESS

Closing Activity

Speaking Have pairs of students draw a coordinate grid complete with positive and negative numbers. Ask them to graph a point with a negative x-coordinate and a positive y-coordinate. Have students explain the meaning of the negative sign.

Practice Masters, p. 82

11-7 Practice

Integration: Geometry
The Coordinate System

Name the ordered pair for each point.

1. K $(1, 3)$ 2. L $(-3, -4)$
3. M $(5, -2)$ 4. N $(-4, 1)$
5. O $(-1, -5)$ 6. P $(2, -4)$
7. Q $(-3, 5)$ 8. R $(5, 2)$
9. S $(-2, 4)$ 10. T $(-2, -3)$
11. U $(4, 4)$ 12. V $(3, -5)$
13. W $(3, 5)$ 14. X $(4, -1)$
15. Y $(-1, 3)$ 16. Z $(-4, -2)$

Graph and label each point on the coordinate grid below.

17. $A(-5, 2)$ 18. $I(2, 1)$
19. $J(1, -3)$ 20. $B(-5, -1)$
21. $C(3, 3)$ 22. $K(-1, 2)$
23. $L(0, -1)$ 24. $D(2, -5)$
25. $E(3, -2)$ 26. $M(-4, -5)$
27. $N(1, 5)$ 28. $F(-2, 5)$
29. $G(-1, -4)$ 30. $O(5, -5)$
31. $P(-3, 4)$ 32. $H(0, 4)$

© Glencoe/McGraw-Hill   T82   *Mathematics: Applications and Connections, Course 1*

Extending the Lesson

Enrichment Masters, p. 82

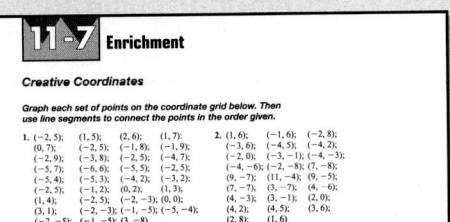

11-7 Enrichment

Creative Coordinates

Graph each set of points on the coordinate grid below. Then use line segments to connect the points in the order given.

Activity Have students use a United States atlas to find three cities that are on or very near the intersection of grid lines. Then, for each city, have them write the latitude and longitude as an ordered pair. For example, New Orleans, Louisiana, is at (40°N, 75°W). You may wish to have students find cities around the world using a world atlas.

GET READY

Objective Students find transformations by using patty paper.

Optional Resources

Hands-On Lab Masters
• worksheet, p. 65

Manipulative Kit
• scissors

MANAGEMENT TIPS

Recommended Time
45 minutes

Getting Started Ask students to read the opening paragraph of the lab. Then use overhead transparency shapes to review geometric figures. Demonstrate transformations.

Activity 1 has students perform a translation. Have students compare their translations with others. Encourage them to ask questions such as the following. *Are the translations the same? If not, how are they different?* **same if** ***B*** **is in the same place**

 patty paper

 scissors

 notebook paper

11-8A **Patty Paper Transformations**

A Preview of Lesson 11-8

Coordinate grids can be used to graph *transformations*, or movements, of figures. This lab will help you understand two types of transformations, *translations* and *reflections*.

TRY THIS

Work with a partner.

❶ To model one type of transformation, follow these steps.

• Draw triangle *A* and point *B* on a sheet of notebook paper. Line up the bottom of triangle *A* with a line on your notebook paper.

• Place a piece of patty paper on top of triangle *A*.
• Trace triangle *A* onto the patty paper.

• Slowly slide the traced triangle to point *B*. Be sure the bottom of the traced triangle slides along the line on your notebook paper. Stop when the top vertex of triangle *A* is on point *B*.

• Draw over the traced triangle. (You will need to press down fairly hard with your pen so that you can see the imprint on your notebook paper.) Then remove the patty paper.
• Trace over this imprint on your notebook paper with your pen. This movement is called a *translation*, or slide, of triangle *A*.

ON YOUR OWN

1. Describe what happened when you made the translation. **The position of the triangle is changed.**
2. How does triangle *A* compare with the new triangle? Is it congruent or similar? **They have the same size and shape; congruent and similar.**

462 Chapter 11 Algebra: Investigating Integers

TRY THIS

Work with a partner.

2 To model another type of transformation, follow these steps.

- Draw triangle *C* and line *m* on a sheet of notebook paper.

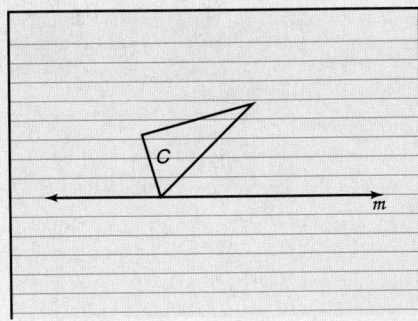

- Place a piece of patty paper on top of your drawing.
- Trace triangle *C* and line *m* onto the patty paper.

- Lift the patty paper up. Turn the patty paper upside down, toward your body. Lay the patty paper on your notebook paper so that line *m* on your patty paper is lined up with the line *m* on your notebook paper.

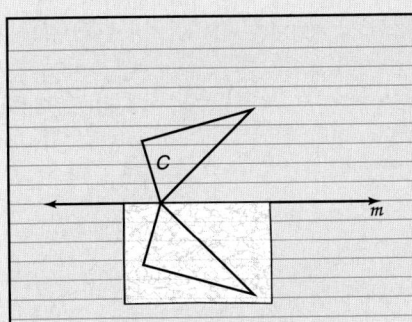

- Draw over the traced triangle, then remove the patty paper.
- Trace over this imprint on your notebook paper with your pen. This movement is called a *reflection*, or flip, of triangle *C*.

3. The new figure is the mirror image of triangle *C*.
4. They are the same size and shape, but are in opposite position.

ON YOUR OWN

3. Describe what happened when you made a reflection.
4. How does triangle *C* compare with the new triangle?
5. **Look Ahead** Look at the clothing you and the other students are wearing. Can you find any patterns in the fabric that have used translations or reflections? Sketch these patterns. **See students' work.**

Lesson 11-8A **HANDS-ON LAB** 463

Math Journal Have students write a paragraph explaining what they have learned about translations and reflections.

ASSESS

Have students complete Exercises 1–4. Watch for students who confuse translation and reflection.

Use Exercise 5 to determine whether students can recognize transformations.

Hands-On Lab Masters, p. 65

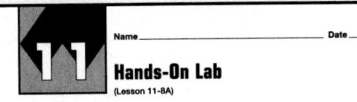

Instructional Resources

- *Study Guide Masters,* p. 83
- *Practice Masters,* p. 83
- *Enrichment Masters,* p. 83
- *Transparencies 11-8, A and B*
- *Assessment and Evaluation Masters,* p. 296

 CD-ROM Program
- Resource Lesson 11-8

Recommended Pacing	
Standard	Days 12 & 13 of 15
Honors	Days 10 & 11 of 13
Block	Day 7 of 8

1 FOCUS

5-Minute Check
(Lesson 11-7)

Name the ordered pair for each point.

1. *A* (−3, 2)
2. *B* (1, −2)
3. *C* (0, 1)

Graph each point.

4. *D*(−2, −4) 5. *E*(1, −3)

 The 5-Minute Check is also available on **Transparency 11-8A** for this lesson.

Motivating the Lesson

Hands-On Activity Various patterns of cloth, wallpaper, art, and so on will be needed. Give each small group a pattern and ask them how translations and reflections could be used to make the item.

11-8

Integration: Geometry
Graphing Transformations

You'll learn to graph transformations on a coordinate grid.

When am I ever going to use this?

Knowing about transformations can help you do computer animations.

Word Wise
transformation
translation
reflection

The Zapotec Indians in Mexico weave colorful tepetes. Tepetes (tah-PAY-tays) are used as rugs and wall hangings.

A **transformation** is a movement of a figure. What transformations do you see in the design of the tepete?

In Hands-On Lab 11-8A, you learned about two kinds of transformations, a **translation** and a **reflection**.

When you slide a figure from one location to another without changing its size or shape, the new figure is called a *translation image.*

When you flip a figure over a line without changing its size or shape, the new figure is called a *reflection image.*

Study Hint

Reading Math The notation A′ is read as A prime. A′ is a point related to point A.

HANDS-ON
MINI-LAB

Work with a partner. grid paper   scissors

Try This

- On grid paper, draw a coordinate grid.
- Graph points $A(-2, 3)$, $B(-1, 1)$, and $C(-3, 1)$.
- Connect the points to make $\triangle ABC$.
- On a separate sheet of paper, trace $\triangle ABC$ and cut it out.
- Place the cut-out triangle on $\triangle ABC$.
- Slide the cut-out triangle 5 units right. Label the new vertices $A′$, $B′$, and $C′$. Then draw $\triangle A′B′C′$.

Talk About It 1. $A′(3, 3)$, $B′(4, 1)$, $C′(2, 1)$

1. What are the coordinates of $A′$, $B′$, and $C′$?
2. What can you say about $\triangle ABC$ and $\triangle A′B′C′$? **See margin.**

Additional Answer for the Mini-Lab

2. $\triangle A′B′C′$ is a translation of $\triangle ABC$. They are the same size and shape.

Example ———— **1**

The vertices of rectangle *DEFG* are *D*(−2, −3), *E*(−2, 1), *F*(−4, 1) and *G*(−4, −3). On a coordinate grid, draw rectangle *DEFG* and its translation image that is 5 units right and 2 units up.

- On grid paper, draw a coordinate grid.

- Graph and label the vertices of rectangle *DEFG*.

- Draw rectangle *DEFG*.

- Translate each vertex 5 units to the right and 2 units up. The coordinates of the new vertices are *D*′(3, −1), *E*′(3, 3), *F*′(1, 3), and *G*′(1, −1).

- Label the new vertices *D*′, *E*′, *F*′, and *G*′.

- Then draw rectangle *D*′*E*′*F*′*G*′.

You can also graph reflections on a coordinate grid.

MINI-LAB

Work with a partner.　　grid paper　　geomirror

Try This

- On grid paper, draw a coordinate grid.
- Graph points *R*(−3, 2), *S*(0, 3), and *T*(0, 1).
- Connect the points to make △*RST*.
- Place a geomirror on the *y*-axis. Draw the reflection of △*RST* you see on the other side of the *y*-axis.
- Label the new vertices *R*′, *S*′, and *T*′.

Talk About It 1–3. See margin.

1. What are the coordinates of *R*′, *S*′, and *T*′?

2. What can you say about △*RST* and △*R*′*S*′*T*′?

3. How is using a geomirror like flipping a piece of patty paper?

Transparency 11-8B contains a teaching aid for this lesson.

Using the Mini-Labs Point out that in the Mini-Lab on page 464, students make a translation image and in the Mini-Lab on page 465, students make a reflection image. In the second Mini-Lab, if geomirrors or other reflective surfaces are unavailable, have students count the squares on the grid to draw the reflection.

In-Class Example

For Example 1
The vertices of square *RSTU* are *R*(−3, 3), *S*(1, 3), *T*(1, −1), and *U*(−3, −1). On a coordinate grid, draw the square *RSTU* and its translation image that is 2 units right and 2 units down.

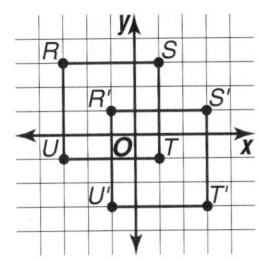

Additional Answers for the Mini-Lab

1. *R*′(3, 2), *S*′(0, 3), *T*′(0, 1)

2. △*R*′*S*′*T*′ is a reflection of △*RST*. They are the same size and shape but are mirror images of each other.

3. Both show the reflection of a shape.

Teaching Tip Before Example 2, review the characteristics of a parallelogram.

In-Class Example

For Example 2

The vertices of parallelogram *JKLM* are *J*(2, 5), *K*(5, 5), *L*(4, 2), and *M*(1, 2). On a coordinate grid, draw the parallelogram *JKLM* and its reflection image over the *y*-axis.

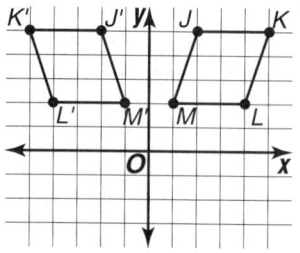

3 PRACTICE/APPLY

Check for Understanding

If students need additional practice or instruction after completing Exercises 1–7, one of these options may be helpful.
• Extra Practice, see p. 588
• Reteaching Activity
• *Study Guide Masters*, p. 83
• *Practice Masters*, p. 83

Study Guide Masters, p. 83

Example ➋ The vertices of parallelogram *WXYZ* are *W*(−2, 1), *X*(−1, 3), *Y*(4, 3), and *Z*(3, 1). On a coordinate grid, draw parallelogram *WXYZ* and its reflection image over the *x*-axis.

• On grid paper, draw a coordinate grid.
• Graph and label the vertices of parallelogram *WXYZ*.
• Draw parallelogram *WXYZ*.
• Reflect the parallelogram by flipping it onto the other side of the *x*-axis. To be a mirror image, each new vertex must be the same distance from the *x*-axis as its corresponding vertex. The coordinates of the new vertices are *W'*(−2, −1), *X'*(−1, −3), *Y'*(4, −3), and *Z'*(3, −1).
• Label the vertices *W'*, *X'*, *Y'*, and *Z'*.
• Draw parallelogram *W'X'Y'Z'*.

2. Translate each vertex of the polygon 6 units left. Then draw the translation image using the new vertices.

CHECK FOR UNDERSTANDING

Communicating Mathematics

Read and study the lesson to answer each question.

1. *Compare and contrast* a translation and a reflection. **See Answer Appendix.**

2. *Explain* how to translate a polygon on a coordinate grid 6 units to the left.

HANDS-ON MATH

3. The vertices of rectangle *ABCD* are *A*(1, −2), *B*(1, −4), *C*(4, −4), and *D*(4, −2). Draw rectangle *ABCD* on a coordinate grid. **a–b. See Answer Appendix.**

   a. On a separate sheet of paper, trace rectangle *ABCD* and cut it out. Place the cut-out rectangle on rectangle *ABCD*. Slide the cut-out rectangle 5 units up. Draw the translation image.

   b. Use a geomirror to reflect rectangle *ABCD* over the *y*-axis.

Guided Practice

4. Tell whether the transformation of △*ABC* to △*A'B'C'* is a *translation* or a *reflection*. **translation**

The vertices of △*EFG* are *E*(−3, 2), *F*(−3, 0), and *G*(0, 0). On a coordinate grid, draw △*EFG* and each transformation image.

5. translation image that is 4 units left and 5 units up **See Answer Appendix.**

6. reflection image over the *y*-axis **See Answer Appendix.**

466 Chapter 11 Algebra: Investigating Integers

Reteaching the Lesson

Activity Use color transparencies of geometric figures on an overhead projector to model transformations on a coordinate grid. For example, show a colored triangle on a grid and ask students to identify and label its vertices. Flip the triangle on an axis to show its reflection. Ask students to identify and label the reflection's vertices.

Error Analysis

Watch for students who reflect figures instead of translating them and vice versa.

Prevent by discussing the meanings of the terms and by reviewing the procedures for each.

7. Nature What type of transformation(s) do you see in the picture of the mountains and the lake? Explain your answer. **Reflection; the mountains are reflected in the lake.**

EXERCISES

Practice Tell whether each transformation is a *translation* or a *reflection*.

8.
reflection

9.
reflection

10.
translation

The vertices of △MNP are M(2, 1), N(2, 3), and P(4, 4). On a coordinate grid, draw △MNP and each transformation image.

11. translation image that is 7 units down   **11–16. See Answer Appendix.**

12. translation image that is 6 units left

13. translation image that is 3 units right and 4 units up

14. translation image that is 2 units left and 5 units down

15. reflection image over the *x*-axis

16. reflection image over the *y*-axis

Applications and Problem Solving

17. *Art* What type of transformation(s) do you see in the drawing by M. C. Escher? Explain your answer.

18. *Design* Draw a pattern for wrapping paper that uses both a translation and a reflection. **See Answer Appendix.**

17. Translations; the winged horses are translations of each other.

19. *Critical Thinking* The first coordinate of each vertex of a polygon is multiplied by −1. The image of the polygon having these new coordinates is drawn. Describe the relationship between the original polygon and its image. **The image is a reflection of the polygon over the y-axis.**

Source: © M.C. Escher/Cordon Art–Baarn–Holland Collection Haags Gemeentemuseum–The Hague

Mixed Review

20. *Geometry* Graph A(2, −3) and B(−3, 2). *(Lesson 11-7)* **See Answer Appendix.**

21. **Standardized Test Practice** An architect made an 8-inch by 10-inch scale drawing of a house. If the scale on the drawing is 1 inch = 5 feet, what are the dimensions of the house? *(Lesson 8-3)* **A**

A 40 ft by 50 ft   **B** 35 ft by 45 ft

C 20 ft by 25 ft   **D** 4 ft by 5 ft

For **Extra Practice**, see page 588.

22. Find the LCM of 15, 20, and 8. *(Lesson 5-7)* **120**

Lesson 11-8 Integration: Geometry   Graphing Transformations   **467**

Extending the Lesson

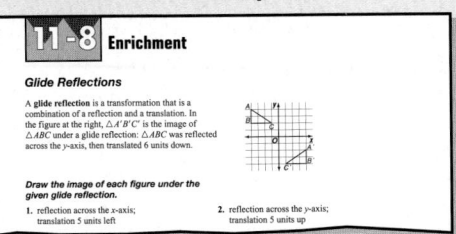
Activity Have students draw △TUV with vertices T(−2, 1), U(−5, 0), and V(−2, −2). Ask them what transformation describes △T'U'V' with vertices T'(0, 1), U'(−3, 0), and V'(0, −2). **Translate △TUV 2 units to the right.**

CHAPTER
11

Study Guide and Assessment

Vocabulary

This section provides a listing of the new terms, properties, and phrases that were introduced in this chapter. Have students define each term and provide an example or two of each, if appropriate.

Understanding and Using the Vocabulary

These exercises check students' understanding of the terms by using a variety of verbal formats including matching, completion, and true/false.

Glossaries

A complete glossary of terms appears on pages 642–648. The glossary also appears in Spanish on pages 649–656.

Additional Answer

12. In a translation, the position of a figure is changed by sliding it. In a reflection, the position of a figure is changed by flipping it over a line.

---

interNET CONNECTION Chapter Review For additional lesson-by-lesson review, visit:
www.glencoe.com/sec/math/mac/mathnet

Vocabulary

After completing this chapter, you should be able to define each term, concept, or phrase and give an example or two of each.

Geometry
coordinate grid (p. 459)
coordinate system (p. 459)
ordered pair (p. 459)
origin (p. 459)
quadrant (p. 459)
reflection (p. 464)
transformation (p. 464)
translation (p. 464)
x-axis (p. 459)
x-coordinate (p. 459)
y-axis (p. 459)
y-coordinate (p. 459)

Number and Operations
integer (p. 434)
negative integer (p. 434)
opposite (p. 435)
positive integer (p. 434)
zero pair (p. 441)

Problem Solving
work backward (p. 454)

Understanding and Using the Vocabulary

State whether each sentence is *true* or *false*. If false, replace the underlined word or number to make a true sentence.

1. Integers that are greater than zero are called <u>negative</u> integers. **false; positive**
2. The opposite of the number 7 is $\frac{1}{7}$. **false; −7**
3. On the number line -21 is to the left of -8, so <u>$-21 < -8$</u>. **true**
4. When adding two negative integers, the answer will <u>always</u> be negative. **true**
5. When subtracting two negative integers, the answer will <u>never</u> be negative. **false; sometimes**
6. When dividing two negative integers, the answer will <u>always</u> be negative. **false; never**
7. When multiplying two negative integers, the answer will <u>sometimes</u> be negative. **false; never**
8. The <u>horizontal</u> line of a coordinate system is called the x-axis. **true**
9. The first number in an ordered pair is the <u>x-coordinate</u>. **true**
10. The x-axis and the y-axis intersect at the <u>quadrant</u>. **false; origin**
11. When you flip a figure, the transformation is called a <u>translation</u>. **false; reflection**

In Your Own Words

12. *Explain* the difference between a translation and a reflection. **See margin.**

MindJogger Videoquizzes

MindJogger Videoquizzes provide an alternative review of concepts presented in this chapter. Students work in teams to answer questions, gaining points for correct answers. The questions are presented in three rounds.
Round 1 Concepts–5 questions
Round 2 Skills–4 questions
Round 3 Problem Solving–4 questions

Objectives & Examples

Upon completing this chapter, you should be able to:

● identify, name, and graph integers
(Lesson 11-1)

Graph −3 on the number line.

```
◄─┼──┼──┼──●──┼──┼──┼──┼──┼──┼──┼──┼──┼─►
 −6 −5 −4 −3 −2 −1  0  1  2  3  4  5  6
```

● compare and order integers
(Lesson 11-2)

Compare −7 and −9.

```
◄─┼──┼──●──┼──┼──┼──┼──●──┼──┼──┼──┼──┼─►
−10 −9 −8 −7 −6 −5 −4 −3 −2 −1  0  1  2
```

−7 is to the right of −9, so −7 > −9.

● add integers using models
(Lesson 11-3)

Use counters to find −4 + 6.

−4 + 6 = 2

● subtract integers using models
(Lesson 11-4)

Use counters to find −4 − 2.

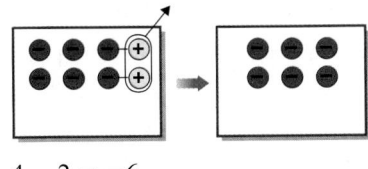

−4 − 2 = −6

Review Exercises

Use these exercises to review and prepare for the chapter test. **13–15. See Answer Appendix.**

Draw a number line from −10 to 10. Graph each integer on the number line.

13. −9   **14.** 6   **15.** −8

16. Write an integer to describe a temperature drop of 13°. **−13**

Replace each ● with <, >, or = to make a true sentence.

17. +4 ● +7 **<**   **18.** +1 ● −6 **>**

19. −7 ● −12 **>**   **20.** −9 ● +11 **<**

21. Order −15, 0, −1, 6, −7, and 10 from least to greatest. **−15, −7, −1, 0, 6, 10**

Find each sum. Use counters or a number line if necessary.

22. −3 + 5 **2**   **23.** 7 + (−7) **0**

24. −2 + (−5) **−7**   **25.** −7 + 1 **−6**

26. 4 + (−3) **1**   **27.** −6 + 0 **−6**

Find each difference. Use counters or a number line if necessary.

28. −2 − (−5) **3**   **29.** −7 − 1 **−8**

30. 3 − (−4) **7**   **31.** 8 − (−3) **11**

32. 6 − 9 **−3**   **33.** −4 − 7 **−11**

Objectives & Examples

This section reviews the skills and concepts of the chapter and shows completely worked examples.

Review Exercises

These exercises provide practice for the corresponding objectives.

Assessment and Evaluation Masters, pp. 283–284

Assessment and Evaluation

Six forms of Chapter 11 Test are available in the *Assessment and Evaluation Masters* as shown in the chart.

Chapter 11 Test, Form 1B, is shown at the right. Chapter 11 Test, Form 2B, is shown on the next page.

1A	Multiple Choice	Honors
1B	Multiple Choice	Average
1C	Multiple Choice	Basic
2A	Free Response	Honors
2B	Free Response	Average
2C	Free Response	Basic

**Assessment and Evaluation
Masters, pp. 289–290**

Objectives & Examples

Review Exercises

● multiply integers using models
(Lesson 11-5)

Use counters to find 2(−3).

$2(−3) = −6$

Find each product. Use counters or a number line if necessary.

34. $6 \times (−2)$ **−12**   **35.** $−3 \times (−5)$ **15**
36. $−4 \times 3$ **−12**   **37.** 5×0 **0**
38. $−5(2)$ **−10**   **39.** $7(−1)$ **−7**

● divide integers using models and patterns
(Lesson 11-6)

Find $14 \div (−2)$.

$−7 \times (−2) = 14$, so $14 \div (−2) = −7$.

Find each quotient. Use counters or patterns if necessary.

40. $35 \div (−7)$ **−5**   **41.** $−36 \div 9$ **−4**
42. $−40 \div 5$ **−8**   **43.** $18 \div (−3)$ **−6**
44. $−30 \div (−5)$ **6**   **45.** $−24 \div (−6)$ **4**

● graph ordered pairs of numbers on a coordinate grid *(Lesson 11-7)*

Graph A(2, −1).
right 2, down 1

Graph B(−3, 2).
left 3, up 2

Graph and label each point.

46. $M(−2, 2)$ **47.** $N(3, 0)$
48. $P(5, 6)$ **49.** $Q(−2, 4)$
50. $R(−2, −5)$ **51.** $S(7, −1)$

46–51. See Answer Appendix.

● graph transformations on a coordinate grid
(Lesson 11-8)

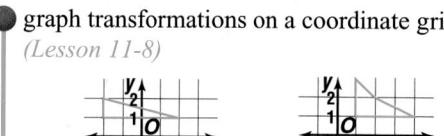

translation   reflection

The vertices of $\triangle ABC$ are $A(−1, 2)$, $B(0, 5)$, and $C(3, 1)$. On a coordinate grid, draw $\triangle ABC$ and each transformation image.

52. translation image that is 3 units left and 2 units down **52–53. See Answer Appendix.**

53. reflection image over the x-axis

Test and Review Software

You may use this software, a combination of an item generator and item bank, to create your own tests or worksheets. Types of items include free response, multiple choice, short answer, and open ended.

CD-ROM Program

The CD-ROM Program contains an Assessment Game whose questions review the concepts in this chapter.

Applications & Problem Solving

54. Weather Low temperatures were recorded for one week in January. Order the temperatures from least to greatest. *(Lesson 11-2)* **−7, −5, −3, −2, 0, 1, 2**

S	M	T	W	T	F	S
−5°	0°	1°	−7°	−3°	2°	−2°

55. Football The Branson Middle School football team is 2 yards from its opponent's goal line. On the next two plays, its offense loses 17 yards and then gains 11 yards. How many yards is the team from the goal line? *(Lesson 11-3)* **8 yd**

56. Work Backward Pearl has money in her savings account. She made withdrawals of $100, $43, and $67. Her balance is now $245. How much did she have in her account before the three withdrawals? *(Lesson 11-6B)* **$455**

57. Crafts Diego wants to make a two-sided ornament out of fabric. He uses a pattern to cut one side of the ornament. Should he use a *reflection* or a *translation* of the pattern for the other side of the ornament? *(Lesson 11-8)* **reflection**

Alternative Assessment

Open Ended

Suppose you are playing a game with a friend and you have decided to be the scorekeeper. During the first round, you scored 6 points and your friend scored 4 points. During the second round, you scored 3 points and your friend lost 3 points. During the third round, you lost 2 points and your friend scored 5 points. Finally, during the fourth round, you lost 1 point and your friend scored 5 points. Explain how to organize the information in order to keep score accurately. **See margin.**

Suppose on the fifth round, you scored 2 points and your friend lost 1 point. Find the total scores. Who is winning the game? **See margin.**

A practice test for Chapter 11 is provided on page 605.

Completing the CHAPTER Project

Use the following checklist to make sure your poster or brochure is complete.

☑ The map is clear and easy to read.

☑ The line plot is correct.

☑ The paragraph discussing the changes in the House of Representatives includes whether your part of the country has gained or lost representatives and how the total number of representatives has changed.

Add any finishing touches that you would like to make your poster or brochure attractive.

Select one exercise that involved graphing from this chapter that you found particularly challenging. Place it in your portfolio.

Applications & Problem Solving

This section provides additional practice in solving real-world problems that involve the skills of this chapter.

Alternative Assessment

The **Open Ended** section provides students with a performance assessment opportunity to evaluate their work and understanding.

CHAPTER Project

Students should complete the final stages of their project and prepare a class demonstration of their results. A scoring guide for the project is available in the *Investigations and Projects Masters*, p. 59.

Students should add to their portfolios at this time.

Assessment and Evaluation Masters, p. 293

11 Name_____ Date_____

Chapter 11 Performance Assessment

Instructions: Demonstrate your knowledge by giving a clear, concise solution to each problem. Be sure to include all relevant drawings and justify your answers. You may show your solutions in more than one way or investigate beyond the requirements of the problems.

1. Draw counters, ⊕ and ⊖, to represent positive and negative integers.

   a. Represent −2 in at least two ways using counters and one way on a number line.

   b. Explain how to represent −5 + (+2) using counters.

   c. Show how to find 4 − (−3) using counters.

   d. Write an expression you would use to find the product of two negative integers. Tell what it means.

   e. Show how to use counters to find the product in part d. Explain each step.

2. a. Tell what is meant by a *translation image*.

   b. On the coordinate grid, draw a translation image of △ABC. Give the coordinates of the translation image of A.

   c. Tell what is meant by a *reflection image*.

   d. Draw the reflection image of △ABC over the x-axis. Give the coordinates of the reflection image of B.

© Glencoe/McGraw-Hill   293   *Mathematics: Applications and Connections, Course 1*

Additional Answers for the Open Ended item

- **Keep a running tally of each player's score. The first round scores were 6 and 4. After the first round, add the integers represented by each score.**

- **After 5 rounds, your score is 8 and your friend's score is 10. Your friend is winning.**

Performance Assessment

Additional performance assessment tasks for this chapter are included in the *Assessment and Evaluation Masters* on page 293. A scoring guide is also provided on page 305.

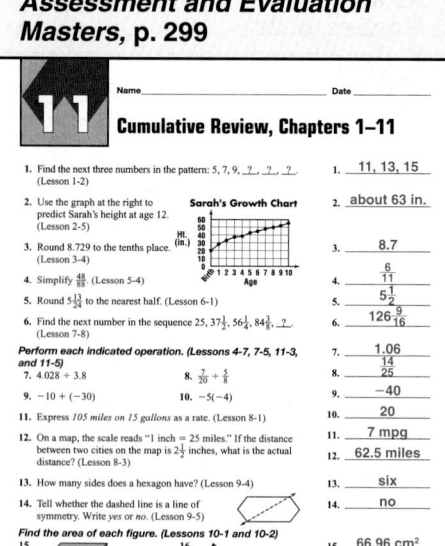

Section One: Multiple Choice

There are twelve multiple choice questions in this section. Choose the best answer. If a correct answer is *not here*, choose the letter for Not Here.

1. Which numbers are factors of 75? **C**

  A 3, 5, and 6

  B 3, 5, and 9

  C 3 and 5

  D 5 and 10

2. If $n = -3$, what is the value of $8 + n$? **H**

  F -5

  G -3

  H 5

  J 11

3. How many lines of symmetry does an equilateral triangle have? **D**

  A 0

  B 1

  C 2

  D 3

4. What are the coordinates of point G on the graph? **F**

  F $(2, -3)$

  G $(3, -2)$

  H $(-3, 2)$

  J $(-2, -3)$

Please note that Questions 5–12 have five answer choices.

5. What integers are graphed? **A**

  A $-5, -1, 2$

  B $-7, -1, 2$

  C $5, 1, 2$

  D $-7, 1, 2$

  E $-2, 1, 5$

6. Write the sentence represented by the model. **J**

  F $4 + (-4) = 0$

  G $4 + (-2) = 2$

  H $4 + (6) = 10$

  J $4 - (-2) = 6$

  K $4 - 2 = 2$

7. One boat is 5.05 meters long, and another is 4.8 meters long. How much space is needed to park the boats end to end? **A**

  A 9.85 meters

  B 9.13 meters

  C 10.3 meters

  D 5.53 meters

  E 0.25 meter

8. A round window in Kevin's house is 40 inches in diameter. Which is a good estimate for the area of the window? **J**

  F 60 square inches

  G 120 square inches

  H 600 square inches

  J 1,200 square inches

  K 4,800 square inches

472 Chapters 1–11 Standardized Test Practice

9. Mr. Orta needs $\frac{7}{8}$ yard of material to upholster a chair seat and $\frac{5}{8}$ yard to upholster the back of the chair. How many yards of material will be needed to cover the chair? **B**

A 1 yard

B $1\frac{1}{2}$ yards

C $1\frac{3}{4}$ yards

D 2 yards

E Not Here

10. Bobbie charges $5.75 per hour for baby-sitting. If she works for 4 hours, how much will she earn? **J**

F $9.75

G $20.75

H $17.25

J $23.00

K Not Here

11. Barbara bought a 3-pound ham and $5\frac{1}{2}$ pounds of steak. How many more pounds of steak did she buy than ham? **B**

A 2 pounds

B $2\frac{1}{2}$ pounds

C $3\frac{1}{2}$ pounds

D $8\frac{1}{2}$ pounds

E Not Here

12. $-3(-13) =$ **H**

F 16   G -16

H 39   J -39

K Not Here

 inter NET CONNECTION Test Practice For additional test practice questions, visit:

www.glencoe.com/sec/math/mac/mathnet

Test-Taking Tip THE PRINCETON REVIEW

You could use educated guesses to help improve your scores. A wild guess involves pure chance, but eliminating possible answers as definitely wrong will allow you to increase your chances of getting a right answer.

Section Two: Free Response

This section contains seven questions for which you will provide short answers. Write your answers on your paper.

13. Find the quotient of 32 and -4. **-8**

14. Find the next two numbers in the sequence 64, 16, 4, 1, ... **$\frac{1}{4}, \frac{1}{16}$**

15. Write the ordered pair represented by M. **(3, 3)**

16. Find 98% of 6. **5.88**

17. Draw the reflection of the letter E over a vertical line. **See margin.**

18. How can you find the surface area of a 3-inch by 4-inch by 5-inch rectangular prism? **See margin.**

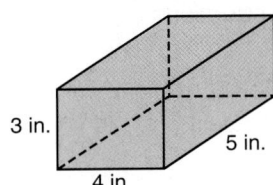

3 in.   5 in.   4 in.

19. Find $3\frac{4}{5} \times 7\frac{1}{2}$. **$28\frac{1}{2}$**

Chapters 1–11 Standardized Test Practice **473**

Test-Taking Tip

Tell students to first find out whether they are penalized for wrong answers. If this is the case, suggest they guess only if they are able to narrow down the answer to two choices.

Assessment and Evaluation Masters, pp. 297–298

11 Name_____ Date_____

Chapter 11 Standardized Test Practice

1. If $s = 5$ and $t = 8$, find the value of $s^3 + t^2$.
   A. 189   B. 89   C. 31   D. none of these   1. ___A___

2. The ages of students in a class are 14, 13, 13, 13, 11, 11, 11, 13, 12, 14, 13, 13, 11, 11, 11, 11, and 12. If a frequency table is constructed by age, which age would have the most tallies or highest frequency?
   A. 11   B. 12   C. 13   D. 14   2. ___A___

3. During a shopping trip, Tanika considered buying a sweater for $16.79, a pair of boots for $27.98, and a necklace for $5.19. To the nearest dollar, how much would Tanika need for these purchases?
   A. $50   B. $48   C. $49   D. none of these   3. ___A___

4. If Saturn orbits the Sun once in 29.46 Earth years, how long will it take for Saturn to go around the Sun four times?
   A. 7.365 years   B. 33.46 years   C. 116.8 years   D. 117.84 years   4. ___D___

5. Lucas has 255 CDs. He wants to give them to several friends so that they each receive the same number of CDs. What are the possible number of friends who could receive CDs?
   A. 3, 5, 15, 17   B. 10, 25, 55   C. 3, 5, 15, 17, 51   D. 2, 3, 5, 17   5. ___C___

6. Alta wants to buy a sweater that costs $24.99. The sales tax is $5\frac{3}{4}$%. Which equation would help Alta estimate the cost of the sweater?
   A. $C = 0.06 \times 25$ B. $C = 0.06 \times 25 + 25$ C. $C = 0.575$ D. none of these   6. ___B___

7. Katie made $8\frac{1}{3}$ cups of soup. How many people can she serve if each serving is $\frac{1}{3}$ cup?
   A. 12   B. 25   C. 9   D. 27   7. ___B___

8. Shane was refilling his iron. The iron holds $\frac{5}{8}$ cup of water. If it took $\frac{3}{8}$ cup to fill, how much water was already in the iron?
   A. $\frac{5}{8}$ cup   B. $\frac{1}{4}$ cup   C. $\frac{1}{2}$ cup   D. 1 cup   8. ___C___

9. A scientific calculator, normally priced at $60, is on sale for $\frac{4}{5}$ of the original price. How much does it cost?
   A. $50   B. $48   C. $45   D. $12   9. ___B___

10. Karly purchased a 15.5 ounce bag of hard candy for $2.49. What was the cost per ounce rounded to the nearest cent?
    A. $0.15/oz   B. $0.16/oz   C. $0.12/oz   D. none of these   10. ___B___

© Glencoe/McGraw-Hill   297   Mathematics: Applications and Connections, Course 1

11 **Chapter 11 Standardized Test Practice (continued)**

11. Ticket sales at a movie theater increased by 105% when ticket prices were cut. Express the percent as a simplified fraction.
    A. $\frac{105}{100}$ B. $1\frac{5}{100}$ C. $1\frac{1}{20}$ D. none of these   11. ___C___

12. Josh wants to design a four-sided mirror with 2 pairs of parallel sides. The mirror will be twice as tall as it is long and have no right angles. What is the shape of the mirror?
    A. parallelogram   B. rectangle   C. square   D. hexagon   12. ___A___

13. The triangular sail on a sailboat is 12 feet tall. The area of the sail is 96 ft². How long is the base of the sail?
    A. 8 ft   B. 13 ft   C. 16 ft   D. 48 ft   13. ___C___

14. Josie wants to give boxes of jelly beans to four of her friends. Each box measures 6 inches by 2 inches by 4 inches. What is the total volume of the boxes she will need?
    A. 48 in³   B. 192 in³   C. 164 in³   D. 196 in³   14. ___B___

15. A piece of modern art is shaped like a triangular pyramid. Each face is painted a different color. How many colors were used?
    A. 2   B. 3   C. 4   D. 5   15. ___C___

16. Which letter has two lines of symmetry?
    A. D   B. H   C. M   D. W   16. ___B___

17. The table shows the average depths of five large bodies of water. Order the bodies of water from deepest to most shallow.

Body of Water	Average Depth
Arctic Ocean	−3,407 ft
Atlantic Ocean	−11,730 ft
Caribbean Sea	−8,448 ft
Indian Ocean	−12,598 ft
Pacific Ocean	−12,925 ft

   A. Pacific, Indian, Atlantic, Caribbean, Arctic
   B. Arctic, Caribbean, Indian, Atlantic, Pacific
   C. Arctic, Caribbean, Atlantic, Indian, Pacific
   D. Pacific, Indian, Atlantic, Arctic, Caribbean   17. ___A___

18. At 6 A.M. the temperature was -7°F, and at noon the temperature was 12°F. What was the difference in temperature?
    A. 5°   B. 19°   C. -5°   D. none of these   18. ___B___

19. The total bill for concert tickets is $372. How much did each ticket cost if six friends are going to the concert?
    A. $53   B. $20   C. $37   D. $62   19. ___D___

20. If the point $(5, 2)$ is reflected around the x-axis, what is its reflection?
    A. $(-5, -2)$ B. $(5, -2)$ C. $(-2, 5)$ D. $(2, 5)$ 20. ___B___

© Glencoe/McGraw-Hill   298   Mathematics: Applications and Connections, Course 1

Additional Answers

17.

18. Add $2(3 \times 4)$ plus $2(4 \times 5)$ plus $2(3 \times 5)$.

Instructional Resources ▶▶▶

Additional standardized test practice is shown at the right and is available in the *Assessment and Evaluation Masters,* pp. 297–298.

Algebra: Exploring Equations

Previewing the Chapter

Overview

This chapter explores algebraic equations and expressions. Students learn to solve equations involving addition, subtraction, multiplication, and division first by using models and then by using properties of equations. Function tables are used to show the output of a given function rule and to determine the function rule when the input and output are given. Coordinate grids are used to graph functions. Students learn to solve problems by using an equation.

Lesson (pages)	Lesson Objectives	NCTM Standards 2000	Standardized Tests	State/Local Objectives
12-1 (476–479)	Solve addition equations by using models.	1, 2, 6–10	MAT	
12-2 (480–483)	Solve subtraction equations by using models.	1, 2, 6–10	MAT	
12-3 (484–487)	Solve multiplication and division equations using models.	1–4, 6–10	MAT	
12-4 (488–491)	Solve two-step equations using models.	1, 2, 6–8, 10	MAT	
12-4B (492–493)	Solve problems by using an equation.	1, 2, 6–9	CAT, MAT	
12-5A (494–495)	Find the input and output for a given function machine.	1, 2, 6–8, 10	CTBS, SAT, TN	
12-5 (496–499)	Complete function tables.	1, 2, 6–10	CTBS, SAT, TN	
12-6 (500–503)	Graph functions from function tables.	1–3, 6–10		

CAT = California Achievement Tests, CTBS = Comprehensive Tests of Basic Skills, ITBS = Iowa Tests of Basic Skills, MAT = Metropolitan Achievement Tests, SAT = Stanford Achievement Tests, TN = Terra Nova
For the key to numbering of NCTM Standards 2000, see page T6.

Organizing the Chapter

The **Interactive Lesson Planner** contains all of the blackline masters and transparencies. This CD-ROM also includes an easy-to-use lesson planning calendar.

LESSON PLANNING GUIDE

Lesson	Extra Practice (Student Edition)	BLACKLINE MASTERS (PAGE NUMBERS)										
		Study Guide	Practice	Enrichment	Assessment & Evaluation	Classroom Games	Diversity	Hands-On Lab	School to Career	Science and Math Lab Manual	Technology	Transparencies A and B
12-1	p. 588	84	84	84				80				12-1
12-2	p. 588	85	85	85	323	33–35						12-2
12-3	p. 589	86	86	86	322, 323				12			12-3
12-4	p. 589	87	87	87			12					12-4
12-4B	p. 589											
12-5A								66				
12-5	p. 590	88	88	88	324						23	12-5
12-6	p. 590	89	89	89	324					21–24	24	12-6
Study Guide/ Assessment					309–321, 325–327							

OTHER CHAPTER RESOURCES

Student Edition

Chapter Project, pp. 475, 478, 487, 503, 507
Math in the Media, p. 479
Let the Games Begin, p. 491

Technology

 MathPASS CD-ROM

Interactive Mathematics Tools Software

Teacher's Classroom Resources

Applications
Family Letters and Activities,
 pp. 23–24
Investigations and Projects
 Masters, pp. 61–64
Meeting Individual Needs
Investigations for the Special
 Education Student, pp. 39–42

Teaching Aids
Answer Key Masters
Block Scheduling Booklet
Lesson Planning Guide
Solutions Manual

Professional Publications
Glencoe Mathematics
 Professional Series

Planning the Chapter

MindJogger Videoquizzes
provide a unique format for reviewing concepts presented in the chapter.

ASSESSMENT RESOURCES

Student Edition

Mixed Review, pp. 479, 483, 487, 491, 499, 503

Mid-Chapter Self Test, p. 487

Math Journal, pp. 482, 501

Study Guide and Assessment, pp. 504–507

Performance Task, p. 507

Portfolio Suggestion, p. 507

Standardized Test Practice, pp. 508–509

Chapter Test, p. 606

Assessment and Evaluation Masters

Multiple-Choice Tests (Forms 1A, 1B, 1C), pp. 309–314

Free-Response Tests (Forms 2A, 2B, 2C), pp. 315–320

Performance Assessment, p. 321

Mid-Chapter Test, p. 322

Quizzes A–D, pp. 323–324

Standardized Test Practice, pp. 325–326

Cumulative Review, p. 327

Teacher's Wraparound Edition

5-Minute Check, pp. 476, 480, 484, 488, 496, 500

Building Portfolios, p. 474

Math Journal, p. 495

Closing Activity, pp. 479, 483, 487, 491, 493, 499, 503

Technology

Test and Review Software

MindJogger Videoquizzes

CD-ROM Program

MATERIALS AND MANIPULATIVES

Lesson 12-1
cups*†
counters*†
equation mat*†

Lesson 12-2
cups*†
counters*†
equation mat*†

Lesson 12-3
cups*†
counters*†
equation mat*†

Lesson 12-4
cups*†
counters*†
equation mat*†
scissors*
beans
index cards
poster board

Lesson 12-5A
scissors*
tape

Lesson 12-6
grid paper†

*Glencoe Manipulative Kit   †Glencoe Overhead Manipulative Resources

PACING CHART

See pages T25–T27 for the Course Planning Calendar.

COURSE	DAY 1	DAY 2	DAY 3	DAY 4	DAY 5	DAY 6	DAY 7
Standard	Chapter Project	Lesson 12-1	Lesson 12-2	Lesson 12-3	Lesson 12-4	Lesson 12-4B	Lessons 12-5A & 12-5
Honors	Chapter Project	Lesson 12-1	Lesson 12-2	Lesson 12-3	Lesson 12-4	Lesson 12-4B	Lesson 12-5
Block	Chapter Project & Lesson 12-1	Lessons 12-2 & 12-3	Lessons 12-4 & 12-4B	Lessons 12-5A, 12-5, & 12-6		Study Guide and Assessment, Chapter Test	

Interactive Mathematics:
Activities and Investigations

is an activity-based program that may be used as an enhancement for chapters in *Mathematics: Applications and Connections.*

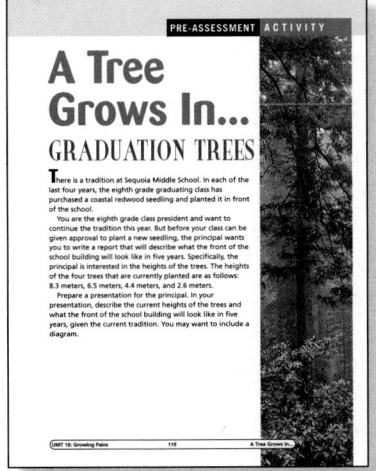

Unit 16,
Pre-Assessment Activity
Use with Lesson 12-4B.

Summary Students are introduced to methods used by scientists to find the age of a tree. They write an equation that could be used to determine the approximate age of a tree.

Math Connection Students use the circumference of a tree to find its age. The circumference can be found by using the formula $C = \pi d$, where d represents the diameter. Students write an equation to determine the approximate age of a tree.

Unit 15, Activity Five
Use with Lesson 12-6.

Summary Students complete tasks that illustrate the relationship between distance and speed, and distance traveled and the number of revolutions a cylindrical object makes. They experiment by rolling objects down ramps and compare the data that they collect.

Math Connection Students conduct experiments rolling objects down ramps of different heights and collecting data to explore momentum, velocity, and acceleration. They sketch graphs of their data and analyze their results.

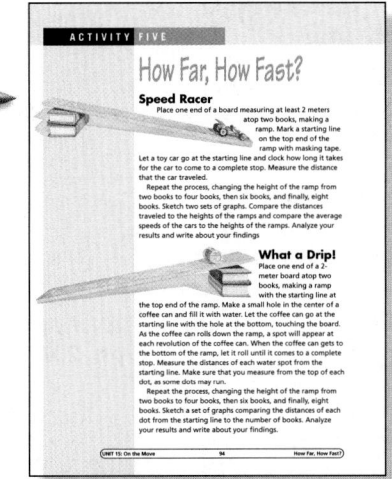

DAY 8	DAY 9	DAY 10	DAY 11	DAY 12	DAY 13	DAY 14	DAY 15
(continue from Day 7)	Lesson 12-6	Study Guide and Assessment	Chapter Test				
(continue from Day 7)	Lesson 12-6	Study Guide and Assessment	Chapter Test				

Enhancing the Chapter

APPLICATIONS

Classroom Games, pp. 33–35

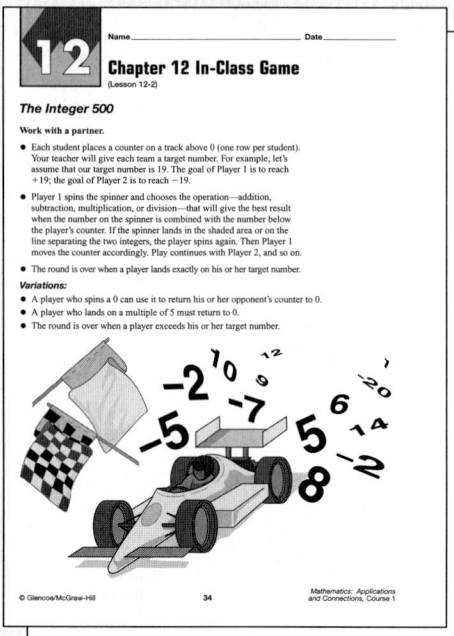

12 Name_____ Date_____

Chapter 12 In-Class Game
(Lesson 12-2)

The Integer 500

Work with a partner.

- Each student places a counter on a track above 0 (one row per student). Your teacher will give each team a target number. For example, let's assume that our target number is 19. The goal of Player 1 is to reach +19; the goal of Player 2 is to reach −19.
- Player 1 spins the spinner and chooses the operation—addition, subtraction, multiplication, or division—that will give the best result when the number on the spinner is combined with the number below the player's counter. If the spinner lands in the shaded area or on the line separating the two integers, the player spins again. Then Player 1 moves the counter accordingly. Play continues with Player 2, and so on.
- The round is over when a player lands exactly on his or her target number.

Variations:
- A player who spins a 0 can use it to return his or her opponent's counter to 0.
- A player who lands on a multiple of 5 must return to 0.
- The round is over when a player exceeds his or her target number.

© Glencoe/McGraw-Hill 34 Mathematics: Applications and Connections, Course 1

Diversity Masters, p. 12

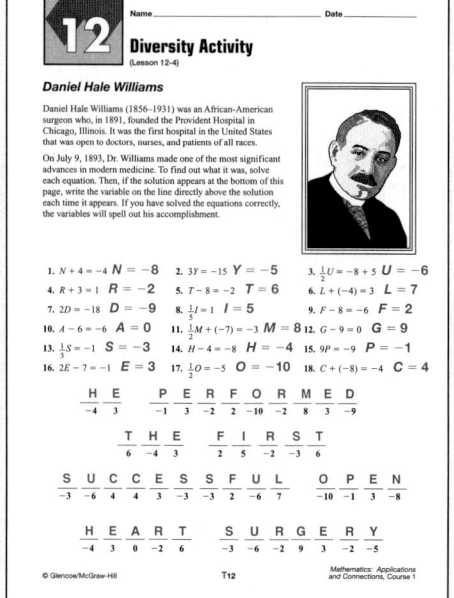

12 Name_____ Date_____

Diversity Activity
(Lesson 12-4)

Daniel Hale Williams

Daniel Hale Williams (1856–1931) was an African-American surgeon who, in 1891, founded the Provident Hospital in Chicago, Illinois. It was the first hospital in the United States that was open to doctors, nurses, and patients of all races.

On July 9, 1893, Dr. Williams made one of the most significant advances in modern medicine. To find out what it was, solve each equation. Then, if the solution appears at the bottom of this page, write the variable on the line directly above the solution each time it appears. If you have solved the equations correctly, the variables will spell out his accomplishment.

1. $N + 4 = -4$ $N = -8$
2. $3Y = -15$ $Y = -5$
3. $\frac{1}{2}U = -8 + 5$ $U = -6$
4. $R + 3 = 1$ $R = -2$
5. $T - 8 = -2$ $T = 6$
6. $L + (-4) = 3$ $L = 7$
7. $2D = -18$ $D = -9$
8. $\frac{1}{5}I = 1$ $I = 5$
9. $F - 8 = -6$ $F = 2$
10. $A - 6 = -6$ $A = 0$
11. $\frac{1}{3}M + (-7) = -3$ $M = 8$
12. $G - 9 = 0$ $G = 9$
13. $\frac{1}{3}S = -1$ $S = -3$
14. $H - 4 = -8$ $H = -4$
15. $9P = -9$ $P = -1$
16. $2E - 7 = -1$ $E = 3$
17. $\frac{1}{2}O = -5$ $O = -10$
18. $C + (-8) = -4$ $C = 4$

$\underset{-4}{H}\ \underset{3}{E}$ $\underset{-1}{P}\ \underset{3}{E}\ \underset{-2}{R}\ \underset{1}{F}\ \underset{-10}{O}\ \underset{-2}{R}\ \underset{8}{M}\ \underset{3}{E}\ \underset{-9}{D}$

$\underset{6}{T}\ \underset{-4}{H}\ \underset{3}{E}$ $\underset{2}{F}\ \underset{5}{I}\ \underset{-2}{R}\ \underset{-3}{S}\ \underset{6}{T}$

$\underset{-3}{S}\ \underset{-6}{U}\ \underset{4}{C}\ \underset{4}{C}\ \underset{3}{E}\ \underset{-3}{S}\ \underset{-3}{S}\ \underset{-2}{F}\ \underset{-6}{U}\ \underset{7}{L}$ $\underset{-10}{O}\ \underset{-1}{P}\ \underset{3}{E}\ \underset{-8}{N}$

$\underset{-4}{H}\ \underset{3}{E}\ \underset{0}{A}\ \underset{-2}{R}\ \underset{6}{T}$ $\underset{-3}{S}\ \underset{-6}{U}\ \underset{-2}{R}\ \underset{9}{G}\ \underset{3}{E}\ \underset{-2}{R}\ \underset{-5}{Y}$

© Glencoe/McGraw-Hill T12 Mathematics: Applications and Connections, Course 1

School to Career Masters, p. 12

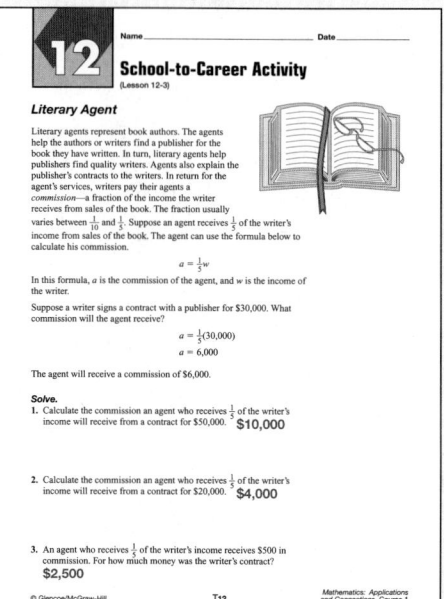

12 Name_____ Date_____

School-to-Career Activity
(Lesson 12-3)

Literary Agent

Literary agents represent book authors. The agents help the authors or writers find a publisher for the book they have written. In turn, literary agents help publishers find quality writers. Agents also explain the publisher's contracts to the writers. In return for the agent's services, writers pay their agents a *commission*—a fraction of the income the writer receives from sales of the book. The fraction usually varies between $\frac{1}{10}$ and $\frac{1}{5}$. Suppose an agent receives $\frac{1}{5}$ of the writer's income from sales of the book. The agent can use the formula below to calculate his commission.

$$a = \frac{1}{5}w$$

In this formula, a is the commission of the agent, and w is the income of the writer.

Suppose a writer signs a contract with a publisher for $30,000. What commission will the agent receive?

$$a = \frac{1}{5}(30,000)$$
$$a = 6,000$$

The agent will receive a commission of $6,000.

Solve.

1. Calculate the commission an agent who receives $\frac{1}{5}$ of the writer's income will receive from a contract for $50,000. **$10,000**

2. Calculate the commission an agent who receives $\frac{1}{5}$ of the writer's income will receive from a contract for $20,000. **$4,000**

3. An agent who receives $\frac{1}{5}$ of the writer's income receives $500 in commission. For how much money was the writer's contract? **$2,500**

© Glencoe/McGraw-Hill T12 Mathematics: Applications and Connections, Course 1

Family Letters and Activities, pp. 23–24

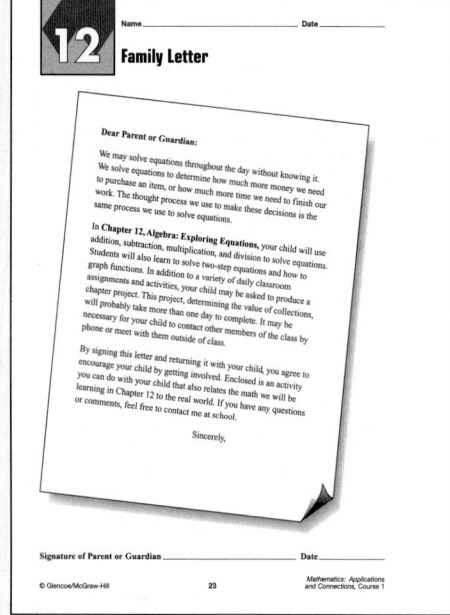

12 Name_____ Date_____

Family Letter

Dear Parent or Guardian:

We may solve equations throughout the day without knowing it. We solve equations to determine how much more money we need to purchase an item, or how much more time we need to finish our work. The thought process we use to make these decisions is the same process we use to solve equations.

In **Chapter 12, Algebra: Exploring Equations,** your child will use addition, subtraction, multiplication, and division to solve equations. Students will also learn to solve two-step equations and how to graph functions. In addition to a variety of daily classroom assignments and activities, your child may be asked to produce a chapter project. This project, determining the value of collections, will probably take more than one day to complete. It may be necessary for your child to contact other members of the class by phone or meet with them outside of class.

By signing this letter and returning it with your child, you agree to encourage your child by getting involved. Enclosed is an activity you can do with your child that also relates the math we will be learning in Chapter 12 to the real world. If you have any questions or comments, feel free to contact me at school.

Sincerely,

Signature of Parent or Guardian_____ Date_____

© Glencoe/McGraw-Hill 23 Mathematics: Applications and Connections, Course 1

12 Name_____ Date_____

Family Activity

Temperature Differences

Watch the news on television, consult the weather section of a newspaper, or visit a weather-related website. Then work with a family member to collect the high and low temperatures for at least nine cities. Write and solve an equation to find how much warmer the high temperature is than the low temperature.

City	Low Temperature	High Temperature	Equation	Solution
1. Austin	72°	91°	72 + t = 91	
2.				
3.				
4.				
5.				
6.				
7.				
8.				
9.				
10.				

1. The high temperature was 19° warmer. 2–10. Answers will vary.

© Glencoe/McGraw-Hill 24 Mathematics: Applications and Connections, Course 1

Science and Math Lab Manual, pp. 21–24

6 Name_____ Date_____

Science and Mathematics Lab
(Course 1, Lesson 12-6)

Ivy League Math

INTRODUCTION

Ivies and most other types of vines are members of a group of plants called *angiosperms*, which means "flowering plants." There are many species of ivy, but the one with which most of us are familiar is the English Ivy or *Hedera helix*. Ivies will climb any rigid structure, such as trees or walls, using aerial roots which develop from their stems.

OBJECTIVES

In this lab, you will:
- measure the length of each vine.
- count the number of leaves on each vine.
- enter your data in a function table.
- draw a graph that represents the relationship between the length of the vine and the number of leaves.
- determine the number of leaves per unit length of vine.

MATERIALS

- ivy or similar vine, cut to four different lengths
- large piece of heavy paper such as blotting paper
- pots and potting soil
- ruler
- paper cups

PROCEDURE

1. Work with a partner. Place each vine on the piece of paper in order from shortest to longest.
2. Label each vine by writing a number from 1–4 above each vine.
3. Use your ruler to measure the length of each vine to the nearest inch. One person can hold the vine straight while the other person measures it. Record the measurements in the Data Table as variable *x*.
4. Count the number of leaves on the vine you have just measured. Record this information in the table as variable *y*.
5. Repeat Steps 3 and 4 for each vine.

© Glencoe/McGraw-Hill 23 Mathematics: Applications and Connections

MANIPULATIVES/MODELING

Hands-On Lab Masters, p. 80

ASSESSMENT/EVALUATION

Assessment and Evaluation Masters, pp. 322–324

TECHNOLOGY/MULTIMEDIA

Technology Masters, pp. 23–24

MEETING INDIVIDUAL NEEDS

Investigations for the Special Education Student, pp. 39–42

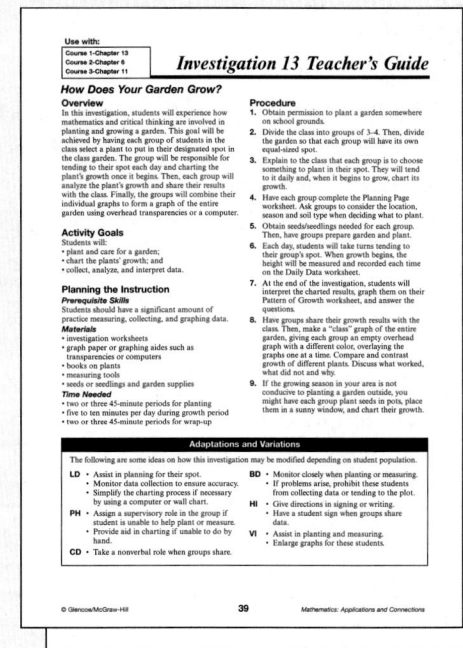

Theme: Collections

Collecting is a popular hobby because a person can collect almost anything of interest. If a person collects objects that are hard to find, the collection can become quite valuable. A single object in a collection can also command a high price. For example, as of 1997, a Michael Jordan retirement basketball card was worth $3,500.00.

Question of the Day Baskets, made in Dresden, Ohio, are collectible, hand-woven, hard-maple baskets. A 1983 Market Basket from the J.W. Collection Series originally sold for $32.95. At an auction in 1997, one of these baskets sold for $1,550. Write an equation to determine how much the value increased. $\$32.95 + x = \$1,550$

Assess Prerequisite Skills

Ask students to read through the list of objectives presented in "What you'll learn in Chapter 12." You may wish to ask them what each of the objectives means or if they have experienced or used any of these math concepts before.

 Building Portfolios

Encourage students to revise their portfolios as they study this chapter. Have them add to their portfolios examples of algebra concepts they have mastered.

 Math and the Family

In the *Family Letters and Activities* booklet (pp. 23–24), you will find a letter to the parents explaining what students will study in Chapter 12. An activity appropriate for the whole family is also available.

What you'll learn in Chapter 12

- to use models to solve equations,
- to solve problems using an equation,
- to complete function tables, and
- to graph functions from function tables.

 CD-ROM Program

Activities for Chapter 12
- Chapter 12 Introduction
- Interactive Lessons 12-2, 12-3, 12-4, 12-6
- Extended Activity 12-5
- Assessment Game
- Resource Lessons 12-1 through 12-6

CHAPTER Project

COLLECT A FORTUNE

In this project, you will start an imaginary collection of at least five items such as sport cards, coins, stamps, or dolls. Or you can use a collection you already have. You will need to research the history of the value of these items. You will prepare a table or some type of display showing the value of your collection to present to your class.

Getting Started

- Look at the table. Which card was worth the most in August, 1996? Which card was worth the most in June, 1997?

- How could you determine whether the value of Kristin's six-card collection increased or decreased in the 10 months between August, 1996 and June, 1997?

Kristin's Card Collection

Player	Value Aug., 1996	Value June, 1997
John Stockton	$10	$7.50
Michael Jordan	$25	$20
Larry Bird	$18	$18
Charles Barkley	$50	$60
Shaquille O'Neal	$80	$30
Rudy Tomjanovich	$15	$15

Technology Tips

- Use a **spreadsheet** to find the value of a collection.

- Use **computer software** to make graphs.

interNET CONNECTION Research For up-to-date information on card collecting, visit:

www.glencoe.com/sec/math/mac/mathnet

Working on the Project

You can use what you'll learn in Chapter 12 to help you make your presentation.

Page	Exercise
478	32
487	33
503	27
507	Alternative Assessment

Instructional Resources ▶ ▶ ▶

A recording sheet to help students organize their data for the Chapter Project is shown at the right and is available in the *Investigations and Projects Masters,* p. 64.

CHAPTER Project
NOTES

Objectives Students should
- research the history and value of collectibles.
- prepare a display of the values of their collection.

Project Pointer You may suggest that students begin a *Project Folder* to keep their work as they complete each stage of the Chapter Project. The completed project may also be added to their portfolios. Encourage students to bring their collections or pictures of them to class for their presentations.

Using the Table Ask students whether each card in Kristin's card collection increased or decreased in value from August 1996 to June 1997.

***Investigations and Projects Masters,* p. 64**

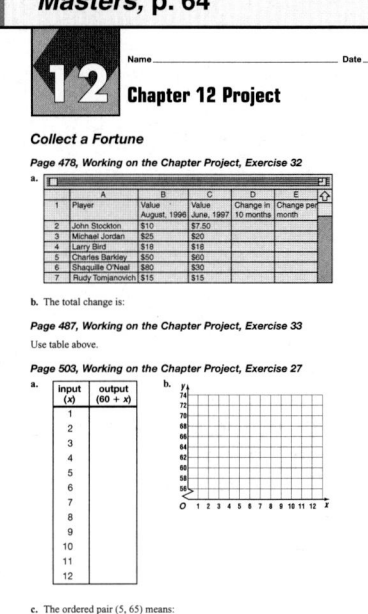

- *Study Guide Masters*, p. 84
- *Practice Masters*, p. 84
- *Enrichment Masters*, p. 84
- Transparencies 12-1, A and B
- *Hands-On Lab Masters*, p. 80

 CD-ROM Program
- Resource Lesson 12-1

Recommended Pacing	
Standard	Day 2 of 11
Honors	Day 2 of 11
Block	Day 1 of 6

1 FOCUS

 5-Minute Check
(Chapter 11)

1. Order −4, 6, 0, and −2 from least to greatest.
   −4, −2, 0, 6

Find each sum, difference, product, or quotient.

2. +5 − (−1) **6**
3. −7 + (−3) **−10**
4. −12(−4) **48**
5. 45 ÷ (−3) **−15**
6. Graph and label point A(−3, 2).

The 5-Minute Check is also available on **Transparency 12-1A** for this lesson.

Motivating the Lesson

Problem Solving Ask students how they would use an addition equation to solve the following problem. *A pie-eating contest is set up for 14 contestants. So far, 8 people have entered the contest. How many openings are left?*

$n + 8 = 14$; $n = 6$

12-1 Solving Addition Equations

What you'll learn

You'll learn to solve addition equations by using models.

When am I ever going to use this?

Knowing how to solve equations can help you determine golf scores.

 Example **Real World APPLICATION** 1

Justin is playing a board game and needs to roll an 8 so he can land on Community Chest. If he rolls a 5 on the first number cube, what must he roll on the second number cube? *This problem will be solved in Example 1.*

You can use cups and counters to solve equations. A cup represents the unknown value, yellow counters represent positive integers, and red counters represent negative integers.

Games Refer to the beginning of the lesson. What must Justin roll on the second number cube?

Explore   The number on the first number cube is 5. Justin wants the total of the two number cubes to be 8.

Plan   Let *d* represent the number tossed on the second number cube. Translate the problem into an equation using the variable *d*. Model the equation and solve.

Solve

number on the first number cube	plus	number on the second number cube	equals	sum of the two numbers
5	+	d	=	8

$$5 + d = 8$$

To get the cup by itself, subtract 5 from each side.

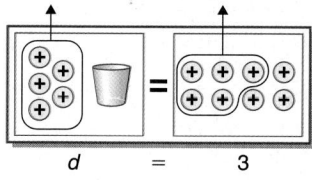

$$d = 3$$

The solution is 3. Justin must roll a 3 on the second number cube.

Examine   Check the solution by replacing the value of the variable in the original equation.

Check: $5 + d = 8$
$5 + 3 \stackrel{?}{=} 8$ *Replace d with 3.*
$8 = 8$ ✓

 ## Cross-Curriculum Cue

Inform the other teachers on your team that your students are studying algebraic equations. Suggestions for curriculum integration are:

Health: daily dietary needs in grams; weight
Social Studies: shifts in population
Physical Education: score-keeping
Earth Science: barometric pressure

Example **2** Use cups and counters to solve $c + 3 = -9$.

Use a cup to represent c. Add 3 positive counters on the left side of the mat to represent $+3$. Place 9 negative counters on the right side of the mat to represent -9.

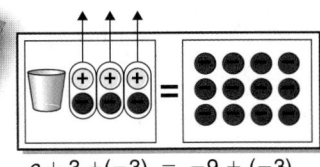

$$c + 3 \qquad = \qquad -9$$

To get the cup by itself, you need to remove 3 positive counters from each side. Since there are no positive counters on the right side of the mat, add 3 negative counters to each side to make 3 zero pairs on the left side of the mat. Then remove the zero pairs.

$$c + 3 + (-3) = -9 + (-3)$$

$$c \qquad = \qquad -12$$

Check: $c + 3 = -9$ *Replace c with –12.*

$$-12 + 3 \stackrel{?}{=} -9$$
$$-9 = -9 \checkmark$$

The solution is -12.

CHECK FOR UNDERSTANDING

Communicating Mathematics

Read and study the lesson to answer each question. 1–2. See margin.

1. *Explain* how the model represents $5 + w = -8$.

2. *Show* how to model the equation $y + 2 = 4$.

Lesson 12-1 Solving Addition Equations   **477**

Reteaching the Lesson

Activity Paper strips and a card labeled *x* will be needed. Without showing students, write a number sentence such as $-1 + 2 = 1$ on a paper strip. Cover one of the numbers with the *x* card. The student who correctly solves the equation writes the next sentence and so on.

Error Analysis

Watch for students who move the sum to the left side of the equation to add or subtract.

Prevent by reminding them to check their answers by replacing the variable with the solution.

Study Guide Masters, **p. 84**

478 Chapter 12

Guided Practice **Solve each equation. Use cups and counters if necessary.**

3. $x + 3 = 9$ **6**   4. $t + 25 = 15$ **−10**   5. $4 + g = 11$ **7**

6. $r + 2 = -5$ **−7**   7. $2 + c = -7$ **−9**   8. $-12 + m = 8$ **20**

9. When n is added to 10, the result is 4. What is the value of n? **−6**

EXERCISES

Practice **Solve each equation. Use cups and counters if necessary.**

10. $y + 7 = 18$ **11**   11. $x + 3 = -2$ **−5**   12. $4 + g = 6$ **2**
13. $n + 4 = 3$ **−1**   14. $-3 + m = -3$ **0**   15. $z + 3 = 5$ **2**
16. $2 + s = -1$ **−3**   17. $2 + b = -4$ **−6**   18. $x + (-3) = -1$ **2**
19. $3 + p = -17$ **−20**   20. $d + 1 = -2$ **−3**   21. $t + 9 = -34$ **−43**

23. **−125**
22. $-3 + c = -5$ **−2**   23. $a + 25 = -100$ 24. $-9 + z = -18$ **−9**
25. $x + (-7) = -9$ **−2**   26. $f + 6 = -8$ **−14**   27. $-2 = m + 6$ **−8**

28. If $8 + c = -12$, what is the value of c? **−20**

29. Find the value of n if $n + (-4) = 6$. **10**

Applications and Problem Solving

30. *Games* In the card game Clubs, it is possible to have a negative score. Suppose your friend had a score of -5 in the second hand. This made her total score after two hands equal -2. What was her score in the first hand? **3**

31. *Sports* On the first day of the Masters golf tournament, Tiger Woods' score was -2. His score on the second day was added to the first day's score, and the total was -8. What was Tiger's score on the second day? **−6**

32. *Working on the* **CHAPTER Project** Refer to the table on page 475. Enter the three columns of the table into a spreadsheet.

a. Label column D *Change in 10 months*. Write a formula for cells D2, D3, D4, D5, D6, and D7 to find the amount of change in value of each basketball card.

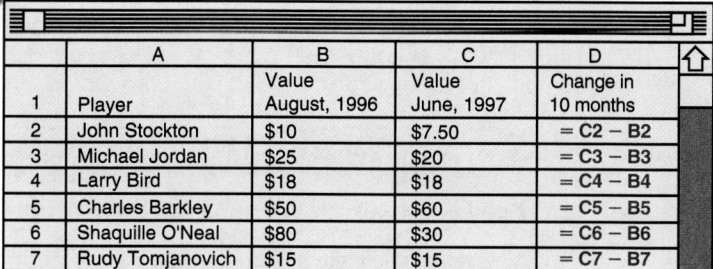

	A	B	C	D
1	Player	Value August, 1996	Value June, 1997	Change in 10 months
2	John Stockton	$10	$7.50	= C2 − B2
3	Michael Jordan	$25	$20	= C3 − B3
4	Larry Bird	$18	$18	= C4 − B4
5	Charles Barkley	$50	$60	= C5 − B5
6	Shaquille O'Neal	$80	$30	= C6 − B6
7	Rudy Tomjanovich	$15	$15	= C7 − B7

b. Write a formula for cell D8 that will find the total change in value of Kristin's six-card collection over the 10-month period. What was the total change in value? **D2 + D3 + D4 + D5 + D6 + D7; $47.50 decrease**

33. *Critical Thinking* Replace the boxes with the numbers 2, 3, 7, 8, and 9 to make a true equation. Use each number exactly once.

 + (−■) = ■ ■ Sample answer: 37 + (−9) = 28

Mixed Review

34. Standardized Test Practice Which of the following illustrates a reflection of the letter L? *(Lesson 11-8)* **A**

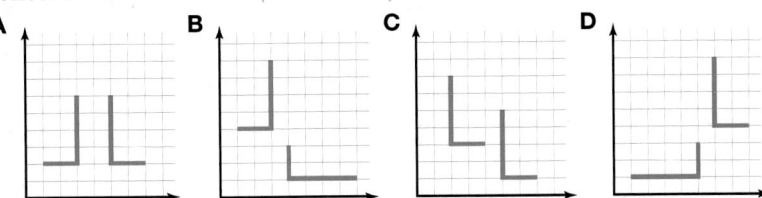

A   B   C   D

35. Find the product of −3 and −7. *(Lesson 11-5)* **21**

36. *Geometry* Find the area of the triangle.
(Lesson 10-2) **369 m²**

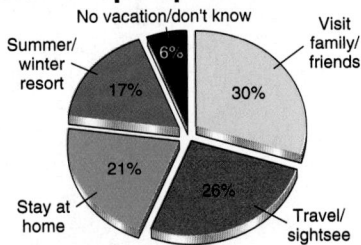

42 m
41 m
18 m

37. *Vacations* Refer to the circle graph. How much greater is the percent of vacationers that travel and sightsee than the percent that go to a resort? *(Lesson 2-4)* **9%**

How People Spend Vacations

No vacation/don't know 6%
Visit family/friends 30%
Summer/winter resort 17%
Stay at home 21%
Travel/sightsee 26%

For **Extra Practice**, see page 588.

MATH IN THE MEDIA

x + 3 = 2x
x = 3

"SAY, WAIT A MINUTE! JUST YESTERDAY SHE SAID X WAS EQUAL TO TWO!"

1. What assumption is the student making about the value of x?

2. How would you check the teacher's solution? **Replace x with 3.**

1. Sample answer: There is a one-to-one correspondence between variables and numbers.

Closing Activity

Modeling Have students use cups and counters to model an addition equation whose solution is 8.
Sample answer: $q + (-2) = 6$

Practice Masters, p. 84

■ Extending the Lesson ■

Enrichment Masters, p. 84

12-1 Enrichment

Try This Balancing Act!

Do you think you can choose four of these numbers and place them on the balance scale at the right so that the two sums are equal?

32, 43, 44, 54, 55

Experiment. Put 32 and 43 on the left part of the scale. The sum is 75. Now try to pick two of the remaining numbers to make a sum of 75. Each pair of numbers you pick will total more than 75. You have to start over again. This time put 43 and 44 on the left part of the scale. The sum is 87. Put 32 and 55 on the right part of the scale. That sum is also 87. You succeeded on the second try!

43 + 44 = 87   32 + 55 = 87

MATH IN THE MEDIA

Discuss with students how the cartoonist found humor in the student's assumption. Ask: *Why do you think the student became confused? How could he have avoided becoming confused?* Have students look through the comics and editorial section of a local Sunday newspaper to find more examples of humor involving mathematics.

Instructional Resources
- *Study Guide Masters*, p. 85
- *Practice Masters*, p. 85
- *Enrichment Masters*, p. 85
- Transparencies 12-2, A and B
- *Assessment and Evaluation Masters*, p. 323
- *Classroom Games*, pp. 33–35

CD-ROM Program
- Resource Lesson 12-2
- Interactive Lesson 12-2

Recommended Pacing	
Standard	Day 3 of 11
Honors	Day 3 of 11
Block	Day 2 of 6

1 FOCUS

5-Minute Check
(Lesson 12-1)

Solve each equation. Use cups and counters if necessary.
1. $4 + f = 10$ **6**
2. $p + 7 = 15$ **8**
3. $-1 + w = -3$ **-2**
4. $t + 5 = -9$ **-14**
5. $x + (-12) = 1$ **13**

The 5-Minute Check is also available on **Transparency 12-2A** for this lesson.

Motivating the Lesson
Communication Ask students how a subtraction equation can be written as an addition equation. Discuss the function of opposite integers in solving equations. Use the penalty system in American football to illustrate how subtracting an integer is the same as adding its opposite.

12-2 Solving Subtraction Equations

12-2

What you'll learn

You'll learn to solve subtraction equations by using models.

When am I ever going to use this?

Knowing how to solve equations can help you describe changes in temperature.

You probably have heard about the greenhouse effect on Earth. Did you know that it also affects other planets? Scientists have determined that, on Mars, the difference between the air temperature with the greenhouse effect and what it would be if it weren't for the greenhouse effect is 5° F. Suppose the temperature would be $-3°$ F on Mars if it weren't for the greenhouse effect. What is the air temperature with the greenhouse effect?

Computer model of Earth's ozone layers.

Example 1
CONNECTION

Earth Science Refer to the beginning of the lesson. What would the temperature be with the greenhouse effect?

Let g represent the temperature with the greenhouse effect. Translate the problem into an equation using the variable g. Then model the equation and solve.

temperature with the greenhouse effect	minus	actual temperature	equals	difference
g	$-$	-3	$=$	5

Rewrite as an addition equation. Remember that subtracting an integer is the same as adding its opposite.

$$g - (-3) = 5 \rightarrow g + 3 = 5$$

Use a cup to represent g. Add 3 positive counters on the left side of the mat to represent $+3$. Place 5 positive counters on the right side of the mat to represent $+5$.

To get the cup by itself, remove 3 positive counters from each side.

The solution is 2. The temperature with the greenhouse effect is 2° F.

Check the solution by replacing the value of the variable in the original equation.

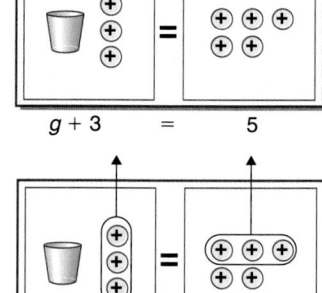

$g + 3 = 5$

$g = 2$

Check: $g - (-3) = 5$
$2 - (-3) \stackrel{?}{=} 5$ *Replace g with 2.*
$2 + 3 \stackrel{?}{=} 5$ *Rewrite as an addition equation.*
$5 = 5$ ✓

◄ **LOOK BACK**
Refer to Lesson 11-4 to review subtracting integers.

Multiple Learning Styles

 Auditory/Musical Have groups of students investigate the speed of sound in various substances. Then have them set up equations to find the difference between speeds in similar substances such as sea water and fresh water.

Study Hint

Reading Math Read the equation

$h - (-4) = -3$

as *h minus negative four equals negative three.*

② Use cups and counters to solve $h - (-4) = -3$.

Rewrite as an addition equation.

$$h - (-4) = -3 \rightarrow h + 4 = -3$$

Use a cup to represent h. Add 4 positive counters beside the cup on the left side of the mat to represent $+4$. Place 3 negative counters on the right side of the mat to represent -3.

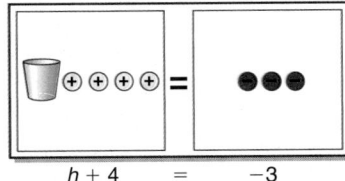

$$h + 4 \quad = \quad -3$$

To get the cup by itself, remove 4 positive counters from each side. Since there are no positive counters on the right side of the mat, add 4 negative counters to each side to make 4 zero pairs on the left side of the mat. Then remove the zero pairs.

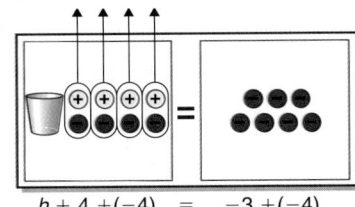

$$h + 4 + (-4) \quad = \quad -3 + (-4)$$

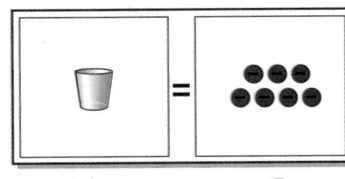

$$h \quad = \quad -7$$

Check: $h - (-4) = -3$

$-7 - (-4) \stackrel{?}{=} -3$ *Replace h with -7.*

$-7 + 4 \stackrel{?}{=} -3$ *Rewrite as an addition equation.*

$-3 = -3$ ✓

The solution is -7.

③ Use cups and counters to solve $x - 6 = -2$.

Rewrite as an addition equation.

$$x - 6 = -2 \rightarrow x + (-6) = -2$$

Use a cup to represent x. Add 6 negative counters on the left side of the mat to represent -6. Place 2 negative counters on the right side of the mat to represent -2.

(continued on the next page)

Lesson 12-2 Solving Subtraction Equations   **481**

Reading Mathematics Have students practice writing an equation from a word problem by using cue words such as difference and total change. Have students write word problems and challenge others to determine the equation needed to solve the problem.

Teaching Tip Before Example 1, have students identify the variable, the number to be subtracted from the variable, and the difference to be sure they are setting up the equation properly.

In-Class Examples

For Example 1
Best Tire Co.'s balance sheet records profits and losses in millions of dollars. Last year's loss was -1. This year's loss was $+2$. What was the change in millions of dollars?
+3 million dollars

For Example 2
Use cups and counters to solve $q - (-8) = 4$. **−4**

For Example 3
Use cups and counters to solve $c - 7 = -1$. **6**

Teaching Tip For students who have difficulty believing that subtracting is the same as adding the opposite, try this activity. To model $h - (-4)$, have students place a cup on one side of the mat. The expression says to subtract -4 from the cup, which is not possible. Add 4 zero pairs to the cup and then have students subtract -4. The result is $h + 4$.

Transparency 12-2B contains a teaching aid for this lesson.

Investigations for the Special Education Student

This blackline master booklet helps you plan for the needs of your special education students by providing long-term projects along with teacher notes. Investigation 13, *How Does Your Garden Grow?*, may be used with this chapter.

Check for Understanding

If students need additional practice or instruction after completing Exercises 1–10, one of these options may be helpful.
- Extra Practice, see p. 588
- Reteaching Activity
- *Study Guide Masters*, p. 85
- *Practice Masters*, p. 85

Additional Answers

1. **Sample answer:** The 3 negative counters and the cup represent $y - 3$ and the 4 positive counters represent 4.

3. **Sample answer:** If the equation involves addition, you subtract counters. If the equation involves subtraction, you add counters.

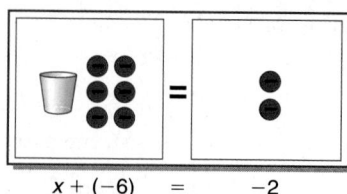

$$x + (-6) = -2$$

To get the cup by itself, remove 6 negative counters from each side. Since there are not enough negative counters on the right side of the mat, add 6 positive counters to each side to make 6 zero pairs on the left side of the mat. Then remove all zero pairs.

$$x + (-6) + 6 = -2 + 6$$

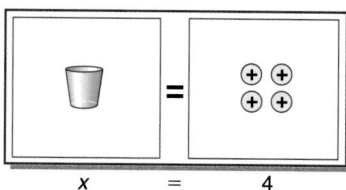

$$x = 4$$

Check: $x - 6 = -2$

$\qquad 4 - 6 \stackrel{?}{=} -2$ *Replace x with 4.*

$\qquad 4 + (-6) \stackrel{?}{=} -2$ *Rewrite as an addition equation.*

$\qquad -2 = -2$ ✓

The solution is 4.

Communicating Mathematics

Read and study the lesson to answer each question.

1. *Explain* how the model represents $y - 3 = 4$. **See margin.**

2. *Show* how to model the equation $x - 2 = 6$. **See students' work.**

Math Journal

3. *Write* a few sentences explaining how you know whether to add or subtract counters from each side of the equation mat. **See margin.**

Guided Practice

Use cups and counters to solve each equation.

4. $x - 8 = 2$ **10**
5. $a - 4 = -6$ **-2**
6. $g - 4 = 11$ **15**
7. $y - 2 = 5$ **7**
8. $c - 2 = -7$ **-5**
9. $z - 7 = 9$ **16**

482   Chapter 12 Algebra: Exploring Equations

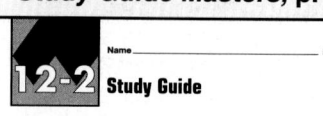

12-2 Study Guide

Solving Subtraction Equations

To **solve an equation** means to find a value for the variable that makes the equation true.

Example   Use cups and counters to solve $m - 2 = 5$.

Rewrite as an addition equation.

$m - 2 = 5 \longrightarrow m + (-2) = 5$

Use a cup to represent m. Add 2 negative counters on the left side of the mat to represent -2. Place 5 positive counters on the right side of the mat to represent $+5$.

$m + (-2) = 5$

To get the cup by itself, you need to remove 2 negative counters from each side. Since there are no negative counters on the right side of the mat, add 2 positive counters to each side to make 2 zero pairs on the left side of the mat. Then remove the zero pairs.

$m + (-2) + 2 = 5 + 2 \qquad m = 7$

Solve each equation. Use cups and counters if necessary.

1. $a - 3 = 5$ **8**
2. $r - 5 = -8$ **-3**
3. $h - 2 = 0$ **-2**
4. $j - 8 = 8$ **16**
5. $77 = d - 12$ **89**
6. $n - 20 = -5$ **15**
7. $r - (-10) = 15$ **5**
8. $y - (-1) = 4$ **3**
9. $n - (-23) = -55$ **-78**
10. If $h - 9 = 25$, what is the value of h? **34**
11. Find the value of c if $c - 19 = -10$. **9**

© Glencoe/McGraw-Hill   T85   *Mathematics: Applications and Connections, Course 1*

Reteaching the Lesson

Activity   Have students create flashcards by writing a subtraction equation on one side of a card and the solution on the other side. Then have pairs of students quiz each other to see who can solve a set of equations first.

Error Analysis

Watch for students who add or subtract counters from only one side of an equation.

Prevent by reminding students that any operation performed on one side of an equation must be performed on the other side as well.

10. Sports After a loss of 5 yards, Ayani had a total of 16 yards. How many yards did he have before the 5-yard loss? **21 yards**

EXERCISES

Practice

Solve each equation. Use cups and counters if necessary.

11. $g - 4 = -6$ **−2**   12. $z - (-3) = 5$ **2**   13. $x - 1 = -3$ **−2**

14. $c - 5 = -5$ **0**   15. $b - 6 = -7$ **−1**   16. $r - 7 = -15$ **−8**

17. $z - 10 = -18$ **−8**   18. $x - (-2) = -1$ **−3** 19. $t - 2 = 3$ **5**

20. $h - (-5) = -2$ **−7** 21. $y - 3 = 4$ **7**   22. $x - 9 = 4$ **13**

23. $d - 5 = -2$ **3**   24. $s - 8 = -1$ **7**   25. $v - 12 = -10$ **2**

26. Find the value of x if $x - (-8) = -14$. **−22**

27. If $t - (-13) = 4$, what is the value of t? **−9**

Applications and Problem Solving

28. **Earth Science** Refer to the graph.
   a. How did the temperature change between January 18 and January 19? **It dropped 9°.**
   b. The low temperature on January 21 was 5 degrees higher than the low on January 20. What was the low on January 21? **3°**

WEEKEND LOW TEMPERATURES
Jan. 18   5°
Jan. 19   −4°
Jan. 20   −2°

29a. $-140 + r = -35$

29. **Diving** A diver begins to go back to the boat from 140 feet below sea level. A few minutes later, the diver is 35 feet below sea level.
   a. Write an addition equation to represent the diver's movement.
   b. How many feet did the diver rise? **105 feet**

30. **Critical Thinking** Describe how you would solve $5 - x = -4$. **See margin.**

Mixed Review

31. **Standardized Test Practice** Sabra collected 6 silver dollars. Her friend Logan gave her some more, and then she had 15. To find out how many silver dollars she was given, Sabra wrote $s + 6 = 15$. What is the value of s? *(Lesson 12-1)* **B**

   A 6   B 9   C 21   D 90

32. **Measurement** Find the area of a circle with a diameter of 6 meters to the nearest tenth. Use 3.14 for pi. *(Lesson 10-3)* **about 28.3 m²**

33. **Geometry** Use a protractor and draw an angle that measures 70°. *(Lesson 9-2)* **See students' work.**

34. **Statistics** Refer to the circle graph of students' favorite sports. How much more of the students' votes were for swimming than tennis? *(Lesson 2-4)* **0.02**

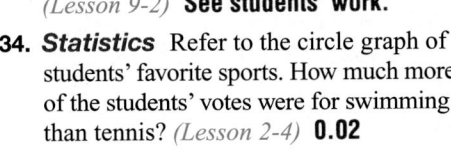
Favorite Sport
Swimming 0.10, Football 0.28, Tennis 0.08, Volleyball 0.16, Baseball 0.21, Basketball 0.17

For **Extra Practice**, see page 588.

Lesson 12-2 Solving Subtraction Equations   **483**

Extending the Lesson

Activity Have groups write subtraction equations with variables on cards placed facedown in a pile. Give each student five marbles. Then have group members take turns selecting a card and solving the equation. Students turn in one marble for each correct answer. The winner is the student who gets rid of his or her marbles first.

Assignment Guide

Core: 11–29 odd, 30–34
Enriched: 12–26 even, 28–34

4 ASSESS

Closing Activity

Speaking Ask students what equation would be used to solve the following question. *How many old pennies did a collector begin with if she traded 36 and has 52 left? x − 36 = 52; 88*

Chapter 12, Quiz A (Lessons 12-1 and 12-2) is available in the *Assessment and Evaluation Masters*, p. 323.

Additional Answer

30. **Sample answer: Use guess and check.** $5 - 3 = 2$; $5 - 6 = -1$; $5 - 9 = -4$; $x = 9$

- *Study Guide Masters*, p. 86
- *Practice Masters*, p. 86
- *Enrichment Masters*, p. 86
- Transparencies 12-3, A and B
- *Assessment and Evaluation Masters*, pp. 322, 323
- *School to Career Masters*, p. 12
- CD-ROM Program
  - Resource Lesson 12-3
  - Interactive Lesson 12-3

Recommended Pacing	
Standard	Day 4 of 11
Honors	Day 4 of 11
Block	Day 2 of 6

1 FOCUS

5-Minute Check
(Lesson 12-2)

Solve each equation. Use cups and counters if necessary.

1. $a - 6 = -8$ −2
2. $x - 6 = 2$ 8
3. $b - 3 = -7$ −4
4. $z - 2 = 5$ 7
5. $y - (-2) = -4$ −6

The 5-Minute Check is also available on **Transparency 12-3A** for this lesson.

Motivating the Lesson

Hands-On Activity Bring in several grocery advertisements from the newspaper. Have students calculate cost per unit for several advertised items by using the equation $n \cdot u = t$, where n is the number of units, u is the unit cost, and t is the total cost. Discuss why smart consumers figure the price per unit for multi-item packages.

12-3 Solving Multiplication and Division Equations

What you'll learn

You'll learn to solve equations involving multiplication and division using models.

When am I ever going to use this?

Knowing how to solve equations involving multiplication and division can help you find your rate of pay.

If you love your dog, don't let it eat chocolate. An ingredient in chocolate, theobromine, can be poisonous to dogs. Just 2 ounces of chocolate could harm a 10-pound pup. Zina determines that half of her chocolate bar is enough to harm a 10-pound pup. How much does her chocolate bar weigh? *This problem will be solved in Example 3.*

Cups and counters can be used to solve multiplication and division equations.

Example 1

Use cups and counters to solve $3s = 15$.

Use three cups to represent $3s$. Place them on the left side of the mat. Place 15 positive counters on the right side of the mat to represent 15.

$$3s \quad = \quad 15$$

Since there are three cups, undo the multiplication by dividing each side by 3. Show division by 3 by forming 3 equal groups on each side of the mat.

$$\frac{3s}{3} = \frac{15}{3}$$
$$s = 5$$

Check: $3s = 15$
$$3(5) \overset{?}{=} 15 \quad \textit{Replace s with 5.}$$
$$15 = 15 \quad \checkmark$$
The solution is 5.

2 Use cups and counters to solve $2x = -4$.

Use two cups to represent $2x$. Place them on the left side of the mat. Place 4 negative counters on the right side of the mat to represent -4.

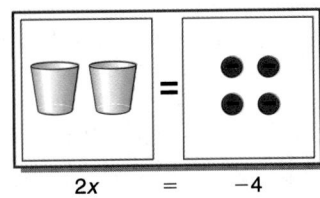

$$2x \quad = \quad -4$$

Undo the multiplication by dividing each side by 2. Show division by 2 by forming 2 equal groups on each side of the mat.

$$\frac{2x}{2} \quad = \quad \frac{-4}{2}$$

$$x \quad = \quad -2$$

Check: $2x = -4$

$2(-2) \stackrel{?}{=} -4$ *Replace x with −2.*

$-4 = -4$ ✓

The solution is -2.

CONNECTION **3** **Life Science** Refer to the beginning of the lesson. How much does Zina's chocolate bar weigh?

First, write an equation to describe the situation. Let b represent the weight of the chocolate bar.

one half of bar	*equals*	*2 ounces*
$\frac{1}{2}b$	$=$	2

Solve the equation $\frac{1}{2}b = 2$.

$\frac{1}{2}b = 2$

$2\left(\frac{1}{2}b\right) = 2(2)$ *Undo the division by multiplying each side by 2.*

$b = 4$

Check: $\frac{1}{2}b = 2$

$\frac{1}{2}(4) \stackrel{?}{=} 2$ *Replace b with 4.*

$2 = 2$ ✓

The solution is 4. Zina's chocolate bar weighs 4 ounces.

MathPASS CD-ROM

This CD-ROM offers a complete, self-paced mathematics curriculum. Each lesson includes a pretest, tutorial, guided practice, and posttest. MathPASS Lesson 39 is correlated to this Student Edition lesson.
For Windows & Macintosh

---

2 TEACH

Transparency 12-3B contains a teaching aid for this lesson.

Thinking Algebraically If students ask how to use counters to solve a problem like Example 3, use the following illustration.

$$\frac{1}{2}n = -8$$

Cut a cup in half to represent $\frac{1}{2}n$ and place on the left side of the mat. Place 8 negative markers on the right side of the mat. Double both the half cup and the counters showing $2 \times \frac{1}{2}n = 2(-8)$. Thus, $n = -16$.

Another method is to model $\frac{1}{2}n = -8$ as described above. Add $\frac{1}{2}$ cup to each side. Since $\frac{1}{2}$ cup $= -8$, replace $\frac{1}{2}$ cup on right side with -8 counters. The result is $n = -16$.

In-Class Examples

Use cups and counters to solve each equation.

For Example 1
Use cups and counters to solve $4x = 12$. **3**

For Example 2
Use cups and counters to solve $3m = -15$. **−5**

For Example 3
In a Walk-a-Thon, $\frac{5}{6}$ of the students who participated brought water bottles. If 36 students participated, how many did *not* bring water bottles? **6**

Teaching Tip After Example 3, lead students to see that multiplication and division equations are solved by using the inverse operation.

Check for Understanding

If students need additional practice or instruction after completing Exercises 1–10, one of these options may be helpful.
- Extra Practice, see p. 589
- Reteaching Activity
- *Study Guide Masters*, p. 86
- *Practice Masters*, p. 86

Assignment Guide

Core: 11–31 odd, 34–38
Enriched: 12–30 even, 31, 32, 34–38
All: Self Test, 1–10

Have students share with the class what they used for counters. On the chalkboard, make a list of equations that students used. Which operation was used most often to solve the equations?

Study Guide Masters, p. 86

12-3 Study Guide

Solving Multiplication and Division Equations

When the variable of an equation is multiplied by a number, divide each side of the equation by the number to get the variable by itself.

Example 1 Use cups and counters to solve $3n = -9$.

When the variable of an equation is divided by a number, multiply each side of the equation by that number to get the variable by itself.

Example 2 Use cups and counters to solve $\frac{1}{3}p = 2$.

Solve each equation. Use cups and counters if necessary.
1. $5t = 15$ **3**
2. $2k = -14$ **−7**
3. $4p = -16$ **−4**
4. $3m = -15$ **−5**
5. $6n = -24$ **−4**
6. $\frac{1}{2}c = 2$ **4**
7. $\frac{1}{3}r = 4$ **12**
8. $\frac{1}{2}f = -3$ **−6**
9. $\frac{1}{2}y = -1$ **−4**

© Glencoe/McGraw-Hill   T86   Mathematics: Applications and Connections, Course 1

Communicating Mathematics

Read and study the lesson to answer each question.

1. *Tell* what equation is represented by the model. Then solve. **$4x = 8$; $x = 2$**

2. *Make* a model to represent the equation $3x = -9$. Then solve the equation. **See Answer Appendix.**

3. Sample answer: They're both correct. Dividing by 2 is the same as multiplying by one-half.

3. *You Decide* Zack says that to solve the equation $2k = 50$ he would divide each side by 2. Aubrey says she would multiply each side by $\frac{1}{2}$. Who is correct? Explain.

Guided Practice

Use items you can find in your home to explain to a family member how you solve an equation involving multiplication or division.

Complete each solution.

4. $3x = 9$ **3, 3; 3**
$\frac{3x}{\blacksquare} = \frac{9}{\blacksquare}$
$x = \blacksquare$

5. $8g = 16$ **8, 8, 2**
$\frac{8g}{\blacksquare} = \frac{16}{\blacksquare}$
$g = \blacksquare$

6. $\frac{1}{4}a = -7$ **4, 4; −28**
$\blacksquare\left(\frac{1}{4}a\right) = \blacksquare(-7)$
$a = \blacksquare$

Solve each equation. Use cups and counters if necessary.

7. $5e = 25$ **5**
8. $2c = 6$ **3**
9. $\frac{1}{2}n = -5$ **−10**

10. *Money Matters* Margie's average weekly earnings in 1997 were three times higher than in 1980. She earned $624 per week in 1997. How much did she earn per week in 1980? **$208**

EXERCISES

Practice

Solve each equation. Use cups and counters if necessary.

11. $9a = 18$ **2**
12. $3x = 3$ **1**
13. $2c = -6$ **−3**
14. $4k = -20$ **−5**
15. $4x = -36$ **−9**
16. $5e = -15$ **−3**
17. $16x = 4$ **$\frac{1}{4}$**
18. $5h = 5$ **1**
19. $4m = 20$ **5**
20. $2x = -16$ **−8**
21. $\frac{1}{8}y = 3$ **24**
22. $\frac{1}{3}x = 12$ **36**
23. $\frac{n}{2} = 19$ **38**
24. $53 = \frac{1}{2}y$ **106**
25. $3.5s = 7$ **2**
26. $24.8 = 1.24a$ **20**
27. $\frac{1}{4}w = -9$ **−36**
28. $-12 = \frac{3}{8}g$ **−32**

29. Solve the equation $3.1t = 25.42$. **8.2**

30. Roni's mother Nikki is 3 times as old as Roni is. Nikki is 39. How old is Roni? **13**

Applications and Problem Solving

31. *Money Matters* In 1995, Michael Jordan's income from endorsements was 10 times his salary for playing basketball. If his income from endorsements was about $40 million, about how much was his salary for playing basketball? **$4 million**

32. *Money Matters* The track team has 19 members. They stopped at a restaurant on the way home from a meet. If the total bill was $90.25, what was the average cost of each team member's meal? **$4.75**

Reteaching the Lesson

Activity Have students use an even number of positive or negative counters. They should then substitute the number of counters for $\blacksquare$ in $2n = \blacksquare$. Ask: *Can you solve the equation by using the counters? How?* Continue with $\frac{1}{2}n = \blacksquare$.

Error Analysis

Watch for students who omit negative signs in their solutions.

Prevent by having them check their solutions in the equations.

33. Working on the 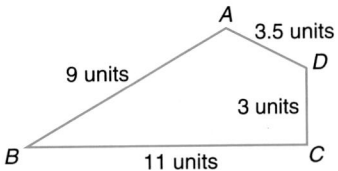 **CHAPTER Project** Refer to the spreadsheet you made for Exercise 32 on page 478. Label column E *Change per month*. Write a formula for cells E2, E3, E4, E5, E6, and E7 to find the change in value per month for each card. **See Answer Appendix.**

34. Critical Thinking Without solving, tell which equation, $\frac{1}{4}x = 13$ or $\frac{1}{8}x = 13$, has the greater solution. Explain. **See Answer Appendix.**

Mixed Review **35. Algebra** Solve the equation $y - 11 = -8$. *(Lesson 12-2)* **3**

36. If the figure at the right is a scale drawing with a scale 1 unit = 100 meters, what is the actual length of $\overline{AB}$? *(Lesson 8-3)* **900 meters**

A
3.5 units
D
9 units
3 units
B
11 units
C

 37. Standardized Test Practice Melika was making a quilt for her room. She had $9\frac{1}{2}$ yards of material. It took 7 yards for the quilt. How much material was not used for the quilt? *(Lesson 6-6)* **C**

A $16\frac{1}{2}$ yd

B $9\frac{1}{2}$ yd

C $2\frac{1}{2}$ yd

D $1\frac{1}{2}$ yd

E Not Here

*For **Extra Practice**, see page 589.*

38. List all the common factors of 20 and 50. *(Lesson 5-3)* **1, 2, 5, 10**

CHAPTER 12

Mid-Chapter Self Test

Solve each equation. Use cups and counters if necessary. *(Lessons 12-1 and 12-2)*

1. $y + 6 = 12$ **6**   **2.** $x + 6 = -3$ **-9**   **3.** $m + (-7) = 14$ **21**   **4.** $t - 8 = 14$ **22**

5. $k - (-10) = -5$ **-15**   **6.** $3g = 18$ **6**   **7.** $2x = -4$ **-2**   **8.** $\frac{1}{3}y = -9$ **-27**

Solve.

9. Transportation Marta's car averages 24 miles per gallon. Her odometer shows that she has driven 72 miles. How many gallons of gasoline has her car used? *(Lesson 12-2)* **3 gallons**

10. Money Matters Lorenzo spends one-third of his monthly allowance on snacks. If he spends $4 on snacks every month, how much money does he get for his allowance? *(Lesson 12-3)* **$12**

Extending the Lesson

Enrichment Masters, p. 86

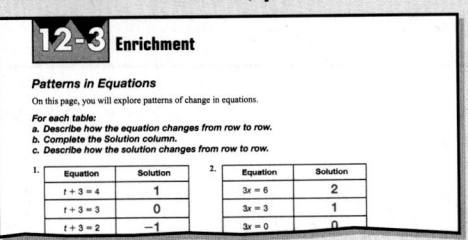

12-3 Enrichment

Patterns in Equations

On this page, you will explore patterns of change in equations.

For each table:
a. Describe how the equation changes from row to row.
b. Complete the Solution column.
c. Describe how the solution changes from row to row.

Equation	Solution
t + 3 = 4	1
t + 3 = 3	0
t + 3 = 2	-1

Equation	Solution
3x = 6	2
3x = 3	1
3x = 0	0

Activity Have students work in pairs to create word problems that can be solved by using multiplication or division equations.

Instructional Resources

- *Study Guide Masters*, p. 87
- *Practice Masters*, p. 87
- *Enrichment Masters*, p. 87
- Transparencies 12-4, A and B
- *Diversity Masters*, p. 12
- CD-ROM Program
  - Resource Lesson 12-4
  - Interactive Lesson 12-4

Recommended Pacing	
Standard	Day 5 of 11
Honors	Day 5 of 11
Block	Day 3 of 6

1 FOCUS

5-Minute Check
(Lesson 12-3)

Solve each equation. Use cups and counters if necessary.

1. $4x = -24$ **−6**
2. $\frac{1}{2}y = -7$ **−14**
3. $\frac{1}{5}k = 30$ **150**
4. $3n = 36$ **12**
5. Marta's car averages 24 miles per gallon of gas. If she drove 72 miles on a trip, how many gallons of gas did her car use? **3**

The 5-Minute Check is also available on **Transparency 12-4A** for this lesson.

Motivating the Lesson

Communication Have students read the opening paragraph. Ask students how many operations would be involved in finding the number of games Lupita bowled. Ask for examples of equations that involve two operations.

12-4 Solving Two-Step Equations

What you'll learn

You'll learn to solve two-step equations using models.

When am I ever going to use this?

Knowing how to solve two-step equations can help you determine total costs when extra charges are added.

Lupita went bowling at Great Lanes Sport Center. Shoe rental was $1, and games were $2 each. If she spent $9 on shoe rental and games, how many games did she bowl?

Examples · **Real World APPLICATION**

LOOK BACK
Refer to Lesson 11-6A to review the work backward strategy.

Sports Refer to the beginning of the lesson. How many games did Lupita bowl?

Let g equal the number of games bowled. Translate the problem into an equation using the variable g. Then model the equation and solve.

$1 for shoe rental	plus	$2 per game	is	total cost
1	+	2g	=	9

The equation is $1 + 2g = 9$. This is a two-step equation because it involves two different operations, addition and multiplication. To solve this equation, you need to work backward using the reverse of the order of operations.

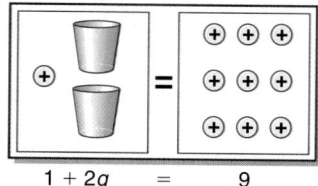

$$1 + 2g = 9$$

To get the cups by themselves, remove 1 positive counter from each side.

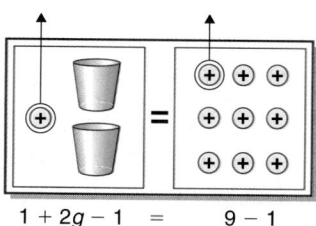

$$1 + 2g - 1 = 9 - 1$$

Multiple Learning Styles

Logical Have students use the work backward strategy to solve equations. For example, use 9 counters to represent $9. Take $1 out for shoe rental; then see how many $2 sets can be formed to find the number of games.

MathPASS CD-ROM

This CD-ROM offers a complete, self-paced mathematics curriculum. Each lesson includes a pretest, tutorial, guided practice, and posttest. MathPASS Lesson 40 is correlated to this Student Edition lesson.
For Windows & Macintosh

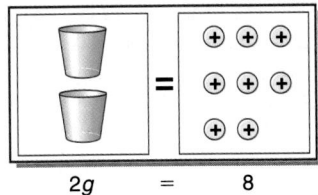

$$2g \quad = \quad 8$$

Since there are 2 cups, undo the multiplication by dividing each side by 2. Form 2 equal groups on each side of the mat.

$$\frac{2g}{2} \quad = \quad \frac{8}{2}$$
$$g \quad = \quad 4$$

The solution is 4. Lupita bowled 4 games.

Check by replacing the value of the variable in the original equation.

Check: $1 + 2g = 9$
$1 + 2(4) \stackrel{?}{=} 9$ *Replace g with 4.*
$9 = 9$ ✓

2 Use cups and counters to solve $2x + 6 = -4$.

Place two cups and 6 positive counters on the left side of the mat to represent $2x + 6$. Place 4 negative counters on the right side of the mat to represent -4.

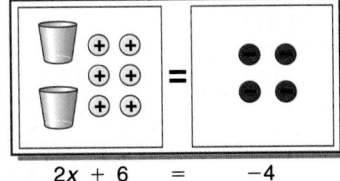

$$2x + 6 \quad = \quad -4$$

To get the cups by themselves, you need to remove 6 positive counters from each side. Since there are no positive counters on the right side of the mat, add 6 negative counters to each side to make 6 zero pairs on the left side of the mat. Then remove the zero pairs.

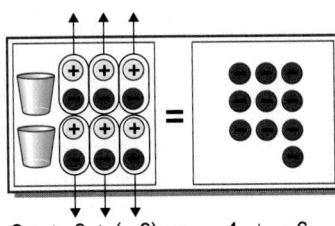

$$2x + 6 + (-6) \quad = \quad -4 + -6$$

(continued on the next page)

Lesson 12-4 Solving Two-Step Equations **489**

2 TEACH

Transparency 12-4B contains a teaching aid for this lesson.

In-Class Examples

For Example 1
A car rental agency charges $10 per day and $2 per mile to rent a car. How many miles did Kohana drive in one day if the car rental bill was $210?
100 miles

For Example 2
Use cups and counters to solve $3x + 7 = -11$. **−6**

Teaching Tip Before Example 2, review the rules for dividing positive and negative integers.

Using Discussion After demonstrating Example 2, ask students why six negative counters were added. Then ask what counters they would add to solve the equation $2x - 3 = -9$.
Add 3 positive counters to each side.

Check for Understanding

If students need additional practice or instruction after completing Exercises 1–6, one of these options may be helpful.
- Extra Practice, see p. 589
- Reteaching Activity
- *Study Guide Masters*, p. 87
- *Practice Masters*, p. 87

Assignment Guide

Core: 7–19 odd, 20–23
Enriched: 8–16 even, 18–23

Additional Answers

4. add 3 to each side; 7
5. add 4 to each side; 20

Study Guide Masters, p. 87

Study Guide 12-4

Solving Two-Step Equations

To solve a two-step equation, undo the addition or subtraction. Then undo the multiplication or division.

Example Use cups and counters to solve $3b - 2 = -5$.

Rewrite as an addition equation.
$$3b - 2 = -5 \longrightarrow 3b + (-2) = -5$$

Place 3 cups and 2 negative counters on the left side of the mat to represent $3b - 2$. Place 5 negative counters on the right side of the mat to represent -5.

$$3b - 2 = -5$$

To get the cups by themselves, you need to remove 2 negative counters from each side.

$$3b + (-2) - (-2) = -5 - (-2)$$

Now the equation is $3b = -3$. Undo the multiplication by dividing each side by 3. Show division by forming 3 equal groups on each side of the mat.

$$\frac{3b}{3} = \frac{-3}{3} \longrightarrow b = -1$$

Solve each equation.
1. $5x + 3 = 23$ **4**   2. $3a - 14 = 4$ **6**   3. $3y + 5 = -19$ **−8**
4. $5c + 6 = -29$ **−7**   5. $42 = 18 - 4v$ **−6**   6. $8 - 5w = -37$ **9**

7. Five less than 4 times a number is nineteen. What is the number? **6**

© Glencoe/McGraw-Hill   T87   Mathematics: Applications and Connections, Course 1

490 Chapter 12

Now the equation is $2x = -10$. Undo the multiplication by dividing each side by 2. Show division by forming 2 equal groups on each side of the mat.

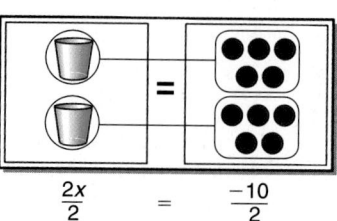

$$\frac{2x}{2} = \frac{-10}{2}$$
$$x = -5$$

Check:
$$2x + 6 = -4$$
$$2(-5) + 6 \stackrel{?}{=} -4 \quad \textit{Replace x with −5.}$$
$$-10 + 6 \stackrel{?}{=} -4$$
$$-4 = -4 \quad \checkmark \text{ The solution is } -5.$$

CHECK FOR UNDERSTANDING

Communicating Mathematics

Read and study the lesson to answer each question.

1. *Write* an equation for the model. Then solve. **$3x + 2 = -1$; $x = -1$**

2. *Make* a model to represent the equation $2x + 3 = -9$. Then solve the equation. **See students' work.; −6**

Guided Practice

Name the first step in solving each equation. Then solve. **4–5. See margin.**

3. subtract 2 from each side; 4

3. $3x + 2 = 14$ 4. $2a - 3 = 11$ 5. $\frac{1}{2}y - 4 = 6$

6. Twice a number, n, plus 7 is -21. What is the value of n? **−14**

EXERCISES

Practice

Solve each equation.

7. $2t + 5 = 13$ **4**   8. $\frac{1}{2}m + 3 = -5$ **−16** 9. $3h - 4 = 5$ **3**
10. $-11 = 4x - 3$ **−2** 11. $2x - (-34) = 16$ **−9** 12. $5r + 1 = 1$ **0**
13. $\frac{1}{4}t - 5 = -13$ **−32** 14. $-1 - 4y = 7$ **−2**   15. $-3y + 15 = 75$ **−20**

16. Ten less than twice a number is sixteen. What is the number? **13**

17. One half a number less five is eleven. Find the number. **32**

Applications and Problem Solving

18. *Money Matters* Claudio ordered three novelty T-shirts from a catalog. The total price including shipping charges was $50. If the total shipping cost was $5, how much did each T-shirt cost? **$15**

19. *Geometry* The perimeter of a rectangle is 40 inches. Find its length if its width is 4 inches. **16 inches**

490 Chapter 12 Algebra: Exploring Equations

Reteaching the Lesson

Activity Have students set up the model shown at the right. What equation does the model represent? What counters would you add to both sides to solve the equation? Solve the equation.
$3x + 2 = -1$; 2 negative counters; −1

20. *Critical Thinking* Use what you know about solving two-step equations to solve the equation $\frac{1}{4}(k - 8) = -3$. **−4**

Mixed Review

21. *Algebra* Solve for q in the equation $-7q = -56$. *(Lesson 12-3)* **8**

22. *Standardized Test Practice* Mr. Vega has 232 seedlings to be planted in flowerpots with 8 plants in each. How many flowerpots will he need to plant the seedlings? *(Lesson 11-6)* **B**

A 32   **B** 29   **C** 27   **D** 19   **E** Not Here

For **Extra Practice,** see page 589.

23. *Patterns* Find the next two numbers in the sequence 34, 36.5, 39, 41.5,... . *(Lesson 7-8)* **44, 46.5**

Let the Games Begin

Four In A Row

Math Skill
Solving Equations

Get Ready   This game is for two to ten players.

    12 index cards   scissors   poster board   beans

Get Set
- Cut three index cards in half. Write an equation using the variable a on each of the 6 cards. Cut another three index cards in half and write an equation using the variable b. Continue until you have six cards with equations for each of the variables, c, and d. No two equations using the same variable should have the same solution. Make a list of the solutions to the equations for each variable.

- Cut ten 6-inch by 5-inch playing cards from the poster board.

- On each playing card, copy the grid shown. Complete each column of the cards with solutions to the equations containing the indicated variable so that no two cards are identical.

a	b	c	d
	FREE		
		FREE	

Go
- Mix the equation cards and place the deck facedown.

- Each player should choose at least one playing card and cover the free spaces with beans.

- After an equation card is turned up, all players should solve the equation.

- When a solution is found on a card, the player should cover it with a bean.

- The winner is the first player to cover four spaces in a row either vertically, horizontally, or diagonally.

interNET **CONNECTION** Visit www.glencoe.com/sec/math/mac/mathnet for more games.

Lesson 12-4 Solving Two-Step Equations   **491**

■ Extending the Lesson ■

Enrichment Masters, p. 87

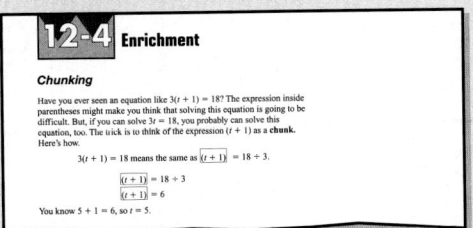

12-4 Enrichment

Chunking

Have you ever seen an equation like $3(t + 1) = 18$? The expression inside parentheses might make you think that solving this equation is going to be difficult. But, if you can solve $3t = 18$, you probably can solve this equation, too. The trick is to think of the expression $(t + 1)$ as a **chunk**.
Here's how.

$3(t + 1) = 18$ means the same as $3 \boxed{(t+1)} = 18 \div 3$.

$\boxed{(t+1)} = 18 \div 3$
$\boxed{(t+1)} = 6$

You know $5 + 1 = 6$, so $t = 5$.

Let the Games Begin

Make variations of Four In A Row by including decks with one-step equations, two-step equations, integer solutions, or non-integer solutions.
Additional resources for this game can be found on page 46 of the Classroom Games.

Practice Masters, p. 87

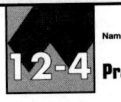

Name _____ Date _____

12-4 Practice

Solving Two-Step Equations

Solve each equation.

1. $2x - 5 = 3$ **4**   2. $4t + 5 = 37$ **8**

3. $7a + 6 = -36$ **−6**   4. $-8g + 7 = 47$ **−5**

5. $-3c - 9 = -24$ **5**   6. $5k - 7 = -52$ **−9**

7. $5s + 4 = -71$ **−15**   8. $6y - 30 = 18$ **8**

9. $7p - 70 = -21$ **7**   10. $-4m + 5 = 25$ **−5**

11. $6z - 1 = 23$ **4**   12. $2b + 12 = -6$ **−9**

13. $\frac{c}{5} + 6 = -2$ **−40**   14. $\frac{d}{4} - 8 = -5$ **12**

15. $\frac{g}{6} + 9 = 3$ **−42**   16. $2v - 3 = 9$ **6**

17. $-3x - 4 = 2$ **−2**   18. $6y + 10 = -8$ **−3**

19. $2w - 7 = -3$ **2**   20. $-4t + 15 = -1$ **4**

21. $-9k - 3 = -21$ **2**   22. $-6h + 7 = -17$ **4**

23. $5n + 3 = -17$ **−4**   24. $12g + 48 = 72$ **2**

25. $7v + 3 = -46$ **−7**   26. $\frac{s}{6} - 19 = 11$ **150**

27. $\frac{d}{4} + 9 = 2$ **28**   28. $\frac{q}{4} - 1 = 12$ **104**

29. $3 - \frac{a}{6} = 7$ **−24**   30. $5 + \frac{n}{-3} = 12$ **−21**

© Glencoe/McGraw-Hill   T87   Mathematics: Applications and Connections, Course 1

---

4 ASSESS

Closing Activity

Writing Have pairs of students write a general rule for solving two-step equations. Suggest that they include an example.

Lesson 12-4   **491**

Objective Students solve problems by using an equation.

Recommended Pacing	
Standard	Day 6 of 11
Honors	Day 6 of 11
Block	Day 3 of 6

1 FOCUS

Getting Started Have students act out the situation presented at the beginning of the lesson. Then have them work in pairs to answer Exercises 1–3. Have the class discuss the results. Then have them solve Exercise 4.

2 TEACH

Teaching Tip Make sure students understand that a variable always represents an unknown number.

In-Class Example

When school pictures were taken, 4 times as many students chose the laser background than the standard background. If 128 students chose the standard background, how many chose the laser background? **512 students**

Teaching Tip Make sure students understand that a variable always represents an unknown number.

Additional Answers

1. **Sample answer:** No; Ed's information may be more useful because it contains all the known amounts.

2. **Sample answer:** Maybe they thought CDs were $3 each.

3. **Sample answer:** Subtract 8 from the solution.

THINKING LAB

PROBLEM SOLVING

12-4B Use an Equation

A Follow-Up of Lesson 12-4

Carol and Ed have just returned from a yard sale where Carol bought a personal CD player and some CDs. Carol bought 8 CDs but thinks she was charged for more. Let's listen in!

Those were good bargains, but I think I was charged for too many CDs.

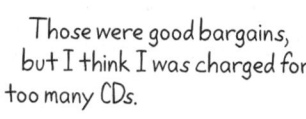
Carol

How many CDs did you get and how much did you pay?

I paid a total of $39 for a $15 CD player and 8 CDs. I can find out if that is correct by adding $15 and $16.

Ed

Or we could let n represent the number of CDs and translate the problem into an equation. The total is $2 times the number of CDs plus $15. This can be written as $39 = 2n + 15$.

But that's a two-step equation!

SALE	
CD Player	$15
All CDs	$2

It's not difficult. First, subtract 15 from each side. Now the equation is $2n = 24$. Dividing each side by 2 shows that you paid for 12 CDs. We better head back and get this straightened out.

THINK ABOUT IT

1–3. See margin.

1. *Compare and contrast* Carol's method of solving the problem to Ed's method. Do both methods contain the same information? If not, which information is more useful? Explain.

2. *Think* of a way to explain why Carol was charged $24 for the CDs.

3. *Tell* how the solution to Ed's equation could be used to find how many CDs were counted twice.

4. *Apply* the **use an equation** strategy to solve the following problem.

   At the same yard sale, Ed paid $27 for 12 CDs in a carrying case. How much did he pay for the case? **$3**

492 Chapter 12 Algebra: Exploring Equations

■ Reteaching the Lesson ■

Activity Have students play "Colored Candy Equations." Ask them to choose two candy colors and assign a point value to each one. Have each player make up problems such as the following. *I have a red one and enough green ones to make 8 points. How many green ones do I have?*

For **Extra Practice**, see page 589.

ON YOUR OWN

5. The third step of the 4-step plan for problem solving asks you to *solve*. **Tell** what other problem-solving strategy you could use to solve Carol's problem. **Sample answer: You could use the guess and check strategy.**

6. *Write a Problem* that can be solved by using an equation. **See students' work.**

7. *Reflect Back* Explain how solving a two-step equation is similar to using the work backward strategy. **See margin.**

MIXED PROBLEM SOLVING

> **STRATEGIES**
>
> Look for a pattern.
> Solve a simpler problem.
> Act it out.
> Guess and check.
> Draw a diagram.
> Make a chart.
> Work backward.

Solve. Use any strategy.

8. *Money Matters* Jillisa bought a clock radio for $9 less than the regular price. If she paid $32, what was the regular price? **$41**

9. *School* The sixth grade class is planning a field trip. There are 589 students in the sixth grade. Each bus holds 48 people. About how many buses will they need? **about 12 buses**

10. *Design* A designer wants to arrange 12 glass bricks into a rectangular shape with the least perimeter possible. How many blocks will be in each row? **3 or 4 blocks**

11. *Money Matters* Scott paid $2.50 in sales tax on a sweatshirt. The total cost was $42.49. What was the price of the sweatshirt before taxes? **$39.99**

12. *Geometry* A kite has two pairs of congruent sides. If two sides are 56 centimeters and 34 centimeters, what is the perimeter of the kite? **180 cm**

34 cm

56 cm

13. *Fashion* A catalog company offers 3 styles of ski sweaters each in 8 different colors. How many combinations of style and color are possible? **24 combinations**

14. *Language Arts* Science fiction books were the most popular items at the Book Fair. On Monday, 86 science fiction books were sold. This is 8 more than twice the amount that were sold on Thursday. How many science fiction books were sold on Thursday? **39 books**

15. *Travel* Kathy lives in Rockwood and works in Somerset. There is no direct route from Rockwood to Somerset, so Kathy goes through either Boulder Creek or Castleton. There is one road between Boulder Creek and Castleton. How many different ways can Kathy drive to work? **4 ways**

16. Standardized Test Practice The Swann family is going to a play. Ticket prices are shown below. Mr. Swann needs 2 adult tickets, 3 student tickets, and 1 child's ticket. Which number sentence could be used to find *T*, the cost in dollars of the tickets? **A**

Ticket Prices	
Adult	$7.25
Student	$3.50
Child under 4	$1.75

A $T = (2 \times 7.25) + (3 \times 3.50) + 1.75$

B $T = 6 \times (7.25 + 3.50 + 1.75)$

C $T = (2 + 3) \times (7.25 + 3.50 + 1.75)$

D $T = 7.25 + 3.50 + 1.75 + 6$

E $T = (2 + 7.25) \times (3 + 3.50) \times (1.75)$

Lesson 12-4B THINKING **LAB** 493

■ Extending the Lesson ■

Activity Have students solve the following problem. *The Saturday matinee at Cinema East sold 120 student tickets at $4.50 each. Some students also bought popcorn. If the theater took in a total of $600 from students that afternoon, what was the total amount students paid for popcorn?* **$60**

Check for Understanding
Use the results from Exercise 4 to determine whether students comprehend how to solve problems by using an equation.

Extra Practice If students need additional practice in problem solving, extra practice is available on the following pages.
- Use an Equation, see p. 589
- Mixed Problem Solving, see pp. 593–594

Assignment Guide
All: 5–16

4 ASSESS

Closing Activity
Writing Have students work in pairs using department store catalogs to create 2-step word problems that can be solved using equations.

Additional Answer
7. Sample answer: In solving a two-step equation, you undo the operations in reverse order of the order of operations.

GET READY

Objective Students find the input and output for a given function machine.

Optional Resources
Hands-On Lab Masters
• worksheet, p. 66

Manipulative Kit
• scissors

MANAGEMENT TIPS

Recommended Time
45 minutes

Getting Started Write the pattern 2, 5, 8, 11, 14, . . . on the chalkboard and have students name the next two numbers. Ask them to write a rule for the pattern. $n + 3$ Before students begin the activity, offer the following tips.
• Paper should be cut in two $4\frac{1}{4}$ in. × 11 in. strips.
• Start numbering the strips about $\frac{1}{3}$ of the way down from the top.

The **Activity** demonstrates using a model to evaluate a function. The activity uses a simple addition function. Students could extend the activity to make function machines for more complex functions and challenge others to make the answer strips.

COOPERATIVE LEARNING

12-5A **Function Machines**

A Preview of Lesson 12-5

✂ scissors

🎞 tape

In this lab, you will use what you have learned about solving equations to help you work with function machines. A *function machine* takes a number called the *input*, performs one or more operations on it, and produces a result called the *output*.

TRY THIS

Work in groups of three.

Make a function machine for the rule $\boxed{+5}$.
• Take a sheet of paper and cut it in half lengthwise.

• On one of the halves, cut four slits — two on each side of the paper. Make each slit at least one inch wide.

• From the other half of the paper, cut two narrow strips lengthwise. These strips should be able to pass through the slits you cut in the other half.

• On one of the narrow strips, write five consecutive numbers starting with 1. On the other narrow strip, write five consecutive numbers starting with 6. The numbers on both strips should align.

1	6
2	7
3	8
4	9
5	10

- Place the strips into the slits so that the numbers can be seen. Show 1 and 6. Once they appear, tape the ends of the strips together. When you pull the strips, they should move together. Mark the left-hand strip *input*, and the right-hand strip *output*. Write the function rule $\boxed{+5}$ between the input and output.

- Make a function table showing the input and the output.

input	output
1	
2	
3	
4	
5	

ON YOUR OWN

1. What is the output when the input is 3? **8**
2. What is the output when the input is 5? **10**
3. Suppose you added more input numbers to the left strip. What would the output be if the input was 8? **13**
4. What is the output if the input is x? **$x + 5$**
5. Make a function machine for the rule $\boxed{\times 3}$.
   a. What is the output when the input is 4? **12**
   b. What is the output when the input is 6? **18**
   c. Suppose you added more input numbers to the left strip. What would the output be if the input was 7? **21**
   d. What was the input if the output was 33? **11**
6. Make up your own function machine. Write pairs of inputs and outputs and have the other members of your group determine the rule. **See students' work.**
7. Temperature is usually measured in Celsius (°C) or Fahrenheit (°F). The formula for changing from Celsius to Fahrenheit is $F = \frac{9}{5} \times C + 32$. This formula is like a function. The input is the Celsius temperature, and the output is the Fahrenheit temperature. Find the output for each input.
   a. 60°C **140°F**   b. 15°C **59°F**   c. 0°C **32°F**   d. −10°C **14°F**

8. *Look Ahead* Use the function machine to find the set of outputs that correspond to the set of inputs 1, 3, 5, and 7. **1, 7, 13, 19**

Have students write a paragraph explaining how a function machine works. Have them include any difficulties they encountered and how they resolved them.

Teaching Tip In Exercise 7, you may suggest that students estimate the Fahrenheit temperatures first by rounding $\frac{9}{5}$ to 2 and 32 to 30. Students can use their estimates to check the reasonableness of their answers.

ASSESS

Have students complete Exercises 1–7. Watch for students who confuse input and output or who don't apply the function rule correctly. Make sure students move the paper strips one number at a time.

Use Exercise 8 to determine whether students understand how to use function machines.

Hands-On Lab Masters, p. 66

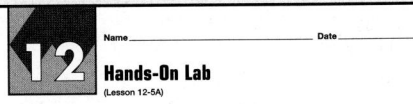

12 Name_____ Date_____
Hands-On Lab
(Lesson 12-5A)

Function Machines

On Your Own
1. The output is ____8____ when the input is 3.
2. The output is ____10____ when the input is 5.
3. The output is ____13____ when the input is 8.
4. The output is ____$x + 5$____ when the input is x.
5. a. The output is ____12____ when the input is 4.
   b. The output is ____18____ when the input is 6.
   c. The output is ____21____ when the input is 7.
   d. The input is ____11____ when the output is 33.

Sample answer:
6.

input	output
1	3
2	4
3	5
4	6
5	7

Rule: $x + 2$

7. a. 60°C = __140°F__
   b. 15°C = __59°F__
   c. 0°C = __32°F__
   d. −10°C = __14°F__

8. **Look Ahead** The set of outputs is __1, 7, 13, 19__.

Instructional Resources

- *Study Guide Masters,* p. 88
- *Practice Masters,* p. 88
- *Enrichment Masters,* p. 88
- Transparencies 12-5, A and B
- *Assessment and Evaluation Masters,* p. 324
- *Technology Masters,* p. 23
- CD-ROM Program
  - Resource Lesson 12-5
  - Extended Activity 12-5

Recommended Pacing

Standard	Days 7 & 8 of 11
Honors	Days 7 & 8 of 11
Block	Day 4 of 6

1 FOCUS

5-Minute Check
(Lesson 12-4)

Solve each equation.

1. $3t + 5 = 17$ **4**
2. $-10 = 4x - 2$ **−2**
3. $\frac{1}{4}m + 3 = 8$ **20**
4. $2k + 5 = 5$ **0**
5. Five less than twice a number is seven. Find the number. **6**

The 5-Minute Check is also available on **Transparency 12-5A** for this lesson.

Motivating the Lesson

Hands-On Activity Have pairs of students use centimeter cubes to make a design such as a capital letter *H.* Ask them how many cubes would be needed to make 2 models of the same design, 5 models of the same design, and *n* models of the same design.

What you'll learn

You'll learn to complete function tables.

When am I ever going to use this?

Knowing how to complete function tables can help you determine the amount of profit a business will make for selling any number of items.

Word Wise

function
function table

Examples
CONNECTION

Did you know? A newborn kangaroo, called a joey, is the size of a paper clip and weighs about 0.03 of an ounce.

A group of kangaroos is called a mob. The amount of plants that a mob of kangaroos eats depends on how many are in the mob. In other words, the amount of plants eaten is a **function** of the number of kangaroos.

A grown kangaroo can eat 14 pounds of grass and other plants per day. About how many pounds a day would be eaten by a mob of 3 grown kangaroos? 4 kangaroos? 5 kangaroos? This problem can be organized in a **function table**. *This problem will be solved in Example 1.*

1 **Life Science** Refer to the beginning of the lesson. **Determine the amount eaten by a mob of 3, 4, and 5 kangaroos.**

To find the amount eaten by a mob of kangaroos in a day (output), you need to multiply the number in the mob (input) by 14.

Input	Function Rule	Output
Number in the Mob (*n*)	14*n*	Amount Eaten in a Day (lb)
3	14(3)	42
4	14(4)	56
5	14(5)	70

A mob of 3 eat 42 pounds of grass and plants, 4 eat 56 pounds, and 5 eat 70 pounds.

2 Find the rule for the function table.

Study the relationship between each input and output.

input (*n*)	output (■)
−2	2
0	4
1	5
3	7

input		output
−2	$+4 \rightarrow$	2
0	$+4 \rightarrow$	4
1	$+4 \rightarrow$	5
3	$+4 \rightarrow$	7

The output is 4 more than the input. So, the function rule is $n + 4$.

Example ──3 **Life Science** Insect-eating bats control insects without
CONNECTION chemicals. The brown bat often eats 600 mosquitoes an hour.
Make a function table showing the number of mosquitoes eaten
in 2, 4, and 6 hours.

You can use the function rule 600h, where h is the number
of hours.

Replace h in the rule 600h with the number of hours.

Replace h with 2.   *Replace h with 4.*   *Replace h with 6.*

$600h = 600 \cdot 2$ $600h = 600 \cdot 4$ $600h = 600 \cdot 6$
$\qquad = 1{,}200$ $\qquad = 2{,}400$ $\qquad = 3{,}600$

A brown bat can eat
1,200 mosquitoes in 2 hours,
2,400 mosquitoes in 4 hours,
and 3,600 mosquitoes in 6 hours.

input (h)	output (600h)
2	1,200
4	2,400
6	3,600

CHECK FOR UNDERSTANDING

Communicating Mathematics

Read and study the lesson to answer each question.

1. *Make* a function table for the function rule $y - 2$. Use inputs of -4, -1, 0, and 3. **See margin.**

2. *Write* the function rule for the table. $n \div 3$

input (n)	output (■)
9	3
0	0
-3	-1
-6	-2

**3. Sample answer:
Juanita is correct. If
you use 4, 5, and 6
for inputs, the outputs
are 1, 2, and 3. Each
output is 3 less than
the input.**

3. *You Decide* The output of a function table is 3 less than each input. Juanita says that the function rule is $x - 3$. Ruby says the rule is $3 - x$. Who is correct? Explain.

Guided Practice

Copy and complete each function table.

4.
input (n)	output (n+3)
-1	■ 2
0	■ 3
3	■ 6

5.
input (n)	output ($\frac{1}{4}n$)
4	■ 1
8	■ 2
12	■ 3

Find the rule for each function table.

6. $4n$
n	■
1	4
2	8
3	12

7. $n \div 2$
n	■
0	0
2	1
4	2

8. If the input values are -2, 0, and 4 and the corresponding outputs are 3, 5, and 9, what is the function rule? $n + 5$

Lesson 12-5 Functions   **497**

Transparency 12-5B contains a teaching aid for this lesson.

Reading Mathematics Make sure students understand that a function rule is simply an expression that is going to be evaluated for several numbers. Have students verbally interpret the function rule before beginning each exercise in the Guided Practice.

In-Class Examples

For Example 1
If Ebony sells her handmade earrings for $4 a pair, how much will she make by selling 6 pairs? 8 pairs? 10 pairs? What is the function rule? **24; 32; 40; 4n**

For Example 2
Find the rule for the function table.

input (n)	output (■)
-1	4
0	5
1	6
2	7

$n + 5$

For Example 3
A bicyclist can pedal 15 miles an hour. Make a function table showing the number of miles traveled in 3, 4, and 5 hours.

input (n)	output (15n)
3	45
4	60
5	75

3 PRACTICE/APPLY

Check for Understanding
If students need additional practice or instruction after completing Exercises 1–9, one of these options may be helpful.
- Extra Practice, see p. 590
- Reteaching Activity
- *Study Guide Masters,* p. 88
- *Practice Masters,* p. 88
- Interactive Mathematics Tools Software

■ **Reteaching the Lesson** ■

Activity Have students play "High Card Rules." Cards numbered from -10 to 10 will be needed. Have players start with the rule $n + 2$. Each player takes a card and uses its number as the input. The player with the greatest output designates the next rule.

Additional Answer

1.
input (y)	output (y − 2)
-4	-6
-1	-3
0	-2
3	1

9. *Money Matters* Marc Wright of Windsor, Ontario, Canada, started his own greeting card business, called Kiddie Cards. Marc makes a profit of $0.75 for every card he sells.

  a. Write the function rule to represent Marc's profits. **0.75c**

  b. How much profit would Marc earn on a sale of 50 cards? **$37.50**

EXERCISES

Practice   **Copy and complete each function table.**

10.

input (n)	output (n + 4)
−3	■ 1
0	■ 4
3	■ 7

11.

input (n)	output (3n)
0	■ 0
3	■ 9
4	■ 12

12.

input (n)	output (5 − n)
5	■ 0
6	■ −1
7	■ −2

13.

input (n)	output ($\frac{1}{8}n$)
−8	■ −1
0	■ 0
12	■ $1\frac{1}{2}$

Find the rule for each function table.

14. $n - 3$

n	■
0	−3
3	0
6	3

15. $5n$

n	■
0	0
3	15
4	20

16. $-2n$

n	■
−2	4
−1	2
3	−6

17. $n \div (-2)$

n	■
−4	2
−2	1
0	0

18. $6 - n$

n	■
1	5
5	1
9	−3

19. n^2

n	■
5	25
−5	25
0	0
−1	1

20. If a function rule is $2n + 1$, what is the output for an input of 2? **5**

21. If a function rule is $6n - 4$, what is the output for an input of −3? **−22**

22. If the input values are 2 and 7 and the corresponding outputs are −6 and −21, what is the function rule? **−3n**

23. If the input values are 5 and 10 and the corresponding outputs are 1 and 2, what is the function rule? **n ÷ 5**

24. If the output values are −5 and −1 and the function rule is $n - 5$, what are the corresponding input values? **0 and 4**

498   **Chapter 12** Algebra: Exploring Equations

Applications and Problem Solving

25. Spreadsheets In the spreadsheet, the number of correct answers on a quiz is entered in column A. The number of questions that were on the quiz are entered in column B. Column C computes the percent correct. The formula in cell C1 is A1/B1*100. The formula acts like the rule of a function. What are the output values for cells C2, C3, C4, and C5? **100, 60, 80, 70**

	A	B	C
1	9	10	90
2	10	10	
3	6	10	
4	8	10	
5	7	10	

26. Money Matters Ebony Hood of Washington, D.C., started her own business selling scarves and fashion pins. Suppose she sells a scarf for $2 and a pin for $4.

a. Write a function rule to represent the total cost of scarves (s) and pins (p). **$2s + 4p$**

b. How much would 5 scarves and 3 pins cost? **$22**

Ebony Hood

27. Critical Thinking Find the rule for the function table. **$2n + 2$**

n	■
-2	-2
-1	0
2	6
3	8

Mixed Review

28. Geometry The area A of a trapezoid can be found by multiplying the height h and one-half the sum of the bases b_1 and b_2. The formula is $A = \frac{1}{2}h(b_1 + b_2)$. The area of the trapezoid at the right is 48 square centimeters. It is 6 centimeters high, and the length of one base is 7 centimeters. What is the length of the other base? *(Lesson 12-4)* **9 cm**

7 cm
6 cm

29. Write an integer to describe a temperature of twelve degrees below zero. *(Lesson 11-1)* **−12**

30. Standardized Test Practice If $\triangle TUV$ is congruent to $\triangle PQR$, then — *(Lesson 9-6)* **B**

Q
22 cm   33 cm
P   50 cm   R   T   U   V

A the measure of side $\overline{TU}$ is equal to the measure of side $\overline{PR}$.

B side $\overline{TV}$ measures 50 centimeters.

C the perimeter of triangle TUV is 100 centimeters.

D the measure of angle P is equal to the measure of angle V.

E the measure of side $\overline{TV}$ is twice the measure of side $\overline{TU}$.

For **Extra Practice**, see page 590.

Lesson 12-5 Functions   **499**

For **Extra Practice**, see page 590.

Extending the Lesson

Enrichment Masters, p. 88

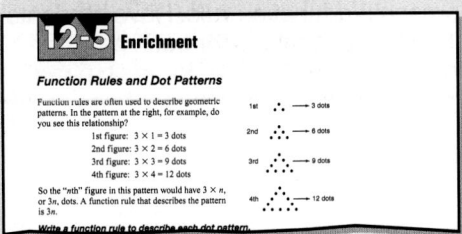

12-5 Enrichment

Function Rules and Dot Patterns

Function rules are often used to describe geometric patterns. In the pattern at the right, for example, do you see this relationship?

1st figure: 3 × 1 = 3 dots
2nd figure: 3 × 2 = 6 dots
3rd figure: 3 × 3 = 9 dots
4th figure: 3 × 4 = 12 dots

1st ••• → 3 dots
2nd ••• ••• → 6 dots
3rd ••• ••• ••• → 9 dots
4th ••• ••• ••• ••• → 12 dots

So the "nth" figure in this pattern would have 3 × n, or 3n, dots. A function rule that describes the pattern is 3n.

Write a function rule to describe each dot pattern.

Activity Rose's parents offered her an allowance of $5 a week or one that pays 2 cents for Week 1, (2 cents)² for Week 2, (2 cents)³ for Week 3, and so on, through Week 10. The Week 10 rate applies thereafter. Which plan would give Rose the greater allowance in the tenth week? Explain. **second plan; (2 cents)¹⁰ > $5**

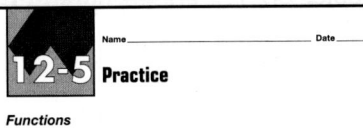

3 PRACTICE/APPLY

Check for Understanding

If students need additional practice or instruction after completing Exercises 1–9, one of these options may be helpful.
- Extra Practice, see p. 590
- Reteaching Activity, see p. 501
- *Study Guide Masters,* p. 89
- *Practice Masters,* p. 89
- Interactive Mathematics Tools Software

Assignment Guide
Core: 11–25 odd, 28–32
Enriched: 10–24 even, 25, 26, 28–32

Additional Answer

8.

input (*x*)	output (*x* − 6)
1	−5
4	−2
5	−1

Study Guide Masters, p. 89

6–7. See Answer Appendix for graphs.

Copy and complete each function table. Then graph the function.

6.

input (*n*)	output (*n* − 5)
4	■ −1
0	■ −5
−2	■ −7

7.

input (*n*)	output ($\frac{n}{2}$)
6.6	■ 3.3
8.4	■ 4.2
10.5	■ 5.25

8. Make a function table for the rule $x - 6$ using 1, 4, and 5 as the input. Then graph the function. **See margin.**

9. Make a function table for the graph. Then determine the rule. **See margin.**

EXERCISES

Practice

10–15. See Answer Appendix.

Graph the functions represented by each function table.

10.

input	output
0	−5
2	−3
4	−1

11.

input	output
5	3
3	1
1	−1

12.

input	output
−2	4
0	0
2	−4

13.

input	output
0	0
4	1
8	2

14.

input	output
2	5
0	−1
−1	−4

15.

input	output
-4	0
0	1
4	2

Copy and complete each function table. Then graph the function.

16–19. See Answer Appendix for graphs.

16.

input (*n*)	output (2*n* + 4)
$5\frac{1}{2}$	■ 15
$4\frac{1}{4}$	■ $12\frac{1}{2}$
0	■ 4

17.

input (*n*)	output (−3*n*)
3	■ −9
0	■ 0
−2	■ 6

18.

input (*n*)	output (2*n* − 3)
−2	■ −7
0	■ −3
2	■ 1
5	■ 7

19.

input (*n*)	output ($\frac{1}{2}n + 1$)
−4	■ −1
−2	■ 0
0	■ 1
2	■ 2

20. Make a function table for the rule $a + 5$ using input values of −5, −3, and 0. Then graph the function. **See Answer Appendix.**

21. Make a function table for the rule $3n - 3$ using input values of −2, 1, and 4. Then graph the function. **See Answer Appendix.**

502 Chapter 12 Algebra: Exploring Equations

Additional Answer

9.

input (*n*)	output (■)
−1	−3
2	0
4	2

The rule is $n - 2$.

Make a function table for each graph. Then determine the rule.

22–24. See Answer Appendix.

22.

23.

24.

Applications and Problem Solving

25a. Jane: $25w - 20$; Julie: $20w$

25c. The point of intersection represents when the total earnings are the same for both girls.

25. *Money Matters* During the summer, Jane earned $25 a week and was required to purchase a uniform for $20. No special clothing was required at Julie's summer job. Julie earned $20 a week.

   a. Write the function rule for each girl's wages.

   b. Graph each function on the same coordinate plane. **See Answer Appendix.**

   c. What does the point of intersection of the two graphs represent?

26. *History* The line graph shows the number of cups of chocolate the Aztec emperor Montezuma drank each day. **a–b. See Answer Appendix.**

   a. Make a function table for the graph.

   b. Determine the function rule.

27a–c. See Answer Appendix.

27. *Working on the* **CHAPTER Project** Refer to the table on page 475.

   You can graph a function to see how the value of a basketball card might change in the future. In June, 1997, the Charles Barkley card was worth $60. The value had been increasing $1 per month.

   a. Make a function table for the rule $60 + x$. Use inputs of 1 through 12 to predict the value of the card over the next 12 months.

   b. Graph the function using graphing software or a graphing calculator.

   c. What does the ordered pair (5, 65) mean in this situation?

28. *Critical Thinking* Determine the rule for the line that passes through $A(-2, 6)$ and $B(3, -6)$. **$-2.4x + 1.2$**

Mixed Review

29. *Algebra* Complete the function table. *(Lesson 12-5)*

input (n)	output (n + 7)
-5	■ 2
0	■ 7
4	■ 11

30. **Standardized Test Practice** If an airplane travels 438 miles per hour, how many miles will it travel in 5 hours? *(Lesson 8-2)* **D**

   A 2,050 mi   **B** 2,090 mi   **C** 2,150 mi   **D** 2,190 mi   **E** Not Here

31. *Geometry* Find the circumference of a circle with a radius of 5 meters. Use 3.14 for pi. *(Lesson 7-4)* **about 31.4 m**

For **Extra Practice,** see page 590.

32. Find the prime factorization of 120. *(Lesson 5-2)* **$2 \times 2 \times 2 \times 3 \times 5$**

Lesson 12-6 Graphing Functions **503**

Extending the Lesson

Enrichment Masters, p. 89

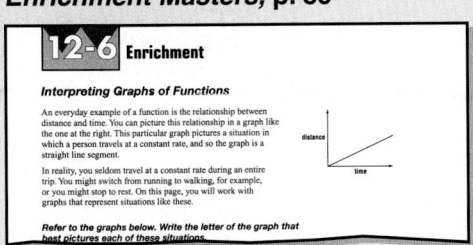

Activity Ask students what role they think math plays in designing a building. Discuss ways in which a coordinate grid could be used to sketch architectural ideas that can be used for scale drawings or blueprints.

Exercise 27 asks students to advance to the next stage of work on the Chapter Project. You may have students compare their graphs for part b. How are the graphs similar? How are they different?

4 ASSESS

Closing Activity

Speaking Have students work in pairs to draw a graph. Ask them to exchange their graph with others to make a function table and determine the rules. Have students discuss how they determined the function rule and whether some rules are difficult to find.

Chapter 12, Quiz D (Lesson 12-6) is available in the *Assessment and Evaluation Masters*, p. 324.

Practice Masters, p. 89

Study Guide and Assessment

CHAPTER 12

Study Guide and Assessment

interNET CONNECTION Chapter Review For additional lesson-by-lesson review, visit: www.glencoe.com/sec/math/mac/mathnet

Vocabulary

Vocabulary

This section provides a listing of the new terms, properties, and phrases that were introduced in this chapter. Have students define each term and provide an example or two of it, if appropriate.

Understanding and Using the Vocabulary

These exercises check students' understanding of the terms by using a variety of verbal formats including matching, completion, and true/false.

Glossaries A complete glossary of terms appears on pages 642–648. The glossary also appears in Spanish on pages 649–656.

Additional Answer

10. **Sample answer: Make a table recording the input and output of the given function. Write the input/output as an ordered pair. Record at least three ordered pairs on the table. Graph these ordered pairs and draw a line connecting the graphed points.**

After completing this chapter, you should be able to define each term, concept, or phrase and give an example or two of each.

Patterns and Functions
function (p. 496)
function machine (p. 494)
function table (p. 496)
input (p. 494)
output (p. 494)

Problem Solving
use an equation (pp. 492–493)

Understanding and Using the Vocabulary

Choose the correct term, number, or equation to complete each sentence.

1. To solve an equation means to find a value for the (coordinate, <u>variable</u>) that makes the equation true.

2. The second step in solving $4b + 3 = 27$ is to (<u>divide</u>, multiply) each side of the equation by 4.

3. In an equation, when a number is (added to, <u>subtracted from</u>) the variable, add the number to each side to solve the equation.

4. A(n) (<u>function</u>, output) describes the relationship between two sets of numbers.

5. A(n) (input, <u>function table</u>) can be helpful in organizing information by using a mathematical rule to assign an output to a given input.

6. The solutions of a function table are found in the (<u>output</u>, input) column.

7. If the function rule is $6n$ and the input value is -3, then the output value is (<u>-18</u>, -2).

8. On the graph of a function, every point has (<u>coordinates</u>, variables) that satisfy the function.

9. The diagram at the right models the equation ($\underline{2x + 3 = -9}$, $x = 6$).

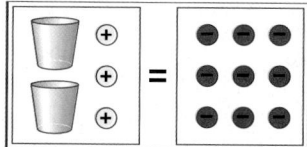

In Your Own Words

10. *Tell* how to graph the function $y = 2x - 1$. **See margin.**

504 Chapter 12 Algebra: Exploring Equations

MindJogger Videoquizzes

MindJogger Videoquizzes provide an alternative review of concepts presented in this chapter. Students work in teams to answer questions, gaining points for correct answers. The questions are presented in three rounds.
Round 1 Concepts–5 questions
Round 2 Skills–4 questions
Round 3 Problem Solving–4 questions

Objectives & Examples

Upon completing this chapter, you should be able to:

● solve addition equations using models
(Lesson 12-1)

Solve $m + (-2) = -5$.

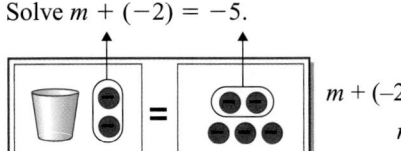

$m + (-2) = -5$
$m = -3$

● solve subtraction equations by using models
(Lesson 12-2)

Solve $t - 3 = 4$.

Rewrite as an addition equation.

$t - 3 = 4 \rightarrow t + (-3) = 4$

$t + (-3) = 4$

Since there are no negative counters on the right side, add 3 positive counters to each side to make 3 zero pairs on the left side. Then remove the zero pairs.

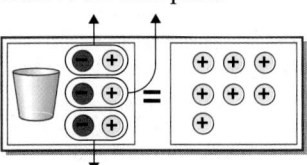

$t + (-3) + 3 = 4 + 3$
$t = 7$

● solve multiplication and division equations using models *(Lesson 12-3)*

Solve $3x = -9$.

$3x = -9$
$x = -3$

Review Exercises

Use these exercises to review and prepare for the chapter test.

Solve each equation. Use cups and counters if necessary.

11. $x + 2 = 5$ **3**   12. $p + 7 = 4$ **−3**
13. $6 + r = -7$ **−13**   14. $-2 + w = -5$ **−3**
15. $a + (-4) = -7$ **−3** 16. $t + 2 = -6$ **−8**

Solve each equation. Use cups and counters if necessary.

17. $x - 1 = 3$ **4**
18. $y - 3 = 11$ **14**
19. $f - 3 = -1$ **2**
20. $g - 4 = -5$ **−1**
21. $h - 9 = -9$ **0**
22. $c - (-8) = -12$ **−20**

Solve each equation. Use cups and counters if necessary.

23. $7q = 28$ **4**   24. $\frac{1}{3}d = 9$ **27**
25. $\frac{1}{5}k = -11$ **−55** 26. $8x = 40$ **5**
27. $3m = -15$ **−5**   28. $2.5g = 15$ **6**
29. $\frac{1}{4}y = -5$ **−20** 30. $-4t = -4$ **1**

Chapter 12 Study Guide and Assessment **505**

Objectives & Examples

This section reviews the skills and concepts of the chapter and shows completely worked examples.

Review Exercises

These exercises provide practice for the corresponding objectives.

Assessment and Evaluation Masters, pp. 311–312

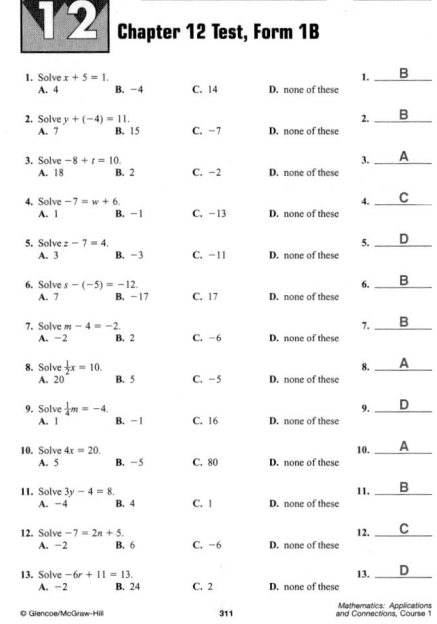

Assessment and Evaluation

Six forms of Chapter 12 Test are available in the *Assessment and Evaluation Masters* as shown in the chart.

Chapter 12 Test, Form 1B, is shown at the right. Chapter 12 Test, Form 2B, is shown on the next page.

1A	Multiple Choice	Honors
1B	Multiple Choice	Average
1C	Multiple Choice	Basic
2A	Free Response	Honors
2B	Free Response	Average
2C	Free Response	Basic

Assessment and Evaluation Masters, pp. 317–318

Objectives & Examples

● **solve two-step equations using models** *(Lesson 12-4)*

Solve $2n + 1 = 7$.

$$2n + 1 = 7$$
$$2n + 1 - 1 = 7 - 1$$
$$2n = 6$$
$$n = 3$$

● **complete function tables** *(Lesson 12-5)*

Find the rule for the function table.

input (n)	output (■)
-1	3
0	4
3	7

$$\left.\begin{array}{l} -1 + 4 = 3 \\ 0 + 4 = 4 \\ 3 + 4 = 7 \end{array}\right\} n + 4$$

● **graph functions from function tables** *(Lesson 12-6)*

Graph the function represented by the function table.

x	x + 4	output	ordered pair
-3	-3 + 4	1	(-3, 1)
0	0 + 4	4	(0, 4)
1	1 + 4	5	(1, 5)

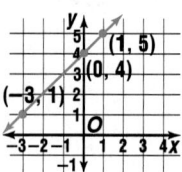

Review Exercises

Solve each equation. Use cups and counters if necessary.

31. $2r - 8 = 4$ **6**

32. $\frac{1}{5}k + 5 = 7$ **10**

33. $2x + 5 = -13$ **-9**

34. $4n + 12.4 = -6.8$ **-4.8**

Copy and complete each function table.

35.
n	3n
-1	■
0	■
2	■

-3
0
6

36.
n	n - 2
-1	■
0	■
5	■

-3
-2
3

37. If a function rule is $2n + 1$, what is the output for $n = -3$? **-5**

Find the rule for each function table.

38.
n	■
-1	5
0	0
3	-15

-5n

39.
n	■
-1	-5
0	-4
3	-1

n - 4

Copy and complete each function table. Then graph the function.

40.
x	4x
-1	■
0	■
2	■

-4
0
8

41.
x	x + 3
-2	■
0	■
2	■

1
3
5

40–41. See Answer Appendix for graphs.

 Test and Review Software

You may use this software, a combination of an item generator and item bank, to create your own tests or worksheets. Types of items include free response, multiple choice, short answer, and open ended.

 CD-ROM Program

The CD-ROM Program contains an Assessment Game whose questions review the concepts in this chapter.

Applications & Problem Solving

42. Health After dieting for 8 weeks and losing 17 pounds, Jeremy weighed 172 pounds. How much did he weigh before the diet? *(Lesson 12-1)* **189 pounds**

43. Use an Equation Keith swam three times as many laps as Dan in the swim meet. Keith swam 24 laps. How many laps did Dan swim? *(Lesson 12-4B)* **8 laps**

44. Money Matters On her vacation, Mrs. Salgado planned to spend less than $120 each day on her hotel room and meals. She found a hotel room for $75 a night. How much can she spend on meals? *(Lesson 12-4)* **less than $45**

45. Money Matters Mr. Jackson got a new shipment of T-shirts to sell at his souvenir shop. The table shows the amount Mr. Jackson paid for each of the three types of T-shirts, and the selling price he marked on the shirts. Find the function rule he used. *(Lesson 12-5)* $n + 3.50$

Amount Paid	Selling Price
$4.00	$7.50
$5.50	$9.00
$6.00	$9.50

Alternative Assessment

● **Open Ended**

Record the temperature of a cup of hot tap water to the nearest degree. Then record the temperature every minute for the next 10 minutes. **See students' work.**

Graph the ordered pairs (time, temperature) on a coordinate plane. **See students' work.**

Estimate the temperature after 30 minutes. Estimate again after 60 minutes.
Answers will vary.

● **Completing the** CHAPTER Project

Use the following checklist to make sure your project is complete.

☑ You have included a list of the items in your collection.

☑ You have included your table or other display showing the value of at least five items in your collection.

☑ You may want to include pictures of the items in your collection.

Add any finishing touches that you would like to make your project attractive.

 PORTFOLIO   Select an item from this chapter that you feel shows your best work. Place it in your portfolio. Explain why you selected it.

A practice test for Chapter 12 is provided on page 606.

 Performance Assessment

Additional performance assessment tasks for this chapter are included in the *Assessment and Evaluation Masters* on page 321. A scoring guide is also provided on page 333.

Applications & Problem Solving

This section provides additional practice in solving real-world problems that involve the skills of this chapter.

Alternative Assessment

The *Open Ended* section provides students with a performance assessment opportunity to evaluate their work and understanding.

CHAPTER Project

Students should complete the final stages of their project and prepare a class demonstration of their results. A scoring guide for the project is available in the *Investigations and Projects Masters*, p. 63.

 PORTFOLIO   Students should add to their portfolios at this time.

Assessment and Evaluation Masters, p. 321

Name_____ Date_____

12 **Chapter 12 Performance Assessment**

Instructions: Demonstrate your knowledge by giving a clear, concise solution to each problem. Be sure to include all relevant drawings and justify your answers. You may show your solutions in more than one way or investigate beyond the requirements of the problems.

1. Draw cups, ⊔, positive counters, ⊕, and negative counters, ⊖, to model each of the following.

   a. Model $x - 3 = 4$. Explain your reasoning.

   b. Use modeling to solve the equation in part a. Explain each step.

   c. Model $4x + 3 = -5$. Explain your reasoning.

   d. Use modeling to solve the equation in part c. Show each step.

   e. Write a word problem concerning integers.

   f. Write an equation for the problem in part e. Solve. Explain each step.

2. a. Write the rule for the table. Then complete the table.

Input (n)	Output
-2	-4
0	0
2	4
3	
-3	

   b. Graph the function in part a.

© Glencoe/McGraw-Hill   321   *Mathematics: Applications and Connections, Course 1*

The Standardized Test Practice may be used to help students prepare for standardized tests. The test items are written in the same style as those in state proficiency tests and standardized tests like CAT, CTBS, ITBS, MAT, SAT, and Terra Nova. The test items cover skills and concepts covered up to this point in the text.

The pages can be used as an overnight assessment. After students have completed the pages, discuss how each problem can be solved, or provide copies of the solutions from the *Solutions Manual*.

***Assessment and Evaluation Masters*, p. 327**

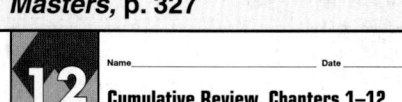

CHAPTERS 1-12

Standardized Test Practice
Assessing Knowledge & Skills

Section One: Multiple Choice

There are eleven multiple-choice questions in this section. Choose the best answer. If a correct answer is *not here*, mark the letter for Not Here.

1. Name the number of faces in a square pyramid. **B**
   A 4
   B 5
   C 6
   D 7

2. What is the solution of the equation $5 + x = 3$? **G**
   F -8
   G -2
   H 2
   J 8

3. Which is a reflection of the letter H? **D**

   A   B

   C   D

4. What numbers complete the function table? **F**

n	$3n$
10	■
0	■
-5	■

   F $30, 0, -15$
   G $30, 20, -10$
   H $13, 3, -2$
   J $13, 3, -10$

5. Which ordered pair is represented by point M? **D**

   A $(5, 4)$
   B $(3, 5)$
   C $(2, 5)$
   D $(5, 3)$

Please note that Questions 6–12 have five answer choices.

6. Diane had 10 coins in her pocket. There were 4 pennies, 1 nickel, 4 dimes, and 1 quarter. If she took out 1 coin at random, what is the probability it would be a dime? **H**
   F $\frac{1}{10}$
   G $\frac{1}{4}$
   H $\frac{2}{5}$
   J $\frac{1}{2}$
   K Not Here

7. Sharon is knitting a sweater. She needs 8 skeins of red yarn that cost $1.89 each and 3 skeins of white yarn that cost $1.29 each. Which number sentence could be used to find S, the total cost in dollars? **E**
   A $S = (1.89 \div 8) + (1.29 \div 3)$
   B $S = (8 \times 1.89) \times (3 \times 1.29)$
   C $S = (1.89 + 1.29) \times 11$
   D $S = (1.89 \div 8) \times (1.29 \div 3)$
   E $S = (8 \times 1.89) + (3 \times 1.29)$

508 Chapters 1–12 Standardized Test Practice

◄◄◄Instructional Resources
Another cumulative review is shown at the left and is available in the *Assessment and Evaluation Masters*, p. 327.

8. Which best describes the two triangles? **H**

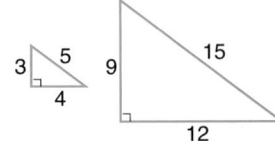

F The triangles are congruent.
G The triangles are reflections.
H The triangles are similar.
J The triangles are equilateral.
K The triangles are symmetrical.

9. Marty bought 5 packages of hamburger. If each package weighed 1.45 pounds, what was the weight of the 5 packages? **D**

A 3.45 lb
B 6.45 lb
C 7.90 lb
D 7.25 lb
E Not Here

10. What is the perimeter of a triangle with sides of $3\frac{1}{2}$ cm, $2\frac{1}{2}$ cm, and $1\frac{3}{4}$ cm? **K**

F 6 cm
G $6\frac{1}{2}$ cm
H $6\frac{3}{4}$ cm
J 7 cm
K Not Here

11. $0.0125 \div 1.7 =$ **E**

A 1   B 0.1
C 0.01   D 0.001
E Not Here

12. $-12 - (-10) =$ **G**

F −22   G −2
H 2   J 22
K Not Here

 Test Practice For additional test practice questions, visit:

www.glencoe.com/sec/math/mac/mathnet

 Test-Taking Tip THE PRINCETON REVIEW

If you solve a problem and the answer you get is not one of the choices, check to see if your answer can be written in a different form. For example, if you solve a problem and get $\frac{x}{4}$ and it is not listed as a choice, try a different form such as $\frac{1}{4}x$. You may have the right answer, but in a different form.

Section Two: Free Response

This section contains six questions for which you will provide short answers. Write your answers on your paper.

13. Find the volume of the rectangular prism.

240 m³

14. Complete the function table.

input (x)	output (x + 7)
−3	4
1	8
5	12

15. In a survey, 17 out of 110 people said they liked boating. How many people would that be out of 100? **about 15 people**

16. The fence around a pool measures 25 feet wide by 60 feet long. If the length is increased by 20 feet, what will the new dimensions be? **25 ft by 80 ft**

17. The base of a cone is a _____. **circle**

18. Make a function table for the rule $x - 2$ using 2, 5, and 8 as the input. Then graph the function. **See Answer Appendix.**

Test-Taking Tip

One of the important skills in test-taking is the ability to recognize the correct answer when multiple choices are given. Guide students to consider every possible form their answer could take before deciding that their answer is not one of the choices.

Assessment and Evaluation Masters, pp. 325–326

12 Chapter 12 Standardized Test Practice

Name_____ Date_____

1. Which of the following is a solution for $12d = 156$?   1. __D__
   A. 4   B. 12   C. 11   D. 13

2. The ordered pair (5, 39) represents the age and weight of a child. If the child's weight increases 5 pounds per year, which ordered pair represents weight at age 8.   2. __B__
   A. (5, 44)   B. (8, 54)   C. (13, 57)   D. (8, 57)

3. The fastest crawling insect, a cockroach, can move at a rate of 4.64 km/hr. The maximum speed of the garden snail is 0.008 km/hr. How much faster does the cockroach travel?   3. __B__
   A. 3.8 km/hr   B. 4.632 km/hr   C. 4.56 km/hr   D. 4.648 km/hr

4. In one year a college student earned $4,582.16 working part-time. What is the approximate average amount she earned in a month?   4. __C__
   A. $4,000   B. $5,000   C. $400   D. $5,500

5. A brick wall is $45\frac{3}{4}$ feet long. Each brick is $8\frac{1}{2}$ inches long. If there is $\frac{1}{2}$ inch of mortar between the bricks, *about* how many bricks are needed for each row?   5. __C__
   A. 5   B. 45   C. 62   D. 90

6. Kane lives $5\frac{1}{4}$ miles from school and $7\frac{1}{6}$ miles from work. How much farther is work than home?   6. __C__
   A. $2\frac{1}{12}$ B. $2\frac{5}{12}$ C. $1\frac{1}{12}$ D. $1\frac{5}{12}$

7. How many nails weighing $\frac{3}{8}$ ounce each are in a 9-ounce bag of nails?   7. __A__
   A. 24   B. $3\frac{3}{8}$ C. $\frac{1}{24}$ D. 8

8. A scale model of the Grand Canyon measures 21.7 inches. How long is the Grand Canyon if the model was built with a scale of 1 inch representing 10 miles?   8. __B__
   A. 21.70 miles   B. 217 miles   C. 2.17 miles   D. none of these

9. The income tax rate for José's family is 9.7%. What is the rate as a decimal?   9. __B__
   A. 0.97   B. 0.097   C. 9.7   D. none of these

10. A jet plane is traveling at 1,000 kilometers per hour north from the state capitol. Due to stormy weather, the plane turns and flies directly east. What angle is formed by the flight path?   10. __B__
    A. 45°   B. 90°   C. 180°   D. none of these

11. Triangle A has a perimeter of 24 centimeters and each side measures 8 centimeters. Triangle B has a perimeter of 48 centimeters and is similar to triangle A. Find the measure for each side of triangle B.   11. __A__
    A. 16 cm   B. 24 cm   C. 32 cm   D. 48 cm

© Glencoe/McGraw-Hill   325   Mathematics: Applications and Connections, Course 1

12 Chapter 12 Standardized Test Practice (continued)

12. An obelisk is an upright four-sided monument topped by a pyramid. How many faces, including the base, does an obelisk have?   12. __D__
    A. 4   B. 7   C. 8   D. 9

13. An art student wants to cover a rectangular prism with mirrors. The prism measures 15 inches by 12 inches by 8 inches. What is the surface area of the prism?   13. __D__
    A. 1,440 in²   B. 492 in²   C. 720 in²   D. 792 in²

14. The beginning balance in Kisha's checking account is $350. In one week, Kisha deposits her paycheck of $250 and withdraws $75 for food. What is Kisha's balance at the end of the week?   14. __B__
    A. $625   B. $525   C. $300   D. $25

15. Luann's dad spends $3.50 a day on gas and tolls to drive his car to work. How much does he spend driving to work for five days?   15. __A__
    A. $17.50   B. $24.50   C. $14.00   D. $21.00

16. The ordered pairs (2, 0), (−2, 0), (2, 2), and (−2, 2) form what shape when graphed?   16. __A__
    A. rectangle   B. square   C. circle   D. triangle

17. Luis has 600 baseball cards. He bought C new cards bringing his total collection to 720. Luis wrote an equation to express the number of cards he owns. Which is the best equation?   17. __A__
    A. $600 + C = 720$ B. $600 + 720 = C$
    C. $720 + C = 600$ D. $C = 120$

18. Trey is paid $5.75 an hour. The equation $s = 5.75 \times t$ could be used to calculate his salary. What is a reasonable estimate for Trey's weekly income if he works $t = 38$ hours in one week?   18. __C__
    A. $180   B. $200   C. $240   D. none of these

19. The perimeter of a rectangle is 92 inches. Find the length if the width is 18 inches.   19. __B__
    A. 24 in.   B. 28 in.   C. 37 in.   D. none of these

20. There is a difference of 3 time zones between New York City, n, and Los Angeles, ℓ. Evaluate the function rule $\ell = n - 3$ to find the time in Los Angeles when it is 1 P.M. in New York City.   20. __D__
    A. 4 P.M.   B. 11 A.M.   C. 2 P.M.   D. none of these

© Glencoe/McGraw-Hill   326   Mathematics: Applications and Connections, Course 1

Instructional Resources ▶▶▶
Additional standardized test practice is shown at the right and is available in the *Assessment and Evaluation Masters,* pp. 325–326.

Interdisciplinary
▼Investigation

GET READY

This optional investigation is designed to be completed by a group of 2 or 3 students over several days or several weeks.

Mathematical Overview

This investigation utilizes the concepts from Chapters 1–12.
- measuring circumference
- graphing functions relating the radius, circumference, and area of circles

Time Management	
Gathering Data	30 minutes
Calculations	30 minutes
Creating Graphs	45 minutes
Summarizing Data	15 minutes
Presentation	10 minutes

Instructional Resources

- *Investigations and Projects Masters*, pp. 13–16
- *Manipulative Kit*
  - tape measures

Investigations and Projects Masters, p. 16

Name_____ Date_____

Interdisciplinary Investigation
(Student Edition, Pages 510–511)

Going In Circles

Use this table to record your data.

Name of Item	Radius (inches)	Circumference (inches)	Area (square inches)

3. Using the formula $C = 2\pi r$, the equation to find the radius is:
5. a. (radius, circumference) b. (radius, area) c. (circumference, area)

© Glencoe/McGraw-Hill   16   Mathematics: Applications and Connections, Course 1

GOING IN CIRCLES

What do these items have in common—a drum, a tambourine, and cymbals? You may have guessed they all have a circular shape. Circles are common in our daily lives.

ⓦhat You'll Do

In this investigation, you will measure the circumference of common circular items. You will graph functions relating the radius, circumference, and area of circles. You will use your graphs to estimate the area of a circle.

Materials string   tape measure   calculator

 grid paper   circular objects

Procedure

1. Work in pairs. Measure the circumference of six different circular items to the nearest $\frac{1}{8}$ inch. To do this, wrap a string around the object and then measure the string or use a tape measure.

2. Make a table similar to the one below. Record the name and circumference of each item measured by you and your partner. Arrange the items from least to greatest circumference. If you use a spreadsheet, convert all fractions to decimals.

Name of Item	Radius (inches)	Circumference (inches)	Area (square inches)
pencil			
vegetable can			

3. Recall that the circumference of a circle can be found using the formula $C = 2\pi r$. Write and solve an equation to find the radius of each item. Record each radius in column 2 of your table.

4. Use the formula $A = \pi r^2$ to find the area of each circle. Record the area in column 4 of your table.

5. Draw three coordinate planes.
   a. For each item in the table, write the ordered pair, (radius, circumference). Then graph each ordered pair.

◀◀◀Instructional Resources
A recording sheet to help students organize their data for this investigation is shown at the left and is available in the *Investigations and Projects Masters*, p. 16.

 Cooperative Learning

This investigation offers an excellent opportunity for using cooperative learning groups. For more information on cooperative learning strategies and group management, see *Cooperative Learning in the Mathematics Classroom*.

b. For each item in the table, write the ordered pair (radius, area). Then graph each ordered pair on the second coordinate plane.

c. For each item in the table, write the ordered pair (circumference, area). Then graph each ordered pair on the third coordinate plane.

6. Write a sentence or two describing each graph.

7. Measure the circumference of a new item. The circumference should be between the smallest and largest items you used for your table. Use the graph from Exercise 5c to estimate the area of the circle. How did your estimate compare to the actual area?

Making the Connection

Use the information about your circles as needed to help in these investigations.

Language Arts

Choose two circles from the investigation. Write directions for finding the side length of two squares that have approximately the same area as the circles.

Physical Education

In the sport of archery, athletes often use a target to improve their skill or for competitions. Research this sport and find the diameter of the target. Use your graphs to estimate the circumference and area of the target.

Technology Tips

- Use a **spreadsheet** to calculate radius and area.

- Use a **graphing calculator** or **graphing software** to display your graphs.

Go Further

- Use a graphing calculator to find equations for the three functions you graphed.

- Research the history of π.

- Find the area of each ring on an archery target.

interNET **CONNECTION** Research **For current information on mathematics, visit:** www.glencoe.com/sec/math/mac/mathnet

You may want to place your work on this investigation in your portfolio.

Instructional Resources ▶▶▶

Sample solutions for this investigation are provided in the *Investigations and Projects Masters* on p. 14. The scoring guide for assessing student performance shown at the right is also available on p. 15.

MANAGEMENT TIPS

Working in Teams Have students take turns measuring the circular items. Have one student make the table and then trade off making the graphs.

Making the Connection

You may wish to alert other teachers on your team that your students may need their assistance in this investigation. *Language Arts* Students may trade their directions to see whether other students can follow them easily. *Physical Education* Students may wish to investigate whether there are different-size targets for different levels of competition.

ASSESS

You may wish to have students determine careers that would require knowledge of circumference and area relationships.

***Investigations and Projects Masters,* p. 15**

SCORING GUIDE

Interdisciplinary Investigation
(Student Edition, Pages 510–511)

Going In Circles

Level	Specific Criteria
3 Superior	• Shows a thorough understanding of the concepts of *applying known formulas to find missing information about circles and constructing coordinate planes and graphing coordinate pairs.* • Uses appropriate strategies to solve problems. • Computations are correct. • Written explanations are exemplary. • Charts, model, and any statements included are appropriate and sensible. • Goes beyond the requirements of some or all problems.
2 Satisfactory, with minor flaws	• Shows understanding of the concepts of *applying known formulas to find missing information about circles and constructing coordinate planes and graphing coordinate pairs.* • Uses appropriate strategies to solve problems. • Computations are mostly correct. • Written explanations are effective. • Charts, model, and any statements included are appropriate and sensible. • Satisfies the requirements of problems.
1 Nearly Satisfactory, with obvious flaws	• Shows understanding of most of the concepts of *applying known formulas to find missing information about circles and constructing coordinate planes and graphing coordinate pairs.* • May not use appropriate strategies to solve problems. • Computations are mostly correct. • Written explanations are satisfactory. • Charts, model, and any statements included are appropriate and sensible. • Satisfies the requirements of problems.
0 Unsatisfactory	• Shows little or no understanding of the concepts of *applying known formulas to find missing information about circles and constructing coordinate planes and graphing coordinate pairs.* • Does not use appropriate strategies to solve problems. • Computations are incorrect. • Written explanations are not satisfactory. • Charts, model, and any statements included are not appropriate or sensible. • Does not satisfy the requirements of the problems.

© Glencoe/McGraw-Hill   15   *Mathematics: Applications and Connections, Course 1*

Using Probability

Overview

This chapter explores probability in a variety of ways. Students learn to find the probability of single events and independent events. They also learn to predict actions of a large group by using a sample. Area models and tree diagrams are used to find outcomes. Students also learn to solve problems by making tables.

Lesson (pages)	Lesson Objectives	NCTM Standards 2000	Standardized Tests	State/Local Objectives
13-1A (514)	Explore fair and unfair games.	1, 2, 5–10		
13-1 (515–518)	Find and interpret the theoretical probability of an event.	1, 2, 5–10	CAT, CTBS, ITBS, MAT, SAT, TN	
13-2A (520–521)	Solve problems by making a table.	1, 2, 5–10	CTBS, MAT, TN	
13-2 (522–525)	Predict the actions of a larger group using a sample.	1–9	CTBS, ITBS, MAT, TN	
13-3 (526–529)	Find probability using area models.	1–10	MAT	
13-3B (530)	Investigate geometric probability by using a graphing calculator.	1–9		
13-4 (531–534)	Find outcomes using lists, tree diagrams, and combinations.	1–10	CTBS, ITBS, MAT, SAT, TN	
13-4B (535)	Explore probability by conducting a simulation.	5–9		
13-5 (536–539)	Find the probability of independent events.	1–10	CAT, CTBS, ITBS, MAT, SAT, TN	

CAT = California Achievement Tests, CTBS = Comprehensive Tests of Basic Skills, ITBS = Iowa Tests of Basic Skills, MAT = Metropolitan Achievement Tests, SAT = Stanford Achievement Tests, TN = Terra Nova
For the key to numbering of NCTM Standards 2000, see page T6.

The **Interactive Lesson Planner** contains all of the blackline masters and transparencies. This CD-ROM also includes an easy-to-use lesson planning calendar.

LESSON PLANNING GUIDE

Lesson	Extra Practice (Student Edition)	BLACKLINE MASTERS (PAGE NUMBERS)										Transparencies A and B
		Study Guide	Practice	Enrichment	Assessment & Evaluation	Classroom Games	Diversity	Hands-On Lab	School to Career	Science and Math Lab Manual	Technology	
13-1A								67				
13-1	p. 590	90	90	90			13					13-1
13-2A	p. 591											
13-2	p. 591	91	91	91	351				13		25	13-2
13-3	p. 591	92	92	92	350, 351			81				13-3
13-3B												
13-4	p. 592	93	93	93	352						26	13-4
13-4B								68				
13-5	p. 592	94	94	94	352	37–40				93–96		13-5
Study Guide/ Assessment					337–349, 353–355							

OTHER CHAPTER RESOURCES

Student Edition

Chapter Project, pp. 513, 518, 529, 543
School to Career, p. 519
Let the Games Begin, p. 539

Technology

 MathPASS CD-ROM

 Interactive Mathematics Tools Software

Teacher's Classroom Resources

Applications
Family Letters and Activities, pp. 25–26
Investigations and Projects Masters, pp. 65–68
Meeting Individual Needs
Investigations for the Special Education Student, pp. 45–46

Teaching Aids
Answer Key Masters
Block Scheduling Booklet
Lesson Planning Guide
Solutions Manual

Professional Publications
Glencoe Mathematics Professional Series

Planning the Chapter

MindJogger Videoquizzes provide a unique format for reviewing concepts presented in the chapter.

ASSESSMENT RESOURCES

Student Edition

Mixed Review, pp. 518, 525, 529, 534, 539

Mid-Chapter Self Test, p. 525

Math Journal, pp. 517, 533

Study Guide and Assessment, pp. 540–543

Performance Task, p. 543

Portfolio Suggestion, p. 543

Standardized Test Practice, pp. 544–545

Chapter Test, p. 607

Assessment and Evaluation Masters

Multiple-Choice Tests (Forms 1A, 1B, 1C), pp. 337–342

Free-Response Tests (Forms 2A, 2B, 2C), pp. 343–348

Performance Assessment, p. 349

Mid-Chapter Test, p. 350

Quizzes A–D, pp. 351–352

Standardized Test Practice, pp. 353–354

Cumulative Review, p. 355

Teacher's Wraparound Edition

5-Minute Check, pp. 515, 522, 526, 531, 536

Building Portfolios, p. 512

Math Journal, pp. 514, 530, 535

Closing Activity, pp. 518, 521, 525, 529, 534, 539

Technology

Test and Review Software

MindJogger Videoquizzes

CD-ROM Program

MATERIALS AND MANIPULATIVES

Lesson 13-1A
number cubes*

Lesson 13-1
newspaper
white paper
black paper
hole punch

Lesson 13-2
newspaper

Lesson 13-3
dot paper†
beans

Lesson 13-3B
graphing calculator
grid paper†
straightedge*†

Lesson 13-4B
two-colored counters*†
cups*†

Lesson 13-5
index cards

*Glencoe Manipulative Kit   †Glencoe Overhead Manipulative Resources

PACING CHART

See pages T25–T27 for the Course Planning Calendar.

COURSE	DAY 1	DAY 2	DAY 3	DAY 4	DAY 5	DAY 6	DAY 7
Honors	Chapter Project	Lesson 13-1	Lesson 13-2A	Lesson 13-2	Lessons 13-3 & 13-3B		Lessons 13-4 & 13-4B

Interactive Mathematics:
Activities and Investigations

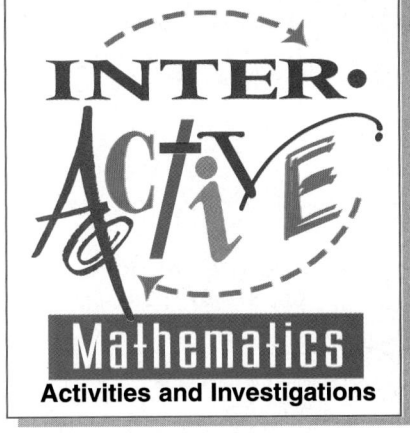

is an activity-based program that may be used as an enhancement for chapters in *Mathematics: Applications and Connections.*

Unit 10, Activity Two
It Happened by Chance
Use with Lesson 13-1.

Summary Students work in groups to complete this activity. Each group selects a fraction card from the deck provided and creates a written situation using that fraction as a probability. The groups write their solutions on posterboard and present them to the class.

Math Connection Students work in groups to explore probability by creating written situations that involve a chosen probability. Probability is the ratio of the number of ways an outcome can occur to the number of possible outcomes.

Unit 10, Activity Three
Use with Lesson 13-5.

Summary Students work in groups to design five random-generating spinners using the clues given on clue cards. Once the group has designed the spinner, students work individually, using compasses and protractors, to make an accurate drawing of the spinner.

Math Connection Students connect probability with geometry and measurement in this activity. They expand their knowledge of circles by designing random-generating spinners. Students use compasses, protractors, and number properties to design and draw their spinners.

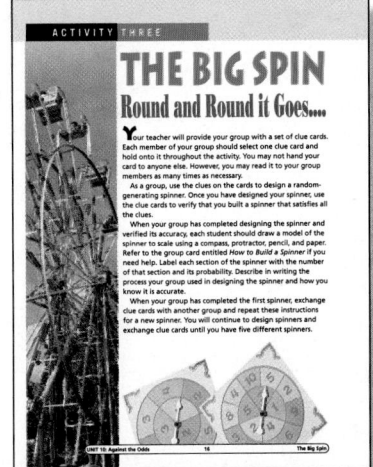

DAY 8	DAY 9	DAY 10	DAY 11	DAY 12	DAY 13	DAY 14	DAY 15
(continue from Day 7)	Lesson 13-5	Study Guide and Assessment	Chapter Test				

Enhancing the Chapter

APPLICATIONS

Classroom Games, pp. 37–40

Diversity Masters, p. 13

School to Career Masters, p. 13

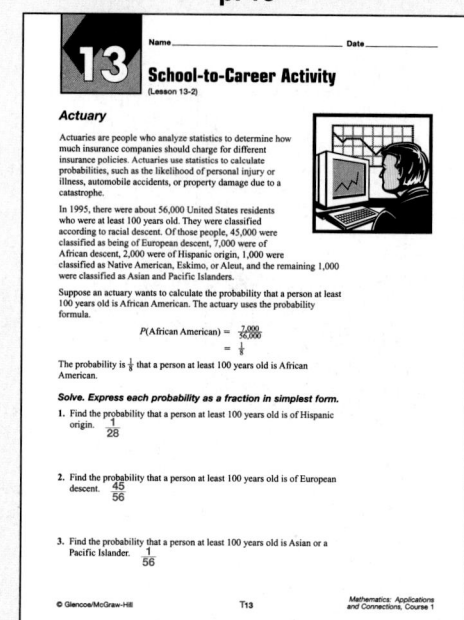
Family Letters and Activities, pp. 25–26

Science and Math Lab Manual, pp. 93–96

Hands-On Lab Masters, p. 81

13 Name _____ Date _____

Lab Activity
(Lesson 13-3)

Probability and Area

1. Count the number of squares in each region to find the area.

   Region 1: **36 squares**

   Region 2: **24 squares**

   Region 3: **4 squares**

   Total Area: **100 squares**

2. Find the ratio $\frac{\text{area of region}}{\text{total area}}$ for each region.

   Region 1: $\frac{9}{25}$

   Region 2: $\frac{6}{25}$

   Region 3: $\frac{1}{25}$

■ Region 1
▨ Region 2
□ Region 3

Drop 50 grains of rice onto the square target from a height of 2 or 3 inches. Mark an X wherever a grain lands inside the target. If a grain does not fall completely inside of one square, mark the X on the square that contains most of the grain. See X's on target for sample answers below.

3. Count the number of grains that landed in each region.

   Region 1: **16 grains**

   Region 2: **11 grains**

   Region 3: **6 grains**

   Total dropped on target: **50 grains**

4. For each region, find the ratio $\frac{\text{number of grains in region}}{\text{number of grains dropped on target}}$

   Region 1: $\frac{8}{25}$

   Region 2: $\frac{11}{50}$

   Region 3: $\frac{3}{25}$

5. Compare the ratios in Exercise 2 to the ratios in Exercise 4 and write a summary of your results. **Sample answer: The area ratios and grain ratios are close, but not exactly the same.**

© Glencoe/McGraw-Hill   81   Mathematics: Applications and Connections, Course 1

Assessment and Evaluation Masters, pp. 350–352

13 Name _____ Date _____

Chapter 13 Mid-Chapter Test
(Lessons 13-1 through 13-3)

A bag contains 8 white marbles, 5 black marbles, and 7 red marbles. Marbles are selected randomly. Find the probability of each event.

1. P(white) 2. P(red)

3. P(blue) 4. P(white or black)

5. P(white or black or red)

6. 100 marbles were selected randomly from the bag and replaced. Make a table showing the expected results.

In a survey at a restaurant, it was found that 12 out of 40 people order french fries with their lunch.

7. What is the sample size?

8. What is the probability that someone will order french fries with their lunch?

9. What is the probability that someone will *not* order french fries with their lunch?

10. If 120 people eat at the restaurant during lunchtime, how many will likely order french fries?

11. A survey of favorite radio stations is taken at an arena after a concert sponsored by a local station. Is this a random survey?

The figure shown represents a dartboard. It is equally likely that a dart will land anywhere on the dartboard. Find each probability for randomly thrown darts.

12. P(shaded) 13. P(unshaded)

14. Suppose you threw a dart 180 times at the dartboard. How many times would you expect it to land in the shaded region?

15. How many times would you expect it to land in the unshaded region?

16. A dart is randomly thrown at the dartboard shown at the right. It is equally likely that a dart will land anywhere on the dartboard. Find the probability of a randomly thrown dart landing in the shaded region.

1. $\frac{2}{5}$
2. $\frac{7}{20}$
3. 0
4. $\frac{13}{20}$
5. 1

6. | Color | Frequency |
   |-------|-----------|
   | white | 40 |
   | black | 25 |
   | red | 35 |

7. 40
8. $\frac{3}{10}$
9. $\frac{7}{10}$
10. 36
11. no

12. $\frac{5}{9}$
13. $\frac{4}{9}$
14. 100
15. 80
16. $\frac{8}{9}$

© Glencoe/McGraw-Hill   350   Mathematics: Applications and Connections, Course 1

Name _____ Date _____

Chapter 13 Quiz A
(Lessons 13-1 and 13-2)

A number cube is rolled. Find the probability of each event.
1. P(6) 2. P(even number)

A sack contains 10 red jelly beans, 8 black jelly beans, and 7 white jelly beans. One jelly bean is chosen at random. Find the probability of each event.
3. P(white) 4. P(red)
5. P(black or red) 6. P(green)

Maria surveyed people buying flats of plants at a garden center. The results are shown in the table.
7. What is the size of the sample?

8. What is the probability that a customer will buy petunias?

9. What is the probability that a customer will buy impatiens or begonias?

10. If the garden center manager plans to order 400 flats of plants, how many flats of geraniums should be ordered?

geraniums	8
petunias	12
impatiens	10
begonias	10

1. $\frac{1}{6}$
2. $\frac{1}{2}$
3. $\frac{7}{25}$
4. $\frac{2}{5}$
5. $\frac{18}{25}$
6. 0
7. 40
8. $\frac{3}{10}$
9. $\frac{1}{2}$
10. 80

Name _____ Date _____

Chapter 13 Quiz B
(Lesson 13-3)

Suppose you threw a dart 100 times at each dartboard shown. How many times would you expect it to land in the shaded region?

1. 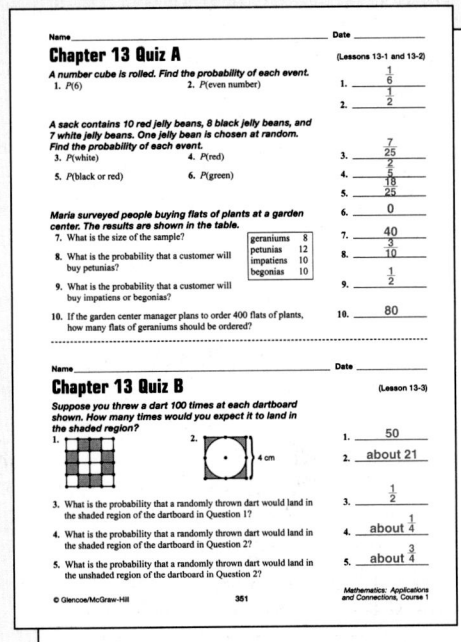 2. ⟡ 4 cm

3. What is the probability that a randomly thrown dart would land in the shaded region of the dartboard in Question 1?

4. What is the probability that a randomly thrown dart would land in the shaded region of the dartboard in Question 2?

5. What is the probability that a randomly thrown dart would land in the unshaded region of the dartboard in Question 2?

1. 50
2. about 21
3. $\frac{1}{2}$
4. about $\frac{1}{4}$
5. about $\frac{3}{4}$

© Glencoe/McGraw-Hill   351   Mathematics: Applications and Connections, Course 1

Technology Masters, pp. 25–26

13 Name _____ Date _____

Calculator Activity
(Lesson 13-2)

Making Predictions Using Samples

Two classes of sixth-grade students were asked to give their favorite brand of athletic shoe. The results are shown at the right.

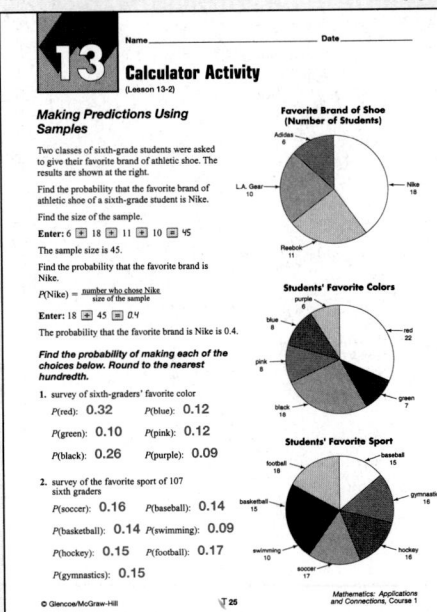

Favorite Brand of Shoe (Number of Students)
Adidas 6, L.A. Gear 10, Nike 18, Reebok 11

Find the probability that the favorite brand of athletic shoe of a sixth-grade student is Nike.

Find the size of the sample.

Enter: 6 ⊞ 18 ⊞ 11 ⊞ 10 ⊟ 45

The sample size is 45.

Find the probability that the favorite brand is Nike.

$P(\text{Nike}) = \frac{\text{number who chose Nike}}{\text{size of the sample}}$

Enter: 18 ⊟ 45 ⊟ 0.4

The probability that the favorite brand is Nike is 0.4.

Find the probability of making each of the choices below. Round to the nearest hundredth.

1. survey of sixth-graders' favorite color

   P(red): **0.32** P(blue): **0.12**

   P(green): **0.10** P(pink): **0.12**

   P(black): **0.26** P(purple): **0.09**

Students' Favorite Colors
purple 6, blue 8, red 22, pink 8, black 18, green 7

2. survey of the favorite sport of 107 sixth graders

   P(soccer): **0.16** P(baseball): **0.14**

   P(basketball): **0.14** P(swimming): **0.09**

   P(hockey): **0.15** P(football): **0.17**

   P(gymnastics): **0.15**

Students' Favorite Sport
football 18, baseball 15, gymnastics 16, hockey 16, swimming 10, soccer 17, basketball 15

© Glencoe/McGraw-Hill   25   Mathematics: Applications and Connections, Course 1

13 Name _____ Date _____

Graphing Calculator Activity
(Lesson 13-4)

Expected and Actual Probability

You can use a graphing calculator to conduct simulations.

Example Suppose you asked 50 people to choose a number from 0 to 9. Find the expected probability of each possible response or outcome.

Possible Outcome	Expected Frequency	Expected Probability	Possible Outcome	Expected Frequency	Expected Probability
0	5	$\frac{1}{10}$	5	5	$\frac{1}{10}$
1	5	$\frac{1}{10}$	6	5	$\frac{1}{10}$
2	5	$\frac{1}{10}$	7	5	$\frac{1}{10}$
3	5	$\frac{1}{10}$	8	5	$\frac{1}{10}$
4	5	$\frac{1}{10}$	9	5	$\frac{1}{10}$

Instead of asking 50 people, you can simulate the data using a graphing calculator.

Enter: MATH ▶ ▶ ▶ ENTER ENTER

The calculator will display a random decimal. Use the individual digits in making up your data as if they were responses. Record them in a table like the one below. Repeat this process until you have 50 responses. Find the actual frequency by counting the tallies. Find the actual probability by using the actual frequency.

Outcome	Tally	Actual Frequency	Actual Probability
0			
1			

Solve.

1. Use a graphing calculator to conduct this simulation. Complete the table using your random data. Then find the actual probabilities. **Check students' tables for the correct actual probabilities.**

2. Compare your data with those of a friend. Why are they not exactly the same? **Since the calculator gives random numbers, no two sets of data will be exactly the same.**

© Glencoe/McGraw-Hill   T 26   Mathematics: Applications and Connections, Course 1

Investigations for the Special Education Student, pp. 45–46

Use with:
Course 1-Chapter 14
Course 2-Chapter 13
Course 3-Chapter 13

Investigation 15 Teacher's Guide

The Game Show

Overview

The purpose of this investigation is for students to recognize that problem-solving and mathematical strategies are needed to play even the most enjoyable games. The problem-solving and mathematical value of several games will be evaluated by students during a three-day game review period. At the end of this time, the class will compile the results of their reviews into one master list of the "top ten" mathematics-related games. This list will then be forwarded to the appropriate school personnel along with a letter of recommendation to include such games as part of the mathematics program at the school.

Activity Goals

Students will:
• explore the problem-solving and mathematical strategies used in games,
• review and give feedback for certain games, and
• participate in selecting and recommending games for the school to purchase.

Planning the Instruction

Prerequisite Skills

Students should have a significant amount of practice reading and following directions, and computing with whole numbers. A basic understanding of probability may be helpful.

Materials
• investigation worksheet
• assortment of games for the classroom
• manila envelopes (one per game)

Time Needed
six 45-minute periods

Procedure

1. Given an example of a well-known game such as checkers, have students brainstorm the problem-solving and mathematical strategies that are necessary to play them. Then, explain to the class that they are about to become game consultants for the school by recommending games that will enhance the problem-solving and mathematical skills of its students.

2. Obtain a variety of games for use in the classroom. Depending on the classroom situation, teachers may bring games from home or have students volunteer to bring them.

3. Students will have three days in class to review as many games as possible. To review a game, students must follow the reviewing procedure on the Game Review worksheet. They will play each game twice, the second time answering the review questions. After reviewing each game, students will place the review sheet for that game in the envelope provided. If time permits, students should review another game using a new Game Review worksheet.

4. At the end of the reviewing periods, the results will be tallied, and, as a class, students and teacher will compile a list of the top ten games.

5. Once the list is established, the class will submit it to the appropriate personnel along with a letter explaining and supporting their research. The letter should also address the need for these games to be part of the mathematics program at the school.

6. An extension of this investigation might require students to create their own game involving the problem-solving and mathematical strategies believed to be the most valuable.

Adaptations and Variations

The following are some ideas on how this investigation may be modified depending on student population.

LD • Simplify rules for easier comprehension.
• Review several games together with the class.
• Allow students to work with a partner.

PH • Allow students to type or word process their review.
• Be sure to choose games suitable to their needs.

CD • Select games suitable to their needs.

BD • Maintain close proximity during the review process.
• If problems arise, have them play alone until they earn their way back to working with others.

HI • Select games suitable to their needs.

VI • Enlarge directions to games.
• Assign an aide to help students with any reading.

© Glencoe/McGraw-Hill   45   Mathematics: Applications and Connections

Theme: Wildlife Animals

Many animals must protect themselves from predators. Camouflage is an adaptation involving colors, patterns, and sometimes textures that enables animals to blend into their environment and become difficult to see. Some animals such as chameleons, flatfish, and shrimp can change color. Stick insects blend in because they look like twigs.

Question of the Day
A sea turtle lays 200 eggs on shore but only 75 survive and make it back to the sea. What is the probability that an egg layed will result in a young turtle making it back to the sea? $\frac{3}{8}$

Assess Prerequisite Skills

Ask students to read through the list of objectives presented in "What you'll learn in Chapter 13." You may wish to ask them what each of the objectives means or if they have experienced or used any of these math concepts before.

Building Portfolios

Encourage students to revise their portfolios as they study this chapter. Have them add work that shows how they determine probability and find outcomes. Encourage students to include predictions for real-world problems along with descriptions of actual outcomes.

Math and the Family

In the *Family Letters and Activities* booklet (pp. 25–26), you will find a letter to the parents explaining what students will study in Chapter 13. An activity appropriate for the whole family is also available.

CHAPTER 13 Using Probability

What you'll learn in Chapter 13

- to find and interpret the probability of an event or events,
- to solve problems by making a table,
- to predict actions of a larger group using a sample,
- to find probability using area models, and
- to find outcomes using lists, tree diagrams, and combinations.

512 Chapter 13 Using Probability

CD-ROM Program

Activities for Chapter 13
- Chapter 13 Introduction
- Interactive Lesson 13-3
- Extended Activity 13-1
- Assessment Game
- Resource Lessons 13-1 through 13-5

CHAPTER Project

HERE TODAY, GONE TOMORROW

In order to survive in their environment, many animals are camouflaged, or hidden, from predators. In this project, you will use probability to explore how camouflage works. You will also research how one animal is camouflaged, make a poster about the animal, and write a report on how a probability experiment can be used to illustrate camouflage.

Getting Started

- You will need black paper, white paper, two sections of the classified ads from the newspaper, a hole punch, and poster board.
- Choose one animal that lives in the wild that you would like to research.
- Research the animal.
  - Where does the animal live?
  - What does the animal eat?
  - Is survival of the animal aided by camouflage?
  - Is the animal an endangered species? Find statistics that tell how many of the animals still exist. What is being done to help the animals survive?

Technology Tips

- Use an **electronic encyclopedia** or the **Internet** to research the animal.
- Use a **word processor** to write a report on how the probability experiment illustrates camouflage.
- Use **computer software** to design your animal poster.

inter NET
CONNECTION Research **For up-to-date information on animal species, visit:**

www.glencoe.com/sec/math/mac/mathnet

Working on the Project

You can use what you'll learn in Chapter 13 to help you explore and understand camouflage.

Page	Exercise
518	27
529	23
543	Alternative Assessment

inter NET
CONNECTION

Instructional Resources ▶▶▶
A recording sheet to help students organize their data for the Chapter Project is shown at the right and is available in the *Investigations and Projects Masters*, p. 68.

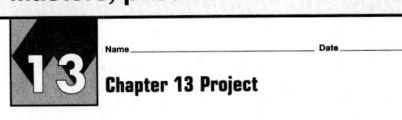

HANDS-ON
LAB

COOPERATIVE LEARNING

13-1A Fair and Unfair Games

A Preview of Lesson 13-1

🎲 number cubes

In this lab, you will explore fair and unfair games. A *fair game* is a game in which players have an equal chance of winning. In an *unfair game*, players do not have an equal chance of winning.

TRY THIS

Work with a partner.

❶ Rules of the game:
• Roll two number cubes.
• Add the two numbers that are face up.
• Player 1 gets one point if the sum is even. Player 2 gets one point if the sum is odd.
• Roll the number cubes 40 times.
• Record each sum in a chart like the one shown.

Sum

❷ Rules of the game:
• Roll two number cubes.
• Multiply the two numbers that are face up.
• Player 1 gets one point if the product is even. Player 2 gets one point if the product is odd.
• Roll the number cubes 40 times.
• Record each product in a chart like the one shown.

Product

ON YOUR OWN

1–5. See Answer Appendix.

1. Compare the number of even sums tossed to the number of odd sums tossed, and the number of even products tossed to the number of odd products tossed.

2. Which game do you think is fair? Which is unfair? Explain your reasoning.

3. Your charts should resemble a bar graph. Describe the shape of each of your graphs.

4. Which sum occurred most often? least often? Which product occurred most often? least often?

5. *Look Ahead* In Game 1, is getting a sum of 12 impossible, less likely than not getting 12, equally likely with not getting 12, more likely than not getting 12, or certain to occur? Explain your reasoning.

514 Chapter 13 Using Probability

Math Journal

Have students write a description of a fair game and an unfair game involving number cubes. Have them include a definition of *fair* and *unfair*.

What you'll learn

You'll learn to find and interpret the theoretical probability of an event.

When am I ever going to use this?

Knowing about probability can help you determine the chance of winning a game at a festival.

Word Wise

theoretical probability
outcomes
event
sample space
complementary events

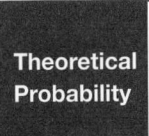

LOOK BACK

You can refer to Lesson 5-4 to review ratios.

On a popular television game show, the contestants spin a wheel that is separated into equal sections marked 5¢, 10¢, 15¢, ... , $1. Each contestant gets two spins. The contestant closest to $1, without going over, wins a spot in the showcase. What is the **theoretical probability**, or chance, that the wheel will land on $1 the first time a contestant spins it?

There are twenty equally likely results, or **outcomes** on the wheel. The specific outcome or type of outcome is called an **event**. In this case, the outcomes are all of the different sections the wheel could stop on, and the event is landing on $1.

The set of all possible outcomes is called the **sample space**. The sample space for the wheel is {5¢, 10¢, 15¢, ..., $1}.

To find the probability of landing on $1, you can use a ratio.

Theoretical Probability	**Words:**	The theoretical probability of an event is the ratio of the number of ways the event can occur to the number of possible outcomes.
	Symbols:	$P(\text{event}) = \dfrac{\text{number of ways the event can occur}}{\text{number of possible outcomes}}$

In the sample space, there is one way to land on $1 and 20 possible outcomes. So, $P(\$1) = \frac{1}{20}$.

You can express the probability of an event as a fraction, decimal, or percent. The probability that an event will occur is a number from 0 to 1. You can interpret probabilities using a number line.

cannot occur	not too likely to occur	50-50 chance	very likely to occur	certain to occur
$P = 0$	$P = \frac{1}{4}$	$P = \frac{1}{2}$	$P = \frac{3}{4}$	$P = 1$
	$= 0.25$	$= 0.5$	$= 0.75$	
$= 0\%$	$= 25\%$	$= 50\%$	$= 75\%$	$= 100\%$

- A probability of 0 means that the event cannot occur.

- A probability of $\frac{1}{2}$ means that there is a 50-50 chance that the event will occur.

- A probability of 1 means that the event is certain to occur.

- The closer a probability is to 1, the more likely the event is to occur.

Lesson 13-1 Theoretical Probability **515**

Instructional Resources

- *Study Guide Masters*, p. 90
- *Practice Masters*, p. 90
- *Enrichment Masters*, p. 90
- Transparencies 13-1, A and B
- *Diversity Masters*, p. 13

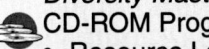 CD-ROM Program
- Resource Lesson 13-1
- Extended Activity 13-1

Recommended Pacing	
Honors	Day 2 of 11

1 FOCUS

 5-Minute Check
(Chapter 12)

Solve each equation.
1. $r - 7 = -18$ **−11**
2. $x + (-5) = 14$ **19**
3. $4n = -32$ **−8**
4. $\frac{1}{5}b = 6$ **30**
5. Complete the following function table. Then graph the function.

input (x)	output ($\frac{1}{4}x$)
−4	■ **−1**
0	■ **0**
8	■ **2**

 The 5-Minute Check is also available on **Transparency 13-1A** for this lesson.

Cross-Curriculum Cue

Inform the teachers on your team that your students are studying probability and area. Suggestions for curriculum integration are:

Physical Education: archery
Life Science: genetics

Motivating the Lesson
Communication Ask these questions about tossing a coin.
- What are the chances that the tossed coin will come up *heads*? **1 out of 2**
- What are the chances that the tossed coin will come up neither *heads* nor *tails*? **0**
- What other situations can you think of that have two equally likely results? **Sample answer: drawing a red or a black card from a deck of playing cards.**

2 TEACH

 Transparency 13-1B contains a teaching aid for this lesson.

Reading Mathematics Have students describe each new term in this lesson in their own words. Then have them use magazines to find examples that illustrate each term.

In-Class Examples

For Example 1
A number cube is marked with 1, 2, 3, 4, 5, and 6 on its faces. You roll the cube once. Find the probability of rolling a 1 or 2. Then tell how likely it is to roll a 1 or 2. $\frac{1}{3}$ **The event is not very likely to occur.**

For Example 2
There are four equally likely outcomes on the spinner.

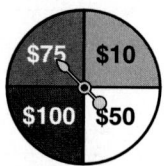

a. Find the probability of spinning $50. $\frac{1}{4}$
b. Find the probability of spinning an amount other than $50. $\frac{3}{4}$

For Example 3
A sportscaster says there is a 60% chance the Bobcats will win the baseball game. What is the probability that the Bobcats will lose the game? **40%**

Study Hint
Reading Math The notation P(less than 3) is read as the probability of a number less than 3 occurring.

1 A set of counters is numbered 1, 2, 3, ... , 10. Suppose you draw one counter without looking. Find the probability of choosing a number less than 3. Then tell how likely it is to choose a number less than 3.

There are two numbers less than 3: 1 and 2.

$\frac{2}{10}$ ← *number of ways to choose a number less than 3*
    ← *number of possible outcomes*

Therefore, $P(\text{less than 3}) = \frac{2}{10}$ or $\frac{1}{5}$.

Since the probability is close to $\frac{1}{4}$, it is not very likely to occur.

2 There are six equally likely outcomes on the spinner.
  a. Find the probability of spinning blue.
  b. Find the probability of spinning a color other than blue.

a. $\frac{2}{6}$ ← *number of ways to spin blue*
       ← *number of possible outcomes*

Therefore, $P(\text{blue}) = \frac{2}{6}$ or $\frac{1}{3}$.

b. $\frac{4}{6}$ ← *number of ways to spin a color other than blue*
       ← *number of possible outcomes*

Therefore, $P(\text{not blue}) = \frac{4}{6}$ or $\frac{2}{3}$.

In Example 2, either one or the other event must take place, but they cannot both happen at the same time. Notice that the sum of the probabilities of the two events is 1. These events are examples of **complementary events**.

Complementary Events	**Words:**	Complementary events are two events in which either one or the other must take place, but they cannot both happen at the same time. The sum of their probabilities is 1.
	Symbols:	$P(\text{event}_1) + P(\text{event}_2) = 1$

Classroom Vignette

"I have students play several games of Paper-Rock-Scissors and record the outcome of each round. I prepare a worksheet asking questions about the probability of the various outcomes during the game. Then they calculate the statistical measure for this data."

Deana Bobzien

Deana Bobzien, Teacher
Rochester Junior High
Rochester, IL

Example 3
CONNECTION

Earth Science A meteorologist predicts a 30% chance of rain. What is the probability that it will not rain?

The probability of no rain is the complement of the probability of rain. To find the probability of no rain, you can use an equation.

$P(\text{rain}) + P(\text{no rain}) = 1$

$0.3 + P(\text{no rain}) = 1$ *Replace P(rain) with 30% or 0.3.*

$P(\text{no rain}) = 1 - 0.3$ *Subtract 0.3 from each side.*

$P(\text{no rain}) = 1.0 - 0.3$ *Rewrite 1 as 1.0.*

$P(\text{no rain}) = 0.7$

So, $P(\text{no rain}) = 0.7$ or 70%.

CHECK FOR UNDERSTANDING

Communicating Mathematics

Read and study the lesson to answer each question.

1. *Draw* a spinner that shows $P(\text{yellow}) = \frac{2}{5}$. **1–3. See Answer Appendix.**

2. *Give two examples* of events in which the probability of each event occurring is 0.

3. *Write* a sentence describing the relationship between complementary events. Then give an example of complementary events.

Guided Practice

A number cube is marked with 1, 2, 3, 4, 5, and 6 on its faces. You roll the cube one time. Find the probability of each event. Then tell how likely the event is to happen. **4–9. For likelihood, see Answer Appendix.**

4. $P(3)$ $\frac{1}{6}$

5. $P(\text{greater than 2})$ $\frac{2}{3}$

6. $P(\text{odd})$ $\frac{1}{2}$

7. $P(5 \text{ or } 6)$ $\frac{1}{3}$

8. $P(\text{not 6})$ $\frac{5}{6}$

9. $P(7)$ **0**

10. *Industry* On a toy assembly line, 3% of the toys are defective. If an inspector selects a product at random, what is the probability the toy will pass inspection? **97%**

EXERCISES

Practice

Suppose you spin the spinner one time. Find the probability of each event. Then tell how likely the event is to happen. **11–17. For likelihood, see Answer Appendix.**

11. $P(\text{red})$ $\frac{1}{4}$

12. $P(\text{blue or red})$ $\frac{3}{8}$

13. $P(\text{green or red})$ $\frac{1}{2}$

14. $P(\text{not yellow})$ $\frac{3}{4}$

A set of 26 counters is lettered a, b, c, ... , z. Suppose you choose one counter without looking. Find the probability of each event. Then tell how likely the event is to happen.

15. $P(\text{m, n, or p})$ $\frac{3}{26}$

16. $P(26)$ **0**

17. $P(\text{consonant})$ $\frac{21}{26}$

Lesson 13-1 Theoretical Probability **517**

Chapter Project

Exercise 27 asks students to advance to the next stage of work on the Chapter Project. In part a, instruct students to pick up the paper circles one at a time. Have students place their paragraph from part c in their Project Folder.

4 ASSESS

Closing Activity

Modeling Have pairs of students design a spinner so that the $P(\text{blue})$ is $\frac{1}{8}$. Then have them find the probability of spinning a color other than blue.

Additional Answers

25b. Sample answer: Sometimes, eliminating the ones that cannot be correct leaves the correct answer.

25c. increase; There would be fewer choices.

28. Sample answer: A set of 10 cards is numbered 1, 2, 3, . . . 10. Suppose you choose one card without looking. Find the probability of choosing a number less than 7.

Practice Masters, p. 90

18–23. See Answer Appendix.

A set of 30 cards is numbered 1, 2, 3, ... , 30. Suppose you choose one card without looking. Find the probability of each event. Then describe the complementary event of each event, and find its probability.

18. $P(12)$
19. $P(\text{odd})$
20. $P(1 \text{ digit})$
21. $P(\text{integer})$
22. $P(\text{less than 1})$
23. $P(\text{greater than 18})$

24. When two number cubes are rolled, the probability of rolling doubles is $\frac{1}{6}$. What is the probability of not rolling doubles? $\frac{5}{6}$

Applications and Problem Solving

25. *School* A multiple-choice test question has five possible answers. Suppose you guess at the answer.
   a. What is the probability of choosing the correct answer? $\frac{1}{5}$
   b. Explain how you can use the problem-solving strategy *eliminating possibilities* to choose the correct answer. **b–c. See margin.**
   c. By eliminating possibilities, would the probability of choosing the correct answer increase or decrease? Explain.

26. *Advertising* A cereal company is having a contest. Each box of cereal contains one of the letters B, A, M, O. In every 20 boxes, there are four Bs, five As, ten Ms, and one O. What is the probability that a box of cereal will have a B? $\frac{1}{5}$

27. *Working on the* **Chapter Project** Place one sheet of the classified ads on the floor. Use a hole punch to cut out 100 holes from each sheet of white paper, black paper, and classified ads. Scatter the circles on the spread-out sheet of classifieds.

27a–b. Answers will vary.

   a. Randomly pick up as many paper circles as you can for 10 seconds. How many circles of each kind do you have?
   b. To find the probability of picking up a black circle, divide the number of black circles picked up by the total number of circles picked up. Find the probability of picking up each color.
   c. Write a paragraph that explains how probability relates to camouflage. Tell whether or not this activity is an example of experimental or theoretical probability. **See students' work.**

For **Extra Practice,** see page 590.

28. *Critical Thinking* Write a problem in which the probability of an event occurring is 0.6. **See margin.**

Mixed Review
29. See Answer Appendix.

29. *Functions* Graph the function represented by the function table shown. *(Lesson 12-6)*
30. Find $-12 + (-6)$. *(Lesson 11-3)* **−18**
31. What is 32% of 148? *(Lesson 8-7)* **47.36**

input	output
4	4
−2	−2
0	0

32. **Standardized Test Practice** Every class that sells 75 tickets to the school play earns an ice cream party. Kate's class has sold 47 tickets. How many more tickets must they sell to earn the ice cream party? *(Lesson 1-1)* **C**
   A 23 **B** 32 **C** 28 **D** 35 **E** Not Here

Extending the Lesson

Enrichment Masters, p. 90

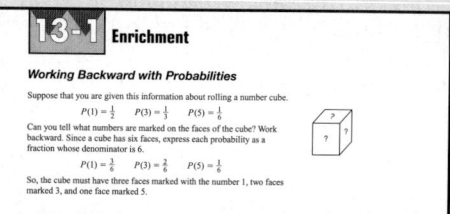

Activity Ask small groups of students to create a game where the probability of winning can change with each turn. A score of 18 is needed to win. **Sample answer: Roll a number cube 6 times. If the number is even, add it to your score. If the number is odd, subtract it.**

BIOLOGICAL SCIENCE

Lyle Allard
Biological Science Technician

Lyle Allard is a biological science technician for the Fish Technology Center in Bozeman, Montana. At the Center, they are developing healthier fish foods. Mr. Allard takes care of experimental fish and watches their growth and behavior. He is a member of the Turtle Mountain Band of the Chippewa Tribe in North Dakota. One of his goals is to help Native American tribes improve their management of fish and wildlife.

To work in biological science, you will need a bachelor's degree in a biology-related field. Some careers in biological science are zoologist, ecologist, naturalist, park ranger, veterinarian, and zookeeper. A zoologist may use mathematics when recording or interpreting data about animals. If you like animals and being outdoors, then you may want to consider a career in biological science.

For more information:
U.S. Fish and Wildlife Service
1849 C Street
Washington, DC 20240

interNET CONNECTION
www.glencoe.com/sec/math/mac/mathnet

I love the outdoors and I think that it would be great to work with wildlife.

Your Turn

Interview a person who works with animals. Ask about the advantages and disadvantages of working with animals and how they use mathematics in their job. Then write a report that summarizes your interview.

School to Career: Biological Science **519**

More About Lyle Allard

- Lyle Allard received an associate's degree from the College of Southern Idaho and a bachelor of arts degree from Montana State University. He believes that it is important to focus on a career while still in school because hard work and devotion in youth can lead to a successful career later in life.

- Mr. Allard became a biological scientist because he enjoyed working outdoors, especially with fish. An avid hiker and camper, he has also worked as a professional hunting guide.

Motivating Students

Wildlife management is necessary to prevent specific animal populations from becoming too large or too small. For example, in the past 150 years, more than 60 species or subspecies of mammals have become extinct. To begin a discussion, ask students these questions.

- Why have certain animals become extinct? **their habitat is developed for human use, pollution**
- Why might people who catch fish be concerned about the health of the fish? **If the fish is sick, the person who eats the fish may become ill.**

Making the Math Connection

Biological scientists use sampling and probability to predict population birth, growth, death, and survival rates. They then use these predictions to plan for future wildlife management.

Working on Your Turn

Encourage students to interview someone who has a job they might like to have themselves. Have them ask the person what education and experience he or she needed to qualify for the position. Have students include this information in their reports. You may also have students read their reports to the class.

An additional School to Career activity is available on page 13 of the School to Career Masters.

PROBLEM SOLVING

13-2A Make a Table

A Preview of Lesson 13-2

Patsy and Adam are organizing their school's upcoming music festival. They are discussing how to conduct a survey to determine which songs the students would prefer to sing. Let's listen in!

Patsy

I have the list of songs to choose from. I think that we should ask all of the chorus members which of the songs they would like to sing.

There isn't enough time to ask everyone. Let's ask every fourth chorus member who comes into chorus practice tonight to choose six songs.

Song Survey		
Song	**Tally**	**Frequency**
Yesterday	IIII	4
You've Lost That Lovin' Feeling	ЖI	6
Georgia On My Mind	III	3
Bridge Over Troubled Water		0
A Whole New World	ЖIII	8
Tomorrow	Ж	5
Just Around The River Bend	II	2
Yellow Rose Of Texas	IIII	4

Adam

OK. I'll make a frequency table like this to record the results of the survey. We'll choose the six songs with the most votes.

THINK ABOUT IT

Work with a partner. 1–3. See margin.

1. **Analyze** the way Patsy and Adam conducted the survey. Do you think the survey reflected the opinions of the entire chorus? Why or why not?

2. **Describe** other types of information that can be concluded from the table.

3. **Tell** an advantage of organizing information in a table.

4. **Apply** the **make a table** strategy to solve the following problem.

   A list of test scores is shown.

71	89	65	77	79	98	84
86	70	97	93	80	91	72
100	75	73	86	99	77	68

   a. *Make a frequency table of the test scores.* **See Answer Appendix.**

   b. *How many more students scored 71 to 80 than 91 to 100?* **2**

For **Extra Practice**, see page 591.

ON YOUR OWN

5. The first step of the 4-step plan for problem solving asks you to *explore* the problem. *Tell* the advantages of exploring the set of data before you make a table. **See margin.**

6. See students' work.

6. *Write a Problem* that can be solved by making a table. Then ask a classmate to solve the problem by making a table.

7. *Explain* how the make a table strategy is used to help conduct the pet survey in Exercise 18 on page 525. **See margin.**

MIXED PROBLEM SOLVING

8. 50 and 36

> **STRATEGIES**
> Look for a pattern.
> Solve a simpler problem.
> Act it out.
> Guess and check.
> Draw a diagram.
> Make a chart.
> Work backward.

Solve. Use any strategy.

8. *Number Sense* The difference between two whole numbers is 14. Their product is 1,800. Find the two numbers.

9. *Life Science* A snail at the bottom of a 10-foot hole crawls up 3 feet each day, but slips back 2 feet each night. How many days will it take the snail to reach the top of the hole and escape? **8 days**

10. *School* The list shows the birth month of the students in Miss Miller's geography class.

June	October	May	April
April	May	October	June
July	August	April	May
March	June	September	July
July	April	December	March
June	October	January	June

    a. Make a frequency table of the students' birth months. **See Answer Appendix.**

    b. How many of the students were born in April? **4**

    c. How many more students were born in June than in August? **4**

11. *Money Matters* Harris spent $5.69 on golf tees. About how much change should he expect to receive if he paid with a $20 bill? **Sample answer: $20–$6 or $14**

12. *Sports* Coach Franco is deciding in which order the players will bat. She looks at the number of hits each player made in the previous game. Use the frequency table shown.

Number of Hits		
Player	**Tally**	**Frequency**
Parker	II	2
Martinez	III	3
Cruz	IIII	4
Plesich	II	2
Higgins	III	3
Reid	I	1
Hartley		0
Wilson	II	2

    a. Who had the most hits? **Cruz**

    b. Who had the least hits? **Hartley**

    c. Find the total number of hits in the previous game. **17**

13. *Standardized Test Practice* There are 4 green, 2 purple, 1 orange, and 5 yellow marbles in a pouch. Forest chooses 1 marble at random, records its color, and replaces it. He repeats this process 25 times. Which color did Forest probably choose the greatest number of times? **D**

    A orange

    B purple

    C green

    D yellow

Lesson 13-2A THINKING **LAB** 521

---

3 PRACTICE/APPLY

Check for Understanding
Have students complete Exercises 1–3 in pairs. Have them ask each other additional questions about the table. Use the results from Exercise 4 to determine whether students understand how to set up a frequency table.

Extra Practice If students need additional practice in problem solving, extra practice is available on the following pages.
- Make a Table, see p. 591
- Mixed Problem Solving, see pp. 593–594

Assignment Guide
All: 5–13

4 ASSESS

Closing Activity
Writing Have students write a paragraph explaining why making a table is a good problem-solving strategy for some problems. Have them include an example of a problem that can be solved by making a table and one that cannot be solved that way.

Additional Answers
5. Sample answer: It enables you to determine a reasonable interval width for the given data.

7. Sample answer: Ashley organized the results of the survey by making a table. The table makes it easy to find information such as the most preferred and the least preferred pet.

Extending the Lesson

Activity Have pairs of students write a survey question that deals with an issue in their school. Discuss how many students would have to be surveyed to answer the question. Have students consider the work involved in a survey and what types of results might be found on the frequency table. Have them conduct the survey and record the data in a frequency table. Sample problem: *What is your favorite cafeteria food? Make a list of food items available in the cafeteria. Survey half the students in the school to find out which items are preferred. Make a frequency table.*

Check for Understanding

If students need additional practice or instruction after completing Exercises 1–7, one of these options may be helpful.
- Extra Practice, see p. 591
- Reteaching Activity
- *Study Guide Masters*, p. 91
- *Practice Masters*, p. 91

Assignment Guide

Core: 9–19 odd, 20–23
Enriched: 8–16 even, 18–23
All: Self Test, 1–5

Additional Answers

1. **Sample answer: Population is the entire group while random sample is a subset of the entire group.**

2. **Sample answer: The conclusions derived from the random sample should reflect the same results derived from the population. Therefore, you should be able to predict the winners of a school board election from the random sample.**

Study Guide Masters, p. 91

13-2 Study Guide

Integration: Statistics
Making Predictions Using Samples

Data gathered by surveying a random sample of the population may be used to make predictions about the entire population.

Example   Joyce surveyed every tenth person entering the school to determine whether they would prefer attending a rock concert or a dance. Of the 60 students surveyed, 35 said they preferred a rock concert, and 25 said they preferred a dance. If 800 students attend the school, predict how many would prefer a rock concert.

$\frac{35}{60}$ or 58% of those surveyed said they preferred a concert.

58% of 800 = 0.58 × 800
         = 464

About 464 students would prefer a rock concert.

Solve.

1. In a random sample of 600 batteries, 3 were found to be defective. If a factory produces 7,000 batteries each day, predict the number that are defective.   **35**

2. Wilson has made 8 out of the last 20 free throws he has attempted. What is the probability that he will make the next free throw?   **$\frac{2}{5}$**

3. The graph shows who has bought tickets so far. What is the probability that a senior citizen will buy the next ticket?   **$\frac{1}{5}$**

Ticket Sales
Adults 36%, Seniors 20%, Students 44%

4. In a poll of 200 people, 82 said they would vote for Peterson for mayor, 106 said they would vote for Sanderson, and 12 were undecided. If 5,200 people vote in the election, predict the number that will vote for Peterson.   **2,132**

5. In a survey, 35% of the students said they would buy a hot dog at a football game, 45% said they would buy a hamburger, and 85% said they would buy a soft drink. If 350 students are expected to attend a football game, how many hot dogs, hamburgers, and soft drinks should be ordered for the concession stand?   **123; 158; 298**

© Glencoe/McGraw-Hill   T91   *Mathematics: Applications and Connections, Course 1*

Communicating Mathematics

Read and study the lesson to answer each question. 1–2. See margin.

1. *Tell* the difference between population and random sample.

2. *Explain* how you can use a random sample to predict the results of a school board election.

HANDS-ON MATH

3. *Find* a newspaper article or advertisement that refers to a survey. Then write one or two sentences describing how the results of the survey can predict the actions of a larger group. **See students' work.**

Guided Practice

Tell whether each of the following is a random sample. Explain your answer. 4–6. See Answer Appendix for explanations.

Type of Survey	Survey Location
4. favorite entertainment	Broadway show **no**
5. favorite flower	shopping center **yes**
6. favorite holiday	fast-food restaurant **yes**

7. *Sports*   In soccer, Karena scored 6 goals in her last 10 attempts.
   a. What is the probability of Karena scoring a goal on her next attempt? $\frac{3}{5}$ **or 60%**
   b. Suppose Karena attempts to score 15 goals. About how many goals will she make?   **about 9**

EXERCISES

Practice

Tell whether each of the following is a random sample. Explain your answer. 8–16. See Answer Appendix for explanations.

Type of Survey	Survey Location
8. favorite color	grocery store **yes**
9. favorite hobby	model train store **no**
10. favorite musician	rock concert **no**
11. favorite sport	mall **yes**
12. favorite season	public library **yes**
13. favorite car	a specific car dealership **no**
14. favorite TV show	skating rink **yes**
15. favorite candy bar	chocolate factory **no**
16. favorite food	Mexican restaurant **no**

17. *Civics*   Louisa conducted a survey to find out which political party people in her county preferred. She surveyed every tenth person standing in line at the Democratic headquarters. Is this a random sample? Explain. **No; no Republicans were included in the survey.**

■ Reteaching the Lesson ■

Activity   Have groups of students conduct a survey among themselves to find out if they prefer hamburgers or tacos. Ask: *Is your group an example of a random sample? What part of your group chose tacos? What is the probability that another student in your class would choose tacos? Predict how many would prefer tacos.*

18. *Life Science* Ashley conducted a survey of students' favorite pets from a random sample of 56 students at Park Middle School. The results are shown in the chart.

a. What is the size of the sample? **56**

b. What is the probability that a student at Park Middle School prefers a gerbil? $\frac{1}{4}$, **or 25%**

c. If there are 252 sixth graders, about how many will prefer gerbils? **about 63**

Pet	Number
Dog	24
Cat	11
Gerbil	14
Bird	7

interNET CONNECTION

For the latest ratings, visit: www.glencoe.com/ sec/math/mac/mathnet

19. *Technology* A ratings company uses a sample of about 970 households in the United States to determine the rankings of TV shows. An estimated 38% of all TV sets in use were tuned to the top rated show. How many sets in the sample were tuned to the top rated show? **about 369**

20. *Critical Thinking* A pre-election poll predicted that a certain candidate for mayor would receive 25% of the vote. The candidate received 15,248 votes. Estimate how many people voted in the mayoral election. **about 60,000 people**

Mixed Review

21. **Standardized Test Practice** A bag contains 2 yellow counters, 1 red counter, 5 blue counters, and 3 green counters. Alec chooses 1 counter at random 20 times, records its color, and then replaces it in the bag. Which color did Alec probably choose the most number of times? *(Lesson 13-1)* **C**

A yellow **B** red **C** blue **D** green

22. *Geometry* An angle measures 91.2°. Is it an obtuse or acute angle? *(Lesson 9-1)* **obtuse**

For **Extra Practice**, see page 591.

23. *Measurement* How many inches are in 5 yards? *(Lesson 5-6)* **180 inches**

CHAPTER **13**

Mid-Chapter Self Test

A bag contains 4 blue marbles, 3 yellow marbles, 6 purple marbles, and 5 green marbles. One marble is chosen at random. Find the probability of each event. *(Lesson 13-1)*

1. $P(\text{yellow})$ $\frac{1}{6}$

2. $P(\text{orange})$ **0**

3. $P(\text{green or blue})$ $\frac{1}{2}$

4. $P(\text{blue or purple})$ $\frac{5}{9}$

5. *Technology* A quality control inspector found that 3 out of 50 computer keyboards were defective. *(Lesson 13-2)*

a. What is the probability that a randomly-chosen computer keyboard will be defective? $\frac{3}{50}$, **or 6%**

b. Suppose the company manufactured 15,000 computer keyboards. How many of the keyboards will be defective? **about 900**

Lesson 13-2 Integration: Statistics Making Predictions Using Samples **525**

Extending the Lesson

Enrichment Masters, p. 91

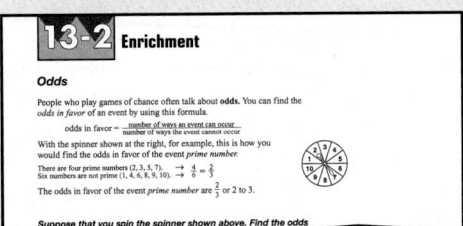

13-2 Enrichment

Odds

People who play games of chance often talk about **odds**. You can find the *odds in favor* of an event by using this formula.

odds in favor = number of ways an event can occur / number of ways the event cannot occur

With the spinner shown at the right, for example, this is how you would find the odds in favor of the event *prime number*.

There are four prime numbers (2, 3, 5, 7). → $\frac{4}{6} = \frac{2}{3}$
Six numbers are not prime (1, 4, 6, 8, 9, 10). → $\frac{2}{3}$

The odds in favor of the event *prime number* are $\frac{2}{3}$ or 2 to 3.

Suppose that you spin the spinner shown above. Find the odds.

Activity Have pairs of students determine how they could use a survey to plan a fund-raising activity. Ask them who they would survey and why. Then have them explain how they would apply the survey results to their fund-raising plan.

- *Study Guide Masters*, p. 92
- *Practice Masters*, p. 92
- *Enrichment Masters*, p. 92
- Transparencies 13-3, A and B
- *Assessment and Evaluation Masters*, pp. 350, 351
- *Hands-On Lab Masters*, p. 81

 CD-ROM Program
- Resource Lesson 13-3
- Interactive Lesson 13-3

Recommended Pacing	
Honors	Days 5 & 6 of 11

1 FOCUS

5-Minute Check
(Lesson 13-2)

A survey was taken to find out how many local residents supported building a new recreation center.

Support Building a New Recreation Center	
Yes	12
No	8
Undecided	5

1. What is the size of the sample? **25**
2. What is the probability that a resident is undecided? $\frac{1}{5}$**, or 20%**
3. Suppose there are 300 residents. How many could be expected to support building a new recreation center? **144 residents**

 The 5-Minute Check is also available on **Transparency 13-3A** for this lesson.

Motivating the Lesson

Problem Solving A round birthday cake serves twelve people and will be cut into twelve equal pieces so that only one of the three roses on the cake would be on a piece. Ask students to determine the probability of receiving a piece with a rose on it. **There would be 3 chances out of 12, or a probability of $\frac{1}{4}$.**

13-3

Integration: Geometry
Probability and Area

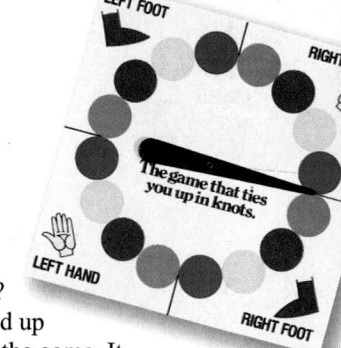

Have you ever played a popular floor game? If so, then you know that it is easy to get tied up in knots! The spinner shown is used to play the game. It has 16 equally likely outcomes. What is the probability of spinning left hand yellow?

There are 16 possible outcomes and 1 way the event can occur. Therefore, $P(\text{left hand, yellow}) = \frac{1}{16}$.

In Lesson 13-1, you learned to relate probability to spinners or number cubes. You can also relate probability to the areas of geometric shapes.

 MINI-LAB

Work with a partner.   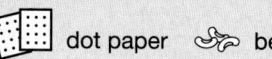 dot paper   beans

Try This
- Draw two squares on dot paper similar to the ones shown.
- Drop 50 beans onto the paper, from about 8 inches above.
- Record the number of beans that land within the large square. Record the number of beans that land within the small square. Do not count those that land outside the squares.

Talk About It
1. Find the ratio $\frac{\text{number of beans in a small square}}{\text{number of beans in a large square}}$. **See students' work.**
2. Find the ratio $\frac{\text{area of small square}}{\text{area of large square}}$. $\frac{1}{4}$
3. Compare the two ratios. **3–4. See students' work.**
4. Combine your results with another group and compare the ratios.

With a very large sample, the experimental probability should be very close to the theoretical probability.

The results of the Mini-Lab suggest the following conclusion.

$$\frac{\text{number landing in small square}}{\text{number landing in large square}} = \frac{\text{area of small square}}{\text{area of large square}}$$

Multiple Learning Styles

 Auditory/Musical Have students count and measure the bars on a toy xylophone. Suggest that they strike each bar and listen to the sound it makes. Then have them determine the probability that a toddler playing randomly will strike a particular bar. Assume that each stroke hits a bar, and only one bar.

Examples

1 The figure shown represents a dartboard.

a. Suppose you threw a dart randomly at the board and it hits the board. Find the probability of the dart landing in region C.

b. Suppose you threw the dart 500 times. How many times would you expect it to land in region C?

a. $P(\text{region C}) = \dfrac{\text{area of region C}}{\text{area of target}}$

$= \dfrac{8}{16} \text{ or } \dfrac{1}{2}$

b. Let c = times the dart lands in region C.

$\dfrac{c}{500} = \dfrac{1}{2}$ ← *area of region C*
           ← *area of dart board*

$c \times 2 = 500 \times 1$ *Find the cross products.*

$2c = 500$

$c = 250$ *Divide each side by 2.*

So, out of 500 times, the dart should land in region C about 250 times.

APPLICATION

Real World

2 **Games** At a county fair, a dart is thrown at the dartboard shown. It is equally likely that the dart will land anywhere on the dartboard. Find the probability that a dart will land in the red region. Then tell how likely the event is to happen.

$P(\text{red region}) = \dfrac{\text{area of red region}}{\text{area of target}}$

Area of red region $= \pi r^2$

$\approx 3.14 \times 1 \times 1$

$\approx 3.14 \text{ in}^2$

Area of target $= s^2$

$= 5 \times 5 \text{ or } 25 \text{ in}^2$

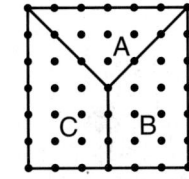
5 in.

1 in.

5 in.

$P(\text{red region}) \approx \dfrac{3.14}{25}$

$\approx \dfrac{3}{24} \text{ or } \dfrac{1}{8}$ *3 and 24 are compatible numbers.*

The probability of landing in the red region is about $\dfrac{1}{8}$ or 12.5%.
The event is not very likely to happen.

Cultural Kaleidoscope

During the 17th century, mathematicians Blaise Pascal and Pierre de Fermat studied the probability of games of chance.

CHECK FOR UNDERSTANDING

Communicating Mathematics

Read and study the lesson to answer each question.

1. *Tell* the probability of a randomly-thrown dart landing in region B of the figure shown. $\dfrac{4}{9}$

2. *Draw* a dartboard in which the probability of landing in a shaded region is $\dfrac{3}{4}$. **See margin.**

A

B

C

Lesson 13-3 Integration: Geometry   Probability and Area   **527**

Transparency 13-3B contains a teaching aid for this lesson.

Using the Mini-Lab If beans are unavailable, rice, popcorn kernels, or puffed cereal may be substituted. Ask students if they think the number of items that fall within the squares will be affected by the height of the drop. Make sure students discover that the larger the sample, the closer the experimental probability gets to the theoretical probability.

In-Class Examples

For Example 1
The figure represents a dartboard.

A

C   B

a. Suppose you threw a dart randomly at the board and it hit the board. Find the probability of the dart landing in region A. $\dfrac{1}{4}$

b. Suppose you threw the dart 300 times. How many times would you expect it to land in region A? **75 times**

For Example 2
Irina lost her contact lens while playing basketball. If it is equally likely that she lost the lens on any part of the court, estimate the probability that Irina lost her lens inside the center circle. **about $\dfrac{1}{47}$, or 2%**

50 ft

6 ft

94 ft

Additional Answer

2. Sample answer:

Check for Understanding

If students need additional practice or instruction after completing Exercises 1–8, one of these options may be helpful.
- Extra Practice, see p. 591
- Reteaching Activity
- *Study Guide Masters*, p. 92
- *Practice Masters*, p. 92
- Interactive Mathematics Tools Software

Assignment Guide

Core: 9–21 odd, 24–27
Enriched: 10–20 even, 21, 22, 24–27

Study Guide Masters, p. 92

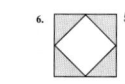

HANDS-ON MATH

3. Use your dartboard from Exercise 2. Drop a bean 50 times onto the target. Then find the ratio that compares the number of times the bean lands in the shaded region to the number of times the bean lands in the target. How does this ratio compare to $\frac{3}{4}$, the theoretical probability of landing in the shaded region? **See students' work.**

Guided Practice

Each figure represents a dartboard. It is equally likely that a dart will land anywhere on the dartboard. Find the probability of a randomly-thrown dart landing in the shaded region.

4. $\frac{7}{25}$

5. 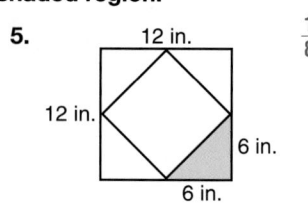 $\frac{1}{8}$

6. about 42
7. about 19

6. Suppose you threw a dart 150 times at the dartboard in Exercise 4. How many times would you expect it to land in the shaded region?

7. Suppose you threw a dart 150 times at the dartboard in Exercise 5. How many times would you expect it to land in the shaded region?

8. *Games* A randomly-thrown dart is thrown at the dartboard shown. It is equally likely that the dart will land anywhere on the dartboard. Find the probability that a dart will land in the shaded region of the figure shown. Then tell how likely the event is to happen.
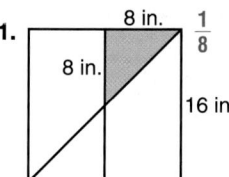
$\frac{15}{16}$; The event is very likely to occur.

EXERCISES

Practice

Each figure represents a dartboard. It is equally likely that a dart will land anywhere on the dartboard. Find the probability of a randomly-thrown dart landing in the shaded region.

9. $\frac{2}{5}$ **10.** $\frac{5}{8}$ **11.** 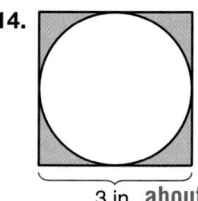 $\frac{1}{8}$

12. $\frac{9}{25}$ **13.** $\frac{4}{25}$ **14.** about $\frac{2}{9}$

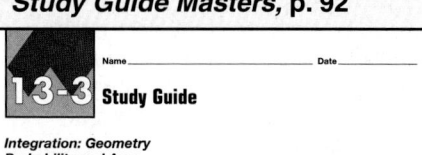

Reteaching the Lesson

Activity Have pairs of students create a square design with red and blue tiles. Have them find the probability of an object landing on a red tile. Then have them use additional tiles to form a new shape and find the probability of an object landing on a red tile in the new shape.

Error Analysis

Watch for students who subtract the area of the region in question from the area of the whole to find the probability.

Prevent by reminding students that a ratio is a comparison of two numbers by division.

Copy and complete.

	Dartboard	Times Dart is Thrown	Times Expected to Land in Shaded Region
15.	Exercise 9	200	about 80
16.	Exercise 10	200	about 125
17.	Exercise 11	250	about 32
18.	Exercise 12	250	about 90
19.	Exercise 13	275	about 44
20.	Exercise 14	275	about 61

Applications and Problem Solving

21. *Entertainment* A sky diver is the featured entertainer for the half-time show of the Johnstown High School homecoming football game. It is equally likely that the sky diver will land on any point of the field. Find the probability that the sky diver will land inside the circle. **about $\frac{1}{40}$, or 2.5%**

160 ft

21 ft

360 ft

22. *Games* A dart is thrown at the dartboard shown. It is equally likely that the dart will land anywhere on the dartboard. What is the probability of the dart landing on the shaded region? Then tell how likely the event is to happen. **See Answer Appendix.**

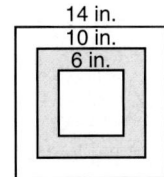

14 in.
10 in.
6 in.

23. *Working on the* **CHAPTER Project** Refer to page 518.

23a–b. See students' work.

24. A-50; B-50; C-about 13; D-25; E-about 13; F-25; G-25

25. No; people in a jeans store may prefer the jeans sold by the store.

a. Suppose you had randomly picked up 100 circles. How many circles of each color would you expect to pick up?

b. Suppose you had randomly picked up 250 circles. How many circles of each color would you expect to pick up?

c. Write a paragraph that explains how this experiment relates to camouflage. **See margin.**

24. *Critical Thinking* Suppose you made a dartboard from the tangram shown. If you throw 200 darts at the dartboard, how many would you expect to land in each region? Assume it is equally likely that the dart lands anywhere in the tangram.

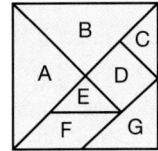

B
C
A
D
E
F
G

Mixed Review

25. *Statistics* Tell whether a survey on favorite jeans at a specific brand of jeans store is a random survey. Explain your answer. *(Lesson 13-2)*

26. *Standardized Test Practice* The area of a rectangle is 153 square feet, and the width is 9 feet. Use the formula $A = \ell w$ to find the length of the rectangle. *(Lesson 12-3)* **A**

  A 17 ft   **B** 144 ft   **C** 162 ft   **D** 1,377 ft

For **Extra Practice,** see page 591.

27. *Geometry* What is the area of a triangle whose base is 52 feet and whose height is 38 feet? *(Lesson 10-2)* **988 ft²**

Lesson 13-3 Integration: Geometry   Probability and Area   **529**

Extending the Lesson

Enrichment Masters, p. 92

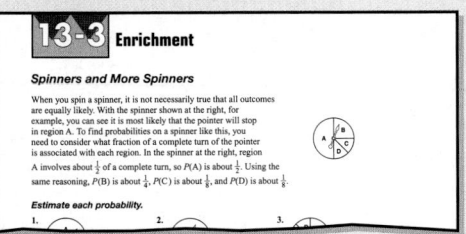

Activity Invite an insurance agent to give a presentation on how probability is used to set rates for accident, life, and hazard insurance. Have students prepare questions and find probabilities with the help of the speaker.

CHAPTER Project

Exercise 23 asks students to advance to the next stage of work on the Chapter Project. You may wish to have students form groups to brainstorm ideas for their paragraphs. Have students place their paragraphs in their Project Folders.

4 ASSESS

Closing Activity

Writing Have students work in pairs to create probability word problems involving any playing field, such as a soccer field or hockey rink.

Chapter 13, Quiz B (Lesson 13-3) is available in the *Assessment and Evaluation Masters,* p. 351.

Mid-Chapter Test (Lessons 13-1 through 13-3) is available in the *Assessment and Evaluation Masters,* p. 350.

Additional Answer

23c. Sample answer: In the experiment, it is easier to see the black and white circles but it is hard to see the newsprint circles. The newsprint circles represent the camouflage trait.

Practice Masters, p. 92

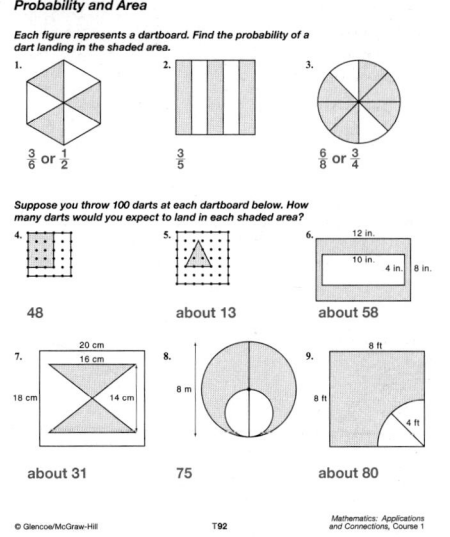

GET READY

Objective Students investigate geometric probability by using a graphing calculator.

Technology Resources
• TI-80, TI-81, TI-82, or TI-83 graphing calculator

MANAGEMENT TIPS

Recommended Time
30 minutes

Getting Started Explain that the calculator program will generate ordered pairs. If students have had little experience with graphing calculators, they will need help entering the program into the memory. Consult the User's Guide for the locations of specific commands.

Explain that the calculator needs an integer seed value to act as a starting point for the random number generator.

Instruct students to count points that fall on the outside edge of the large square or unshaded square as inside the particular square.

Using a Spreadsheet
Spreadsheet software may also be used to generate the needed random numbers.

ASSESS

After students answer Exercises 1–5, ask them to compare their graphs. Have students with similar graphs compare their ratios for Exercises 1 and 4. Are these ratios also close? **They should be.**

13-3B Probability

A Follow-Up of Lesson 13-3

 graphing calculator

 grid paper

 straightedge

In Lesson 13-3, you used area to find a probability. You can experiment with area and probability by using a graphing calculator.

TRY THIS

Work with a partner.

• Use a straightedge to draw the figure shown on grid paper. Then shade the figure as shown.

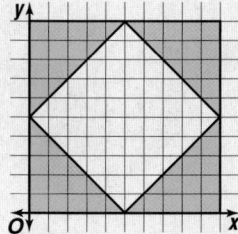

• Use the program to generate 50 random ordered pairs. When you run the program, it will ask you how many ordered pairs you want: type "50" and push the ENTER key. It will then ask you for a seed number. Type in any number and push the ENTER key. This helps the calculator pick random numbers. The calculator will now start giving you pairs of coordinates. The first number is *x* and the second number is *y*. Each time you push the ENTER key, it will give you another pair of numbers until it has given you 50 of them.

• Graph each pair on the grid paper. Keep a tally of how many points are in the shaded regions and how many points are in the unshaded region.

```
:Fix 1
:Disp "Number of Pairs"
:Input P
:Disp "Seed Number"
:Input N
:N → rand
:For (J,1,P,1)
:10 * rand → X
:Disp X
:10 * rand → Y
:Disp Y
:Disp " "
:Pause
:End
```

ON YOUR OWN

1. Write a ratio that compares the number of points graphed in the shaded regions to the total number of points graphed. **1–4. See Answer Appendix.**

2. Use the formulas for the area of a triangle and the area of a square to find the ratio that compares the area of the shaded regions to the area of the square.

3. How do the ratios compare?

4. Generate and graph 50 more ordered pairs by changing the seed number. Add the results to your previous results. What fraction of the 100 points generated are in the shaded region? How does this fraction compare to the fraction of the square that is shaded?

5. Suppose you wanted to plot points on a grid in which the *x*- and *y*-coordinates went from 0 to 20, instead of 0 to 10. What change would you need to make in the program? **Sample answer: In the program, change 10 to 20.**

530 **Chapter 13** Using Probability

 Math Journal Have students write a paragraph about their reaction to the close link between are a and probability. Were they surprised? Why or why not?

Finding Outcomes

What you'll learn

You'll learn to find outcomes using lists, tree diagrams, and combinations.

When am I ever going to use this?

Knowing how to find the number of possible outcomes can help you determine options when ordering a pizza.

Word Wise

tree diagram
combinations

Study Hint

Problem Solving
Use the draw-a-diagram strategy.

Mr. Mason wrote the suffixes *-ness, -er,* and *-ly* on the chalkboard. He then asked his students to form words using the given suffixes and the words *quick, slow,* and *happy*. How many different words can be made using the suffixes and the words?

To solve the problem, you can determine the sample space by making a list.

quickness	quicker	quickly
slowness	slower	slowly
happiness	happier	happily

There are 9 different words that can be formed.

You can also use a **tree diagram** to show the sample space.

Word	Suffix	Outcome
quick	-ness	quickness
	-er	quicker
	-ly	quickly
slow	-ness	slowness
	-er	slower
	-ly	slowly
happy	-ness	happiness
	-er	happier
	-ly	happily

Study Hint

Reading Math The outcome TC means Thin crust Cheese pizza.

Example 1

At Pizza House, you can order a thin crust or deep dish pizza with cheese, pepperoni, or sausage. Draw a tree diagram that shows all of the ways you can order a one-topping pizza.

Pizza	Topping	Outcome
thin crust (T)	cheese (C)	TC
	pepperoni (P)	TP
	sausage (S)	TS
deep dish (D)	cheese (C)	DC
	pepperoni (P)	DP
	sausage (S)	DS

There are six ways to order a one-topping pizza.

Lesson 13-4 Finding Outcomes **531**

Multiple Learning Styles

Verbal/Linguistic Have students write a short story involving at least 3 different decisions with at least 2 choices for each decision. Have students make a tree diagram of their story and list all possible outcomes.

Instructional Resources

- *Study Guide Masters,* p. 93
- *Practice Masters,* p. 93
- *Enrichment Masters,* p. 93
- Transparencies 13-4, A and B
- *Assessment and Evaluation Masters,* p. 352
- *Technology Masters,* p. 26
- CD-ROM Program
  - Resource Lesson 13-4

Recommended Pacing	
Honors	Day 7 of 11

1 FOCUS

5-Minute Check
(Lesson 13-3)

Each figure represents a dartboard. It is equally likely that a dart will land anywhere on the dartboard. Find the probability of a randomly thrown dart landing in the shaded region.

1. $\frac{1}{9}$

2. $\frac{1}{4}$

7 ft

12 ft

3. Suppose you threw a dart 100 times at each dartboard shown in Exercise 1. How many times would you expect it to land in each shaded region? **11, 25**

The 5-Minute Check is also available on **Transparency 13-4A** for this lesson.

Problem Solving Ask students how they would determine which package of wrapping paper has more possible combinations.

- six paper patterns, four ribbon colors
- five color patterns, two ribbon colors, two styles of cord

Sample answers: make a list, make a table, draw a diagram

2 TEACH

 Transparency 13-4B contains a teaching aid for this lesson.

Reading Mathematics Make sure students know how to read the path from left to right through the tree diagram to the outcome and what the outcome means.

In-Class Examples

For Example 1
A canoe can be purchased in either red or green. You also may choose plastic, aluminum, or cane seats. Draw a tree diagram that shows all the buying options.

```
 Color     Seats     Outcome
           plastic(P)→ RP
  red(R) ← alum.  (A)→ RA
           cane   (C)→ RC
           plastic(P)→ GP
 green(G)← alum.  (A)→ GA
           cane   (C)→ GC
```

For Example 2
A penny, a nickel, and a quarter are tossed. Find the probability of getting a head on the penny, a tail on the nickel, and a head on the quarter. $\frac{1}{8}$

For Example 3
A teacher must select a pair of students to represent the class at a tree-planting ceremony. There are six students eligible to be chosen because of their excellent attendance at school. In how many ways can the pair be chosen? **15**

Example ❷ Each spinner is spun once. Find the probability of spinning blue, green, and red in that order.

Spinner 1   Spinner 2   Spinner 3

Find all of the possible outcomes.

Spinner 1	Spinner 2	Spinner 3	Outcome

```
                        white (W) ──→ PTW
              tan (T) <
                        red (R)   ──→ PTR
  pink (P) <
                        white (W) ──→ PGW
              green (G)<
                        red (R)   ──→ PGR

                        white (W) ──→ BTW
              tan (T) <
                        red (R)   ──→ BTR
  blue (B) <
                        white (W) ──→ BGW
              green (G)<
                        red (R)   ──→ BGR
```

One outcome has blue, green, red in that order. There are eight possible outcomes. Therefore, $P(\text{BGR}) = \frac{1}{8}$.

Arrangements or listings where order is not important are called **combinations**. Combinations are another way to determine a sample space. To find combinations, you can make a list.

Example ❸ **APPLICATION**

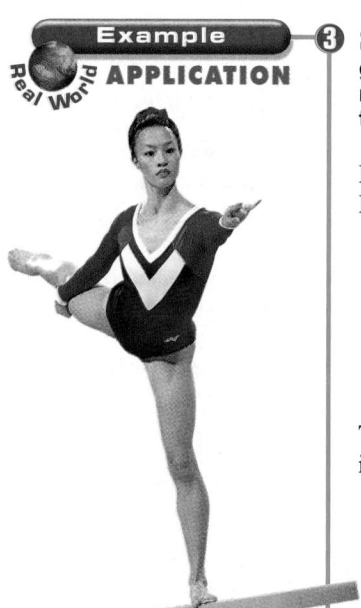

Sports At Teyas Middle School, there are five members on the gymnastics team. Coach Reyes must choose two of the members to be team captains. In how many ways can he choose two captains from five team members?

Let V, W, X, Y, and Z represent the team members.
List all of the ways two team captains can be chosen.

VW	VX	VY	VZ	WV
WX	WY	WZ	XV	XW
XY	XZ	YV	YW	YX
YZ	ZV	ZW	ZX	ZY

Then count all of the *different* arrangements. Since order is not important, VW and WV are the same.

VW	VX	VY	VZ	WX
WY	WZ	XY	XZ	YZ

There are 10 ways Coach Reyes can choose two team captains.

 Investigations for the Special Education Student

This blackline master booklet helps you plan for the needs of your special education students by providing long-term projects along with teacher notes. Investigation 15, *The Game Show,* may be used with this chapter.

Communicating Mathematics

1. See Answer Appendix.

Read and study the lesson to answer each question.

1. *Write a Problem* that can be solved by using the tree diagram shown.

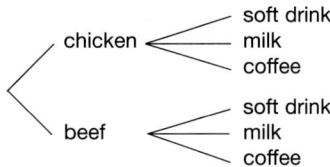

chicken — soft drink, milk, coffee
beef — soft drink, milk, coffee

2. *Draw* a tree diagram that shows the results of tossing a nickel, a dime, and a quarter. Then find the probability of getting three tails. **See margin.**

3. *Write* about the advantages of using a tree diagram to count outcomes. Are there any disadvantages of tree diagrams? **See Answer Appendix.**

Guided Practice

For each situation, make a list and draw a tree diagram to show the sample space. 4–5. See Answer Appendix.

4. a choice of a hot dog or hamburger and a choice of iced tea or lemonade

5. a choice of a blue or red shirt with blue, black, or red shorts

6. How many ways can a person choose two magazines from four magazines? **6 ways**

7. *School* A science quiz has one multiple-choice question with answer choices A, B, and C, and two true/false questions.

   a. Draw a tree diagram that shows all of the ways a student can answer the questions. **See Answer Appendix.**

   b. What is the probability of answering all three questions correctly by guessing? $\frac{1}{12}$

Family Activity

Make a diagram of your family tree going back to your great-grandparents. Explain how your diagram is like a tree diagram.

EXERCISES

Practice

For each situation, make a list and draw a tree diagram to show the sample space. 8–13. See Answer Appendix.

8. a choice of lemon, apple, or pecan pie with milk or tea

9. a choice of a leather or nylon backpack in purple, green, black, or brown

10. rolling two number cubes

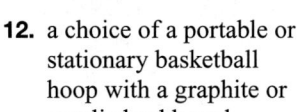

11. spinning each spinner once

12. a choice of a portable or stationary basketball hoop with a graphite or acrylic backboard

13. a choice of a tower or spinner CD holder made from wood or plastic that holds 60, 100, or 250 CDs

Lesson 13-4 Finding Outcomes **533**

---

3 PRACTICE/APPLY

Check for Understanding

If students need additional practice or instruction after completing Exercises 1–7, one of these options may be helpful.
- Extra Practice, see p. 592
- Reteaching Activity
- *Study Guide Masters,* p. 93
- *Practice Masters,* p. 93

Assignment Guide

Core: 9–17 odd, 19–22
Enriched: 8–16 even, 17–22

Family Activity

An alternative activity would be to have students make a tree of how their school staff is organized, beginning with the principal.

Additional Answer

2. See students' diagrams; outcomes are HHH, HHT, HTH, HTT, THH, THT, TTH, TTT. $P(TTT) = \frac{1}{8}$

Study Guide Masters, p. 93

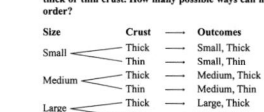

Reteaching the Lesson

Activity Ask students to predict how many different figures they would have if they drew squares and triangles each in red, black, green, and yellow. **8** Have them draw the shapes and make a tree diagram to check their prediction. Ask what the probability would be of randomly choosing a green triangle. $\frac{1}{8}$

Error Analysis

Watch for students who repeat patterns within a tree diagram.

Prevent by having them multiply the number of choices to check the number of outcomes.

Closing Activity

Act It Out In situation one, four students stand in front of the class. How many handshakes need to occur so that each student shakes hands with the other three students? Have a volunteer list the handshakes on the chalkboard. **6 handshakes**

In situation two, have four students put their names in a hat for a raffle. The first name drawn wins first prize, and second wins second prize. How many possible first and second place winner arrangements are there? **12 arrangements**

Chapter 13, Quiz C (Lesson 13-4) is available in the *Assessment and Evaluation Masters,* p. 352.

14. How many different combinations of 2 recipes can a chef choose from 3 different recipes? **3 ways**

15. How many different ways can a person choose 3 kittens from a litter of 5 kittens? **10 ways**

16. How many different ways can a teacher choose 3 three-dimensional figures to put on a quiz from 4 different three-dimensional figures? **4 ways**

Applications and Problem Solving

17. *Food* At Otani Sushi Restaurant, customers can choose from the following six Nigiri-Sushi, or fish: Maguro (tuna), Ika (squid), Tako (octopus), Ebi (shrimp), Kani (crab), and Saba (mackerel). In how many ways can a customer choose two of the six Nigiri-Sushi? **15 ways**

18. *Fashion* Awenasa is buying a new navy sweater. The sweater will coordinate with her black, white, red, and yellow blouses and her blue, plaid, and black pants.
   a. How many different outfits will she have? **12 outfits**
   b. Suppose Awenasa chooses one blouse and one pair of pants at random. What is the probability that she will choose the yellow blouse and the blue pants or the red blouse and the black pants? $\frac{1}{6}$

19. *Critical Thinking* There are three 2-sided counters in a cup. One is red on one side and blue on the other, one is red and white, and the third is blue and white. Amiri shakes the cup and tosses out the chips. He receives one point if the chips are all different colors. Irene receives one point if two chips match. Use a tree diagram to help you determine whether or not this is a fair game. If this is not a fair game, how could you make it fair? **See Answer Appendix.**

Mixed Review

20. *Probability* The figure shown represents a dartboard. It is equally likely that the dart will land anywhere on the dartboard. Find the probability of a randomly-thrown dart landing in the shaded region. *(Lesson 13-3)* **about $\frac{2}{5}$ or 40%**

21. **Standardized Test Practice** Solve $n = -145 \div (-29)$. *(Lesson 11-6)* **C**
   A -5 **B** 4   **C** 5   **D** -3 **E** Not Here

For **Extra Practice**, see page 592.

22. *Food* Refer to the graph. Suppose 2,000 people participated in the peanut butter survey. How many people can be expected to prefer creamy peanut butter? *(Lesson 8-6)* **940 people**

Peanut Butter Preference
Creamy 47%
Other 2%
Natural 18%
Crunchy 33%

Source: The Adult Peanut Butter Lover's Fan Club, Peanut Advisory Board

Enrichment Masters, p. 93

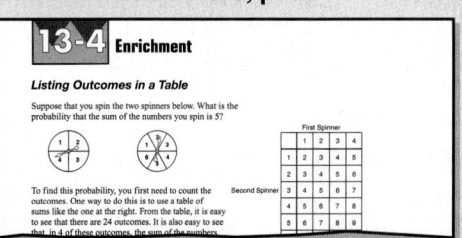

Activity On a restaurant menu, a person can order 1 item from column A listing 6 main courses, 2 items from column B listing 10 side dishes, and 1 item from column C listing 5 desserts. How many different meals are possible? Have students discuss their answers. **1,350 meals**

COOPERATIVE LEARNING

13-4B Simulations

A Follow-Up of Lesson 13-4

- two-colored counters
- cups

A simulation is an application of the Acting It Out problem-solving strategy.

A *simulation* is a way of acting out a problem. You can conduct a simulation by using manipulatives such as counters or number cubes. In this lab, you will conduct a simulation to explore the probability that in a family with three children, at least two of them are girls.

It is equally likely that a boy or a girl will be born. Similarly, it is equally likely that a two-colored counter will land on one color or the other. So, you can toss a two-colored counter to simulate outcomes.

TRY THIS

Work with a partner.

To explore the probability that at least two of the three children in a family are girls, follow these steps.

Step 1 Place three counters in a cup and toss them onto your desk.

Step 2 Count the number of counters that land with the red side up. This represents the number of boys. Count the number of counters that land with the yellow side up. This represents the number of girls.

Step 3 Record the results in a table like the one shown.

Step 4 Repeat Steps 1-3 until you have 50 trials.

Outcome			
Trial 1	B	B	G
Trial 2	G	G	G
Trial 3	G	G	B
Trial 4	B	B	G

Suppose 23 of the 50 trials have at least two girls. The experimental probability that at least two of the three children in a family are girls is $\frac{23}{50}$.

You can refer to Lesson 5-4B for information on experimental probability.

ON YOUR OWN

1. Based on your results of the simulation, what is the experimental probability that, in a family with three children, at least two of them are girls? **1–4. See Answer Appendix.**

2. Make a list showing all of the possible outcomes of the experiment. What is the theoretical probability that, in a family with three children, at least two of them are girls?

3. Compare the experimental probability with the theoretical probability.

4. *Reflect Back* Find the probability that in a family with four children, all four of them are girls. Then describe a simulation that you can use to explore this probability. Conduct the simulation. Record and explain your results.

Lesson 13-4B HANDS-ON **LAB** **535**

Have students write a paragraph describing another situation where a simulation would be useful. Have them include a sample simulation.

HANDS-ON
13-4B LAB Notes

GET READY

Objective Students explore probability by conducting a simulation.

Optional Resources
Hands-On Lab Masters
- counters, p. 6
- pattern for cup, p. 8
- worksheet, p. 68

Overhead Manipulative Resources
- counters
- cups

Manipulative Kit
- counters
- cups

MANAGEMENT TIPS

Recommended Time
30 minutes

Getting Started Ask students how they think three counters and a cup will be used to investigate the problem of this lab. Then ask: *How many counters would be needed for a family with one child? two children? n children?* **1; 2; n**

The **Activity** requires students to toss 3 counters and record results. The phrase "at least 2 boys" means that students will count all outcomes with 2 or 3 boys for their experimental probability. Have students pool all their experiments to get an experimental probability for the class for no boys, 1 boy, 2 boys, and 3 boys. If there are students who are one of 3 children, use your class data to determine the probability for the siblings in their families.

ASSESS

Have students complete Exercises 1–4. If students are having difficulty with Exercise 4, remind them that a tree diagram is very helpful for finding theoretical probabilities.

- *Study Guide Masters*, p. 94
- *Practice Masters*, p. 94
- *Enrichment Masters*, p. 94
- Transparencies 13-5, A and B
- *Assessment and Evaluation Masters*, p. 352
- *Classroom Games*, pp. 37–40
- *Science and Math Lab Manual*, pp. 93–96

 CD-ROM Program
- Resource Lesson 13-5

Recommended Pacing	
Honors	Day 9 of 11

1 FOCUS

5-Minute Check
(Lesson 13-4)

1. For a class project, you can make a display, write a report, or build a model about a person, locale, or object. Draw a tree diagram to show all of the outcomes.

```
Project    Subject    Outcome
            person(P) → DP
display(D)  locale(L) → DL
            object(O) → DO
            person(P) → RP
report(R)   locale(L) → RL
            object(O) → RO
            person(P) → MP
model(M)    locale(L) → ML
            object(O) → MO
```

2. Find the number of games that would be played in the first round of a five-team tournament where each team plays every other team. **10 games**

 The 5-Minute Check is also available on **Transparency 13-5A** for this lesson.

Motivating the Lesson
Communication Ask students to discuss how they would determine the probability that a set of fraternal twins would be two boys. **Possibilities are BB, BG, GB, GG; $P = \frac{1}{4}$**

13-5 Probability of Independent Events

You'll learn to find the probability of independent events.

When am I ever going to use this?

Knowing how to find the probability of independent events can help you determine the chance of rolling doubles in Monopoly.

Word Wise

independent event

While on a nature walk with their baby-sitter, Margarita and Billy collected acorns, walnuts, and stones. The table shows the contents of each of their bags. Suppose they each reach into their respective bag and randomly choose an object. What is the probability that Billy chooses an acorn and Margarita chooses a stone?

Name	Acorns	Walnuts	Stones
Billy	6	8	10
Margarita	12	12	16

The object that Billy chooses does not affect the object that Margarita chooses. They are called **independent events**.

To find the probability of two independent events, you multiply their probabilities.

Probability of Two Independent Events		
	Words:	The probability of two independent events, A and B, is the product of the probability of event A and the probability of event B.
	Symbols:	$P(A \text{ and } B) = P(A) \cdot P(B)$

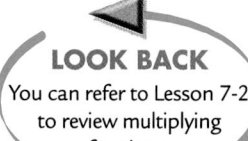

LOOK BACK
You can refer to Lesson 7-2 to review multiplying fractions.

$P(\text{acorn}) = \frac{6}{24}$ ← *number of ways Billy can choose an acorn*
← *number of possible outcomes: 6 + 10 + 8 = 24*

$P(\text{stone}) = \frac{16}{40}$ ← *number of ways Margarita can choose a stone*
← *number of possible outcomes: 12 + 16 + 12 = 40*

Multiply to find the probability.

$$\frac{6}{24} \times \frac{16}{40} = \frac{\overset{1}{6}}{\underset{4}{24}} \times \frac{\overset{2}{16}}{\underset{5}{40}} \quad \textit{The GCF of 6 and 24 is 6.}$$
$$\textit{The GCF of 16 and 40 is 8.}$$
$$= \frac{2}{20} \text{ or } \frac{1}{10}$$

The probability that Billy chooses an acorn and Margarita chooses a stone is $\frac{1}{10}$. The event is not too likely to occur.

Multiple Learning Styles

 Logical Have students research sports statistics to determine the probability that a professional athlete will make a free throw in basketball, score a goal in hockey, get a hit in baseball, serve an ace in tennis, and so on.

1 A number cube is rolled, and the spinner shown is spun. Find the probability of rolling 5 and landing on a consonant.

$$P(5) = \frac{1}{6} \qquad P(\text{consonant}) = \frac{3}{4}$$

$$P(5 \text{ and consonant}) = \frac{1}{6} \times \frac{3}{4}$$

$$= \frac{3}{24} \text{ or } \frac{1}{8}$$

The probability of rolling a 5 and landing on a consonant is $\frac{1}{8}$.

CONNECTION **2** **Life Science** Owls lay two to five rounded, white eggs. Suppose an owl lays two eggs. What is the probability that the first egg hatched is a female owl and the second egg hatched is a male owl?

Explore You know the probability of female and the probability of male. You need to find the probability that the first egg hatched is a female owl and the second egg hatched is a male owl.

Plan Multiply to find the probability.

Solve $P(\text{female owl}) = \frac{1}{2} \qquad P(\text{male owl}) = \frac{1}{2}$

$$\frac{1}{2} \times \frac{1}{2} = \frac{1}{4}$$

So, $P(\text{female owl, then male owl}) = \frac{1}{4}$.

Examine Use a tree diagram. One outcome has a female owl and then a male owl. There are four possible outcomes. Therefore, the probability is $\frac{1}{4}$.

First Egg	Second Egg	Outcome
female (F)	female	FF
	male	FM
male (M)	female	MF
	male	MM

Did you know The largest owls in the world are eagle owls, which grow to be about 710 millimeters long. The smallest owls are pygmy owls, which grow to be about 120 millimeters long. While eagle owls are found in Europe, Asia, and North Africa, pygmy owls are found in South and Central America.

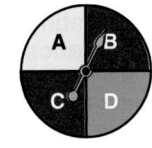 **Transparency 13-5B** contains a teaching aid for this lesson.

Thinking Algebraically Students' knowledge of tree diagrams can help them deduce the formula for the probability of two independent events. For each possibility in A, there are all of the possibilities of B. So if A has 6 branches and B has 3, the total number is 6 · 3 or 18 possibilities.

Teaching Tip After Example 1, have students make a tree diagram to verify their answer.

In-Class Examples

For Example 1
A number cube is rolled and a coin is tossed. Find the probability of rolling a 2 and landing on heads. $\frac{1}{12}$

For Example 2
To win the grand prize, Ted has to choose one of 10 keys to unlock Treasure Chest A, B, or C. The winning combination is Key 3 in Treasure Chest A. What are Ted's chances of winning? $\frac{1}{30}$

Classroom Vignette

"I have students interview adults and write a report about how they use math in their job or in everyday life. They are encouraged to use their creativity in preparing their report. They also use computers to prepare their reports."

Deana Bobzien, Teacher
Rochester Junior High
Rochester, IL

Deana Bobzien

Study Guide
and Assessment

Vocabulary

This section provides a listing of the new terms, properties, and phrases that were introduced in this chapter. Have students define each term and provide an example or two of it, if appropriate.

Understanding and Using the Vocabulary

These exercises check students' understanding of the terms by using a variety of verbal formats including matching, completion, and true/false.

Glossaries A complete glossary of terms appears on pages 642–648. The glossary also appears in Spanish on pages 649–656.

Additional Answer

11. Sample answer: Multiply the probability of the first event by the probability of the second event.

■*inter*NET CONNECTION Chapter Review For additional lesson-by-lesson review, visit: www.glencoe.com/sec/math/mac/mathnet

Vocabulary

After completing this chapter, you should be able to define each term, concept, or phrase and give an example or two of each.

Problem Solving
make a table (pp. 520-521)

Statistics and Probability
combinations (p. 532)
complementary events (p. 516)
event (p. 515)
fair game (p. 514)
independent events (p. 536)

outcomes (p. 515)
population (p. 522)
random (p. 522)
sample (p. 522)
sample space (p. 515)
simulation (p. 535)
theoretical probability (p. 515)
tree diagram (p. 531)
unfair game (p. 514)

Understanding and Using the Vocabulary

Choose the letter of the term that best matches each phrase.

1. arrangements or listings where order is not important **e**
2. the ratio of the number of ways an event can occur to the number of possible outcomes **i**
3. a specific outcome or type of outcome **g**
4. the entire group from which samples are taken **a**
5. a diagram used to show all of the possible outcomes **b**
6. a randomly selected group chosen for the purpose of collecting data **h**
7. a word that means the same as results **c**
8. when one event's occurring does not affect another event **j**
9. two events in which either one or the other can occur, but not both **d**
10. events that happen by chance **f**

a. population
b. tree diagram
c. outcomes
d. complementary events
e. combinations
f. random events
g. event
h. sample
i. probability
j. independent events
k. simulation

In Your Own Words

11. *Explain* how to find the probability of two independent events. **See margin.**

MindJogger Videoquizzes

MindJogger Videoquizzes provide an alternative review of concepts presented in this chapter. Students work in teams to answer questions, gaining points for correct answers. The questions are presented in three rounds.
Round 1 Concepts–5 questions
Round 2 Skills–4 questions
Round 3 Problem Solving–4 questions

Objectives & Examples

Upon completing this chapter, you should be able to:

● find and interpret the theoretical probability of an event *(Lesson 13-1)*

There are six equally likely outcomes on the spinner. Find the probability of spinning blue.

$\frac{1}{6}$ ← *number of ways to spin blue*

$\;$ ← *number of possible outcomes*

So, $P(\text{blue}) = \frac{1}{6}$.

● predict the actions of a larger group using a sample *(Lesson 13-2)*

If 12 out of 50 people prefer to watch TV after 11 P.M., how many people out of 1,000 would prefer to watch TV after 11 P.M.?

Let p represent the number of people who would prefer to watch TV after 11 P.M.

$$\frac{12}{50} = \frac{p}{1,000}$$

$$12 \times 1,000 = 50 \times p$$

$$12,000 = 50p$$

$$\frac{12,000}{50} = \frac{50p}{50}$$

$$240 = p$$

Of the 1,000 people, 240 would prefer to watch TV after 11 P.M.

Review Exercises

Use these exercises to review and prepare for the chapter test.

Suppose you spin the spinner shown at the left once. Find the probability of each event. Then tell how likely the event is to happen. 12–15. See Answer Appendix.

12. $P(\text{green})$ **13.** $P(\text{red or white})$

14. $P(\text{pink})$ **15.** $P(\text{not blue})$

A bag contains a nickel, dime, and penny. Suppose you choose one coin without looking. Find the probability of each event. Then tell how likely the event is to happen. 16–17. See Answer Appendix.

16. $P(\text{nickel})$ **17.** $P(\text{dime or penny})$

Tell whether each of the following is a random survey. Explain your answer.

Type of Survey	Survey Location
18. favorite fast food	beach **18–20. See Answer Appendix.**
19. favorite sport	football game
20. favorite pet	mall

21. The results of a survey showed that 14 out of 40 students at West Middle School are interested in publishing a school newspaper. **a. See Answer Appendix.**

   a. What is the probability that a student at this school would be interested in publishing a school newspaper?

   b. If there are 420 students, how many would be interested in publishing a school newspaper? **147 students**

Objectives & Examples

This section reviews the skills and concepts of the chapter and shows completely worked examples.

Review Exercises

These exercises provide practice for the corresponding objectives.

Assessment and Evaluation Masters, pp. 339–340

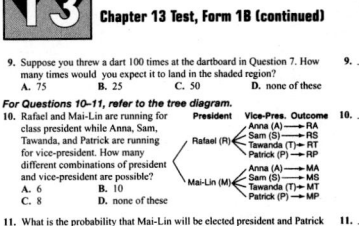

Assessment and Evaluation

Six forms of Chapter 13 Test are available in the *Assessment and Evaluation Masters* as shown in the chart.

Chapter 13 Test, Form 1B, is shown at the right. Chapter 13 Test, Form 2B, is shown on the next page.

1A	Multiple Choice	Honors
1B	Multiple Choice	Average
1C	Multiple Choice	Basic
2A	Free Response	Honors
2B	Free Response	Average
2C	Free Response	Basic

Additional Answers

22. $\frac{5}{6}$

23. about $\frac{5}{16}$ or 31.25%

Assessment and Evaluation Masters, pp. 345–346

Chapter 13 Test, Form 2B

A set of 25 cards is numbered 1, 2, 3, ..., 25. Suppose you draw one card without looking. Find the probability of each event.

1. $P(8)$ 1. $\frac{1}{25}$

2. $P(25)$ 2. $\frac{1}{25}$

3. $P(1 \text{ or } 9)$ 3. $\frac{2}{25}$

4. $P(\text{an even number})$ 4. $\frac{12}{25}$

5. $P(\text{a multiple of } 4)$ 5. $\frac{6}{25}$

In a survey of customers at a video store, 12 customers preferred action films, 5 customers preferred comedies, 3 customers preferred horror films, and 10 customers preferred dramas. The shop owner plans to order 90 new films. How many of each type should she order?

6. action   6. 36

7. comedy   7. 15

8. drama   8. 30

Suppose you threw a dart 100 times at each dartboard below. How many times would you expect it to land in the shaded region of each dartboard?

9.   10.

9. 25

10. 25

11.   11. about 33

© Glencoe/McGraw-Hill   345   Mathematics: Applications and Connections, Course 1

Chapter 13 Test, Form 2B (continued)

12. Make a frequency table that represents the expected results of a spinner numbered 1–4 being spun 100 times.

12.
Number	Frequency
1	25
2	25
3	25
4	25

Use the tree diagram to answer the questions.

13. How many possible outcomes are there?   13. 9

14. What is the probability of a small vanilla?   14. $\frac{1}{9}$

15. What is $P(\text{medium})$?   15. $\frac{1}{3}$

16. What is $P(\text{chocolate})$?   16. $\frac{1}{3}$

Suppose you roll a 6-sided number cube and spin the spinner shown. Find the probability of each of the following.

17. $P(3 \text{ and white})$ 17. $\frac{1}{24}$

18. $P(\text{even number and blue})$ 18. $\frac{1}{8}$

19. $P(\text{not 1 and blue})$ 19. $\frac{5}{24}$

20. $P(\text{prime and white})$ 20. $\frac{1}{6}$

© Glencoe/McGraw-Hill   346   Mathematics: Applications and Connections, Course 1

Chapter 13   Study Guide and Assessment

Objectives & Examples

● find probability using area models *(Lesson 13-3)*

The figure shown represents a dartboard. Find the probability that a randomly-thrown dart lands in the shaded region.

$$P\left(\frac{\text{shaded}}{\text{region}}\right) = \frac{\text{area of shaded region}}{\text{area of target}}$$

$$= \frac{8}{30} \text{ or } \frac{4}{15}$$

● find outcomes using lists, tree diagrams, and combinations *(Lesson 13-4)*

In how many ways can a person choose a 1-dip ice cream cone from two types of cones and three flavors of ice cream?

Cone	Flavor	Outcome
	grape (G) →	SG
sugar (S)	mint (M) →	SM
	peach (P) →	SP
	grape (G) →	WG
waffle (W)	mint (M) →	WM
	peach (P) →	WP

There are 6 ways.

● find the probability of independent events *(Lesson 13-5)*

Two number cubes are rolled. Find $P(\text{odd and } 4)$.

$$P(\text{odd}) = \frac{1}{2} \quad P(4) = \frac{1}{6}$$

$$P(\text{odd and } 4) = \frac{1}{2} \times \frac{1}{6} \text{ or } \frac{1}{12}$$

Review Exercises

Each figure represents a dartboard. It is equally likely that a dart will land anywhere on the dartboard. Find the probability of a randomly-thrown dart landing in the shaded region.

22.   23.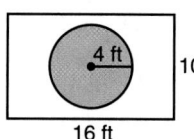

22–23. See margin.

24. Suppose you threw a dart 150 times at the dartboard in Exercise 22. How many times would you expect it to land in the shaded region? **125**

For each situation, make a list and draw a tree diagram to show the sample space.

25. a choice of black or blue jeans in tapered leg, straight leg, or baggy style

26. a choice of soup or salad with beef, chicken, fish, or pasta

27. a choice of going to a basketball game, an amusement park, or a concert on a Friday or a Saturday

28. Tell how many different ways a person can choose four movies from a list of five movies. **5 ways**

25–27. See Answer Appendix.

A coin is tossed and a number cube is rolled. Find the probability of each event.

29. $P(\text{heads and even})$ $\frac{1}{4}$

30. $P(\text{heads and 1})$ $\frac{1}{12}$

31. $P(\text{tails and 5 or 6})$ $\frac{1}{6}$

32. $P(\text{tails and 2, 3, or 4})$ $\frac{1}{4}$

542   Chapter 13 Using Probability

Test and Review Software

You may use this software, a combination of an item generator and item bank, to create your own tests or worksheets. Types of items include free response, multiple choice, short answer, and open ended.

CD-ROM Program

The CD-ROM Program contains an Assessment Game whose questions review the concepts in this chapter.

Applications & Problem Solving

33. *Make a Table* The table shows the results of a survey on the number of hours teenagers use a computer on the weekend. *(Lesson 13-2A)*

Weekend Computer Use		
Hours	**Tally**	**Frequency**
0-2	卌 卌	10
3-4	卌 卌 I	11
5-6	卌	5
7 or more	卌 I	6

a. How many teenagers use a computer 5 or more hours during the weekend? **11**

b. How many teenagers participated in the survey? **32**

34. *Earth Science* The probability of rain on Saturday is 0.6. The probability of rain on Sunday is 0.3. What is the probability that it will rain on both days? *(Lesson 13-5)* **0.18**

35. *School* The cheerleaders at Ross Middle School have three different skirts they can wear as part of their uniforms. One is purple, one is white, and one is yellow. They also have a choice of a yellow vest or a purple sweater to wear. Make a list and a tree diagram to show all of the possible uniform combinations. *(Lesson 13-4)* **See Answer Appendix.**

36. *Party Planning* According to a survey of 30 students, 13 prefer chicken, and 17 prefer hot dogs. If 750 students will be attending the picnic, how many will prefer each selection? *(Lesson 13-2)*
325 will prefer chicken;
425 will prefer hot dogs

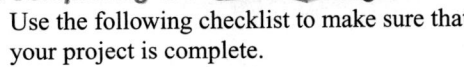

Alternative Assessment

● **Open Ended**

Suppose you are taking pictures to be used in the school yearbook. You can choose either color or black and white film. When the pictures are developed, you can choose a glossy or matte finish, and the pictures can be developed into 3 × 5, 4 × 6, 5 × 5, or 8 × 10 size prints. How can you determine the number of different ways you can develop a photo? **See Answer Appendix.**

Draw a tree diagram to show all of the sample space. If the prints can also be cut with square or rounded corners, how many outcomes are possible? **See Answer Appendix.**

A practice test for Chapter 13 is provided on page 607.

● **Completing the** CHAPTER Project

Use the following checklist to make sure that your project is complete.

☑ The data about the animal is included on the poster.

☑ The paragraph that explains how probability relates to camouflage is included.

☑ Add any finishing touches that you would like to make your project complete.

 PORTFOLIO Select one of the assignments from this chapter and place it in your portfolio. Attach a note to it explaining why you selected it.

 Performance Assessment

Additional performance assessment tasks for this chapter are included in the *Assessment and Evaluation Masters* on page 349. A scoring guide is also provided on page 361.

Applications & Problem Solving

This section provides additional practice in solving real-world problems that involve the skills of this chapter.

Alternative Assessment

The *Open Ended* section provides students with a performance assessment opportunity to evaluate their work and understanding.

CHAPTER *Project*

Students should complete the final stages of their project and prepare a class demonstration of their results. A scoring guide for the project is available in the *Investigations and Projects Masters*, p. 67.

 PORTFOLIO Students should add to their portfolios at this time.

Assessment and Evaluation Masters, p. 349

---

13 Name_____ Date_____

Chapter 13 Performance Assessment

Instructions: Demonstrate your knowledge by giving a clear, concise solution to each problem. Be sure to include all relevant drawings and justify your answers. You may show your solutions in more than one way or investigate beyond the requirements of the problems.

1. a. Tell what a probability of 0 means. Give an example of an event with probability 0.

  b. Tell what a probability of 1 means. Give an example of an event with probability 1.

  c. Tell what it means for an event to have a probability of $\frac{1}{2}$. Give an example of such an event.

  d. Tell in your own words what is meant by independent events.

  e. Write a word problem that uses the probability of two independent events.

  f. Solve the problem in part e and tell in your own words what the answer means.

2. Wendy is interviewing students on her bus to see for whom they plan to vote for student body president. She found that 18 plan to vote for Kevin and 22 plan to vote for Juanita.

  a. According to Wendy's poll, what is the probability that Kevin will win? that Juanita will win?

  b. Tell why Wendy's sample may not be a random sample of students in the school.

  c. Explain how Wendy could choose a more random sample.

3. A pizza is divided into eight slices. One fourth of the pizza is mushroom, one fourth is pepperoni, one fourth is sausage, and one fourth is green pepper.

  a. If Elaine tosses an anchovy onto the pizza, what is the probability that it will land on a slice with green pepper?

  b. Reggie wants to eat a total of three different pieces of pizza. Draw a tree diagram to show his choices if he has already eaten a slice of mushroom pizza.

© Glencoe/McGraw-Hill   349   *Mathematics: Applications and Connections, Course 1*

The Standardized Test Practice may be used to help students prepare for standardized tests. The test items are written in the same style as those in state proficiency tests and standardized tests like CAT, CTBS, ITBS, MAT, SAT, and Terra Nova. The test items cover skills and concepts covered up to this point in the text.

The pages can be used as an overnight assessment. After students have completed the pages, discuss how each problem can be solved, or provide copies of the solutions from the *Solutions Manual.*

Section One: Multiple Choice

There are thirteen multiple-choice questions in this section. Choose the best answer. If a correct answer is *not here*, choose the letter for Not Here.

1. Find $6^3 \div 3^2 + 2$. **D**
- **A** 6
- **B** 216
- **C** 132
- **D** 26

2. How many lines of symmetry does the figure have? **G**
- **F** 2
- **G** 3
- **H** 4
- **J** 5

3. Which expression represents the volume of a cube with side r? **C**
- **A** $6r$
- **B** $6r^2$
- **C** r^3
- **D** $3r^3$

4. What is the probability of a randomly-thrown dart landing in the shaded region of the figure? **G**
- **F** 30%
- **G** 50%
- **H** 60%
- **J** 75%

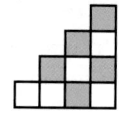

5. Which two-dimensional figure best describes the base of a cone? **B**
- **A** square
- **B** circle
- **C** triangle
- **D** rectangle

6. Which number is missing from this sequence? **G**
$$\ldots, 27, 81, \underline{?}, 729, 2{,}187, \ldots$$
- **F** 357
- **G** 243
- **H** 261
- **J** 539

Please note that Questions 7–13 have five answer choices.

7. Taye bought 3 bags of chips for $0.39 each and 2 cans of soft drink for $0.55 each. Which expression can be used to find the cost in dollars of the items? **D**
- **A** $3 \times 0.39 \times 5 \times 0.55$
- **B** $3 \div 0.39 + 2 \div 0.55$
- **C** $3 \times 0.39 + 5 \times 0.55$
- **D** $3 \times 0.39 + 2 \times 0.55$
- **E** $3 \div 0.39 \times 2 \div 0.55$

8. In a survey, Akili found that 8 out of 40 students were the oldest child in their family. If 250 students had participated in the survey, how many would be expected to be the oldest child? **J**
- **F** 120
- **G** 75
- **H** 60
- **J** 50
- **K** 85

9. What percent of the numbers from 1 to 25 contain the digit 3? **A**
- **A** about 10%
- **B** about 20%
- **C** about 30%
- **D** about 40%
- **E** about 50%

10. In May, about 78 tools were rented each day at The Rent Center. Estimate the number of tools rented for the entire month of May. **G**
- **F** 2,000
- **G** 2,400
- **H** 2,800
- **J** 3,200
- **K** 3,600

Assessment and Evaluation Masters, p. 355

◀◀◀**Instructional Resources**
Another cumulative review is shown at the left and is available in the *Assessment and Evaluation Masters,* p. 355.

11. The perimeter of the triangle is $2\frac{3}{8}$ inches. Find the value of y. **C**

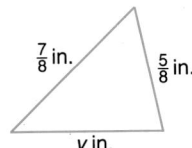

A $\frac{3}{8}$

B $\frac{1}{2}$

C $\frac{7}{8}$

D $\frac{5}{8}$

E Not Here

12. Ms. Hayashi made a tablecloth for her kitchen. She bought $4\frac{3}{4}$ yards of material. She used $3\frac{1}{8}$ yards of material to make the tablecloth. How much material was not used to make the tablecloth? **K**

F $7\frac{3}{8}$ yd   G $6\frac{1}{2}$ yd

H $7\frac{7}{8}$ yd   J $6\frac{3}{4}$ yd

K Not Here

13. What is the area of the octagon? **C**

  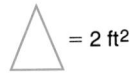 $= 2\ ft^2$

A 6 ft²

B 10 ft²

C 16 ft²

D 20 ft²

E Not Here

Test Practice **For additional test practice questions, visit:**

www.glencoe.com/sec/math/mac/mathnet

Section Two: Free Response

This section contains three questions for which you will provide short answers. Write your answers on your paper.

14. A rectangular aquarium has sides measuring 28 inches long, 16 inches wide, and 12 inches high. The aquarium is filled with water to a height of 10 inches. What is the volume of the water? **4,480 in³**

15. A bag contains 3 yellow marbles, 5 red marbles, 6 blue marbles, and 16 green marbles. **a–b. See margin.**

   a. Suppose you choose one marble without looking, record its color, and then replace the marble. What is the probability of choosing a red marble?

   b. Suppose you choose one marble without looking, record its color, replace the marble, and then choose another marble. What is the probability of choosing a yellow marble and then a green marble?

16. How many different words can be made using the words *college*, *game*, *season*, and *election* and the prefixes *pre-* and *post-*? **8**

Assessment and Evaluation Masters, pp. 353–354

Additional Answers

15a. $\frac{1}{6}$

15b. $\frac{4}{75}$

Instructional Resources ▶▶▶

Additional standardized test practice is shown at the right and is available in the *Assessment and Evaluation Masters*, pp. 353–354.

Student Handbook
Table of Contents

Basic Skills

Place Value

Write the place-value position for each digit in 721,056,938,504,550.

1. 4 thousands   2. 2 ten trillions   3. 6 billions   4. 8 millions

5. 3 ten millions   6. 7 hundred trillions   7. 1 trillions   8. 9 hundred millions

Write each number in words.

9. 47,900 **forty-seven thousand nine hundred**

10. 2,013 **two thousand thirteen**

11. 540,006,000 **five hundred forty million six thousand**

12. 7,036,000,000 **seven billion thirty-six million**

13. 263 **two hundred sixty-three**

14. 95,000,100,000,000 **ninety-five trillion one hundred million**

15. 7,261 **seven thousand two hundred sixty-one**

16. 120,760 **one hundred twenty thousand seven hundred sixty**

17. 102,000,016 **one hundred two million sixteen**

18. 582 **five hundred eighty-two**

19. 8,000,070,000,600 **eight trillion seventy million six hundred**

20. 67,826 **sixty-seven thousand eight hundred twenty-six**

Write each number in standard form.

21. seventy-six million **76,000,000**

22. nine trillion **9,000,000,000,000**

23. six hundred thousand **600,000**

24. forty-two **42**

25. fifty-five trillion **55,000,000,000,000**

26. three billion **3,000,000,000**

27. seven hundred seventy-one **771**

28. sixteen thousand **16,000**

29. one hundred twenty-four million **124,000,000**

30. six thousand nine hundred **6,900**

31. eighty-eight billion **88,000,000,000**

32. three hundred seventy trillion **370,000,000,000,000**

Replace each ● with a number to make a true sentence.

33. 67,000 = ● hundreds **670**

34. 39,000,000 = ● hundred thousands **390**

35. 1,400,000,000,000 = ● millions **1,400,000**

36. 760,000 = ● thousands **760**

37. 4,200 = ● hundreds **42**

38. 86,000,000 = ● thousands **86,000**

39. ● = 17 millions **17,000,000**

40. ● = 930 ten thousands **9,300,000**

Basic Skills

Adding Whole Numbers

1. $\begin{array}{r} 40 \\ + 8 \\ \hline 48 \end{array}$
2. $\begin{array}{r} 32 \\ + 5 \\ \hline 37 \end{array}$
3. $\begin{array}{r} 63 \\ + 6 \\ \hline 69 \end{array}$
4. $\begin{array}{r} 41 \\ + 8 \\ \hline 49 \end{array}$
5. $\begin{array}{r} 53 \\ + 4 \\ \hline 57 \end{array}$

6. $\begin{array}{r} 30 \\ +60 \\ \hline 90 \end{array}$
7. $\begin{array}{r} 20 \\ +50 \\ \hline 70 \end{array}$
8. $\begin{array}{r} 47 \\ +20 \\ \hline 67 \end{array}$
9. $\begin{array}{r} 85 \\ +10 \\ \hline 95 \end{array}$
10. $\begin{array}{r} 56 \\ +33 \\ \hline 89 \end{array}$

11. $\begin{array}{r} 600 \\ + 50 \\ \hline 650 \end{array}$
12. $\begin{array}{r} 506 \\ + 30 \\ \hline 536 \end{array}$
13. $\begin{array}{r} 225 \\ + 40 \\ \hline 265 \end{array}$
14. $\begin{array}{r} 704 \\ + 35 \\ \hline 739 \end{array}$
15. $\begin{array}{r} 628 \\ + 71 \\ \hline 699 \end{array}$

16. $\begin{array}{r} 500 \\ +200 \\ \hline 700 \end{array}$
17. $\begin{array}{r} 320 \\ +430 \\ \hline 750 \end{array}$
18. $\begin{array}{r} 405 \\ +503 \\ \hline 908 \end{array}$
19. $\begin{array}{r} 342 \\ +127 \\ \hline 469 \end{array}$
20. $\begin{array}{r} 315 \\ +583 \\ \hline 898 \end{array}$

21. $\begin{array}{r} 27 \\ + 4 \\ \hline 31 \end{array}$
22. $\begin{array}{r} 76 \\ + 9 \\ \hline 85 \end{array}$
23. $\begin{array}{r} 59 \\ + 7 \\ \hline 66 \end{array}$
24. $\begin{array}{r} 25 \\ +68 \\ \hline 93 \end{array}$
25. $\begin{array}{r} 24 \\ +48 \\ \hline 72 \end{array}$

26. $\begin{array}{r} 304 \\ + 57 \\ \hline 361 \end{array}$
27. $\begin{array}{r} 845 \\ + 29 \\ \hline 874 \end{array}$
28. $\begin{array}{r} 637 \\ + 36 \\ \hline 673 \end{array}$
29. $\begin{array}{r} 304 \\ +509 \\ \hline 813 \end{array}$
30. $\begin{array}{r} 228 \\ +534 \\ \hline 762 \end{array}$

31. $\begin{array}{r} 83 \\ +56 \\ \hline 139 \end{array}$
32. $\begin{array}{r} 94 \\ +72 \\ \hline 166 \end{array}$
33. $\begin{array}{r} 62 \\ +85 \\ \hline 147 \end{array}$
34. $\begin{array}{r} 380 \\ +270 \\ \hline 650 \end{array}$
35. $\begin{array}{r} 761 \\ +187 \\ \hline 948 \end{array}$

36. $\begin{array}{r} 684 \\ + 67 \\ \hline 751 \end{array}$
37. $\begin{array}{r} 495 \\ + 48 \\ \hline 543 \end{array}$
38. $\begin{array}{r} 347 \\ + 59 \\ \hline 406 \end{array}$
39. $\begin{array}{r} 676 \\ +276 \\ \hline 952 \end{array}$
40. $\begin{array}{r} 733 \\ +197 \\ \hline 930 \end{array}$

41. $\begin{array}{r} 24 \\ 76 \\ +53 \\ \hline 153 \end{array}$
42. $\begin{array}{r} 67 \\ 28 \\ +44 \\ \hline 139 \end{array}$
43. $\begin{array}{r} 55 \\ 89 \\ +23 \\ \hline 167 \end{array}$
44. $\begin{array}{r} 368 \\ 275 \\ +256 \\ \hline 899 \end{array}$
45. $\begin{array}{r} 275 \\ 384 \\ +633 \\ \hline 1,292 \end{array}$

46. $\begin{array}{r} 4,680 \\ +3,945 \\ \hline 8,625 \end{array}$
47. $\begin{array}{r} 5,126 \\ +2,899 \\ \hline 8,025 \end{array}$
48. $\begin{array}{r} 2,973 \\ +1,689 \\ \hline 4,662 \end{array}$
49. $\begin{array}{r} 52,046 \\ +41,388 \\ \hline 93,434 \end{array}$
50. $\begin{array}{r} 96,277 \\ +27,563 \\ \hline 123,840 \end{array}$

Basic Skills

Adding Whole Numbers

1. 50
    $\underline{+\ 9}$
    59

2. 46
    $\underline{+\ 3}$
    49

3. 23
    $\underline{+\ 2}$
    25

4. 62
    $\underline{+\ 5}$
    67

5. 81
    $\underline{+\ 4}$
    85

6. 20
    $\underline{+60}$
    80

7. 40
    $\underline{+30}$
    70

8. 38
    $\underline{+20}$
    58

9. 61
    $\underline{+10}$
    71

10. 58
    $\underline{+11}$
    69

11. 100
    $\underline{+\ 70}$
    170

12. 207
    $\underline{+\ 40}$
    247

13. 563
    $\underline{+\ 20}$
    583

14. 716
    $\underline{+\ 81}$
    797

15. 334
    $\underline{+\ 53}$
    387

16. 300
    $\underline{+500}$
    800

17. 240
    $\underline{+530}$
    770

18. 621
    $\underline{+347}$
    968

19. 406
    $\underline{+273}$
    679

20. 748
    $\underline{+111}$
    859

21. 17
    $\underline{+\ 5}$
    22

22. 34
    $\underline{+\ 8}$
    42

23. 78
    $\underline{+\ 4}$
    82

24. 57
    $\underline{+24}$
    81

25. 22
    $\underline{+39}$
    61

26. 517
    $\underline{+\ 64}$
    581

27. 266
    $\underline{+\ 29}$
    295

28. 742
    $\underline{+\ 38}$
    780

29. 354
    $\underline{+\ 37}$
    391

30. 635
    $\underline{+\ 46}$
    681

31. 44
    $\underline{+72}$
    116

32. 35
    $\underline{+83}$
    118

33. 56
    $\underline{+92}$
    148

34. 580
    $\underline{+340}$
    920

35. 174
    $\underline{+261}$
    435

36. 674
    $\underline{+\ 36}$
    710

37. 398
    $\underline{+\ 43}$
    441

38. 264
    $\underline{+\ 89}$
    353

39. 593
    $\underline{+327}$
    920

40. 786
    $\underline{+114}$
    900

41. 62
    37
    $\underline{+46}$
    145

42. 28
    54
    $\underline{+19}$
    101

43. 71
    96
    $\underline{+12}$
    179

44. 265
    612
    $\underline{+117}$
    994

45. 422
    536
    $\underline{+314}$
    1,272

46. 3,276
    $\underline{+4,563}$
    7,839

47. 6,127
    $\underline{+1,932}$
    8,059

48. 2,985
    $\underline{+1,316}$
    4,301

49. 47,864
    $\underline{+32,297}$
    80,161

50. 93,760
    $\underline{+42,163}$
    135,923

Basic Skills

Subtracting Whole Numbers

1. 98
  − 5
  93

2. 87
  − 4
  83

3. 56
  − 3
  53

4. 45
  − 5
  40

5. 29
  − 7
  22

6. 60
  −20
  40

7. 80
  −50
  30

8. 56
  −40
  16

9. 90
  −60
  30

10. 78
  −24
  54

11. 798
  − 45
  753

12. 955
  − 23
  932

13. 354
  − 34
  320

14. 865
  − 52
  813

15. 697
  − 83
  614

16. 800
  −500
  300

17. 650
  −300
  350

18. 854
  −630
  224

19. 355
  −103
  252

20. 695
  −132
  563

21. 93
  − 7
  86

22. 47
  − 8
  39

23. 54
  − 5
  49

24. 78
  −59
  19

25. 60
  −38
  22

26. 760
  − 36
  724

27. 382
  − 67
  315

28. 630
  − 23
  607

29. 460
  −248
  212

30. 373
  −126
  247

31. 578
  − 93
  485

32. 247
  − 83
  164

33. 623
  − 93
  530

34. 738
  −165
  573

35. 954
  −372
  582

36. 232
  −184
  48

37. 540
  −275
  265

38. 727
  −538
  189

39. 660
  −383
  277

40. 840
  −496
  344

41. 315
  −227
  88

42. 712
  −555
  157

43. 408
  −209
  199

44. 705
  −509
  196

45. 400
  −189
  211

46. 6,791
  − 899
  5,892

47. 3,406
  − 408
  2,998

48. 5,690
  − 792
  4,898

49. 6,243
  −4,564
  1,679

50. 7,092
  −6,895
  197

51. 64,700
  − 3,792
  60,908

52. 41,905
  − 4,916
  36,989

53. 52,009
  − 7,314
  44,695

54. 80,490
  −60,495
  19,995

55. 68,418
  −39,529
  28,889

Basic Skills

Subtracting Whole Numbers

1. $\begin{array}{r} 67 \\ -\ 4 \\ \hline \mathbf{63} \end{array}$
2. $\begin{array}{r} 25 \\ -\ 5 \\ \hline \mathbf{20} \end{array}$
3. $\begin{array}{r} 78 \\ -\ 6 \\ \hline \mathbf{72} \end{array}$
4. $\begin{array}{r} 93 \\ -\ 2 \\ \hline \mathbf{91} \end{array}$
5. $\begin{array}{r} 56 \\ -\ 3 \\ \hline \mathbf{53} \end{array}$

6. $\begin{array}{r} 40 \\ -10 \\ \hline \mathbf{30} \end{array}$
7. $\begin{array}{r} 70 \\ -30 \\ \hline \mathbf{40} \end{array}$
8. $\begin{array}{r} 62 \\ -40 \\ \hline \mathbf{22} \end{array}$
9. $\begin{array}{r} 90 \\ -70 \\ \hline \mathbf{20} \end{array}$
10. $\begin{array}{r} 86 \\ -32 \\ \hline \mathbf{54} \end{array}$

11. $\begin{array}{r} 726 \\ -\ 14 \\ \hline \mathbf{712} \end{array}$
12. $\begin{array}{r} 584 \\ -\ 32 \\ \hline \mathbf{552} \end{array}$
13. $\begin{array}{r} 963 \\ -\ 51 \\ \hline \mathbf{912} \end{array}$
14. $\begin{array}{r} 497 \\ -\ 83 \\ \hline \mathbf{414} \end{array}$
15. $\begin{array}{r} 677 \\ -\ 21 \\ \hline \mathbf{656} \end{array}$

16. $\begin{array}{r} 600 \\ -400 \\ \hline \mathbf{200} \end{array}$
17. $\begin{array}{r} 730 \\ -300 \\ \hline \mathbf{430} \end{array}$
18. $\begin{array}{r} 961 \\ -520 \\ \hline \mathbf{441} \end{array}$
19. $\begin{array}{r} 874 \\ -352 \\ \hline \mathbf{522} \end{array}$
20. $\begin{array}{r} 519 \\ -116 \\ \hline \mathbf{403} \end{array}$

21. $\begin{array}{r} 43 \\ -\ 7 \\ \hline \mathbf{36} \end{array}$
22. $\begin{array}{r} 72 \\ -\ 5 \\ \hline \mathbf{67} \end{array}$
23. $\begin{array}{r} 95 \\ -\ 8 \\ \hline \mathbf{87} \end{array}$
24. $\begin{array}{r} 86 \\ -27 \\ \hline \mathbf{59} \end{array}$
25. $\begin{array}{r} 40 \\ -13 \\ \hline \mathbf{27} \end{array}$

26. $\begin{array}{r} 461 \\ -\ 28 \\ \hline \mathbf{433} \end{array}$
27. $\begin{array}{r} 532 \\ -\ 17 \\ \hline \mathbf{515} \end{array}$
28. $\begin{array}{r} 670 \\ -\ 52 \\ \hline \mathbf{618} \end{array}$
29. $\begin{array}{r} 982 \\ -\ 36 \\ \hline \mathbf{946} \end{array}$
30. $\begin{array}{r} 621 \\ -\ 12 \\ \hline \mathbf{609} \end{array}$

31. $\begin{array}{r} 726 \\ -\ 43 \\ \hline \mathbf{683} \end{array}$
32. $\begin{array}{r} 942 \\ -\ 61 \\ \hline \mathbf{881} \end{array}$
33. $\begin{array}{r} 527 \\ -\ 52 \\ \hline \mathbf{475} \end{array}$
34. $\begin{array}{r} 438 \\ -229 \\ \hline \mathbf{209} \end{array}$
35. $\begin{array}{r} 855 \\ -472 \\ \hline \mathbf{383} \end{array}$

36. $\begin{array}{r} 860 \\ -472 \\ \hline \mathbf{388} \end{array}$
37. $\begin{array}{r} 215 \\ -167 \\ \hline \mathbf{48} \end{array}$
38. $\begin{array}{r} 742 \\ -563 \\ \hline \mathbf{179} \end{array}$
39. $\begin{array}{r} 936 \\ -478 \\ \hline \mathbf{458} \end{array}$
40. $\begin{array}{r} 487 \\ -199 \\ \hline \mathbf{288} \end{array}$

41. $\begin{array}{r} 417 \\ -358 \\ \hline \mathbf{59} \end{array}$
42. $\begin{array}{r} 324 \\ -137 \\ \hline \mathbf{187} \end{array}$
43. $\begin{array}{r} 707 \\ -309 \\ \hline \mathbf{398} \end{array}$
44. $\begin{array}{r} 602 \\ -408 \\ \hline \mathbf{194} \end{array}$
45. $\begin{array}{r} 500 \\ -279 \\ \hline \mathbf{221} \end{array}$

46. $\begin{array}{r} 7,213 \\ -\ 426 \\ \hline \mathbf{6,787} \end{array}$
47. $\begin{array}{r} 2,146 \\ -\ 347 \\ \hline \mathbf{1,799} \end{array}$
48. $\begin{array}{r} 6,290 \\ -\ 794 \\ \hline \mathbf{5,496} \end{array}$
49. $\begin{array}{r} 7,418 \\ -2,439 \\ \hline \mathbf{4,979} \end{array}$
50. $\begin{array}{r} 6,052 \\ -5,456 \\ \hline \mathbf{596} \end{array}$

51. $\begin{array}{r} 64,205 \\ -\ 3,746 \\ \hline \mathbf{60,459} \end{array}$
52. $\begin{array}{r} 88,644 \\ -\ 9,657 \\ \hline \mathbf{78,987} \end{array}$
53. $\begin{array}{r} 30,716 \\ -\ 4,755 \\ \hline \mathbf{25,961} \end{array}$
54. $\begin{array}{r} 64,658 \\ -23,659 \\ \hline \mathbf{40,999} \end{array}$
55. $\begin{array}{r} 91,273 \\ -86,594 \\ \hline \mathbf{4,679} \end{array}$

Basic Skills

Multiplying Whole Numbers

1. 40
   × 5
   ─────
   200

2. 30
   × 6
   ─────
   180

3. 20
   × 8
   ─────
   160

4. 60
   × 4
   ─────
   240

5. 50
   × 7
   ─────
   350

6. 23
   × 3
   ─────
   69

7. 44
   × 2
   ─────
   88

8. 81
   × 6
   ─────
   486

9. 72
   × 3
   ─────
   216

10. 61
   × 7
   ─────
   427

11. 721
   × 4
   ─────
   2,884

12. 513
   × 3
   ─────
   1,539

13. 234
   × 2
   ─────
   468

14. 634
   × 2
   ─────
   1,268

15. 831
   × 3
   ─────
   2,493

16. 46
   × 5
   ─────
   230

17. 53
   × 7
   ─────
   371

18. 82
   × 6
   ─────
   492

19. 27
   × 4
   ─────
   108

20. 68
   × 8
   ─────
   544

21. 704
   × 6
   ─────
   4,224

22. 409
   × 5
   ─────
   2,045

23. 806
   × 8
   ─────
   6,448

24. 307
   × 9
   ─────
   2,763

25. 208
   × 7
   ─────
   1,456

26. 28
   ×10
   ─────
   280

27. 86
   ×10
   ─────
   860

28. 51
   ×10
   ─────
   510

29. 247
   × 10
   ─────
   2,470

30. 4,328
   × 10
   ─────
   43,280

31. 52
   ×20
   ─────
   1,040

32. 37
   ×50
   ─────
   1,850

33. 26
   ×40
   ─────
   1,040

34. 175
   × 30
   ─────
   5,250

35. 1,469
   × 80
   ─────
   117,520

36. 75
   ×19
   ─────
   1,425

37. 54
   ×27
   ─────
   1,458

38. 45
   ×81
   ─────
   3,645

39. 52
   ×64
   ─────
   3,328

40. 80
   ×76
   ─────
   6,080

41. 89
   ×45
   ─────
   4,005

42. 64
   ×37
   ─────
   2,368

43. 78
   ×62
   ─────
   4,836

44. 56
   ×82
   ─────
   4,592

45. 83
   ×59
   ─────
   4,897

46. 414
   × 22
   ─────
   9,108

47. 321
   × 43
   ─────
   13,803

48. 522
   × 34
   ─────
   17,748

49. 613
   × 32
   ─────
   19,616

50. 202
   × 24
   ─────
   4,848

Basic Skills

Dividing Whole Numbers

1. $5\overline{)95}$ = 19
2. $2\overline{)58}$ = 29
3. $4\overline{)92}$ = 23
4. $3\overline{)78}$ = 26
5. $8\overline{)88}$ = 11

6. $4\overline{)848}$ = 212
7. $6\overline{)984}$ = 164
8. $3\overline{)351}$ = 117
9. $6\overline{)762}$ = 127
10. $2\overline{)276}$ = 138

11. $32\overline{)96}$ = 3
12. $19\overline{)95}$ = 5
13. $13\overline{)78}$ = 6
14. $21\overline{)63}$ = 3
15. $17\overline{)68}$ = 4

16. $32\overline{)256}$ = 8
17. $64\overline{)192}$ = 3
18. $97\overline{)679}$ = 7
19. $72\overline{)360}$ = 5
20. $16\overline{)144}$ = 9

21. $31\overline{)620}$ = 20
22. $14\overline{)980}$ = 70
23. $22\overline{)220}$ = 10
24. $29\overline{)870}$ = 30
25. $12\overline{)600}$ = 50

26. $8\overline{)576}$ = 72
27. $23\overline{)644}$ = 28
28. $56\overline{)952}$ = 17
29. $13\overline{)481}$ = 37
30. $46\overline{)690}$ = 15

31. $27\overline{)2,592}$ = 96
32. $68\overline{)3,060}$ = 45
33. $85\overline{)1,020}$ = 12
34. $53\overline{)4,081}$ = 77
35. $39\overline{)3,198}$ = 82

36. $19\overline{)4,902}$ = 258
37. $59\overline{)9,558}$ = 162
38. $23\overline{)5,175}$ = 225
39. $18\overline{)7,614}$ = 423
40. $12\overline{)6,264}$ = 522

41. $3\overline{)97}$ = 32 R1
42. $4\overline{)65}$ = 16 R1
43. $5\overline{)87}$ = 17 R2
44. $8\overline{)93}$ = 11 R5
45. $7\overline{)74}$ = 10 R4

46. $5\overline{)273}$ = 54 R3
47. $9\overline{)858}$ = 95 R3
48. $6\overline{)412}$ = 68 R4
49. $3\overline{)136}$ = 45 R1
50. $7\overline{)529}$ = 75 R4

51. $13\overline{)68}$ = 5 R3
52. $16\overline{)97}$ = 6 R1
53. $14\overline{)33}$ = 2 R5
54. $24\overline{)54}$ = 2 R6
55. $18\overline{)71}$ = 3 R17

56. $34\overline{)162}$ = 4 R26
57. $19\overline{)135}$ = 7 R2
58. $51\overline{)426}$ = 8 R18
59. $68\overline{)345}$ = 5 R5
60. $46\overline{)234}$ = 5 R4

61. $65\overline{)58,974}$ = 907 R19
62. $47\overline{)32,569}$ = 692 R45
63. $12\overline{)14,586}$ = 1,215 R6
64. $52\overline{)74,853}$ = 1,439 R25
65. $29\overline{)62,185}$ = 2,144 R9

66. $100\overline{)902}$ = 9 R2
67. $100\overline{)764}$ = 7 R64
68. $200\overline{)536}$ = 2 R136
69. $300\overline{)847}$ = 2 R247
70. $500\overline{)604}$ = 1 R104

71. $300\overline{)1,475}$ = 4 R275
72. $400\overline{)3,206}$ = 8 R6
73. $200\overline{)2,568}$ = 12 R168
74. $600\overline{)9,612}$ = 16 R12
75. $500\overline{)8,520}$ = 17 R20

Extra Practice

Lesson 1-1 *(Pages 4–7)*
Use the four-step plan to solve each problem.

1. On a map of Ohio, each inch represents approximately 9 miles. Chad is planning to travel from Cleveland to Cincinnati. If the distance on the map from Cleveland to Cincinnati is about 23 inches, how far will he travel? **207 miles**

2. Sylvia has $102. If she made three purchases of $13, $37, and $29, how much money does she have left? **$23**

3. It took Jason 56 hours to paint a house. It only took Nolan 43 hours and 16 minutes to paint an identical house. How many more hours did it take Jason to paint the house than it took Nolan? **12 h and 44 min**

4. A cassette tape holds sixty minutes of music. If Logan has already taped eight songs that are each five minutes long on the tape, how many more minutes of music can she still tape on the cassette? **20 min**

5. The Cornells want to buy a car that costs $4,260. They plan to make a down payment of $1,500 and pay the rest in twelve equal payments. What will be the amount of each payment? **$230**

Lesson 1-2 *(Pages 8–11)*
Find the next three numbers or shapes for each pattern.

1.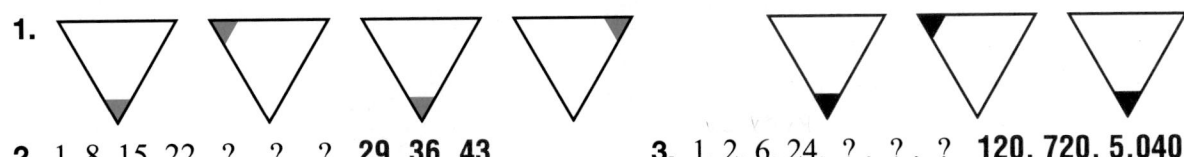

2. 1, 8, 15, 22, _?_, _?_, _?_ **29, 36, 43**

3. 1, 2, 6, 24, _?_, _?_, _?_ **120, 720, 5,040**

Solve by using patterns.

4. Sarah is conditioning for track. On the first day, she ran 2 laps. The second day she ran 3 laps. The third day she ran 5 laps, and on the fourth day she ran 8 laps. If this pattern continues, how many laps will she run on the seventh day? **23 laps**

5. The times that a new movie is showing are 9:30 A.M., 11:12 A.M., 12:54 P.M., and 2:36 P.M. What are the next three times this movie will be shown?
4:18 P.M., 6:00 P.M., 7:42 P.M.

Lesson 1-3 *(Pages 12–15)*
Round each number to the underlined place-value position.

1. 4̲6 **50**
2. 1,2̲49 **1,200**
3. 9̲,499 **9,000**
4. 2,96̲0 **2,960**
5. 6̲,001 **6,000**
6. 16̲3 **160**
7. 6̲58 **700**
8. 6̲,710 **7,000**
9. 12,6̲50 **12,700**
10. 18̲,305 **18,000**
11. 156,9̲99 **157,000**
12. 960,7̲15 **960,700**

Estimate. State whether the answer shown is reasonable. 13–20. See Answer Appendix.

13. $61 \times 5 = 234$
14. $889 - 43 = 846$
15. $2.94 + $6.13 + $9.25 = 18.32
16. $415 \times 4 = 1,660$
17. $385 \div 5 = 65$
18. $2,107 - 182 = 1,625$
19. $108 + 496 + 229 = 833$
20. $5,627 \div 331 = 17$

Lesson 1-4 *(Pages 16–19)*
Find the value of each expression.

1. $14 - 5 + 7$ **16**   **2.** $12 + 10 - 5 - 6$ **11**   **3.** $50 - 6 + 12 + 4$ **60**

4. $12 - 2 \times 3$ **6**   **5.** $16 + 4 \times 5$ **36**   **6.** $5 + 3 \times 4 - 7$ **10**

7. $2 \times 3 + 9 \times 2$ **24**   **8.** $6 \times 8 + 4 \div 2$ **50**   **9.** $7 \times 6 - 14$ **28**

10. $8 + 12 \times 4 \div 8$ **14**   **11.** $13 - 6 \times 2 + 1$ **2**   **12.** $80 \div 10 \times 8$ **64**

13. $1 + 2 + 3 + 4$ **10**   **14.** $1 \times 2 \times 3 \times 4$ **24**   **15.** $6 + 6 \times 6$ **42**

16. $14 - 2 \times 7 + 0$ **0**   **17.** $156 - 6 \times 0$ **156**   **18.** $30 - 14 \times 2 + 8$ **10**

Lesson 1-5 *(Pages 22–25)*
Evaluate each expression if $m = 2$ and $n = 4$.

1. $m + m$ **4**   **2.** $n - m$ **2**   **3.** mn **8**   **4.** $2m$ **4**   **5.** $2n$ **8**

6. $2n + 2m$ **12**   **7.** $m \times 0$ **0**   **8.** $64 \div n$ **16**   **9.** $12 - m$ **10**   **10.** $2mn$ **16**

Evaluate each expression if $a = 3$, $b = 4$, and $c = 12$.

11. $a + b$ **7**   **12.** $c - a$ **9**   **13.** $a + b + c$ **19**   **14.** $b - a$ **1**

15. $c - a \times b$ **0**   **16.** $a + 2 \times b$ **11**   **17.** $b + c \div 2$ **10**   **18.** ab **12**

19. $a + 3b$ **15**   **20.** $a + c \div 6$ **5**   **21.** $25 + c \div b$ **28**   **22.** abc **144**

23. $144 - abc$ **0**   **24.** $c \div a + 10$ **14**   **25.** $2b - a$ **5**   **26.** $2ab$ **24**

Lesson 1-6 *(Pages 28–31)*
Write each product using exponents.

1. $2 \cdot 2 \cdot 2 \cdot 2 \cdot 2$ **2^5**   **2.** $6 \cdot 6 \cdot 6 \cdot 7 \cdot 7$ **$6^3 \cdot 7^2$**   **3.** $9 \cdot 9 \cdot 9 \cdot 9 \cdot 9 \cdot 9 \cdot 10$ **$9^6 \cdot 10$**

4. $k \cdot k \cdot k \cdot t \cdot t \cdot t$ **$k^3 \cdot t^3$**   **5.** $14 \cdot 14 \cdot 6$ **$14^2 \cdot 6$**   **6.** $3 \cdot 3 \cdot 3 \cdot 3 \cdot y \cdot y$ **$3^4 \cdot y^2$**

Write each power as a product.

7. 13^4 **$13 \cdot 13 \cdot 13 \cdot 13$**   **8.** 9^6 **$9 \cdot 9 \cdot 9 \cdot 9 \cdot 9 \cdot 9$**   **9.** $2^3 \cdot 3^2$ **$2 \cdot 2 \cdot 2 \cdot 3 \cdot 3$**

10. x^5 **$x \cdot x \cdot x \cdot x \cdot x$**   **11.** 169^3 **$169 \cdot 169 \cdot 169$**   **12.** $13{,}410^2$ **$13{,}410 \cdot 13{,}410$**

Evaluate each expression.

13. 5^6 **15,625**   **14.** 17^3 **4,913**   **15.** 2^{12} **4,096**   **16.** $3^5 \cdot 2^3$ **1,944**

17. $6^4 \cdot 3$ **3,888**   **18.** $2^2 \cdot 3^2 \cdot 4^2$ **576**   **19.** 176^2 **30,976**   **20.** $6 \cdot 4^3$ **384**

Lesson 1-7A *(Pages 32–33)*
Solve.

1. Find an even number between 70 and 80 that is divisible by 2 and 9. **72**

2. Last week the Tri-River Animal Shelter sent a total of 34 cats and dogs to new homes. There were 8 more cats than dogs. How many of each were adopted? **13 dogs, 21 cats**

3. Admission to the Cincinnati Zoo is $8 for adults, $5 for children, and $3 for senior citizens. Eleven members of the Ruiz family paid a total of $55 for admission. If 6 children were in the group, how many adults and senior citizens were in the group? **2 adults, 3 senior citizens**

4. Sylvia's soccer team played a total of 18 matches. Her team won twice as many matches as they lost. How many matches did they win? **12 matches**

5. Jordan makes $5 per hour mowing lawns and $7 per hour painting houses during the summer. This week, Jordan made $102. If he worked twice as many hours mowing lawns as he did painting houses, how many hours did he work at each job? **12 hours mowing, 6 hours painting**

Lesson 1-7 *(Pages 34–37)*
Tell whether the equation is *true* or *false* by replacing the variable with the given value.

1. $q - 7 = 7$; $q = 28$ **false**
2. $g - 3 = 10$; $g = 13$ **true**
3. $r - 3 = 4$; $r = 7$ **true**
4. $t + 3 = 21$; $t = 24$ **false**

Identify the solution to each equation from the list given.

5. $7 + a = 10$; 3, 13, 17 **3**
6. $14 + m = 24$; 7, 10, 34 **10**
7. $j \div 3 = 2$; 4, 6, 8 **6**
8. $20 = 24 - n$; 2, 3, 4 **4**

Solve each equation mentally.

9. $b + 7 = 12$ **5**
10. $s + 10 = 23$ **13**
11. $4x = 36$ **9**
12. $6 = t \div 5$ **30**
13. $b - 3 = 12$ **15**
14. $w \div 2 = 8$ **16**

Lesson 2-1 *(Pages 46–49)*
Make a frequency table for each set of data.

1. To the nearest mile, how many miles did members of the track team run during practice yesterday? **See Answer Appendix.**
   1 4 3 5 2 3 3 2 1 4 3 2 3 1 5 3 4 2 3 1 5 2

2. What were the high temperatures in Indiana cities on March 13? **See Answer Appendix.**
   52 57 48 53 52 49 48 52 51
   47 51 49 57 53 48 52 52 49

Use the frequency table to the right to answer Exercises 3–4.

3. Describe the data shown in the table.

4. Which flavor should the ice cream shop stock the most? **vanilla**

3. **6 flavors of ice cream are being sold, with vanilla being the most purchased and peach the least purchased**

ICE CREAM FLAVORS SOLD IN JULY		
Flavor	Tally	Frequency
Vanilla	ⅢⅢ ⅢⅢ ⅢⅢ ⅢⅢ IIII	24
Chocolate	ⅢⅢ ⅢⅢ ⅢⅢ III	18
Strawberry	ⅢⅢ ⅢⅢ II	12
Chocolate Chip	ⅢⅢ ⅢⅢ ⅢⅢ I	16
Peach	ⅢⅢ III	8
Butter Pecan	ⅢⅢ ⅢⅢ I	11

Lesson 2-2 *(Pages 50–53)*

Choose an appropriate scale and an interval for each set of data.

1. 2, 7, 13, 3, 4, 12, 9 **0 to 13; 1**   **2.** 11, 15, 13, 18, 19, 20 **11 to 20; 1**

3. 56, 85, 23, 78, 42, 63 **21 to 85; 5**   **4.** 10, 25, 88, 64, 99, 37 **0 to 100; 10**

5. 165, 167, 169, 164, 170, 166, 167, 165, 169 **161 to 170; 1**

6. 132, 865, 465, 672, 318, 940, 573, 689 **100 to 1,000; 100**

7. 1,450; 7,896; 5,638; 7,142; 4,287; 8,612 **1,000 to 9,000; 1,000**

Lesson 2-3 *(Pages 54–57)*

Make a bar graph for each set of data.

1. a vertical bar graph

Favorite Subject

Subject	Frequency
Math	4
Science	6
History	2
English	8
Phys. Ed.	12

2. a horizontal bar graph

Final Grades

Subject	Score
Math	88
Science	82
History	92
English	94

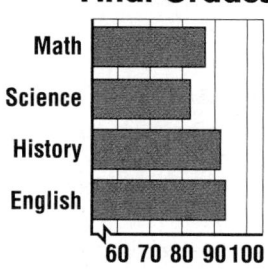

Make a line graph for each set of data.

3.

Test	Score
1	62
2	75
3	81
4	83
5	78
6	92

4.

Day	Absences
Mon.	3
Tues.	6
Wed.	2
Thur.	1
Fri.	8

Homeroom Absences

Lesson 2-3B *(Pages 58–59)*

The double bar graph shows the quarterly sales (in millions of dollars) of two companies. Use the graph to answer the following questions.

1. In which quarter did Company A have its lowest sales? **1st quarter**

2. About how much higher are the sales for Company A than Company B in the 3rd quarter? **about $45 million**

3. The sales of Company A in the 2nd quarter are about equal to the sales of Company B in which quarter? **1st quarter**

4. In which quarter is there the least difference between the sales of Company A and the sales of Company B? **1st quarter**

Lesson 2-4 *(Pages 60–63)*
The circle graph shows the favorite subject
of students at Midland Middle School.

1. The percents are 5%, 12%, 20%, 25%, and 38%.
Match each percent with the appropriate section
of the graph. **1–2. See Answer Appendix.**

2. Suppose math and history were combined. Would
the combination be preferred by $\frac{1}{4}$ of the students?

3. Which two subjects together are preferred by the
same percent as English? **history and science**

4. Which two subjects together are preferred by half
of the students? **math and phys. ed.**

Students' Favorite Subjects

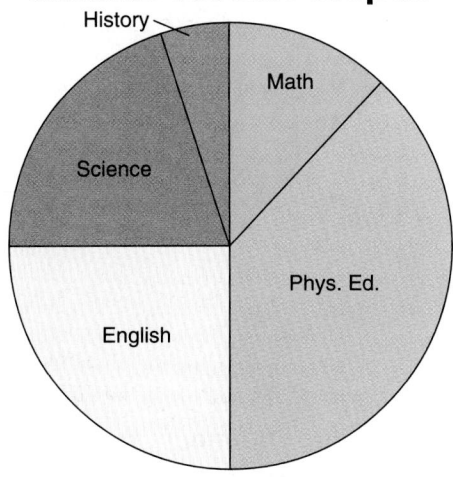

Lesson 2-5 *(Pages 64–67)*
Use the following graph to solve each problem.

Average Starting Salaries

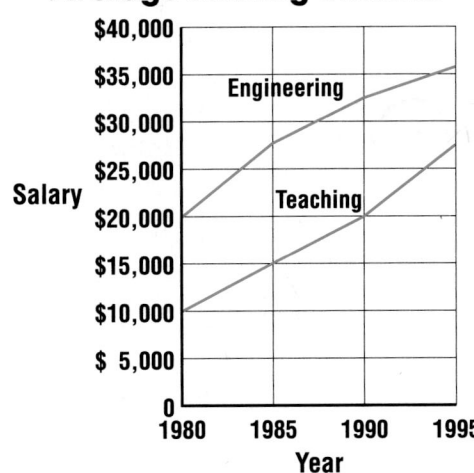

1. Give the expected starting salary in 1988 for:
  a. an engineer **about $31,000**
  b. a teacher **about $18,000**

2. How much more did an engineer make than
a teacher in 1980? **$10,000**

3. Which of these two professions do you think
will start with a higher salary in 2000? **engineering**

4. How much less was the difference in salaries
in 1995 than in 1980? **about $1,000**

Lesson 2-6 *(Pages 68–70)*
Make a stem-and-leaf plot for each set of data.

1. 23, 15, 39, 68, 57, 42, 51, 52, 41, 18, 29

2. 5, 14, 39, 28, 14, 6, 7, 18, 13, 28, 9, 14

3. 189, 182, 196, 184, 197, 183, 196, 194, 184

4. 71, 82, 84, 95, 76, 92, 83, 74, 81, 75, 96

1.
Stem	Leaf
1	5 8
2	3 9
3	9
4	1 2
5	1 2 7
6	8

1|5 = 15

2.
Stem	Leaf
0	5 6 7 9
1	3 4 4 4 8
2	8 8
3	9

0|5 = 5

3.
Stem	Leaf
18	2 3 4 4 9
19	4 6 6 7

18|9 = 189

4.
Stem	Leaf
7	1 4 5 6
8	1 2 3 4
9	2 5 6

7|1 = 71

Lesson 2-7 *(Pages 71–75)*

Find the mean, median, mode, and range for each set of data. 6. 710, 721, no mode, 495

1. 1, 5, 9, 1, 2, 4, 8, 2 **4; 3; 1, 2, and 8**

2. 2, 5, 8, 9, 7, 6, 3, 5 **5.6, 5.5, 5, 7**

3. 1, 2, 4, 2, 2, 1, 2 **2, 2, 2, 3**

4. 12, 13, 15, 12, 12, 11 **12.5, 12, 12, 4**

5. 256, 265, 247, 256 **256, 256, 256, 18**

6. 957, 562, 462, 848, 721

7. 46, 54, 66, 54, 46, 66
   55.33; 54; 46, 54, and 66; 20

8. 81, 82, 83, 84, 85, 86, 87 **84, 84, no mode, 6**

Lesson 2-8 *(Pages 78–81)*

**Tell whether the mean, median, or mode would be best to describe each
set of data. Explain each answer.**

1. 627, 452, 573, 602, 498 **mean–the numbers are all about the same**

2. Favorite bagel flavor **mode–want to find the most frequent**

3. $42,360; $51,862; $47,650; $23,400; $52,961 **median–$23,400 is much lower than the rest**

The graphs below display the same information.

4. Explain why these graphs look different. **They have different vertical scales.**

5. If Mr. Roush wishes to show that SAT scores have improved greatly since
   he became principal in 1993, which graph should he use?
   **Answers may vary. Sample answer: He should use Graph B
   because the increase looks greater.**

Lesson 2-9 *(Pages 82–85)*

Use the grid at the right to name the point for each ordered pair.

1. (6, 2) **P** 2. (3, 5) **J** 3. (1, 3) **R** 4. (6, 0) **M** 5. (5, 8) **Q**

6. (2, 7) **L** 7. (0, 6) **S** 8. (4, 3) **D** 9. (10, 4) **T** 10. (1, 9) **N**

Use the grid at the right to name the ordered pair for each point.

11. *L* **(2, 1)** 12. *I* **(4, 2)** 13. *C* **(7, 2)** 14. *R* **(6, 8)** 15. *T* **(3, 7)**

16. *X* **(1, 7)** 17. *Z* **(1, 5)** 18. *K* **(5, 1)** 19. *Y* **(8, 2)** 20. *N* **(6, 3)**

Lesson 3-1 *(Pages 95–98)*
Write each fraction or mixed number as a decimal.

1. $\frac{4}{10}$ **0.4**
2. $\frac{66}{100}$ **0.66**
3. $\frac{73}{100}$ **0.73**
4. $\frac{5}{100}$ **0.05**
5. $\frac{79}{100}$ **0.79**

6. $\frac{94}{100}$ **0.94**
7. $6\frac{85}{1,000}$ **6.085**
8. $\frac{875}{10,000}$ **0.0875**
9. $\frac{1,264}{1,000}$ **1.264**
10. $\frac{527}{10,000}$ **0.0527**

Write each expression as a decimal.

11. two hundredths **0.02**
12. sixteen hundredths **0.16**

13. four tenths **0.4**
14. two and twenty-seven hundredths **2.27**

15. nine and twelve hundredths **9.12**
16. fifty-six and nine tenths **56.9**

17. twenty-seven thousandths **0.027**
18. one hundred ten-thousandths **0.0100**

19. two ten-thousandths **0.0002**
20. twenty and six hundred thousandths **20.600**

21. two thousand, four hundred seventy-five and six tenths **2,475.6**

22. twelve thousand, ninety-seven and sixty-two thousandths **12,097.062**

Lesson 3-2 *(Pages 102–104)*
Use a centimeter ruler to measure each line segment.

1. _____ **3.4 cm**
2. _____ **4.8 cm**

3. _____ **1.9 cm**
4. _____ **3.7 cm**

5. _____ **3.0 cm**
6. _____ **4.1 cm**

7. ____ **1.0 cm**
8. _____ **1.8 cm**

Lesson 3-3 *(Pages 105–108)*
State the greater number in each group.

1. 0.112 or 0.121 **0.121**
2. 0.9985 or 0.998 **0.9985**
3. 0.556 or 0.519 **0.556**

4. 1.19 or 11.9 **11.9**
5. 0.6, 6.0 or 0.06 **6.0**
6. 0.0009 or 0.001 **0.001**

Order each set of decimals from least to greatest.

7.		8.		9.		10.	
415.65	**415.56**	0.0256	**0.0009**	1.2356	**1.2335**	50.12	**5.012**
451.65	**415.65**	0.2056	**0.0255**	1.2355	**1.2353**	5.012	**5.901**
451.66	**451.56**	0.0255	**0.0256**	1.25	**1.2355**	50.22	**50.02**
451.56	**451.65**	0.0009	**0.2056**	1.2335	**1.2356**	5.901	**50.12**
415.56	**451.66**	0.2560	**0.2560**	1.2353	**1.25**	50.02	**50.22**

Order each set of decimals from greatest to least.

11.		12.		13.		14.	
13.664	**13.664**	26.6987	**26.9688**	1.00065	**1.00165**	2.014	**22.14**
13.446	**13.446**	26.9687	**26.9687**	1.00100	**1.00100**	2.010	**22.00**
1.3666	**1.6333**	26.9666	**26.9666**	1.00165	**1.00065**	22.00	**2.014**
1.6333	**1.3666**	26.9688	**26.6987**	1.00056	**1.00056**	22.14	**2.010**

Lesson 3-4 *(Pages 109–111)*

Round each number to the underlined place-value position.

1. 5.6̲4 **5.6**
2. 12.37̲6 **12.38**
3. 0.053̲62 **0.054**
4. 6̲.17 **6**

5. 15.2̲98 **15.3**
6. 0.0026̲325 **0.0026**
7. 758.99̲9 **759.00**
8. 4̲.25 **4**

9. 32.658̲3 **32.658**
10. 0̲.025 **0**
11. 1.004̲9 **1.005**
12. 9.2̲5 **9.3**

13. 67.49̲2 **67.49**
14. 25.1̲9 **25.2**
15. 26.9̲6 **27.0**
16. 4.00̲098 **4.00**

Lesson 3-5 *(Pages 112–115)*

Estimate using rounding.

1. 0.245   **0.25**
    +0.256 **+0.26**
          0.51

2. 2.45698   **2.5**
    −1.26589 **−1.3**
          1.2

3. 0.5962   **0.6**
    +1.2598 **+1.3**
          1.9

4. 17.985   **18.0**
    − 9.001 **− 9.0**
          9

5. 0.256 + 0.6589
   0.26 + 0.66; 0.92

6. 1.2568 − 0.1569
   1.3 − 0.2; 1.1

7. 12.999 + 5.048
   13 + 5; 18

Estimate using clustering.

8. 4.5 + 4.95 + 5.2 + 5.49 **5 × 4 = 20**

9. 2.25 + 1.69 + 2.1 + 2.369 **2 × 4 = 8**

10. $12.15 + $11. 63 + $12 + $11.89
    $12 × 4 = $48

11. 0.569 + 1.005 + 1.265 + 0.765 **1 × 4 = 4**

Lesson 3-6A *(Pages 116–117)*

Solve.

1. Jaleel bought a t-shirt at a concert. He paid for the $17.49 shirt with a $20 bill. Should he expect about $4 or about $2 in change? **about $2**

2. There are 3,261 seats in the Northmore High School stadium. What is a reasonable number of rows in the stadium if each row holds about 55 people? **about 60 rows**

3. Jayson wants to spend his allowance on CD ROM games for his computer. He has saved $80. About how many games can Jayson buy if each CD ROM costs $29.95? **about 2 games**

4. Lucas needs to buy school supplies. He found a backpack for $29.95, a notebook for $8.49, and a package of pens and pencils for $3.70. Is $30 or $50 needed to pay for these supplies? **$50**

5. When Jamilah added 0.00276 and 0.0149 the calculator showed 0.1766. Is this answer reasonable? **no**

Lesson 3-6 *(Pages 118–121)*
Add or subtract.
1. $0.46 + 0.72$ **1.18**
2. $13.7 + 2.6$ **16.3**
3. $17.9 + 7.41$ **25.31**
4. $19.2 + 7.36$ **26.56**
5. $0.5113 + 0.62148$ **1.13278**
6. $12.56 - 10.21$ **2.35**
7. $0.2154 - 0.1526$ **0.0628**
8. $2.3125 + 1.02$ **3.3325**
9. $1.025 - 0.58697$ **0.43803**
10. $14.526 - 12.654$ **1.872**
11. $2.3568 + 5$ **7.3568**
12. $20 - 5.98671$ **14.01329**
13. $15.256 + 0.236$ **15.492**
14. $3.7 + 1.5 + 0.2$ **5.4**
15. $0.23 + 1.2 + 0.36$ **1.79**
16. $0.896352 - 0.25639$ **0.639962**
17. $25.6 - 2.3$ **23.3**
18. $13.5 - 2.8456$ **10.6544**
19. $1.265 + 1.654$ **2.919**
20. $24.56 - 24.32$ **0.24**
21. $0.256 - 0.255$ **0.001**

Lesson 4-1 *(Pages 133–136)*
Multiply.
1. $\begin{array}{r} 0.2 \\ \times\ 65 \\ \hline 13 \end{array}$
2. $\begin{array}{r} 0.73 \\ \times\ 12 \\ \hline 8.76 \end{array}$
3. $\begin{array}{r} 0.65 \\ \times\ 27 \\ \hline 17.55 \end{array}$
4. $\begin{array}{r} 9.6 \\ \times\ 13 \\ \hline 124.8 \end{array}$
5. $\begin{array}{r} 12.15 \\ \times\ 6 \\ \hline 72.9 \end{array}$
6. $\begin{array}{r} 0.91 \\ \times\ 16 \\ \hline 14.56 \end{array}$
7. $\begin{array}{r} 0.265 \\ \times\ 7 \\ \hline 1.855 \end{array}$
8. $\begin{array}{r} 2.612 \\ \times\ 14 \\ \hline 36.568 \end{array}$
9. $\begin{array}{r} 0.003 \\ \times\ 55 \\ \hline 0.165 \end{array}$
10. $\begin{array}{r} 0.67 \\ \times\ 21 \\ \hline 14.07 \end{array}$

Solve each equation.
11. $r = 19 \times 0.111$ **2.109**
12. $1.65 \times 72 = a$ **118.8**
13. $9.6 \times 101 = q$ **969.6**
14. $24 \times 1.201 = d$ **28.824**
15. $610 \times 7.5 = j$ **4,575**
16. $z = 0.001 \times 6$ **0.006**
17. $x = 510 \times 0.0135$ **6.885**
18. $b = 9.2 \times 17$ **156.4**
19. $14.1235 \times 4 = m$ **56.494**

Lesson 4-2 *(Pages 137–139)*
Find each product mentally. Use the distributive property.
1. 5×18 **90**
2. 9×27 **243**
3. 8×83 **664**
4. 7×21 **147**
5. 3×47 **141**
6. 2×106 **212**
7. 6×34 **204**
8. 56×3 **168**
9. 27×8 **216**
10. 5×3.4 **17**
11. 6×40.7 **244.2**
12. 1.5×30 **45**
13. 0.9×71 **63.9**
14. 30×2.08 **62.4**
15. 16×7 **112**
16. 33×4 **132**
17. 0.6×12 **7.2**
18. 80×7.9 **632**

Lesson 4-3 *(Pages 141–143)*
Multiply.

1. $9.6 \cdot 10.5$ **100.8**

2. $3.2 \cdot 0.1$ **0.32**

3. $1.5 \cdot 9.6$ **14.4**

4. $5.42 \cdot 0.21$ **1.1382**

5. $7.42 \cdot 0.2$ **1.484**

6. $0.001 \cdot 0.02$ **0.00002**

7. $0.6 \cdot 542$ **325.2**

8. $6.7 \cdot 5.8$ **38.86**

9. $3.24 \cdot 6.7$ **21.708**

Solve each equation.

10. $9.8 \cdot 4.62 = s$ **45.276**

11. $7.32 \cdot 9.7 = v$ **71.004**

12. $t = 0.008 \cdot 0.007$ **0.000056**

13. $a = 0.001 \cdot 56$ **0.056**

14. $c = 4.5 \cdot 0.2$ **0.9**

15. $9.6 \cdot 2.3 = h$ **22.08**

16. $5.63 \cdot 8.1 = q$ **45.603**

17. $10.35 \cdot 9.1 = u$ **94.185**

18. $t = 28.2 \cdot 3.9$ **109.98**

19. $g = 102.13 \cdot 1.221$ **124.70073**

20. $n = 2.02 \times 1.25$ **2.525**

21. $z = 8.37 \times 89.6$ **749.952**

Lesson 4-4 *(Pages 145–148)*
Find the perimeter of each figure.

1.

2.

3.

Find the perimeter and area of each figure.

4. $19 \text{ cm} \times 3 \text{ cm}$ **44 cm, 57 cm²**

5. $5 \text{ in.} \times 3 \text{ in.}$ **16 in., 15 in²**

6. 9 ft square **36 ft, 81 ft²**

7. 4.3 m square **17.2 m, 18.49 m²**

8.

14 yd, 10 yd²

9.
21.2 cm, 28.09 cm²

10.
27.4 in., 39.36 in²

Lesson 4-5A *(Pages 150–151)*
Solve.

1. Genaro wants to carpet a den that measures 18 feet by 24 feet. In the center of the room is a tile hearth for his stove which he does not want to carpet. If the hearth measures 6 feet by 6 feet, how much carpet does he need? **396 ft²**

2. Jamika and Jordan are carving pumpkins for a Halloween party. Jamika can carve 3 pumpkins in 2 hours. Jordan can carve 2 pumpkins in 1 hour. If they work the same amount of time, how long will it take to carve 14 pumpkins? **4 hours**

3. Lonny has 24 feet of fence to make a pen for his rabbit. What dimensions should he make the pen so the area is the greatest possible? **6 ft by 6 ft**

4. How many cuts must be made to divide a 6-foot submarine sandwich equally among 10 people? **9 cuts**

Lesson 4-5 *(Pages 152–155)*
Find each quotient.

1. $6\overline{)1.26}$ **0.21**   2. $8\overline{)23.2}$ **2.9**   3. $6\overline{)89.22}$ **14.87**   4. $15\overline{)54.75}$ **3.65**

5. $13\overline{)128.31}$ **9.87**   6. $9\overline{)2.583}$ **0.287**   7. $47\overline{)11.28}$ **0.24**   8. $26\overline{)32.5}$ **1.25**

9. $37.1 \div 14$ **2.65**   10. $5.88 \div 4$ **1.47**   11. $3.7 \div 5$ **0.74**

12. $41.4 \div 18$ **2.3**   13. $9.87 \div 3$ **3.29**   14. $8.45 \div 25$ **0.338**

Round each quotient to the nearest tenth.

15. $26.5 \div 4$ **6.6**   16. $46.25 \div 8$ **5.8**   17. $19.38 \div 9$ **2.2**

18. $8.5 \div 2$ **4.3**   19. $90.88 \div 14$ **6.5**   20. $23.1 \div 4$ **5.8**

Round each quotient to the nearest hundredth.

21. $19.5 \div 27$ **0.72**   22. $26.5 \div 19$ **1.39**   23. $46.23 \div 25$ **1.85**

24. $46.25 \div 25$ **1.85**   25. $4.26 \div 9$ **0.47**   26. $18.74 \div 19$ **0.99**

Lesson 4-6 *(Pages 157–159)*
Find each quotient.

1. $0.5\overline{)18.45}$ **36.9**   2. $0.08\overline{)5.2}$ **65**   3. $2.6\overline{)0.65}$ **0.25**   4. $1.3\overline{)12.831}$ **9.87**

5. $0.87\overline{)5.133}$ **5.9**   6. $2.54\overline{)24.13}$ **9.5**   7. $3.7\overline{)35.89}$ **9.7**   8. $26\overline{)32.5}$ **1.25**

9. $5.88 \div 0.4$ **14.7**   10. $3.7 \div 0.5$ **7.4**   11. $6.72 \div 2.4$ **2.8**

12. $9.87 \div 0.3$ **32.9**   13. $8.45 \div 2.5$ **3.38**   14. $90.88 \div 14.2$ **6.4**

15. $33.6 \div 8.4$ **4**   16. $25.389 \div 4.03$ **6.3**   17. $85.92 \div 4.8$ **17.9**

18. $63.18 \div 16.2$ **3.9**   19. $18.49 \div 4.3$ **4.3**   20. $9.363 \div 0.003$ **3,121**

21. $1.02 \div 0.3$ **3.4**   22. $6.4 \div 0.8$ **8**   23. $7.2 \div 0.9$ **8**

Lesson 4-7 *(Pages 161–163)*
Find each quotient to the nearest hundredth.

1. $9\overline{)0.36}$ **0.04**   2. $13\overline{)39.39}$ **3.03**   3. $45\overline{)0.585}$ **0.01**   4. $8\overline{)0.24}$ **0.03**

5. $6\overline{)0.312}$ **0.05**   6. $7\overline{)0.161}$ **0.02**   7. $7\overline{)7.21}$ **1.03**   8. $3\overline{)9.18}$ **3.06**

9. $\$0.72 \div 12$ **\$0.06**   10. $0.36 \div 9$ **0.04**   11. $0.56 \div 14$ **0.04**

12. $32.2 \div 8$ **4.03**   13. $0.3869 \div 5.3$ **0.07**   14. $0.39 \div 7.8$ **0.05**

Solve each equation.

15. $0.0426 \div 71 = q$ **0.0006**   16. $f = 0.1185 \div 7.9$ **0.015**   17. $j = 0.84 \div 12$ **0.07**

18. $m = 4.544 \div 64$ **0.071**   19. $v = 0.384 \div 9.6$ **0.04**   20. $0.2262 \div 8.7 = d$ **0.026**

Lesson 4-8 *(Pages 164–166)*

Write the unit that you would use to measure each of the following. Then estimate the mass or capacity.

1. a bag of sugar **kilogram; 2 kg**

2. a pitcher of fruit punch **liter; 2 L**

3. the mass of a dime **gram; 10 g**

4. the amount of water in an ice cube **milliliter; 20 mL**

5. a vitamin **gram; 1 g**

6. a pencil **gram; 20 g**

7. the mass of a puppy **kilogram; 5 kg**

8. a bottle of perfume **milliliter; 20 mL**

9. a grain of sand **milligram; 1 mg**

10. the mass of a car **kilogram; 1,000 kg**

Lesson 4-9 *(Pages 167–169)*

Complete.

1. 400 mm = **40** cm

2. 4 kg = **4,000** g

3. 660 cm = **6.6** m

4. 0.3 L = **300** mL

5. 30 mm = **3** cm

6. 84.5 g = **0.0845** kg

7. **0.54** m = 54 cm

8. **0.563** L = 563 mL

9. **21,000** mg = 21 g

10. 4 L = **4,000** mL

11. 61.2 mg = **0.0612** g

12. 4,497 mL = **4.497** L

13. **450** mm = 45 cm

14. 632 mL = **0.632** L

15. 61 g = **61,000** mg

16. **510,000** mg = 0.51 kg

17. 0.63 L = **630** mL

18. 18 km = **1,800,000** cm

Lesson 5-1 *(Pages 178–180)*

Determine whether the first number is divisible by the second number.

1. 89; 3 **no**

2. 64; 2 **yes**

3. 125; 5 **yes**

4. 156; 4 **yes**

5. 216; 9 **yes**

6. 330; 10 **yes**

7. 225; 3 **yes**

8. 524; 6 **no**

State whether each number is divisible by 2, 3, 5, 6, 9, and 10.

9. 1,986 **2, 3, 6**

10. 2,052 **2, 3, 6, 9**

11. 110 **2, 5, 10**

12. 315 **3, 5, 9**

13. 405 **3, 5, 9**

14. 918 **2, 3, 6, 9**

15. 243 **3, 9**

16. 735 **3, 5**

17. 1,233 **3, 9**

18. 5,103 **3, 9**

19. 8,001 **3, 9**

20. 9,270 **2, 3, 5, 6, 9, 10**

Lesson 5-2 *(Pages 182–184)*

Tell whether each number is *prime, composite,* or *neither*.

1. 20 **composite**   2. 65 **composite**   3. 37 **prime**   4. 26 **composite**   5. 54 **composite**

6. 155 **composite**   7. 201 **composite**   8. 0 **neither**   9. 49 **composite**   10. 17 **prime**

Find the prime factorization of each number.

11. 72 $2^3 \times 3^2$ 12. 2,648 $2^3 \times 331$ 13. 32 2^5 14. 86 2×43 15. 120 $2^3 \times 3 \times 5$

16. 576 $2^6 \times 3^2$ 17. 68 $2^2 \times 17$ 18. 240 $2^4 \times 3 \times 5$ 19. 24 $2^3 \times 3$ 20. 70 $2 \times 5 \times 7$

21. 102 $2 \times 3 \times 17$ 22. 121 11^2 23. 164 $2^2 \times 41$ 24. 225 $5^2 \times 3^2$ 25. 54 2×3^3

Lesson 5-3A *(Pages 186–187)*

Solve.

1. Mychal needs to go to the bank, the post office, and the bicycle shop. In how many different orders can she do this? **6 different orders**

2. How many different four digit numbers can be made from the digits 2, 5, 7, and 9? **24 numbers**

3. Ai-lien usually buys her lunch from the a la carte line in the cafeteria. Today, she has a choice of chicken, fish, or spaghetti; soup or salad; and fresh fruit or yogurt. How many possible choices does she have? **12 choices**

4. A shoe company offers 8 different styles of running shoes in 4 different colors. How many combinations of style and color are possible? **32 combinations**

Lesson 5-3 *(Pages 188–190)*

Find the GCF of each set of numbers by making a list.

1. 8, 18 **2**   2. 6, 9 **3**   3. 4, 12 **4**   4. 18, 24 **6**

5. 25, 30 **5**   6. 36, 54 **9**   7. 64, 32 **32**   8. 16, 32, 56 **8**

Find the GCF of each set of numbers by using prime factorization.

9. 6, 15 **3**   10. 8, 24 **8**   11. 14, 22 **2**   12. 12, 27 **3**

13. 17, 51 **17**   14. 48, 60 **12**   15. 54, 72 **18**   16. 14, 28, 42 **14**

Find the GCF of each set of numbers using either method.

17. 5, 20 **5**   18. 9, 21 **3**   19. 10, 25 **5**   20. 12, 28 **4**

21. 16, 24 **8**   22. 42, 48 **6**   23. 60, 75 **15**   24. 27, 45, 63 **9**

Lesson 5-4 *(Pages 193–196)*

Replace each ■ with a number so that the fractions are equivalent.

1. $\frac{12}{16} = \frac{■}{4}$ **3**
2. $\frac{7}{8} = \frac{■}{32}$ **28**
3. $\frac{3}{4} = \frac{75}{■}$ **100**
4. $\frac{8}{16} = \frac{■}{2}$ **1**

5. $\frac{6}{18} = \frac{1}{■}$ **3**
6. $\frac{27}{36} = \frac{3}{■}$ **4**
7. $\frac{1}{4} = \frac{16}{■}$ **64**
8. $\frac{9}{18} = \frac{■}{2}$ **1**

State whether each fraction or ratio is in simplest form. If not, write each fraction or ratio in simplest form.

9. $\frac{50}{100}$ **no; $\frac{1}{2}$**
10. $\frac{24}{40}$ **no; $\frac{3}{5}$**
11. 2:5 **yes**
12. 8 out of 24 **no; 1 out of 3**

13. 20 to 27 **yes**
14. $\frac{4}{10}$ **no; $\frac{2}{5}$**
15. $\frac{3}{5}$ **yes**
16. 14:19 **yes**

17. 9:12 **no; 3:4**
18. $\frac{6}{8}$ **no; $\frac{3}{4}$**
19. $\frac{15}{18}$ **no; $\frac{5}{6}$**
20. 9 out of 20 **yes**

Lesson 5-5 *(Pages 198–201)*

Express each mixed number as an improper fraction.

1. $3\frac{1}{16}$ **$\frac{49}{16}$**
2. $2\frac{3}{4}$ **$\frac{11}{4}$**
3. $1\frac{3}{8}$ **$\frac{11}{8}$**
4. $1\frac{5}{12}$ **$\frac{17}{12}$**
5. $7\frac{3}{5}$ **$\frac{38}{5}$**

6. $6\frac{5}{8}$ **$\frac{53}{8}$**
7. $3\frac{1}{3}$ **$\frac{10}{3}$**
8. $1\frac{7}{9}$ **$\frac{16}{9}$**
9. $2\frac{3}{16}$ **$\frac{35}{16}$**
10. $1\frac{2}{3}$ **$\frac{5}{3}$**

Express each improper fraction as a mixed number.

11. $\frac{33}{10}$ **$3\frac{3}{10}$**
12. $\frac{103}{25}$ **$4\frac{3}{25}$**
13. $\frac{22}{5}$ **$4\frac{2}{5}$**
14. $\frac{13}{2}$ **$6\frac{1}{2}$**
15. $\frac{29}{6}$ **$4\frac{5}{6}$**

16. $\frac{101}{100}$ **$1\frac{1}{100}$**
17. $\frac{21}{8}$ **$2\frac{5}{8}$**
18. $\frac{19}{6}$ **$3\frac{1}{6}$**
19. $\frac{23}{5}$ **$4\frac{3}{5}$**
20. $\frac{99}{50}$ **$1\frac{49}{50}$**

Lesson 5-6 *(Pages 202–205)*

Draw a line segment of each length. See students' work.

1. $2\frac{1}{4}$ inches
2. $1\frac{3}{8}$ inches
3. $\frac{3}{4}$ inch

4. $1\frac{1}{2}$ inches
5. $3\frac{1}{8}$ inches
6. $2\frac{1}{4}$ inches

Find the length of each line segment to the nearest half, fourth, or eighth inch.

7. ——————— $1\frac{1}{4}$ in.
8. ——————————— $1\frac{1}{2}$ in.

9. ————— 1 in.
10. ——————————— $1\frac{3}{8}$ in.

Lesson 5-7 *(Pages 206–209)*

Determine whether the first number is a multiple of the second number.

1. 30; 7 **no**
2. 42; 14 **yes**
3. 10; 8 **no**
4. 30; 10 **yes**

5. 13; 7 **no**
6. 84; 28 **yes**
7. 150; 25 **yes**
8. 21; 14 **no**

Find the LCM for each set of numbers.

9. 5, 15 **15**
10. 13, 39 **39**
11. 16, 24 **48**
12. 18, 20 **180**

13. 8, 12 **24**
14. 12, 15 **60**
15. 9, 27 **27**
16. 5, 6 **30**

17. 12, 18, 3 **36**
18. 12, 35, 10 **420**
19. 21, 14, 6 **42**

20. 3, 6, 9 **18**
21. 6, 10, 15 **30**
22. 15, 75, 25 **75**

Lesson 5-8 *(Pages 210–213)*

Find the LCD for each pair of fractions.

1. $\frac{2}{5}$ $\frac{4}{15}$ **15**
2. $\frac{2}{28}$ $\frac{15}{42}$ **84**
3. $\frac{8}{16}$ $\frac{14}{24}$ **48**
4. $\frac{9}{25}$ $\frac{21}{30}$ **150**

Replace each ● with <, >, or = to make a true sentence.

5. $\frac{1}{2}$ ● $\frac{1}{3}$ **>**
6. $\frac{2}{3}$ ● $\frac{3}{4}$ **<**
7. $\frac{5}{9}$ ● $\frac{4}{5}$ **<**
8. $\frac{3}{6}$ ● $\frac{6}{12}$ **=**

9. $\frac{12}{23}$ ● $\frac{15}{19}$ **<**
10. $\frac{9}{27}$ ● $\frac{13}{39}$ **=**
11. $\frac{7}{8}$ ● $\frac{9}{13}$ **>**
12. $\frac{5}{9}$ ● $\frac{7}{8}$ **<**

13. $\frac{25}{100}$ ● $\frac{3}{8}$ **<**
14. $\frac{6}{7}$ ● $\frac{8}{15}$ **>**
15. $\frac{5}{9}$ ● $\frac{19}{23}$ **<**
16. $\frac{120}{567}$ ● $\frac{1}{2}$ **<**

17. $\frac{5}{7}$ ● $\frac{2}{3}$ **>**
18. $\frac{9}{36}$ ● $\frac{7}{28}$ **=**
19. $\frac{2}{5}$ ● $\frac{2}{6}$ **>**
20. $\frac{5}{9}$ ● $\frac{12}{13}$ **<**

Lesson 5-9 *(Pages 214–216)*

Express each decimal as a fraction or mixed number in simplest form.

1. 0.5 $\frac{1}{2}$
2. 0.8 $\frac{4}{5}$
3. 0.32 $\frac{8}{25}$
4. 0.875 $\frac{7}{8}$

5. 0.54 $\frac{27}{50}$
6. 0.38 $\frac{19}{50}$
7. 0.744 $\frac{93}{125}$
8. 0.101 $\frac{101}{1,000}$

9. 0.303 $\frac{303}{1,000}$
10. 0.486 $\frac{243}{500}$
11. 0.626 $\frac{313}{500}$
12. 0.448 $\frac{56}{125}$

13. 0.074 $\frac{37}{500}$
14. 0.008 $\frac{1}{125}$
15. 9.36 $9\frac{9}{25}$
16. 10.18 $10\frac{9}{50}$

17. 0.06 $\frac{3}{50}$
18. 0.75 $\frac{3}{4}$
19. 0.48 $\frac{12}{25}$
20. 0.9 $\frac{9}{10}$

21. 0.005 $\frac{1}{200}$
22. 0.4 $\frac{2}{5}$
23. 1.875 $1\frac{7}{8}$
24. 5.08 $5\frac{2}{25}$

Lesson 5-10 *(Pages 217–219)*

Write each repeating decimal using bar notation.

1. 0.757575... **0.$\overline{75}$**
2. 0.444444... **0.$\overline{4}$**
3. 2.875875... **2.$\overline{875}$**
4. 0.333333... **0.$\overline{3}$**

5. 6.404040... **6.$\overline{40}$**
6. 5.272727... **5.$\overline{27}$**
7. 0.8521685216... **0.$\overline{85216}$**
8. 0.833333... **0.8$\overline{3}$**

Express each fraction or mixed number as a decimal. Use bar notation to show a repeating decimal.

9. $\frac{3}{16}$ **0.1875**
10. $\frac{8}{33}$ **0.$\overline{24}$**
11. $\frac{7}{12}$ **0.58$\overline{3}$**
12. $\frac{14}{25}$ **0.56**

13. $\frac{7}{10}$ **0.7**
14. $\frac{5}{8}$ **0.625**
15. $\frac{11}{15}$ **0.7$\overline{3}$**
16. $\frac{8}{9}$ **0.$\overline{8}$**

17. $\frac{15}{16}$ **0.9375**
18. $\frac{1}{12}$ **0.08$\overline{3}$**
19. $\frac{7}{20}$ **0.35**
20. $\frac{5}{18}$ **0.2$\overline{7}$**

Lesson 6-1 *(Pages 228–231)*

Round each number to the nearest half.

1. $\frac{11}{12}$ **1**
2. $\frac{5}{8}$ **$\frac{1}{2}$**
3. $\frac{2}{5}$ **$\frac{1}{2}$**
4. $\frac{1}{10}$ **0**
5. $\frac{1}{6}$ **0**
6. $\frac{2}{3}$ **$\frac{1}{2}$**

7. $\frac{9}{10}$ **1**
8. $\frac{1}{8}$ **0**
9. $\frac{4}{9}$ **$\frac{1}{2}$**
10. $1\frac{1}{8}$ **1**
11. $\frac{12}{11}$ **1**
12. $2\frac{4}{5}$ **3**

13. $\frac{7}{9}$ **1**
14. $7\frac{1}{10}$ **7**
15. $10\frac{2}{3}$ **$10\frac{1}{2}$**
16. $\frac{1}{3}$ **$\frac{1}{2}$**
17. $\frac{7}{16}$ **$\frac{1}{2}$**
18. $\frac{5}{7}$ **$\frac{1}{2}$**

1. $14 - 7 = 7$
2. $8 + 2 = 10$
3. $5 + 8 = 13$
4. $12 - 5 = 7$
5. $3 - 1 = 2$
6. $4 + 1 = 5$
7. $5 - 2 = 3$
8. $5 + 10 = 15$
9. $7 - 3 = 4$
10. $2 + 1 = 3$
11. $18 - 13 = 5$
12. $13 + 9 = 22$
13. $9 - 6 = 3$
14. $3 - 2\frac{1}{2} = \frac{1}{2}$
15. $9 - 0 = 9$
16. $12 - 1 = 11$
17. $2 + 2 = 4$
18. $9 - 8 = 1$
19. $9 + 5 = 14$
20. $1 + 7 = 8$

Lesson 6-2 *(Pages 232–234)*

Estimate. 1–20. Sample answers are given.

1. $14\frac{1}{10} - 6\frac{4}{5}$
2. $8\frac{1}{3} + 2\frac{1}{6}$
3. $4\frac{7}{8} + 7\frac{3}{4}$
4. $11\frac{11}{12} - 5\frac{1}{4}$

5. $3\frac{2}{5} - 1\frac{1}{4}$
6. $4\frac{2}{5} + \frac{5}{6}$
7. $4\frac{7}{12} - 1\frac{3}{4}$
8. $4\frac{2}{3} + 10\frac{3}{8}$

9. $7\frac{7}{15} - 3\frac{1}{12}$
10. $2\frac{1}{20} + 1\frac{1}{3}$
11. $18\frac{1}{4} - 12\frac{3}{5}$
12. $12\frac{5}{9} + 8\frac{5}{8}$

13. $8\frac{2}{3} - 5\frac{1}{2}$
14. $3\frac{1}{8} - 2\frac{3}{5}$
15. $9\frac{2}{7} - \frac{1}{3}$
16. $11\frac{7}{8} - \frac{5}{6}$

17. $2\frac{2}{5} + 2\frac{1}{4}$
18. $8\frac{1}{2} - 7\frac{4}{5}$
19. $8\frac{3}{4} + 4\frac{2}{3}$
20. $1\frac{1}{8} + 7\frac{1}{10}$

Lesson 6-2B *(Pages 236–237)*
Solve.

1. Ben wants a part-time job. There are three 10 hour per week jobs available. One pays $45 per week. One pays $4.75 per hour. One pays $3.25 per hour plus tips which average $20 per week. If Ben wants to take the job that pays the most, for which job should he apply? **$3.25 per hour plus tips**

2. Micaela gave the clerk $50 to pay for a $21.79 hat and a $17.33 belt. Should she expect $10, $20, or $40 change? **$10**

3. Jackie used her calculator to multiply 678 and 34. Should she expect the product to be about 2,305, 23,050 or 230,500? **23,050**

4. If Carl blinks 15 times per minute, about how many times does he blink in one day? **c**
   a. 216 times
   b. 2,160 times
   c. 21,600 times
   d. 216,000 times

Lesson 6-3 *(Pages 238–241)*
Add or subtract. Write the answer in simplest form.

1. $\frac{2}{5} + \frac{2}{5}$ **$\frac{4}{5}$**
2. $\frac{5}{8} + \frac{3}{8}$ **1**
3. $\frac{9}{11} - \frac{3}{11}$ **$\frac{6}{11}$**
4. $\frac{3}{14} + \frac{5}{14}$ **$\frac{4}{7}$**

5. $\frac{7}{8} - \frac{3}{8}$ **$\frac{1}{2}$**
6. $\frac{3}{4} - \frac{1}{4}$ **$\frac{1}{2}$**
7. $\frac{15}{27} - \frac{7}{27}$ **$\frac{8}{27}$**
8. $\frac{1}{36} + \frac{5}{36}$ **$\frac{1}{6}$**

9. $\frac{2}{9} - \frac{1}{9}$ **$\frac{1}{9}$**
10. $\frac{7}{8} + \frac{5}{8}$ **$1\frac{1}{2}$**
11. $\frac{9}{16} - \frac{5}{16}$ **$\frac{1}{4}$**
12. $\frac{6}{8} + \frac{4}{8}$ **$1\frac{1}{4}$**

13. $\frac{1}{2} + \frac{1}{2}$ **1**
14. $\frac{1}{3} - \frac{1}{3}$ **0**
15. $\frac{8}{9} + \frac{7}{9}$ **$1\frac{2}{3}$**
16. $\frac{5}{6} - \frac{3}{6}$ **$\frac{1}{3}$**

17. $\frac{3}{9} + \frac{8}{9}$ **$1\frac{2}{9}$**
18. $\frac{8}{40} + \frac{12}{40}$ **$\frac{1}{2}$**
19. $\frac{56}{90} - \frac{26}{90}$ **$\frac{1}{3}$**
20. $\frac{2}{9} + \frac{8}{9}$ **$1\frac{1}{9}$**

Lesson 6-4 *(Pages 243–245)*
Add or subtract. Write the answer in simplest form.

1. $\frac{1}{3} + \frac{1}{2}$ **$\frac{5}{6}$**
2. $\frac{2}{9} + \frac{1}{3}$ **$\frac{5}{9}$**
3. $\frac{1}{2} + \frac{3}{4}$ **$1\frac{1}{4}$**
4. $\frac{1}{4} + \frac{3}{12}$ **$\frac{1}{2}$**

5. $\frac{5}{9} - \frac{1}{3}$ **$\frac{2}{9}$**
6. $\frac{5}{8} - \frac{2}{5}$ **$\frac{9}{40}$**
7. $\frac{3}{4} - \frac{1}{2}$ **$\frac{1}{4}$**
8. $\frac{7}{8} - \frac{3}{16}$ **$\frac{11}{16}$**

9. $\frac{9}{16} + \frac{13}{24}$ **$1\frac{5}{48}$**
10. $\frac{8}{15} + \frac{2}{3}$ **$1\frac{1}{5}$**
11. $\frac{5}{14} + \frac{11}{28}$ **$\frac{3}{4}$**
12. $\frac{11}{12} + \frac{7}{8}$ **$1\frac{19}{24}$**

13. $\frac{2}{3} - \frac{1}{6}$ **$\frac{1}{2}$**
14. $\frac{9}{16} - \frac{1}{2}$ **$\frac{1}{16}$**
15. $\frac{5}{8} - \frac{11}{20}$ **$\frac{3}{40}$**
16. $\frac{14}{15} - \frac{2}{9}$ **$\frac{32}{45}$**

17. $\frac{9}{20} + \frac{2}{15}$ **$\frac{7}{12}$**
18. $\frac{5}{6} + \frac{4}{5}$ **$1\frac{19}{30}$**
19. $\frac{23}{25} - \frac{27}{50}$ **$\frac{19}{50}$**
20. $\frac{19}{25} - \frac{1}{2}$ **$\frac{13}{50}$**

Lesson 6-5 *(Pages 246–249)*

Add or subtract. Write the answer in simplest form.

1. $5\frac{1}{2} + 3\frac{1}{4}$ $8\frac{3}{4}$

2. $2\frac{2}{3} + 4\frac{1}{9}$ $6\frac{7}{9}$

3. $7\frac{4}{5} + 9\frac{3}{10}$ $17\frac{1}{10}$

4. $9\frac{4}{7} - 3\frac{5}{14}$ $6\frac{3}{14}$

5. $13\frac{1}{5} - 10$ $3\frac{1}{5}$

6. $3\frac{3}{4} + 5\frac{5}{8}$ $9\frac{3}{8}$

7. $3\frac{2}{5} + 7\frac{6}{15}$ $10\frac{4}{5}$

8. $10\frac{2}{3} + 5\frac{6}{7}$ $16\frac{11}{21}$

9. $15\frac{6}{9} - 13\frac{5}{12}$ $2\frac{1}{4}$

10. $13\frac{7}{12} - 9\frac{1}{4}$ $4\frac{1}{3}$

11. $5\frac{2}{3} - 3\frac{1}{2}$ $2\frac{1}{6}$

12. $17\frac{2}{9} + 12\frac{1}{3}$ $29\frac{5}{9}$

13. $6\frac{5}{12} + 12\frac{5}{8}$ $19\frac{1}{24}$

14. $8\frac{3}{5} - 2\frac{1}{5}$ $6\frac{2}{5}$

15. $23\frac{2}{3} - 4\frac{1}{2}$ $19\frac{1}{6}$

Lesson 6-6 *(Pages 250–253)*

Subtract. Write the answer in simplest form.

1. $11\frac{2}{3} - 8\frac{11}{12}$ $2\frac{3}{4}$

2. $3\frac{4}{7} - 1\frac{2}{3}$ $1\frac{19}{21}$

3. $7\frac{1}{8} - 4\frac{1}{3}$ $2\frac{19}{24}$

4. $18\frac{1}{9} - 12\frac{2}{5}$ $5\frac{32}{45}$

5. $12\frac{3}{10} - 8\frac{3}{4}$ $3\frac{11}{20}$

6. $43 - 5\frac{1}{5}$ $37\frac{4}{5}$

7. $8\frac{1}{5} - 4\frac{1}{4}$ $3\frac{19}{20}$

8. $14\frac{1}{6} - 3\frac{2}{3}$ $10\frac{1}{2}$

9. $25\frac{4}{7} - 21$ $4\frac{4}{7}$

10. $17\frac{3}{9} - 4\frac{3}{5}$ $12\frac{11}{15}$

11. $18\frac{1}{9} - 1\frac{3}{7}$ $16\frac{43}{63}$

12. $16\frac{1}{4} - 7\frac{1}{5}$ $9\frac{1}{20}$

13. $18\frac{1}{5} - 6\frac{1}{4}$ $11\frac{19}{20}$

14. $4 - 1\frac{2}{3}$ $2\frac{1}{3}$

15. $26 - 4\frac{1}{9}$ $21\frac{8}{9}$

Lesson 6-7 *(Pages 254–257)*

Complete.

1. 2 h 10 min = 1 h __70__ min

2. 3 h 65 min = __4__ h 5 min

3. 3 min 14 s = 2 min __74__ s

4. 1 h 15 min 10 s = __75__ min 10 s

Add or subtract. Rename if necessary.

5.   6 h 14 min
    −2 h 8 min
    4 h 6 min

6.   5 h 35 min 25 s
    +   45 min 35 s
    6 h 21 min 0 s

7.   5 h 4 min 45 s
    −2 h 40 min 5 s
    2 h 24 min 40 s

8.   15 h 16 min
    − 8 h 35 min 16 s
    6 h 40 min 44 s

9.   9 h 20 min 10 s
    +1 h 39 min 55 s
    11 h 0 min 5 s

10.   2 h 40 min 20 s
    +3 h 5 min 50 s
    5 h 46 min 10 s

Find the elapsed time.

11. 10:30 A.M. to 6:00 P.M. $7\frac{1}{2}$ **hours**

12. 8:45 P.M. to 1:30 A.M. $4\frac{3}{4}$ **hours or 4 hours 45 min**

Lesson 7-1 *(Pages 268–270)*

Round each fraction to 0, $\frac{1}{2}$, or 1.

1. $\frac{3}{4}$ **1**
2. $\frac{5}{8}$ $\frac{1}{2}$
3. $\frac{3}{25}$ **0**
4. $\frac{1}{20}$ **0**
5. $\frac{5}{11}$ $\frac{1}{2}$
6. $\frac{11}{18}$ $\frac{1}{2}$
7. $\frac{1}{3}$ $\frac{1}{2}$

Round each mixed number to the nearest whole number.

8. $6\frac{4}{9}$ **6**
9. $19\frac{3}{4}$ **20**
10. $2\frac{1}{15}$ **2**
11. $17\frac{2}{7}$ **17**
12. $8\frac{9}{16}$ **9**
13. $1\frac{3}{5}$ **2**
14. $15\frac{41}{45}$ **16**

Estimate each product.

15. $\frac{2}{3} \times \frac{4}{5}$ $\frac{1}{2} \times 1 = \frac{1}{2}$
16. $\frac{1}{6} \times \frac{2}{5}$ $0 \times 0 = 0$
17. $\frac{4}{9} \times \frac{3}{7}$ $\frac{1}{2} \times \frac{1}{2} = \frac{1}{4}$
18. $\frac{5}{12} \times \frac{6}{11}$ $\frac{1}{2} \times \frac{1}{2} = \frac{1}{4}$
19. $\frac{3}{8} \times \frac{8}{9}$ $\frac{1}{2} \times 1 = \frac{1}{2}$
20. $\frac{3}{5} \times \frac{5}{12}$ $\frac{1}{2} \times \frac{1}{2} = \frac{1}{4}$
21. $\frac{2}{5} \times \frac{5}{8}$ $\frac{1}{2} \times \frac{1}{2} = \frac{1}{4}$
22. $5\frac{3}{7} \times \frac{4}{5}$ $5 \times 1 = 5$

Lesson 7-2 *(Pages 273–276)*

Find each product. Write in simplest form.

1. $\frac{5}{6} \times \frac{15}{16}$ $\frac{25}{32}$
2. $\frac{6}{14} \times \frac{12}{18}$ $\frac{2}{7}$
3. $\frac{2}{3} \times \frac{3}{13}$ $\frac{2}{13}$
4. $\frac{4}{9} \times \frac{1}{6}$ $\frac{2}{27}$
5. $\frac{3}{4} \times \frac{5}{6}$ $\frac{5}{8}$
6. $\frac{9}{10} \times \frac{3}{4}$ $\frac{27}{40}$
7. $\frac{8}{9} \times \frac{2}{3}$ $\frac{16}{27}$
8. $\frac{6}{7} \times \frac{4}{5}$ $\frac{24}{35}$
9. $\frac{8}{11} \times \frac{11}{12}$ $\frac{2}{3}$
10. $\frac{5}{6} \times \frac{3}{5}$ $\frac{1}{2}$
11. $\frac{6}{7} \times \frac{7}{21}$ $\frac{2}{7}$
12. $\frac{8}{9} \times \frac{9}{10}$ $\frac{4}{5}$

Solve each equation. Write the solution in simplest form.

13. $q = \frac{7}{11} \times \frac{12}{15}$ $\frac{28}{55}$
14. $r = \frac{7}{9} \times \frac{5}{7}$ $\frac{5}{9}$
15. $\frac{8}{13} \times \frac{2}{11} = a$ $\frac{16}{143}$
16. $m = \frac{4}{7} \times \frac{2}{9}$ $\frac{8}{63}$
17. $d = \frac{4}{9} \times \frac{24}{25}$ $\frac{32}{75}$
18. $\frac{1}{9} \times \frac{6}{13} = s$ $\frac{2}{39}$
19. $j = \frac{4}{7} \times 6$ $3\frac{3}{7}$
20. $\frac{7}{10} \times 5 = p$ $3\frac{1}{2}$
21. $10 \times 3\frac{1}{5} = k$ **32**

Lesson 7-3 *(Pages 277–279)*

Express each mixed number as an improper fraction.

1. $2\frac{1}{3}$ $\frac{7}{3}$
2. $2\frac{1}{2}$ $\frac{5}{2}$
3. $2\frac{2}{3}$ $\frac{8}{3}$
4. $3\frac{1}{2}$ $\frac{7}{2}$
5. $1\frac{1}{4}$ $\frac{5}{4}$

Find each product. Write in simplest form.

6. $3\frac{5}{8} \times 4\frac{1}{2}$ $16\frac{5}{16}$
7. $\frac{4}{5} \times 2\frac{3}{4}$ $2\frac{1}{5}$
8. $6\frac{1}{8} \times 5\frac{1}{7}$ $31\frac{1}{2}$
9. $2\frac{2}{3} \times 2\frac{1}{4}$ **6**
10. $6\frac{2}{3} \times 7\frac{3}{5}$ $50\frac{2}{3}$
11. $7\frac{1}{5} \times 2\frac{4}{7}$ $18\frac{18}{35}$
12. $8\frac{3}{4} \times 2\frac{2}{5}$ **21**
13. $4\frac{1}{3} \times 2\frac{1}{7}$ $9\frac{2}{7}$

Solve each equation. Write the solution in simplest form.

14. $4\frac{3}{5} \times 2\frac{1}{2} = c$ $11\frac{1}{2}$
15. $z = 5\frac{5}{6} \times 4\frac{2}{7}$ **25**
16. $6\frac{8}{9} \times 3\frac{5}{6} = f$ $26\frac{11}{27}$
17. $2\frac{1}{9} \times 1\frac{1}{2} = x$ $3\frac{1}{6}$
18. $4\frac{7}{15} \times 3\frac{3}{4} = h$ $16\frac{3}{4}$
19. $k = 5\frac{7}{9} \times 6\frac{3}{8}$ $36\frac{5}{6}$

Lesson 7-4 *(Pages 280–283)*

Find the circumference of each circle shown or described to the nearest tenth. Use $\frac{22}{7}$ or 3.14 for π.

1.
9 cm
28.3 cm

2.
2.1 yd
13.2 yd

3.
0.6 m
3.8 m

4.
10 in.
31.4 in.

5. $d = 5.6$ m **17.6 m**

6. $r = 3.21$ yd **20.2 yd**

7. $r = 0.5$ in. **3.1 in.**

8. $d = 4$ m **12.6 m**

9. $r = 16$ cm **100.5 cm**

10. $d = 9.1$ m **28.6 m**

11. $r = 0.1$ yd **0.6 yd**

12. $d = 65.7$ m **206.3 m**

13. $r = 1$ cm **6.3 cm**

Lesson 7-5 *(Pages 285–288)*

Find the reciprocal of each number.

1. $\frac{12}{13}$ $\frac{13}{12}$

2. $\frac{7}{11}$ $\frac{11}{7}$

3. 5 $\frac{1}{5}$

4. $\frac{1}{4}$ **4**

5. $\frac{7}{9}$ $\frac{9}{7}$

6. $\frac{9}{2}$ $\frac{2}{9}$

7. $\frac{1}{5}$ **5**

Find each quotient. Write in simplest form.

8. $\frac{2}{3} \div \frac{1}{2}$ $1\frac{1}{3}$

9. $\frac{3}{5} \div \frac{2}{5}$ $1\frac{1}{2}$

10. $\frac{7}{10} \div \frac{3}{8}$ $1\frac{13}{15}$

11. $\frac{5}{9} \div \frac{2}{3}$ $\frac{5}{6}$

12. $4 \div \frac{2}{3}$ **6**

13. $8 \div \frac{4}{5}$ **10**

14. $9 \div \frac{5}{9}$ $16\frac{1}{5}$

15. $\frac{2}{7} \div 7$ $\frac{2}{49}$

Solve each equation. Write the solution in simplest form.

16. $\frac{1}{14} \div 7 = b$ $\frac{1}{98}$

17. $\frac{2}{13} \div \frac{5}{26} = y$ $\frac{4}{5}$

18. $g = \frac{4}{7} \div \frac{6}{7}$ $\frac{2}{3}$

19. $w = \frac{7}{8} \div \frac{1}{3}$ $2\frac{5}{8}$

20. $15 \div \frac{3}{5} = n$ **25**

21. $\frac{9}{14} \div \frac{3}{4} = v$ $\frac{6}{7}$

22. $u = \frac{8}{9} \div \frac{5}{6}$ $1\frac{1}{15}$

23. $j = \frac{4}{9} \div 36$ $\frac{1}{81}$

24. $d = \frac{15}{16} \div \frac{5}{8}$ $1\frac{1}{2}$

Lesson 7-6 *(Pages 289–291)*

Write each mixed number as an improper fraction. Then write its reciprocal.

1. $4\frac{1}{5}$ $\frac{21}{5}; \frac{5}{21}$

2. $3\frac{2}{9}$ $\frac{29}{9}; \frac{9}{29}$

3. $2\frac{3}{8}$ $\frac{19}{8}; \frac{8}{19}$

4. $5\frac{3}{5}$ $\frac{28}{5}; \frac{5}{28}$

Find each quotient. Write in simplest form.

5. $\frac{3}{5} \div 1\frac{2}{3}$ $\frac{9}{25}$

6. $2\frac{1}{2} \div 1\frac{1}{4}$ **2**

7. $7 \div 4\frac{9}{10}$ $1\frac{3}{7}$

8. $1\frac{3}{7} \div 10$ $\frac{1}{7}$

9. $3\frac{3}{5} \div \frac{4}{5}$ $4\frac{1}{2}$

10. $8\frac{2}{5} \div 4\frac{1}{2}$ $1\frac{13}{15}$

11. $6\frac{1}{3} \div 2\frac{1}{2}$ $2\frac{8}{15}$

12. $5\frac{1}{4} \div 2\frac{1}{3}$ $2\frac{1}{4}$

Solve each equation. Write the solution in simplest form.

13. $n = 4\frac{1}{8} \div 3\frac{2}{3}$ $1\frac{1}{8}$

14. $p = 2\frac{5}{8} \div \frac{1}{2}$ $5\frac{1}{4}$

15. $1\frac{5}{6} \div 3\frac{2}{3} = z$ $\frac{1}{2}$

16. $k = 21 \div 5\frac{1}{4}$ **4**

17. $b = 12 \div 3\frac{3}{5}$ $3\frac{1}{3}$

18. $q = 18 \div 2\frac{1}{4}$ **8**

Lesson 7-7 *(Pages 292–294)*
Complete.

1. 3 gal = _?_ pt **24**
2. 24 pt = _?_ gal **3**
3. 20 lb = _?_ oz **320**
4. 2 gal = _?_ fl oz **256**
5. 20 pt = _?_ qt **10**
6. 18 qt = _?_ pt **36**
7. 2,000 lb = _?_ T **1**
8. 3 T = _?_ lb **6,000**
9. 6 lb = _?_ oz **96**
10. 9 lb = _?_ oz **144**
11. 15 qt = _?_ gal **$3\frac{3}{4}$**
12. 4 pt = _?_ c **8**
13. 4 gal = _?_ qt **16**
14. 4 qt = _?_ fl oz **128**
15. 12 pt = _?_ c **24**
16. 10 pt = _?_ qt **5**
17. 24 fl oz = _?_ c **3**
18. 1.5 pt = _?_ c **3**
19. $\frac{1}{4}$ lb = _?_ oz **4**
20. 5 T = _?_ lb **10,000**
21. 2 lb = _?_ oz **32**

Lesson 7-8A *(Pages 296–297)*
Solve.

1. What are the next three numbers in the pattern? 6, 7, 9, 12, 16, . . . **21, 27, 34**

2. Kip and Celia began working for the same company in 1997. Celia earned $19,000 per year, and Kip earned $16,500 per year. Each year Kip received a $1,500 raise and Celia received a $1,000 raise.
   a. In what year will they earn the same amount of money? **2002**
   b. What will be their annual salary in that year? **$24,000**

3. What is the missing measurement in the pattern?
   . . . $\frac{1}{2}$ in., $\frac{1}{4}$ in., ___ in., $\frac{1}{16}$ in., . . . **$\frac{1}{8}$**

4. Daria eats half of a pizza at 12:00 P.M. At 2:00 P.M., she eats half of what was left of her pizza from lunch. At 4:00 P.M., she eats half of what was left from the pizza. If Daria continues eating at this rate for six more hours, how much of the pizza has she eaten? **$\frac{63}{64}$**

5. At Snowfalls Middle School, the bell rings at 8:05, 8:55, 9:00, and 9:50 each morning. If this pattern continues, when would the next three bells ring? **9:55, 10:45, 10:50**

Lesson 7-8 *(Pages 298–300)*
Find the next two numbers in each sequence.

1. 14, 21, 28, 35, . . . **42, 49**
2. 36, 42, 48, 54, . . . **60, 66**
3. 3, 9, 27, 81, . . . **243, 729**
4. 2, 6, 10, 14, . . . **18, 22**
5. 1,600, 800, 400, 200, . . . **100, 50**
6. 192, 96, 48, 24, . . . **12, 6**
7. 15, $14\frac{1}{3}$, $13\frac{2}{3}$, 13, . . . **$12\frac{1}{3}$, $11\frac{2}{3}$**
8. 11, $11\frac{1}{2}$, 12, $12\frac{1}{2}$, . . . **13, $13\frac{1}{2}$**
9. $\frac{1}{5}$, 2, 20, 200, . . . **2,000, 20,000**
10. 36, 6, 1, $\frac{1}{6}$, . . . **$\frac{1}{36}$, $\frac{1}{216}$**

Find the missing number in each sequence.

11. 5, 10, _?_, 40, . . . **20**
12. _?_, 193, 293, 393, . . . **93**
13. 8, 32, 128, _?_, . . . **512**
14. 11, _?_, 19, 23, . . . **15**
15. 9, $8\frac{3}{4}$, _?_, $8\frac{1}{4}$, . . . **$8\frac{1}{2}$**
16. 64, _?_, 16, 8, . . . **32**
17. _?_, 19, 26, 33, . . . **12**
18. $\frac{1}{2}$, $1\frac{1}{2}$, $4\frac{1}{2}$, _?_, . . . **$13\frac{1}{2}$**
19. $\frac{1}{81}$, _?_, 1, 9, . . . **$\frac{1}{9}$**
20. 12, _?_, 432, 2,592, . . . **72**

Lesson 8-1 *(Pages 312–315)*

Express each ratio as a fraction in simplest form.

1. 21 sugar cookies out of an assortment of 75 cookies. $\frac{7}{25}$

2. 10 girls in a class of 25 students. $\frac{2}{5}$

3. 34 non-smoking tables in a restaurant with 50 tables. $\frac{17}{25}$

4. 7 striped ties out of 21 ties. $\frac{1}{3}$

Express each ratio as a rate.

5. $2.00 for 5 cans of tomato soup **$0.40/can**

6. $200.00 for 40 hours of work **$5/hour**

7. 540 parts produced in 18 hours **30 parts/hour**

Lesson 8-2 *(Pages 317–320)*

Use cross products to determine whether each pair of ratios forms a proportion.

1. $\frac{3}{10}, \frac{7}{25}$ **no**　　2. $\frac{5}{12}, \frac{3}{8}$ **no**　　3. $\frac{12}{16}, \frac{9}{12}$ **yes**　　4. $\frac{5}{4}, \frac{125}{100}$ **yes**　　5. $\frac{4}{5}, \frac{80}{100}$ **yes**

Solve each proportion.

6. $\frac{15}{21} = \frac{5}{b}$ **7**　　7. $\frac{22}{25} = \frac{n}{100}$ **88**　　8. $\frac{24}{48} = \frac{h}{50}$ **25**　　9. $\frac{9}{27} = \frac{y}{42}$ **14**　　10. $\frac{4}{7} = \frac{16}{x}$ **28**

11. $\frac{4}{6} = \frac{a}{9}$ **6**　　12. $\frac{6}{14} = \frac{21}{m}$ **49**　　13. $\frac{3}{7} = \frac{21}{d}$ **49**　　14. $\frac{4}{10} = \frac{18}{e}$ **45**　　15. $\frac{9}{10} = \frac{27}{f}$ **30**

Lesson 8-3A *(Pages 322–323)*　　**3. Clara, Sam, Toma, Benito, Emma**

Solve.

1. Four cars were crossing a bridge. The red car was behind the yellow car. The green car was last. The blue car was not first. In what order did the cars cross the bridge? **yellow, red, blue, green**

2. The streets in Sandra's town are arranged in square blocks. Sandra left school and walked 5 blocks west and 3 blocks south to Marcia's house. She then walked 1 block south and 3 blocks east to the park. Finally she walked 2 blocks east and 2 blocks north to get home. How far is Sandra's home from the school? **2 blocks south**

3. Nida arranged five friends in a line for a photograph. Benito stood between Emma and Toma. Sam stood between Toma and Clara. Clara was on the left. In what order were the five people arranged for the photograph?

4. How many different rectangles can be made with 36 one-inch tiles? **5 rectangles**

5. In how many different ways can Amelia, Bob, Cornelia, and Damien seat themselves in four chairs at a round table? **24 ways**

Lesson 8-3 *(Pages 324–327)*

The map at the right has a scale of $\frac{1}{4}$ in. = 5 km. Use a ruler to measure each map distance to the nearest $\frac{1}{4}$ inch. Then find the actual distances.

1. Bryan to Napoleon **40 km**
2. Stryker to Evansport **10 km**
3. Ney to Bryan **10 km**
4. Defiance to Napoleon **25 km**
5. Ridgeville to Bryan **30 km**
6. Brunersburg to Ney **15 km**

Lesson 8-4 *(Pages 330–333)*

Express each percent as a fraction in simplest form.

1. 13% $\frac{13}{100}$
2. 25% $\frac{1}{4}$
3. 8% $\frac{2}{25}$
4. 105% $\frac{21}{20}$ or $1\frac{1}{20}$
5. 60% $\frac{3}{5}$
6. 70% $\frac{7}{10}$
7. 80% $\frac{4}{5}$
8. 45% $\frac{9}{20}$
9. 20% $\frac{1}{5}$
10. 14% $\frac{7}{50}$
11. 75% $\frac{3}{4}$
12. 120% $\frac{6}{5}$ or $1\frac{1}{5}$
13. 5% $\frac{1}{20}$
14. 2% $\frac{1}{50}$
15. 450% $\frac{9}{2}$ or $4\frac{1}{2}$

Express each fraction as a percent.

16. $\frac{77}{100}$ **77%**
17. $\frac{3}{4}$ **75%**
18. $\frac{17}{20}$ **85%**
19. $\frac{3}{25}$ **12%**
20. $\frac{3}{10}$ **30%**
21. $\frac{27}{50}$ **54%**
22. $\frac{2}{5}$ **40%**
23. $\frac{3}{50}$ **6%**
24. $\frac{9}{20}$ **45%**
25. $\frac{8}{5}$ **160%**
26. $\frac{1}{4}$ **25%**
27. $\frac{1}{5}$ **20%**
28. $\frac{19}{20}$ **95%**
29. $\frac{7}{10}$ **70%**
30. $\frac{11}{25}$ **44%**

Lesson 8-5 *(Pages 334–336)*

Express each percent as a decimal.

1. 5% **0.05**
2. 22% **0.22**
3. 50% **0.50**
4. 420% **4.2**
5. 75% **0.75**
6. 1% **0.01**
7. 100% **1.00**
8. 3.7% **0.037**
9. 0.9% **0.009**
10. 9% **0.09**
11. 90% **0.9**
12. 900% **9.00**
13. 78% **0.78**
14. 62.5% **0.625**
15. 15% **0.15**

Express each decimal as a percent.

16. 0.02 **2%**
17. 0.2 **20%**
18. 0.002 **0.2%**
19. 1.02 **102%**
20. 0.66 **66%**
21. 0.11 **11%**
22. 0.354 **35.4%**
23. 0.31 **31%**
24. 0.09 **9%**
25. 5.2 **520%**
26. 2.22 **222%**
27. 0.008 **0.8%**
28. 0.275 **27.5%**
29. 0.3 **30%**
30. 6.0 **600%**

Lesson 8-6 *(Pages 337–339)*

Estimate each percent.

1. 11% of 48 **5**
2. 1.9% of 50 **1**
3. 29% of 500 **150**
4. 41% of 50 **20**
5. 32% of 300 **100**
6. 411% of 50 **200**
7. 149% of 60 **90**
8. 4.1% of 50 **2**
9. 62% of 200 **120**
10. 58% of 100 **58**
11. 52% of 400 **200**
12. 68% of 30 **21**
13. 9% of 25 **2.5**
14. 48% of 1000 **500**
15. 98% of 725 **725**

Estimate the percent of each figure that is shaded.

16. **50%**
17. **25%**
18. **66$\frac{2}{3}$%**

Lesson 8-7 *(Pages 340–343)*

Find the percent of each number.

1. 38% of 150 **57**
2. 20% of 75 **15**
3. 0.2% of 500 **1**
4. 25% of 70 **17.5**
5. 10% of 90 **9**
6. 16% of 30 **4.8**
7. 39% of 40 **15.6**
8. 250% of 100 **250**
9. 6% of 86 **5.16**
10. 12.5% of 160 **20**
11. 9% of 29 **2.61**
12. 3% of 46 **1.38**
13. 66$\frac{2}{3}$% of 60 **40**
14. 89% of 47 **41.83**
15. 435% of 30 **130.5**
16. 25% of 48 **12**
17. 5% of 420 **21**
18. 55% of 134 **73.7**
19. 28% of 4 **1.12**
20. 14% of 40 **5.6**
21. 14% of 14 **1.96**
22. 90% of 140 **126**
23. 40% of 45 **18**
24. 0.5% of 200 **1**

Lesson 9-1 *(Pages 352–355)*

Use a protractor to find the measure of each angle. Then classify the angle as *acute*, *right*, or *obtuse*.

1. 60°; acute
2. 120°; obtuse
3. 90°; right
4. 20°; acute

Classify each angle measure as *acute*, *right*, or *obtuse*.

5. 86° **acute**
6. 101° **obtuse**
7. 90° **right**
8. 145.6° **obtuse**

Classify each pair of angles as *complementary*, *supplementary*, or *neither*.

9. supplementary
10. neither
11. complementary

Lesson 9-1B *(Pages 356–357)*
Solve.

1. At Morgon Middle School, 37 of the eighth grade students are involved in a club activity, 63 play sports, and 21 are involved in both sports and clubs.
   a. How many students participate in only clubs? **16**
   b. How many students participate in only sports? **42**
   c. What is the total number of students who participate in extracurricular activities? **79**

2. In a class of 26 students going on a field trip, 8 have backpacks, 13 have lunch bags, and 6 have both backpacks and lunch bags. How many have neither a lunch bag nor a backpack? **11**

3. What are the next two figures in the pattern? ↑ ↖ ← ↙   ↓ ↘

4. Of the 320 students at Lincoln Junior High, 75 are in the orchestra, 120 are in the marching band, and 45 are in both orchestra and marching band. How many students are in neither orchestra nor marching band? **170**

Lesson 9-2 *(Pages 358–361)* **1–4. See students' work.**
Use a protractor to draw angles having the following measurements.

1. 165°
2. 20°
3. 90°
4. 41°

Estimate the measure of each angle.

5.

about 45°

6.

about 90°

7.

about 90°

8.

about 135°

Lesson 9-3 *(Pages 364–367)* **1–8. See students' work.**
Draw the angle or line segment with the given measurement. Then use a straightedge and a compass to bisect each angle or line segment.

1. 3 in.
2. 5 cm
3. 110°
4. 48 mm

5. 70°
6. 33 mm
7. 25°
8. 150°

Lesson 10-4 *(Pages 412–414)*

Name each figure.

1. **cone**

2. **rectangular prism**

3. **triangular pyramid**

4. **cylinder**

5. **pentagonal prism**

6. **sphere**

State the number of faces, edges, and vertices in each figure.

7. square prism **6; 12; 8**

8. triangular pyramid **4; 6; 4**

9. cone **0; 0; 0**

10. pentagonal pyramid **6; 10; 6**

Lesson 10-5A *(Pages 416–417)*   **1. Sample answer: 15 in. × 3 in. × 6 in.**
Solve.

1. Ten 3-inch cubes fit in a carton. What are the possible dimensions of the carton?

2. Eve is making a pyramid-shaped display of boxes of soda. Each box is a cube. The bottom layer of the pyramid has 8 boxes. If there is one less box in each layer and there are 6 layers in the pyramid, how many boxes will Eve need to make the display? **33 boxes**

3. A construction worker wants to arrange 20 cement bricks into the shape of a rectangle with the smallest perimeter possible. How many bricks will be in each row? **4 five-rows or 5 four-rows**

4. A rectangular prism can be formed by using exactly 10 cubes. Find the length, width, and height of the prism. **Sample answer: 5 cubes × 2 cubes × 1 cube**

Lesson 10-5 *(Pages 418–420)*
Find the volume of each rectangular prism to the nearest tenth.

1. 2 in. 14 in. 18 in.
504 in³

2. 41 ft 38 ft 96 ft
149,568 ft³

3. 3 m 6 m 5 m
90 m³

4. 9 mm 9 mm 9 mm
729 mm³

5. 3 cm 3 cm 20 cm
180 cm³

6. 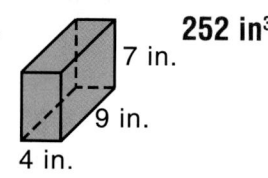 7 in. 9 in. 4 in.
252 in³

7. length = 8 in.
   width = 5 in.
   height = 2 in. **80 in³**

8. length = 10 cm
   width = 2 cm
   height = 8 cm **160 cm³**

9. length = 20 ft
   width = 5 ft
   height = 6 ft **600 ft³**

Lesson 10-6 *(Pages 421–424)*

Find the surface area of each rectangular prism to the nearest tenth.

1.
2 in. 14 in. 12 in. **440 in²**

2.
10,980 ft² 41 ft 30 ft 60 ft

3.
78 m² 3 m 3 m 5 m

4.
7 mm 9 mm 9 mm **414 mm²**

5.
3 cm 3 cm 20 cm **258 cm²**

6.
7 in. 6 in. 8 in. **292 in²**

7. length = 4 mm
width = 12 mm
height = 1.5 mm **144 mm²**

8. length = 16 cm
width = 20 cm
height = 20.4 cm **2,108.8 cm²**

9. length = 8.5 m
width = 2.1 m
height = 7.6 m **196.8 m²**

Lesson 11-1 *(Pages 434–436)* **1–7. See Answer Appendix.**

Draw a number line from −10 to 10. Graph each integer on the number line.

1. −3 **2.** 3 **3.** −1 **4.** −8 **5.** 9 **6.** 10 **7.** 6

Write an integer to describe each situation.

8. a loss of 15 dollars **−15**

9. 9 degrees below zero **−9**

Write the opposite of each integer.

10. 7 **−7** **11.** −3 **3** **12.** 11 **−11** **13.** −9 **9** **14.** −13 **13** **15.** 101 **−101** **16.** 0 **0**

Lesson 11-2 *(Pages 437–439)*

Replace each ● with <, >, or = to make a true sentence.

1. −5 ● −55 **>** **2.** 4 ● −66 **>** **3.** −777 ● −77 **<** **4.** −75 ● −75 **=**

5. −898 ● −99 **<** **6.** 0 ● 44 **<** **7.** 56 ● −1 **>** **8.** −82 ● −9 **<**

9. −6 ● −7 **>** **10.** 90 ● 101 **<** **11.** 4 ● −2,000 **>** **12.** −3 ● 0 **<**

Order each set of integers from least to greatest.

13. 8, 0, −808, −8, −88, 88, −888 **−888, −808, −88, −8, 0 , 8, 88**

14. 0, 3, −21, 9, −89, 8, −65, −56, **−89, −65, −56, −21, 0, 3, 8, 9**

15. 70, −9, 67, −78, 0, 45, −36, −19 **−78, −36, −19, −9, 0, 45, 67, 70**

16. 0, −90, −56, −29, −92, −87, −35 **−92, −90, −87, −56, −35, −29, 0**

17. −239, −999, 458, −29, −77, 200, −818 **−999, −818, −239, −77, −29, 200, 458**

Lesson 11-3 *(Pages 441–444)*

Find each sum. Use counters or a number line if necessary.

1. $-4 + (-7)$ **−11**
2. $-1 + 0$ **−1**
3. $7 + (-13)$ **−6**
4. $-20 + 2$ **−18**
5. $4 + (-6)$ **−2**
6. $-12 + 9$ **−3**
7. $-12 + (-10)$ **−22**
8. $5 + (-15)$ **−10**
9. $17 + 9$ **26**
10. $18 + (-18)$ **0**
11. $-4 + (-4)$ **−8**
12. $0 + (-9)$ **−9**
13. $-12 + (-9)$ **−21**
14. $-8 + 7$ **−1**
15. $3 + (-6)$ **−3**
16. $-9 + 16$ **7**
17. $-5 + (-3)$ **−8**
18. $-5 + 5$ **0**
19. $-3 + (-3)$ **−6**
20. $-11 + 6$ **−5**
21. $-10 + 6$ **−4**
22. $-5 + (-9)$ **−14**
23. $18 + (-20)$ **−2**
24. $-4 + (-4)$ **−8**
25. $2 + (-4)$ **−2**
26. $-3 + (-11)$ **−14**
27. $-17 + 9$ **−8**
28. $-6 + 10$ **4**
29. $-6 + (-12)$ **−18**
30. $8 + 8$ **16**
31. $-9 + 0$ **−9**
32. $4 + (-5)$ **−1**

Lesson 11-4 *(Pages 445–448)*

Find each difference. Use counters or a number line if necessary.

1. $7 - (-4)$ **11**
2. $-4 - (-9)$ **5**
3. $13 - (-3)$ **16**
4. $2 - (-5)$ **7**
5. $-9 - 5$ **−14**
6. $-11 - (-18)$ **7**
7. $-4 - (-7)$ **3**
8. $-6 - (-6)$ **0**
9. $-6 - 6$ **−12**
10. $17 - 9$ **8**
11. $-12 - (-9)$ **−3**
12. $0 - (-4)$ **4**
13. $-7 - 0$ **−7**
14. $-12 - (-10)$ **−2**
15. $-2 - (-1)$ **−1**
16. $3 - (-5)$ **8**
17. $5 - (-1)$ **6**
18. $-5 - (-6)$ **1**
19. $9 - (-1)$ **10**
20. $1 - 9$ **−8**
21. $-5 - 1$ **−6**
22. $-1 - 4$ **−5**
23. $0 - (-7)$ **7**
24. $8 - 13$ **−5**
25. $-4 - (-6)$ **2**
26. $9 - 9$ **0**
27. $-7 - (-7)$ **0**
28. $7 - 5$ **2**
29. $8 - (-5)$ **13**
30. $5 - 8$ **−3**
31. $1 - 6$ **−5**
32. $-8 - (-8)$ **0**

Lesson 11-5 *(Pages 449–452)*

Find each product. Use counters or a number line if necessary.

1. $3 \times (-5)$ **−15**
2. -5×1 **−5**
3. $-8 \times (-4)$ **32**
4. $6 \times (-3)$ **−18**
5. -3×2 **−6**
6. $-1 \times (-4)$ **4**
7. $8 \times (-2)$ **−16**
8. $-5 \times (-7)$ **35**
9. $3 \times (-9)$ **−27**
10. -9×4 **−36**
11. $-4 \times (-5)$ **20**
12. $5 \times (-2)$ **−10**
13. $-8(3)$ **−24**
14. $-9(-1)$ **9**
15. $7(-3)$ **−21**
16. $2(3)$ **6**
17. $-6(0)$ **0**
18. $-5(-1)$ **5**
19. $5(-5)$ **−25**
20. $-2(-3)$ **6**
21. $8(-4)$ **−32**
22. $-2(4)$ **−8**
23. $-4(-4)$ **16**
24. $2(9)$ **18**
25. $-2(-12)$ **24**
26. $7 \times (-4)$ **−28**
27. $-5 \times (-9)$ **45**
28. -2×11 **−22**
29. $4(-2)$ **−8**
30. $4(-4)$ **−16**
31. $-3(-11)$ **33**
32. $-3(3)$ **−9**

Lesson 11-6A *(Pages 454–455)*
Solve.

1. Morgan and Stephen want to get ready for the fall football season that starts August 29. Before the season starts, they plan to spend 3 to 4 weeks practicing plays. Before practicing plays, they plan to spend 6 to 8 weeks running and exercising. What are the earliest and latest dates that Morgan and Stephen can begin getting ready for the football season? **June 6, June 27**

2. Daniella and Wayne must arrive at school no later than 7:25 A.M. weekday mornings. It takes 20 minutes to get from Wayne's house to the school. Daniella picks up Wayne, but it takes her 15 minutes to get to Wayne's house. If it takes Daniella 55 minutes to get ready in the morning, what is the latest she should get out of bed? **5:55 A.M.**

3. Melina bought some school supplies. She spent $4.35 on paper, pens, and pencils and 3 times that on notebooks. After paying for the items, she had $7.26 left. How much money did she have before she went shopping? **$24.66**

4. In the trivia bowl, each finalist must answer four questions correctly. Each question is worth twice as much as the question before it. The fourth question is worth $6,000. How much is the first question worth? **$750**

5. Connor, Petra, Daria, and Lyle each handed in term papers of the Industrial Revolution. Petra's paper was 4 pages shorter than Connor's. Daria's paper was 7 pages longer than Petra's. Lyle's paper was half as long as Daria's. Lyle's paper was 14 pages long. How long was Connor's paper? **25 pages long**

Lesson 11-6 *(Pages 456–458)*
Find each quotient. Use counters or patterns if necessary.

1. $12 \div (-6)$ **−2**
2. $-7 \div (-1)$ **7**
3. $-4 \div 4$ **−1**
4. $6 \div (-6)$ **−1**
5. $0 \div (-4)$ **0**
6. $45 \div (-9)$ **−5**
7. $15 \div (-5)$ **−3**
8. $-6 \div 2$ **−3**
9. $-28 \div (-7)$ **4**
10. $20 \div (-2)$ **−10**
11. $-40 \div (-8)$ **5**
12. $12 \div (-4)$ **−3**
13. $-18 \div 6$ **−3**
14. $9 \div (-1)$ **−9**
15. $-30 \div 6$ **−5**
16. $-54 \div (-9)$ **6**
17. $28 \div (-7)$ **−4**
18. $-24 \div 8$ **−3**
19. $24 \div (-4)$ **−6**
20. $-14 \div 7$ **−2**
21. $9 \div 3$ **3**
22. $-18 \div (-6)$ **3**
23. $-9 \div (-1)$ **9**
24. $18 \div (-9)$ **−2**
25. $-25 \div (-5)$ **5**
26. $15 \div (-3)$ **−5**
27. $-36 \div 9$ **−4**
28. $-4 \div 2$ **−2**
29. $-40 \div 8$ **−5**
30. $-32 \div 4$ **−8**
31. $-27 \div (-9)$ **3**
32. $-8 \div 8$ **−1**

Lesson 11-7 *(Pages 459–461)*
Name the ordered pair for each point.

1. M **(−3, 1)**
2. A **(−4, 4)**
3. D **(2, −4)**
4. E **(3, 2)**
5. P **(−4, −3)**
6. Q **(1, −1)**
7. B **(−2, 3)**
8. C **(3, −2)**
9. F **(−2, −4)**
10. G **(−2, −2)**
11. N **(−4, −2)**
12. R **(0, 0)**
13. K **(1, 4)**
14. H **(1, 3)**

Graph and label each point. 15–22. See Answer Appendix.

15. $S(4, -1)$
16. $T(-3, -2)$
17. $W(2, 1)$
18. $Y(-5, 3)$
19. $Z(-1, -3)$
20. $U(3, -3)$
21. $V(1, 2)$
22. $X(-1, 4)$

Lesson 11-8 *(Pages 464–467)*

The vertices of △*QRS* are *Q*(1, −2), *R*(3, 4), and *S*(−2, 2). On a coordinate grid, draw △*QRS* and each transformation image. 1–5. **See Answer Appendix.**

1. translation image that is 5 units down

2. translation image that is 4 units left

3. translation image that is 2 units right and 3 units up

4. translation image that is 1 unit left and 8 units down

5. reflection image over the *x*-axis

Lesson 12-1 *(Pages 476–479)*

Solve each equation. Use cups and counters if necessary.

1. $x + 4 = 14$ **10**

2. $b + (-10) = 0$ **10**

3. $-2 + w = -5$ **−3**

4. $k + (-3) = -5$ **−2**

5. $-4 + h = 6$ **10**

6. $-7 + d = -3$ **4**

7. $m + 11 = 9$ **−2**

8. $f + (-9) = -19$ **−10**

9. $p + 66 = 22$ **−44**

10. $-34 + t = 41$ **75**

11. $e + 56 = -24$ **−80**

12. $-29 + a = -54$ **−25**

13. $17 + m = -33$ **−50**

14. $b + (-44) = -34$ **10**

15. $w + (-39) = 55$ **94**

Lesson 12-2 *(Pages 480–483)*

Solve each equation. Use cups and counters if necessary.

1. $y - (-7) = 2$ **−5**

2. $a - 10 = -22$ **−12**

3. $g - (-1) = 9$ **8**

4. $c - 8 = 5$ **13**

5. $z - (-2) = 7$ **5**

6. $n - 1 = -87$ **−86**

7. $j - 15 = -22$ **−7**

8. $x - 12 = 45$ **57**

9. $y - 65 = -79$ **−14**

10. $q - 16 = -31$ **−15**

11. $q - (-6) = 12$ **6**

12. $j - 18 = -34$ **−16**

13. $k - (-2) = -8$ **−10**

14. $r - 76 = 41$ **117**

15. $n - 63 = -81$ **−18**

Lesson 12-3 *(Pages 484–487)*
Solve each equation. Use cups and counters if necessary.

1. $5x = 30$ **6**
2. $18w = 2$ $\frac{1}{9}$
3. $\frac{1}{2}a = 7$ **14**
4. $2d = -28$ **−14**
5. $\frac{1}{4}c = -3$ **−12**
6. $11n = 77$ **7**
7. $\frac{1}{3}z = 15$ **45**
8. $9y = -63$ **−7**
9. $6m = -54$ **−9**
10. $5f = -75$ **−15**
11. $20p = 5$ $\frac{1}{4}$
12. $\frac{1}{4}x = 16$ **64**
13. $4t = -24$ **−6**
14. $7b = 21$ **3**
15. $19h = 0$ **0**
16. $22d = -66$ **−3**
17. $\frac{1}{3}y = 11$ **33**
18. $3m = -78$ **−26**
19. $8x = -2$ $-\frac{1}{4}$
20. $9c = -72$ **−8**
21. $\frac{1}{2}p = 35$ **70**
22. $\frac{1}{5}k = 20$ **100**
23. $33y = 99$ **3**
24. $6z = -5$ $-\frac{5}{6}$

Lesson 12-4 *(Pages 488–491)*
Solve each equation.

1. $3x + 7 = 13$ **2**
2. $\frac{1}{2}r + 6 = -3$ **−18**
3. $2h - 5 = 7$ **6**
4. $-10 = 5x + 5$ **−3**
5. $2x - (-16) = 26$ **5**
6. $6r + 2 = 2$ **0**
7. $\frac{1}{5}t - 6 = -12$ **−30**
8. $-2 - 3y = -11$ **3**
9. $-4y + 16 = 64$ **−12**

Lesson 12-4B *(Pages 492–493)*
Solve.

1. Eric bought a personal CD player for $12 less than the regular price. If he paid $54, what was the regular price? **$66**

2. Lisa paid $2.58 in sales tax on an Ohio State Buckeyes sweatshirt. The total cost was $45.57. What was the price of the sweatshirt before taxes? **$42.99**

3. School T-shirts are the most popular item sold in the school store. On Monday, 49 T-shirts were sold. This is 3 more than twice the amount that were sold on Tuesday. How many T-shirts were sold on Tuesday? **23**

4. Jayson made a long-distance phone call to his grandmother. The first 5 minutes cost $3, and each minute after that cost $0.50. How many minutes did they talk on the phone if the cost of the call was $12? **23 minutes**

5. Paige went bowling at Champion Bowling Center. Shoe rental was $1.75 and games were $2.25 each. If she spent $8.50 on shoe rental and games, how many games did she play? **3 games**

Lesson 12-5 *(Pages 496–499)*

Copy and complete each function table.

1.

input (n)	output (n − 4)
5	1
2	−2
−1	−5

2.

input (n)	output (3n)
1	3
0	0
−2	−6

Find the rule for each function table.

3. $n + 5$

n	■
−1	4
0	5
3	8

4. $\frac{n}{2}$

n	■
−6	−3
0	0
8	4

Lesson 12-6 *(Pages 500–503)* **1–6. See Answer Appendix for graphs.**

Copy and complete each function table. Then graph the function.

1.

input (x)	output (x + 1)
2	■ 3
0	■ 1
−3	■ −2

2.

input (x)	output (2x)
2	■ 4
0	■ 0
−3	■ −6

3.

input (x)	output (x − 3)
4	■ 1
0	■ −3
−1	■ −4

4.

input (x)	output $\left(\frac{x}{5}\right)$
10	■ 2
0	■ 0
−5	■ −1

5.

input (x)	output (−3x)
2	■ −6
−1	■ 3
−2	■ 6

6.

input (x)	output (2x − 3)
2	■ 1
0	■ −3
−1	■ −5

Lesson 13-1 *(Pages 515–518)*

A set of 30 tickets are placed in a bag. There are 6 baseball tickets, 4 hockey tickets, 4 basketball tickets, 2 football tickets, 3 symphony tickets, 2 opera tickets, 4 ballet tickets, and 5 theater tickets. One ticket is drawn without looking. Find the probability of each event. Then tell how likely the event is to happen. 1–18. See Answer Appendix.

1. P(basketball) $\frac{2}{15}$

2. P(sports event) $\frac{8}{15}$

3. P(opera or ballet) $\frac{1}{5}$

4. P(soccer) **0**

5. P(not symphony) $\frac{9}{10}$

6. P(theater) $\frac{1}{6}$

7. P(basketball or hockey) $\frac{4}{15}$

8. P(not a sports event) $\frac{7}{15}$

9. P(not opera) $\frac{14}{15}$

10. P(baseball) $\frac{1}{5}$

11. P(football) $\frac{1}{15}$

12. P(not soccer) **1**

13. P(opera) $\frac{1}{15}$

14. P(not theater) $\frac{5}{6}$

15. P(symphony) $\frac{1}{10}$

16. P(soccer or football) $\frac{1}{15}$

17. P(opera or theater) $\frac{7}{30}$

18. P(hockey) $\frac{2}{15}$

Lesson 13-2A *(Pages 520–521)*
Solve.

1. Sean made this frequency table to show the time it took his classmates to run 100 meters.

100 Meter Times (in seconds)		
Time	**Tally**	**Frequency**
13.0 – 13.9	III	3
14.0 – 14.9	IIII I	6
15.0 – 15.9	IIII IIII I	11
16.0 – 16.9	IIII IIII III	13
17.0 – 17.9	IIII	4
18.0 – 18.9	II	2

a. How many students ran 100 meters in less than 16 seconds? **20**

b. How many students took 17 seconds or longer to run 100 meters? **6**

c. How many students did Sean survey? **39**

d. In what interval did the greatest number of times occur? **16.0-16.9**

e. How many students ran 100 meters in 15.0 - 16.9 seconds? **24**

2. The list shows the birth month of the students in Mrs. Barr's geometry class. **a. See Answer Appendix.**
   a. Make a frequency table of the students birth month.
   b. How many of the students were born in September? **3**
   c. Which months were not represented?
   January, April, May, November

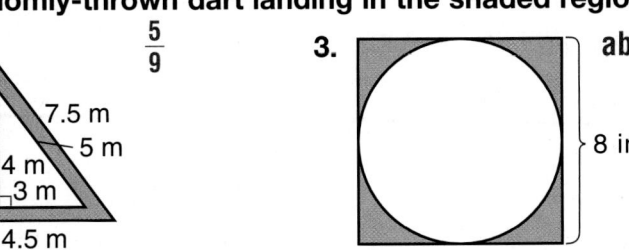

September   October   July
June   February   October
October   July   July
October   October   February
February   March   December
March   June   March
September   August   September

Lesson 13-2 *(Pages 522–525)*
Tell whether each of the following is a random sample. Explain your answer. 1–10. See Answer Appendix.

Type of Survey	**Survey Location**
1. favorite television show	department store
2. favorite baseball team	a specific baseball park
3. favorite movie	shopping center
4. favorite cookie	park
5. favorite sport	soccer game
6. favorite ice cream flavor	school
7. favorite entertainer	Garth Brooks concert
8. favorite fruit	apple orchard
9. favorite food	county fair
10. favorite vacation	popular theme park

Lesson 13-3 *(Pages 526–529)*
Each figure represents a dartboard. It is equally likely that a dart will land anywhere on the dartboard. Find the probability of a randomly-thrown dart landing in the shaded region.

1. 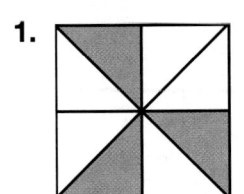 $\frac{3}{8}$

2. $\frac{5}{9}$

7.5 m
6 m   4 m   5 m
3 m
4.5 m

3. about $\frac{3}{14}$

8 in.

Lesson 13-4 *(Pages 531–534)*

For each situation, make a list and draw a tree diagram to show the sample space.

1. tossing a quarter and rolling a number cube

2. spinning each spinner once

1–4. See Answer Appendix.

3. a choice of a red, blue, or green sweater with a white, black, or tan skirt.

4. a choice of a chicken, ham, turkey, or bologna sandwich with coffee, milk, juice, or soda

5. How many ways can a person choose to watch two television shows from four television shows? **6 ways**

EXTRA PRACTICE

Lesson 13-5 *(Pages 536–539)*

The spinner shown is spun and a card is chosen from the set of cards shown. Find the probability of each event.

1. $P(15 \text{ and } C)$ $\frac{1}{36}$

2. $P(\text{even and } H)$ $\frac{1}{12}$

3. $P(\text{odd and a vowel})$ $\frac{1}{6}$

4. $P(\text{multiple of 5 and } O)$ $\frac{1}{3}$

5. $P(\text{multiple of 10 and consonant})$ $\frac{1}{3}$

6. $P(\text{composite and } L)$ $\frac{5}{36}$

A bag contains 3 quarters and 5 dimes. Another bag contains 12 pennies and 8 nickels. One coin is randomly-chosen from each bag. Find the probability of each event.

7. $P(\text{dime and nickel})$ $\frac{1}{4}$

8. $P(\text{quarter})$ $\frac{3}{8}$

9. $P(\text{quarter and penny})$ $\frac{9}{40}$

10. $P(\text{not a nickel})$ $\frac{3}{5}$

11. $P(\text{dime and penny})$ $\frac{3}{8}$

12. $P(\text{not a dime and nickel})$ $\frac{3}{20}$

Mixed Problem Solving

Solve using any strategy.

1. *Money Matters* The Martin family bought tickets to the Science Museum. Admission is $8 for adults and $5 for children under 12. They spent $49 for admission. How many adult and children tickets did the Martin family purchase? **3 adults, 5 children**

2. How many 3-digit numbers can you make using the even digits from 1 through 9, without repeating the same digit twice in any number? **24**

3. *Life Science* Your heart at rest beats approximately 72 times per minute. At this rate, about how many times per day does your heart beat? **a.**
   a. 103,680
   b. 10,368
   c. 1,368
   d. 1,036,800

4. *Sports* Mrs. Zimmer sent her grandson an autographed souvenir baseball from the Baseball Hall of Fame in Cooperstown, N.Y. The baseball arrived in a cube-shaped box. Each side of the box measured 4 inches. Make a pattern for this box.

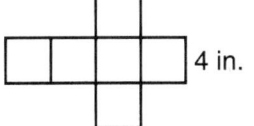
4 in.

5. *Money Matters* Marcus belongs to a teen book club. He purchases a new paperback at $3.95 every other week for a full year. At this rate, how much will he pay over a 3-year period? **$308.10**

6. The bus leaves downtown for the mall at 7:35 A.M., 8:10 A.M., 8:45 A.M., and 9:20 A.M. If the bus continues to run on this schedule, what time does the bus leave between 10:00 A.M. and 11:00 A.M.? **10:30 A.M.**

7. *Civics* The American flag has 50 white stars on a blue background. The stars are arranged in alternating rows of 5 and 6. How many rows are there on the American flag? **9**

8. Cadet Girl Scout Troop 548 held their annual cookie sale. Bethany sold half as many boxes of cookies as Olivia. Julie sold 15 more boxes than Bethany. Kara sold 9 fewer boxes than Alaina. Olivia sold three times as many boxes as Kara. How many boxes of cookies did Troop 548 sell if Julie sold 39 boxes? **152 boxes**

Mixed Problem Solving

Solve using any strategy.

1. **Sports** The Chicago Cubs play 81 games each year. If 2,225,000 people attend the games, what is a reasonable estimate of the number of people that attend each game, 28,000 or 280,000? **28,000**

2. **Money Matters** The Changs had their washing machine repaired. They were charged $45 for the first 15 minutes and $12 for every 15 minutes after that. The Chang's bill, excluding parts and tax, was $93. How many minutes did the repair work take? **75 minutes or 1 hour 15 minutes**

3. **School** Of the 100 6th grade students at the John Glenn Middle School, 30 are taking French, 40 are taking Spanish, and 15 are taking both French and Spanish. How many students are taking either French or Spanish? **55 students**

4. **School** Jared has to read a mystery novel for English class. If the novel contains 168 pages, how many pages must he read per day to finish the book in 7 days? **24 pages**

5. **Geometry** The Parks Commission is preparing a triangular section of Evening Shade Park in order to plant flowers. The base of the triangular region measures 18.4 feet, and the height is 12.5 feet. What is the area of the triangular flower garden? **115 square feet**

6. The graph shows the types of footwear men say they wear in their home.

   a. Which two types of footwear are worn for about the same frequency? **sneakers and barefoot**

   b. Which two types of footwear make up about 60% of the type of footwear worn? **socks and slippers**

Happy Feet

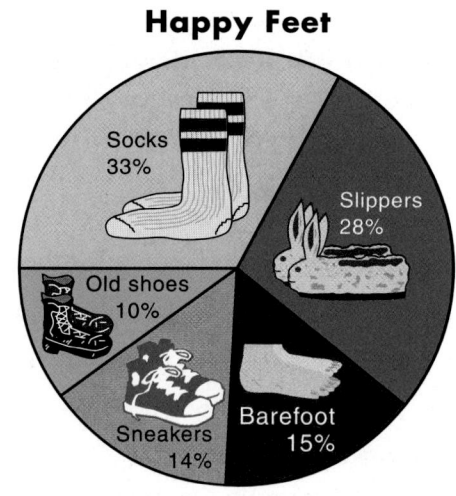

Source: L.B. Evans

7. **Sports** Vicki wants to try out for the basketball team on Saturday. Tryouts begin at 9:30 A.M. sharp. She wants to arrive 20 minutes early to practice her foul shots. It takes her 35 minutes to eat breakfast and get ready. She plans to walk 10 minutes to her friend Madison's house. Vicki and Madison will then walk the remaining 15 minutes to the tryouts. What time should Vicki plan to get up on Saturday morning? **8:10 A.M.**

Use the four-step plan to solve.

1. *Geography* Amad and Marisela went hiking and canoeing down the Danube River, Europe's second largest river. They traveled from its source in the Black Forest 1,760 miles to its end at the Black Sea. If they averaged 11 miles each day, how long was the trip? **160 days**

Find the next three numbers or draw the next three shapes for each pattern.

2. 192, 96, 48, 24, _?_, _?_, _?_ **12, 6, 3**

3.

Round each number to the underlined place-value position.

4. 7<u>5</u>4 **750**

5. <u>4</u>,839 **5,000**

Estimate. State whether the answer shown is reasonable.

6. $198 \div 5 = 50$
   $200 \div 5 = 40$; **not reasonable**

7. $1,492 + 1,941 = 3,300$
   $1,000 + 2,000 = 3,000$; **reasonable**

8. *Earth Science* Each year, 16,000,000 thunderstorms occur throughout the world. About how many thunderstorms occur each week? **about 300,000**

Find the value of each expression.

9. $48 - 24 \div 3 \times 6$ **0**

10. $63 \div 7 - 2 \times 3$ **3**

Evaluate each expression if $m = 2$, $n = 7$, and $p = 21$.

11. $p - m$ **19**

12. $m + p \div n$ **5**

13. Write $5 \cdot 5 \cdot 5 \cdot 5$ using exponents. **5^4**

14. Write d^6 as a product. **$d \cdot d \cdot d \cdot d \cdot d \cdot d$**

Evaluate each expression.

15. 10^4 **10,000**

16. 3 cubed **27**

Identify the solution to each equation from the given list.

17. $32 \div x = 2$; 16, 30, 64 **16**

18. $y + 7 = 23$; 5, 16, 7 **16**

Solve each equation mentally.

19. $5z = 55$ **11**

20. $15 - w = 9$ **6**

Test

1. The test scores of the students in Mrs. Wimberly's history class are shown below. Make a frequency table of the data. **See Answer Appendix.**

72	95	87	77	88	79	92	97	100
82	75	93	92	75	77	71	98	99
85	84	77	80	91	91	85	83	89

Geography The lengths, in miles, of the Great Lakes are Lake Superior, 350; Lake Michigan, 307; Lake Huron, 206; Lake Erie, 241; and Lake Ontario, 193.

2. What scale would you use for the vertical axis of a vertical bar graph? **0 to 350**

3. Make a bar graph for this data. **See Answer Appendix.**

4. Find the median length of the lakes. **241 miles**

Refer to the circle graph for Exercises 5–6.

5. Which color is the most popular? **red**

6. Which three colors together are favored by about half the students? **yellow, green, and blue**

Students' Favorite Colors

Jobs David mows lawns, rakes leaves, shovels snow, and does other outdoor jobs. Last year, his earnings were: January–$55, February–$70, March–$35, April–$23, May–$38, June–$55, July–$74, August–$78, September–$69, October–$55, November–$38, December–$58.

7. Find David's mean monthly earnings. **$54**

8. Find the mode. **$55**

9. Find the median. **$55**

10. David wants to buy a new bike that costs $179. If his earnings this year are the same as last year, when will he have enough to buy the bike? **April**

11. Make a line graph for this data. **See Answer Appendix.**

12. Change your graph to make it misleading. **See Answer Appendix.**

Make a stem-and-leaf plot for each set of data.

13. 86, 85, 92, 73, 75, 96, 84, 92, 74, 87 **See Answer Appendix.**

14. 46¢, 59¢, 42¢, 69¢, 55¢, 48¢, 66¢, 43¢, 85¢ **See Answer Appendix.**

Use the grid to name the point for each ordered pair.

15. (3, 1) **H**   16. (4, 0) **E**   17. (2, 5) **C**

Use the grid to name the ordered pair for each point.

18. A **(0, 4)**   19. B **(1, 2)**   20. D **(3, 4)**

CHAPTER 3

Test

Write each fraction or mixed number as a decimal.

1. $\frac{341}{10,000}$ **0.0341**
2. $7\frac{13}{1,000}$ **7.013**
3. $\frac{9}{100}$ **0.09**

4. Write two hundred and six thousandths as a decimal. **200.006**

Use a centimeter ruler to measure each line segment.

5. _____ **6.8 cm or 68 mm** _____
6. _____ **4.4 cm or 44 mm** _____

Use a centimeter ruler to measure one side of each figure.

7. **1 cm**

8. **2.5 cm**

9. *School* Jennifer's semester math average is 76.7. Her twin sister, Julie, is close with an average of 76.35. Whose average is higher? **Jennifer's**

10. Order 17.4, 1.747, 1.8, 17.36, and 17.09 from least to greatest. **1.747, 1.8, 17.09, 17.36, 17.4**

11. Order 0.89, 0.98, 0.889, 0.982, and 0.88 from greatest to least. **0.982, 0.98, 0.89, 0.889, 0.88**

12. *Money Matters* Sonia and four friends ate at a restaurant. Dividing the bill, each owed $7.146. What should each have paid? **$7.15**

Round each number to the underlined place-value position.

13. 901.263 **901.3**
14. 0.999 **1.00**
15. 2.445 **2.4**
16. 78.1 **78**

Estimate using any strategy. **17.** $7 + 7 + 7 + 7 = 28$ **19.** $5 + 6 + 2 = 13$

17. 7.14 + 7 + 6.7 + 6.9
18. 45.9 − 6.12 **46 − 6 = 40**
19. 5.34 + 6.33 + 1.9

20. *Earth Science* The table shows the five most common elements in Earth's crust along with the percent of the crust each element represents. About how much more is the percent that is silicon than the percent that is aluminum? **about 20%**

Element	Percent
Oxygen	46.60
Silicon	27.72
Aluminum	8.13
Iron	5.00
Calcium	3.63

21. *Money Matters* At breakfast, Phil ordered juice for $0.89, scrambled eggs and toast for $3.69, and a glass of milk for $0.59. Did he spend about $6 or $4? **about $6**

Add or subtract.

22. 9.04 **21.84**
+12.8

23. 54.29 − 3.8 **50.49**
24. 54 + 1.8 **55.8**

25. 71.34 **27.56**
−43.78

Multiply.

1. $\begin{array}{r} 0.81 \\ \times\ 22 \end{array}$ **17.82**

2. 22.38×803 **17,971.14**

3. $\begin{array}{r} 30.98 \\ \times\ 5.6 \end{array}$ **173.488**

Find each product mentally. Use the distributive property.

4. 6×17 **102**

5. 7×9.3 **65.1**

6. 21.8×30 **654**

Solve each equation.

7. $x = 47.3 \times 5.6$ **264.88**

8. $20.86 \cdot 4.11 = m$ **85.7346**

9. *Algebra* Evaluate $b(a + c)$ if $a = 7.8$, $b = 5.05$, and $c = 0.02$. **39.491**

Find the perimeter of each figure.

10. 24 m   25 m   7 m   **56 m**

11. a square with sides of length 5.4 inches **21.6 in.**

12. 17.1 in.   10.5 in.   **55.2 in.**

Find the area of each figure.

13. rectangle: ℓ, 10.5 mi; w, 17.1 mi **179.55 mi²**

14. square: s, 2.5 cm **6.25 cm²**

Find each quotient.

15. $19.36 \div 44$ **0.44**

16. $21.6\overline{)49.68}$ **2.3**

Solve each equation.

17. $x = 58.305 \div 11.5$ **5.07**

18. $1,274.7 \div 2.1 = t$ **607**

19. *Algebra* Evaluate $c \div d$ if $c = 108.9$ and $d = 3.3$. **33**

Write the unit that you would use to measure each of the following. Then estimate the mass or capacity. **20. liter, 4 L**

20. a bottle of windshield-washer fluid

21. a potato **gram, 200 g**

Complete.

22. 739 mL = _?_ L **0.739**

23. _?_ mg = 2.1 kg **2,100,000**

24. *Transportation* Danielle drove 11.5 kilometers each day for 5 days. How far did she travel in all? **57.5 kilometers**

25. Find the area of the figure. **683 ft²**

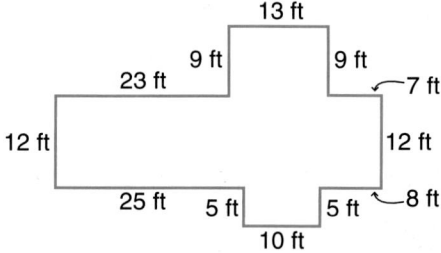

13 ft
9 ft   9 ft
23 ft   7 ft
12 ft   12 ft
25 ft   5 ft   5 ft   8 ft
10 ft

CHAPTER TEST

State whether each number is divisible by 2, 3, 5, 6, 9, or 10.

1. 75 **3, 5**

2. 864 **2, 3, 6, 9**

3. Games In one card game, all 52 cards are to be dealt out to the players. If there are six players, will all players have the same number of cards? Explain. **Sample answer:**

4. Which of the numbers 21, 31, 54, or 75 is prime? **31**

No; 52 is not divisible by 3.

Find the prime factorization of each number.

5. 72 $2^3 \times 3^2$

6. 108 $2^2 \times 3^3$

7. 58 2×29

8. List all of the factors of 20 from least to greatest. **1, 2, 4, 5, 10, 20**

Find the GCF of each set of numbers.

9. 27, 45 **9**

10. 18, 48 **6**

11. 21, 38, 42 **1**

State whether each fraction is in simplest form. If not, write each fraction or ratio in simplest form.

12. $\frac{40}{100}$ **no;** $\frac{2}{5}$

13. $\frac{6}{25}$ **yes**

14. $\frac{45}{50}$ **no;** $\frac{9}{10}$

Express each mixed number as an improper fraction.

15. $2\frac{5}{7}$ $\frac{19}{7}$

16. $4\frac{1}{3}$ $\frac{13}{3}$

17. $12\frac{4}{5}$ $\frac{64}{5}$

Express each improper fraction as a mixed number.

18. $\frac{7}{3}$ $2\frac{1}{3}$

19. $\frac{16}{5}$ $3\frac{1}{5}$

20. $\frac{21}{4}$ $5\frac{1}{4}$

21. Draw a line segment that is $1\frac{7}{8}$ inches long. **See Answer Appendix.**

Find the LCM for each set of numbers.

22. 6, 16 **48**

23. 12, 18 **36**

24. 3, 9, 15 **45**

Replace each ● with < , >, or = to make a true sentence.

25. $\frac{5}{6}$ ● $\frac{7}{9}$ **>**

26. $\frac{6}{11}$ ● $\frac{4}{9}$ **>**

27. $\frac{8}{12}$ ● $\frac{12}{18}$ **=**

Express each decimal as a fraction or mixed number in simplest form.

28. 0.05 $\frac{1}{20}$

29. 5.1 $5\frac{1}{10}$

30. 0.42 $\frac{21}{50}$

Express each fraction or mixed number as a decimal. Use bar notation to show a repeating decimal.

31. $6\frac{5}{6}$ **6.8$\overline{3}$**

32. $\frac{7}{16}$ **0.4375**

33. *Food* The Pretzel Factory sells salted, unsalted, cinnamon, herb, and chocolate pretzels in two sizes, regular and jumbo. How many different ways can a person buy a pretzel? **10 ways**

Round each number to the nearest half unit.

1. $\dfrac{7}{15}$ $\dfrac{1}{2}$

2. $7\dfrac{2}{11}$ **7**

3. $\dfrac{11}{14}$ **1**

4. *Decorating* One wall space in Eric's room is $24\dfrac{3}{8}$ inches wide. When looking for a poster to fit in that space, should he round up or down? **down**

Estimate.

5. $4\dfrac{7}{10} - 2\dfrac{1}{5}$ **5 − 2 = 3**

6. $\dfrac{7}{8} + \dfrac{1}{6}$ **1 + 0 = 1**

7. $\dfrac{15}{16} - \dfrac{4}{9}$ $\mathbf{1 - \dfrac{1}{2} = \dfrac{1}{2}}$

Add or subtract. Write the answer in simplest form.

8. $\dfrac{3}{17} + \dfrac{16}{17}$ $\mathbf{1\dfrac{2}{17}}$

9. $\dfrac{7}{8} + \dfrac{1}{6}$ $\mathbf{1\dfrac{1}{24}}$

10. $6\dfrac{3}{10} - 2\dfrac{9}{10}$ $\mathbf{3\dfrac{2}{5}}$

11. $4\dfrac{2}{9} + 5\dfrac{2}{9}$ $\mathbf{9\dfrac{4}{9}}$

12. $12 - 7\dfrac{3}{8}$ $\mathbf{4\dfrac{5}{8}}$

13. $3\dfrac{1}{8} - 1\dfrac{1}{16}$ $\mathbf{2\dfrac{1}{16}}$

14. $\dfrac{15}{16} - \dfrac{7}{16}$ $\mathbf{\dfrac{1}{2}}$

15. $\dfrac{2}{15} + \dfrac{3}{10} - \dfrac{1}{5}$ $\mathbf{\dfrac{7}{30}}$

16. $5\dfrac{7}{8} + 1\dfrac{5}{6}$ $\mathbf{7\dfrac{17}{24}}$

Solve each equation. Write the solution in simplest form.

17. $m = \dfrac{15}{16} - \dfrac{11}{16}$ $\mathbf{\dfrac{1}{4}}$

18. $y = \dfrac{4}{5} + \dfrac{3}{5}$ $\mathbf{1\dfrac{2}{5}}$

19. $9\dfrac{4}{5} = 7\dfrac{3}{5} + t$ $\mathbf{2\dfrac{1}{5}}$

20. $d - 8\dfrac{3}{8} = 7\dfrac{5}{24}$ $\mathbf{15\dfrac{7}{12}}$

21. *Gardening* Mr. Hannon had $\dfrac{1}{2}$ ton of dirt for his garden delivered on Tuesday. On Thursday, another $\dfrac{1}{4}$ ton was delivered. How much dirt was delivered in all? $\mathbf{\dfrac{3}{4}}$ **ton**

22. *Tickets* Emeka got to TicketCentral at 4:52 A.M. to wait in line for concert tickets. If TicketCentral opened at 7:30 A.M., how long did he wait? **2 h 38 min**

Add or subtract.   23. **5 h 22 min**

23. 10 h 12 min
    − 4 h 50 min

24.   3 h 4 min 10 s
    +9 h 58 min 28 s
    13 h 2 min 38 s

25.   6 h 55 min
    −5 h 49 min
    1 h 6 min

Estimate each product.

1. $6\frac{7}{8} \times 8\frac{1}{6}$ **7 × 8 = 56**

2. $37 \times \frac{4}{9}$ **40 × $\frac{1}{2}$ = 20**

3. $\frac{9}{10} \times \frac{5}{8}$ **1 × $\frac{1}{2}$ = $\frac{1}{2}$**

Find the product. Write in simplest form.

4. $1\frac{4}{5} \times 2\frac{2}{3}$ **$4\frac{4}{5}$**

5. $\frac{9}{10} \times \frac{5}{8}$ **$\frac{9}{16}$**

6. $3\frac{1}{5} \times 1\frac{1}{4}$ **4**

7. *Cooking* Kahlil's chocolate chip pie recipe calls for $1\frac{1}{2}$ cups of sugar. How much sugar will he need to make half of the recipe? **$\frac{3}{4}$ cup**

8. *Civics* In Homeland, U.S.A., $\frac{3}{4}$ of the adult residents are registered to vote. In the last May primary election, $\frac{2}{3}$ of those registered voted. What portion of the adult residents voted? **$\frac{1}{2}$**

Solve each equation. Write the solution in simplest form.

9. $4 \times \frac{3}{5} = z$ **$2\frac{2}{5}$**

10. $r = \frac{1}{8} \div \frac{3}{4}$ **$\frac{1}{6}$**

11. $k = 3\frac{2}{3} \times 2\frac{1}{3}$ **$8\frac{5}{9}$**

12. $g = 6 \div 1\frac{4}{5}$ **$3\frac{1}{3}$**

13. $\frac{3}{8} \times \frac{2}{5} = f$ **$\frac{3}{20}$**

14. $m = 5\frac{3}{4} \div 1\frac{1}{2}$ **$3\frac{5}{6}$**

Find the circumference of each circle shown or described. Use $\frac{22}{7}$ or 3.14 for π. Round decimal answers to the nearest tenth.

15. **109.0 m**

34.7 m

16. $r = 3\frac{1}{2}$ in. **22 in.**

17. 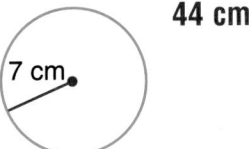 **44 cm**

7 cm

Find each quotient. Write in simplest form.

18. $\frac{3}{4} \div \frac{4}{7}$ **$1\frac{5}{16}$**

19. $2\frac{2}{3} \div 1\frac{5}{9}$ **$1\frac{5}{7}$**

20. $\frac{2}{3} \div \frac{8}{9}$ **$\frac{3}{4}$**

Complete.

21. $2\frac{1}{2}$ qt = _?_ c **10**

22. 9,000 lb = _?_ T **$4\frac{1}{2}$**

23. 8 c = _?_ fl oz **64**

Find the next two numbers in each sequence.

24. $4, 6\frac{1}{2}, 9, 11\frac{1}{2}, \ldots$ **14, $16\frac{1}{2}$**

25. $810, 270, 90, 30, \ldots$ **10, $3\frac{1}{3}$**

Find the area of each figure to the nearest tenth.

1. **48 m²**
4 m · 4.3 m
12 m

2.
5 in.
78.5 in²

3.
5 m · 3.5 m · 10 m
21 m² 12 m

4.
1 mi
1.7 mi
4 mi
4 mi²

5. **95.0 cm²**
11 cm

6. **7 ft²**
7.3 ft
2 ft
7 ft

7. *Traffic Signs* A triangular yield sign has a base of 32 inches and a height of 30 inches. Find the area of the sign. **480 in²**

8. *Gardening* Keisha plans to plant bulbs in a circular flower bed that has a radius of 2 meters. If she will plant 40 bulbs per square meter, how many bulbs should she buy? **502 bulbs**

Name each figure.

9. **cone**

10. **rectangular pyramid**

11. **rectangular prism**

12. State the number of faces, edges, and vertices in a triangular prism. **5; 9; 6**

Find the volume of each rectangular prism in Exercises 13–16 to the nearest tenth.

13. 2 mm **132 mm³**
6 mm
11 mm

14. **94.8 cm³**
8.1 cm
4.5 cm
2.6 cm

15. length, 11 inches; width, 8 inches; height, $5\frac{1}{2}$ inches **484 in³**

16. length, 4.5 meters; width, 2 meters; height, 5 meters **45 m³**

17. Find the surface area of the rectangular prism in Exercise 13. **200 mm²**

18. Find the surface area of the rectangular prism in Exercise 14. **138.42 cm²**

19. Find the surface area of a rectangular prism whose length is 20 yards, width is 30 yards, and height is 10 yards. **2,200 yd²**

20. *Pools* A rectangular diving pool is 20 feet by 15 feet by 8 feet. How much water is required to fill the pool? **2,400 ft³**

1. Write an integer to describe a loss of 12 dollars. **−12**

2. Write the integer that is the opposite of −5. **+5**

3. Graph −3 on a number line.

$$\xleftarrow{\;\;}\overset{\bullet}{\underset{\substack{-10\;-8\;-6\;-4\;-2\;\;\;0\;\;\;2\;\;\;4\;\;\;6\;\;\;8\;\;10}}{\rule{6cm}{0.4pt}}}\xrightarrow{\;\;}$$

Replace each ● with >, <, or = to make a true sentence.

4. 8 ● −12 **>**

5. −77 ● −777 **>**

6. −127 ● −9 **<**

7. Order −10, 0, −12, 3, −1, and 11 from least to greatest. **−12, −10, −1, 0, 3, 11**

Find each sum or difference. Use counters or a number line if necessary.

8. −5 + (−7) **−12**

9. 6 − (−19) **25**

10. −13 + 10 **−3**

11. −4 − (−9) **5**

12. *Weather* The temperature at 6:00 A.M. was −5°F. What was the temperature at 8:00 A.M. if it was 7 degrees warmer? **2°F**

Find each product or quotient. Use counters, a number line, or patterns if necessary.

13. 21 ÷ (−7) **−3**

14. 6 × (−7) **−42**

15. −60 ÷ (−6) **10**

16. −8(3) **−24**

17. *Health* While Jane was recovering from the flu, her temperature dropped 1°F each hour for 3 hours. What was the total drop? **−3°**

Name the ordered pair for each point.

18. K **(2, 1)**

19. R **(4, −1)**

20. M **(−3, −2)**

On grid paper, draw a coordinate grid. Then graph and label each point.

21. A(5, −1)

22. B(−2, −3)

23. C(−4, 5)

21–23. See Answer Appendix.

The vertices of △ABC are A(2, 3), B(−4, 1), and C(−1, 0). On a coordinate grid, draw △ABC and each transformation image. 24–25. See Answer Appendix.

24. a translation 3 units down

25. a reflection over the *x*-axis

Solve each equation. Use cups and counters if necessary.

1. $x + (-3) = -1$ **2**

2. $r - 2 = 5$ **7**

3. $w + 4 = -3$ **-7**

4. $b - 4 = -1$ **3**

5. $\frac{1}{10}p = 2$ **20**

6. $5m = 30$ **6**

7. $\frac{1}{4}w = -8$ **-32**

8. $4x + 1 = -15$ **-4**

9. $10 = \frac{1}{3}n - 2$ **36**

10. What number should replace the cup on the equation mat at the right? **5**

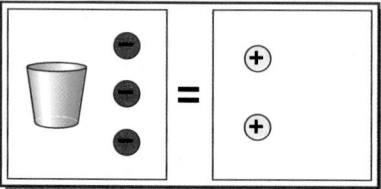

11. *Earth Science* The temperature at 10:00 P.M. was half what it was at noon. If the temperature at 10:00 P.M. was 26°, what was it at noon? **52°**

12. *Sports* Rodney was sacked for a 12-yard loss. On the next play, he had a gain of 5 yards. What was his net yardage on the two plays? **-7**

13. *Money Matters* Jeannette bought a sweater. The sale price was $38, which was $15 less than the original price. Find the original price. **$53**

Copy and complete each function table.

14.

input (n)	output ($n + 5$)
-5	■ 0
0	■ 5
1	■ 6

15.

input (n)	output ($6n$)
-3	■ -18
-1	■ -6
1	■ 6

Find the rule for each function table.

16. $n - 3$

input (n)	output (■)
-2	-5
0	-3
3	0

17. $7n$

input (n)	output (■)
-2	-14
0	0
3	21

18. *Age* Bret is 12 years old, and his father is 35 years old. When Bret is 20, his father will be 43 years old. Write a function rule for this relationship. **$B + 23$**

19. *Patterns* The triangles below were formed using toothpicks.

   a. Write the function rule to find the number of toothpicks for any number of triangles. **$2t + 1$**

   b. How many toothpicks will be needed to make 8 triangles? **17**

20. Graph the function given by the rule $\frac{1}{2}n$. **See Answer Appendix.**

A set of 20 cards has two cards numbered 10, three cards numbered 15, three cards numbered 20, and one card for each of the numbers 1 through 12. Suppose you choose one card without looking. Find the probability of each event.

1. $P(8)$ $\frac{1}{20}$

2. $P(3 \text{ or } 10)$ $\frac{1}{5}$

3. $P(\text{multiple of } 5)$ $\frac{1}{2}$

4. $P(15)$ $\frac{3}{20}$

5. $P(\text{a multiple of } 3)$ $\frac{7}{20}$

6. $P(\text{prime})$ $\frac{1}{4}$

Tell whether each of the following is a random sample.

Type of Survey	Survey Location
7. favorite brand of tennis shoes	library **yes**
8. favorite subject	science fair **no**
9. favorite TV show	department store **yes**

10. *Entertainment* According to a survey, 52 out of 100 people prefer listening to country music. Suppose 375 people participated in the survey. How many people can be expected to prefer listening to country music? **about 195 people**

Each figure represents a dartboard. It is equally likely that a dart will land anywhere on the dartboard. Find the probability of a randomly-thrown dart landing in the shaded region.

11. $\frac{1}{2}$

12. $\frac{1}{3}$

13. about $\frac{4}{5}$

14. Suppose you throw a dart 135 times at the dartboard in Exercise 12. How many times would you expect it to land in the shaded region? **about 45**

15. Suppose you throw a dart 150 times at the dartboard in Exercise 13. How many times would you expect it to land in the shaded region? **about 120**

16. *Food* At The Snack Shack, a person has a choice of iced tea or soda and nachos, popcorn, or a chocolate bar.

   a. Make a list and draw a tree diagram to show the sample space. **See Answer Appendix.**

   b. How many possible outcomes are there? **6 possible outcomes**

   c. What is the probability the next customer who orders a beverage and a snack will choose an iced tea and nachos? $\frac{1}{6}$

A coin is tossed, and the spinner shown is spun. Find the probability of each event.

17. $P(\text{tails and blue})$ $\frac{1}{8}$

18. $P(\text{heads and not green})$ $\frac{3}{8}$

19. $P(\text{not heads and red})$ $\frac{1}{8}$

20. $P(\text{heads or tails and yellow})$ $\frac{1}{4}$

Getting Acquainted with the Graphing Calculator

When some students first see a graphing calculator, they think, "Oh, no! Do we **have** to use one?", while others may think, "All right! We get to use these neat calculators!" There are as many thoughts and feelings about graphing calculators as there are students, but one thing is for sure: a graphing calculator *can* help you learn mathematics. Keep reading for answers to some frequently asked questions.

What is it?

So what is a graphing calculator? Very simply, it is a calculator that draws graphs. This means that it will do all of the things that a "regular" calculator will do, *plus* it will draw graphs of equations.

What does it do?

A graphing calculator can do more than just calculate and draw graphs. For example, you can program it and work with data to make statistical graphs and computations. If you need to generate random numbers, you can do that on the graphing calculator. If you need to find the absolute value of a number, you can do that too. It's really a very powerful tool, so powerful that it is often called a pocket computer.

Graphing Keys

Special Feature Keys

These keys are found on any scientific calculator

These keys allow you to move the cursor up, down, left, and right on the screen.

Basic Keystrokes

- The yellow commands written above the calculator keys are accessed with the [2nd] key, which is also yellow. Similarly, the green characters above the keys are accessed with the [ALPHA] key, which is also green. In this text, commands that are accessed by the [2nd] and [ALPHA] keys are shown in brackets. For example, [2nd] [QUIT] means to press the [2nd] key followed by the key below the yellow [QUIT] command.
- [2nd] [ENTRY] copies the previous calculation so you can edit and use it again.
- [2nd] [QUIT] will return you to the home (or text) screen.
- Negative numbers are entered using the [(-)] key, not the minus sign, [−].
- [2nd] [OFF] turns the calculator off.

Order of Operations

As with any scientific calculator, the graphing calculator observes the order of operations.

Example	Keystrokes	Display
4 + 13	4 [+] 13 [ENTER]	4 + 13 17
5^3	5 [∧] 3 [ENTER]	5 ^ 3 125
4 (9 + 18)	4 [(] 9 [+] 18 [)] [ENTER]	4(9 + 18) 108
$\sqrt{24}$	[2nd] [√] 24 [ENTER]	√(24 4.8989 79486

Programming

Programming features allow you to write and execute a series of commands for tasks that may be too complex or cumbersome to perform otherwise. Each program is given a name. Commands begin with a colon (:), which the calculator enters automatically, followed by an expression or an instruction.

When you press [PRGM], you see three menus: EXEC, EDIT, and NEW. EXEC allows you to execute a stored program, EDIT allows you to edit or change a program, and NEW allows you to create a program.

- To begin entering a new program, press [PRGM] [▶] [▶] [ENTER].
- You do not need to type each letter using the [ALPHA] key. Any command that contains lowercase letters should be entered by choosing it from a menu. Check your user's guide to find any commands that are unfamiliar.
- After a program is entered, press [2nd] [QUIT] to exit the program mode and return to the home screen.
- To execute a program, press [PRGM]. Then use the down arrow key to locate the program name and press [ENTER] twice, or press the number or letter next to the program name followed by [ENTER].
- If you wish to edit a program, press [PRGM] [▶] and choose the program from the menu.
- To immediately re-execute a program after it is run, press [ENTER] when Done appears on the screen.
- To stop a program during execution, press [ON] or [2nd] [QUIT].

While a graphing calculator cannot do everything, it can make some things easier and help your understanding of math. To prepare for whatever lies ahead, you should try to learn as much as you can. Who knows? Maybe one day you will be designing the next satellite or building the next skyscraper with the help of a graphing calculator!

Getting Acquainted with Spreadsheets

What do you think of when people talk about computers? Maybe you think of computer games or using a word processor to write a school paper. But a computer is a powerful tool that can be used for many things.

One of the most common computer applications is a spreadsheet program. Here are answers to some of the questions you may have if you're new to using spreadsheets.

What is it?

You have probably seen tables of numbers in newspapers and magazines. Similar to those tables, a spreadsheet is a table that you can use to organize information. But a spreadsheet is more than just a table. You can also use a spreadsheet to perform calculations or make graphs.

Why use a spreadsheet?

The advantage a spreadsheet has over a simple calculator is that when a number is changed, the entire spreadsheet is recalculated and the new results are displayed. So with a spreadsheet, you can see patterns in data and investigate what happens if one or more of the numbers is changed.

How do I use a spreadsheet?

A spreadsheet is organized into boxes called *cells*. The cells are named by a letter, that identifies the column, and a number, that identifies the row. In the spreadsheet below, cell C4 is highlighted.

	A	B	C
1	Width	Length	Area
2	3	4	12
3	2	10	20
4	5	12	60
5	8	14	112

To enter information in a spreadsheet, simply move the cursor to the cell you want to access and click the mouse. Then type in the information and press Enter.

How do I enter formulas?

If you want to use the spreadsheet as a calculator, begin by choosing the cell where you want the result to appear.

- For a simple calculation, type = followed by the formula. For example, in the spreadsheet above, the formula in cell C2 is entered as "=A2*B2." *Notice that * is the symbol for multiplication in a spreadsheet.*

- Sometimes you will want similar formulas in more than one cell. First type the formula in one cell. Then select the cell and click the copy button. Finally select the cells where you want to copy the formula and click the paste button.

- Often it is useful to find the sum or average of a row or column of numbers. The spreadsheet allows you to choose from several functions like this instead of entering the formula manually. To enter a function, click the cell where you want the result to appear. Then click on the = button above the cells. A list of formulas will appear to the left. Click the down arrow button and choose your function. The spreadsheet will enter a range, which you may alter. For example, to find the average of row 2 of the spreadsheet below, the function chooses to find the average of cells B2, C2, and D2.

	A	B	C	D	E
1	Student	Test 1	Test 2	Test 3	Average
2	Kathy	88	85	91	88
3	Ben	86	89	92	89
4	Carmen	92	86	92	90
5	Anthony	80	88	87	85

The formula for cell E2 is =(B2+C2+D2)/3.

Spreadsheet software is one of the most common tools used in business today. You should try to learn as much as you can to prepare for your future. Who knows? Maybe you'll use what you're learning today as a company president tomorrow!

Selected Answers

Chapter 1
Problem Solving, Numbers, and Algebra

Pages 6–7   Lesson 1-1

1. Explore–Decide what facts you know and what you need to find out.   Plan–Make a plan for solving the problem and estimate the answer. Solve–Solve the problem. Make a new plan if necessary.   Examine–Check to see if your answer makes sense.   **5.** about 15 million   **7.** 180 miles   **9.** $40   **11.** 65°F   **13.** 84,480 pennies   **15.** Yes; Sample answer: a team can score 7 field goals and 1 safety or 3 touchdowns, 2 two-point conversions, and 1 one-point conversion.

Pages 10–11   Lesson 1-2

3.

Number of Folds	1	2	3	4
Number of Thicknesses	2	4	8	16

Sample answer: The number of thicknesses doubles.
5. 8, 4, 2   **7.** 3, 4, 3   **9.** 512, 2,048, 8,192
11. 17, 22, 28   **13.** 21, 31, 43   **15.** 5:10 P.M.
17. 256   **19.** C

Pages 14–15   Lesson 1-3

1. On the number line, 957 is closer to 1,000 than 900.   **5.** 400   **7.** 300   **9.** 10,000   **11.** 900 − 400 = 500; reasonable   **13.** 500 ÷ 50 = 10; not reasonable   **15.** 100   **17.** 50   **19.** 440
21. 5,500   **23.** 3,700   **25.** 5,600   **27.** 10,000
29. 2,000   **31.** 9,000   **33.** 80 × 3 = 240; reasonable   **35.** 100−20 = 80; not reasonable
37. 5,000 + 5,000 = 10,000; reasonable   **39.** 800 − 200 = 600; reasonable   **41.** $5.00 + $35.00 = $40.00; not reasonable   **43.** Sample answer: 200 + 60 + 600 + 300 = 1,160; about 1,160 lbs
45a. $75 + $36 + $21 + $6 + $2 + $2 + $10 = $152   **47.** 11, 16, 22   **49.** 10:22 A.M., 11:02 A.M., 11:06 A.M.   **51.** C

Pages 18–19   Lesson 1-4

1. Multiply and divide in order from left to right. Then add and subtract in order from left to right.   **3.** +; 14

5. ×; 33   **7a.** 12 × $15 + 28 × $6   **7b.** $348
9. 117   **11.** 43   **13.** 15   **15.** 23   **17.** 9   **19.** 55
21a. 2 × 15 + 1 × 14 + 3 × 18   **21b.** 98 g
23a. Sample answer: 3 × $29.95 + 2 × $16.95 + $12.95 = $136.70   **25.** 9,000   **27.** B

Page 19   Mid-Chapter Self Test

1. $7   **3.** 37, 45, 53   **5.** 150   **7.** 18,000 ÷ 300 = 60
9. 9

Pages 20–21   Lesson 1-5A

1. the unknown value   **3.** 13   **5.** the unknown value   **7.** 5 bags

Pages 24–25   Lesson 1-5

1. 5 × r or 5 · r **3.** Nicholas; 2 + 14 ÷ 2 = 9
5. 4   **7.** 18   **9.** 16   **11.** 15   **13.** 10   **15.** 22
17. 105   **19.** 60   **21.** 35   **23.** 22   **25.** 9
27. 18   **29.** 54   **31.** 9   **33.** 24   **35.** 30   **37.** 9
39. 12 inches   **41.** yes; 30   **43.** 21   **45.** A

Page 26   Lesson 1-5B

1. 3   **3.** 28   **5.** 14   **7.** 20   **9.** Yes, unless the scientific calculator does not have parentheses keys.

Pages 29–31   Lesson 1-6

1. An exponent is a number that tells how many times a number, called the base, is used as a factor. A power is a number that is expressed using exponents.   **3.** Tamika; $3^2 + 2^4 \cdot 6 = 105$.   **5.** m^5
7. $c \cdot c \cdot c$ **9.** $h \cdot h \cdot h \cdot h \cdot h$ **11.** 100,000
13. about 1,000,000,000 people   **15.** 3^6
17. $3^2 \cdot 4^4$ **19.** r^4 **21.** $6^3 \cdot 1^3$ **23.** 14 · 14
25. 7 · 7 · 7 · 7 · 7   **27.** 16 · 16 · 16 · 16 · 16 · 16
29. $x \cdot x \cdot x \cdot y \cdot y \cdot y \cdot y$ **31.** 1,000   **33.** 32
35. 9   **37.** 1,027   **39.** 103   **41.** 1; 1; 10; 1
43. 5,832 in^3 **45.** 18   **47.** 400 + 700 + 200 = 1,300; reasonable   **49.** 379 students

Pages 32–33   Lesson 1-7A

3. The piece that is beside the top left-hand puzzle piece. It will connect to the corner piece.

5. Sample answer: When making a plan to solve a problem, you can use the guess-and-check strategy to guess an answer and compare the answer to the problem. If your answer does not work, then you know to make another guess. **7.** Sample answer: You could guess values for p to find what number divided by 5 is 45. **9.** 15 dogs, 9 cats **11.** There are 8 bones in the wrist, 14 in the fingers, and 5 in the palm. **13.** 67,740 feet per minute **15.** B

Pages 35–37 Lesson 1-7

1. Sample answer: Both algebraic expressions and equations can contain variables, operations, and numbers. Whereas an equation contains an equals sign, an algebraic expression does not contain an equals sign. **3.** false **5.** 7 **7.** 4 **9.** 9 **11.** 10 **13.** true **15.** true **17.** false **19.** 15 **21.** 7 **23.** 13 **25.** 7 **27.** 44 **29.** 26 **31.** 7 **33.** 3 **35.** 225 **37.** 2 **39.** 16 **41a.** $19 + g = 65$ **41b.** 46 grams **43.** C **45.** 12 **47.** about $70

Pages 38–41 Study Guide and Assessment

1. multiply and divide **3.** 4 **5.** 3 and 4 **7.** 2^5 **9.** 10 **11.** 11 **13.** $39.92 **15.** 531 votes

17.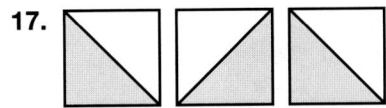

19. 48, 56, 64 **21.** 30 **23.** 650 **25.** 2 **27.** 2 **29.** 7 **31.** 16 **33.** 7 **35.** 21 **37.** 44 **39.** 4,096 **41.** 125 **43.** t^5 **45.** 3 **47.** 63 **49.** 9 **51.** 6 **53.** 13 years 10 months **55.** about 63,000

Pages 42–43 Standardized Test Practice

1. B **3.** B **5.** D **7.** E **9.** B **11.** A **13.** 10 ft **15.** 21 **17.** 27

Chapter 2 Statistics: Graphing Data

Pages 48–49 Lesson 2-1

1. Sample answer: to make it easier to study the data.

5a.

Age	Tally	Frequency
10	I	1
11	I	1
12	IIII	5
13	III	3
14	II	2

5b. 12

7.

Days Absent	Tally	Frequency
0	IIII	5
1	IIII I	6
2	II	2
3	III	3
4		0
5	II	2

9a. Sample answer: All the shoes sold were between sizes 9 and 11. **9b.** 77 pairs of shoes **9c.** 10 **11a.** Sample answer: Based on the data in the table, they should keep potato chips and corn chips well stocked. **11b.** Sample answer: There are too few to tell. **13.** A

Pages 51–53 Lesson 2-2

1. Sample answer: The scale must include all of the data. Since the shortest distance is 12 and the longest distance is 63, a scale from 10 to 70 is appropriate. **5.** 2; 10 is too large.

7a.

Shelby's Video Game Scores		
Score	Tally	Frequency
60,000–69,900	I	1
50,000–59,900	I	1
40,000–49,900	IIII	4
30,000–39,900	IIII	5
20,000–29,900	IIII	4
10,000–19,900	II	2
0–9,900	I	1

7b. Most of her scores were between 30,000 and 39,900. **9.** a **11.** a **13.** b

15.

Amount	Tally	Frequency
81–100	I	1
61–80		0
41–60	IIII	4
21–40	I	1
0–20	II	2

17a. No; since Texas is a much larger state, the distances will be larger. If she used the same scale the frequency table would not include all the distances. **17b.** Sample answer: Yes; however, the table will have a large number of rows. **19a.** Sample answer: 5,000–20,999

19b.

Elevation	Tally	Frequency
19,000–20,999	I	1
17,000–18,999		0
15,000–16,999		0
13,000–14,999	JHT III	8
11,000–12,999	IIII	4
9,000–10,999		0
7,000–8,999	II	2
5,000–6,999	JHT II	7

21.

Number of Hits	Tally	Frequency
0	I	1
1	II	2
2	III	3
3	II	2
4	I	1

23. D

Pages 55–57   Lesson 2-3

1. Call Them   **3.** Sample answer: If the vertical scale is much higher than the highest value, it makes the graph flatter. Changing the interval does not affect either type of graph.   **5.** 0–70; 10

7.

Favorite Soft Drinks

9.

11. Sample answer: 0 to 300   **13.** Table A; It shows the change and direction of change over time.

15.

Super Bowl Ticket Prices

19. B   **21.** 4

Pages 58–59   Lesson 2-3B

3. Sample answer: Mickey's; It is the second favorite and the healthiest.   **7.** $30
9. 1,380 miles   **11.** C

Pages 62–63   Lesson 2-4

1. Sample answer: When you want to represent data that looks at part to whole relationships.
5a. 13%–Special; 15%–egg noodles; 31%–short pasta; 41%–long pasta   **5b.** special and egg noodles
5c. 72%   **5d.** special and egg noodles   **5e.** either long pasta and special (54%) or short pasta and egg noodles (46%)   **7a.** LP album, 7-12 in. singles and music videos   **7b.** cassette single–5%; cassette album–25%; CDs–68%

9.

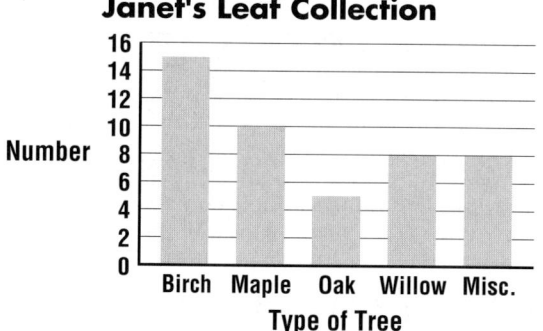

Janet's Leaf Collection

Pages 65–67   Lesson 2-5

1. Sample answer: If the extension aligns with the segment between 1980 to 1990, world population could be about 7 billion.   **5a.** Sample answer: It will continue to bounce higher.   **5b.** Sample answer: It will bounce about as high as it did when dropped from 110 cm.   **5c.** Sample answer: Ball A might be a Super Ball.   **5d.** Sample answer: No; at some point both balls will begin to level off. If you dropped Ball A from 100 feet it will not bounce 100 feet.   **7.** The point where they cross indicates the times were the same.   **9.** D

Page 67 Mid-Chapter Self Test

1.

Height	Tally	Frequency
54	I	1
55	I	1
56	I	1
57	IIII	4
58	I	1
59	I	1
60	II	2
61		0
62		0
63	I	1

3.

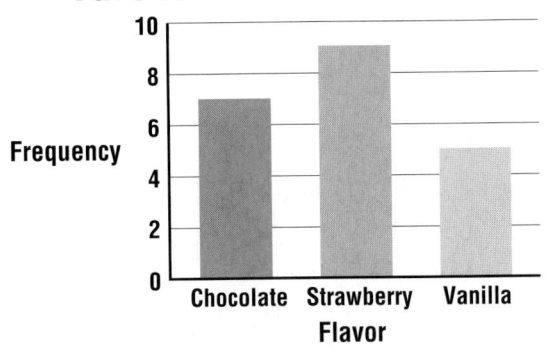

Favorite Ice Cream Flavor

5a. the 5th week **5b.** the 11th week **5c.** Sample answer: No; the horizontal scale doesn't extend far enough.

Pages 69–70 Lesson 2-6

1. when there are many numbers in a set of data

5.

Stem	Leaf
2	0 4 7
3	4 5 6 6 8
4	3 5 7
5	3 4 8 8
6	
7	8 2|7 = 27

7. 1, 2, 3, 4, 5

9. 0, 1, 2, 3, 4

11.

Stem	Leaf
9	2 4 9 9
10	
11	
12	4 4
13	0 2 3
14	0
15	
16	2 7 12|4 = 124

13.

Stem	Leaf
0	9
1	
2	7 8 9
3	4 4 4
4	5 6
5	3 6 6 7 7 7 8

$5|3 = 53°$

15a.

Stem	Leaf
0	5 5 6 7 8 9 9 9 9 9
1	0 1 1 3 4 6 7 8 8 9 9
2	2 2 3 6 7 7 9
3	7
4	1 1|0 = 10

15b. 9 days **17.** Sample answer: 400

Pages 73–74 Lesson 2-7

1. The mean because the numbers do not differ greatly. **5.** 10, 26, 27, 29, 36, 37, 57, 83, 88; 36; no mode; ≈ 43.7; 78 **7.** 44; 44; no mode; 22 **9.** 15; 15; 14 and 16; 4 **11.** 31; 31; 31; 26 **13.** The mean would be lower. **15.** yes; Sample answer: The total would be higher so the mean would also be higher. **17.** Sample answer: The mode because she would want to know what size they sold the most shakes.

19.

Stem	Leaf
0	0 2 2 4 5 7 7 9
1	0 2 3 3 8 9
2	0 3 2|0 = 20

Page 77 Lesson 2-7B

1.

3.

Pages 79–81 Lesson 2-8

1. Sample answer: Using different scales and not having a title. **3.** Sample answer: If the range is very high the mean could be misleading. If the set of data has a gap between two groups of numbers that are all about the same, the mean could be misleading. For example, 1, 2, 3, 2, and 8, 7, 6, 9, 8. **5.** mode–want to find the most frequent **7a.** Graph B is misleading because the distance between 0 and 25 is the same as the distance between 25 and 30.

7b. Graph A because it shows a general rise in price. **9.** $1\frac{1}{2}$; median **11.** $1962; mean **13.** There may be a few very low priced CDs, thus giving a lower average. **15a.** mean: 134 ÷ 24 ≈ 5.6 or 6 pets; median: 3 pets; mode: 2 pets

15b. Sample answer: The median best represents the data. The student with 24 pets has a big effect on the mean. **17.** A **19.** 25, 36, 49

Pages 84–85 Lesson 2-9

1. From the origin, go 7 units left, then up 9 units.
3. Sample answer: Raul; to graph (8, 3) you move 8 units right and 3 units up and to graph (3, 8) you move 3 units right and 8 units up. **5.** F **7.** (8, 0) **9.** (5, 6) **11.** C **13.** K **15.** Q **17.** L **19.** M **21.** (7, 4) **23.** (3, 7) **25.** (0, 9) **27.** (0, 0) **29.** (9, 8) **35.** C **37.** 7

Pages 86–89 Study Guide and Assessment

1. f **3.** a **5.** c **7.** i **9.** j **11.** Sample answer: A bar graph represents data using rectangles to show the frequency of responses. A line graph uses dots at the frequency points connected by segments to show how data changes over time.

13.

Favorite Color	Tally	Frequency
blue	IIII	4
red	IIII	4
pink	II	2
orange	I	1
yellow	I	1
green	II	2
brown	I	1

15. scale = 0 to 50, interval 5 **17.** scale = 0 to 160, interval 20

19.

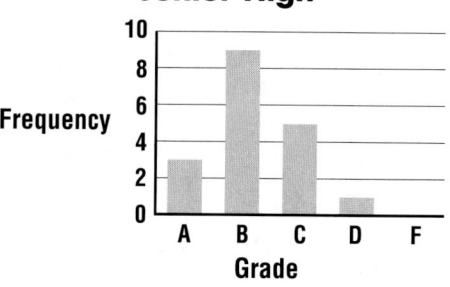

Alma's Grades During Junior High

21. less **23.** 22 **25.** 25 **27.** median **29.** mean **31.** A **33.** (3, 6)

35.

Stem	Leaf
4	0 5
5	0
6	5 9
7	5 5
8	5
9	0 2 5

$9|0 = 90$

Pages 90–91 Standardized Test Practice

1. D **3.** B **5.** B **7.** C **9.** C **11.** E **13.** $7 + r = 22$; 15 **15.** 25

....

Chapter 3 Adding and Subtracting Decimals

Page 94 Lesson 3-1A

1. thirty hundredths
3. 9 tenths;

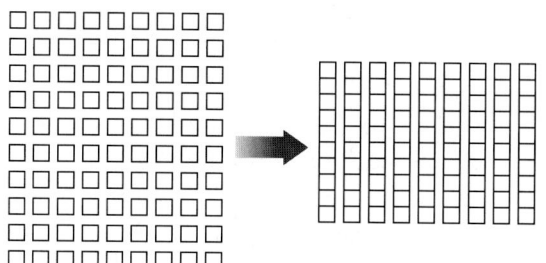

Pages 97–98 Lesson 3-1

1. 0.05, $\frac{5}{100}$, five hundredths **3.** Mercedes is correct because the last digit, 8, is in the thousandths place. **5.** 0.43 **7.** 4.0029 **9.** 0.0702 **11.** 0.3 **13.** 0.07 **15.** 19.53 **17.** 0.009 **19.** 47.047 **21.** 172.0001 **23.** 20.9 **25.** 3.003 **27.** 0.0801 **29.** 0.01 **31.** greatest: 0.750; least: 0.057 **33.** B **35.** $19

Page 101 Lesson 3-2A

3. Students should notice that the measures are related to powers of 10 and start to notice how decimals are used.

Pages 103–104 Lesson 3-2

5. cm; about 2.5 cm **7.** 3.2 cm or 32 mm **9.** cm; about 90 cm **11.** m; about 5 m **13.** 1.3 cm or 13 mm **15.** 3.8 cm or 38 mm **17.** 3 cm or 30 mm **19.** 2 cm or 20 mm **21.** 300 cm **25.** C **27.** 10

Pages 107–108 Lesson 3-3

1.

3. 1.63 > 1.54 **5.** 0.06 **7.** 13.05, 13.507, 13.84, 13.9 **9.** 389.225, 388.404, 388.246, 385.867,

385.841 **11.** 0.331 **13.** 1.018 **15.** 47.553
17. 0.7 **19.** 14.95, 15, 15.01, 15.8 **21.** 0.0316,
0.0306, 0.025, 0.0249, 0.0208 **23.** 397.877, 379.9,
379.88, 379.8778, 378.87 **25.** 0.603 **27a.** 2.1,
2.9, 4.2, 5.1, 5.8, 7.0, 9.0, 13.0, 14.0 **27b.** 5.8
29. 5.7 cm or 57 mm **31.** Sample answer: 95, 91,
93, 89; no number occurs more often than the others

Pages 110–111   Lesson 3-4

1. Sample answer: Since the digit to the right of the
ones place is greater than 5, add one to the ones
place. $10.79 rounded to the nearest dollar is $11.
3. Sharon is correct. Carlos rounded to the nearest
hundred. **5.** 8.20 **7.** 20 **9.** 18 **11.** 20.5
13. 49.8 **15.** 19.78 **17.** 100.0 **19.** 7.000
21. $2.00 **23.** 102 **25.** Sample answer: Using
the exact data in this case would be most appropriate.
27. No, because no numbers differ greatly.

Page 111   Mid-Chapter Self Test

1. 0.7 **3.** 0.681 **5.** 3 cm **7.** 638.178 **9.** 3.40

Pages 114–115   Lesson 3-5

1. Sample answer: Round both amounts to the
nearest dollar. $17 − $4 = $13 **5.** 20 + 30 = 50
7. 11 + 11 + 11 + 11 = 44 **9.** 20 + 20 + 20 =
60 **11.** Sample answer: Round 0.38 to 0.4 and
round 0.21 to 0.2. 0.4 + 0.2 = 0.6. Since 0.6 > 0.5
both samples cannot be stored in the 0.5-liter
container. **13.** 9−5 = 4 **15.** 32 + 17 = 49
17. $30−$20 = $10 **19.** $58−$27 = $31 **21.** 4
+ 4 + 4 = 12 **23.** 1 + 1 + 1 +1 = 4 **25.** $54
+ $54 + $54 = $162 **27.** $65−$40 = $25
29. $200−$110 = $90 **31.** 102°F − 99°F = 3°F
33. about 1 million square feet **35a.** Sample
answer: An estimate for Mandy's family is $9 + $9
+ $9 + $4 or $31. Since all costs were rounded up,
her whole family can go on the tour for less than
$35. **35b.** Sample answer: An estimate for each
meal is $5 for breakfast, $7 for lunch, and $12 for
dinner. The estimate for one person would be $5 +
$7 + $12 or $24. The estimate for a family of 4
would be $24 + $24 + $24 + $24 or $96. This
could be rounded up to $100. **37.** 0.270 **39.** 21
41. 8

Pages 116–117   Lesson 3-6A

3. Sample answer: If you round to the nearest
hundred, the 1986 and 1987 amounts or the 1987

and 1988 amounts total 200 million. If you round to
the nearest ten the 1986 and 1988 amounts total 200
million. **9a.** They sold 12 subscriptions during
week three. **9b.** Since each symbol means 4
subscriptions, a half-magazine means 2
subscriptions. **9c.** They sold 16 subscriptions
during week two. **11.** Sample answer: By drawing
a linc graph and extending it to match the segment
between 1993 and 1994, over 1.6 million CDs will
be distributed in 2000. **13.** B

Pages 119–121   Lesson 3-6

1. Sample answer: Annex two zeros. Then line up
the decimal points, rename and subtract. **5.** 2.24
7. 0.75 **9.** 6.592 **11.** 6.4 **13.** 0.24 **15.** $11.77
17. 1.747 **19.** 2.02 **21.** 13.253 **23.** 151.575
25. $12.10 **27.** 26.42 **29.** 2.1 **31.** 10.72
33a. 2.6 pounds **33b.** 18 pounds **35.** 0.2 −
0.1876543 = 0.0123457 **37.** B **39.** 3

Pages 122–125   Study Guide and Assessment

1. false, less **3.** false, one hundredth **5.** false,
centimeters **7.** false, 600.012 **9.** true **11.** 0.08
13. 14.017 **15.** 0.2 **17.** 0.053 **19.** eight ten-
thousandths **21.** 6 cm **23.** 2 cm **25.** 11.6
27. 0.0289, 0.0319, 0.032, 0.31 **29.** 6.75, 6.39,
6.32, 6.02 **31.** 7 **33.** 13.6 **35.** 5 − 1 = 4
37. 6 + 6 + 6 + 6 + 6 = 30 **39.** 12.912
41. 77.1 **43.** 7320.4, 7321.5, 7321.539, 7342.98,
7346.24, 7346.4 **45.** about $210

Pages 126–127   Standardized Test Practice

1. A **3.** C **5.** A **7.** D **9.** B **11.** D **13.** divide
120 by 8 **15.** 241 miles **17.** 68 **19.** mode

Chapter 4
Multiplying and Dividing Decimals

Page 132   Lesson 4-1A

1.

3.

5. 3.2

5.

Pages 134–136   Lesson 4-1
1. Sample answer: Round 40.32 to 40 and round 251 to 250. You can find 40×250 since 4 and 25 are compatible numbers.   **3.** Sample answer: Yes; by rounding 34.78 to 30 and rounding 452 to 500, the product of 30 and 500 is 15,000.   **5.** 239.4   **7.** 1.6   **9.** 0.32   **11.** 66,593.12 miles per hour   **13.** 1.12   **15.** 30.78   **17.** 64.2   **19.** 2,606.5   **21.** 9.425   **23.** 0.252   **25.** 3,940.2   **27.** 21,286.734   **29.** Sample answer: Since 0.5 is less than 5, 0.5×5 will be less than 25.   **31.** \$29.25   **33.** Sample answer: 5×9.178 **35.** Sample answer: 80   **37a.** Sample answer: 800 points   **37b.** Sample answer: Use clustering to total the hundreds and use rounding to estimate to the nearest ten.
37c. Sample answer: You would round to the nearest ten because rounding to the nearest hundred they would all be the same.

Pages 138–139   Lesson 4-2
1. First find 8^2. Then add 64 and 6. Finally, multiply 70(9).   **5.** $80 + 64 = 144$ **7.** $30 + 2 = 32$
9. $100 + 25 = 125$ **11.** $3 \times 20 + 3 \times 7$ **13.** 84
15. 216   **17.** 48.6   **19.** 124.2   **21.** 92.7   **23.** 630
25. \$15.75   **27a.** 0.32   **27b.** 0.05   **27c.** 0.54
27d. 7.3125   **29.** 35.9 in.

Page 140   Lesson 4-3A
1. 0.6×1.9
3.
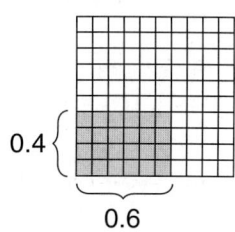

Pages 142–143   Lesson 4-3
1. Sample answer: The total decimal places of the factors are 5. 0.40563   **3.** 4.08   **5.** 27.9258
7. 0.0078   **9.** 69.608   **11.** 0.49   **13.** 13.0968
15. 16,688.0428   **17.** 9.49   **19.** 0.0186
21. 0.00212   **23.** 5.82788   **25.** 108.8472
27. 0.00696   **29.** 5.41   **31.** Sample answer:
0.1×0.6 **33.** D   **35.** 216

Page 144   Lesson 4-3B
1. E4   **3.** \$28.79, \$37.49, \$25.41, \$12.00, \$12.34, \$17.95   **5.** No; you would still multiply.

Pages 147–148   Lesson 4-4
5. 7.5 in.   **7.** $P = 121.6$ cm; $A = 924.16$ cm^2
9. 43 m   **11.** 27 m   **13.** $P = 6$ in.; $A = 2.25$ in.^{2}
15. $P = 12.8$ m; $A = 7.68$ m^2 **17.** $P = 46.4$ in.;
$A = 135.56$ in.^{2} **19.** 15 in^2; 20 in.
21a. perimeter   **21b.** 880 ft^2
23.   **25.** C

Page 149   Lesson 4-4B
1a.

Length	Width	Area
7	1	7
6	2	12
5	3	15
4	4	16

1b.

Length	Width	Area
8	1	8
7	2	14
6	3	18
5	4	20

1c.

Length	Width	Area
9	1	9
8	2	16
7	3	21
6	4	24
5	5	25

3. Sample answer: The longer the length and shorter the width, the lesser the area of the rectangular shape.

Pages 150–151   Lesson 4-5A

1. Sample answer: She thought she was dividing the length into 2-foot sections.   **3.** 17 cuts   **5.** Sample answer: This strategy allows you to break a difficult problem into manageable parts.   **7.** 28 feet
9a. $40 million   **9b.** $50 million   **9c.** $3 million
11. His competition average was 17 pins higher than his previous average.   **13.** D

Pages 153–155   Lesson 4-5

1. Sample answer: The estimate tells you the answer is close to 1.   **3.** Sample answer: Estimate 80 ÷ 40 = 2; The estimate shows that the answer is reasonable.   **5.** 0.415   **7.** 7.9   **9.** 2.6   **11.** 0.25
13. 21.2   **15.** 9.23   **17.** 2.7   **19.** 3.3   **21.** 22.42
23. 9.79   **25.** 5.5   **27.** 4.53   **29.** $14.67
31. $0.19, $0.07, $0.06   **33.** Sample answer: 0.9984 ÷ 8   **35.** about 27 cm   **37.** B

Page 155   Mid-Chapter Self Test

1. $20,000   **3.** 420   **5.** 0.0204   **7.** 9.8 cm, 0.94 cm²   **9.** 9.63

Page 156   Lesson 4-6A

1. 2   **3.** 30   **5.** 3

Pages 158–159   Lesson 4-6

1. Sample answer: 1.84 ÷ 0.8.   **3.** 19   **5.** 694
7. 54.3   **9.** 2.2   **11.** 112   **13.** 0.4   **15.** 0.9
17. 2,967   **19.** 0.6   **21.** 8.37   **23.** 107   **25.** 3.9
27. 3.41   **29.** 0.84   **31.** 19 tanks   **33.** Sample answer: 0.896 ÷ 0.35 = 2.56   **35.** two hundred four and two thousand three hundred ninety-eight ten-thousandths   **37.** 7

Pages 162–163   Lesson 4-7

1. Sample answer: 4.53 ÷ 15   **3.** Sample answer: Multiply the divisor and dividend by 10. The problem becomes 1,561.4 ÷ 148. Estimate: 1,500 ÷ 150 = 10.   **5.** 4.03   **7.** 5.02   **9.** 17.05   **11.** 10.2
13. 301   **15.** 5.21   **17.** 10.94   **19.** 20.26
21. 10.42   **23.** 2.00   **25.** 101   **27.** 0.807
29. 0.0032   **31.** 6.08 m   **33.** never   **35.** D
37. Sample answer: 0 to 120

Pages 165–166   Lesson 4-8

1. kilogram   **3.** kilogram; 500 kg   **5.** liter; 2 L
7. Sample answer: The fruit is heavier, so the loaf has to be smaller to have the same mass.   **9.** milliliter, 200 mL   **11.** kilogram, 100 kg   **13.** kilogram, 2 kg   **15.** milligram, 1 mg   **17.** gram, 100 g
19. milligram, 500 mg   **23.** 1.765 g   **25a.** 4,389 g
25b. more than 4 kg   **27.** 201.5   **29.** C

Pages 168–169   Lesson 4-9

1. divide by 1,000   **3.** Sample answer: Parker and Dinh are both incorrect. Parker multiplied by 10 and Dinh divided by 10. They should have multiplied by 1,000.   **5.** multiply; 7   **7.** multiply; 5,020
9. divide; 0.15   **11.** 21   **13.** 2,500   **15.** 5.24
17. 81.7   **19.** 1.953   **21.** 3,290   **23.** 5,250
25. 10   **27.** 0.0067   **29.** 58 cm   **31.** 0.213 L
33. about 5.6 cans   **35.** liters   **37.** 77.65

Pages 170–173   Study Guide and Assessment

1. true   **3.** false, perimeter   **5.** true   **7.** true
9. true   **11.** false, multiply   **13.** Sample answer: Round 6.9 to 7 and 88 to 90. 7 × 90 = 630
15. 488.05   **17.** 47.46   **19.** 96,819.2   **21.** 322.8
23. 34   **25.** 0.204   **27.** 62.0984   **29.** 539.76
31. 27.3 m   **33.** 41 mi; 104.16 mi²   **35.** 30.4 ft, 57.76 sq ft   **37.** 6.37   **39.** 0.52175   **41.** 19.21
43. 141   **45.** 5.9   **47.** 0.01   **49.** 0.08   **51.** 5.436
53. kilogram, 5 kg   **55.** milliliter, 15 mL
57. 0.001   **59.** 5.2 kilometers   **61.** $319.52

Pages 174–175   Standardized Test Practice

1. D   **3.** C   **5.** C   **7.** C   **9.** B   **11.** C   **13.** 88, 93, 95   **15.** liters   **17.** 0.0235   **19.** Sample answer: The 539-gram can of soup is a better buy. It costs 0.135¢ per gram while the 306-gram can costs 0.137¢ per gram.

Chapter 5
Using Number Patterns, Fractions, and Ratios

Pages 179–180   Lesson 5-1
1. Sample answer:

2 Children

12 Children

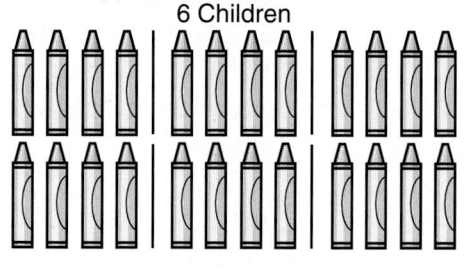

6 Children

3. 2: if the ones digit is divisible by 2. 3: if the sum of the digits is divisible by 3. 5: if the ones digit is 0 or 5. 6: if the number is divisible by 2 and 3. 9: if the sum of the digits is divisible by 9. 10: if the ones digit is zero.   **5.** no   **7.** none   **9.** 2, 3, 6   **11.** yes   **13.** yes   **15.** no   **17.** yes   **19.** yes   **21.** 2, 3, 6, 9   **23.** none   **25.** 3, 9   **27.** 2, 5, 10   **29.** yes   **31.** no   **33.** Sample answer: 90   **35.** Yes; each chaperone will have 15 students.   **37.** 50   **39.** 275.856

Page 181   Lesson 5-2A
1.

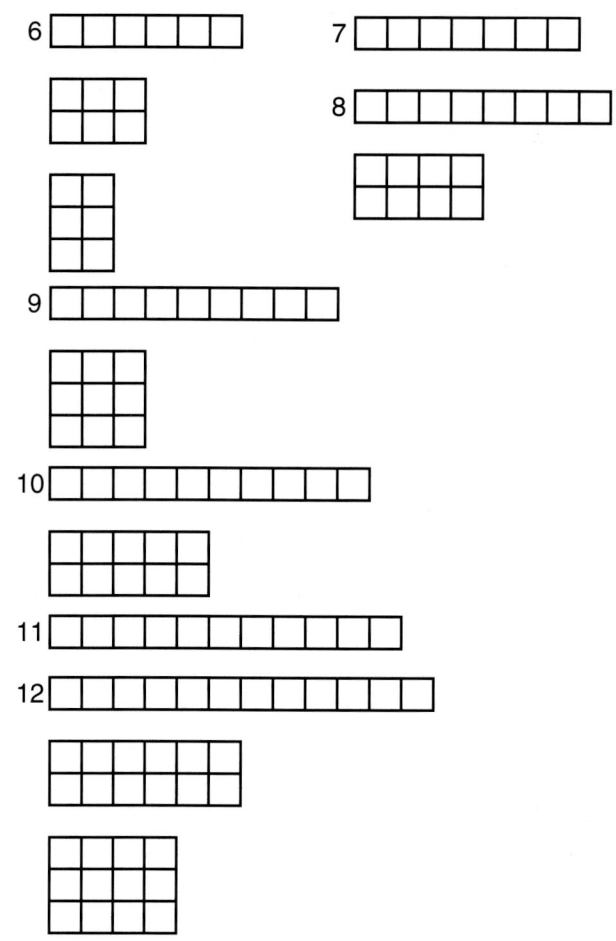

3. 4, 6, 8, 9, 10, 12   **5.** 12, 14, 15, 16, 18, 20, 21, 22, 24; these numbers have several factors.

Pages 183–184   Lesson 5-2
1.

1×10

2×5

So, 10 is a composite number.   **3.** Both are correct. The factors are arranged in a different order.
5. neither   **7.** composite   **9.** 3×5^2 **11.** $2^3 \times 13$ **13.** neither   **15.** prime   **17.** composite   **19.** composite   **21.** composite   **23.** composite   **25.** $2 \times 3 \times 7$ **27.** 5×13 **29.** prime   **31.** 2×3^2 **33.** $2 \times 3 \times 17$ **35.** $2^3 \times 3 \times 5$ **37.** 83   **39.** 2; Two is the only even number that has exactly 2 factors, 1 and itself.   **41.** 3 and 5, 5 and 7, 11 and 13, 17 and 19, 29 and 31, 41 and 43, 59 and 61, 71 and 73   **43.** yes   **45.** 4.36   **47.** $17 \times 17 \times 17 \times 17 \times 17 \times 17 \times 17$

Pages 186–187   Lesson 5-3A
3. 12 possible options   **7.** 30   **9.** 6   **11.** $1,680   **13.** C

Pages 189–190   Lesson 5-3

1. Sample answer: Find the prime factorization of 12 and 18. Multiply all common factors of both numbers to find the greatest common factor.   **3.** 5
5. 7   **7.** 8   **9.** 8 ft   **11.** 2   **13.** 15   **15.** 11
17. 17   **19.** 12   **21.** 6   **23.** 3   **25.** 17   **27.** 19
29. 3   **31a.** 8 in. by 8 in.   **31b.** 18   **33.** Sample answer: 8 and 9   **35.** 24.9 yd^2 **37.** 9.016

Pages 191–192   Lesson 5-4A

1. 5 out of 6, 5 to 6, or 5:6; $\frac{5}{6}$ **3.** 5 out of 9, 5 to 9, or 5:9; $\frac{5}{9}$ **5.** $\frac{3}{4}, \frac{6}{8}$

7.

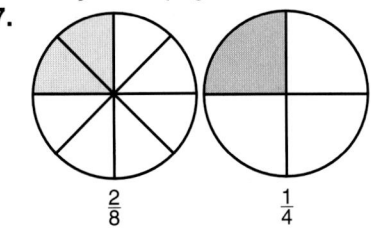

$\frac{2}{8}$ $\frac{1}{4}$

Pages 195–196   Lesson 5-4

1a. $\frac{8}{12}$ **1b.** 4   **1c.** $\frac{2}{3}$ **1d.**
3. 9   **5.** 3   **7.** no; 1 to 9
9. yes   **11.** 4   **13.** 9
15. 24   **17.** 6   **19.** 20   **21.** no; $\frac{5}{19}$ **23.** no; 3 out of 4   **25.** no; $\frac{3}{20}$ **27.** no; 3:5   **29.** no; $\frac{21}{25}$ **31.** no; 1 out of 4   **33.** Sample answer: $\frac{4}{6}$ **35a.** Gwynn, $\frac{2}{5}$; Ripken, $\frac{1}{3}$; Gonzalez, $\frac{11}{36}$; Williams, $\frac{8}{21}$; Bonds, $\frac{1}{3}$; Rodriguez, $\frac{5}{14}$ **35b.** Ripken and Bonds   **37.** $\frac{36}{48}$
39. C   **41.** 26.98, 27.025, 27.13, 27.131, 27.9

Page 197   Lesson 5-4B

1. $\frac{7}{48}$ **3.** $\frac{17}{48}$

Pages 200–201   Lesson 5-5

1. Sample answer: a fraction with a numerator greater than or equal to the denominator.

3.

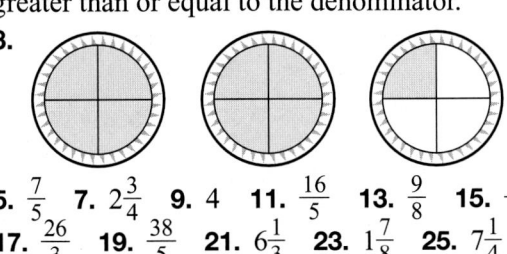

5. $\frac{7}{5}$ **7.** $2\frac{3}{4}$ **9.** 4   **11.** $\frac{16}{5}$ **13.** $\frac{9}{8}$ **15.** $\frac{16}{9}$
17. $\frac{26}{3}$ **19.** $\frac{38}{5}$ **21.** $6\frac{1}{3}$ **23.** $1\frac{7}{8}$ **25.** $7\frac{1}{4}$
27. $2\frac{1}{9}$ **29.** $3\frac{4}{7}$ **31.** $\frac{55}{8}$ **33.** Kentucky Derby–$\frac{5}{4}$; Preakness Stakes–$\frac{19}{16}$; Belmont Stakes–$\frac{3}{2}$ **35.** Sample answer: If the numerator is less than the denominator, then the fraction is less than one. If the numerator is the same as the denominator, then the fraction is equal to one. If the numerator is greater than the denominator, then the fraction is greater than one.
37. $2^2 \times 3 \times 17$ **39.** 0.13

Page 201   Mid-Chapter Self Test

1. 3, 5   **3.** 2, 5, 10   **5.** $2^3 \times 11$ **7.** 18   **9.** 4:25

Pages 203–205   Lesson 5-6

1. Divide 24 by 12.   **3.** A cubit is about 18 in. A span is about 8 to 9 in.   **5.** 3
7. ▬▬▬▬▬▬▬▬▬▬▬▬▬▬▬▬▬▬
9. $\frac{7}{8}$ in.   **11.** 5   **13.** 108   **15.** 10,560
17. ▬▬▬▬▬▬▬▬▬▬   **19.** ▬
21. ▬▬▬▬▬▬▬▬▬▬▬▬   **23.** $\frac{1}{2}$ in.
25. $1\frac{3}{8}$ in.   **27.** $\frac{1}{4}$ in.   **29.** $1\frac{1}{2}$ ft   **31.** 1 in., $\frac{1}{2}$ in., $\frac{1}{4}$ in., $\frac{1}{8}$ in.   **33a.** 1 in.   **33b.** $1\frac{3}{4}$ in.   **33c.** $2\frac{1}{8}$ in.
33d. $3\frac{7}{8}$ in.   **33e.** 3 in.   **33f.** $\frac{3}{4}$ in.   **35.** $\frac{43}{8}$ **37.** C

Pages 208–209   Lesson 5-7

1. The least common multiple is the least number, other than zero, that is a multiple of two or more numbers.   **3.** 30   **5.** yes   **7.** 9   **9.** 22   **11.** 4 packages of hot dogs, 5 packages of hot dog buns, 2 packages of plates   **13.** yes   **15.** yes   **17.** no
19. no   **21.** 12   **23.** 21   **25.** 80   **27.** 208
29. 36   **31.** 280   **33.** 18   **35.** 12   **37.** Sample answer: 18 and 24, 36 and 72   **39.** $9\frac{2}{5}$
41. Sample answer: 6 + 234 = 240

Pages 212–213   Lesson 5-8

1. Use the LCM of the denominators to rename fractions so they will have the same denominators. Then compare the numerators.   **3.** The LCD of $\frac{2}{5}$ and $\frac{4}{9}$ is 45. So, rename the fractions with a denominator of 45. $\frac{2}{5} = \frac{18}{45}$ and $\frac{4}{9} = \frac{20}{45}$. Since 18 < 20, $\frac{2}{5} < \frac{4}{9}$.   **5.** 20   **7.** =   **9.** kitchen   **11.** 12
13. 45   **15.** >   **17.** =   **19.** >   **21.** <   **23.** =
25. $\frac{2}{7}$ **27.** $\frac{3}{5}, \frac{3}{7}, \frac{2}{5}, \frac{1}{6}$ **29.** $\frac{16}{90}$ and $\frac{8}{45}$; Since $\frac{16}{90} = \frac{8}{45}$, the cost is the same.   **31.** 300   **33.** $\frac{25}{28}$ **35.** 23

Pages 215–216   Lesson 5-9

1. Sample answer: Write the decimal as a fraction with a denominator of 100. Then simplify by using the GCF.   **3.** Ann; The decimal is written to the hundredths place. So, the denominator will be 100.
5. $\frac{9}{20}$ **7.** $4\frac{3}{8}$ **9.** $3\frac{1}{5}$ **11.** $8\frac{13}{20}$ **13.** $5\frac{16}{25}$
15. $2\frac{2}{5}$ **17.** $13\frac{9}{1,000}$ **19.** $7\frac{89}{100}$ **21.** 0.38; $\frac{19}{50}$
23. $\frac{1}{2}$ mi; $\frac{2}{5}$ mi; $\frac{3}{10}$ mi

25. krypton: $83\frac{4}{5}$; selenium: $78\frac{24}{25}$; sulfur: $32\frac{3}{50}$; carbon: $12\frac{11}{1,000}$ **27.** $\frac{3}{7}$ **29.** D

31.
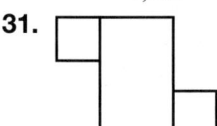

Pages 218–219 Lesson 5-10
1. Divide the numerator by the denominator. **3.** $0.\overline{4}$
5. 0.375 **7.** $0.58\overline{3}$ **9.** $0.\overline{7}$ **11.** $2.\overline{45}$ **13.** $0.8\overline{31}$
15. 0.75 **17.** $0.\overline{2}$ **19.** $0.\overline{45}$ **21.** $0.91\overline{6}$ **23.** $4.\overline{09}$
25. $0.1\overline{6}$ oz **29.** $29\frac{3}{4}$ **31.** D

Pages 220–223 Study Guide and Assessment
1. g **3.** e **5.** b **7.** f **9.** 3 **11.** 3, 9
13. prime **15.** neither **17.** 2×3^3 **19.** $2^2 \times 31$
21. 6 **23.** 2 **25.** 20 **27.** no; $\frac{5}{6}$ **29.** no; 7 to 8
31. $\frac{18}{5}$ **33.** $3\frac{4}{5}$ **35.** ▬▬▬▬
37. $1\frac{3}{4}$ inches **39.** 75 **41.** 84 **43.** 20 **45.** >
47. $\frac{4}{5}$ **49.** $3\frac{13}{20}$ **51.** 0.625 **53.** 24 ways
55. $30.40

Pages 224–225 Standardized Test Practice
1. A **3.** B **5.** A **7.** B **9.** A **11.** C **13.** D
15. 129 **17.** $20.49 **19.** $5.63

··

Chapter 6
Adding and Subtracting Fractions

Pages 230–231 Lesson 6-1
1.

3. Sample answer: If the numerator is close in value to the denominator, round up. If the numerator is about half the denominator, round to $\frac{1}{2}$. If the numerator is much smaller than the denominator, round down. **5.** 4 **7.** $\frac{1}{2}$ **9.** down
11. $2\frac{1}{2}$ cups **13.** 1 **15.** $6\frac{1}{2}$ **17.** $\frac{1}{2}$ **19.** 12
21. 4 **23.** $10\frac{1}{2}$ **25.** $5\frac{1}{2}$ **27.** down **29.** up
31. up **33a.** $\frac{23}{28}, \frac{2}{7}, \frac{5}{28}, \frac{1}{2}, \frac{11}{14}, \frac{17}{28}, \frac{5}{7}, \frac{3}{4}$
33b. salads, turkey **33c.** popcorn, chicken, frozen yogurt **35.** Sample answer: $5\frac{3}{8}, 5\frac{7}{16}, 5\frac{3}{5}$
37. sixteen ten-thousandths **39.** D

Pages 233–234 Lesson 6-2
1.

3. Sample answer: Rounding $4\frac{3}{8}$ to 4 is correct, but since the measure was rounded down, there would not be enough material to complete the picture frame. Nina should buy 20 inches of framing material. **5–9.** Sample answers are given.
5. $7 + 4 = 11$ **7.** $2\frac{1}{2} - \frac{1}{2} = 2$ **9.** $6 + 10 = 16$
11–27. Sample answers are given. **11.** $1 + \frac{1}{2} = 1\frac{1}{2}$
13. $8 - 1 = 7$ **15.** $1 + \frac{1}{2} = 1\frac{1}{2}$ **17.** $1 + 6 = 7$
19. $9 + 0 = 9$ **21.** $22 + 5 = 27$ **23.** 5 min − 1 min = 4 min **25.** 20 cups − 11 cups = 9 cups
27. $7 + 7 + 7 + 7 + 7 = 35$ **29.** 64 in. − 62 in. = 2 in. **31.** Sample answer: $\frac{5}{8}$ and $\frac{7}{16}$ **33.** $\frac{17}{100}$
35. 400,000 cm

Pages 236–237 Lesson 6-2B
1. Sample answer: Franco and Cesar eliminated the routes that they could not take to see which route they could. **3.** C **5.** Sample answer: Is $15,840 \div 18$ equal to 80, 88, 880, or 8,800? **7.** Viho is 8 years old. His father is 32 and his grandfather is 64.
9. 50¢ **11.** about 7 cups **13.** 12 **15.** D

Pages 240–241 Lesson 6-3
1. Sample answer: Add numerators and keep the denominators the same.
3.
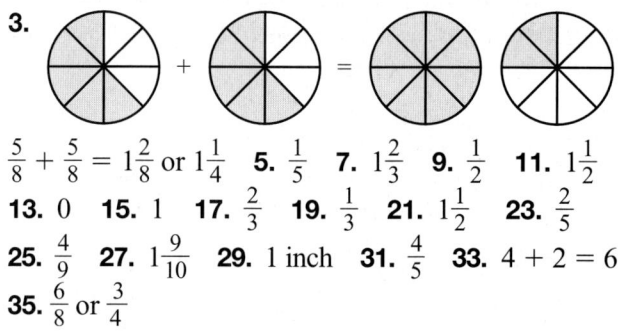

$\frac{5}{8} + \frac{5}{8} = 1\frac{2}{8}$ or $1\frac{1}{4}$ **5.** $\frac{1}{5}$ **7.** $1\frac{2}{3}$ **9.** $\frac{1}{2}$ **11.** $1\frac{1}{2}$
13. 0 **15.** 1 **17.** $\frac{2}{3}$ **19.** $\frac{1}{3}$ **21.** $1\frac{1}{2}$ **23.** $\frac{2}{5}$
25. $\frac{4}{9}$ **27.** $1\frac{9}{10}$ **29.** 1 inch **31.** $\frac{4}{5}$ **33.** $4 + 2 = 6$
35. $\frac{6}{8}$ or $\frac{3}{4}$

Page 242 Lesson 6-4A
1. Sample answer: you rename the units so that the answer makes sense. **5.** Sample answer: find a common denominator.

Pages 244–245 Lesson 6-4
1. Sample answer: You rename fractions with unlike denominators to get a common unit name.
3. $\frac{7}{16}$ **5.** $\frac{1}{12}$ **7.** $\frac{1}{4}$ **9.** $\frac{7}{8}$ **11.** $\frac{1}{16}$ **13.** $1\frac{1}{10}$
15. $\frac{8}{15}$ **17.** $\frac{7}{24}$ **19.** $\frac{7}{20}$ **21.** $\frac{17}{36}$ **23.** $\frac{3}{8}$

25. $\frac{5}{16}$ inch **27.** $\frac{3}{4}$ **29.** $\frac{1}{12}$ **31.** $1\frac{3}{10}$ **33.** $1\frac{1}{2}$
35. 30 feet **37.** Sample answer: $\frac{2}{8}$ or $\frac{1}{4}$ in. **39.** D

Pages 248–249 Lesson 6-5

1. Sample answer: Find the LCM of the denominators. **3.** Sample answer:

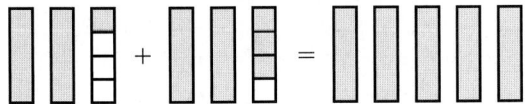

5. $10\frac{3}{4}$ **7.** $28\frac{1}{10}$ **9.** $7\frac{1}{15}$ **11.** 20 inches
13. $2\frac{2}{3}$ **15.** $19\frac{1}{12}$ **17.** $2\frac{1}{4}$ **19.** $8\frac{2}{5}$ **21.** $\frac{5}{24}$
23. $9\frac{13}{80}$ **25.** $14\frac{31}{40}$ **27.** $2\frac{1}{2}$ **29.** $1\frac{1}{4}$ pounds
31. Sample answer: How much more cotton was planted in 1996 than was estimated to be planted in 1997? **33.** D **35.** 0.8 kg

Page 249 Mid-Chapter Self Test

1. Sample answer: To avoid ruining the chili, you should round down to one-half teaspoon of salt. You can always add more. **3.** $22 - 15 = 7$ **5.** $\frac{3}{10}$
7. $\frac{7}{30}$ **9.** $20\frac{1}{6}$

Pages 251–253 Lesson 6-6

1. Sample answer:

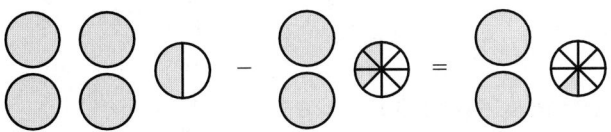

3. Sample answer: When Gail borrowed one from 10 she just carried it next to the 1 in $\frac{1}{5}$ and made it $\frac{11}{5}$. **5.** 30 **7.** $2\frac{5}{6}$ **9.** $\frac{7}{8}$ **11.** 2 **13.** 7 **15.** 29
17. $5\frac{1}{2}$ **19.** $3\frac{7}{10}$ **21.** $4\frac{7}{12}$ **23.** $7\frac{5}{12}$ **25.** $9\frac{3}{4}$
27. $7\frac{34}{35}$ **29.** $\frac{2}{3}$ **31.** $1\frac{23}{30}$ **33.** $1\frac{2}{3}$ **35a.** softball; $2\frac{5}{8}$ to $3\frac{1}{8}$ in. larger **35b.** softball; 1 to 2 ounces heavier **37b.** $1\frac{3}{4}$ in. **39.** $2\frac{17}{24}$ **41.** 1,010.5
43. 11

Pages 255–257 Lesson 6-7

1. 11 minutes **3.** Sample answer: Adding and subtracting measures of time is similar to adding and subtracting mixed numbers because you have to rename. **5.** 10 **7.** 10 min 45 s **9.** 3 h 50 min 40 s
11. 6 h 45 min **13.** $28 **15.** 68 **17.** 6; 27
19. 27; 23 **21.** 10 h 38 min **23.** 16 h 1 min
25. 20 min **27.** 16 min 55 s **29.** 16 h 15 min 20 s
31. 10 h 26 min 20 s **33.** 3 h 50 min 40 s

35. 59 min **37.** 10 h 30 min **39.** 21 h 20 min 10 s
41. 45 min **43.** 10:29 A.M. **45.** $3\frac{3}{4}$ in. **47.** B
49. 100,000,000 miles

Pages 258–261 Study Guide and Assessment

1. 5 **3.** $\frac{4}{5}$ **5.** LCD **7.** $5\frac{1}{2}$ **9.** 80 **11.** $\frac{1}{2}$
13. $11\frac{1}{2}$ **15.** down **17.** up **19.** $8 - 4 = 4$
21. $0 + 5 = 5$ **23.** $1\frac{4}{15}$ **25.** $\frac{3}{4}$ **27.** $\frac{1}{2}$ **29.** $1\frac{5}{18}$
31. $5\frac{2}{7}$ **33.** $1\frac{3}{10}$ **35.** $4\frac{7}{8}$ **37.** $5\frac{1}{3}$ **39.** $5\frac{7}{8}$
41. 68 **43.** 7 h 36 min **45.** 59 min 52 s
47. $8.50 **49.** $1\frac{1}{6}$ miles

Pages 262–263 Standardized Test Practice

1. B **3.** D **5.** C **7.** C **9.** E **11.** A
13. when both factors are less than one **15.** $\frac{5}{9}$
17. $1\frac{1}{16}$ **19.** 14 h 10 min

Chapter 7 Multiplying and Dividing Fractions

Pages 269–270 Lesson 7-1

1. Round $3\frac{1}{2}$ to 4. Round $9\frac{1}{8}$ to 9. Since $4 \times 9 = 36$, $3\frac{1}{2} \times 9\frac{1}{8} \approx 36$. **3.** Both Juan and Odina are correct. If you round $8\frac{1}{2}$ to 9 and $6\frac{1}{4}$ to 6, the product is 9×6, or 54. If you round $8\frac{1}{2}$ to 8 and $6\frac{1}{4}$ to 6, the product is 8×6, or 48. **5.** $\frac{1}{2}$ **7–9.** Sample answers are given. **7.** $\frac{1}{8} \times 16 = 2$ **9.** $3 \times 9 = 27$ **11.** $\frac{1}{2}$
13. $\frac{1}{2}$ **15.** 6 **17.** 3 or 4 **19–29.** Sample answers are given. **19.** $\frac{1}{4} \times 32 = 8$ **21.** $\frac{1}{7} \times 21 = 3$
23. $\frac{1}{6} \times 42 = 7$ **25.** $\frac{4}{9} \times 45 = 20$ **27.** $8 \times 3 = 24$
29. $15 \times 7 = 105$ **31.** about $\frac{2}{3} \times 6$, or about 4 million **33.** 1 h 3 min 51 s **35.** 0.498

Page 271–272 Lesson 7-2A

1. 6 square units **3.** $\frac{1}{6}$ **5.** $\frac{1}{12}$ **7.** To multiply fractions, multiply the numerators and then multiply the denominators.

Pages 275–276 Lesson 7-2

1. The rectangle is separated into thirds. Then the rectangle is separated into halves. The shaded portion shows overlap between $\frac{1}{3}$ of the rectangle and $\frac{1}{2}$ of the rectangle. This area represents the product, $\frac{1}{6}$. **3.** To find the product of fractions, you need to multiply the numerators and then multiply the denominators. If necessary, simplify the answer. **5.** $\frac{3}{20}$ **7.** $\frac{2}{15}$ **9.** $\frac{1}{3}$ **11.** about 105 pounds **13.** $\frac{8}{27}$ **15.** $\frac{1}{9}$ **17.** $\frac{2}{15}$ **19.** $\frac{2}{3}$ **21.** $\frac{10}{27}$ **23.** $\frac{2}{27}$ **25.** $6\frac{2}{3}$ **27.** $\frac{1}{12}$ **29.** $\frac{4}{9}$ **31.** $10\frac{1}{2}$ **33.** $\frac{4}{15}$ **35a.** $\frac{9}{64}$ **35b.** $\frac{16}{25}$ **37.** $\frac{3}{4} \times 36 = 27$ **39.** 2, 3, 6

Pages 278–279 Lesson 7-3

1. To multiply mixed numbers, express each mixed number as an improper fraction and then multiply as with fractions. **3.** $\frac{19}{3}$ **5.** $\frac{23}{4}$ **7.** $3\frac{3}{5}$ **9.** 38 **11.** $1\frac{1}{9}$ **13a.** $\frac{3}{4}$ **13b.** $\frac{3}{8}$ **15.** $\frac{23}{3}$ **17.** $\frac{14}{3}$ **19.** $\frac{33}{5}$ **21.** $\frac{35}{4}$ **23.** $6\frac{2}{3}$ **25.** $10\frac{1}{2}$ **27.** $4\frac{7}{8}$ **29.** 42 **31.** 21 **33.** $8\frac{1}{7}$ **35.** $7\frac{1}{3}$ **37.** 30 **39.** $7\frac{1}{2}$ **41.** $8\frac{1}{4}$ sq ft **43.** more; $2\frac{2}{3} \times 4\frac{1}{2} \approx 3 \times 4$ or 12 **45.** $3\frac{5}{12}$ **47.**

Phone Calls

Pages 282–283 Lesson 7-4

1. Sample answer: Multiply 2 by π by 3. **5.** $\pi = \frac{22}{7}$; $7\frac{6}{7}$ yd **7.** 6.0 m **9.** 12.6 in. **11.** $\pi = \frac{22}{7}$; $7\frac{1}{3}$ in. **13.** 37.7 yd **15.** 25.1 ft **17.** 9.7 yd **19.** 52.8 cm **21.** $\pi = \frac{22}{7}$; $15\frac{5}{7}$ ft **23.** The circumference is twice as long. **25.** $\frac{1}{2}$

Page 283 Mid-Chapter Self Test

1–3. Sample answers are given. **1.** $16 \times \frac{3}{4} = 12$ **3.** $3 \times \frac{1}{2} = 1\frac{1}{2}$ **5.** $\frac{1}{4}$ **7.** $3\frac{3}{8}$ **9.** 42.7 cm

Page 284 Lesson 7-5A

1.

3.

5. 2

Pages 287–288 Lesson 7-5

1. Multiply $\frac{1}{2}$ by $\frac{3}{2}$. **3.** 2 **5.** $\frac{1}{8}$ **7.** $\frac{1}{6}$ **9.** $1\frac{1}{8}$ **11.** 20 **13.** $1\frac{2}{3}$ **15.** $\frac{1}{5}$ **17.** 3 **19.** 7 **21.** 1 **23.** $\frac{5}{9}$ **25.** $\frac{4}{5}$ **27.** $\frac{1}{10}$ **29.** $\frac{1}{3}$ **31.** $\frac{5}{16}$ **33.** $\frac{8}{9}$ **35.** $\frac{2}{3}$ **37.** $\frac{9}{10}$ **39.** $\frac{2}{9}$ **41.** $3\frac{1}{2}$ **43.** 8 quarters **45a.** $\frac{11}{10}$ **45b.** $\frac{11}{10}$ **47.** $0.\overline{7}$ **49.** about 4 inches

Pages 290–291 Lesson 7-6

1. First, write $4\frac{5}{8}$ as the improper fraction $\frac{37}{8}$. Then invert the numerator and the denominator. The reciprocal of $4\frac{5}{8}$ is $\frac{8}{37}$. **3.** Change each mixed number to an improper fraction. Multiply the first fraction by the reciprocal of the second fraction. Divide 8 and 12 by the GCF, 4. Multiply $\frac{3}{1}$ and $\frac{3}{2}$ to find the product $\frac{9}{2}$, or $4\frac{1}{2}$. **5.** $\frac{23}{3}$; $\frac{3}{23}$ **7.** $3\frac{1}{5}$ **9.** $4\frac{1}{2}$ **11.** $1\frac{1}{7}$ **13.** 36 slices **15.** $\frac{32}{5}$; $\frac{5}{32}$ **17.** $\frac{14}{5}$; $\frac{5}{14}$ **19.** $\frac{15}{4}$; $\frac{4}{15}$ **21.** $\frac{37}{4}$; $\frac{4}{37}$ **23.** $7\frac{3}{5}$ **25.** 12 **27.** $\frac{4}{5}$ **29.** $4\frac{3}{8}$ **31.** $\frac{2}{3}$ **33.** 26 **35.** $\frac{2}{3}$

37. $8\frac{1}{3}$ **39a.** $\frac{7}{10}, 5\frac{11}{12}, 9\frac{5}{8}$ **39b.** $\frac{1}{10}, \frac{7}{12}, 6\frac{3}{8}$
39c. $\frac{3}{25}, 8\frac{2}{3}, 13$ **39d.** $1\frac{1}{3}, 1\frac{7}{32}, 4\frac{12}{13}$ **41.** 6
photographs **43.** Greater than; $\frac{2}{3}$ is less than $\frac{3}{4}$.
45. $\frac{10}{21}$ **47.** B **49.** two tenths; seven hundredths; four thousandths

Page 293–294 Lesson 7-7

1. fluid ounce, cup, pint, quart, gallon, ounce, pound, and ton **3.** 8 **5.** 4 **7.** 2 **9.** about 13,000 pounds **11.** 6 **13.** 144 **15.** 2 **17.** 40 **19.** 4,500 **21.** 10 **23.** $1\frac{1}{2}$ **25.** 40 **27.** 500 pounds **29.** 16 **31.** 3, 5, 9 **33.** E

Page 295 Lesson 7-7B

1.

Planet/Moon	Amount of water	Weight compared to Earth	Weight compared to Jupiter
Sun	28 cups	more	more
Mercury	$\frac{1}{3}$ cups	less	less
Venus	$\frac{9}{10}$ cups	less	less
Moon	$\frac{1}{6}$ cups	less	less
Mars	$\frac{3}{8}$ cups	less	less
Jupiter	3 cups	more	

3. 66 pounds **5.** 6 ounces

Pages 296–297 Lesson 7-8A

3.

5. Sample answer: Once you identify the pattern, then you can continue the pattern to solve the problem. **9a.** $\frac{31}{32}$ **9b.** Richard will not finish the sandwich, but the amount will be so small that it will be like he did eat it all. **11.** 1,476 sq cm **13.** C

Pages 299–300 Lesson 7-8

1. Sample answer: A sequence is a list of numbers in a specific order. **3.** Joshua; In the sequence, $2\frac{1}{2}$ is added to each number. The next number is $12\frac{1}{2} + 2\frac{1}{2}$, or 15. **5.** 17, 10 **7.** 125 **9.** 75, 90 **11.** $\frac{3}{4}, \frac{3}{8}$
13. 432, 2,592 **15.** 33 **17.** 1 **19.** 400 **21.** x^5
23. $\frac{1}{16}$ (sixteenth note), $\frac{1}{32}$ (thirty-second note), and $\frac{1}{64}$ (sixty-fourth note) **25a.** $\frac{1}{2}, \frac{1}{4}, \frac{1}{8}, \frac{1}{16}, \frac{1}{32}, \frac{1}{64}, \frac{1}{128}, \frac{1}{256}, \frac{1}{512}, \frac{1}{1,024}$ **25b.** 1 **27.** A

Page 301 Lesson 7-8B

1. Multiply the value in cell B5 by the value in cell B2. **3.** 8.000 m, 3.200 m, 1.280 m, 0.512 m, 0.2048 m, 0.08192 m

Pages 302–305 Study Guide and Assessment

1. k **3.** i **5.** h **7.** f **9.** d **11–16.** Sample answers are given. **11.** $10 \times 3 = 30$
13. $1 \times 13 = 13$ **15.** $\frac{2}{3} \times 18 = 12$ **17.** $\frac{7}{10}$
19. $7\frac{1}{2}$ **21.** $4\frac{1}{2}$ **23.** $13\frac{1}{2}$ **25.** 57.1 ft
27. $\pi = \frac{22}{7}; 5\frac{1}{2}$ yd **29.** $1\frac{1}{9}$ **31.** $\frac{2}{3}$ **33.** $\frac{1}{3}$
35. $\frac{21}{40}$ **37.** 11,000 **39.** 48 **41.** 176, 156
43. 2 **45.** 57 students **47.** 144 one-cup servings

Pages 306–307 Standardized Test Practice

1. C **3.** B **5.** B **7.** B **9.** D **11.** A
13. $5.05 **15.** $\frac{1}{2}$ yd **17.**

Chapter 8
Exploring Ratio, Proportion, and Percent

Page 311 Lesson 8-1A

1a. $\frac{1}{2}$ square unit **1b.** Triangle C is $\frac{1}{2}$ the size of triangle B. **3a.** $\frac{1}{2}$ **3b.** $\frac{1}{4}$ **3c.** 1 **3d.** $\frac{2}{1}$ **3e.** $\frac{1}{2}$
3f. $\frac{1}{2}$

Pages 313–315 Lesson 8-1

1. A ratio is a comparison of two numbers by division. A rate is a ratio of two measurements that have different units. **3.** Sample answer: Rates would be useful when shopping in the grocery store. They allow you to determine better buys. **5.** Sample answer: 15 to 34, $\frac{15}{34}$, 15 out of 34 **7.** $\frac{2}{5}$ **9.** $0.65 per soft drink **11–15.** Sample answers are given. **11.** 9 out of 16, 9 to 16, 9:16 **13.** 18 out of 29, 18 to 29, 18:29 **15.** 23 out of 25, 23 to 25, 23:25
17. $\frac{1}{3}$ **19.** $\frac{7}{9}$ **21.** $\frac{4}{9}$ **23.** 79 kilometers per hour **25.** $8.75 per ticket **27.** $0.11 per egg **29.** Sample answer: 13 out of 24; 13 to 24; 13:24 **31a.** $\frac{2}{25}$
31b. $\frac{6}{25}$ **33.** 25 miles **35a.** $\frac{1}{144}$ **35b.** $\frac{1}{64}$

37. $4\frac{5}{8}$ **39a.** 6.6 billion lb   **39b.** 34.1 billion lb

Page 316   Lesson 8-1B

1. $\frac{1}{4}$; $\frac{3}{4}$ **3.** Sample answer: The results are about the same.   **5.** 0.625

Pages 319–320   Lesson 8-2

1. A proportion is an equation stating that two ratios are equivalent.   **5.** no   **7.** 72   **9.** 120 dentists
11. yes   **13.** no   **15.** no   **17.** 8   **19.** 11
21. 100   **23.** 100   **25.** 6 pairs   **27.** 1,404
29. 15   **31.** $7\frac{1}{6}$ **33.** D

Page 321   Lesson 8-2B

1. Multiply the contents of cell B2 by 2.   **3.** 6 cups of mayonnaise, 24 T of mustard, 24 T of relish, 12 T of vinegar, 3 t of salt, $1\frac{1}{2}$ t of pepper, 60 cups of potatoes, 3 cups of parsley

Pages 322–323   Lesson 8-3A

1.

3. 15 handshakes   **5.** A diagram will help you understand and picture the information more clearly.

7.

$\frac{7}{8}$ in.
$\frac{1}{4}$ = 28 in.
$\frac{1}{4}$ = 28 in.
$\frac{1}{4}$ = 28 in.
$\frac{1}{2}$ of $\frac{1}{4}$ = 14 in.

9. Reynelda, Juliet, Keela, Pedro, Daniel
11. 417.5 kg   **13.** 6 cuts

Pages 325–327   Lesson 8-3

1. An architect would make a scale drawing or a model in order to show a building exactly as it looks, but smaller.   **3a.** $2\frac{1}{4}$ feet   **3b.** $3\frac{1}{2}$ feet
3c. $3\frac{1}{2}$ feet   **5a.** $1\frac{2}{3}$ yards   **5b.** $1\frac{1}{3}$ yards   **5c.** 2 yards   **7a.** $14\frac{1}{4}$ miles   **7b.** $23\frac{3}{4}$ miles   **7c.** $16\frac{5}{8}$ miles   **7d.** $45\frac{1}{8}$ miles   **7e.** $8\frac{5}{16}$ miles   **9.** 20 feet
11a. length: 5.18 m; width: 2.16 m; height: 1.58 m
11b. length: 4.93 m; width: 1.92 m; height: 1.47 m
13. 5.4

Page 327   Mid-Chapter Self Test

1. Sample answer: 11 to 19, $\frac{11}{19}$, 11:19   **3.** $\frac{3}{7}$
5. 60 mph   **7.** 96   **9.** 2.8

Page 329   Lesson 8-4A

1a.   **1b.**

1c.   **1d.**

1e.

3. Sample answer: Grid C from the first set is the same as grid A from the second set. Grid A from the first set is the same as grid B from the second set. Grid B from the first set is the same as grid C from the second set. Grid D from the first set is the same as grid D from the second set. Grid E from the first set is the same as grid E from the second set.

Pages 332–333   Lesson 8-4

1a. 25%   **1b.** 47%   **1c.** $33\frac{1}{3}$%   **1d.** 80%
1e. 50%   **1f.** $66\frac{2}{3}$%   **5.** $\frac{11}{20}$ **7.** 34%   **9.** 125%
11. $\frac{7}{50}$ **13.** $\frac{1}{100}$ **15.** $1\frac{3}{10}$ **17.** $1\frac{1}{20}$ **19.** $\frac{17}{100}$
21.   **23.**

25. 63%   **27.** 150%   **29.** 74%   **31.** 76%
33. 45%   **35a.** 48%   **35b.** 9%   **37a.** $\frac{1}{144}$, 0.01, 1%   **37b.** $\frac{1}{64}$, 0.02, 2%   **39.** 55 miles   **41.** $1\frac{1}{4}$
43. 30

Pages 335–336   Lesson 8-5

1.   **3.** Betty is correct. The decimal 3.78 is equivalent to 378%. Therefore, it is more than 100%.   **5.** 0.81   **7.** 0.008
9. 90%   **11.** 2%   **13.** 0.32

15. 0.01 **17.** 0.06 **19.** 0.003 **21.** 0.39 **23.** 0.04 **25.** 96% **27.** 36.4% **29.** 71.6% **31.** 7% **33.** 8% **35.** 20% **37.** 1.8% **39a.** 0.0321, 0.12, 0.09, 26.5 **39b.** $\frac{7}{100}$, $1\frac{129}{1,000}$, $\frac{3}{100}$, $\frac{47}{1}$ **39c.** 4%, 53.8%, 60%, 37.5% **41a.** 18% **41b.** 82% **43.** $1\frac{14}{25}$ **45.** D **47.** 5.4

Pages 338–339   Lesson 8-6

1. 75% = $\frac{3}{4}$. Round 1,976 to 2,000. $\frac{3}{4} \times 2,000 =$ 1,500. So, 75% of 1,976 is about 1,500. **5.** Sample answer: $\frac{1}{4} \times 200 = 50$ **7–17.** Sample answers are given. **7.** 50% **9.** $\frac{1}{5} \times 35 = \$7$ **11.** $\frac{1}{3} \times 60 =$ 20 **13.** $\frac{1}{2} \times 50 = 25$ **15.** $\frac{2}{5} \times 100 = 40$ **17.** 1 $\times 300 = 300$ **19.** 75% **21.** $66\frac{2}{3}\%$ **23.** 100% **25–27.** Sample answers are given. **25.** $\frac{3}{8} \times 48 = 18$ **27.** $\frac{1}{100} \times 10 = \frac{1}{10}$ **29.** 50% $\times$ 5,000 = 2,500; 20% $\times$ 5,000 = 1,000; 2,500 $-$ 1,000 = 1,500 **31.** *c*; because *a* and *b* equal 11 while *c* equals 0.11. **33.** 23.04 m² **35.** 38

Pages 342–343   Lesson 8-7

1. Sample answer: **Method 1:** Change the percent to a fraction. First, change the percent to a fraction. Then multiply the number by the fraction. **Method 2:** Change the percent to a decimal. First, change the percent to a decimal. Then multiply the number by the decimal. **Method 4:** Use a calculator. First, enter the percent by entering the number ⌜2nd⌝ [%]. Then press ⌜×⌝ and the number by which you are multiplying. Press ⌜=⌝. **3.** Kosey is correct. 125% = 1.25. 1.25 $\times$ 150 = 187.5. So, 125% of 150 is 187.5 **5.** 6.72 **7.** 5.88 **9.** 18 **11.** 92 **13.** 6 **15.** 98.98 **17.** 181.25 **19.** 137 **21.** 219 **23.** 6.4 **25a.** $45.00 **25b.** $33.75 **27a.** 20% **27b.** 84 **27c.** 300 **29.** Sample answer: $\frac{3}{8} \times 64 = 24$

Pages 344–347   Study Guide and Assessment

1. false; division **3.** true **5.** false; proportion **7.** true **9.** true **11.** true **13.** false; 34.6% **15.** Sample answer: Express the percent as a fraction with a denominator of 100 and then simplify. **17.** $\frac{11}{20}$ **19.** 15.75 pounds per week **21.** yes **23.** 25 **25.** 30 **27.** 1.5 units **29.** $\frac{3}{100}$ **31.** $1\frac{1}{2}$ **33.** 60% **35.** 55% **37.** 5% **39.** 0.38 **41.** 0.66 **43.** 130% **45.** 59.1% **47.** Sample answer: $\frac{1}{4} \times 80 = 20$ **49.** Sample answer: $\frac{2}{5} \times 240 = 96$ **51.** 16.02 **53.** 17 **55.** 0.162 **57.** 50 mph **59.** 8 cans

Pages 348–349   Standardized Test Practice

1. C **3.** A **5.** D **7.** D **9.** D **11.** C **13.** D **15.** 60% **17.** $1\frac{3}{8}$ inches **19.** 21

....

Chapter 9
Geometry: Investigating Patterns

Pages 353–355   Lesson 9-1

1. Sample answer: **Step 1:** Place the center of the protractor on the vertex of the angle with the straightedge along one side. **Step 2:** Using the scale that begins with 0° on the side of the angle, read the angle measure where the other side crosses the same scale. **3.** 50°; acute **5.** obtuse **7.** acute **9.** 74° **11.** 65°; acute **13.** 135°; obtuse **15.** 15°; acute **17.** right **19.** obtuse **21.** acute **23.** acute **25.** neither **27.** acute **29.** 18° **31.** Sample answer: A right angle is formed by the two pieces. The angles on the inside corner are obtuse and the angles on the outside corner are acute. **33a.** cut into the hill and flatten the road **33b.** larger **35.** $0.76 = \frac{19}{25}$; $0.15 = \frac{3}{20}$; $0.09 = \frac{9}{100}$ **37.** 52

Pages 356–357   Lesson 9-1B

1. Sample answer: Jesse's and Estella's thinking does make sense because 22 + 33 = 55, the number of students who play sports. **3.** 82 students **5.** You found that 5 students have only lunch bags, 10 have only backpacks, and 9 have neither a lunch bag nor a backpack. 5 + 10 + 9 = 24. So, there are 24 students going on the trip. **7.** A right angle measures 90°. The measure of the angle given is 90.4°. Since 90.4° is greater than 90°. It is only logical that the angle is an obtuse angle. **9.** 456 **11a.** Sample answer:

11b. Each figure has one more side than the previous figure, so the next figure must have six sides. **13.** C

Pages 360–361   Lesson 9-2

3. The corner of a sheet of paper is a 90° angle. A 45° angle is half of a 90° angle. So, to show a 45° angle, you can fold the corner in half.

5.

7. Sample answer: about 120°

9. about equal to

11.

13.

15.

17.

19–23. Sample answers are given. **19.** about 40°
21. about 55° **23.** about 70° **25a.** south **25b.** 180°

27.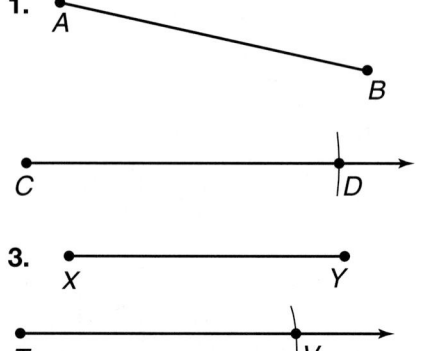

29. acute **31.** 120

Pages 362–363 Lesson 9-3A

1.

3.

5.

7.

Page 366 Lesson 9-3

1. To separate something into two congruent parts.

3. The crease bisects the angle.

5.

7.

9.

11.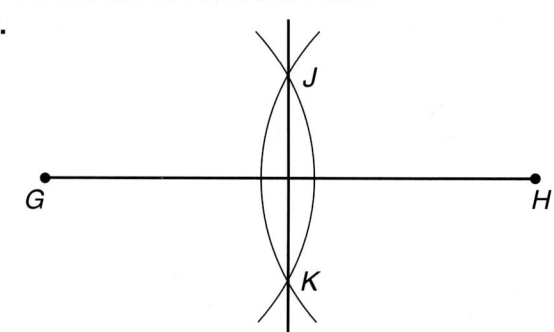

13–15. Answer not drawn to scale.

13.

15.

17. The diagonals bisect the corners of the square.

21. $\frac{37}{50}$

23.

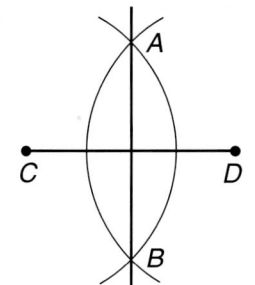

25. pentagon, hexagon
27a. quadrilaterals, pentagons, hexagons, octagons   **27b.** 360°; 540°; 360°; 1,080°

29.

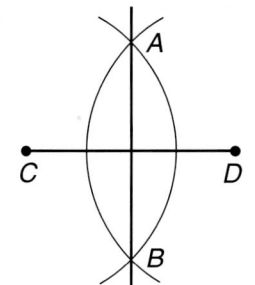

31. B

Pages 368–369   Lesson 9-4A

1. acute   **3.** right   **5.** Sample answer: The quadrilateral has two sides that are congruent.

7. Sample answer: The opposite sides of the quadrilateral are parallel.

Page 373   Mid-Chapter Self Test

1. 125°; obtuse   **3.** 90°; right   **5.** about 30°

7.

9.

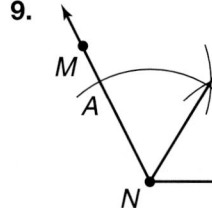

Page 374   Lesson 9-4B

1. The second net did not cover the cube. The "top" and "bottom" covers are on the same side of the cube.

3. Sample answer: Each net contains six squares. Each net has four squares lined up in a row. Each net has two squares positioned on opposite sides of the row of four squares.

Pages 372–373   Lesson 9-4

1. Sample answer: A chalkboard is a rectangle and a piece of floor tile is a square.   **3.** Jonathan; All squares are parallelograms since both sets of opposite sides of a square are parallel. Victoria is incorrect. Some parallelograms are not squares since some parallelograms do not have right angles.

5. equilateral triangle; yes   **7.** Alike: All sides are congruent. All angles are congruent.   Different: pentagon has 5 sides and square has 4 sides

9.

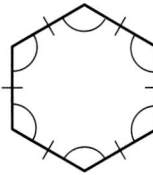

11. pentagon; yes   **13.** square; yes   **15.** Alike: all sides congruent; all angles congruent Different: triangle has three sides and square has four sides

17. Alike: quadrilaterals; at least 1 pair of parallel sides   Different: square has all sides congruent and four right angles

19.

21.

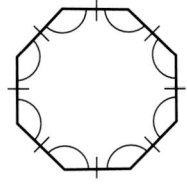

Pages 376–378   Lesson 9-5

5. yes

7.

9.

11. yes   **13.** yes   **15.** yes   **17.** yes   **19.** no

21.

23.

25. 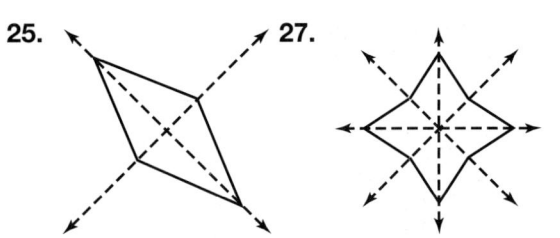 **27.**

29. yes **31.** no **33.** yes **35.** 8 **37.** 1 **41.** $6\frac{1}{3}$
43. 525 people

Pages 380–382   Lesson 9-6

1. The angles are congruent, they have the same shape, and they are different sizes. **5.** congruent
7. 3 **9.** neither **11.** neither **13.** congruent
15a. 2.5 m **15b.** $\overline{NM}$ **17.** A and D; A and F; A and G; B and D; B and F; B and G; F and D; A and B; D and G; F and G

19.

21. B **23.** $5\frac{3}{4}$

Pages 384–385   Lesson 9-6B

1.   **3.**

5.   **7.**

Pages 386–389   Study Guide and Assessment

1. f **3.** a **5.** e **7.** b **9.** d **11.** If an angle measures less than 90°, it is an acute angle. If an angle measures 90°, it is a right angle. If an angle measures between 90° and 180°, it is an obtuse angle. **13.** 42°; acute **15.** acute **17.** acute
19.

21. about 90°

23.

25.

27. pentagon; no

29.

31. yes

33.

35. similar

37.

Pages 390–391 Standardized Test Practice

1. C   **3.** D   **5.** A   **7.** B   **9.** A   **11.** C
13. 126 feet   **15.** $\frac{1}{8}$ **17.** 26 inches by 18 inches

Chapter 10
Geometry: Understanding Area and Volume

Pages 396–397 Lesson 10-1A

7–11. Sample answers are given.   **7.** 5 square units
9. $4\frac{1}{2}$ square units   **11.** The areas are the same.

Pages 400–401 Lesson 10-1

1. A rectangle is a special parallelogram.   **3.** If the lengths of the bases and the heights are the same, the areas will be the same.   **5.** 13.6 sq m   **7.** 54 in²
9. 38.8 cm²   **11.** 70 m²   **13.** 42.7 cm²
15. 4,611 cm²   **17a.** The area doubles.
17b. The area is increased four times.   **19.** 2, 3, 6

Pages 404–405 Lesson 10-2

1. Two congruent triangles form a parallelogram.
3. Ebony is correct. If 5.8 is used as the height, then the base is the length of the side to which the height is drawn, the 7 inch side.   **5.** 35 mm²   **7.** 1,136 m²
9. 13.5 units²   **11.** 51 ft²   **13.** 41.3 cm²
15. 1,400 in²   **17.** 128 cm²   **19.** 14 ft³; 16 ft
21. Sample answer: An elephant's ears expands its overall surface area, allowing it more space to release heat and cool itself.   **25.** 320 mm²
27. 46.4 ounces

Pages 407–409 Lesson 10-3

1. The circle can be cut and arranged into a figure like a parallelogram to find the area.   **5.** 254.3 m²
7. 1.4 ft²   **9.** 28.3 in²   **11.** 615.4 ft²   **13.** 95.0 in²
15. 379.9 in²   **17.** 63.6 m²   **19.** 379.9 mm²
21. 95.0 m²   **23.** about 63.6 m²   **25.** The area is multiplied by 4.   **27.** A

Page 411 Lesson 10-3B

1. Sample answer: The circle graph, because it allows a visual comparison of the proportions.
3. Sample answers: data that doesn't equal 100%; a bar or line graph

5.

World Population

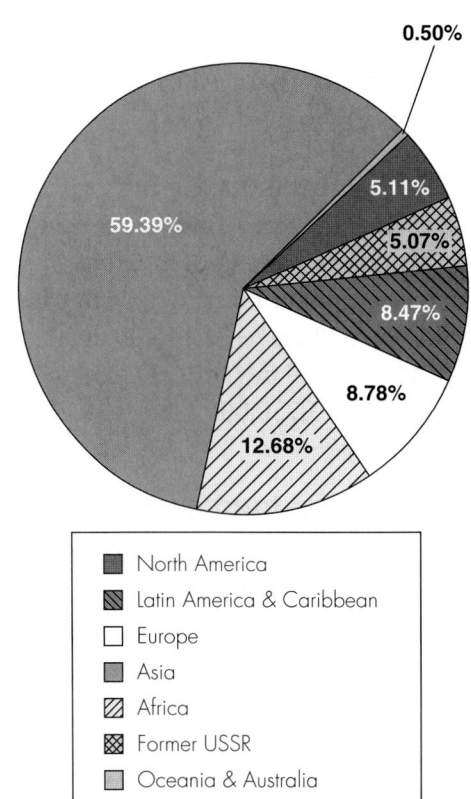

7. The area of the circle is divided into parts to represent the portion of the whole for each category.

Pages 413–414 Lesson 10-4

1. square pyramid   **5.** cone   **7.** 5; 9; 6
9. cylinder   **11.** triangular prism   **13.** cone
15. 4; 6; 4   **17.** none; none; none   **19.** 8; 18; 12
21a. 8; 12; 6   **21b.** yes   **23.** 1,519.76 in²   **25.** B

Page 414 Mid-Chapter Self Test

1. 3,850 ft²   **3.** 12.6 in²   **5.** cylinder

Page 415 Lesson 10-4B

1. the sides that are rectangles 3 units long and 2 units wide   **2.** yes   **3.** Draw the hexagonal base first. Then from each vertex, draw a line to represent the depth. Then connect the ends of the segments.
5.

Page 417 Lesson 10-5A

1. Sample answer: It allowed them to build a small pyramid with easy-to-move boxes first.   **3.** Emilio

7. **9.**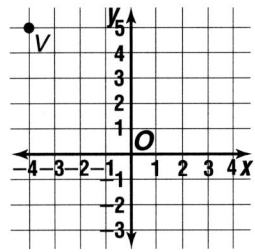

11. $(-3, 1)$ **13.** $(4, -3)$ **15.** $(2, 3)$ **17.** $(0, -2)$
19. $(-2, -3)$ **21.** $(-4, 4)$

23. **25.**

27. **29.**

31a. **31b.** yes

33. $(1, -5), (2, -3), (3, 0), (4, 5), (5, 8)$

 35.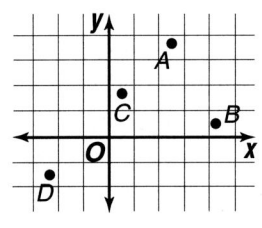

37. C   **39.** 83

Pages 462–463   Lesson 11-8A
1. The position of the triangle is changed.   **3.** The new figure is the mirror image of triangle *C*.

Pages 466–467   Lesson 11-8
1. Both translations and reflections are transformations. In translations and reflections, the image is the same size and shape as the figure. The translation image has the same orientation as the figure, but the reflection image is a flip of the figure.

3a. **3b.**

5.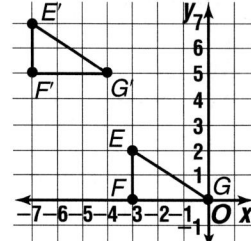

7. Reflection; the mountains are reflected in the lake.   **9.** reflection

11. **13.**

15.

17. Translations; the winged horses are translations of each other.   **19.** The image is a reflection of the polygon over the *y*-axis.
21. A

Pages 468–471   Study Guide and Assessment
1. false; positive   **3.** true   **5.** false; sometimes
7. false; never   **9.** true   **11.** false; reflection
13.

15.

17. < **19.** > **21.** $-15, -7, -1, 0, 6, 10$ **23.** 0
25. -6 **27.** -6 **29.** -8 **31.** 11 **33.** -11
35. 15 **37.** 0 **39.** -7 **41.** -4 **43.** -6 **45.** 4

47.   **49.**

51.   **53.**

55. 8 yd **57.** reflection

Pages 472–473 Standardized Test Practice

1. C **3.** D **5.** A **7.** A **9.** B **11.** B **13.** -8
15. (3, 3) **17.** ⊒ **19.** $28\frac{1}{2}$

....

Chapter 12
Algebra: Exploring Equations

Pages 477–479 Lesson 12-1

1. Sample answer: The 5 positive counters and the cup represent $x + 5$ and the 8 negative counters represent -8. **3.** 6 **5.** 7 **7.** -9 **9.** -6
11. -5 **13.** -1 **15.** 2 **17.** -6 **19.** -20
21. -43 **23.** -125 **25.** -2 **27.** -8 **29.** 10
31. -6 **33.** Sample answer: $37 + (-9) = 28$
35. 21 **37.** 9%

Pages 482–483 Lesson 12-2

1. Sample answer: The 3 negative counters and the cup represent $y - 3$ and the 4 positive counters represent 4. **3.** Sample answer: If the equation involves addition, you subtract counters. If the equation involves subtraction, you add counters.
5. -2 **7.** 7 **9.** 16 **11.** -2 **13.** -2 **15.** -1

17. -8 **19.** 5 **21.** 7 **23.** 3 **25.** 2 **27.** -9
29a. $-140 + r = -35$ **29b.** 105 feet **31.** B

Pages 486–487 Lesson 12-3

1. $4x = 8; x = 2$ **3.** Sample answer: They're both correct. Dividing by 2 is the same as multiplying by one-half. **5.** 8, 8, 2 **7.** 5 **9.** -10 **11.** 2
13. -3 **15.** -9 **17.** $\frac{1}{4}$ **19.** 5 **21.** 24 **23.** 38
25. 2 **27.** -36 **29.** 8.2 **31.** $4 million
33.

E
Change per month
D2/10
D3/10
D4/10
D5/10
D6/1
D7/10

35. 3 **37.** C

Page 487 Mid-Chapter Self Test

1. 6 **3.** 21 **5.** -15 **7.** -2 **9.** 3 gallons

Pages 490–491 Lesson 12-4

1. $3x + 2 = -1; x = -1$ **3.** subtract 2 from each side; 4 **5.** add 4 to each side; 20 **7.** 4 **9.** 3
11. -9 **13.** -32 **15.** -20 **17.** 32
19. 16 inches **21.** 8 **23.** 44, 46.5

Pages 492–493 Lesson 12-4B

1. Sample answer: no; Ed's information may be more useful because it contains all the known amounts. **3.** Sample answer: Subtract 8 from the solution. **5.** Sample answer: You could use the guess and check strategy. **7.** Sample answer: In solving a two-step equation, you undo the operations in reverse order of the order of operations. **9.** about 12 buses **11.** $39.99 **13.** 24 combinations
15. 4 ways

Page 495 Lesson 12-5A

1. 8 **3.** 13 **5a.** 12 **5b.** 18 **5c.** 21 **5d.** 11
7. 1, 7, 13, 19

Pages 497–499 Lesson 12-5

1.

input (y)	output (y−2)
−4	−6
−1	−3
0	−2
3	1

3. Sample answer: Juanita is correct. If you use 4, 5, and 6 for inputs, the outputs are 1, 2, and 3. Each output is 3 less than the input.

5.

input (n)	output $\left(\frac{1}{4}n\right)$
4	1
8	2
12	3

7. $n \div 2$ **9a.** $0.75c$ **9b.** $37.50

11.

input (n)	output (3n)
0	0
3	9
4	12

13.

input (n)	output $\left(\frac{1}{8}n\right)$
−8	−1
0	0
12	$1\frac{1}{2}$

15. $5n$ **17.** $n \div -2$ **19.** n^2 **21.** -22 **23.** $n \div 5$
25. 100, 60, 80, 70   **27.** $2n + 2$ **29.** -12

Pages 501–503   Lesson 12-6

1. Sample answer: Let the input values represent the x-coordinates and let the output values represent the corresponding y-coordinates.   **3.** Sample answer: Make a table recording the input and output of the given function. Write the input/output as an ordered pair. Record at least three ordered pairs on the table. Graph these ordered pairs and draw a line connecting the graphed points.

5.

7.

input (n)	output $\left(\frac{n}{2}\right)$
6	3
8	4
10	5

The rule is $n - 2$.

9.

input (n)	output (■)
−1	−3
2	0
4	2

11.

13.

15.
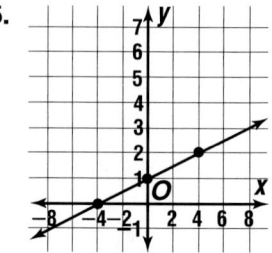

17.

input (n)	output (−3n)
3	−9
0	0
−2	6

19.

input (n)	output $\left(\frac{1}{2}n + 1\right)$
−4	−1
−2	0
0	1
2	2

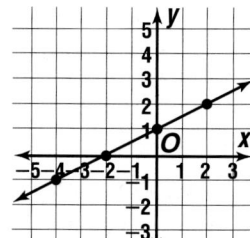

21.

input (n)	output (3n − 3)
−2	−9
1	0
4	9

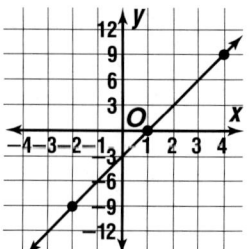

23.

input (*n*)	output (■)
0	0
4	2
8	4

The rule is $\frac{n}{2}$

25a. Jane: $25w - 20$; Julie: $20w$

25b.

25c. The point of intersection represents when the total earnings are the same for both girls.

27a.

input	output
1	61
2	62
3	63
4	64
5	65
6	66
7	67
8	68
9	69
10	70
11	71
12	72

27b.

27c. In 5 months, the card will be worth $65.

29.

input (*n*)	output (*n* + 7)
−5	2
0	7
4	11

31. about 31.4 meters

Pages 504–507 Study Guide and Assessment

1. variable   **3.** subtracted from   **5.** function table
7. −18   **9.** $2x + 3 = -9$ **11.** 3   **13.** −13
15. −3   **17.** 4   **19.** 2   **21.** 0   **23.** 4   **25.** −55
27. −5   **29.** −20   **31.** 6   **33.** −9   **35.** −3, 0, 6
37. −5   **39.** $n - 4$
41. 1, 3, 5

43. 8 laps   **45.** $n + 3.50$

Pages 508–509   Standardized Test Practice

1. B   **3.** D   **5.** D   **7.** E   **9.** D   **11.** E
13. 240 m³   **15.** about 15 people
17. circle

Chapter 13
Using Probability

Page 514   Lesson 13-1A

1. Sample answer: The number of even sums tossed and the number of odd sums tossed should be about the same. The number of even products tossed should be greater than the number of odd products tossed.   **3.** Sample answer: For the game involving sums, the bar graph resembled an isosceles triangle and is symmetrical about the axis which contains the sum of 7. For the products game, the bar graph reaches a maximum height at products 6 and 12 and the overall graph is not symmetrical.   **5.** Sample answer: A sum of 12 is less likely to occur since out of 36 results, a sum of 12 can only occur one way.

Pages 517–518   Lesson 13-1

1. Sample answer:

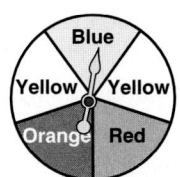

3. Sample answer: Complementary events are two events in which either one or the other can occur, but not both. The sum of their probabilities is 1. An example is the probability of snow and the probability of no snow. **5.** $\frac{2}{3}$; The event is very likely to occur. **7.** $\frac{1}{3}$; The event is not too likely to occur. **9.** 0; The event cannot occur. **11.** $\frac{1}{4}$; The event is not too likely to occur. **13.** $\frac{1}{2}$; The event is equally likely to occur. **15.** $\frac{3}{26}$; The event is not too likely to occur. **17.** $\frac{21}{26}$; The event is very likely to occur. **19.** $\frac{1}{2}$; not odd; $\frac{1}{2}$ **21.** 1; not an integer; 0 **23.** $\frac{2}{5}$; not greater than 18; $\frac{3}{5}$ **25a.** $\frac{1}{5}$ **25b.** Sample answer: Sometimes, eliminating the ones that cannot be correct leaves the correct answer. **25c.** increase; There would be fewer choices. **29.**

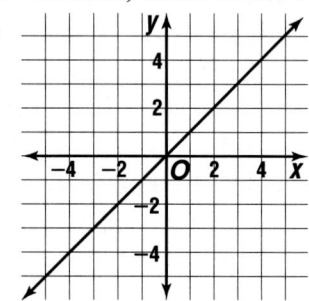

31. 47.36

Pages 520–521 Lesson 13-2A

1. Sample answer: Yes; surveying every fourth member provides an adequate sample. **3.** Sample answer: The information is easy to locate and it is easier to draw conclusions from organized data. **5.** Sample answer: It enables you to determine a reasonable interval width for the given data. **7.** Sample answer: Ashley organized the results of the survey by making a table. The table makes it easy to find information such as the most preferred and the least preferred pet. **9.** 8 days **11.** Sample answer: $20−$6 or $14. **13.** D

Pages 524–525 Lesson 13-2

1. Sample answer: Population is the entire group while random sample is a subset of the entire group. **5.** yes; There is probably a diverse group of people at a shopping center. **7a.** $\frac{3}{5}$, or 60% **7b.** about 9 **9.** no; You would probably survey people whose hobby is model trains. **11.** yes; A mall would have a diverse group of people. **13.** no; You would probably find many people who prefer the type of cars sold by the dealership. **15.** no; A lot of chocolate lovers would be in a chocolate factory. **17.** no; No Republicans were included in the survey. **19.** about 369 **21.** C **23.** 180 inches

Page 525 Mid-Chapter Self Test

1. $\frac{1}{6}$ **3.** $\frac{1}{2}$ **5a.** $\frac{3}{50}$, or 6% **5b.** about 900

Pages 527–529 Lesson 13-3

1. $\frac{4}{9}$ **5.** $\frac{1}{8}$ **7.** about 19 **9.** $\frac{2}{5}$ **11.** $\frac{1}{8}$ **13.** $\frac{4}{25}$ **15.** about 80 **17.** about 32 **19.** about 44 **21.** about $\frac{1}{40}$, or 2.5% **23c.** Sample answer: In the experiment, it is easier to see the black and white circles but it is hard to see the newsprint circles. The newsprint circles represent the camouflage trait. **25.** No; people in a jeans store may prefer the jeans sold by the store. **27.** 988 ft^2

Page 530 Lesson 13-3B

1. Sample answer: $\frac{27}{50}$ **3.** Sample answer: The fractions should be about the same. **5.** Sample answer: In the program, change each 10 to 20.

Pages 533–534 Lesson 13-4

1. Sample answer: At a restaurant, a customer can choose either a chicken or beef dinner and one of three beverages. How many possible outcomes are there? **3.** Sample answer: Tree diagrams are useful for organizing the outcomes. One disadvantage is that there could be too many outcomes. **5.** blue shirt, blue shorts; blue shirt, black shorts; blue shirt, red shorts; red shirt, blue shorts; red shirt, black shorts; red shirt, red shorts

7a.

			Outcome
A	T	T	ATT
		F	ATF
	F	T	AFT
		F	AFF
B	T	T	BTT
		F	BTF
	F	T	BFT
		F	BFF
C	T	T	CTT
		F	CTF
	F	T	CFT
		F	CFF

7b. $\frac{1}{2}$ **9.** leather, purple; leather, green; leather, black; leather, brown; nylon, purple; nylon, green; nylon, black; nylon, brown **11.** blue, red; blue, green; blue, white; blue, black; orange, red; orange,

green; orange, white; orange, black; yellow, red; yellow, green; yellow, white; yellow, black
13. tower, wood, 60; tower, wood, 100; tower, wood, 250; tower, plastic, 60; tower, plastic, 100; tower, plastic, 250; spinner, wood, 60; spinner, wood, 100; spinner, wood, 250; spinner, plastic, 60; spinner, plastic, 100; spinner, plastic, 250 **15.** 10 ways
17. 15 ways **19.** Sample answer: This is not a fair game. Only in two of the eight outcomes are all chips different. It could be made a fair game by giving Amiri 3 points or changing the second counter from red and white to green and white. **21.** C

Page 535 Lesson 13-4B
1. Sample answer: $\frac{22}{50}$ **3.** They are about the same.

Pages 538–539 Lesson 13-5
1. Multiply the probability of the first event by the probability of the second event. **3.** Flora is correct. The probability of a 4 or 5 is $\frac{2}{6}$, and the probability of a 6 is $\frac{1}{6}$. $\frac{1}{3} \times \frac{1}{6} = \frac{1}{18}$. **5.** $\frac{1}{10}$ **7a.** $\frac{2}{5}$
7b. $\frac{3}{10}$ **7c.** $\frac{3}{25}$ **9.** $\frac{1}{4}$ **11.** 0 **13.** $\frac{1}{3}$ **15.** $\frac{3}{8}$
17. $\frac{5}{18}$ **19a.** 0.48 **19b.** 0.08 **21.** 20 ways **23.** D

Pages 540–543 Study Guide and Assessment
1. e **3.** g **5.** b **7.** c **9.** d **11.** Sample answer: Multiply the probability of the first event by the probability of the second event. **13.** $\frac{1}{3}$; The event is not too likely to occur. **15.** $\frac{5}{6}$; The event is very likely to occur. **17.** $\frac{2}{3}$; The event is very likely to occur. **19.** no; At a football game, you would most likely find people who prefer football. **21a.** $\frac{7}{20}$ or 35% **21b.** 147 students **23.** about $\frac{5}{16}$ or 31.25% **25.** black jeans–tapered; black jeans–straight; black jeans–baggy; blue jeans–tapered; blue jeans–straight; blue jeans–baggy **27.** ball game–Friday; ball game–Saturday; amusement park–Friday; amusement park–Saturday; concert–Friday; concert–Saturday; **29.** $\frac{1}{4}$ **31.** $\frac{1}{6}$ **33a.** 11 **33b.** 32 **35.** purple skirt–yellow vest; purple skirt–purple sweater; white skirt–yellow vest; white skirt–purple sweater; yellow skirt–yellow vest; yellow skirt–purple sweater

Pages 544–545 Standardized Test Practice
1. D **3.** C **5.** B **7.** D **9.** A **11.** C **13.** C **15a.** $\frac{1}{6}$ **15b.** $\frac{4}{75}$

Photo Credits

Researchers; **377** Fred Bavendam/Peter Arnold, Inc.; **379** Jeff Greenberg/Peter Arnold, Inc.; **382** Matt Meadows; **389** John Evans; **392** (t)Matt Meadows, (c)Diane Graham-Henry & Kathleen-Aguilar, (b)Doug Martin; **393** (t)Mark Steinmetz, (c)BLT Productions, (b)KS Studio; **394** (bkgd)Richard Passmore/Tony Stone Images, (l)Aaron Haupt, (r)KS Studio; **394-395** Doug Martin; **398** Focus on Sports; **401** Mike Timo/Tony Stone Images; **402** Paul Souders/Corbis; **404** SuperStock; **405** James L. Amos/Peter Arnold, Inc.; **408** Aaron Haupt; **409** courtesy Matt Ghaffari/USA Wrestling; **412** (t)Craig Wells/Tony Stone Images, (b)Wil & Deni McIntyre/Photo Researchers; **416** (t)Matt Meadows, (b)Scott Cunningham; **419** Aaron Haupt; **422** Spencer Jones/FPG; **424** Marc Chamberlain/ Tony Stone Images; **429** Audrey Gibson/The Stock Market; **432** (bkgd)courtesy Tony Hall's Office, courtesy Marcy Kaptur; **432-433** Joe Sohm/Photo Researchers; **434** Steve Kaufman/ Peter Arnold, Inc.; **435** Janice Rubin/Black Star; **437** David Ball/The Stock Market; **439** Robert Dunne/Photo Researchers; **441** Doug Martin; **443** TSADO/Tom Stack & Assoc.; **445** Rafael Macia/Photo Researchers; **449** Vanessa Vick/Photo Researchers; **450** John Shaw/Tom Stack & Assoc.; **452** Charles Krebs/The Stock Market; **453** (t)Doug Martin, (c)US Dept. of Commerce, (bl)Richard T. Nowitz, (br)Aaron Haupt; **454** (l c) Doug Martin, (r)Aaron Haupt; **456** Everett Collection; **457** Aaron Haupt; **460** Van Bucher/Photo Researchers; **461 463** Aaron Haupt; **464** Bob Firth; **467** (t)John Shaw/Tom Stack & Assoc., (b)M.C. Escher/Cordon Art B.V.; **471** Aaron Haupt; **474** (l)Aaron Haupt, (r)Doug Martin; **474** Aaron Haupt; **476** (t b)Matt Meadows, (cl)Latent Image; **477** Matt Meadows; **478** Jonathon Eric/Sports Photo Masters; **480** NASA; **484** (t)Franz Gorski/Peter Arnold, Inc., (b)Kevin R. Morris/Corbis; **485** GK & Vikki Hart/The Stock Market; **487** Universal-Amblin/ Shooting Star; **489** Aaron Haupt; **492** (t)Kenji Kerins, (c b)Matt Meadows; **496** Tom McHugh/Photo Researchers; **497** Merlin D. Tuttle/Bat Conservation International; **498** Gordana Stavanovic/ *Windsor Star*; **499** Daniel R. Westergren/ National Geographic Society; **500** Matt Meadows; **507** David Barnes/Tony Stone Images; **510 511** Doug Martin; **512** (bkgd)J.H. Pete Car-michael/Image Bank, Brian Stablyk/Tony Stone Images; **512** Art Wolfe/Tony Stone Images; **515** David Young-Wolff/ Photo-Edit; **516** Aaron Haupt; **517** David Brownell; **518** Michael Keller/The Stock Market; **519** (bkgd)SuperStock, (t)Pat & Tom Leeson/Photo Researchers, (bl)J.K. Lawrence Photography, (br)KS Studio; **520** KS Studio; **522** (t)Lowell Georgia/Photo Researchers, (b)Bill Aron/ PhotoEdit; **523** Dennis MacDonald/ PhotoEdit; **524** Doris J. Brooks; **525** GK & Vikki Hart/The Image Bank; **526** Doug Martin; **529** Joseph McBride/Tony Stone Images; **532** Jon Feingersh/The Stock Market; **534** Comstock; **536** Mark Burnett; **537** Michael Gionecci/Photo Researchers; **547** (t br)Aaron Haupt, (c)TSADO/Tom Stack & Assoc., (bl)KS Studio, (bc)Doug Martin; **608** Aaron Haupt.
Teacher's Wraparound Edition: iv v viii Mark Burnett; **ix** (l)Hickson & Assoc., (lc)AT&T, (r)Mark Burnett, (rc)Bob Mullenix; **x** Thomas Kitchin/Tom Stack & Assoc.; **xi** Aaron Haupt; **xii** Don Valentine/Tony Stone Images; **xiii** Courtesy Biney & Smith; **xiv** Elisabeth Weiland/Photo Researchers; **xv** William Blake/Corbis; **xvi** Doug Martin; **xvii** Bill Bachman/Photo Researchers; **xviii** SuperStock; **xix** Steve Kaufman/Peter Arnold, Inc.; **xx** John Cancalosi/Peter Arnold, Inc.; **xxi** GK & Vikki Hart/The Image Bank; **T05** Scott Cunningham; **T10** (t)John Shaw/Tom Stack & Assoc., (cb) Doug Martin, (l)Dominic Oldershaw, (r)BLT Productions; **T11** (t)Scott Cunningham, (b)KS Studio; **T12** KS Studio; **T13** Aaron Haupt; **T14** KS Studio; **T15** Scott Cunningham; **T16** BLT Productions; **T17 T18 T19** KS Studio; **T21** Scott Cunningham; **T22 T23** Geoff Butler; **T24** (t)Tim Courlas, (b)George Haling/Photo Researchers; **T30 T31** KS Studio; **2A** (t)Matt Meadows (b)Aaron Haupt; **44A** Ted Horowitz/The Stock Market; **92A** (t)Aaron Haupt, (b)Robert Houser/Index Stock; **130A** Ed Taylor Studio/FPG; **176A** Doug Martin; **226A** Telegraph Colour Library/FPG; **250A** Mark Burnett/Photo Researchers; **266A** Doug Martin; **308A** Index Stock; **394A** Richard Passmore/Tony Stone Images; **432A** Joe Sohm/Photo Researchers; **474A** Aaron Haupt; **512A** J.H. Pete Charmichael/The Image Bank.

Glossary

A

acute angle (352) An angle with a measure greater than 0° and less than 90°.

algebra (22) A mathematical language that uses letters along with numbers. The letters stand for numbers that are unknown. $10x - 3 = 17$ is an example of an algebra equation.

algebraic expression (22) A combination of variables, numbers, and at least one operation.

angle (352) Two rays with a common endpoint form an angle.

angle *BAC* or ∠*BAC*

area (146) The number of square units needed to cover a surface enclosed by a geometric figure.

average (71) The sum of two or more quantities divided by the number of quantities; the mean.

B

bar graph (54) A graph using bars to compare quantities. The height or length of each bar represents a designated number.

bar notation (218) In repeating decimals, the line or bar placed over the digits that repeat. For example, $2.\overline{63}$ indicates the digits 63 repeat.

base (28) In a power, the number used as a factor. In 10^3, the base is 10. That is, $10^3 = 10 \times 10 \times 10$.

base (398) Any side of a parallelogram.

base (412) The faces on the top and bottom of a three-dimensional figure.

bisect (364) To separate something into two congruent parts.

box-and-whisker plot (76) A diagram that summarizes data using the median, the upper and lower quartiles, and the extreme values. A box is drawn around the quartile value and whiskers extend from each quartile to the extreme data points.

C

cell (144) The basic unit of a spreadsheet. A cell can contain data, labels, or formulas.

center (280, 413) The given point from which all points on a circle or a sphere are the same distance.

centimeter (100) A metric unit of length. One centimeter equals one-hundredth of a meter.

circle (280) The set of all points in a plane that are the same distance from a given point called the center.

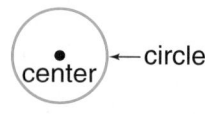

circle graph (60) A graph used to compare parts of a whole. The circle represents the whole and is separated into parts of the whole.

circumference (280) The distance around a circle.

clustering (113) A method used to estimate decimal sums and differences by rounding a group of closely related numbers to the same whole number.

combination (532) An arrangement or listing of objects in which order is not important.

common multiples (206) Multiples that are shared by two or more numbers. For example, some common multiples of 2 and 3 are 6, 12, and 18.

compass (362) An instrument used for drawing circles or parts of circles.

compatible numbers (133, 268) Two numbers that are easy to divide mentally. They are often members of fact families.

complementary (353) Two angles are complementary if the sum of their measures is 90°.

complementary events (516) Two events in which either one or the other must take place, but they cannot both happen at the same time. The sum of their probabilities is 1.

composite number (181, 182) Any whole number greater than 1 that has more than two factors.

cone (413) A three-dimensional figure with curved surfaces, a circular base and one vertex.

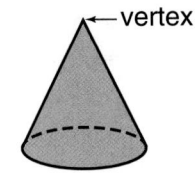

congruent angles (363) Angles that have the same angle measure.

congruent figures (379) Figures that are the same size and shape. The symbol ≅ means *is congruent to*.

congruent segments (362) Segments having the same length.

coordinate grid (459) Another name for a coordinate system.

coordinate system (82, 459) A plane in which a horizontal number line and a vertical number line intersect at their zero points.

cross products (318) The products of the terms on the diagonals when two ratios are compared. If the cross products are equal, then the ratios form a proportion. In the proportion $\frac{3}{6} = \frac{4}{8}$, the cross products are 3×8 and 6×4.

cubed (28) The product in which a number is a factor three times. Two cubed is 8 because $2 \times 2 \times 2 = 8$.

cup (292) A customary unit of capacity equal to 8 fluid ounces.

cylinder (413) A three-dimensional figure with all curved surfaces, two circular bases and no vertices.

D

data (46) Numerical information gathered for statistical purposes.

decagon (370) A polygon having ten sides.

degree (352) The most common unit of measure for angles.

diameter (280) The distance across a circle through its center.

distributive property (137) For any numbers a, b, and c, $a(b + c) = ab + ac$ and $(b + c)a = ba + ca$.

E

edge (352, 412) The intersection of faces of a three-dimensional figure.

equation (34) A mathematical sentence that contains the equal sign, =.

equilateral triangle (371) A triangle with three congruent sides.

equivalent fractions (193) Fractions that name the same number. $\frac{3}{4}$ and $\frac{6}{8}$ are equivalent.

evaluate (22) To find the value of an expression by replacing variables with numerals.

event (515) A specific outcome or type of outcome.

experimental probability (197) An estimated probability based on the relative frequency of positive outcomes occurring during an experiment.

exponent (28) In a power, the number of times the base is used as a factor. In 5^3, the exponent is 3. That is, $5^3 = 5 \times 5 \times 5$.

extreme value (76) The least value or the greatest value in a set of data.

F

face (412) The flat surfaces of a three-dimensional figure.

factor (28) A number that divides into a whole number with a remainder of zero. 5 is a factor of 30.

factor tree (183) A diagram showing the prime factorization of a number. The factors branch out from the previous factors until all the factors are prime numbers.

fair game (514) A game in which players have an equal chance of winning.

fluid ounce (292) A customary unit of capacity.

foot (202) A customary unit of length equal to 12 inches.

frequency table (46) A table for organizing a set of data that shows the number of times each item or number appears.

function (496) A relation in which each element of the input is paired with exactly one element of the output according to a specified rule.

function machine (494) A machine that uses a number called the input, performs one or more operations on it, and produces a result called the output.

function table (496) A table organizing the input, rule, and output of a function.

gallon (292) A customary unit of capacity equal to 4 quarts.

gram (164) The basic unit of mass in the metric system.

greatest common factor (GCF) (188) The greatest of the common factors of two or more numbers. The GCF of 24 and 30 is 6.

height (398) The shortest distance from the base of a parallelogram to its opposite side.

hexagon (370) A polygon having six sides.

improper fraction (198) A fraction that has a numerator that is greater than or equal to the denominator.

inch (202) A customary unit of length. Twelve inches equal one foot.

independent events (536) Two or more events in which the outcome of one event does *not* affect the outcome(s) of the other event(s).

input (494) Information or data given to a function machine to produce output or results.

integer (434) The whole numbers and their opposites. . . . , $-3, -2, -1, 0, 1, 2, 3, . . .$

interval (50) The difference between successive values on a scale.

kilogram (164) A metric unit of mass. One kilogram equals one thousand grams.

L

leaf (68) The units digit written to the right of the vertical line in a stem-and-leaf plot.

least common denominator (LCD) (210) The least common multiple of the denominators of two or more fractions.

least common multiple (LCM) (206) The least of the common multiples of two or more numbers. The LCM of 2 and 3 is 6.

like fractions (238) Fractions with the same denominator.

line graph (54) A graph used to show change and direction of change over a period of time.

line of symmetry (375) A line that divides a figure into two halves that are reflections of each other.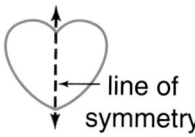

line segment (362) Two endpoints and the straight path between them. A line segment is named by its endpoints. A representation of line segment *ST (ST)* is shown below.

liter (164) The basic unit of capacity in the metric system. A liter is a little more than a quart.

lower quartile (77) The median of the lower half of a set of data.

M

mean (71) The sum of the numbers in a set of data divided by the number of pieces of data.

measures of central tendency (71) Numbers or pieces of data that can represent the whole set of data. These common measures of central tendency are *mean*, *median*, and *mode*.

median (71) The middle number in a set of data when the data are arranged in numerical order. If the data has an even number, the median is the mean of the two middle numbers.

meter (102) The basic unit of length in the metric system.

metric system (102) A base-ten system of weights and measures. The meter is the basic unit of length, the gram is the basic unit of weight, and the liter is the basic unit of capacity.

mile (202) A customary unit of length equal to 5,280 feet or 1,760 yards.

milligram (164) A metric unit of mass. One milligram equals one-thousandth of a gram.

milliliter (164) A metric unit of capacity. One milliliter equals one-thousandth of a liter.

millimeter (100) A metric unit of length. One millimeter equals one-thousandth of a meter.

mixed number (198) The sum of a whole number and a fraction. $1\frac{1}{2}$, $2\frac{3}{4}$, and $4\frac{5}{8}$ are mixed numbers.

mode (71) The number(s) or item(s) that appear most often in a set of data.

multiple (206) The product of the number and any whole number.

N

negative integer (434) Integer that is less than zero.

net (374) The shape that is formed by "unfolding" a three-dimensional figure. The net shows all the faces that make up the surface area of the figure.

O

obtuse angle (352) Any angle that measures greater than 90° but less than 180°.

octagon (370) A polygon having eight sides.

opposite (435) Two integers are opposites if they are represented on the number line by points that are the same distance from zero, but in opposite directions from zero. The sum of opposites is zero.

ordered pair (82, 459) A pair of numbers used to locate a point in the coordinate system. The ordered pair is written in this form: (*x*-coordinate, *y*-coordinate).

order of operations (16, 28) The rules to follow when more than one operation is used.
1. Do all powers before other operations.
2. Do all multiplications and divisions from left to right.
3. Then do all additions and subtractions from left to right.

origin (82, 459) The point of intersection of the *x*-axis and *y*-axis in a coordinate system.

ounce (292) A customary unit of weight. 16 ounces equals one pound.

outcomes (515) Possible results of a probability event. For example, 4 is an outcome when a number cube is rolled.

output (494) The result of input that has had one or more operations performed on it in a function machine.

P

parallel (371) Lines going in the same direction and always being the same distance apart. Parallel lines never meet or cross each other.

parallelogram (371) A quadrilateral that has both pairs of opposite sides equal and parallel.

pentagon (370) A polygon with five sides.

percent (330) A ratio with a denominator of 100.

perimeter (145) The distance around any closed figure.

pint (292) A customary unit of capacity equal to two cups.

place value (95) A system for writing numbers in which the position of the digit determines its value.

polygon (368, 370) A simple closed figure in a plane formed by three or more line segments.

population (522) The entire group of items or individuals from which the samples under consideration are taken.

positive integer (434) Integer that is greater than zero.

pound (292) A customary unit of weight equal to 16 ounces.

power (28) A number that can be written using an exponent. The power 3^2 is read *three to the second power*, or *three squared*.

prime factorization (183) Expressing a composite number as the product of prime numbers. For example, the prime factorization of 63 is $3 \times 3 \times 7$.

prime number (181, 182) A whole number greater than 1 that has exactly two factors, 1 and itself.

prism (412) A three-dimensional figure that has two parallel and congruent bases in the shape of polygons and at least three lateral faces shaped like rectangles. The shape of the bases tells the name of the prism.

proportion (317) An equation that shows that two ratios are equivalent, $\frac{a}{b} = \frac{c}{d}$, $b \neq 0$, $d \neq 0$.

protractor (352) An instrument used to measure angles.

pyramid (412) A solid figure that has a polygon for a base and triangles for sides. A pyramid is named for the shape of its base.

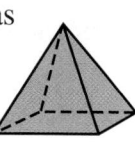

Q

quadrant (459) One of the four regions into which two perpendicular number lines separate the plane.

quadrilateral (368, 370) A polygon with four sides.

quart (292) A customary unit of capacity equal to two pints.

R

radius (280) The distance from the center of a circle to any point on the circle.

radius

random (522) When an outcome is chosen without any preference the outcome occurs at random.

range (72) The difference between the greatest number and the least number in a set of data.

rate (312) A ratio of two measurements having different units.

ratio (191, 193) A comparison of two numbers by division. The ratio of 2 to 3 can be stated as 2 out of 3, 2 to 3, 2:3, or $\frac{2}{3}$.

ray (363) A part of a line that extends indefinitely from one point in one direction. A representation of ray DE $(\overrightarrow{DE})$ is shown below.

D   E

reciprocals (285) Any two numbers whose product is 1. Since $\frac{5}{6} \times \frac{6}{5} = 1$, the reciprocal of $\frac{5}{6}$ is $\frac{6}{5}$.

rectangle (371) A quadrilateral with four congruent angles.

rectangular prism (412) A three-dimensional figure with six rectangular shaped faces. A rectangular prism has a total of six faces, twelve edges, and eight vertices.

reflection (375, 464) A type of transformation where a figure is flipped over a line.

regular polygon (370) A polygon having all sides congruent and all angles congruent.

repeating decimal (218) A decimal whose digits repeat in groups of one or more. 0.181818... can also be written $0.\overline{18}$. The bar above the digits indicates those digits repeat.

right angle (352) An angle that measures 90°.

S

sample (522) A randomly-selected group that is used to represent a whole population.

sample space (515) The set of all possible outcomes.

scale (50) The set of all possible values of a given measurement, including the least and greatest numbers in the set, separated by the intervals used.

scale drawing (324) A drawing that is similar but either larger or smaller than the actual object.

sequence (298) A list of numbers in a certain order, such as, 0, 1, 2, 3, or 2, 4, 6, 8.

sides (145) Line segments that enclose a polygon.

similar figures (379) Figures that have the same shape but different sizes. The symbol ~ means *is similar to*.

simplest form (194) The form of a fraction when the GCF of the numerator and the denominator is 1. The fraction $\frac{3}{4}$ is in simplest form because the GCF of 3 and 4 is 1.

simulation (535) The process of acting out a problem.

solution (34) Any number that makes an equation true. The solution for $12 = x + 7$ is 5.

solve (34) To replace a variable with a number that makes an equation true.

sphere (413) A three-dimensional figure with no faces, bases, edges, or vertices. All of its points are the same distance from a given point called the center.

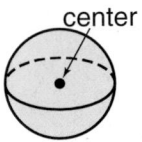
center

spreadsheet (144) A tool used for organizing and analyzing data.

square (371) A parallelogram with all sides congruent and all angles congruent.

squared (28) A number multiplied by itself; 4×4, or 4^2.

square pyramid (412) A pyramid with a square base.

statistics (46) The study of collecting, analyzing, and presenting data.

stem (68) The greatest place value common to all the data that is written to the left of the line in a stem-and-leaf plot.

stem-and-leaf plot (68) A system used to condense a set of data where the greatest place value of the data forms the stem and the next greatest place value forms the leaves.

straightedge (358) Any object with a straight side that can be used to draw a straight line.

supplementary (353) Two angles are supplementary if the sum of their measures is 180°.

surface area (421) The sum of the areas of all the surfaces (faces) of a three-dimensional figure.

T

terminating decimal (214) A decimal whose digits end. Every terminating decimal can be written as a fraction with a denominator of 10, 100, 1000, and so on.

theoretical probability (515) The ratio of the number of ways an event can occur to the number of possible outcomes.

three-dimensional figure (412) A figure that encloses a part of space.

ton (292) A customary unit of weight equal to 2,000 pounds.

transformation (464) Movement of geometric figures to new points in a coordinate system.

translation (384, 464) One type of transformation where a figure is slid horizontally, vertically, or both.

tree diagram (531) A diagram used to show the total number of possible outcomes in a probability experiment.

triangle (368, 370) A polygon with three sides.

U

unfair game (514) A game in which players do not have an equal chance of winning.

upper quartile (77) The median of the upper half of a set of numbers.

variable (22) A symbol, usually a letter, used to represent a number.

vertex (352) A vertex of a polygon is a point where two sides of the polygon intersect.

vertex (412) The point where the edges of a three-dimensional figure intersect.

volume (418) The amount of space that a three-dimensional figure contains. Volume is expressed in cubic units.

x-**axis** (82, 459) The horizontal line of the two perpendicular number lines in a coordinate plane.

x-**coordinate** (82, 459) The first number of an ordered pair.

yard (202) A customary unit of length equal to 3 feet, or 36 inches.

y-**axis** (82, 459) The vertical line of the two perpendicular number lines in a coordinate plane.

y-**coordinate** (82, 459) The second number of an ordered pair.

zero pair (441) The result of pairing one positive counter with one negative counter.

Spanish Glossary/Glosario

acute angle / ángulo agudo (352) Ángulo que mide más de 0° y menos de 90°.

algebra / álgebra (22) Lenguaje matemático que usa letras y números. Las letras representan números desconocidos.

$10x - 3 = 17$ es un ejemplo de ecuación algebraica.

algebraic expression / expresión algebraica (22) Combinación de variables, números y al menos una operación.

angle / ángulo (352) Dos rayos con un extremo común forman un ángulo.

ángulo *BAC* ó ∠*BAC*

area / área (146) Número de unidades cuadradas que se requieren para cubrir la superficie cerrada por una figura geométrica.

average / promedio (71) Suma de dos o más cantidades dividida entre el número de cantidades; la media.

bar graph / gráfica de barras (54) Gráfica que usa barras para comparar cantidades. La altura o longitud de cada barra representa un número específico.

bar notation / notación de barras (218) En los decimales periódicos, la línea o barra que se coloca encima de los dígitos que se repiten. En 2.6̄3̄, la barra encima de 63 indica que el bloque de dos dígitos, 63, se repite indefinidamente.

base / base (28) Número que se usa como factor en una potencia. En 10^3, la base es 10, es decir, $10^3 = 10 \times 10 \times 10$.

base / base (398) Cualquier lado de un paralelogramo.

base / base (412) Caras inferior y superior de una figura tridimensional.

bisect / bisecar (364) Separar algo en dos partes congruentes.

box-and-whisker plot / diagrama de caja y patillas (76) Diagrama que resume información usando la mediana, los cuartiles superior e inferior y los valores extremos. Se dibuja una caja alrededor de los cuartiles y se trazan patillas uniendo los cuartiles a los valores extremos respectivos.

cell / celda (144) Unidad básica de una hoja de cálculos. Las celdas pueden contener datos, rótulos o fórmulas.

center / centro (280, 413) Un punto dado del cual equidistan todos los puntos de un círculo o de una esfera.

centimeter / centímetro (100) Unidad métrica de longitud. Un centímetro es igual a la centésima parte de un metro.

circle / círculo (280) Conjunto de todos los puntos en un plano que equidistan de un punto dado llamado centro.

centro ←círculo

circle graph / gráfica circular (60) Gráfica que se usa para comparar las partes de un todo. El círculo representa el todo y aparece dividido en las partes en las que el todo ha sido separado.

circumference / circunferencia (280) La distancia alrededor de un círculo.

clustering / agrupamiento (113) Método que se usa para estimar sumas y restas de decimales, redondeando al mismo número entero un grupo de números estrechamente relacionados.

combination / combinación (532) Arreglo o lista de objetos en la que el orden no es importante.

integer / entero (434) Los números enteros y sus opuestos.
..., −3, −2, −1, 0, 1, 2, 3, ...

interval / intervalo (50) La diferencia entre valores sucesivos de una escala.

kilogram / kilogramo (164) Unidad métrica de masa. Un kilogramo equivale a mil gramos.

leaf / hoja (68) El dígito de las unidades que se escribe a la derecha de la línea divisoria vertical en un diagrama de tallo y hojas.

least common denominator (LCD) / mínimo común denominador (mcd) (210) El menor múltiplo común de los denominadores de dos o más fracciones.

least common multiple (LCM) / mínimo común múltiplo (mcm) (206) El menor múltiplo común de dos o más números. El mcm de 2 y 3 es 6.

like fractions / fracciones con igual denominador (238) Fracciones que tienen el mismo denominador.

line graph / gráfica lineal (54) Gráfica que se usa para mostrar cambio y la dirección del cambio, durante un período de tiempo.

line of symmetry / eje de simetría (375) Recta que divide una figura en dos mitades que son reflexiones una de la otra.

eje de simetría

line segment / segmento de recta (362) Dos puntos y la senda rectilínea entre ellos. Un segmento de recta recibe el nombre de los puntos que la unen. A continuación se muestra una representación del segmento de recta ST ($\overline{ST}$).

S ———————— T

liter / litro (164) Unidad fundamental de capacidad del sistema métrico. Un litro es un poco más de un cuarto de galón.

lower quartile / cuartil inferior (77) La mediana de la mitad inferior de un conjunto de datos.

mean / media (71) La suma de los números en un conjunto de datos dividida entre el número total de datos.

measures of central tendency / medidas de tendencia central (71) Números o piezas de datos que pueden representar el conjunto completo de datos. Las medidas comunes de tendencia central son la *media*, la *mediana* y la *modal*.

median / mediana (71) El número central de un conjunto de datos, una vez que los datos se han ordenado numéricamente. Si hay un número par de datos, la mediana es la media de los dos datos centrales.

meter / metro (102) Unidad fundamental de longitud del sistema métrico.

metric system / sistema métrico (102) Sistema de pesos y medidas de base diez. El metro es la unidad fundamental de longitud; el gramo es la unidad fundamental de masa; y el litro es la unidad fundamental de capacidad.

mile / milla (202) Unidad de longitud del sistema inglés que equivale a 5,280 pies ó 1,760 yardas.

milligram / miligramo (164) Unidad métrica de masa. Un miligramo equivale a la milésima parte de un gramo.

milliliter / mililitro (164) Unidad métrica de capacidad. Un mililitro equivale a la milésima parte de un litro.

millimeter / milímetro (100) Unidad métrica de longitud. Un milímetro equivale a la milésima parte de un metro.

mixed number / número mixto (198) La suma de un entero y una fracción. $1\frac{1}{2}$, $2\frac{3}{4}$ y $4\frac{5}{8}$ son números mixtos.

mode / modal (71) Número(s) o ítem(es) de un conjunto de datos que aparece(n) más frecuentemente.

multiple / múltiplo (206) El múltiplo de un número entero es el producto del número por cualquier otro número entero.

N

negative integer / entero negativo (434) Entero que es menor que cero.

net / red (374) Forma que se obtiene al "desdoblar" una figura tridimensional. La red muestra todas las caras que integran la superficie de una figura.

O

obtuse angle / ángulo obtuso (352) Cualquier ángulo que mide más de 90° pero menos de 180°.

octagon / octágono (370) Polígono de ocho lados.

opposite / opuestos (435) Dos enteros son opuestos si, en la recta numérica, están representados por puntos que equidistan de cero, pero en direcciones opuestas. La suma de opuestos es cero.

ordered pair / par ordenado (82, 459) Par de números que se utiliza para ubicar un punto en un plano de coordenadas. Se escribe de la siguiente forma: (coordenada x, coordenada y).

order of operations / orden de las operaciones (16, 28) Reglas a seguir cuando hay más de una operación involucrada.
1. Ejecuta todas las potencias antes que cualquier otra operación.
2. Ejecuta todas las multiplicaciones y divisiones de izquierda a derecha, en el orden que aparezcan.
3. Luego ejecuta todas las sumas y restas de izquierda a derecha, en el orden que aparezcan.

origin / origen (82, 459) Punto de intersección axial en un plano de coordenadas.

ounce / onza (292) Unidad de peso del sistema inglés de medidas. 16 onzas equivalen a una libra.

outcomes / resultados (515) Resultados posibles de un experimento probabilístico. Por ejemplo, 4 es un resultado posible cuando se lanza un dado.

output / salida (494) Resultado de una entrada sobre la que se han realizado una o más operaciones, en una máquina de función.

P

parallel / paralelas (371) Rectas que se extienden en la misma dirección y que se mantienen siempre a la misma distancia una de la otra. Las rectas paralelas nunca se intersecan o cruzan.

parallelogram / paralelogramo (371) Cuadrilátero cuyos pares de lados opuestos son congruentes y paralelos.

pentagon / pentágono (370) Polígono de cinco lados.

percent / tanto por ciento (330) Razón cuyo denominador es 100. Por ejemplo, 7% y $\frac{7}{100}$ indican el mismo número. 7% se lee 7 *por ciento*.

perimeter / perímetro (145) Medida del contorno de una figura cerrada.

pint / pinta (292) Unidad de capacidad del sistema inglés de medidas que equivale a dos tazas.

place value / valor de posición (95) Sistema de escritura de números en el que la posición de cada dígito de un número determina su valor.

polygon / polígono (368, 370) Figura simple cerrada en un plano, formada por tres o más segmentos de recta.

population / población (522) El grupo total de artículos o individuos del cual se toman las muestras bajo estudio.

positive integer / entero positivo (434) Entero que es mayor que cero.

pound / libra (292) Unidad de peso del sistema inglés de medidas que equivale a 16 onzas.

power / potencia (28) Número que puede escribirse usando un exponente. La potencia

3^2 se lee *tres a la segunda potencia* o *tres al cuadrado*.

prime factorization / factorización prima (183) Forma de expresar un número compuesto como el producto de números primos. La factorización prima de 63, por ejemplo, es $3 \times 3 \times 7$.

prime number / número primo (181, 182) Número entero mayor que 1 que sólo tiene dos factores, 1 y sí mismo.

prism / prisma (412) Figura tridimensional que posee dos bases paralelas y congruentes con forma de polígono, y por lo menos, tres caras laterales con forma de rectángulo. La forma de las bases identifica el prisma.

proportion / proporción (317) Ecuación que demuestra la igualdad de dos razones, $\frac{a}{b} = \frac{c}{d}$, $b \neq 0$, $d \neq 0$.

protractor / transportador (352) Instrumento que se usa para medir ángulos.

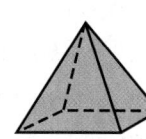

pyramid / pirámide (412) Figura tridimensional que tiene una base poligonal y caras triangulares. Las pirámides se clasifican según la forma de su base.

quadrant / cuadrante (459) Una de las cuatro regiones en que dos rectas perpendiculares dividen un plano.

quadrilateral / cuadrilátero (368, 370) Polígono de cuatro lados.

quart / cuarto de galón (292) Unidad de capacidad del sistema inglés de medidas que equivale a dos pintas.

radius / radio (280) Distancia del centro de un círculo a cualquier punto del mismo.

radio

random / aleatorio (522) Un resultado ocurre aleatoriamente o al azar si se escoge sin preferencia alguna.

range / rango (72) Diferencia entre los valores máximo y mínimo de un conjunto de datos.

rate / tasa (312) Razón de dos medidas que tienen distintas unidades de medida.

ratio / razón (191, 193) Comparación de dos números mediante división. La razón de 2 a 3 puede escribirse como 2 de cada 3, 2 a 3, 2:3 ó $\frac{2}{3}$.

ray / rayo (363) Parte de una recta que se extiende indefinidamente en una dirección. A continuación se muestra una representación del rayo DE ($\overrightarrow{DE}$).

reciprocals / recíprocos (285) Dos números cuyo producto es 1. Como $\frac{5}{6} \times \frac{6}{5} = 1$, el recíproco de $\frac{5}{6}$ es $\frac{6}{5}$ y viceversa.

rectangle / rectángulo (371) Cuadrilátero cuyos cuatro ángulos son congruentes entre sí.

rectangular prism / prisma rectangular (412) Figura tridimensional que posee seis caras rectangulares. Un prisma rectangular tiene en total seis caras, doce aristas y ocho vértices.

reflection / reflexión (375, 464) Transformación en que a una figura se le da vuelta de campana por encima de una recta.

regular polygon / polígono regular (370) Polígono cuyos lados, así como sus ángulos, son todos congruentes.

repeating decimal / decimal periódico (218) Decimal en el cual los dígitos, en algún momento, comienzan a repetirse en bloques de uno o más números. 0.181818... puede también escribirse $0.\overline{18}$. La barra encima de los dígitos indica que estos dígitos se repiten.

right angle / ángulo recto (352) Ángulo que mide 90°.

sample / muestra (522) Grupo escogido al azar o aleatoriamente que se usa para representar la población entera.

sample space / espacio muestral (515) Conjunto de todos los resultados posibles de un experimento probabilístico.

scale / escala (50) Conjunto de todos los posibles valores de una medida dada, el cual incluye los valores máximo y mínimo del conjunto, separados mediante los intervalos que se han usado.

scale drawing / dibujo a escala (324) Dibujo que es semejante, pero más grande o más pequeño que el objeto real.

sequence / sucesión (298) Lista de números en cierto orden como, por ejemplo, 0, 1, 2, 3 ó 2, 4, 6, 8.

sides / lados (145) Segmentos de recta que encierran un polígono.

similar figures / figuras semejantes (379) Figuras que tienen la misma forma, pero no necesariamente el mismo tamaño. El símbolo ~ se lee *es semejante a*.

simplest form / forma reducida (194) Forma de una fracción en que el MCD de su numerador y denominador es 1. La fracción $\frac{3}{4}$ está escrita en forma reducida pues el MCD de 3 y 4 es 1.

simulation / simulación (535) Proceso de representar un problema.

solution / solución (34) Cualquier número que satisface una ecuación. La solución de $12 = x + 7$ es 5.

solve / resolver (34) Proceso de encontrar el número o números que satisfagan una ecuación.

sphere / esfera (413) Figura tridimensional que carece de caras, bases, aristas o vértices. Conjunto de todos los puntos en el espacio que equidistan de un punto dado llamado centro.

centro

spreadsheet / hoja de cálculos (144) Herramienta que se usa para organizar y analizar datos.

square / cuadrado (371) Paralelogramo cuyos lados, así como sus ángulos, son todos congruentes.

squared / al cuadrado (28) Número multiplicado por sí mismo; 4×4 ó 4^2.

square pyramid / pirámide cuadrada (412) Pirámide cuya base es un cuadrado.

statistics / estadística (46) Estudio de la recolección, análisis y presentación de datos.

stem / tallo (68) El mayor valor de posición común a todos los datos, el cual se escribe a la izquierda de la línea divisoria vertical en un diagrama de tallo y hojas.

stem-and-leaf plot / diagrama de tallo y hojas (68) Sistema que se usa para condensar un conjunto de datos y en el cual el mayor valor de posición de los datos forma el tallo y el segundo mayor valor de posición de los datos forma las hojas.

straightedge / regla (358) Cualquier objeto con un lado recto que se usa para trazar rectas.

supplementary / suplementarios (353) Dos ángulos son suplementarios si la suma de sus medidas es 180°.

surface area / área de superficie (421) Suma de las áreas de todas las superficies de una figura tridimensional.

T

terminating decimal / decimal terminal (214) Decimal cuyos dígitos terminan. Todo decimal terminal puede escribirse como una fracción con un denominador de 10, 100, 1,000, etc.

theoretical probability / probabilidad teórica (515) La razón del número de maneras en que puede ocurrir un evento al número total de resultados posibles.

three-dimensional figure / figura tridimensional (412) Figura que encierra parte del espacio.

ton / tonelada (292) Unidad de peso del sistema inglés que equivale a 2,000 libras.

transformation / transformación (464) Movimiento de figuras geométricas en un sistema de coordenadas a otros puntos del sistema.

translation / traslación (384, 464) Tipo de transformación en que una figura se desliza horizontalmente, verticalmente o de ambas maneras.

tree diagram / diagrama de árbol (531) Diagrama que se utiliza para encontrar y mostrar el número total de resultados posibles de un experimento probabilístico.

triangle / triángulo (368, 370) Polígono de tres lados.

unfair game / juego injusto (514) Juego en que los jugadores no tienen la misma oportunidad de ganar.

upper quartile / cuartil superior (77) La mediana de la mitad superior de un conjunto de números o datos.

variable / variable (22) Un símbolo, por lo general, una letra que se usa para representar números.

vertex / vértice (352) Un vértice de un polígono es el punto de intersección de dos lados del polígono.

vertex / vértice (412) Punto en que se intersecan las aristas de una figura tridimensional.

volume / volumen (418) Cantidad de espacio que encierra una figura tridimensional. Se expresa en unidades cúbicas.

x*-axis / eje *x (82, 459) La recta horizontal de las dos rectas numéricas perpendiculares, en un plano de coordenadas.

x*-coordinate / coordenada *x (82, 459) Primer número de un par ordenado.

yard / yarda (202) Unidad de longitud del sistema inglés que equivale a 3 pies ó 36 pulgadas.

y*-axis / eje *y (82, 459) La recta vertical de las dos rectas numéricas perpendiculares, en un plano de coordenadas.

y*-coordinate / coordenada *y (82, 459) Segundo número de un par ordenado.

zero pair / par nulo (441) Resultado de aparear una ficha positiva con una negativa.

Index

INDEX

INDEX

INDEX

INDEX

Answer Appendix

CHAPTER 1
Problem Solving, Numbers, and Algebra

Pages 18–19, Lesson 1-4

22a. $24 \times 15 + 24 \times 20 + 24 \times 15$

23a. Sample answer: $3 \times \$29.95 + 2 \times \$16.95 + \$12.95 = \$136.70$

Page 26, Lesson 1-5B

9. Yes; unless the scientific calculator does not have parentheses keys.

Pages 38–41, Chapter 1
Study Guide and Assessment

17.

CHAPTER 2
Statistics: Graphing Data

Pages 48–49, Lesson 2-1

6.

Hours	Tally	Frequency
1	III	3
2	IIII	4
3	II	2
4	I	1

7.

Days Absent	Tally	Frequency
0	HH	5
1	HHI	6
2	II	2
3	III	3
4		0
5	II	2

8.

Temperature	Tally	Frequency
92	I	1
91	HH	5
90	HHIIII	9
89		0
88	HHHH	10
87	IIII	4
86		0
85	I	1

Pages 51–53, Lesson 2-2

7a.

Shelby's Video Game Scores		
Score	Tally	Frequency
60,000–69,000	I	1
50,000–59,900	I	1
40,000–49,900	IIII	4
30,000–39,900	HH	5
20,000–29,900	IIII	4
10,000–19,900	II	2
0–9,900	I	1

14.

Amount	Tally	Frequency
16–20	I	1
11–15	I	1
6–10	II	2
0–5	III	3

15.

Amount	Tally	Frequency
81–100	I	1
61–80		0
41–60	IIII	4
21–40	I	1
0–20	II	2

16.

Amount	Tally	Frequency
401–500	I	1
301–400	I	1
201–300	III	3
101–200	III	3
0–100	II	2

Pages 55–57, Lesson 2-3

6b.

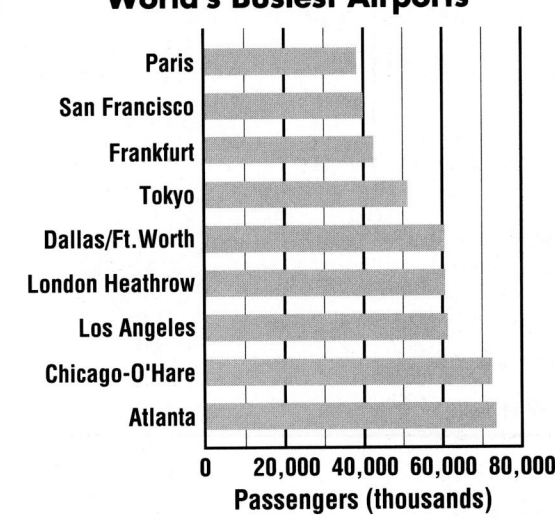

World's Busiest Airports

7.

Favorite Soft Drinks

14.

Entertainment Expenses per Person

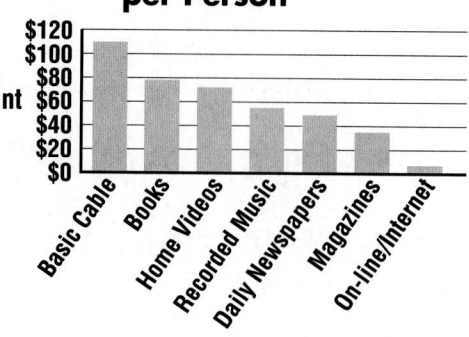

8. **Average Event Day Attendance**

15. **Super Bowl Ticket Prices**

Pages 62–63, Lesson 2-4

9. **Average Snowfall for Brighton, Utah**

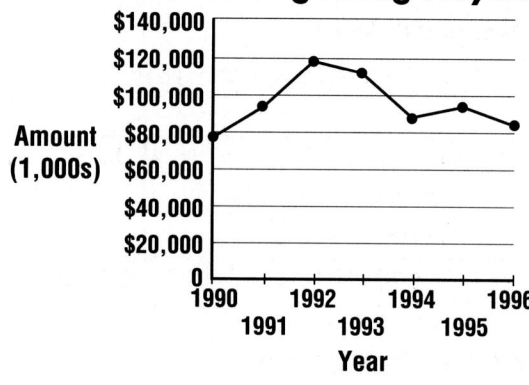

10. **U.S. Sales of Sing-Along Players**

9. **Janet's Leaf Collection**

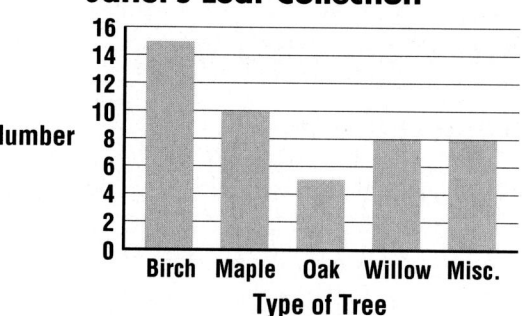

Page 67, Mid-Chapter Self Test

1.

Height	Tally	Frequency
54	I	1
55	I	1
56	I	1
57	IIII	4
58	I	1
59	I	1
60	II	2
61		0
62		0
63	I	1

2c.

Number	Tally	Frequency
81–100	IIII	4
61–80	II	2
41–60	IIII	4
21–40	II	2
0–20	II	2

3.

Favorite Ice Cream Flavor

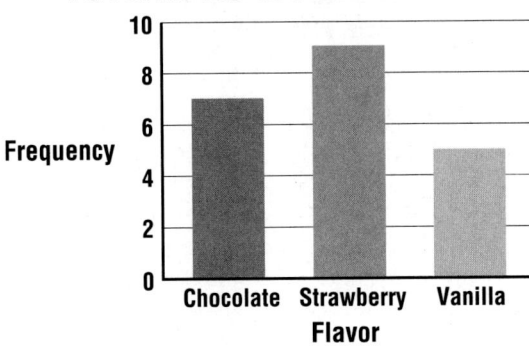

Pages 69–70, Lesson 2-6

5.

Stem	Leaf
2	0 4 7
3	4 5 6 6 8
4	3 5 7
5	3 4 8 8
6	
7	8

2|7 = 27

6a.

Stem	Leaf
3	2 3 8 9
4	1 5 6
5	0 1 2 2 3 9
6	1 1 2 6 7 9
7	0 2

3|2 = 32

10.

Stem	Leaf
2	1 2 4 7 7 8 8 9
3	0 1 1 2 3 5 8 8
4	4 5

2|1 = 21

11.

Stem	Leaf
9	2 4 9 9
10	
11	
12	4 4
13	0 2 3
14	0
15	
16	2 7

12|4 = 124

12.

Stem	Leaf
5	4 4
6	
7	5
8	3 5 9
9	2 4 6

5|4 = 54¢

13.

Stem	Leaf
0	9
1	
2	7 8 9
3	4 4 4
4	5 6
5	3 6 6 7 7 7 8

5|3 = 53°

14a.

Stem	Leaf
0	7 8 9
1	0 1 2 2 2 3 4 5 6 6 8 8 9
2	0 1 2

1|0 = 10

15a.

Stem	Leaf
0	5 5 6 7 8 9 9 9 9 9
1	0 1 1 3 4 6 7 8 8 9 9
2	2 2 3 6 7 7 9
3	7
4	1

1|0 = 10

Pages 73–74, Lesson 2-7

5. 10, 26, 27, 29, 36, 37, 57, 83, 88; 36; no mode; ≈ 43.7; 78

15. yes; Sample answer: The total would be higher so the mean would also be higher.

17. Sample answer: The mode because she would want to know what size they sold the most shakes.

18. Sample answer: 12, 12, 14, 14, 15, 17

19.

Stem	Leaf
0	0 2 2 4 5 7 7 9
1	0 2 3 3 8 9
2	0 3

2|0 = 20

Page 77, Lesson 2-7B

1.

3.

Pages 79–81, Lesson 2-8

3. Sample answer: If the range is very high the mean could be misleading. If the set of data has a gap between two groups of numbers that are all about the same, the mean could be misleading. For example, 1, 2, 3, 2, and 8, 7, 6, 9, 8.

Pages 84–85, Lesson 2-9

36.

Top Animal Speeds

Pages 86–89, Chapter 2
Study Guide and Assessment

12.

Number of Brothers and Sisters	Tally	Frequency
0	IIII	4
1	IIII II	7
2	III	3
3	III	3
4	I	1

13.

Favorite Color	Tally	Frequency
blue	IIII	4
red	IIII	4
pink	II	2
orange	I	1
yellow	I	1
green	II	2
brown	I	1

15. scale = 0 to 50, interval 5

16. scale = 0 to 20, interval 3

17. scale = 0 to 160, interval 20

18.

Alma's Grades During Junior High

19.

Alma's Grades During Junior High

35.

Stem	Leaf
4	0 5
5	0
6	5 9
7	5 5
8	5
9	0 2 5

$9|0 = 90$

CHAPTER 3
Adding and Subtracting Decimals

Page 94, Lesson 3-1A

3.

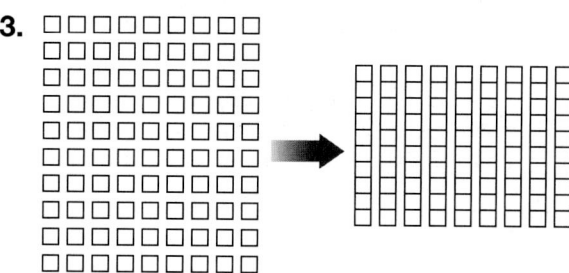

Pages 97-98, Lesson 3-1

2.

Pages 103-104, Lesson 3-2

2. Sample answer: centimeters; The length of the book is smaller than a meter.

26.

Guinea Pig Weights

Pages 107–108, Lesson 3-3

1.

Pages 110–111, Lesson 3-4

1. Sample answer: Since the digit to the right of the ones place is greater than 5, add one to the ones place. $10.79 rounded to the nearest dollar is $11.

2.

25. Sample answer: Using the exact data would be most appropriate. Since there are only 9 numbers in the set of data, rounding is not necessary.

27. No, because no numbers differ greatly.

Pages 114–115, Lesson 3-5

35a. Answers will vary. Sample answer: An estimate for Mandy's family is $9 + $9 + $9 + $4 or $31. Since all costs were rounded up, her whole family can go on the tour for less than $35.

35b. Answers will vary. Sample answer: An estimate for each meal is $5 for breakfast, $7 for lunch, and $12 for dinner. The estimate for one person would be $5 + $7 + $12 or $24. The estimate for a family of 4 would be $24 + $24 + $24 + $24 or $96. This could be rounded up to $100.

CHAPTER 4
Multiplying and Dividing Decimals

Page 132, Lesson 4-1A

1.

2.

3.

Page 140, Lesson 4-3A

3. **4.**

5.

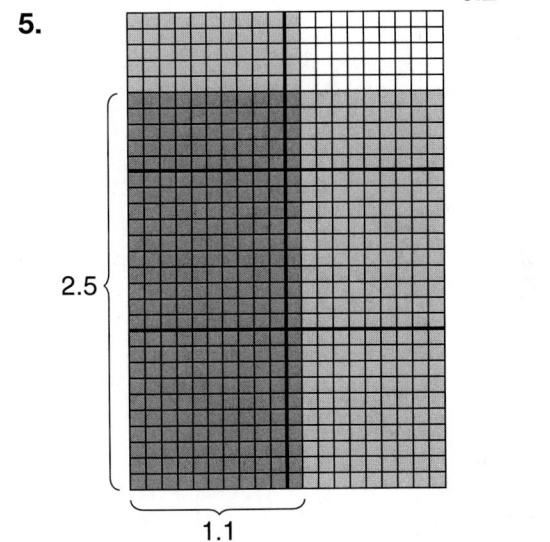

Page 149, Lesson 4-4B

1a.

Length	Width	Area
7	1	7
6	2	12
5	3	15
4	4	16

1b.

Length	Width	Area
8	1	8
7	2	14
6	3	18
5	4	20

Length	Width	Area
9	1	9
8	2	16
7	3	21
6	4	24

CHAPTER 5
Using Number Patterns, Fractions, and Ratios

Pages 179–180, Lesson 5-1

1. Sample answer:

2 Children

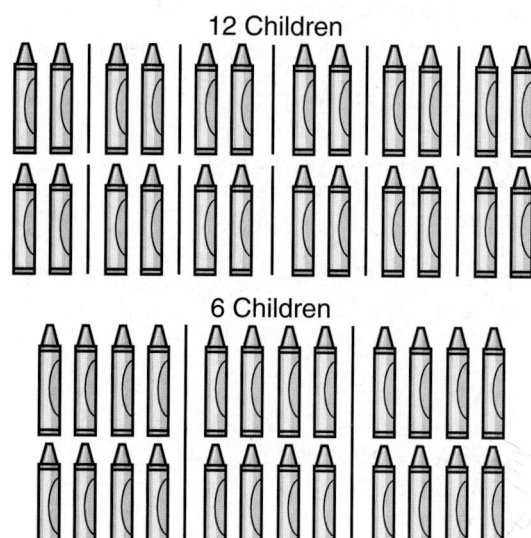

12 Children

6 Children

Page 181, Lesson 5-2A

1.

2 ☐☐

3 ☐☐☐

4 ☐☐☐☐

☐☐
☐☐

5 ☐☐☐☐☐

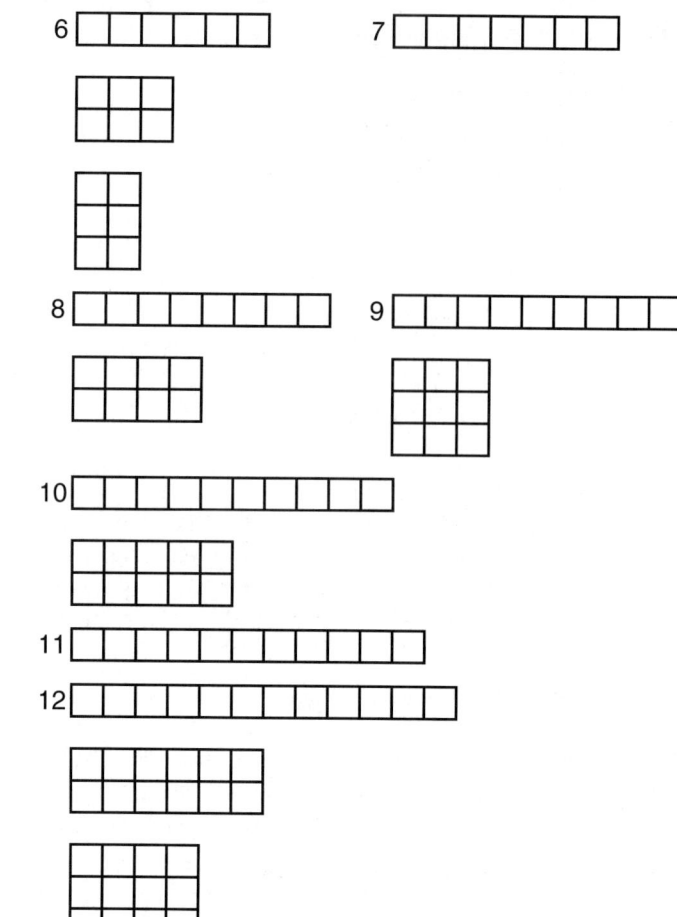

6 ☐☐☐☐

7 ☐☐☐☐☐☐

8 ☐☐☐☐☐☐

9 ☐☐☐☐☐☐

10 ☐☐☐☐☐☐☐

11 ☐☐☐☐☐☐☐☐☐☐☐

12 ☐☐☐☐☐☐☐☐☐☐☐☐

Pages 183–184, Lesson 5-2

1.

1×10

2×5

So, 10 is a composite number.

2. Sample answer: While a composite number has more than two factors, a prime number has exactly two factors, 1 and the number itself.

3. Both are correct. The factors are arranged in a different order.

Pages 189–190, Lesson 5-3

1. Sample answer: Find the prime factorization of 12 and 18. Multiply all common factors of both numbers to find the greatest common factor.

2. Sample answer: It could be one of the numbers if one number is a factor of the other number. Example #1: The GCF of 3 and 9 is 3. Example #2: The GCF of 4 and 16 is 4.

Pages 191–192, Lesson 5-4A

6.

$\frac{1}{3}$ $\frac{2}{6}$

7.

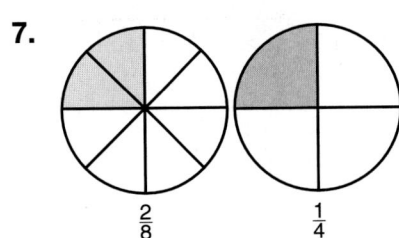

$$\frac{2}{8} \qquad \frac{1}{4}$$

Pages 200–201, Lesson 5-5

34a. Movie A: $\frac{88}{60}$; Movie B: $\frac{76}{60}$; Movie C: $\frac{84}{60}$; Movie D: $\frac{69}{60}$

34b. Movie A: $1\frac{7}{15}$; Movie B: $1\frac{4}{15}$; Movie C: $1\frac{2}{5}$; Movie D: $1\frac{3}{20}$

35. Sample answer: If the numerator is less than the denominator, then the fraction is less than one. If the numerator is the same as the denominator, then the fraction is equal to one. If the numerator is greater than the denominator, then the fraction is greater than one.

Pages 203–205, Lesson 5-6

17. ├────────────┤
18. ├──────────┤
19. ├──┤
20. ├──────────────┤
21. ├──────────┤
22. ├────┤

Pages 208–209, Lesson 5-7

38. ├────┤

Pages 215–216, Lesson 5-9

1. Sample answer: Write the decimal as a fraction with a denominator of 100. Then simplify by using the GCF.

3. Ann; The decimal is written to the hundredths place. So, the denominator will be 100.

Pages 218–219, Lesson 5-10

1. Divide the numerator by the denominator.

2. Sample answer: terminating decimal: 0.8; repeating decimal: 0.890890890…

Pages 220–223, Chapter 5 Study Guide and Assessment

35. ├──────────────┤
36. ├────────────────────┤

CHAPTER 6
Adding and Subtracting Fractions

Pages 230–231, Lesson 6-1

38.

Raul's Earnings

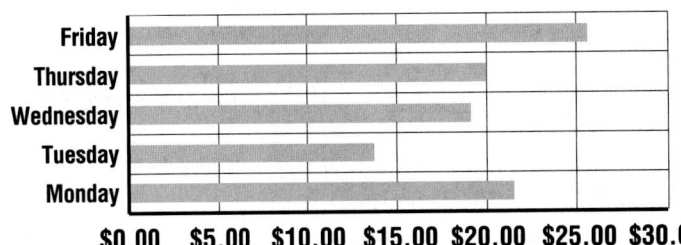

See students' work for the additional graph.

Pages 233–234, Lesson 6-2

1.

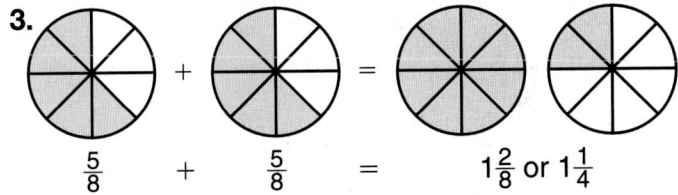

3. Sample answer: Nina should buy 20 inches of framing material. Rounding $4\frac{3}{8}$ to 4 is correct, but since you rounded down, there would not be enough material to complete the picture frame.

10. Margie has $5\frac{2}{3}$ yards of material. She uses $1\frac{1}{4}$ yards for a scarf. About how much material does she have left?

Pages 240–241, Lesson 6-3

3.

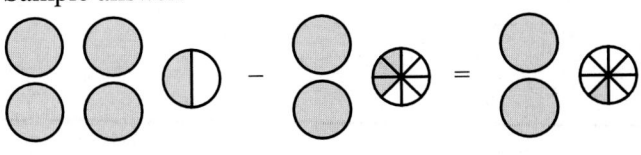

$$\frac{5}{8} \quad + \quad \frac{5}{8} \quad = \quad 1\frac{2}{8} \text{ or } 1\frac{1}{4}$$

Page 248–249, Lesson 6-5

3. Sample answer:

Pages 251–253, Lesson 6-6

1. Sample answer:

3. Sample answer: When Gail borrowed one from 10 she just carried it next to the 1 in $\frac{1}{5}$ and made it $\frac{11}{5}$.

Pages 254–257, Lesson 6-7

2. Sample answer:

7:50 A.M. to 12:00 noon is 4 h 10 min. 12:00 noon to 2:35 P.M. is 2 h 35 min. The elapsed time is 4 h 10 min + 2 h 35 min or 6 h 45 min.

Page 261, Performance Task

Sample answer: To estimate the sum or difference of mixed numbers round each number to the nearest whole number. Then add or subtract.

Sample answer: Since you need the amounts shown, round all the mixed numbers up.

13 + 11 + 19 = 43 yards

Sample answer: Subtract similar to subtracting decimals.

$$
\begin{array}{cc}
9{:}18 & 8{:}78 \\
-7{:}30 \quad \rightarrow & -7{:}30 \\
\hline
& 1{:}48 \text{ or } 1\text{ h } 48 \text{ min}
\end{array}
$$

Sample answer: It is similar to subtracting mixed numbers involving renaming because you rename hours as minutes. For example, 9 h 18 min = 8 h 78 min.

CHAPTER 7
Multiplying and Dividing Fractions

Pages 269–270, Lesson 7-1

1. Round $3\frac{1}{2}$ to 4. Round $9\frac{1}{8}$ to 9. Since $4 \times 9 = 36$, $3\frac{1}{2} \times 9\frac{1}{8} \approx 36$.

2. $\frac{1}{4}$ and 8 are compatible numbers. Since $\frac{1}{4} \times 8 = 2$, it follows that $\frac{3}{4} \times 8 = 2 \times 3$, or 6. So, $\frac{3}{4} \times 9 \approx 6$.

3. Both Juan and Odina are correct. If you round $8\frac{1}{2}$ to 9 and $6\frac{1}{4}$ to 6, the product is 9×6, or 54. If you round $8\frac{1}{2}$ to 8 and $6\frac{1}{4}$ to 6, the product is 8×6, or 48.

19-27. Sample answers are given.

19. $\frac{1}{4} \times 32 = 8$ **20.** $\frac{1}{2} \times \frac{1}{2} = \frac{1}{4}$

21. $\frac{1}{7} \times 21 = 3$ **22.** $2 \times 6 = 12$

23. $\frac{1}{6} \times 42 = 7$ **24.** $1 \times 3 = 3$

25. $\frac{4}{9} \times 45 = 20$ **26.** $\frac{1}{6} \times 1 = \frac{1}{6}$

27. $8 \times 3 = 24$

Pages 271–272, Lesson 7-2A

8.

Pages 278–279, Lesson 7-3

1. To multiply mixed numbers, express each mixed number as an improper fraction and then multiply as with fractions.

2. Express $3\frac{1}{2}$ as the improper fraction $\frac{7}{2}$. Express $1\frac{1}{2}$ as the improper fraction $\frac{3}{2}$. Then multiply $\frac{7}{2}$ and $\frac{3}{2}$: $\frac{7}{2} \times \frac{3}{2} = \frac{21}{4}$, or $5\frac{1}{4}$.

Page 284, Lesson 7-5A

1.

2.

3.

4.

Pages 290–291, Lesson 7-6

1. First, write $4\frac{5}{8}$ as the improper fraction $\frac{37}{8}$. Then invert the numerator and the denominator. The reciprocal of $4\frac{5}{8}$ is $\frac{8}{37}$.

2. More; there are eight $\frac{1}{2}$'s in 4.

3. Change each mixed number to an improper fraction. Multiply the first fraction by the reciprocal of the second fraction. Divide 8 and 12 by the GCF, 4. Multiply $\frac{3}{1}$ and $\frac{3}{2}$ to find the product $\frac{9}{2}$, or $4\frac{1}{2}$.

Page 295, Lesson 7-7B

1.

Planet/ Moon	Amount of water	Weight compared to Earth	Weight compared to Jupiter
Sun	28 cups	more	more
Mercury	$\frac{1}{3}$ cups	less	less
Venus	$\frac{9}{10}$ cups	less	less
Moon	$\frac{1}{6}$ cups	less	less
Mars	$\frac{3}{8}$ cups	less	less
Jupiter	3 cups	more	—

2. The container labeled *Jupiter*. It has the most water.

Pages 296–297, Lesson 7-8A

3.

Pages 299–300, Lesson 7-8

3. Joshua is correct. In the sequence, $2\frac{1}{2}$ is added to each number. The next number is $12\frac{1}{2} + 2\frac{1}{2}$, or 15.

Pages 302–305, Chapter 7 Study Guide and Assessment

11-16. Sample answers are given.

11. $10 \times 3 = 30$ **12.** $4 \times 6 = 24$

13. $1 \times 13 = 13$ **14.** $1 \times \frac{1}{2} = \frac{1}{2}$

15. $\frac{2}{3} \times 18 = 12$ **16.** $8 \times \frac{1}{4} = 2$

CHAPTER 8 Exploring Ratio, Proportion, and Percent

Pages 313–315, Lesson 8-1

36.

total number of students	−	number of students at or above 85%	=	number of students below 85%
24	−	18	=	6

Ratio of the number of students scoring below 85% to the total number of students is 6:24.

  a. The ratio 18:24 represents the number of students who received 85% or better.

  b. The ratio 24:6 is reversed from what Mr. Sarmiento asked. This ratio compares the total students to the number of students below 85%.

  c. The ratio 24:18 compares the total number of students to those who received 85% or above.

Page 329, Lesson 8-4A

1a.   **1b.**

1c.   **1d.**

1e.

2a.   **2b.**

2c.   **2d.**

2e.

3. Sample answer: Grid C from the first set is the same as grid A from the second set. Grid A from the first set is the same as grid B from the second set. Grid B from the first set is the same as grid C from the second set. Grid D from the first set is the same as grid D from the second set. Grid E from the first set is the same as grid E from the second set.

Pages 332–333, Lesson 8-4

21.   **22.**

23.   **24.**

Pages 335–336, Lesson 8-5

1.

2. First, express 0.008 as the fraction $\frac{8}{1,000}$. Next, divide the numerator and denominator by 10 so that the denominator is 100. $\frac{8}{1,000} = \frac{0.8}{100}$. Then express the fraction as the percent 0.8%.

3. Betty is correct. The decimal 3.78 is equivalent to 378%. Therefore, it is more than 100%.

Pages 338–339, Lesson 8-6

1. 75% = $\frac{3}{4}$. Round 1,976 to 2,000. $\frac{3}{4} \times 2,000 = 1,500$. So, 75% of 1,976 is about 1,500.

16. Sample answer: $\frac{2}{3} \times 90 = 60$

17. Sample answer: $1 \times 300 = 300$

18. Sample answer: $\frac{1}{4} \times 280 = 70$

CHAPTER 9
Geometry: Investigating Patterns

Pages 353–355, Lesson 9-1

1. Sample answer: See students' drawings;

Step 1   Place the center of the protractor on the vertex of the angle with the straightedge along one side.

Step 2   Using the scale that begins with 0° on the side of the angle, read the angle measure where the other side crosses the same scale.

Pages 356–357, Lesson 9-1B

6. Sample answer: In a line of 24 people waiting for a city bus, 12 have umbrellas, 10 have raincoats, and 7 have both umbrellas and raincoats. The rest of the people have neither a raincoat nor an umbrella. How many people only have umbrellas?

Pages 360–361, Lesson 9-2

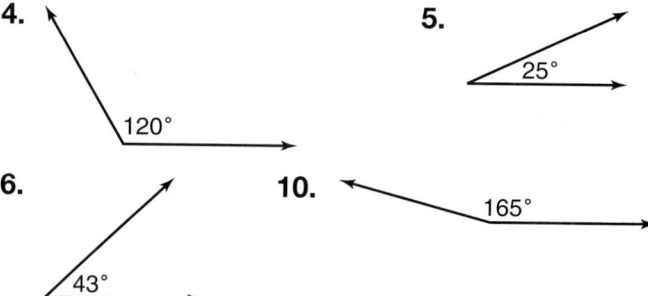

4. 120°   **5.** 25°

6. 43°   **10.** 165°

11.

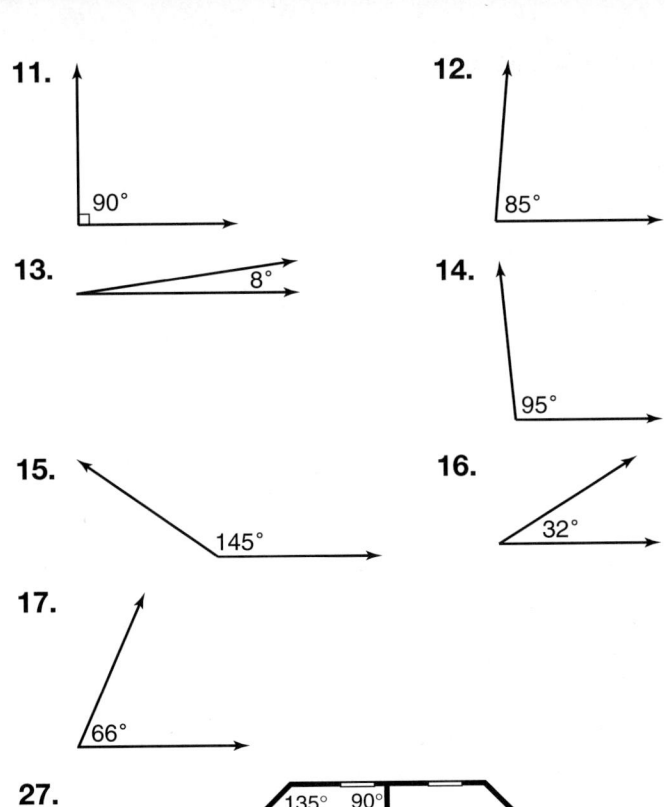

90°

12.

85°

13.

8°

14.

95°

15.

145°

16.

32°

17.

66°

27.

135°   90°
Bedroom #2   Bedroom #1
45°   Closet   90°   Closet
45°
Great Room
90° 135°   90°
135° Dining Room   Bathroom
110°   135° 90°
Entry
70°   Kitchen
Deck

Pages 362–363, Lesson 9-3A

1.

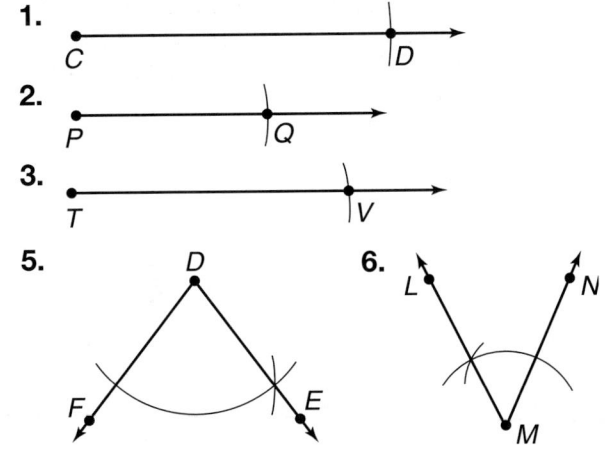

C ——————————— D

2.

P ————— Q —————

3.

T ————— V —————

5.

D
F   E

6.

L   N
M

7.

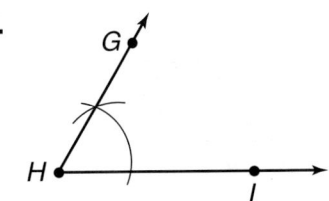

G
H   I

Page 366, Lesson 9-3

1. To separate something into two congruent parts.

2. First, place the compass at one end of the line segment. Then set the compass to more than half the length of the line segment and draw two arcs. Next, using the same compass setting, place the compass at the other end of the line segment and draw two more arcs. Then, using a straightedge, draw a line through the arcs.

3. See students' work. The crease bisects the angle.

4. Note: Art is not drawn to scale.

X
A ——————————— B
Z

5.

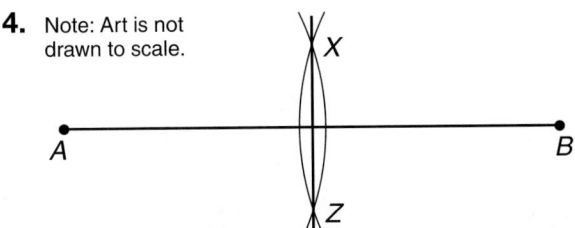

B
X   Z
A
Y   C

6.

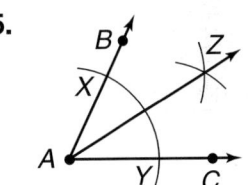

A
X ——————————— Y
B

7.

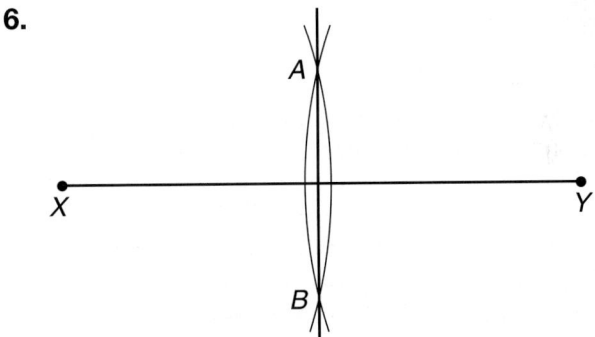

C
A   X
59.5°
D   B   E

8.

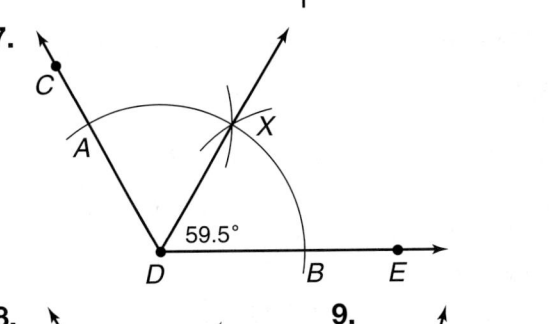

M
R   T
N   S   P

9.

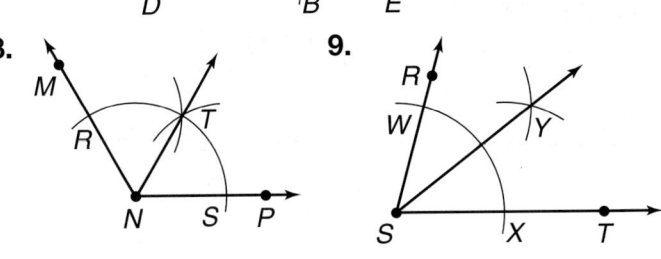

R
W   Y
S   X   T

10.

11. **12.**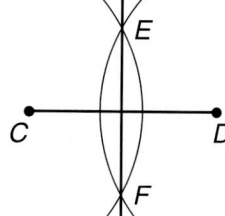

13. Note: Art is not drawn to scale.

14.

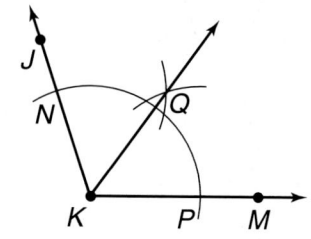

15. Note: Art is not drawn to scale.

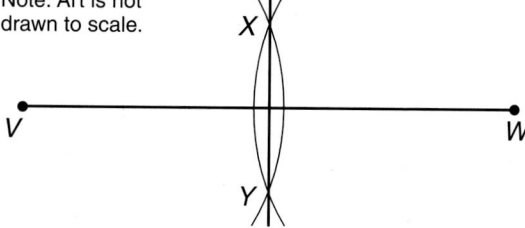

17. The diagonals bisect the corners of the square.

18. See students' work.

Pages 372–373, Lesson 9-4

1. Sample answer: A chalkboard is a rectangle and a piece of floor tile is a square.

2. Sample answer:

8. **9.**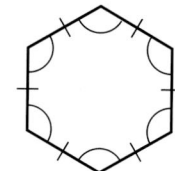

15. Alike: all sides congruent; all angles congruent
Different: triangle has three sides and square has four sides

16. Alike: all sides congruent; all angles congruent
Different: triangle has three sides; octagon has eight sides

17. Alike: quadrilaterals; at least 1 pair of parallel sides
Different: square has all sides congruent and four right angles

18. Sample answer: **19.** Sample answer:

20. **21.**

22. Sample answer: **23.**

29.

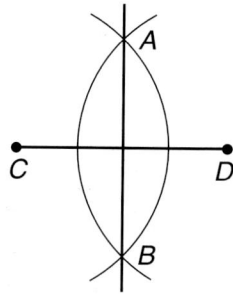

Page 373, Mid-Chapter Self Test

7.

8.

9.

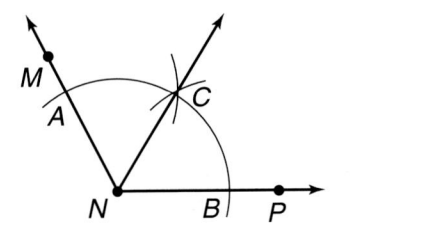

Page 374, Lesson 9-4B

2. Sample answer:

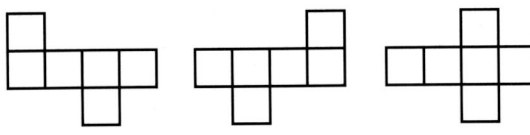

3. Sample answer: Each net contains six squares. Each net has four squares lined up in a row. Each net has two squares positioned on opposite sides of the row of four squares.

Pages 380–382, Lesson 9-6

18a.

7 in.

5 in.

3.5 in.

2.5 in.

19.

Pages 384–385, Lesson 9-6B

1.

2.

3.

5.

6.

7.

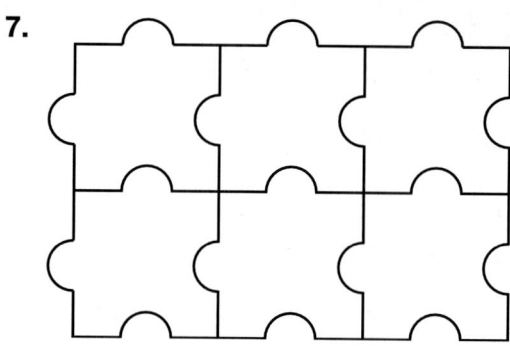

Pages 386–389, Chapter 9
Study Guide and Assessment

18.

36°

19.

127°

22. Note: Art is not drawn to scale.

23.

24.

25.

28. Sample answer:

29.

37.

38.

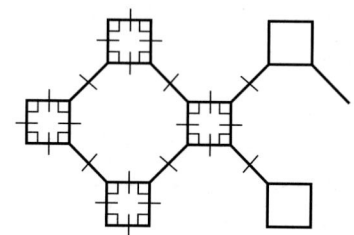

CHAPTER 10
Geometry: Understanding Area and Volume

Page 411, Lesson 10-3B

4.

Film Time in Camera

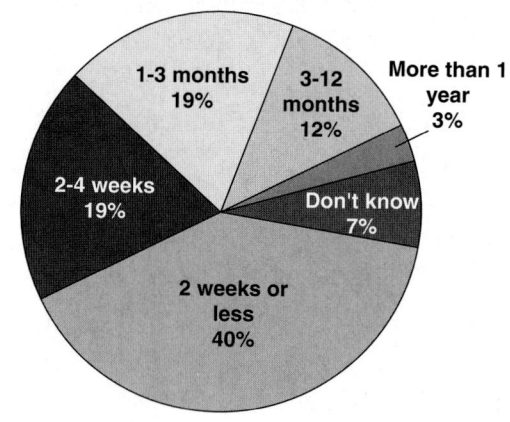

1-3 months 19%

3-12 months 12%

More than 1 year 3%

2-4 weeks 19%

Don't know 7%

2 weeks or less 40%

5. **World Population**

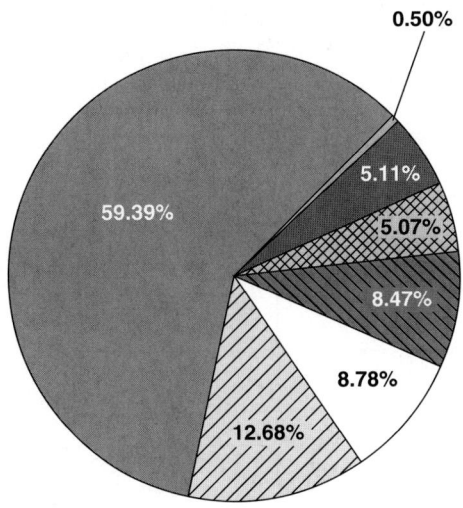

0.50%

5.11%

5.07%

8.47%

59.39%

8.78%

12.68%

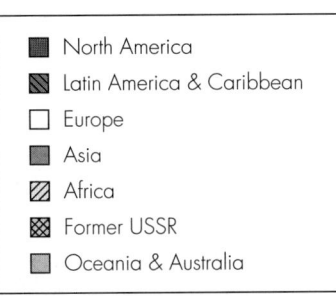

■ North America
▨ Latin America & Caribbean
□ Europe
▦ Asia
▨ Africa
▨ Former USSR
▨ Oceania & Australia

Pages 413–414, Lesson 10-4

2. Sample answer: A two-dimensional figure is flat, it has only width and length. A three-dimensional figure is not flat, it has width, length, and depth.

Page 415, Lesson 10-4B

4.   **5.**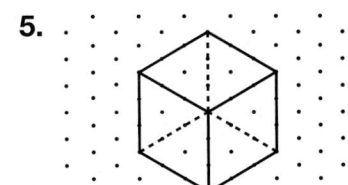

Page 425, Lesson 10-6B

5. When one dimension is doubled, the volume doubles. When two dimensions are doubled, the volume is multiplied by four. When all three dimensions are doubled, the volume is multiplied by eight. The volumes are changed in this way because if any one dimension is multiplied by 2, the volume is multiplied by 2.

6. When one or two dimensions are doubled, the surface area is increased. When all three dimensions are doubled, the surface area is multiplied by four. The surface area is changed because as one dimension is doubled, the areas of four faces are affected, but two are unchanged. When three dimensions are doubled, the areas of all six faces are quadrupled, so the surface area is quadrupled.

CHAPTER 11
Algebra: Investigating Integers

Pages 435–436, Lesson 11-1

2.

-6 and 6 are the same distance from 0 in opposite directions.

4.

5.

6.

12.

14.

15.

16.

17.

18.

19.

20.

21.

36.

37.

38.

42. Both a number line and a thermometer measure positive and negative numbers. A number line is usually horizontal, so the negative values are to the left of 0 and the positive values are to the right of 0. A thermometer is vertical, so the negative values are below 0 and the positive values are above 0.

Pages 438–439, Lesson 11-2

1. Graph the numbers on a number line. The number to the left is less than the number to the right.

2. Sample answer: A scuba diver is 20 ft below the surface of the water. Another diver is 30 ft below the surface. Which diver is farther from the surface of the water?

3. Cordelia; since -5 is to the left of -3 on the number line, $-5 < -3$.

24.

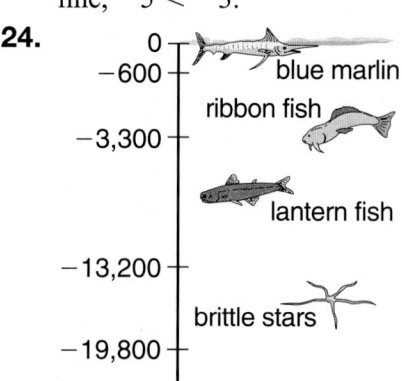

Pages 443–444, Lesson 11-3

2.

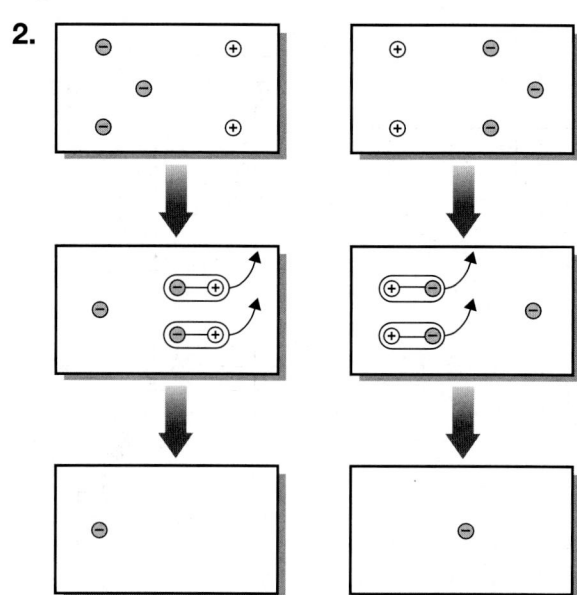

Pages 447–448, Lesson 11-4

21.

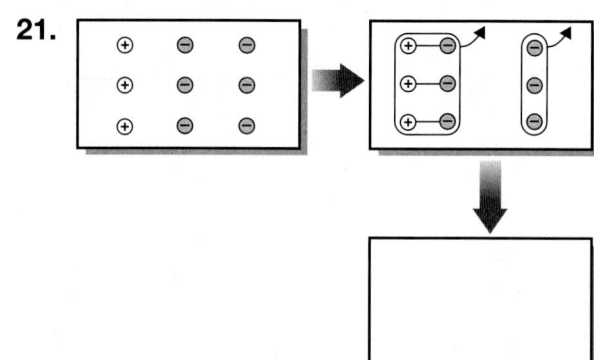

Pages 451–452, Lesson 11-5

2.

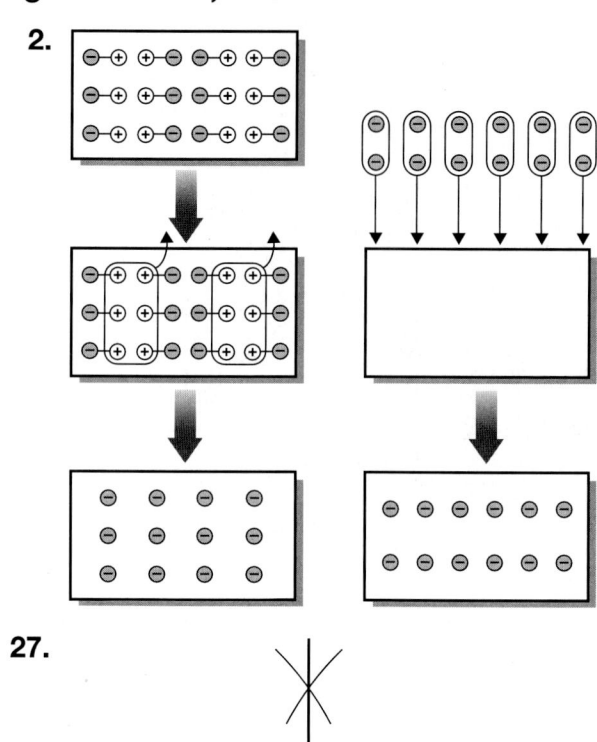

27.

Pages 460–461, Lesson 11-7

2a-b. **7.**

8. **9.**

23.

24.

25.

26.

27.

28.

29.

30.

31a.

33.

35a-d.

3a.

3b.

5.

6.

11.

12.

13.

14.

15.

16.

18. Sample answer:

20.

Pages 466–467, Lesson 11-8

1. Both translations and reflections are transformations. In translations and reflections, the image is the same size and shape as the figure. The translation image has the same orientation as the figure, but the reflection image is a flip of the figure.

Pages 468–471, Chapter 11
Study Guide and Assessment

13.

14.

15.

46-51.

52.   **53.**

CHAPTER 12
Algebra: Exploring Equations

Pages 486–487, Lesson 12-3

2. [diagram of cups and counters balance]

33.

E
Change per month
= D2/10
= D3/10
= D4/10
= D5/10
= D6/10
= D7/10

34. The solution to $\frac{1}{8}x = 13$ will be greater because you have to multiply by a greater number (8) to solve it.

Pages 501–503, Lesson 12-6

1. Sample answer: Let the input values represent the x-coordinates and let the output values represent the corresponding y-coordinates.

2. The graph in the third quadrant represents negative time.

3. Sample answer: Make a table recording the input and output of the given function. Write the input/output as an ordered pair. Record at least three ordered pairs on the table. Graph these ordered pairs and draw a line connecting the graphed points.

4.   **5.**

6.   **7.**

10.   **11.**

12.   **13.**

14.   **15.**

16.   **17.**

18.   **19.**

20.

input (a)	output (a + 5)
−5	0
−3	2
0	5

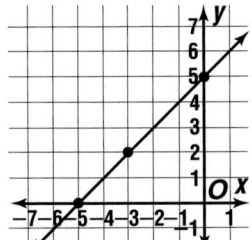

21.

input (n)	output (3n − 3)
−2	−9
1	0
4	9

22.

input (n)	output (○)
−2	−6
0	0
2	6

The rule is $3n$.

23.

input (n)	output (○)
0	0
4	2
8	4

The rule is $\frac{n}{2}$.

24.

input (n)	output (○)
0	−2
2	0
4	2

The rule is $n - 2$.

25b.

26a.

input	output
0	0
1	50
2	100
3	150

26b. The function rule is $50n$.

27a.

input	output
1	61
2	62
3	63
4	64
5	65
6	66
7	67
8	68
9	69
10	70
11	71
12	72

27b.

27c. In 5 months, the card will be worth $65.

Pages 504–507, Chapter 12
Study Guide and Assessment

40.   **41.**

Pages 508–509, Standardized Test Practice

18.

x	x − 2
2	0
5	3
8	6

Page 514, Lesson 13-1A

1. Sample answer: The number of even sums tossed and the number of odd sums tossed should be about the same. The number of even products tossed should be greater than the number of odd products tossed.

2. Sample answer: The game involving sums is fair. If you toss two number cubes, there are 36 possible results. Eighteen sums are even and eighteen sums are odd. The game involving products is unfair. If you toss two number cubes, there are 36 possible results. Twenty-seven products are even and nine products are odd. So, you would have a greater chance of tossing an even product than an odd product.

3. Sample answer: For the game involving sums, the bar graph resembled an isosceles triangle and is symmetrical about the axis which contains the sum of 7. For the products game, the bar graph reaches a maximum height at products 6 and 12 and the overall graph is not symmetrical.

4. Sample answer: The sum of 7 occurred most often and the sums of 2 and 12 occurred least often. The products of 6 and 12 occurred most often and the products of 1, 9, 16, 25, and 36 occurred least often.

5. Sample answer: A sum of 12 is less likely to occur since out of 36 results, a sum of 12 can only occur one way.

Pages 517–518, Lesson 13-1

1. Sample answer:

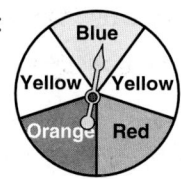

2. Sample answer: The probability of rolling a 9 on a number cube labeled 1 to 6. The probability of the sun not rising.

3. Sample answer: Complementary events are two events in which either one or the other can occur, but not both. The sum of their probabilities is 1. An example is the probability of snow or the probability of no snow.

4. The event is not too likely to occur.
5. The event is very likely to occur.
6. The event is equally likely to occur.
7. The event is not too likely to occur.
8. The event is very likely to occur.
9. The event cannot occur.
11. The event is not too likely to occur.
12. The event is not too likely to occur.
13. The event is equally likely to occur.

14. The event is very likely to occur.
15. The event is not too likely to occur.
16. The event cannot occur.
17. The event is very likely to occur.
18. $\frac{1}{30}$; not 12; $\frac{29}{30}$
19. $\frac{1}{2}$; not odd; $\frac{1}{2}$
20. $\frac{3}{10}$; not a 1 digit number; $\frac{7}{10}$
21. 1; not an integer; 0
22. 0; not less than 1; 1
23. $\frac{2}{5}$; not greater than 18; $\frac{3}{5}$
29.

Pages 520–521, Lesson 13-2A

4a.

Test Scores		
Score	Tally	Frequency
91–100	卌I	6
81–90	IIII	4
71–80	卌III	8
61–70	III	3

10a.

Students' Birth Months		
Month	Tally	Frequency
January	I	1
February		0
March	II	2
April	IIII	4
May	III	3
June	卌	5
July	III	3
August	I	1
September	I	1
October	III	3
November		0
December	I	1

Pages 524–525, Lesson 13-2

4. You are probably surveying people whose main interest is a Broadway show.

5. There is probably a diverse group of people at a shopping center.

6. There is probably a fair sampling of people at a fast-food restaurant.

8. There is probably a fair sampling of people at a grocery store.

9. You would probably survey people whose hobby is model trains.

10. You would probably survey people who prefer the musician.

11. A mall would have a diverse group of people.

12. There would be a diverse group of people at the library.

13. You would probably find many people who prefer the type of cars sold by the dealership.

14. There would be a diverse group of people at a skating rink.

15. A lot of chocolate lovers would be in a chocolate factory.

16. The customers may prefer Mexican food.

Pages 527–529, Lesson 13-3

22. $\frac{16}{49}$, or about 32.7%; The event is not too likely to happen.

Page 530, Lesson 13-3B

1. Sample answer: $\frac{27}{50}$

2. $\frac{1}{2}$

3. Sample answer: The fractions should be about the same.

4. Sample answer: The fractions should be closer than the fractions compared in Exercise 3.

Pages 533–534, Lesson 13-4

1. Sample answer: At a restaurant, a customer can choose either a chicken or a beef dinner and one of three beverages. How many possible outcomes are there?

3. Sample answer: Tree diagrams are useful for organizing the outcomes. One disadvantage is that there could be too many outcomes.

4. See students' diagrams; outcomes are hot dog, iced tea; hot dog, lemonade; hamburger, iced tea; hamburger, lemonade.

5. See students' diagrams; outcomes are blue shirt, blue shorts; blue shirt, black shorts; blue shirt, red shorts; red shirt, blue shorts; red shirt, black shorts; red shirt, red shorts.

7a. See students' diagrams; outcomes are ATT, ATF, AFT, AFF, BTT, BTF, BFT, BFF, CTT, CTF, CFT, CFF.

8. See students' diagrams; outcomes are lemon, milk; lemon, tea; apple, milk; apple, tea; pecan, milk; pecan, tea.

9. See students' diagrams; outcomes are leather, purple; leather, green; leather, black; leather, brown; nylon, purple; nylon, green; nylon, black; nylon, brown.

10. See students' diagrams; outcomes are 1, 1; 1, 2; 1, 3; 1, 4; 1, 5; 1, 6; 2, 1; 2, 2; 2, 3; 2, 4; 2, 5; 2, 6; 3, 1; 3, 2; 3, 3; 3, 4; 3, 5; 3, 6; 4, 1; 4, 2; 4, 3; 4, 4; 4, 5; 4, 6; 5, 1; 5, 2; 5, 3; 5, 4; 5, 5; 5, 6; 6, 1; 6, 2; 6, 3; 6, 4; 6, 5; 6, 6.

11. See students' diagrams; outcomes are blue, red; blue, green; blue, white; blue, black; orange, red; orange, green; orange, white; orange, black; yellow, red; yellow, green; yellow, white; yellow, black.

12. See students' diagrams; outcomes are portable, graphite; portable, acrylic; stationary, graphite; stationary, acrylic.

13. See students' diagrams; outcomes are tower, wood, 60; tower, wood, 100; tower, wood, 250; tower, plastic, 60; tower, plastic, 100; tower, plastic, 250; spinner, wood, 60; spinner, wood, 100; spinner, wood, 250; spinner, plastic, 60; spinner, plastic, 100; spinner, plastic, 250.

19. Sample answer: This is not a fair game. Only in two of the eight outcomes are all chips different. It could be made a fair game by giving Amiri 3 points or changing the second counter from red and white to green and white.

Page 535, Lesson 13-4B

1. Sample answer: $\frac{22}{50}$

2. BBB, BBG, BGB, BGG, GBG, GGB, GBB, GGG; $\frac{4}{8}$ or $\frac{1}{2}$

3. They are about the same.

4. $\frac{1}{16}$; Repeat steps 1 to 4, but in step 1, place four counters in a cup. See students' work.

Pages 540–543, Chapter 13
Study Guide and Assessment

12. $\frac{1}{6}$; The event is not too likely to occur.

13. $\frac{1}{3}$; The event is not too likely to occur.

14. 0; The event cannot occur.

15. $\frac{5}{6}$; The event is very likely to occur.

16. $\frac{1}{3}$; The event is not too likely to occur.

17. $\frac{2}{3}$; The event is very likely to occur.

18. yes; There will be many people at the beach with all different interests.

19. no; At a football game, you would most likely find people who prefer football.

20. yes; There would be many people at the mall who would prefer different types of pets.

21a. $\frac{7}{20}$ or 35%

25. See students' diagrams; outcomes are black jeans, tapered; black jeans, straight; black jeans, baggy; blue jeans, tapered; blue jeans, straight; blue jeans, baggy.

26. See students' diagrams; outcomes are soup, beef; soup, chicken; soup, fish; soup, pasta; salad, beef; salad, chicken; salad, fish; salad, pasta.

27. See students' diagrams; outcomes are ball game, Friday; ball game, Saturday; amusement park, Friday; amusement park, Saturday; concert, Friday; concert, Saturday.

35. See students' diagrams; outcomes are purple skirt, yellow vest; purple skirt, purple sweater; white skirt, yellow vest; white skirt, purple sweater; yellow skirt, yellow vest; yellow skirt, purple sweater.

Page 543, Performance Task

- Make a tree diagram to show all of the possibilities; outcomes are color, glossy, 3×5; color, glossy, 4×6; color, glossy, 5×5; color, glossy, 8×10; color, matte, 3×5; color, matte, 4×6; color, matte, 5×5; color, matte, 8×10; black and white, glossy, 3×5; black and white, glossy, 4×6; black and white, glossy, 5×5; black and white, glossy, 8×10; black and white, matte, 3×5; black and white, matte, 4×6; black and white, matte, 5×5; black and white, matte, 8×10.

- There are 16 possible outcomes. If the pictures can also be cut square or rounded, there would be 32 possible outcomes.

Page 557, Extra Practice, Lesson 1-3

13. $60 \times 5 = 300$; not reasonable

14. $900 - 40 = 860$; reasonable

15. $\$3 + \$6 + \$9 = \$18$; reasonable

16. $400 \times 4 = 1,600$; reasonable

17. $400 \div 5 = 80$; not reasonable

18. $2,000 - 200 = 1,800$; not reasonable

19. $100 + 500 + 200 = 800$; reasonable

20. $6,000 \div 300 = 20$; reasonable

Page 559, Extra Practice, Lesson 2-1

1.

# of miles	Tally	Frequency
1	IIII	4
2	HHt	5
3	HHt II	7
4	III	3
5	III	3

2.

Temperature	Tally	Frequency
47	I	1
48	III	3
49	III	3
51	II	2
52	HHt	5
53	II	2
57	II	2

Page 561, Extra Practice, Lesson 2-4

1. 5% – history; 12% – math; 20% – science; 25% – English; 38% – phys. ed.

2. Sample answer: No; the combination of math and history is not $\frac{1}{4}$ of the circle.

Page 582, Extra Practice, Lesson 9-4

Sample answers:

5. same length sides, different number of sides, different angles

6. same length sides, same number of sides, different angles

7. same number of sides, one has 3 equal angles and the other has 2 equal angles and a right angle

Page 585, Extra Practice, Lesson 11-1

1-7.

Page 587, Extra Practice, Lesson 11-7

15-22.

Page 588, Extra Practice, Lesson 11-8

1.

2.

3.

4.

5.

Page 590, Extra Practice, Lesson 12-6

1.

2.

3.

4.

5.

6.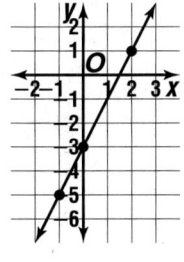

Page 590, Extra Practice, Lesson 13-1

1. not too likely to occur
2. equally likely to occur
3. not too likely to occur
4. cannot occur
5. very likely to occur
6. not too likely to occur
7. not too likely to occur
8. equally likely to occur

9. very likely to occur
10. not too likely to occur
11. not too likely to occur
12. certain to occur
13. not too likely to occur
14. very likely to occur
15. not too likely to occur
16. not too likely to occur
17. not too likely to occur
18. not too likely to occur

Page 591, Extra Practice,

2a.

Month	Tally	
February	III	
March	III	
June	II	2
July	III	3
August	I	1
September	III	3
October	HHH	5
December	I	1

Page 591, Extra Practice, Lesson 13-2

1. yes; A department store would have a diverse group of people.
2. no; You would probably find many fans of the specific baseball team.
3. yes: There would be a diverse group of people at a shopping center.
4. yes; A park would have a diverse group of people.
5. no; You would probably find many people who prefer soccer.
6. yes; A school would have a diverse group of students.
7. no; You would probably find many people who like Garth Brooks.
8. no; You would probably find many people who like apples.
9. yes; There would be a diverse group of people at a county fair.
10. no; Many of the people would probably prefer to go to the popular theme park for vacation.

Page 592, Extra Practice, Lesson 13-4

1. See students' diagrams; outcomes are heads, 1; heads, 2; heads, 3; heads, 4; heads, 5; heads, 6; tails, 1; tails, 2; tails, 3; tails, 4; tails, 5; tails, 6.
2. See students' diagrams; outcomes are red, red; red, blue; red, yellow; green, red; green, blue; green, yellow; blue, red; blue, blue; blue, yellow; yellow, red; yellow, blue; yellow, yellow.

grams; outcomes are red, white; red, blue, white; blue, black; blue, tan; green, black; green, tan.

diagrams; outcomes are chicken, ~~chi~~cken, milk; chicken, juice; chicken, soda; ~~coff~~ee; ham, milk; ham, juice; ham, soda; ~~c~~offee; turkey, milk; turkey, juice; turkey, ~~b~~ologna, coffee; bologna, milk; bologna, juice; ~~bolog~~na, soda.

596, Chapter 2 Test

Score	Tally	Frequency
96–100	III	4
91–95	HHH I	6
86–90	III	3
81–85	HHH	5
76–80	HHH	5
71–75	IIII	4

3.

11.

Line graph: Earnings ($) vs months Jan.–Dec.

12.

Line graph: Jan.–Dec.

13.

Stem	Leaf
7	3 4 5
8	4 5 6 7
9	2 2 6 *9|2 = 92*

14.

Stem	Leaf
4	2 3 6 8
5	5 9
6	6 9
7	
8	5 *8|5 = 85*

21. ▬▬▬▬▬

8.

12.

13.

14.

15.

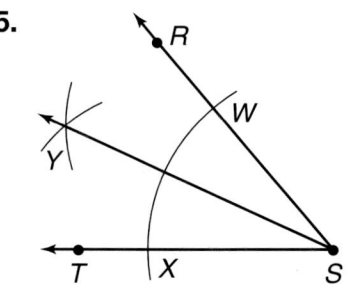

ANSWER APPENDIX

Page 605, Chapter 11 Test

21.

22.

23.

24.

25.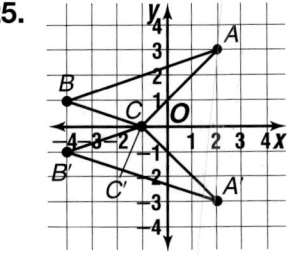

Page 606, Chapter 12 Test

20.

Page 607, Chapter 13 Test

16a. See students' diagrams; outcomes are iced tea, nachos; iced tea, popcorn; iced tea, chocolate; soda, nachos; soda, popcorn; soda, chocolate.